# ANALYSIS AND DESIGN OF ANALOG INTEGRATED CIRCUITS

Fourth Edition

K. SANTHOSH

# ANALYSIS AND DESIGN OF ANALOG INTEGRATED CIRCUITS

## Fourth Edition

**PAUL R. GRAY**
*University of California, Berkeley*

**PAUL J. HURST**
*University of California, Davis*

**STEPHEN H. LEWIS**
*University of California, Davis*

**ROBERT G. MEYER**
*University of California, Berkeley*

**WILEY-INDIA**

**ANALYSIS AND DESIGN OF ANALOG INTEGRATED CIRCUITS**
*Fourth Edition*

Wiley also publishes its books in a variety of electronic formats. Some content that appears in print may not be available in electronic books. For more information about Wiley products, visit our website at www.wiley.com.

Reprint: 2008

Printed at: Gopaljee Enterprises, Delhi

ISBN : 978-81-265-1569-1

*To Liz, Barbara, Robin, and Judy*

# Preface

In the 23 years since the publication of the first edition of this book, the field of analog integrated circuits has developed and matured. The initial groundwork was laid in bipolar technology, followed by a rapid evolution of MOS analog integrated circuits. Furthermore, BiCMOS technology (incorporating both bipolar and CMOS devices on one chip) has emerged as a serious contender to the original technologies. A key issue is that CMOS technologies have become dominant in building digital circuits because CMOS digital circuits are smaller and dissipate less power than their bipolar counterparts. To reduce system cost and power dissipation, analog and digital circuits are now often integrated together, providing a strong economic incentive to use CMOS-compatible analog circuits. As a result, an important question in many applications is whether to use pure CMOS or a BiCMOS technology. Although somewhat more expensive to fabricate, BiCMOS allows the designer to use both bipolar and MOS devices to their best advantage, and also allows innovative combinations of the characteristics of both devices. In addition, BiCMOS can reduce the design time by allowing direct use of many existing cells in realizing a given analog circuit function. On the other hand, the main advantage of pure CMOS is that it offers the lowest overall cost. Twenty years ago, CMOS technologies were only fast enough to support applications at audio frequencies. However, the continuing reduction of the minimum feature size in integrated-circuit (IC) technologies has greatly increased the maximum operating frequencies, and CMOS technologies have become fast enough for many new applications as a result. For example, the required bandwidth in video applications is about 4 MHz, requiring bipolar technologies as recently as 15 years ago. Now, however, CMOS can easily accommodate the required bandwidth for video and is even being used for radio-frequency applications.

In this fourth edition, we have combined the consideration of MOS and bipolar circuits into a unified treatment that also includes MOS-bipolar connections made possible by BiCMOS technology. We have written this edition so that instructors can easily select topics related to only CMOS circuits, only bipolar circuits, or a combination of both. We believe that it has become increasingly important for the analog circuit designer to have a thorough appreciation of the similarities and differences between MOS and bipolar devices, and to be able to design with either one where this is appropriate.

Since the SPICE computer analysis program is now readily available to virtually all electrical engineering students and professionals, we have included extensive use of SPICE in this edition, particularly as an integral part of many problems. We have used computer analysis as it is most commonly employed in the engineering design process—both as a more accurate check on hand calculations, and also as a tool to examine complex circuit behavior beyond the scope of hand analysis. In the problem sets, we have also included a number of open-ended design problems to expose the reader to real-world situations where a whole range of circuit solutions may be found to satisfy a given performance specification.

This book is intended to be useful both as a text for students and as a reference book for practicing engineers. For class use, each chapter includes many worked problems; the problem sets at the end of each chapter illustrate the practical applications of the material in the text. All the authors have had extensive industrial experience in IC design as well as in the teaching of courses on this subject, and this experience is reflected in the choice of text material and in the problem sets.

Although this book is concerned largely with the analysis and design of ICs, a considerable amount of material is also included on applications. In practice, these two subjects are closely linked, and a knowledge of both is essential for designers and users of ICs. The latter compose the larger group by far, and we believe that a working knowledge of IC design is a great advantage to an IC user. This is particularly apparent when the user must choose from among a number of competing designs to satisfy a particular need. An understanding of the IC structure is then useful in evaluating the relative desirability of the different designs under extremes of environment or in the presence of variations in supply voltage. In addition, the IC user is in a much better position to interpret a manufacturer's data if he or she has a working knowledge of the internal operation of the integrated circuit.

The contents of this book stem largely from courses on analog integrated circuits given at the University of California at the Berkeley and Davis campuses. The courses are undergraduate electives and first-year graduate courses. The book is structured so that it can be used as the basic text for a sequence of such courses. The more advanced material is found at the end of each chapter or in an appendix so that a first course in analog integrated circuits can omit this material without loss of continuity. An outline of each chapter is given below together with suggestions for material to be covered in such a first course. It is assumed that the course consists of three hours of lecture per week over a 15-week semester and that the students have a working knowledge of Laplace transforms and frequency-domain circuit analysis. It is also assumed that the students have had an introductory course in electronics so that they are familiar with the principles of transistor operation and with the functioning of simple analog circuits. Unless otherwise stated, each chapter requires three to four lecture hours to cover.

Chapter 1 contains a summary of bipolar transistor and MOS transistor device physics. We suggest spending one week on selected topics from this chapter, the choice of topics depending on the background of the students. The material of Chapters 1 and 2 is quite important in IC design because there is significant interaction between circuit and device design, as will be seen in later chapters. A thorough understanding of the influence of device fabrication on device characteristics is essential.

Chapter 2 is concerned with the technology of IC fabrication and is largely descriptive. One lecture on this material should suffice if the students are assigned to read the chapter.

Chapter 3 deals with the characteristics of elementary transistor connections. The material on one-transistor amplifiers should be a review for students at the senior and graduate levels and can be assigned as reading. The section on two-transistor amplifiers can be covered in about three hours, with greatest emphasis on differential pairs. The material on device mismatch effects in differential amplifiers can be covered to the extent that time allows.

In Chapter 4, the important topics of current mirrors and active loads are considered. These configurations are basic building blocks in modern analog IC design, and this material should be covered in full, with the exception of the material on band-gap references and the material in the appendices.

Chapter 5 is concerned with output stages and methods of delivering output power to a load. Integrated-circuit realizations of Class A, Class B, and Class AB output stages are described, as well as methods of output-stage protection. A selection of topics from this chapter should be covered.

Chapter 6 deals with the design of operational amplifiers (op amps). Illustrative examples of dc and ac analysis in both MOS and bipolar op amps are performed in detail, and the limitations of the basic op amps are described. The design of op amps with improved characteristics in both MOS and bipolar technologies is considered. This key chapter on amplifier design requires at least six hours.

In Chapter 7, the frequency response of amplifiers is considered. The zero-value time-constant technique is introduced for the calculations of the $-3$-dB frequency of complex circuits. The material of this chapter should be considered in full.

Chapter 8 describes the analysis of feedback circuits. Two different types of analysis are presented: two-port and return-ratio analyses. Either approach should be covered in full with the section on voltage regulators assigned as reading.

Chapter 9 deals with the frequency response and stability of feedback circuits and should be covered up to the section on root locus. Time may not permit a detailed discussion of root locus, but some introduction to this topic can be given.

In a 15-week semester, coverage of the above material leaves about two weeks for Chapters 10, 11, and 12. A selection of topics from these chapters can be chosen as follows. Chapter 10 deals with nonlinear analog circuits, and portions of this chapter up to Section 10.3 could be covered in a first course. Chapter 11 is a comprehensive treatment of noise in integrated circuits, and material up to and including Section 11.4 is suitable. Chapter 12 describes fully differential operational amplifiers and common-mode feedback and may be best suited for a second course.

We are grateful to the following colleagues for their suggestions for and/or evaluation of this edition: R. Jacob Baker, Bernhard E. Boser, A. Paul Brokaw, John N. Churchill, David W. Cline, Ozan E. Erdoğan, John W. Fattaruso, Weinan Gao, Edwin W. Greeneich, Alex Gros-Balthazard, Tünde Gyurics, Ward J. Helms, Timothy H. Hu, Shafiq M. Jamal, John P. Keane, Haideh Khorramabadi, Pak-Kim Lau, Thomas W. Matthews, Krishnaswamy Nagaraj, Khalil Najafi, Borivoje Nikolić, Robert A. Pease, Lawrence T. Pileggi, Edgar Sánchez-Sinencio, Bang-Sup Song, Richard R. Spencer, Eric J. Swanson, Andrew Y. J. Szeto, Yannis P. Tsividis, Srikanth Vaidianathan, T. R. Viswanathan, Chorng-Kuang Wang, and Dong Wang. We are also grateful to Kenneth C. Dyer for allowing us to use on the cover of this book a die photograph of an integrated circuit he designed and to Zoe Marlowe for her assistance with word processing. Finally, we would like to thank the people at Wiley and Publication Services for their efforts in producing this fourth edition.

The material in this book has been greatly influenced by our association with Donald O. Pederson, and we acknowledge his contributions.

*Berkeley and Davis, CA, 2001*

*Paul R. Gray*
*Paul J. Hurst*
*Stephen H. Lewis*
*Robert G. Meyer*

# Contents

**CHAPTER 4**

# Current Mirrors, Active Loads, and References    253

**Symbol Convention**

Unless otherwise stated, the following symbol convention is used in this book. *Bias* or *dc* quantities, such as transistor collector current $I_C$ and collector-emitter voltage $V_{CE}$, are represented by uppercase symbols with uppercase subscripts. *Small-signal* quantities, such as the incremental change in transistor collector current $i_c$, are represented by lowercase symbols with lowercase subscripts. Elements such as transconductance $g_m$ in small-signal equivalent circuits are represented in the same way. Finally, quantities such as *total* collector current $I_c$, which represent the sum of the bias quantity *and* the signal quantity, are represented by an uppercase symbol with a lowercase subscript.

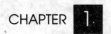

# Models for Integrated-Circuit Active Devices

## 1.1 Introduction

The analysis and design of integrated circuits depend heavily on the utilization of suitable models for integrated-circuit components. This is true in hand analysis, where fairly simple models are generally used, and in computer analysis, where more complex models are encountered. Since any analysis is only as accurate as the model used, it is essential that the circuit designer have a thorough understanding of the origin of the models commonly utilized and the degree of approximation involved in each.

This chapter deals with the derivation of large-signal and small-signal models for integrated-circuit devices. The treatment begins with a consideration of the properties of *pn* junctions, which are basic parts of most integrated-circuit elements. Since this book is primarily concerned with circuit analysis and design, no attempt has been made to produce a comprehensive treatment of semiconductor physics. The emphasis is on summarizing the basic aspects of semiconductor-device behavior and indicating how these can be modeled by equivalent circuits.

## 1.2 Depletion Region of a *pn* Junction

The properties of reverse-biased *pn* junctions have an important influence on the characteristics of many integrated-circuit components. For example, reverse-biased *pn* junctions exist between many integrated-circuit elements and the underlying substrate, and these junctions all contribute voltage-dependent parasitic capacitances. In addition, a number of important characteristics of active devices, such as breakdown voltage and output resistance, depend directly on the properties of the depletion region of a reverse-biased *pn* junction. Finally, the basic operation of the junction field-effect transistor is controlled by the width of the depletion region of a *pn* junction. Because of its importance and application to many different problems, an analysis of the depletion region of a reverse-biased *pn* junction is considered below. The properties of forward-biased *pn* junctions are treated in Section 1.3 when bipolar-transistor operation is described.

Consider a *pn* junction under reverse bias as shown in Fig. 1.1. Assume *constant doping densities* of $N_D$ atoms/cm$^3$ in the *n*-type material and $N_A$ atoms/cm$^3$ in the *p*-type material. (The characteristics of junctions with nonconstant doping densities will be described later.) Due to the difference in carrier concentrations in the *p*-type and *n*-type regions, there exists a region at the junction where the mobile holes and electrons have been removed, leaving the fixed acceptor and donor ions. Each acceptor atom carries a negative charge and each donor atom carries a positive charge, so that the region near the junction is one of significant space charge and resulting high electric field. This is called

Figure 1.1  The abrupt junction under reverse bias $V_R$. (a) Schematic. (b) Charge density. (c) Electric field. (d) Electrostatic potential.

the *depletion* region or *space-charge* region. It is assumed that the edges of the depletion region are sharply defined as shown in Fig. 1.1, and this is a good approximation in most cases.

For zero applied bias, there exists a voltage $\psi_0$ across the junction called the *built-in potential*. This potential opposes the diffusion of mobile holes and electrons across the junction in equilibrium and has a value[1]

$$\psi_0 = V_T \ln \frac{N_A N_D}{n_i^2}  \tag{1.1}$$

where

$$V_T = \frac{kT}{q} \approx 26\,\text{mV} \quad \text{at} \quad 300°\text{K}$$

the quantity $n_i$ is the intrinsic carrier concentration in a pure sample of the semiconductor and $n_i \approx 1.5 \times 10^{10}\,\text{cm}^{-3}$ at $300°\text{K}$ for silicon.

In Fig. 1.1 the built-in potential is augmented by the applied reverse bias, $V_R$, and the total voltage across the junction is $(\psi_0 + V_R)$. If the depletion region penetrates a distance $W_1$ into the $p$-type region and $W_2$ into the $n$-type region, then we require

$$W_1 N_A = W_2 N_D  \tag{1.2}$$

because the total charge per unit area on either side of the junction must be equal in magnitude but opposite in sign.

Poisson's equation in one dimension requires that

$$\frac{d^2V}{dx^2} = -\frac{\rho}{\epsilon} = \frac{qN_A}{\epsilon} \quad \text{for} \quad -W_1 < x < 0 \tag{1.3}$$

where $\rho$ is the charge density, $q$ is the electron charge ($1.6 \times 10^{-19}$ coulomb), and $\epsilon$ is the permittivity of the silicon ($1.04 \times 10^{-12}$ farad/cm). The permittivity is often expressed as

$$\epsilon = K_S \epsilon_0 \tag{1.4}$$

where $K_S$ is the dielectric constant of silicon and $\epsilon_0$ is the permittivity of free space ($8.86 \times 10^{-14}$ F/cm). Integration of (1.3) gives

$$\frac{dV}{dx} = \frac{qN_A}{\epsilon}x + C_1 \tag{1.5}$$

where $C_1$ is a constant. However, the electric field $\mathscr{E}$ is given by

$$\mathscr{E} = -\frac{dV}{dx} = -\left(\frac{qN_A}{\epsilon}x + C_1\right) \tag{1.6}$$

Since there is zero electric field outside the depletion region, a boundary condition is

$$\mathscr{E} = 0 \quad \text{for} \quad x = -W_1$$

and use of this condition in (1.6) gives

$$\mathscr{E} = -\frac{qN_A}{\epsilon}(x + W_1) = -\frac{dV}{dx} \quad \text{for} \quad -W_1 < x < 0 \tag{1.7}$$

Thus the dipole of charge existing at the junction gives rise to an electric field that varies linearly with distance.

Integration of (1.7) gives

$$V = \frac{qN_A}{\epsilon}\left(\frac{x^2}{2} + W_1 x\right) + C_2 \tag{1.8}$$

If the zero for potential is arbitrarily taken to be the potential of the neutral *p*-type region, then a second boundary condition is

$$V = 0 \quad \text{for} \quad x = -W_1$$

and use of this in (1.8) gives

$$V = \frac{qN_A}{\epsilon}\left(\frac{x^2}{2} + W_1 x + \frac{W_1^2}{2}\right) \quad \text{for} \quad -W_1 < x < 0 \tag{1.9}$$

At $x = 0$, we define $V = V_1$, and then (1.9) gives

$$V_1 = \frac{qN_A}{\epsilon}\frac{W_1^2}{2} \tag{1.10}$$

If the potential difference from $x = 0$ to $x = W_2$ is $V_2$, then it follows that

$$V_2 = \frac{qN_D}{\epsilon}\frac{W_2^2}{2} \tag{1.11}$$

and thus the total voltage across the junction is

$$\psi_0 + V_R = V_1 + V_2 = \frac{q}{2\epsilon}(N_A W_1^2 + N_D W_2^2) \tag{1.12}$$

Substitution of (1.2) in (1.12) gives

$$\psi_0 + V_R = \frac{qW_1^2 N_A}{2\epsilon}\left(1 + \frac{N_A}{N_D}\right) \tag{1.13}$$

From (1.13), the penetration of the depletion layer into the p-type region is

$$W_1 = \left[\frac{2\epsilon(\psi_0 + V_R)}{qN_A\left(1 + \frac{N_A}{N_D}\right)}\right]^{1/2} \tag{1.14}$$

*depletion width*

Similarly

*$w, w_1 \propto (\psi_0 + V_R)$*

$$W_2 = \left[\frac{2\epsilon(\psi_0 + V_R)}{qN_D\left(1 + \frac{N_D}{N_A}\right)}\right]^{1/2} \tag{1.15}$$

Equations 1.14 and 1.15 show that the depletion regions extend into the p-type and n-type regions in *inverse* relation to the impurity concentrations and in proportion to $\sqrt{\psi_0 + V_R}$. If either $N_D$ or $N_A$ is much larger than the other, the depletion region exists almost entirely in the *lightly doped* region.

■ **EXAMPLE**

An abrupt pn junction in silicon has doping densities $N_A = 10^{15}$ atoms/cm³ and $N_D = 10^{16}$ atoms/cm³. Calculate the junction built-in potential, the depletion-layer depths, and the maximum field with 10 V reverse bias.

From (1.1)

$$\psi_0 = 26\ln\frac{10^{15}\times 10^{16}}{2.25\times 10^{20}}\,\text{mV} = 638\,\text{mV}\quad\text{at}\quad 300°\text{K}$$

From (1.14) the depletion-layer depth in the p-type region is

$$W_1 = \left(\frac{2\times 1.04\times 10^{-12}\times 10.64}{1.6\times 10^{-19}\times 10^{15}\times 1.1}\right)^{1/2} = 3.5\times 10^{-4}\text{cm}$$

$$= 3.5\,\mu\text{m}\quad(\text{where }1\,\mu\text{m} = 1\text{ micrometer} = 10^{-6}\text{ m})$$

The depletion-layer depth in the more heavily doped n-type region is

$$W_2 = \left(\frac{2\times 1.04\times 10^{-12}\times 10.64}{1.6\times 10^{-19}\times 10^{16}\times 11}\right)^{1/2} = 0.35\times 10^{-4}\text{ cm} = 0.35\,\mu\text{m}$$

Finally, from (1.7) the maximum field that occurs for $x = 0$ is

$$\mathscr{E}_{max} = -\frac{qN_A}{\epsilon}W_1 = -1.6\times 10^{-19}\times\frac{10^{15}\times 3.5\times 10^{-4}}{1.04\times 10^{-12}}$$

$$= -5.4\times 10^4\text{ V/cm}$$

■ Note the large magnitude of this electric field.

### 1.2.1 Depletion-Region Capacitance

Since there is a *voltage-dependent charge Q* associated with the depletion region, we can calculate a small-signal capacitance $C_j$ as follows:

$$C_j = \frac{dQ}{dV_R} = \frac{dQ}{dW_1}\frac{dW_1}{dV_R} \tag{1.16}$$

Now

$$dQ = AqN_A dW_1 \tag{1.17}$$

where $A$ is the cross-sectional area of the junction. Differentiation of (1.14) gives

$$\frac{dW_1}{dV_R} = \left[\frac{\epsilon}{2qN_A\left(1 + \dfrac{N_A}{N_D}\right)(\psi_0 + V_R)}\right]^{1/2} \tag{1.18}$$

Use of (1.17) and (1.18) in (1.16) gives

$$C_j = A\left[\frac{q\epsilon N_A N_D}{2(N_A + N_D)}\right]^{1/2}\frac{1}{\sqrt{\psi_0 + V_R}} \tag{1.19}$$

The above equation was derived for the case of reverse bias $V_R$ applied to the diode. However, it is valid for positive bias voltages as long as the forward current flow is small. Thus, if $V_D$ represents the bias on the junction (positive for forward bias, negative for reverse bias), then (1.19) can be written as

$$C_j = A\left[\frac{q\epsilon N_A N_D}{2(N_A + N_D)}\right]^{1/2}\frac{1}{\sqrt{\psi_0 - V_D}} \tag{1.20}$$

$$= \frac{C_{j0}}{\sqrt{1 - \dfrac{V_D}{\psi_0}}} \tag{1.21}$$

where $C_{j0}$ is the value of $C_j$ for $V_D = 0$.

Equations 1.20 and 1.21 were derived using the assumption of constant doping in the *p*-type and *n*-type regions. However, many practical diffused junctions more closely approach a *graded* doping profile as shown in Fig. 1.2. In this case a similar calculation yields

$$C_j = \frac{C_{j0}}{\sqrt[3]{1 - \dfrac{V_D}{\psi_0}}} \tag{1.22}$$

Note that both (1.21) and (1.22) predict values of $C_j$ approaching infinity as $V_D$ approaches $\psi_0$. However, the current flow in the diode is then appreciable and the equations no longer valid. A more exact analysis[2,3] of the behavior of $C_j$ as a function of $V_D$ gives the result shown in Fig. 1.3. For forward bias voltages up to about $\psi_0/2$, the values of $C_j$ predicted by (1.21) are very close to the more accurate value. As an approximation, some computer programs approximate $C_j$ for $V_D > \psi_0/2$ by a linear extrapolation of (1.21) or (1.22).

If $V_{D \text{ forward}} \approx \psi_0$, No forward current due to built in $Vi$

Figure 1.2 Charge density versus distance in a graded junction.

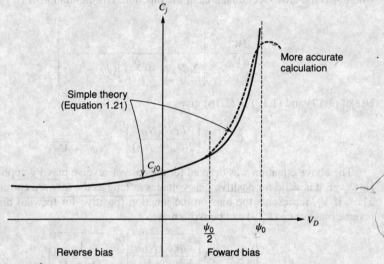

Figure 1.3 Behavior of $pn$ junction depletion-layer capacitance $C_j$ as a function of bias voltage $V_D$.

■ EXAMPLE

If the zero-bias capacitance of a diffused junction is 3 pF and $\psi_0 = 0.5$ V, calculate the capacitance with 10 V reverse bias. Assume the doping profile can be approximated by an abrupt junction.

From (1.21)

$$C_j = \frac{3}{\sqrt{1 + \dfrac{10}{0.5}}}\text{pF} = 0.65 \text{ pF}$$

■

### 1.2.2 Junction Breakdown

From Fig. 1.1c it can be seen that the maximum electric field in the depletion region occurs at the junction, and for an abrupt junction (1.7) yields a value

$$\mathscr{E}_{\max} = -\frac{qN_A}{\epsilon} W_1 \qquad (1.23)$$

Substitution of (1.14) in (1.23) gives

$$|\mathscr{E}_{max}| = \left[ \frac{2qN_AN_DV_R}{\epsilon\,(N_A + N_D)} \right]^{1/2} \tag{1.24}$$

where $\psi_0$ has been neglected. Equation 1.24 shows that the maximum field increases as the doping density increases and the reverse bias increases. Although useful for indicating the functional dependence of $\mathscr{E}_{max}$ on other variables, this equation is strictly valid for an ideal plane junction only. Practical junctions tend to have edge effects that cause somewhat higher values of $\mathscr{E}_{max}$ due to a concentration of the field at the curved edges of the junction.

Any reverse-biased *pn* junction has a small reverse current flow due to the presence of minority-carrier holes and electrons in the vicinity of the depletion region. These are swept across the depletion region by the field and contribute to the leakage current of the junction. As the reverse bias on the junction is increased, the maximum field increases and the carriers acquire increasing amounts of energy between lattice collisions in the depletion region. At a critical field $\mathscr{E}_{crit}$ the carriers traversing the depletion region acquire sufficient energy to create new hole-electron pairs in collisions with silicon atoms. This is called the *avalanche process* and leads to a sudden increase in the reverse-bias leakage current since the newly created carriers are also capable of producing avalanche. The value of $\mathscr{E}_{crit}$ is about $3 \times 10^5$ V/cm for junction doping densities in the range of $10^{15}$ to $10^{16}$ atoms/cm³, but it increases slowly as the doping density increases and reaches about $10^6$ V/cm for doping densities of $10^{18}$ atoms/cm³.

A typical *I-V* characteristic for a junction diode is shown in Fig. 1.4, and the effect of avalanche breakdown is seen by the large increase in reverse current, which occurs as the reverse bias approaches the breakdown voltage *BV*. This corresponds to the maximum field $\mathscr{E}_{max}$ approaching $\mathscr{E}_{crit}$. It has been found empirically[4] that if the normal reverse bias current of the diode is $I_R$ with no avalanche effect, then the actual reverse current near the breakdown voltage is

$$I_{RA} = MI_R \tag{1.25}$$

**Figure 1.4** Typical *I-V* characteristic of a junction diode showing avalanche breakdown.

where $M$ is the *multiplication factor* defined by

$$M = \cfrac{1}{1 - \left(\cfrac{V_R}{BV}\right)^n} \qquad (1.26)$$

In this equation, $V_R$ is the reverse bias on the diode and $n$ has a value between 3 and 6.

The operation of a $pn$ junction in the breakdown region is not inherently destructive. However, the avalanche current flow must be limited by external resistors in order to prevent excessive power dissipation from occurring at the junction and causing damage to the device. Diodes operated in the avalanche region are widely used as voltage references and are called *Zener diodes*. There is another, related process called *Zener breakdown*,[5] which is different from the avalanche breakdown described above. Zener breakdown occurs only in very heavily doped junctions where the electric field becomes large enough (even with small reverse-bias voltages) to strip electrons away from the valence bonds. This process is called *tunneling*, and there is no multiplication effect as in avalanche breakdown. Although the Zener breakdown mechanism is important only for breakdown voltages below about 6 V, all breakdown diodes are commonly referred to as Zener diodes.

The calculations so far have been concerned with the breakdown characteristic of plane abrupt junctions. Practical diffused junctions differ in some respects from these results and the characteristics of these junctions have been calculated and tabulated for use by designers.[5] In particular, edge effects in practical diffused junctions can result in breakdown voltages as much as 50 percent below the value calculated for a plane junction.

■  **EXAMPLE**

An abrupt plane $pn$ junction has doping densities $N_A = 5 \times 10^{15}$ atoms/cm$^3$ and $N_D = 10^{16}$ atoms/cm$^3$. Calculate the breakdown voltage if $\mathscr{E}_{crit} = 3 \times 10^5$ V/cm.

The breakdown voltage is calculated using $\mathscr{E}_{max} = \mathscr{E}_{crit}$ in (1.24) to give

$$
\begin{aligned}
BV &= \frac{\epsilon\,(N_A + N_D)}{2qN_A N_D}\mathscr{E}_{crit}^2 \\
&= \frac{1.04 \times 10^{-12} \times 15 \times 10^{15}}{2 \times 1.6 \times 10^{-19} \times 5 \times 10^{15} \times 10^{16}} \times 9 \times 10^{10}\ \text{V} \\
&= 88\ \text{V}
\end{aligned}
$$

■

## 1.3 Large-Signal Behavior of Bipolar Transistors

In this section, the large-signal or dc behavior of bipolar transistors is considered. Large-signal models are developed for the calculation of total currents and voltages in transistor circuits, and such effects as breakdown voltage limitations, which are usually not included in models, are also considered. Second-order effects, such as current-gain variation with collector current and Early voltage, can be important in many circuits and are treated in detail.

The sign conventions used for bipolar transistor currents and voltages are shown in Fig. 1.5. All bias currents for both $npn$ and $pnp$ transistors are assumed positive going into the device.

Figure 1.5 Bipolar transistor sign convention.

npn          pnp

$\boxed{V_{BE}: \text{fwd}, \; V_{BC}: \text{reverse}}$

## 1.3.1 Large-Signal Models in the Forward-Active Region

A typical *npn* planar bipolar transistor structure is shown in Fig. 1.6a, where collector, base, and emitter are labeled C, B, and E, respectively. The method of fabricating such transistor structures is described in Chapter 2. It is shown there that the impurity doping density in the base and the emitter of such a transistor is not constant but varies with distance from the top surface. However, many of the characteristics of such a device can be predicted by analyzing the idealized transistor structure shown in Fig. 1.6b. In this structure the base and emitter doping densities are assumed constant, and this is sometimes called a *uniform-base* transistor. Where possible in the following analyses, the equations for the uniform-base analysis are expressed in a form that applies also to nonuniform-base transistors.

A cross section AA' is taken through the device of Fig. 1.6b and carrier concentrations along this section are plotted in Fig. 1.6c. Hole concentrations are denoted by p and electron concentrations by n with subscripts p or n representing p-type or n-type regions. The n-type emitter and collector regions are distinguished by subscripts E and C, respectively. The carrier concentrations shown in Fig. 1.6c apply to a device in the *forward-active region*. That is, the base-emitter junction is forward biased and the base-collector junction is reverse biased. The minority-carrier concentrations in the base at the edges of the depletion regions can be calculated from a Boltzmann approximation to the Fermi-Dirac distribution function to give[6]

$$n_p(0) = n_{po} \exp \frac{V_{BE}}{V_T} \tag{1.27}$$

$$n_p(W_B) = n_{po} \exp \frac{V_{BC}}{V_T} \approx 0 \tag{1.28}$$

where $W_B$ is the width of the base from the base-emitter depletion layer edge to the base-collector depletion layer edge and $n_{po}$ is the equilibrium concentration of electrons in the base. Note that $V_{BC}$ is negative for an *npn* transistor in the forward-active region and thus $n_p(W_B)$ is very small. Low-level injection conditions are assumed in the derivation of (1.27) and (1.28). This means that the minority-carrier concentrations are always assumed much smaller than the majority-carrier concentration.

If *recombination* of holes and electrons in the base is small, it can be shown that[7] the minority-carrier concentration $n_p(x)$ in the base varies *linearly* with distance. Thus a straight line can be drawn joining the concentrations at $x = 0$ and $x = W_B$ in Fig. 1.6c.

For charge neutrality in the base, it is necessary that

$$N_A + n_p(x) = p_p(x) \tag{1.29}$$

**Figure 1.6** (*a*) Cross section of a typical *npn* planar bipolar transistor structure. (*b*) Idealized transistor structure. (*c*) Carrier concentrations along the cross section *AA'* of the transistor in (*b*). Uniform doping densities are assumed. (Not to scale.)

and thus

$$p_p(x) - n_p(x) = N_A \qquad (1.30)$$

where $p_p(x)$ is the hole concentration in the base and $N_A$ is the base doping density that is assumed constant. Equation 1.30 indicates that the hole and electron concentrations are separated by a constant amount and thus $p_p(x)$ also varies linearly with distance.

Collector current is produced by minority-carrier electrons in the base diffusing in the direction of the concentration gradient and being swept across the collector-base depletion region by the field existing there. The diffusion current density due to electrons in the base is

$$J_n = qD_n \frac{dn_p(x)}{dx} \qquad (1.31)$$

*[handwritten top margin: fwd —||— minority Carrer diffusion // ⟶ —||— n → holes diffusion (mjechon)]*

where $D_n$ is the diffusion constant for electrons. From Fig. 1.6c

$$J_n = -qD_n \frac{n_p(0)}{W_B}$$ (1.32)

If $I_C$ is the collector current and is taken as positive flowing *into* the collector, it follows from (1.32) that

$$I_C = qAD_n \frac{n_p(0)}{W_B}$$ (1.33)

where $A$ is the cross-sectional area of the emitter. Substitution of (1.27) into (1.33) gives

$$I_C = \frac{qAD_n n_{po}}{W_B} \exp \frac{V_{BE}}{V_T}$$ (1.34)

*[handwritten left: $W_B \ll L'$ (diffusion) ↳ recomb distance]*

$$= I_S \exp \frac{V_{BE}}{V_T}$$ (1.35)

where

$$I_S = \frac{qAD_n n_{po}}{W_B}$$ (1.36)

and $I_S$ is a constant used to describe the transfer characteristic of the transistor in the forward-active region. Equation 1.36 can be expressed in terms of the base doping density by noting that[8] (see Chapter 2)

$$n_{po} = \frac{n_i^2}{N_A}$$ (1.37)

and substitution of (1.37) in (1.36) gives     *[handwritten: A: emmitter area]*

$$I_S = \frac{qAD_n n_i^2}{W_B N_A} = \frac{qA\bar{D}_n n_i^2}{Q_B}$$ (1.38)

where $Q_B = W_B N_A$ is the number of doping atoms in the base per unit area of the emitter and $n_i$ is the intrinsic carrier concentration in silicon. In this form (1.38) applies to both uniform- and nonuniform-base transistors and $D_n$ has been replaced by $\bar{D}_n$, which is an average effective value for the electron diffusion constant in the base. This is necessary for nonuniform-base devices because the diffusion constant is a function of impurity concentration. Typical values of $I_S$ as given by (1.38) are from $10^{-14}$ to $10^{-16}$ A.

Equation 1.35 gives the collector current as a function of base-emitter voltage. The base current $I_B$ is also an important parameter and, at moderate current levels, consists of two major components. One of these ($I_{B1}$) represents recombination of holes and electrons in the base and is proportional to the minority-carrier charge $Q_e$ in the base. From Fig. 1.6c, the minority-carrier charge in the base is

$$Q_e = \frac{1}{2} n_p(0) W_B qA$$ (1.39)

and we have

$$I_{B1} = \frac{Q_e}{\tau_b} = \frac{1}{2} \frac{n_p(0) W_B qA}{\tau_b}$$ (1.40)

*[handwritten bottom: rev: —||— drift /swept comers: by E]*

where $\tau_b$ is the minority-carrier lifetime in the base. $I_{B1}$ represents a flow of majority holes from the base lead into the base region. Substitution of (1.27) in (1.40) gives

$$I_{B1} = \frac{1}{2} \frac{n_{po} W_B q A}{\tau_b} \exp \frac{V_{BE}}{V_T}$$

(1.41)

The second major component of base current (usually the dominant one in integrated-circuit $npn$ devices) is due to injection of holes from the base into the emitter. This current component depends on the gradient of minority-carrier holes in the emitter and is[9]

$$I_{B2} = \frac{qAD_p}{L_p} p_{nE}(0)$$

(1.42)

where $D_p$ is the diffusion constant for holes and $L_p$ is the diffusion length (assumed small) for holes in the emitter. $p_{nE}(0)$ is the concentration of holes in the emitter at the edge of the depletion region and is

$$p_{nE}(0) = p_{nEo} \exp \frac{V_{BE}}{V_T}$$

(1.43)

If $N_D$ is the donor atom concentration in the emitter (assumed constant), then

$$p_{nEo} \simeq \frac{n_i^2}{N_D}$$

(1.44)

The emitter is deliberately doped much more heavily than the base, making $N_D$ large and $p_{nEo}$ small, so that the base-current component, $I_{B2}$, is minimized. Substitution of (1.43) and (1.44) in (1.42) gives

$$I_{B2} = \frac{qAD_p}{L_p} \frac{n_i^2}{N_D} \exp \frac{V_{BE}}{V_T}$$

(1.45)

The total base current, $I_B$, is the sum of $I_{B1}$ and $I_{B2}$:

$$I_B = I_{B1} + I_{B2} = \left( \frac{1}{2} \frac{n_{po} W_B q A}{\tau_b} + \frac{qAD_p}{L_p} \frac{n_i^2}{N_D} \right) \exp \frac{V_{BE}}{V_T}$$

(1.46)

Although this equation was derived assuming uniform base and emitter doping, it gives the correct functional dependence of $I_B$ on device parameters for practical double-diffused nonuniform-base devices. Second-order components of $I_B$, which are important at low current levels, are considered later.

Since $I_C$ in (1.35) and $I_B$ in (1.46) are both proportional to $\exp(V_{BE}/V_T)$ in this analysis, the base current can be expressed in terms of collector current as

$$I_B = \frac{I_C}{\beta_F}$$

(1.47)

where $\beta_F$ is the forward current gain. An expression for $\beta_F$ can be calculated by substituting (1.34) and (1.46) in (1.47) to give

$$\beta_F = \frac{\dfrac{qAD_n n_{po}}{W_B}}{\dfrac{1}{2}\dfrac{n_{po} W_B q A}{\tau_b} + \dfrac{qAD_p n_i^2}{L_p N_D}} = \frac{1}{\dfrac{W_B^2}{2\tau_b D_n} + \dfrac{D_p}{D_n}\dfrac{W_B}{L_p}\dfrac{N_A}{N_D}}$$

(1.48)

where (1.37) has been substituted for $n_{po}$. Equation 1.48 shows that $\beta_F$ is maximized by minimizing the base width $W_B$ and maximizing the ratio of emitter to base doping densities $N_D/N_A$. Typical values of $\beta_F$ for $npn$ transistors in integrated circuits are 50 to 500, whereas lateral $pnp$ transistors (to be described in Chapter 2) have values 10 to 100. Finally, the emitter current is

$$I_E = -(I_C + I_B) = -\left(I_C + \frac{I_C}{\beta_F}\right) = -\frac{I_C}{\alpha_F} \qquad (1.49)$$

where

$$\alpha_F = \frac{\beta_F}{1 + \beta_F} \qquad (1.50)$$

The value of $\alpha_F$ can be expressed in terms of device parameters by substituting (1.48) in (1.50) to obtain

$$\alpha_F = \frac{1}{1 + \frac{1}{\beta_F}} = \frac{1}{1 + \frac{W_B^2}{2\tau_b D_n} + \frac{D_p}{D_n}\frac{W_B}{L_p}\frac{N_A}{N_D}} \approx \alpha_T \gamma \qquad (1.51)$$

where

$$\alpha_T = \frac{1}{1 + \frac{W_B^2}{2\tau_b D_n}} \qquad (1.51a)$$

$$\gamma = \frac{1}{1 + \frac{D_p}{D_n}\frac{W_B}{L_p}\frac{N_A}{N_D}} \qquad (1.51b)$$

The validity of (1.51) depends on $W_B^2/2\tau_b D_n \ll 1$ and $(D_p/D_n)(W_B/L_p)(N_A/N_D) \ll 1$, and this is always true if $\beta_F$ is large [see (1.48)]. The term $\gamma$ in (1.51) is called the *emitter injection efficiency* and is equal to the ratio of the electron current ($npn$ transistor) injected into the base from the emitter to the total hole and electron current crossing the base-emitter junction. Ideally $\gamma \rightarrow 1$, and this is achieved by making $N_D/N_A$ large and $W_B$ small. In that case very little reverse injection occurs from base to emitter.

The term $\alpha_T$ in (1.51) is called the *base transport factor* and represents the fraction of carriers injected into the base (from the emitter) that reach the collector. Ideally $\alpha_T \rightarrow 1$ and this is achieved by making $W_B$ small. It is evident from the above development that fabrication changes that cause $\alpha_T$ and $\gamma$ to approach unity also maximize the value of $\beta_F$ of the transistor.

The results derived above allow formulation of a large-signal model of the transistor suitable for bias-circuit calculations with devices in the forward-active region. One such circuit is shown in Fig. 1.7 and consists of a base-emitter diode to model (1.46) and a controlled collector-current generator to model (1.47). Note that the collector voltage ideally has no influence on the collector current and the collector node acts as a high-impedance current source. A simpler version of this equivalent circuit, which is often useful, is shown in Fig. 1.7b, where the input diode has been replaced by a battery with a value $V_{BE(on)}$, which is usually 0.6 to 0.7 V. This represents the fact that in the forward-active region the base-emitter voltage varies very little because of the steep slope of the exponential characteristic. In some circuits the temperature coefficient of $V_{BE(on)}$ is important, and a typical value for this is $-2$ mV/°C. The equivalent circuits of Fig. 1.7 apply for $npn$ transistors. For $pnp$ devices the corresponding equivalent circuits are shown in Fig. 1.8.

$$I_B = \frac{I_S}{\beta_F} \exp \frac{V_{BE}}{V_T}$$

(a)

(b)

**Figure 1.7** Large-signal models of *npn* transistors for use in bias calculations. (*a*) Circuit incorporating an input diode. (*b*) Simplified circuit with an input voltage source.

$$I_B = -\frac{I_S}{\beta_F} \exp -\frac{V_{BE}}{V_T}$$

(a)

(b)

**Figure 1.8** Large-signal models of *pnp* transistors corresponding to the circuits of Fig. 1.7.

## 1.3.2 Effects of Collector Voltage on Large-Signal Characteristics in the Forward-Active Region

In the analysis of the previous section, the collector-base junction was assumed reverse biased and ideally had no effect on the collector currents. This is a useful approximation for first-order calculations, but is not strictly true in practice. There are occasions where the influence of collector voltage on collector current is important, and this will now be investigated.

The collector voltage has a dramatic effect on the collector current in two regions of device operation. These are the saturation ($V_{CE}$ approaches zero) and breakdown ($V_{CE}$ very large) regions that will be considered later. For values of collector-emitter voltage $V_{CE}$ between these extremes, the collector current increases slowly as $V_{CE}$ increases. The reason for this can be seen from Fig. 1.9, which is a sketch of the minority-carrier concentration in the base of the transistor. Consider the effect of changes in $V_{CE}$ on the carrier concentration for constant $V_{BE}$. Since $V_{BE}$ is constant the change in $V_{CB}$ equals the change in $V_{CE}$ and this causes an increase in the collector-base depletion-layer width as shown. The change in the base width of the transistor, $\Delta W_B$, equals the change in the depletion-layer width and causes an increase $\Delta I_C$ in the collector current.

From (1.35) and (1.38) we have

$$I_C = \frac{qA\bar{D}_n n_i^2}{Q_B} \exp \frac{V_{BE}}{V_T} \tag{1.52}$$

Differentiation of (1.52) yields

$$\frac{\partial I_C}{\partial V_{CE}} = -\frac{qA\bar{D}_n n_i^2}{Q_B^2} \left( \exp \frac{V_{BE}}{V_T} \right) \frac{dQ_B}{dV_{CE}} \tag{1.53}$$

and substitution of (1.52) in (1.53) gives

$$\frac{\partial I_C}{\partial V_{CE}} = -\frac{I_C}{Q_B} \frac{dQ_B}{dV_{CE}} \tag{1.54}$$

→ Base-width modulation

**Figure 1.9** Effect of increases in $V_{CE}$ on the collector depletion region and base width of a bipolar transistor.

*(handwritten annotations on figure)*
→ reverse

$V_{CC}$ changes the depletion width → $W_B$

$V_{CE}\uparrow$, $W_B\downarrow$

For a uniform-base transistor $Q_B = W_B N_A$, and (1.54) becomes

$$\frac{\partial I_C}{\partial V_{CE}} = -\frac{I_C}{W_B}\frac{dW_B}{dV_{CE}} \qquad (1.55)$$

Note that since the base width *decreases* as $V_{CE}$ increases, $dW_B/dV_{CE}$ in (1.55) is negative and thus $\partial I_C/\partial V_{CE}$ is positive. The magnitude of $dW_B/dV_{CE}$ can be calculated from (1.18) for a uniform-base transistor. This equation predicts that $dW_B/dV_{CE}$ is a function of the bias value of $V_{CE}$, but the variation is typically small for a reverse-biased junction and $dW_B/dV_{CE}$ is often assumed constant. The resulting predictions agree adequately with experimental results.

Equation 1.55 shows that $\partial I_C/\partial V_{CE}$ is proportional to the collector-bias current and inversely proportional to the transistor base width. Thus narrow-base transistors show a greater dependence of $I_C$ on $V_{CE}$ in the forward-active region. The dependence of $\partial I_C/\partial V_{CE}$ on $I_C$ results in typical transistor output characteristics as shown in Fig. 1.10. In accordance with the assumptions made in the foregoing analysis, these characteristics are shown for constant values of $V_{BE}$. However, in most integrated-circuit transistors the base current is dependent only on $V_{BE}$ and not on $V_{CE}$, and thus constant-base-current characteristics can often be used in the following calculation. The reason for this is that the base current is usually dominated by the $I_{B2}$ component of (1.45), which has no dependence on $V_{CE}$. Extrapolation of the characteristics of Fig. 1.10 back to the $V_{CE}$ axis gives an intercept $V_A$ called the Early voltage, where

$$V_A = \frac{I_C}{\dfrac{\partial I_C}{\partial V_{CE}}} \qquad (1.56)$$

Substitution of (1.55) in (1.56) gives

$$V_A = -W_B \frac{dV_{CE}}{dW_B} \qquad (1.57)$$

which is a constant, independent of $I_C$. Thus all the characteristics extrapolate to the same point on the $V_{CE}$ axis. The variation of $I_C$ with $V_{CE}$ is called the Early effect, and $V_A$ is a common model parameter for circuit-analysis computer programs. Typical values of $V_A$

**Figure 1.10**  Bipolar transistor output characteristics showing the Early voltage, $V_A$.

for integrated-circuit transistors are 15 to 100 V. The inclusion of Early effect in dc bias calculations is usually limited to computer analysis because of the complexity introduced into the calculation. However, the influence of the Early effect is often dominant in small-signal calculations for high-gain circuits and this point will be considered later.

Finally, the influence of Early effect on the transistor large-signal characteristics in the forward-active region can be represented approximately by modifying (1.35) to

$$I_C = I_S\left(1 + \frac{V_{CE}}{V_A}\right)\exp\frac{V_{BE}}{V_T} \quad\longrightarrow \mathcal{I}_{mp} \tag{1.58}$$

This is a common means of representing the device output characteristics for computer simulation.

### 1.3.3 Saturation and Inverse-Active Regions

Saturation is a region of device operation that is usually avoided in analog circuits because the transistor gain is very low in this region. Saturation is much more commonly encountered in digital circuits, where it provides a well-specified output voltage that represents a logic state.

In saturation, both emitter-base and collector-base junctions are forward biased. Consequently, the collector-emitter voltage $V_{CE}$ is quite small and is usually in the range 0.05 to 0.3 V. The carrier concentrations in a saturated $npn$ transistor with uniform base doping are shown in Fig. 1.11. The minority-carrier concentration in the base at the edge of the depletion region is again given by (1.28) as

$$n_p(W_B) = n_{po}\exp\frac{V_{BC}}{V_T} \tag{1.59}$$

but since $V_{BC}$ is now positive, the value of $n_p(W_B)$ is no longer negligible. Consequently, changes in $V_{CE}$ with $V_{BE}$ held constant (which cause equal changes in $V_{BC}$) directly affect $n_p(W_B)$. Since the collector current is proportional to the slope of the minority-carrier concentration in the base [see (1.31)], it is also proportional to $[n_p(0) - n_p(W_B)]$ from Fig. 1.11. Thus changes in $n_p(W_B)$ directly affect the collector current, and the collector node of the transistor appears to have a *low impedance*. As $V_{CE}$ is decreased in saturation with $V_{BE}$ held constant, $V_{BC}$ increases, as does $n_p(W_B)$ from (1.59). Thus from Fig. 1.11 the collector

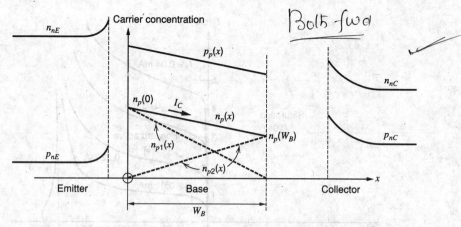

Figure 1.11  Carrier concentrations in a saturated *npn* transistor. (Not to scale.)

current decreases because the slope of the carrier concentration decreases. This gives rise to the saturation region of the $I_C - V_{CE}$ characteristic shown in Fig. 1.12. The slope of the $I_C - V_{CE}$ characteristic in this region is largely determined by the resistance in series with the collector lead due to the finite resistivity of the *n*-type collector material. A useful model for the transistor in this region is shown in Fig. 1.13 and consists of a fixed voltage source to represent $V_{BE(on)}$, and a fixed voltage source to represent the collector-emitter voltage $V_{CE(sat)}$. A more accurate but more complex model includes a resistor in series with the collector. This resistor can have a value ranging from 20 to 500 $\Omega$, depending on the device structure.

An additional aspect of transistor behavior in the saturation region is apparent from Fig. 1.11. For a given collector current, there is now a much larger amount of stored charge in the base than there is in the forward-active region. Thus the base-current contribution represented by (1.41) will be larger in saturation. In addition, since the collector-base junction is now forward biased, there is a new base-current component due to injection of carriers from the base to the collector. These two effects result in a base current $I_B$ in saturation, which is larger than in the forward-active region for a given collector current $I_C$. Ratio $I_C/I_B$ in saturation is often referred to as the *forced β* and is always less than $β_F$. As the forced β is made lower with respect to $β_F$, the device is said to be more *heavily saturated*.

The minority-carrier concentration in saturation shown in Fig. 1.11 is a straight line joining the two end points, assuming that recombination is small. This can be represented as a linear superposition of the two dotted distributions as shown. The justification for this is that the terminal currents depend *linearly* on the concentrations $n_p(0)$ and $n_p(W_B)$. This picture of device carrier concentrations can be used to derive some general equations describing transistor behavior. Each of the distributions in Fig. 1.11 is considered separately and the two contributions are combined. The *emitter* current that would result from $n_{p1}(x)$ above is given by the classical diode equation

$$I_{EF} = -I_{ES}\left(\exp\frac{V_{BE}}{V_T} - 1\right) \tag{1.60}$$

where $I_{ES}$ is a constant that is often referred to as the *saturation current* of the junction (no connection with the transistor saturation previously described). Equation 1.60 predicts that the junction current is given by $I_{EF} \approx I_{ES}$ with a reverse-bias voltage applied. However,

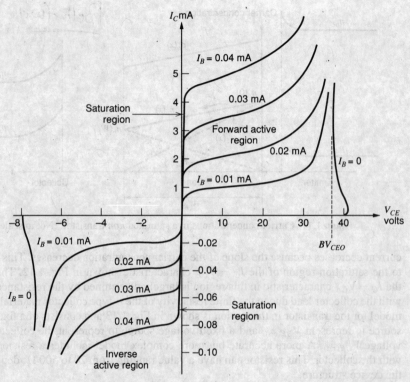

**Figure 1.12** Typical $I_C$-$V_{CE}$ characteristics for an *npn* bipolar transistor. Note the different scales for positive and negative currents and voltages.

**Figure 1.13** Large-signal models for bipolar transistors in the saturation region.

in practice (1.60) is applicable only in the forward-bias region, since second-order effects dominate under reverse-bias conditions and typically result in a junction current several orders of magnitude larger than $I_{ES}$. The junction current that flows under reverse-bias conditions is often called the *leakage current* of the junction.

Returning to Fig. 1.11, we can describe the *collector* current resulting from $n_{p2}(x)$ alone as

$$I_{CR} = -I_{CS}\left(\exp\frac{V_{BC}}{V_T} - 1\right) \tag{1.61}$$

where $I_{CS}$ is a constant. The total collector current $I_C$ is given by $I_{CR}$ plus the fraction of $I_{EF}$ that reaches the collector (allowing for recombination and reverse emitter injection). Thus

$$I_C = \alpha_F I_{ES}\left(\exp\frac{V_{BE}}{V_T} - 1\right) - I_{CS}\left(\exp\frac{V_{BC}}{V_T} - 1\right) \tag{1.62}$$

where $\alpha_F$ has been defined previously by (1.51). Similarly, the total emitter current is composed of $I_{EF}$ plus the fraction of $I_{CR}$ that reaches the emitter with the transistor acting in an inverted mode. Thus

$$I_E = -I_{ES}\left(\exp \frac{V_{BE}}{V_T} - 1\right) + \alpha_R I_{CS}\left(\exp \frac{V_{BC}}{V_T} - 1\right) \tag{1.63}$$

where $\alpha_R$ is the ratio of emitter to collector current with the transistor operating *inverted* (i.e., with the collector-base junction forward biased and emitting carriers into the base and the emitter-base junction reverse biased and collecting carriers). Typical values of $\alpha_R$ are 0.5 to 0.8. An inverse current gain $\beta_R$ is also defined

$$\beta_R = \frac{\alpha_R}{1 - \alpha_R} \tag{1.64}$$

and has typical values 1 to 5. This is the current gain of the transistor when operated inverted and is much lower than $\beta_F$ because the device geometry and doping densities are designed to maximize $\beta_F$. The inverse-active region of device operation occurs for $V_{CE}$ negative in an *npn* transistor and is shown in Fig. 1.12. In order to display these characteristics adequately in the same figure as the forward-active region, the negative voltage and current scales have been expanded. The inverse-active mode of operation is rarely encountered in analog circuits.

Equations 1.62 and 1.63 describe *npn* transistor operation in the saturation region when $V_{BE}$ and $V_{BC}$ are both positive, and also in the forward-active and inverse-active regions. These equations are the *Ebers-Moll* equations. In the forward-active region, they degenerate into a form similar to that of (1.35), (1.47), and (1.49) derived earlier. This can be shown by putting $V_{BE}$ positive and $V_{BC}$ negative in (1.62) and (1.63) to obtain

$$I_C = \alpha_F I_{ES}\left(\exp \frac{V_{BE}}{V_T} - 1\right) + I_{CS} \tag{1.65}$$

$$I_E = -I_{ES}\left(\exp \frac{V_{BE}}{V_T} - 1\right) - \alpha_R I_{CS} \tag{1.66}$$

Equation 1.65 is similar in form to (1.35) except that leakage currents that were previously neglected have now been included. This minor difference is significant only at high temperatures or very low operating currents. Comparison of (1.65) with (1.35) allows us to identify $I_S = \alpha_F I_{ES}$, and it can be shown[10] in general that

$$\alpha_F I_{ES} = \alpha_R I_{CS} = I_S \tag{1.67}$$

where this expression represents a reciprocity condition. Use of (1.67) in (1.62) and (1.63) allows the Ebers-Moll equations to be expressed in the general form

$$I_C = I_S\left(\exp \frac{V_{BE}}{V_T} - 1\right) - \frac{I_S}{\alpha_R}\left(\exp \frac{V_{BC}}{V_T} - 1\right) \tag{1.62a}$$

$$I_E = -\frac{I_S}{\alpha_F}\left(\exp \frac{V_{BE}}{V_T} - 1\right) + I_S\left(\exp \frac{V_{BC}}{V_T} - 1\right) \tag{1.63a}$$

This form is often used for computer representation of transistor large-signal behavior.

The effect of leakage currents mentioned above can be further illustrated as follows. In the forward-active region, from (1.66)

$$I_{ES}\left(\exp \frac{V_{BE}}{V_T} - 1\right) = -I_E - \alpha_R I_{CS} \tag{1.68}$$

Substitution of (1.68) in (1.65) gives

$$I_C = -\alpha_F I_E + I_{CO} \tag{1.69}$$

where

$$I_{CO} = I_{CS}(1 - \alpha_R \alpha_F) \tag{1.69a}$$

and $I_{CO}$ is the collector-base leakage current with the emitter open. Although $I_{CO}$ is given theoretically by (1.69a), in practice, surface leakage effects dominate when the collector-base junction is reverse biased and $I_{CO}$ is typically several orders of magnitude larger than the value given by (1.69a). However, (1.69) is still valid if the appropriate measured value for $I_{CO}$ is used. Typical values of $I_{CO}$ are from $10^{-10}$ to $10^{-12}$ A at 25°C, and the magnitude doubles about every 8°C. As a consequence, these leakage terms can become very significant at high temperatures. For example, consider the base current $I_B$. From Fig. 1.5 this is

$$I_B = -(I_C + I_E) \tag{1.70}$$

If $I_E$ is calculated from (1.69) and substituted in (1.70), the result is

$$I_B = \frac{1 - \alpha_F}{\alpha_F} I_C - \frac{I_{CO}}{\alpha_F} \tag{1.71}$$

But from (1.50)

$$\beta_F = \frac{\alpha_F}{1 - \alpha_F} \tag{1.72}$$

and use of (1.72) in (1.71) gives

$$I_B = \frac{I_C}{\beta_F} - \frac{I_{CO}}{\alpha_F} \tag{1.73}$$

Since the two terms in (1.73) have opposite signs, the effect of $I_{CO}$ is to *decrease* the magnitude of the external base current at a given value of collector current.

▪ **EXAMPLE**
If $I_{CO}$ is $10^{-10}$ A at 24°C, estimate its value at 120°C.
Assuming that $I_{CO}$ doubles every 8°C, we have

$$I_{CO}(120°C) = 10^{-10} \times 2^{12}$$
$$= 0.4 \ \mu A$$

### 1.3.4 Transistor Breakdown Voltages

In Section 1.2.2 the mechanism of avalanche breakdown in a *pn* junction was described. Similar effects occur at the base-emitter and base-collector junctions of a transistor and these effects limit the maximum voltages that can be applied to the device.

First consider a transistor in the common-base configuration shown in Fig. 1.14a and supplied with a constant emitter current. Typical $I_C - V_{CB}$ characteristics for an *npn* transistor in such a connection are shown in Fig. 1.14b. For $I_E = 0$ the collector-base junction breaks down at a voltage $BV_{CBO}$, which represents collector-base breakdown with the emitter open. For finite values of $I_E$, the effects of avalanche multiplication are apparent for values of $V_{CB}$ below $BV_{CBO}$. In the example shown, the effective common-base current

**Figure 1.14** Common-base transistor connection. (a) Test circuit. (b) $I_C - V_{CB}$ characteristics.

gain $\alpha_F = I_C/I_E$ becomes larger than unity for values of $V_{CB}$ above about 60 V. Operation in this region (but below $BV_{CBO}$) can, however, be safely undertaken if the device power dissipation is not excessive. The considerations of Section 1.2.2 apply to this situation, and neglecting leakage currents, we can calculate the collector current in Fig. 1.14a as

$$I_C = -\alpha_F I_E M \tag{1.74}$$

where $M$ is defined by (1.26) and thus

$$I_C = -\alpha_F I_E \cfrac{1}{1 - \left(\cfrac{V_{CB}}{BV_{CBO}}\right)^n} \tag{1.75}$$

One further point to note about the common-base characteristics of Fig. 1.14b is that for low values of $V_{CB}$ where avalanche effects are negligible, the curves show very little of the Early effect seen in the common-emitter characteristics. Base widening still occurs in this configuration as $V_{CB}$ is increased, but unlike the common-emitter connection, it produces little change in $I_C$. This is because $I_E$ is now fixed instead of $V_{BE}$ or $I_B$, and in Fig. 1.9, this means the slope of the minority-carrier concentration at the emitter edge of the base is fixed. Thus the collector current remains almost unchanged.

Now consider the effect of avalanche breakdown on the common-emitter characteristics of the device. Typical characteristics are shown in Fig. 1.12, and breakdown occurs at a value $BV_{CEO}$, which is sometimes called the sustaining voltage $LV_{CEO}$. As in previous cases, operation near the breakdown voltage is destructive to the device only if the current (and thus the power dissipation) becomes excessive.

The effects of avalanche breakdown on the common-emitter characteristics are more complex than in the common-base configuration. This is because hole-electron *pairs* are produced by the avalanche process and the holes are swept into the base, where they effectively contribute to the base current. In a sense the avalanche current is then *amplified* by the transistor. The base current is still given by

$$I_B = -(I_C + I_E)$$ (1.76)

Equation 1.74 still holds, and substitution of this in (1.76) gives

$$I_C = \frac{M\alpha_F}{1 - M\alpha_F} I_B$$ (1.77)

where

$$M = \frac{1}{1 - \left(\dfrac{V_{CB}}{BV_{CBO}}\right)^n}$$ (1.78)

Equation 1.77 shows that $I_C$ approaches infinity as $M\alpha_F$ approaches unity. That is, the effective $\beta$ approaches infinity because of the additional base-current contribution from the avalanche process itself. The value of $BV_{CEO}$ can be determined by solving

$$M\alpha_F = 1$$ (1.79)

If we assume that $V_{CB} \simeq V_{CE}$, this gives

$$\left.\frac{\alpha_F}{1 - \left(\dfrac{BV_{CEO}}{BV_{CBO}}\right)^n} = 1 \right\}$$ (1.80)

and this results in

$$\frac{BV_{CEO}}{BV_{CBO}} = \sqrt[n]{1 - \alpha_F}$$

and thus

$$BV_{CEO} \simeq \frac{BV_{CBO}}{\sqrt[n]{\beta_F}}$$ (1.81)

Equation 1.81 shows that $BV_{CEO}$ is less than $BV_{CBO}$ by a substantial factor. However, the value of $BV_{CBO}$, which must be used in (1.81), is the *plane* junction breakdown of the collector-base junction, neglecting any edge effects. This is because it is only collector-base avalanche current actually under the emitter that is amplified as described in the previous calculation. However, as explained in Section 1.2.2, the measured value of $BV_{CBO}$ is usually determined by avalanche in the curved region of the collector, which is remote from the active base. Consequently, for typical values of $\beta_F = 100$ and $n = 4$, the value of $BV_{CEO}$ is about one-half of the measured $BV_{CBO}$ and not 30 percent as (1.81) would indicate.

Equation 1.81 explains the shape of the breakdown characteristics of Fig. 1.12 if the dependence of $\beta_F$ on collector current is included. As $V_{CE}$ is increased from zero with $I_B = 0$, the initial collector current is approximately $\beta_F I_{CO}$ from (1.73); since $I_{CO}$ is typically several picoamperes, the collector current is very small. As explained in the next section, $\beta_F$ is small at low currents, and thus from (1.81) the breakdown voltage is high. However, as avalanche breakdown begins in the device, the value of $I_C$ increases and thus $\beta_F$ increases. From (1.81) this causes a *decrease* in the breakdown voltage and the characteristic bends back as shown in Fig. 1.12 and exhibits a negative slope. At higher collector currents, $\beta_F$ approaches a constant value and the breakdown curve with $I_B = 0$ becomes perpendicular to the $V_{CE}$ axis. The value of $V_{CE}$ in this region of the curve is usually defined to be $BV_{CEO}$, since this is the maximum voltage the device can sustain. The value of $\beta_F$ to be used to calculate $BV_{CEO}$ in (1.81) is thus the *peak* value of $\beta_F$. Note from (1.81) that high-$\beta$ transistors will thus have low values of $BV_{CEO}$.

The base-emitter junction of a transistor is also subject to avalanche breakdown. However, the doping density in the emitter is made very large to ensure a high value of $\beta_F [N_D$ is made large in (1.45) to reduce $I_{B2}]$. Thus the base is the more lightly doped side of the junction and determines the breakdown characteristic. This can be contrasted with the collector-base junction, where the collector is the more lightly doped side and results in typical values of $BV_{CBO}$ of 20 to 80 V or more. The base is typically an order of magnitude more heavily doped than the collector, and thus the base-emitter breakdown voltage is much less than $BV_{CBO}$ and is typically about 6 to 8 V. This is designed $BV_{EBO}$. The breakdown voltage for inverse-active operation shown in Fig. 1.12 is approximately equal to this value because the base-emitter junction is reverse biased in this mode of operation.

The base-emitter breakdown voltage of 6 to 8 V provides a convenient reference voltage in integrated-circuit design, and this is often utilized in the form of a *Zener* diode. However, care must be taken to ensure that all other transistors in a circuit are protected against reverse base-emitter voltages sufficient to cause breakdown. This is because, unlike collector-base breakdown, base-emitter breakdown *is* damaging to the device. It can cause a large degradation in $\beta_F$, depending on the duration of the breakdown-current flow and its magnitude.[11] If the device is used purely as a Zener diode, this is of no consequence, but if the device is an amplifying transistor, the $\beta_F$ degradation may be serious.

■ **EXAMPLE**

If the collector doping density in a transistor is $2 \times 10^{15}$ atoms/cm$^3$ and is much less than the base doping, calculate $BV_{CEO}$ for $\beta = 100$ and $n = 4$. Assume $\mathscr{E}_{crit} = 3 \times 10^5$ V/cm.

The plane breakdown voltage in the collector can be calculated from (1.24) using $\mathscr{E}_{max} = \mathscr{E}_{crit}$:

$$BV_{CBO} = \frac{\epsilon (N_A + N_D)}{2qN_AN_D}\mathscr{E}_{crit}^2$$

Since $N_D \ll N_A$, we have

$$BV_{CBO}|_{plane} = \frac{\epsilon}{2qN_D}\mathscr{E}_{crit}^2 = \frac{1.04 \times 10^{-12}}{2 \times 1.6 \times 10^{-19} \times 2 \times 10^{15}} \times 9 \times 10^{10} \text{ V} = 146 \text{ V}$$

From (1.81)

$$BV_{CEO} = \frac{146}{\sqrt[4]{100}}\text{V} = 46 \text{ V}$$

■

## 1.3.5 Dependence of Transistor Current Gain $\beta_F$ on Operating Conditions

Although most first-order analyses of integrated circuits make the assumption that $\beta_F$ is constant, this parameter does in fact depend on the operating conditions of the transistor. It was shown in Section 1.3.2, for example, that increasing the value of $V_{CE}$ increases $I_C$ while producing little change in $I_B$, and thus the effective $\beta_F$ of the transistor increases. In Section 1.3.4 it was shown that as $V_{CE}$ approaches the breakdown voltage, $BV_{CEO}$, the collector current increases due to avalanche multiplication in the collector. Equation 1.77 shows that the effective current gain approaches infinity as $V_{CE}$ approaches $BV_{CEO}$.

In addition to the effects just described, $\beta_F$ also varies with both temperature and transistor collector current. This is illustrated in Fig. 1.15, which shows typical curves of $\beta_F$ versus $I_C$ at three different temperatures for an *npn* integrated circuit transistor. It is evident that $\beta_F$ increases as temperature increases, and a typical temperature coefficient for $\beta_F$ is +7000 ppm/°C (where ppm signifies *parts per million*). This temperature dependence of $\beta_F$ is due to the effect of the extremely high doping density in the emitter,[12] which causes the emitter injection efficiency $\gamma$ to increase with temperature.

The variation of $\beta_F$ with collector current, which is apparent in Fig. 1.15, can be divided into three regions. Region I is the low-current region, where $\beta_F$ decreases as $I_C$ decreases. Region II is the midcurrent region, where $\beta_F$ is approximately constant. Region III is the high-current region, where $\beta_F$ decreases as $I_C$ increases. The reasons for this behavior of $\beta_F$ with $I_C$ can be better appreciated by plotting base current $I_B$ and collector current $I_C$ on a log scale as a function of $V_{BE}$. This is shown in Fig. 1.16, and because of the log scale on the vertical axis, the value of $\ln \beta_F$ can be obtained directly as the distance between the two curves.

At moderate current levels represented by region II in Figs. 1.15 and 1.16, both $I_C$ and $I_B$ follow the ideal behavior, and

$$I_C = I_S \exp \frac{V_{BE}}{V_T} \tag{1.82}$$

$$I_B \simeq \frac{I_S}{\beta_{FM}} \exp \frac{V_{BE}}{V_T} \tag{1.83}$$

where $\beta_{FM}$ is the maximum value of $\beta_F$ and is given by (1.48).

At low current levels, $I_C$ still follows the ideal relationship of (1.82), and the decrease in $\beta_F$ is due to an additional component in $I_B$, which is mainly due to recombination of carriers in the base-emitter depletion region and is present at any current level. However, at higher current levels the base current given by (1.83) dominates, and this additional component has little effect. The base current resulting from recombination in the depletion region is[5]

$$I_{BX} \simeq I_{SX} \exp \frac{V_{BE}}{mV_T} \tag{1.84}$$

where

$$m \simeq 2$$

Figure 1.15 Typical curves of $\beta_F$ versus $I_C$ for an *npn* integrated-circuit transistor with 6 μm² emitter area.

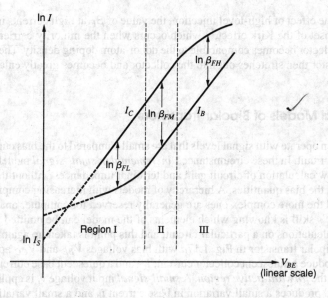

**Figure 1.16** Base and collector currents of a bipolar transistor plotted on a log scale versus $V_{BE}$ on a linear scale. The distance between the curves is a direct measure of $\ln \beta_F$.

At very low collector currents, where (1.84) dominates the base current, the current gain can be calculated from (1.82) and (1.84) as

$$\beta_{FL} \simeq \frac{I_C}{I_{BX}} = \frac{I_S}{I_{SX}} \exp \frac{V_{BE}}{V_T}\left(1 - \frac{1}{m}\right) \qquad (1.85)$$

Substitution of (1.82) in (1.85) gives

$$\beta_{FL} \simeq \frac{I_S}{I_{SX}} \left(\frac{I_C}{I_S}\right)^{[1-(1/m)]} \qquad (1.86)$$

If $m \simeq 2$, then (1.86) indicates that $\beta_F$ is proportional to $\sqrt{I_C}$ at very low collector currents.

At high current levels, the base current $I_B$ tends to follow the relationship of (1.83), and the decrease in $\beta_F$ in region III is due mainly to a decrease in $I_C$ below the value given by (1.82). (In practice the measured curve of $I_B$ versus $V_{BE}$ in Fig. 1.16 may also deviate from a straight line at high currents due to the influence of voltage drop across the base resistance.) The decrease in $I_C$ is due partly to the effect of high-level injection, and at high current levels the collector current approaches[7]

$$I_C \simeq I_{SH} \exp \frac{V_{BE}}{2V_T} \qquad (1.87)$$

The current gain in this region can be calculated from (1.87) and (1.83) as

$$\beta_{FH} \simeq \frac{I_{SH}}{I_S} \beta_{FM} \exp\left(-\frac{V_{BE}}{2V_T}\right) \qquad (1.88)$$

Substitution of (1.87) in (1.88) gives

$$\beta_{FH} \simeq \frac{I_{SH}^2}{I_S} \beta_{FM} \frac{1}{I_C} \qquad (1.88)$$

Thus $\beta_F$ decreases rapidly at high collector currents.

In addition to the effect of high-level injection, the value of $\beta_F$ at high currents is also decreased by the onset of the Kirk effect,[13] which occurs when the minority-carrier concentration in the collector becomes comparable to the donor-atom doping density. The base region of the transistor then stretches out into the collector and becomes greatly enlarged.

## 1.4 Small-Signal Models of Bipolar Transistors

Analog circuits often operate with signal levels that are small compared to the bias currents and voltages in the circuit. In these circumstances, *incremental* or *small-signal* models can be derived that allow calculation of circuit gain and terminal impedances without the necessity of including the bias quantities. A hierarchy of models with increasing complexity can be derived, and the more complex ones are generally reserved for computer analysis. Part of the designer's skill is knowing which elements of the model can be omitted when performing hand calculations on a particular circuit, and this point is taken up again later.

Consider the bipolar transistor in Fig. 1.17a with bias voltages $V_{BE}$ and $V_{CC}$ applied as shown. These produce a quiescent collector current, $I_C$, and a quiescent base current, $I_B$, and the device is in the *forward-active region*. A *small-signal* input voltage $v_i$ is applied in series with $V_{BE}$ and produces a small variation in base current $i_b$ and a small variation in collector current $i_c$. Total values of base and collector currents are $I_b$ and $I_c$, respectively, and thus $I_b = (I_B + i_b)$ and $I_c = (I_C + i_c)$. The carrier concentrations in the base of the transistor corresponding to the situation in Fig. 1.17a are shown in Fig. 1.17b. With only

**Figure 1.17** Effect of a small-signal input voltage applied to a bipolar transistor. (*a*) Circuit schematic. (*b*) Corresponding changes in carrier concentrations in the base when the device is in the forward-active region.

bias voltages applied, the carrier concentrations are given by the solid lines. Application of the small-signal voltage $v_i$ causes $n_p(0)$ at the emitter edge of the base to increase, and produces the concentrations shown by the dotted lines. These pictures can now be used to derive the various elements in the small-signal equivalent circuit of the bipolar transistor.

### 1.4.1 Transconductance

The transconductance is defined as

$$g_m = \frac{dI_C}{dV_{BE}} \tag{1.89}$$

Since

$$\Delta I_C = \frac{dI_C}{dV_{BE}} \Delta V_{BE}$$

we can write

$$\Delta I_C = g_m \Delta V_{BE}$$

and thus

$$i_c = g_m v_i \tag{1.90}$$

The value of $g_m$ can be found by substituting (1.35) in (1.89) to give

$$g_m = \frac{d}{dV_{BE}} I_S \exp \frac{V_{BE}}{V_T} = \frac{I_S}{V_T} \exp \frac{V_{BE}}{V_T} = \frac{I_C}{V_T} = \frac{qI_C}{kT} \tag{1.91}$$

The transconductance thus depends linearly on the bias current $I_C$ and is 38 mA/V for $I_C = 1$ mA at 25°C for any bipolar transistor of either polarity ($npn$ or $pnp$), of any size, and made of any material (Si, Ge, GaAs).

To illustrate the limitations on the use of small-signal analysis, the foregoing relation will be derived in an alternative way. The total collector current in Fig. 1.17a can be calculated using (1.35) as

$$I_c = I_S \exp \frac{V_{BE} + v_i}{V_T} = I_S \exp \frac{V_{BE}}{V_T} \exp \frac{v_i}{V_T} \tag{1.92}$$

But the collector bias current is

$$I_C = I_S \exp \frac{V_{BE}}{V_T} \tag{1.93}$$

and use of (1.93) in (1.92) gives

$$I_c = I_C \exp \frac{v_i}{V_T} \tag{1.94}$$

If $v_i < V_T$, the exponential in (1.94) can be expanded in a power series,

$$I_c = I_C \left[ 1 + \frac{v_i}{V_T} + \frac{1}{2}\left(\frac{v_i}{V_T}\right)^2 + \frac{1}{6}\left(\frac{v_i}{V_T}\right)^3 + \cdots \right] \tag{1.95}$$

Now the incremental collector current is

$$i_c = I_c - I_C \tag{1.96}$$

and substitution of (1.96) in (1.95) gives

$$i_c = \frac{I_C}{V_T} v_i + \frac{1}{2}\frac{I_C}{V_T^2} v_i^2 + \frac{1}{6}\frac{I_C}{V_T^3} v_i^3 + \cdots \tag{1.97}$$

If $v_i \ll V_T$, (1.97) reduces to (1.90), and the small-signal analysis is valid. The criterion for use of small-signal analysis is thus $v_i = \Delta V_{BE} \ll 26$ mV at 25°C. In practice, if $\Delta V_{BE}$ is less than 10 mV, the small-signal analysis is accurate within about 10 percent.

## 1.4.2 Base-Charging Capacitance

Figure 1.17b shows that the change in base-emitter voltage $\Delta V_{BE} = v_i$ has caused a change $\Delta Q_e = q_e$ in the minority-carrier charge in the base. By charge-neutrality requirements, there is an equal change $\Delta Q_h = q_h$ in the majority-carrier charge in the base. Since majority carriers are supplied by the base lead, the application of voltage $v_i$ requires the supply of charge $q_h$ to the base, and the device has an apparent input capacitance

$$C_b = \frac{q_h}{v_i} \tag{1.98}$$

The value of $C_b$ can be related to fundamental device parameters as follows. If (1.39) is divided by (1.33), we obtain

$$\frac{Q_e}{I_C} = \frac{W_B^2}{2D_n} = \tau_F \tag{1.99}$$

The quantity $\tau_F$ has the dimension of time and is called the base transit time in the forward direction. Since it is the ratio of the charge in transit $(Q_e)$ to the current flow $(I_C)$, it can be identified as the average time per carrier spent in crossing the base. To a first order it is independent of operating conditions and has typical values 10 to 500 ps for integrated npn transistors and 1 to 40 ns for lateral pnp transistors. Practical values of $\tau_F$ tend to be somewhat lower than predicted by (1.99) for diffused transistors that have nonuniform base doping.[14] However, the functional dependence on base width $W_B$ and diffusion constant $D_n$ is as predicted by (1.99).

From (1.99)

$$\Delta Q_e = \tau_F \Delta I_C \tag{1.100}$$

But since $\Delta Q_e = \Delta Q_h$, we have

$$\Delta Q_h = \tau_F \Delta I_C \tag{1.101}$$

and this can be written

$$q_h = \tau_F i_c \tag{1.102}$$

Use of (1.102) in (1.98) gives

$$C_b = \tau_F \frac{i_c}{v_i} \tag{1.103}$$

and substitution of (1.90) in (1.103) gives

$$C_b = \tau_F g_m \tag{1.104}$$

$$= \tau_F \frac{qI_C}{kT} \tag{1.105}$$

Thus the small-signal, base-charging capacitance is proportional to the collector bias current.

In the inverse-active mode of operation, an equation similar to (1.99) relates stored charge and current via a time constant $\tau_R$. This is typically orders of magnitude larger than $\tau_F$ because the device structure and doping are optimized for operation in the forward-active region. Since the saturation region is a combination of forward-active and inverse-active operation, inclusion of the parameter $\tau_R$ in a SPICE listing will model the large charge storage that occurs in saturation.

### 1.4.3 Input Resistance

In the forward-active region, the base current is related to the collector current by (1.47) as

$$I_B = \frac{I_C}{\beta_F} \tag{1.47}$$

Small changes in $I_B$ and $I_C$ can be related using (1.47):

$$\Delta I_B = \frac{d}{dI_C}\left(\frac{I_C}{\beta_F}\right)\Delta I_C \tag{1.106}$$

and thus

$$\beta_0 = \frac{\Delta I_C}{\Delta I_B} = \frac{i_c}{i_b} = \left[\frac{d}{dI_C}\left(\frac{I_C}{\beta_F}\right)\right]^{-1} \tag{1.107}$$

where $\beta_0$ is the *small-signal* current gain of the transistor. Note that if $\beta_F$ is constant, then $\beta_F = \beta_0$. Typical values of $\beta_0$ are close to those of $\beta_F$, and in subsequent chapters little differentiation is made between these quantities. A single value of $\beta$ is often assumed for a transistor and then used for both ac and dc calculations.

Equation 1.107 relates the change in base current $i_b$ to the corresponding change in collector current $i_c$, and the device has a small-signal input resistance given by

$$r_\pi = \frac{v_i}{i_b} \tag{1.108}$$

Substitution of (1.107) in (1.108) gives

$$r_\pi = \frac{v_i}{i_c}\beta_0 \tag{1.109}$$

and use of (1.90) in (1.109) gives

$$\boxed{r_\pi = \frac{\beta_0}{g_m}} \tag{1.110}$$

Thus the small-signal input shunt resistance of a bipolar transistor depends on the current gain and is inversely proportional to $I_C$.

### 1.4.4 Output Resistance

In Section 1.3.2 the effect of changes in collector-emitter voltage $V_{CE}$ on the large-signal characteristics of the transistor was described. It follows from that treatment that small changes $\Delta V_{CE}$ in $V_{CE}$ produce corresponding changes $\Delta I_C$ in $I_C$, where

$$\Delta I_C = \frac{\partial I_C}{\partial V_{CE}}\Delta V_{CE} \tag{1.111}$$

Substitution of (1.55) and (1.57) in (1.111) gives

$$\frac{\Delta V_{CE}}{\Delta I_C} = \frac{V_A}{I_C} = r_o \tag{1.112}$$

where $V_A$ is the Early voltage and $r_o$ is the small-signal output resistance of the transistor. Since typical values of $V_A$ are 50 to 100 V, corresponding values of $r_o$ are 50 to 100 k$\Omega$ for $I_C = 1$mA. Note that $r_o$ is inversely proportional to $I_C$, and thus $r_o$ can be related to $g_m$, as are many of the other small-signal parameters.

$$r_o = \frac{1}{\eta g_m} \; = \; \frac{V_A}{I_c} \; = \; \frac{V_A}{g_m V_T} \tag{1.113}$$

where

$$\eta = \frac{kT}{qV_A} \tag{1.114}$$

If $V_A = 100$ V, then $\eta = 2.6 \times 10^{-4}$ at 25°C. Note that $1/r_o$ is the slope of the output characteristics of Fig. 1.10.

### 1.4.5 Basic Small-Signal Model of the Bipolar Transistor

Combination of the above small-signal circuit elements yields the small-signal model of the bipolar transistor shown in Fig. 1.18. This is valid for both *npn* and *pnp* devices in the forward-active region and is called the *hybrid-π* model. Collector, base, and emitter nodes are labeled *C, B* and *E*, respectively. The elements in this circuit are present in the equivalent circuit of *any* bipolar transistor and are specified by relatively few parameters ($\beta$, $\tau_F$, $\eta$, $I_C$). Note that in the evaluation of the small-signal parameters for *pnp* transistors, the *magnitude only* of $I_C$ is used. In the following sections, further elements are added to this model to account for parasitics and second-order effects.

### 1.4.6 Collector-Base Resistance

Consider the effect of variations in $V_{CE}$ on the minority charge in the base as illustrated in Fig. 1.9. An increase in $V_{CE}$ causes an increase in the collector depletion-layer width and consequent reduction of base width. This causes a reduction in the total minority-carrier charge stored in the base and thus a reduction in base current $I_B$ due to a reduction in $I_{B1}$ given by (1.40). Since an increase $\Delta V_{CE}$ in $V_{CE}$ causes a *decrease* $\Delta I_B$ in $I_B$, this effect can be modeled by inclusion of a resistor $r_\mu$ from collector to base of the model of Fig. 1.18. If $V_{BE}$ is assumed held constant, the value of this resistor can be determined as follows.

$$r_\mu = \frac{\Delta V_{CE}}{\Delta I_{B1}} = \frac{\Delta V_{CE}}{\Delta I_C}\frac{\Delta I_C}{\Delta I_{B1}} \tag{1.115}$$

$$r_\pi = \frac{\beta}{g_m}, r_o = \frac{1}{\eta g_m}, g_m = \frac{qI_C}{kT}, C_b = \tau_F g_m$$

**Figure 1.18**  Basic bipolar transistor small-signal equivalent circuit.

Substitution of (1.112) in (1.115) gives

$$r_\mu = r_o \frac{\Delta I_C}{\Delta I_{B1}} \tag{1.116}$$

If the base current $I_B$ is composed entirely of component $I_{B1}$, then (1.107) can be used in (1.116) to give

$$r_\mu = \beta_0 r_o \tag{1.117}$$

This is a lower limit for $r_\mu$. In practice, $I_{B1}$ is typically less than 10 percent of $I_B$ [component $I_{B2}$ from (1.42) dominates] in integrated $npn$ transistors, and since $I_{B1}$ is very small, the change $\Delta I_{B1}$ in $I_{B1}$ for a given $\Delta V_{CE}$ and $\Delta I_C$ is also very small. Thus a typical value for $r_\mu$ is greater than $10\beta_0 r_o$. For lateral $pnp$ transistors, recombination in the base is more significant, and $r_\mu$ is in the range $2\beta_0 r_o$ to $5\beta_0 r_o$.

### 1.4.7 Parasitic Elements in the Small-Signal Model

The elements of the bipolar transistor small-signal equivalent circuit considered so far may be considered basic in the sense that they arise directly from essential processes in the device. However, technological limitations in the fabrication of transistors give rise to a number of parasitic elements that must be added to the equivalent circuit for most integrated-circuit transistors. A cross section of a typical $npn$ transistor in a junction-isolated process is shown in Fig. 1.19. The means of fabricating such devices is described in Chapter 2.

As described in Section 1.2, all $pn$ junctions have a voltage-dependent capacitance associated with the depletion region. In the cross section of Fig. 1.19, three depletion-region capacitances can be identified. The base-emitter junction has a depletion-region capacitance $C_{je}$ and the base-collector and collector-substrate junctions have capacitances $C_\mu$ and $C_{cs}$, respectively. The base-emitter junction closely approximates an abrupt junction due to the steep rise of the doping density caused by the heavy doping in the emitter. Thus the variation of $C_{je}$ with bias voltage is well approximated by (1.21). The collector-base junction behaves like a graded junction for small bias voltages since the doping density is a function of distance near the junction. However, for larger reverse-bias values (more than about a volt), the junction depletion region spreads into the collector, which is

**Figure 1.19** Integrated-circuit $npn$ bipolar transistor structure showing parasitic elements. (Not to scale.)

uniformly doped, and thus for devices with thick collectors the junction tends to behave like an abrupt junction with uniform doping. Many modern high-speed processes, however, have very thin collector regions (of the order of one micron), and the collector depletion region can extend all the way to the buried layer for quite small reverse-bias voltages. When this occurs, both the depletion region and the associated capacitance vary quite slowly with bias voltage. The collector-base capacitance $C_\mu$ thus tends to follow (1.22) for very small bias voltages and (1.21) for large bias voltages in thick-collector devices. In practice, measurements show that the variation of $C_\mu$ with bias voltage for most devices can be approximated by

$$C_\mu = \frac{C_{\mu 0}}{\left(1 - \dfrac{V}{\psi_o}\right)^n} \tag{1.117a}$$

where $V$ is the forward bias on the junction and $n$ is an exponent between about 0.2 and 0.5. The third parasitic capacitance in a monolithic $npn$ transistor is the collector-substrate capacitance $C_{cs}$, and for large reverse bias voltages this varies according to the abrupt junction equation (1.21) for junction-isolated devices. In the case of oxide-isolated devices, however, the deep $p$ diffusions used to isolate the devices are replaced by oxide. The sidewall component of $C_{cs}$ then consists of a fixed oxide capacitance. Equation 1.117a may then be used to model $C_{cs}$, but a value of $n$ less than 0.5 gives the best approximation. In general, (1.117a) will be used to model all three parasitic capacitances with subscripts $e$, $c$, and $s$ on $n$ and $\psi_0$ used to differentiate emitter-base, collector-base, and collector-substrate capacitances, respectively. Typical zero-bias values of these parasitic capacitances for a minimum-size $npn$ transistor in a modern oxide-isolated process are $C_{je0} \simeq 10$ fF, $C_{\mu 0} \simeq 10$ fF, and $C_{cs0} \simeq 20$ fF. Values for other devices are summarized in Chapter 2.

As described in Chapter 2, lateral $pnp$ transistors have a parasitic capacitance $C_{bs}$ from base to substrate in place of $C_{cs}$. Note that the substrate is always connected to the most negative voltage supply in the circuit in order to ensure that all isolation regions are separated by reverse-biased junctions. Thus the substrate is an ac ground, and all parasitic capacitance to the substrate is connected to ground in an equivalent circuit.

The final elements to be added to the small-signal model of the transistor are resistive parasitics. These are produced by the finite resistance of the silicon between the top contacts on the transistor and the active base region beneath the emitter. As shown in Fig. 1.19, there are significant resistances $r_b$ and $r_c$ in series with the base and collector contacts, respectively. There is also a resistance $r_{ex}$ of several ohms in series with the emitter lead that can become important at high bias currents. (Note that the collector resistance $r_c$ is actually composed of three parts labeled $r_{c1}$, $r_{c2}$, and $r_{c3}$.) Typical values of these parameters are $r_b = 50$ to $500\ \Omega$, $r_{ex} = 1$ to $3\ \Omega$, and $r_c = 20$ to $500\ \Omega$. The value of $r_b$ varies significantly with collector current because of *current crowding*.[15] This occurs at high collector currents where the dc base current produces a lateral voltage drop in the base that tends to forward bias the base-emitter junction preferentially around the edges of the emitter. Thus the transistor action tends to occur along the emitter periphery rather than under the emitter itself, and the distance from the base contact to the active base region is reduced. Consequently, the value of $r_b$ is reduced, and in a typical $npn$ transistor, $r_b$ may decrease 50 percent as $I_C$ increases from 0.1 mA to 10 mA.

The value of these parasitic resistances can be reduced by changes in the device structure. For example, a large-area transistor with multiple base and emitter stripes will have a smaller value of $r_b$. The value of $r_c$ is reduced by inclusion of the low-resistance buried $n^+$ layer beneath the collector.

**Figure 1.20**  Complete bipolar transistor small-signal equivalent circuit.

The addition of the resistive and capacitive parasitics to the basic small-signal circuit of Fig. 1.18 gives the complete small-signal equivalent circuit of Fig. 1.20. The internal base node is labeled $B'$ to distinguish it from the external base contact $B$. The capacitance $C_\pi$ contains the base-charging capacitance $C_b$ and the emitter-base depletion layer capacitance $C_{je}$.

$$C_\pi = C_b + C_{je}$$ (1.118)

Note that the representation of parasitics in Fig. 1.20 is an approximation in that lumped elements have been used. In practice, as suggested by Fig. 1.19, $C_\mu$ is distributed across $r_b$ and $C_{cs}$ is distributed across $r_c$. This lumped representation is adequate for most purposes but can introduce errors at very high frequencies. It should also be noted that while the parasitic resistances of Fig. 1.20 can be very important at high bias currents or for high-frequency operation, they are usually omitted from the equivalent circuit for low-frequency calculations, particularly for collector bias currents less than 1 mA.

■ **EXAMPLE**

Derive the complete small-signal equivalent circuit for a bipolar transistor at $I_C = 1$ mA, $V_{CB} = 3$ V, and $V_{CS} = 5$ V. Device parameters are $C_{je0} = 10$ fF, $n_e = 0.5$, $\psi_{0e} = 0.9$ V, $C_{\mu0} = 10$ fF, $n_c = 0.3$, $\psi_{0c} = 0.5$ V, $C_{cs0} = 20$ fF, $n_s = 0.3$, $\psi_{0s} = 0.65$ V, $\beta_0 = 100$, $\tau_F = 10$ ps, $V_A = 20$ V, $r_b = 300$ Ω, $r_c = 50$ Ω, $r_{ex} = 5$ Ω, $r_\mu = 10$ $\beta_0 r_o$.

Since the base-emitter junction is forward biased, the value of $C_{je}$ is difficult to determine for reasons described in Section 1.2.1. Either a value can be determined by computer or a reasonable estimation is to double $C_{je0}$. Using the latter approach, we estimate

$$C_{je} = 20 \text{ fF}$$

Using (1.117a) gives, for the collector-base capacitance,

$$C_\mu = \frac{C_{\mu0}}{\left(1 + \dfrac{V_{CB}}{\psi_{0c}}\right)^{n_c}} = \frac{10}{\left(1 + \dfrac{3}{0.5}\right)^{0.3}} = 5.6 \text{ fF}$$

The collector-substrate capacitance can also be calculated using (1.117a)

$$C_{cs} = \frac{C_{cs0}}{\left(1 + \dfrac{V_{CS}}{\psi_{0s}}\right)^{n_s}} = \frac{20}{\left(1 + \dfrac{5}{0.65}\right)^{0.3}} = 10.5 \text{ fF}$$

From (1.91) the transconductance is

$$g_m = \frac{qI_C}{kT} = \frac{10^{-3}}{26 \times 10^{-3}} \text{A/V} = 38 \text{ mA/V}$$

From (1.104) the base-charging capacitance is

$$C_b = \tau_F g_m = 10 \times 10^{-12} \times 38 \times 10^{-3} \text{ F} = 0.38 \text{ pF}$$

The value of $C_\pi$ from (1.118) is

$$C_\pi = 0.38 + 0.02 \text{ pF} = 0.4 \text{ pF}$$

The input resistance from (1.110) is

$$r_\pi = \frac{\beta_0}{g_m} = 100 \times 26 \ \Omega = 2.6 \text{ k}\Omega$$

The output resistance from (1.112) is

$$r_o = \frac{20}{10^{-3}} \ \Omega = 20 \text{ k}\Omega$$

and thus the collector-base resistance is

$$r_\mu = 10\beta_0 r_o = 10 \times 100 \times 20 \text{ k}\Omega = 20 \text{ M}\Omega$$

■    The equivalent circuit with these parameter values is shown in Fig. 1.21.

### 1.4.8 Specification of Transistor Frequency Response

The high-frequency gain of the transistor is controlled by the capacitive elements in the equivalent circuit of Fig. 1.20. The frequency capability of the transistor is most often specified in practice by determining the frequency where the magnitude of the short-circuit, common-emitter current gain falls to unity. This is called the *transition frequency*, $f_T$, and is a measure of the maximum useful frequency of the transistor when it is used as an amplifier. The value of $f_T$ can be measured as well as calculated, using the ac circuit of Fig. 1.22. A small-signal current $i_i$ is applied to the base, and the output current $i_o$ is measured with the collector short-circuited for ac signals. A small-signal equivalent circuit can be formed for this situation by using the equivalent circuit of Fig. 1.20 as shown in Fig. 1.23, where $r_{ex}$ and $r_\mu$ have been neglected. If $r_c$ is assumed small, then $r_o$ and $C_{cs}$ have no

**Figure 1.21** Complete small-signal equivalent circuit for a bipolar transistor at $I_C = 1$ mA, $V_{CB} = 3$ V, and $V_{CS} = 5$ V. Device parameters are $C_{je0} = 10$ fF, $n_e = 0.5$, $\psi_{0e} = 0.9$ V, $C_{\mu 0} = 10$ fF, $n_c = 0.3$, $\psi_{0c} = 0.5$ V, $C_{cs0} = 20$ fF, $n_s = 0.3$, $\psi_{0s} = 0.65$ V, $\beta_0 = 100$, $\tau_F = 10$ ps, $V_A = 20$ V, $r_b = 300 \ \Omega$, $r_c = 50 \ \Omega$, $r_{ex} = 5 \ \Omega$, $r_\mu = 10\beta_0 r_o$.

Figure 1.22  Schematic of ac circuit for measurement of $f_T$.

Figure 1.23  Small-signal equivalent circuit for the calculation of $f_T$.

influence, and we have

$$v_1 \simeq \frac{r_\pi}{1 + r_\pi(C_\pi + C_\mu)s}i_i$$  (1.119)

If the current fed forward through $C_\mu$ is neglected,

$$i_o \simeq g_m v_1$$  (1.120)

Substitution of (1.119) in (1.120) gives

$$i_o \simeq i_i \frac{g_m r_\pi}{1 + r_\pi(C_\pi + C_\mu)s}$$

and thus

$$\frac{i_o}{i_i}(j\omega) = \frac{\beta_0}{1 + \beta_0 \dfrac{C_\pi + C_\mu}{g_m}j\omega}$$  (1.121)

using (1.110).

Now if $i_o/i_i(j\omega)$ is written as $\beta(j\omega)$ (the high-frequency, small-signal current gain), then

$$\beta(j\omega) = \frac{\beta_0}{1 + \beta_0 \dfrac{C_\pi + C_\mu}{g_m}j\omega}$$  (1.122)

At high frequencies the imaginary part of the denominator of (1.122) is dominant, and we can write

$$\beta(j\omega) \simeq \frac{g_m}{j\omega\,(C_\pi + C_\mu)}$$  (1.123)

From (1.123), $|\beta(j\omega)| = 1$ when

$$\omega = \omega_T = \frac{g_m}{C_\pi + C_\mu}$$  (1.124)

**Figure 1.24** Magnitude of small-signal ac current gain $|\beta(j\omega)|$ versus frequency for a typical bipolar transistor.

and thus

$$f_T = \frac{1}{2\pi}\frac{g_m}{C_\pi + C_\mu} \qquad (1.125)$$

The transistor behavior can be illustrated by plotting $|\beta(j\omega)|$ using (1.122) as shown in Fig. 1.24. The frequency $\omega_\beta$ is defined as the frequency where $|\beta(j\omega)|$ is equal to $\beta_0/\sqrt{2}$ (3 dB down from the low-frequency value). From (1.122) we have

$$\omega_\beta = \frac{1}{\beta_0}\frac{g_m}{C_\pi + C_\mu} = \frac{\omega_T}{\beta_0} \qquad (1.126)$$

From Fig. 1.24 it can be seen that $\omega_T$ can be determined by measuring $|\beta(j\omega)|$ at some frequency $\omega_x$ where $|\beta(j\omega)|$ is falling at 6 dB/octave and using

$$\omega_T = \omega_x|\beta(j\omega_x)| \qquad (1.127)$$

This is the method used in practice, since deviations from ideal behavior tend to occur as $|\beta(j\omega)|$ approaches unity. Thus $|\beta(j\omega)|$ is typically measured at some frequency where its magnitude is about 5 or 10, and (1.127) is used to determine $\omega_T$.

It is interesting to examine the time constant, $\tau_T$, associated with $\omega_T$. This is defined as

$$\tau_T = \frac{1}{\omega_T} \qquad (1.128)$$

and use of (1.124) in (1.128) gives

$$\tau_T = \frac{C_\pi}{g_m} + \frac{C_\mu}{g_m} \qquad (1.129)$$

Substitution of (1.118) and (1.104) in (1.129) gives

$$\tau_T = \frac{C_b}{g_m} + \frac{C_{je}}{g_m} + \frac{C_\mu}{g_m} = \tau_F + \frac{C_{je}}{g_m} + \frac{C_\mu}{g_m} \qquad (1.130)$$

Equation 1.130 indicates that $\tau_T$ is dependent on $I_C$ (through $g_m$) and approaches a constant value of $\tau_F$ at high collector bias currents. At low values of $I_C$, the terms involving $C_{je}$ and $C_\mu$ dominate, and they cause $\tau_T$ to *rise* and $f_T$ to *fall* as $I_C$ is decreased. This behavior is illustrated in Fig. 1.25, which is a typical plot of $f_T$ versus $I_C$ for an integrated-circuit $npn$ transistor. The decline in $f_T$ at high collector currents is not predicted by this simple theory and is due to an increase in $\tau_F$ caused by high-level injection and Kirk effect at high

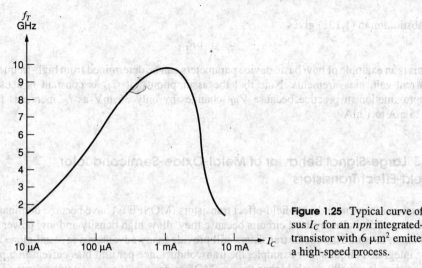

**Figure 1.25** Typical curve of $f_T$ versus $I_C$ for an $npn$ integrated-circuit transistor with 6 $\mu m^2$ emitter area in a high-speed process.

currents. These are the same mechanisms that cause a decrease in $\beta_F$ at high currents as described in Section 1.3.5.

■ **EXAMPLE**

A bipolar transistor has a short-circuit, common-emitter current gain at 1 GHz of 8 with $I_C = 0.25$ mA and 9 with $I_C = 1$ mA. Assuming that high-level injection effects are negligible, calculate $C_{je}$ and $\tau_F$, assuming both are constant. The measured value of $C_\mu$ is 10 fF.

From the data, values of $f_T$ are

$$f_{T1} = 8 \times 1 = 8 \text{ GHz} \quad \text{at} \quad I_C = 0.25 \text{ mA}$$
$$f_{T2} = 9 \times 1 = 9 \text{ GHz} \quad \text{at} \quad I_C = 1 \text{ mA}$$

Corresponding values of $\tau_T$ are

$$\tau_{T1} = \frac{1}{2\pi f_{T1}} = 19.9 \text{ ps}$$

$$\tau_{T2} = \frac{1}{2\pi f_{T2}} = 17.7 \text{ ps}$$

Using these data in (1.130), we have

$$19.9 \times 10^{-12} = \tau_F + 104(C_\mu + C_{je}) \tag{1.131}$$

at $I_C = 0.25$ mA. At $I_C = 1$ mA we have

$$17.7 \times 10^{-12} = \tau_F + 26(C_\mu + C_{je}) \tag{1.132}$$

Subtraction of (1.132) from (1.131) yields

$$C_\mu + C_{je} = 28.2 \text{ fF}$$

Since $C_\mu$ was measured as 10 fF, the value of $C_{je}$ is given by

$$C_{je} \simeq 18.2 \text{ fF}$$

Substitution in (1.131) gives

$$\tau_F \doteq 17 \text{ ps}$$

This is an example of how basic device parameters can be determined from high-frequency current-gain measurements. Note that the assumption that $C_{je}$ is constant is a useful approximation in practice because $V_{BE}$ changes by only 36 mV as $I_C$ increases from
■  0.25 mA to 1 mA.

## 1.5 Large-Signal Behavior of Metal-Oxide-Semiconductor Field-Effect Transistors

Metal-oxide-semiconductor field-effect transistors (MOSFETs) have become dominant in the area of digital integrated circuits because they allow high density and low power dissipation. In contrast, bipolar transistors still provide many advantages in stand-alone analog integrated circuits. For example, the transconductance per unit bias current in bipolar transistors is usually much higher than in MOS transistors. So in systems where analog techniques are used on some integrated circuits and digital techniques on others, bipolar technologies are often preferred for the analog integrated circuits and MOS technologies for the digital. To reduce system cost and increase portability, both increased levels of integration and reduced power dissipation are required, forcing the associated analog circuits to use MOS-compatible technologies. One way to achieve these goals is to use a processing technology that provides both bipolar and MOS transistors, allowing great design flexibility. However, all-MOS processes are less expensive than combined bipolar and MOS processes. Therefore, economic considerations drive integrated-circuit manufacturers to use all-MOS processes in many practical cases. As a result, the study of the characteristics of MOS transistors that affect analog integrated-circuit design is important.

### 1.5.1 Transfer Characteristics of MOS Devices

A cross section of a typical enhancement-mode $n$-channel MOS (NMOS) transistor is shown in Fig. 1.26. Heavily doped $n$-type source and drain regions are fabricated in a $p$-type substrate (often called the body). A thin layer of silicon dioxide is grown over the

**Figure 1.26**  Typical enhancement-mode NMOS structure.

substrate material and a conductive gate material (metal or polycrystalline silicon) covers the oxide between source and drain. Note that the gate is horizontal in Fig. 1.26, and we will use this orientation in all descriptions of the physical operation of MOS devices. In operation, the gate-source voltage modifies the conductance of the region under the gate, allowing the gate voltage to control the current flowing between source and drain. This control can be used to provide gain in analog circuits and switching characteristics in digital circuits.

The enhancement-mode NMOS device of Fig. 1.26 shows significant conduction between source and drain only when an $n$-type channel exists under the gate. This observation is the origin of the *n-channel* designation. The term *enhancement mode* refers to the fact that no conduction occurs for $V_{GS} = 0$. Thus, the channel must be *enhanced* to cause conduction. MOS devices can also be made by using an $n$-type substrate with a $p$-type conducting channel. Such devices are called enhancement-mode $p$-channel MOS (PMOS) transistors. In complementary MOS (CMOS) technology, both device types are present.

The derivation of the transfer characteristics of the enhancement-mode NMOS device of Fig. 1.26 begins by noting that with $V_{GS} = 0$, the source and drain regions are separated by back-to-back $pn$ junctions. These junctions are formed between the $n$-type source and drain regions and the $p$-type substrate, resulting in an extremely high resistance (about $10^{12}\ \Omega$) between drain and source when the device is off.

Now consider the substrate, source, and drain grounded with a positive voltage $V_{GS}$ applied to the gate as shown in Fig. 1.27. The gate and substrate then form the plates of a capacitor with the $SiO_2$ as a dielectric. Positive charge accumulates on the gate and negative charge in the substrate. Initially, the negative charge in the $p$-type substrate is manifested by the creation of a *depletion region* and the exclusion of holes under the gate as described in Section 1.2 for a $pn$-junction. The depletion region is shown in Fig. 1.27. The results of Section 1.2 can now be applied. Using (1.10), the depletion-layer width $X$ under the oxide is

$$X = \left(\frac{2\epsilon\phi}{qN_A}\right)^{1/2} \tag{1.133}$$

where $\phi$ is the potential in the depletion layer at the oxide-silicon interface, $N_A$ is the doping density (assumed constant) of the $p$-type substrate in atoms/cm$^3$, and $\epsilon$ is the permittivity of the silicon. The charge per area in this depletion region is

$$Q = qN_A X = \sqrt{2qN_A\epsilon\phi} \tag{1.134}$$

Figure 1.27   Idealized NMOS device cross section with positive $V_{GS}$ applied, showing depletion regions and the induced channel.

When the surface potential in the silicon reaches a critical value equal to twice the Fermi level $\phi_f$, a phenomenon known as *inversion* occurs.[16] The Fermi level $\phi_f$ is defined as

$$\phi_f = \frac{kT}{q} \ln\left[\frac{N_A}{n_i}\right]$$  (1.135)

where $k$ is Boltzmann's constant. Also, $n_i$ is the intrinsic carrier concentration, which is

$$n_i = \sqrt{N_c N_v} \exp\left(-\frac{E_g}{2kT}\right)$$  (1.136)

where $E_g$ is the band gap of silicon at $T = 0°K$, $N_c$ is the density of allowed states near the edge of the conduction band, and $N_v$ is the density of allowed states near the edge of the valence band, respectively. The Fermi level $\phi_f$ is usually about 0.3 V. After the potential in the silicon reaches $2\phi_f$, further increases in gate voltage produce no further changes in the depletion-layer width but instead induce a thin layer of electrons in the depletion layer at the surface of the silicon directly under the oxide. Inversion produces a continuous $n$-type region with the source and drain regions and forms the conducting channel between source and drain. The conductivity of this channel can be modulated by increases or decreases in the gate-source voltage. In the presence of an inversion layer, and without substrate bias, the depletion region contains a fixed charge density

$$Q_{b0} = \sqrt{2qN_A\epsilon 2\phi_f}$$  (1.137)

If a substrate bias voltage $V_{SB}$ (positive for $n$-channel devices) is applied between the source and substrate, the potential required to produce inversion becomes $(2\phi_f + V_{SB})$, and the charge density stored in the depletion region in general is

$$Q_b = \sqrt{2qN_A\epsilon(2\phi_f + V_{SB})}$$  (1.138)

The gate-source voltage $V_{GS}$ required to produce an inversion layer is called the threshold voltage $V_t$ and can now be calculated. This voltage consists of several components. First, a voltage $[2\phi_f + (Q_b/C_{ox})]$ is required to sustain the depletion-layer charge $Q_b$, where $C_{ox}$ is the gate oxide capacitance per unit area. Second, a work-function difference $\phi_{ms}$ exists between the gate metal and the silicon. Third, positive charge density $Q_{ss}$ always exists in the oxide at the silicon interface. This charge is caused by crystal discontinuities at the $Si - SiO_2$ interface and must be compensated by a gate-source voltage contribution of $-Q_{ss}/C_{ox}$. Thus we have a threshold voltage

$$V_t = \phi_{ms} + 2\phi_f + \frac{Q_b}{C_{ox}} - \frac{Q_{ss}}{C_{ox}}$$  (1.139)

$$= \phi_{ms} + 2\phi_f + \frac{Q_{b0}}{C_{ox}} - \frac{Q_{ss}}{C_{ox}} + \frac{Q_b - Q_{b0}}{C_{ox}}$$

$$= V_{t0} + \gamma\left(\sqrt{2\phi_f + V_{SB}} - \sqrt{2\phi_f}\right)$$  (1.140)

where (1.137) and (1.138) have been used, and $V_{t0}$ is the threshold voltage with $V_{SB} = 0$. The parameter $\gamma$ is defined as

$$\gamma = \frac{1}{C_{ox}}\sqrt{2q\epsilon N_A}$$  (1.141)

and

$$C_{ox} = \frac{\epsilon_{ox}}{t_{ox}} \qquad (1.142)$$

where $\epsilon_{ox}$ and $t_{ox}$ are the permittivity and the thickness of the oxide, respectively. A typical value of $\gamma$ is 0.5 $V^{1/2}$, and $C_{ox} = 3.45$ fF/$\mu$m$^2$ for $t_{ox} = 100$ angstroms.

In practice, the value of $V_{t0}$ is usually adjusted in processing by implanting additional impurities into the channel region. Extra $p$-type impurities are implanted in the channel to set $V_{t0}$ between 0.5 V and 1.5 V for $n$-channel enhancement devices. By implanting $n$-type impurities in the channel region, a conducting channel can be formed even for $V_{GS} = 0$, forming a *depletion* device with typical values of $V_{t0}$ in the range $-1$ V to $-4$ V. If $Q_i$ is the charge density due to the implant, then the threshold voltage given by (1.139) is shifted by approximately $Q_i/C_{ox}$.

The preceding equations can now be used to calculate the large-signal characteristics of an $n$-channel MOSFET. In this analysis, the source is assumed grounded and bias voltages $V_{GS}$, $V_{DS}$, and $V_{SB}$ are applied as shown in Fig. 1.28. If $V_{GS} > V_t$, inversion occurs and a conducting channel exists. The channel conductivity is determined by the vertical electric field, which is controlled by the value of $(V_{GS} - V_t)$. If $V_{DS} = 0$, the current $I_D$ that flows from drain to source is zero because the horizontal electric field is zero. Nonzero $V_{DS}$ produces a horizontal electric field and causes current $I_D$ to flow. The value of the current depends on both the horizontal and the vertical electric fields, explaining the term *field-effect* transistor. Positive voltage $V_{DS}$ causes the reverse bias from the drain to the substrate to be larger than from the source to substrate, and thus the widest depletion region exists at the drain. For simplicity, however, we assume that the voltage drop along the channel itself is small so that the depletion-layer width is constant along the channel.

The drain current $I_D$ is

$$I_D = \frac{dQ}{dt} \qquad (1.143)$$

where $dQ$ is the incremental channel charge at a distance $y$ from the source in an incremental length $dy$ of the channel, and $dt$ is the time required for this charge to cross length $dy$. The charge $dQ$ is

$$dQ = Q_I W dy \qquad (1.144)$$

where $W$ is the width of the device perpendicular to the plane of Fig. 1.28 and $Q_I$ is the induced electron charge per unit area of the channel. At a distance $y$ along the channel, the voltage with respect to the source is $V(y)$ and the gate-to-channel voltage at that point is

**Figure 1.28** NMOS device with bias voltages applied.

$V_{GS} - V(y)$. We assume this voltage exceeds the threshold voltage $V_t$. Thus the induced electron charge per unit area in the channel is

$$Q_I(y) = C_{ox}[V_{GS} - V(y) - V_t] \qquad (1.145)$$

Also,

$$dt = \frac{dy}{v_d(y)} \qquad (1.146)$$

where $v_d$ is the electron drift velocity at a distance $y$ from the source. Combining (1.144) and (1.146) gives

$$I_D = WQ_I(y)v_d(y) \qquad (1.147)$$

The drift velocity is determined by the horizontal electric field. When the horizontal electric field $\mathcal{E}(y)$ is small, the drift velocity is proportional to the field and

$$v_d(y) = \mu_n\mathcal{E}(y) \qquad (1.148)$$

where the constant of proportionality $\mu_n$ is the average electron mobility in the channel. In practice, the mobility depends on both the temperature and the doping level but is almost constant for a wide range of normally used doping levels. Also, $\mu_n$ is sometimes called the surface mobility for electrons because the channel forms at the surface of the silicon. Typical values range from about 500 cm$^2$/(V-s) to about 700 cm$^2$/(V-s), which are much less than the mobility of electrons in the bulk of the silicon (about 1400 cm$^2$/V-s) because surface defects not present in the bulk impede the flow of electrons in MOS transistors.[17] The electric field $\mathcal{E}(y)$ is

$$\mathcal{E}(y) = \frac{dV}{dy} \qquad (1.149)$$

where $dV$ is the incremental voltage drop along the length of channel $dy$ at a distance $y$ from the source. Substituting (1.145), (1.148), and (1.149) into (1.147) gives

$$I_D = WC_{ox}[V_{GS} - V - V_t]\mu_n\frac{dV}{dy} \qquad (1.150)$$

Separating variables and integrating gives

$$\int_0^L I_D \, dy = \int_0^{V_{DS}} W\mu_nC_{ox}(V_{GS} - V - V_t) \, dV \qquad (1.151)$$

Carrying out this integration gives

$$I_D = \frac{k'}{2}\frac{W}{L}[2(V_{GS} - V_t)V_{DS} - V_{DS}^2] \qquad (1.152)$$

where

$$k' = \mu_nC_{ox} = \frac{\mu_n\epsilon_{ox}}{t_{ox}} \qquad (1.153)$$

When $V_{DS} \ll 2(V_{GS} - V_t)$, (1.152) predicts that $I_D$ is approximately proportional to $V_{DS}$. This result is reasonable because the average horizontal electric field in this case is $V_{DS}/L$, and the average drift velocity of electrons is proportional to the average field when the field is small. Equation 1.152 is important and describes the $I$-$V$ characteristics of an MOS transistor, assuming a continuous induced channel. A typical value of $k'$ for $t_{ox} = 100$ angstroms is about 200 $\mu$A/V$^2$ for an $n$-channel device.

As the value of $V_{DS}$ is increased, the induced conducting channel narrows at the drain end and (1.145) indicates that $Q_I$ at the drain end approaches zero as $V_{DS}$ approaches $(V_{GS} - V_t)$. That is, the channel is no longer connected to the drain when $V_{DS} > V_{GS} - V_t$. This phenomenon is called *pinch-off* and can be understood by writing a KVL equation around the transistor:

$$V_{DS} = V_{DG} + V_{GS} \tag{1.154}$$

Therefore, when $V_{DS} > V_{GS} - V_t$,

$$V_{DG} + V_{GS} > V_{GS} - V_t \tag{1.155}$$

Rearranging (1.155) gives

$$V_{GD} < V_t \tag{1.156}$$

Equation 1.156 shows that when drain-source voltage is greater than $(V_{GS} - V_t)$, the gate-drain voltage is less than a threshold, which means that the channel no longer exists at the drain. This result is reasonable because we know that the gate-to-channel voltage at the point where the channel disappears is equal to $V_t$ by the definition of the threshold voltage. Therefore, at the point where the channel pinches off, the channel voltage is $(V_{GS} - V_t)$. As a result, the average horizontal electric field across the channel in pinch-off does not depend on the the drain-source voltage but instead on the voltage across the channel, which is $(V_{GS} - V_t)$. Therefore, (1.152) is no longer valid if $V_{DS} > V_{GS} - V_t$. The value of $I_D$ in this region is obtained by substituting $V_{DS} = V_{GS} - V_t$ in (1.152), giving

$$I_D = \frac{k'}{2} \frac{W}{L} (V_{GS} - V_t)^2 \tag{1.157}$$

Equation 1.157 predicts that the drain current is independent of $V_{DS}$ in the pinch-off region. In practice, however, the drain current in the pinch-off region varies slightly as the drain voltage is varied. This effect is due to the presence of a depletion region between the physical pinch-off point in the channel at the drain end and the drain region itself. If this depletion-layer width is $X_d$, then the *effective* channel length is given by

$$L_{\text{eff}} = L - X_d \tag{1.158}$$

If $L_{\text{eff}}$ is used in place of $L$ in (1.157), we obtain a more accurate formula for current in the pinch-off region

$$I_D = \frac{k'}{2} \frac{W}{L_{\text{eff}}} (V_{GS} - V_t)^2 \tag{1.159}$$

Because $X_d$ (and thus $L_{\text{eff}}$) are functions of the drain-source voltage in the pinch-off region, $I_D$ varies with $V_{DS}$. This effect is called *channel-length modulation*. Using (1.158) and (1.159), we obtain

$$\frac{\partial I_D}{\partial V_{DS}} = -\frac{k'}{2} \frac{W}{L_{\text{eff}}^2} (V_{GS} - V_t)^2 \frac{dL_{\text{eff}}}{dV_{DS}} \tag{1.160}$$

and thus

$$\frac{\partial I_D}{\partial V_{DS}} = \frac{I_D}{L_{\text{eff}}} \frac{dX_d}{dV_{DS}} \tag{1.161}$$

This equation is analogous to (1.55) for bipolar transistors. Following a similar procedure, the Early voltage can be defined as

$$V_A = \frac{I_D}{\partial I_D / \partial V_{DS}} \tag{1.162}$$

and thus

$$V_A = L_{\text{eff}} \left( \frac{dX_d}{dV_{DS}} \right)^{-1} \tag{1.163}$$

For MOS transistors, a commonly used parameter for the characterization of channel-length modulation is the reciprocal of the Early voltage,

$$\lambda = \frac{1}{V_A} \tag{1.164}$$

As in the bipolar case, the large-signal properties of the transistor can be approximated by assuming that $\lambda$ and $V_A$ are constants, independent of the bias conditions. Thus we can include the effect of channel-length modulation in the $I$-$V$ characteristics by modifying (1.157) to

$$I_D = \frac{k'}{2} \frac{W}{L} (V_{GS} - V_t)^2 \left( 1 + \frac{V_{DS}}{V_A} \right) \cong \frac{k'}{2} \frac{W}{L} (V_{GS} - V_t)^2 (1 + \lambda V_{DS}) \tag{1.165}$$

In practical MOS transistors, variation of $X_d$ with voltage is complicated by the fact that the field distribution in the drain depletion region is not one-dimensional. As a result, the calculation of $\lambda$ from the device structure is quite difficult,[18] and developing effective values of $\lambda$ from experimental data is usually necessary. The parameter $\lambda$ is inversely proportional to the effective channel length and a decreasing function of the doping level in the channel. Typical values of $\lambda$ are in the range 0.05 V$^{-1}$ to 0.005 V$^{-1}$.

Plots of $I_D$ versus $V_{DS}$ with $V_{GS}$ as a parameter are shown in Fig. 1.29 for an NMOS transistor. The device operates in the pinch-off region when $V_{DS} > (V_{GS} - V_t)$. The pinch-off region for MOS devices is often called the *saturation* region. In saturation, the output characteristics are almost flat, which shows that the current depends mostly on the gate-source voltage and only to a small extent on the drain-source voltage. On the other hand, when $V_{DS} < (V_{GS} - V_t)$, the device operates in the *Ohmic* or *triode* region, where the device can be modeled as a nonlinear voltage-controlled resistor connected between the drain and source. The resistance of this resistor is *nonlinear* because the $V_{DS}^2$ term in (1.152) causes the resistance to depend on $V_{DS}$. Since this term is small when $V_{DS}$ is small, however, the nonlinearity is also small when $V_{DS}$ is small, and the triode region is also sometimes called the *linear* region. The boundary between the triode and saturation regions occurs when $V_{DS} = (V_{GS} - V_t)$. On this boundary, both (1.152) and (1.157) correctly predict $I_D$. Since $V_{DS} = (V_{GS} - V_t)$ along the boundary between triode and saturation, (1.157) shows that the boundary is $I_D = (k'/2)(W/L)V_{DS}^2$. This parabolic function

**Figure 1.29** NMOS device characteristics.

of $V_{DS}$ is shown in Fig. 1.29. For depletion $n$-channel MOS devices, $V_t$ is negative, and $I_D$ is nonzero even for $V_{GS} = 0$. For PMOS devices, all polarities of voltages and currents are reversed.

The results derived above can be used to form a large-signal model of the NMOS transistor in saturation. The model topology is shown in Fig. 1.30, where $I_D$ is given by (1.152) in the triode region and (1.157) in saturation, ignoring the effect of channel-length modulation. To include the effect of channel-length modulation, (1.159) or (1.165) should be used instead of (1.157) to find the drain current in saturation.

### 1.5.2 Comparison of Operating Regions of Bipolar and MOS Transistors

Notice that the meaning of the word *saturation* for MOS transistors is quite different than for bipolar transistors. Saturation in bipolar transistors refers to the region of operation where both junctions are forward biased and the collector-emitter voltage is approximately constant or saturated. On the other hand, saturation in MOS transistors refers to the region of operation where the channel is attached only to the source but not to the drain and the current is approximately constant or saturated. To avoid confusion, the term *active region* will be used in this book to describe the flat region of the MOS transistor characteristics, as shown in Fig. 1.29. This wording is selected to form a link between the operation of MOS and bipolar transistors. This link is summarized in the table of Fig. 1.31, which reviews the operating regions of $npn$ bipolar and $n$-channel MOS transistors.

When the emitter junction is forward biased and the collector junction is reverse biased, bipolar transistors operate in the forward-active region. They operate in the reverse-active region when the collector junction is forward biased and the emitter junction is reverse biased. This distinction is important because integrated-circuit bipolar transistors are typically not symmetrical in practice; that is, the collector operates more efficiently as a collector of minority carriers than as an emitter. Similarly, the emitter operates more efficiently as an emitter of minority carriers than as a collector. One reason for this asymmetry is that the collector region surrounds the emitter region in integrated-circuit bipolar transistors, as shown in Fig. 1.19. A consequence of this asymmetry is that the current gain in the forward-active region $\beta_F$ is usually much greater than the current gain in the reverse-active region $\beta_R$.

**Figure 1.30** Large-signal model for the NMOS transistor.

| $npn$ Bipolar Transistor | | | $n$-channel MOS Transistor | | |
|---|---|---|---|---|---|
| Region | $V_{BE}$ | $V_{BC}$ | Region | $V_{GS}$ | $V_{GD}$ |
| Cutoff | $< V_{BE(on)}$ | $< V_{BC(on)}$ | Cutoff | $< V_t$ | $< V_t$ |
| Forward Active | $\geq V_{BE(on)}$ | $< V_{BC(on)}$ | Saturation(Active) | $\geq V_t$ | $< V_t$ |
| Reverse Active | $< V_{BE(on)}$ | $\geq V_{BC(on)}$ | Saturation(Active) | $< V_t$ | $\geq V_t$ |
| Saturation | $\geq V_{BE(on)}$ | $\geq V_{BC(on)}$ | Triode | $\geq V_t$ | $\geq V_t$ |

**Figure 1.31** Operating regions of $npn$ bipolar and $n$-channel MOS transistors.

In contrast, the source and drain of MOS transistors are completely interchangeable based on the preceding description. (In practice, the symmetry is good but not perfect.) Therefore, distinguishing between the forward-active and reverse-active regions of operation of an MOS transistor is not necessary.

Figure 1.31 also shows that $npn$ bipolar transistors operate in cutoff when both junctions are reversed biased. Similarly, MOS transistors operate in cutoff when the gate is biased so that inversion occurs at neither the source nor the drain. Furthermore, $npn$ transistors operate in saturation when both junctions are forward biased, and MOS transistors operate in the triode region when the gate is biased so that the channel is connected to both the source and the drain. Therefore, this comparison leads us to view the voltage required to invert the surface of an MOS transistor as analogous to the voltage required to forward bias a $pn$ junction in a bipolar transistor. To display this analogy, we will use the circuit symbols in Fig. 1.32a to represent MOS transistors. These symbols are intentionally chosen to appear similar to the symbols of the corresponding bipolar transistors. In bipolar-transistor symbols, the arrow at the emitter junction represents the direction of current flow when the emitter junction is forward biased. In MOS transistors, the $pn$ junctions between the source and body and the drain and body are reverse biased for normal operation. Therefore, the arrows in Fig. 1.32a do not indicate $pn$ junctions. Instead they indicate the direction of current flow when the terminals are biased so that the terminal labeled as the drain operates as the drain and the terminal labeled as the source operates as the source. In NMOS transistors, the source is the source of electrons; therefore, the source operates at a lower voltage than the drain, and the current flows in a direction opposite that of the electrons in the channel. In PMOS transistors, the source is the source of holes; therefore, the source operates at a higher voltage than the drain, and the current flows in the same direction as the holes in the channel.

In CMOS technology, one device type is fabricated in the substrate, which is common to all devices, invariably connected to a dc power-supply voltage, and usually not shown on the circuit diagram. The other device type, however, is fabricated in separate isolation

**Figure 1.32** (a) NMOS and PMOS symbols used in CMOS circuits. (b) NMOS and PMOS symbols used when the substrate connection is nonstandard. (c) Depletion MOS device symbols.

regions called *wells*, which may or may not be connected together and which may or may not be connected to a power-supply voltage. If these isolation regions are connected to the appropriate power supply, the symbols of Fig. 1.32a will be used, and the substrate connection will not be shown. On the other hand, if the individual isolation regions are connected elsewhere, the devices will be represented by the symbols of Fig. 1.32b, where the substrate is labeled B. Finally, symbols for depletion-mode devices, for which a channel forms for $V_{GS} = 0$, are shown in Fig. 1.32c.

### 1.5.3 Decomposition of Gate-Source Voltage

The gate-source voltage of a given MOS transistor is usually separated into two parts: the threshold, $V_t$, and the voltage over the threshold, $V_{GS} - V_t$. We will refer to this latter part of the gate-source voltage as the *overdrive*. This decomposition is used because these two components of the gate-source voltage have different properties. Assuming square-law behavior as in (1.157), the overdrive is

$$V_{ov} = V_{GS} - V_t = \sqrt{\frac{2I_D}{k'(W/L)}} \tag{1.166}$$

Since the transconductance parameter $k'$ is proportional to mobility, and since mobility falls with increasing temperature, the overdrive rises with temperature. In contrast, the next section shows that the threshold falls with increasing temperature. Furthermore, (1.140) shows that the threshold depends on the source-body voltage, but not on the current; (1.166) shows that the overdrive depends directly on the current, but not on the source-body voltage.

### 1.5.4 Threshold Temperature Dependence

Assume that the source-body voltage is zero. Substituting (1.138) into (1.139) gives

$$V_t = \frac{\sqrt{2qN_A\epsilon(2\phi_f)}}{C_{ox}} + 2\phi_f + \phi_{ms} - \frac{Q_{ss}}{C_{ox}} \tag{1.167}$$

Assume that $\phi_{ms}$, $Q_{ss}$, and $C_{ox}$ are independent of temperature.[19] Then differentiating (1.167) gives

$$\frac{dV_t}{dT} = \frac{\sqrt{2qN_A\epsilon(2)}}{2C_{ox}\sqrt{\phi_f}}\frac{d\phi_f}{dT} + 2\frac{d\phi_f}{dT} = \frac{d\phi_f}{dT}\left[2 + \frac{1}{C_{ox}}\sqrt{\frac{qN_A\epsilon}{\phi_f}}\right] \tag{1.168}$$

Substituting (1.136) into (1.135) gives

$$\phi_f = \frac{kT}{q}\ln\left[\frac{N_A\exp\left(\dfrac{E_g}{2kT}\right)}{\sqrt{N_cN_v}}\right] \tag{1.169}$$

Assume both $N_c$ and $N_v$ are independent of temperature.[20] Then differentiating (1.169) gives

$$\frac{d\phi_f}{dT} = \frac{kT}{q}\left[-\frac{E_g}{2kT^2}\right] + \frac{k}{q}\ln\left[\frac{N_A\exp\left(\dfrac{E_g}{2kT}\right)}{\sqrt{N_cN_v}}\right] \tag{1.170}$$

Substituting (1.169) into (1.170) and simplifying gives

$$\frac{d\phi_f}{dT} = -\frac{E_g}{2qT} + \frac{\phi_f}{T} = -\frac{1}{T}\left[\frac{E_g}{2q} - \phi_f\right]$$    (1.171)

Substituting (1.141) and (1.171) into (1.168) gives

$$\frac{dV_t}{dT} = -\frac{1}{T}\left[\frac{E_g}{2q} - \phi_f\right]\left[2 + \frac{\gamma}{\sqrt{2\phi_f}}\right]$$    (1.172)

Equation 1.172 shows that the threshold voltage falls with increasing temperature if $\phi_f < E_g/(2q)$. The slope is usually in the range of $-0.5$ mV/°C to $-4$ mV/°C.[21]

■ **EXAMPLE**

Assume $T = 300°$K, $N_A = 10^{15}$ cm$^{-3}$, and $t_{ox} = 100$ Å. Find $dV_t/dT$.
From (1.135),

$$\phi_f = (25.8 \text{ mV}) \ln\left(\frac{10^{15}\text{cm}^{-3}}{1.45 \times 10^{10}\text{cm}^{-3}}\right) = 287 \text{ mV}$$    (1.173)

Also

$$\frac{E_g}{2q} = \frac{1.12 \text{ eV}}{2q} = 0.56 \text{ V}$$    (1.174)

Substituting (1.173) and (1.174) into (1.171) gives

$$\frac{d\phi_f}{dT} = -\frac{1}{300}(560 - 287) \frac{\text{mV}}{°\text{K}} = -0.91 \frac{\text{mV}}{°\text{K}}$$    (1.175)

From (1.142),

$$C_{ox} = \frac{3.9\,(8.854 \times 10^{-14} \text{ F/cm})}{100 \times 10^{-8} \text{ cm}} = 3.45 \frac{\text{fF}}{\mu\text{m}^2}$$    (1.176)

Also,

$$\frac{\gamma}{\sqrt{2\phi_f}} = \frac{1}{C_{ox}}\sqrt{\frac{(2)(1.6 \times 10^{-19} \text{ C})(11.7)(8.854 \times 10^{-14} \text{ F/cm})(10^{15} \text{ cm}^{-3})}{(2)(0.287 \text{ V})}}$$

$$= \frac{2.4 \times 10^{-8} \text{ F/cm}^2}{3.45 \times 10^{-15} \text{ F/}\mu\text{m}^2} = \frac{2.4 \times 10^{-16} \text{ F/}\mu\text{m}^2}{3.45 \times 10^{-15} \text{ F/}\mu\text{m}^2} = 0.07$$    (1.177)

Substituting (1.173) - (1.177) into (1.172) gives

$$\frac{dV_t}{dT} = \left(-0.91 \frac{\text{mV}}{°\text{K}}\right)(2 + 0.07) \approx -1.9 \frac{\text{mV}}{°\text{K}} = -1.9 \frac{\text{mV}}{°\text{C}}$$    (1.178)

■

### 1.5.5 MOS Device Voltage Limitations

The main voltage limitations in MOS transistors are described next.[22,23] Some of these limitations have a strong dependence on the gate length $L$; others have little dependence on $L$. Also, some of the voltage limitations are inherently destructive; others cause no damage as long as overheating is avoided.

**Junction Breakdown.** For long channel lengths, the drain-depletion region has little effect on the channel, and the $I_D$-versus-$V_{DS}$ curves closely follow the ideal curves of Fig. 1.29. For increasing $V_{DS}$, however, eventually the drain-substrate $pn$-junction breakdown voltage is exceeded, and the drain current increases abruptly by avalanche breakdown as described in Section 1.2.2. This phenomenon is not inherently destructive.

**Punchthrough.** If the depletion region around the drain in an MOS transistor touches the depletion region around the source before junction breakdown occurs, increasing the drain-source voltage increases the drain current by reducing the barrier to electron flow between the source and drain. This phenomenon is called *punchthrough*. Since it depends on the two depletion regions touching, it also depends on the gate length. Punchthrough is not inherently destructive and causes a more gradual increase in the drain current than is caused by avalanche breakdown. Punchthrough normally occurs below the surface of the silicon and is often prevented by an extra ion implantation below the surface to reduce the size of the depletion regions.

**Hot Carriers.** With sufficient horizontal or vertical electric fields, electrons or holes may reach sufficient velocities to be injected into the oxide, where most of them increase the gate current and some of them become trapped. Such carriers are called *hot* because the required velocity for injection into the oxide is usually greater than the random thermal velocity. Carriers trapped in the oxide shift the threshold voltage and may cause a transistor to remain on when it should turn off or vice versa. In this sense, injection of hot carriers into the oxide is a destructive process. This process is most likely to be problematic in short-channel technologies, where horizontal electric fields are likely to be high.

**Oxide Breakdown.** In addition to $V_{DS}$ limitations, MOS devices must also be protected against excessive gate voltages. Typical gate oxides break down with an electric field of about $6 \times 10^6$ V/cm to $7 \times 10^6$ V/cm,[24,25] which corresponds to 6 to 7 V applied from gate to channel with an oxide thickness of 100 angstroms. Since this process depends on the vertical electrical field, it is independent of channel length. However, this process is destructive to the transistor, resulting in resistive connections between the gate and the channel. Oxide breakdown can be caused by static electricity and can be avoided by using $pn$ diodes and resistors to limit the voltage range at sensitive nodes internal to the integrated circuit that connect to bonding pads.

## 1.6 Small-Signal Models of MOS Transistors

As mentioned in Section 1.5, MOS transistors are often used in analog circuits. To simplify the calculation of circuit gain and terminal impedances, *small-signal* models can be used. As in the case for bipolar transistors, a hierarchy of models with increasing complexity can be derived, and choosing the simplest model required to do a given analysis is important in practice.

Consider the MOS transistor in Fig. 1.33 with bias voltages $V_{GS}$ and $V_{DD}$ applied as shown. These bias voltages produce quiescent drain current $I_D$. If $V_{GS} > V_t$ and $V_{DD} > (V_{GS} - V_t)$, the device operates in the saturation or active region. A small-signal input voltage $v_i$ is applied in series with $V_{GS}$ and produces a small variation in drain current $i_d$. The total value of the drain current is $I_d = (I_D + i_d)$.

**Figure 1.33** Schematic of an MOS transistor with biasing.

## 1.6.1 Transconductance

Assuming square-law operation, the transconductance from the gate can be determined from (1.165) by differentiating.

$$g_m = \frac{\partial I_D}{\partial V_{GS}} = k'\frac{W}{L}(V_{GS} - V_t)(1 + \lambda V_{DS}) \tag{1.179}$$

If $\lambda V_{DS} \ll 1$, (1.179) simplifies to

$$g_m = k'\frac{W}{L}(V_{GS} - V_t) = \sqrt{2k'\frac{W}{L}I_D} \tag{1.180}$$

Unlike the bipolar transistor, the transconductance of the MOS transistor is proportional to the square root of the bias current and depends on device geometry (oxide thickness via $k'$ and $W/L$). Another key difference between bipolar and MOS transistors can be seen by calculating the ratio of the transconductance to the current. Using (1.157) and (1.180) for MOS transistors shows that

$$\frac{g_m}{I_D} = \frac{2}{V_{GS} - V_t} = \frac{2}{V_{ov}} \tag{1.181}$$

Also, for bipolar transistors, (1.91) shows that

$$\frac{g_m}{I_C} = \frac{q}{kT} = \frac{1}{V_T} \tag{1.182}$$

At room temperature, the thermal voltage $V_T$ is about equal to 26 mV. In contrast, the overdrive $V_{ov}$ for MOS transistors in many applications is chosen to be approximately several hundred mV so that MOS transistors are fast enough for the given application. (Section 1.6.8 shows that the transition frequency $f_T$ of an MOS transistor is proportional to the overdrive.) Under these conditions, the transconductance per given current is much higher for bipolar transistors than for MOS transistors. One of the key challenges in MOS analog circuit design is designing high-quality analog circuits with a low transconductance-to-current ratio.

The transconductance calculated in (1.180) is valid for small-signal analysis. To determine the limitation on the use of small-signal analysis, the change in the drain current resulting from a change in the gate-source voltage will be derived from a large-signal standpoint. The total drain current in Fig. 1.33 can be calculated using (1.157) as

$$I_d = \frac{k'}{2}\frac{W}{L}(V_{GS} + v_i - V_t)^2 = \frac{k'}{2}\frac{W}{L}\left[(V_{GS} - V_t)^2 + 2(V_{GS} - V_t)v_i + v_i^2\right] \tag{1.183}$$

Substituting (1.157) in (1.183) gives

$$I_d = I_D + \frac{k'}{2}\frac{W}{L}\left[2(V_{GS} - V_t)v_i + v_i^2\right] \tag{1.184}$$

Rearranging (1.184) gives

$$i_d = I_d - I_D = k'\frac{W}{L}(V_{GS} - V_t)v_i\left[1 + \frac{v_i}{2(V_{GS} - V_t)}\right] \tag{1.185}$$

If the magnitude of the small-signal input $|v_i|$ is much less than twice the overdrive defined in (1.166), substituting (1.180) into (1.185) gives

$$i_d \simeq g_m v_i \tag{1.186}$$

In particular, if $|v_i| = |\Delta V_{GS}|$ is less than 20 percent of the overdrive, the small-signal analysis is accurate within about 10 percent.

## 1.6.2 Intrinsic Gate-Source and Gate-Drain Capacitance

If $C_{ox}$ is the oxide capacitance per unit area from gate to channel, then the total capacitance under the gate is $C_{ox}WL$. This capacitance is intrinsic to the device operation and models the gate control of the channel conductance. In the triode region of device operation, the channel exists continuously from source to drain, and the gate-channel capacitance is usually lumped into two equal parts at the drain and source with

$$C_{gs} = C_{gd} = \frac{C_{ox}WL}{2} \tag{1.187}$$

In the saturation or active region, however, the channel pinches off before reaching the drain, and the drain voltage exerts little influence on either the channel or the gate charge. As a consequence, the intrinsic portion of $C_{gd}$ is essentially zero in the saturation region. To calculate the value of the intrinsic part of $C_{gs}$ in the saturation or active region, we must calculate the total charge $Q_T$ stored in the channel. This calculation can be carried out by substituting (1.145) into (1.144) and integrating to obtain

$$Q_T = WC_{ox}\int_0^L [V_{GS} - V(y) - V_t]dy \tag{1.188}$$

Solving (1.150) for $dy$ and substituting into (1.188) gives

$$Q_T = \frac{W^2C_{ox}^2\mu_n}{I_D}\int_0^{V_{GS}-V_t} (V_{GS} - V - V_t)^2 dV \tag{1.189}$$

where the limit $y = L$ corresponds to $V = (V_{GS} - V_t)$ in the saturation or active region. Solution of (1.189) and use of (1.153) and (1.157) gives

$$Q_T = \frac{2}{3}WLC_{ox}(V_{GS} - V_t) \tag{1.190}$$

Therefore, in the saturation or active region,

$$C_{gs} = \frac{\partial Q_T}{\partial V_{GS}} = \frac{2}{3}WLC_{ox} \tag{1.191}$$

and

$$C_{gd} = 0 \tag{1.192}$$

### 1.6.3 Input Resistance

The gate of an MOS transistor is insulated from the channel by the $SiO_2$ dielectric. As a result, the low-frequency gate current is essentially zero and the input resistance is essentially infinite. This characteristic is important in some circuits such as sample-and-hold amplifiers, where the gate of an MOS transistor can be connected to a capacitor to sense the voltage on the capacitor without leaking away the charge that causes that voltage. In contrast, bipolar transistors have small but nonzero base current and finite input resistance looking into the base, complicating the design of bipolar sample-and-hold amplifiers.

### 1.6.4 Output Resistance

In Section 1.5.1, the effect of changes in drain-source voltage on the large-signal characteristics of the MOS transistor was described. Increasing drain-source voltage in an $n$-channel MOS transistor increases the width of the depletion region around the drain and reduces the effective channel length of the device in the saturation or active region. This effect is called channel-length modulation and causes the drain current to increase when the drain-source voltage is increased. From that treatment, we can calculate the change in the drain current $\Delta I_D$ arising from changes in the drain-source voltage $\Delta V_{DS}$ as

$$\Delta I_D = \frac{\partial I_D}{\partial V_{DS}} \Delta V_{DS} \tag{1.193}$$

Substitution of (1.161), (1.163), and (1.164) in (1.193) gives

$$\frac{\Delta V_{DS}}{\Delta I_D} = \frac{V_A}{I_D} = \frac{1}{\lambda I_D} = r_o \tag{1.194}$$

where $V_A$ is the Early voltage, $\lambda$ is the channel-length modulation parameter, $I_D$ is the drain current without channel-length modulation given by (1.157), and $r_o$ is the small-signal output resistance of the transistor.

### 1.6.5 Basic Small-Signal Model of the MOS Transistor

Combination of the preceding small-signal circuit elements yields the small-signal model of the MOS transistor shown in Fig. 1.34. This model was derived for $n$-channel transistors in the saturation or active region and is called the *hybrid-$\pi$* model. Drain, gate, and source nodes are labeled $D$, $G$, and $S$, respectively. When the gate-source voltage is increased, the model predicts that the incremental current $i_d$ flowing from drain to source increases. Since the dc drain current $I_D$ also flows from drain to source in an $n$-channel transistor,

**Figure 1.34** Basic small-signal model of an MOS transistor in the saturation or active region.

increasing the gate-source voltage also increases the total drain current $I_d$. This result is reasonable physically because increasing the gate-source voltage in an $n$-channel transistor increases the channel conductivity and drain current.

The model shown in Fig. 1.34 is also valid for $p$-channel devices. Therefore, the model again shows that increasing the gate-source voltage increases the incremental current $i_d$ flowing from drain to source. Unlike in the $n$-channel case, however, the dc current $I_D$ in a $p$-channel transistor flows from source to drain because the source acts as the source of holes. Therefore, the incremental drain current flows in a direction opposite to the dc drain current when the gate-source voltage increases, reducing the total drain current $I_d$. This result is reasonable physically because increasing the gate-source voltage in a $p$-channel transistor reduces the channel conductivity and drain current.

## 1.6.6 Body Transconductance

The drain current is a function of both the gate-source and body-source voltages. On the one hand, the gate-source voltage controls the vertical electric field, which controls the channel conductivity and therefore the drain current. On the other hand, the body-source voltage changes the threshold, which changes the drain current when the gate-source voltage is fixed. This effect stems from the influence of the substrate acting as a second gate and is called the *body effect*. Note that the body of an MOS transistor is usually connected to a constant power-supply voltage, which is a small-signal or ac ground. However, the source connection can have a significant ac voltage impressed on it, which changes the body-source voltage when the body voltage is fixed. Therefore, when the body-source voltage is not constant, two transconductance terms are required to model MOS transistors: one associated with the main gate and the other associated with the body or second gate.

Using (1.165), the transconductance from the body or second gate is

$$g_{mb} = \frac{\partial I_D}{\partial V_{BS}} = - k' \frac{W}{L}(V_{GS} - V_t)(1 + \lambda V_{DS})\frac{\partial V_t}{\partial V_{BS}} \tag{1.195}$$

From (1.140)

$$\frac{\partial V_t}{\partial V_{BS}} = - \frac{\gamma}{2 \sqrt{2\phi_f + V_{SB}}} = -\chi \tag{1.196}$$

This equation defines a factor $\chi$, which is the rate of change of threshold voltage with body bias voltage. Substitution of (1.141) in (1.196) and use of (1.20) gives

$$\chi = \frac{C_{js}}{C_{ox}} \tag{1.197}$$

where $C_{js}$ is the capacitance per unit area of the depletion region under the channel, assuming a one-sided step junction with a built-in potential $\psi_0 = 2\phi_f$. Substitution of (1.196) in (1.195) gives

$$g_{mb} = \frac{\gamma k'(W/L)(V_{GS} - V_t)(1 + \lambda V_{DS})}{2 \sqrt{2\phi_f + V_{SB}}} \tag{1.198}$$

If $\lambda V_{DS} \ll 1$, we have

$$g_{mb} = \frac{\gamma k'(W/L)(V_{GS} - V_t)}{2 \sqrt{2\phi_f + V_{SB}}} = \gamma \sqrt{\frac{k'(W/L)I_D}{2(2\phi_f + V_{SB})}} \tag{1.199}$$

The ratio $g_{mb}/g_m$ is an important quantity in practice. From (1.179) and (1.198), we find

$$\frac{g_{mb}}{g_m} = \frac{\gamma}{2\sqrt{2\phi_f + V_{SB}}} = \chi \tag{1.200}$$

The factor $\chi$ is typically in the range 0.1 to 0.3; therefore, the transconductance from the main gate is typically a factor of about 3 to 10 times larger than the transconductance from the body or second gate.

### 1.6.7 Parasitic Elements in the Small-Signal Model

The elements of the small-signal model for MOS transistors described above may be considered basic in the sense that they arise directly from essential processes in the device. As in the case of bipolar transistors, however, technological limitations in the fabrication of the devices give rise to a number of parasitic elements that must be added to the equivalent circuit for most integrated-circuit transistors. A cross section and top view of a typical $n$-channel MOS transistor are shown in Fig. 1.35. The means of fabricating such devices is described in Chapter 2.

All $pn$ junctions in the MOS transistor should be reverse biased during normal operation, and each junction exhibits a voltage-dependent parasitic capacitance associated with its depletion region. The source-body and drain-body junction capacitances shown in Fig. 1.35a are $C_{sb}$ and $C_{db}$, respectively. If the doping levels in the source, drain, and body regions are assumed to be constant, (1.21) can be used to express these capacitances as follows:

$$C_{sb} = \frac{C_{sb0}}{\left(1 + \dfrac{V_{SB}}{\psi_0}\right)^{1/2}} \tag{1.201}$$

(a)

(b)

**Figure 1.35** (a) Cross section and (b) top view of an $n$-channel MOS transistor.

$$C_{db} = \frac{C_{db0}}{\left(1 + \dfrac{V_{DB}}{\psi_0}\right)^{1/2}}$$

(1.202)

These capacitances are proportional to the source and drain region areas (including side-walls). Since the channel is attached to the source in the saturation or active region, $C_{sb}$ also includes depletion-region capacitance from the induced channel to the body. A detailed analysis of the channel-body capacitance is given in Tsividis.[26]

In practice, $C_{gs}$ and $C_{gd}$, given in (1.187) for the triode region of operation and in (1.191) and (1.192) for the saturation or active region, are increased due to parasitic oxide capacitances arising from gate overlap of the source and drain regions. These overlap capacitances $C_{ol}$ are shown in Fig. 1.35a, and their values are calculated in Chapter 2.

Capacitance $C_{gb}$ between gate and body or substrate models parasitic oxide capacitance between the gate-contact material and the substrate outside the active-device area. This capacitance is independent of the gate-body voltage and models coupling from polysilicon and metal interconnects to the underlying substrate, as shown by the shaded regions in the top view of Fig. 1.35b. Parasitic capacitance of this type underlies all polysilicon and metal traces on integrated circuits. Such parasitic capacitance should be taken into account when simulating and calculating high-frequency circuit and device performance. Typical values depend on oxide thicknesses. With a silicon dioxide thickness of 100 Å, the capacitance is about 3.45 fF per square micron. Fringing capacitance becomes important for lines narrower in width than several microns.

Parasitic resistance in series with the source and drain can be used to model the nonzero resistivity of the contacts and diffusion regions. In practice, these resistances are often ignored in hand calculations for simplicity but included in computer simulations. These parasitic resistances have an inverse dependence on channel width $W$. Typical values of these resistances are 50 $\Omega$ to 100 $\Omega$ for devices with $W$ of about 1 $\mu$m. Similar parasitic resistances in series with the gate and body terminals are sometimes included but often ignored because very little current flows in these terminals, especially at low frequencies. The small-signal model including capacitive parasitics but ignoring resistive parasitics is shown in Fig. 1.36.

### 1.6.8 MOS Transistor Frequency Response

As for a bipolar transistor, the frequency capability of an MOS transistor is usually specified by finding the transition frequency $f_T$. For an MOS transistor, $f_T$ is defined as the

Figure 1.36  Small-signal MOS transistor equivalent circuit.

**Figure 1.37** Circuits for calculating the $f_T$ of an MOS transistor: (a) ac schematic and (b) small-signal equivalent.

frequency where the magnitude of the short-circuit, common-source current gain falls to unity. Although the dc gate current of an MOS transistor is essentially zero, the high-frequency behavior of the transistor is controlled by the capacitive elements in the small-signal model, which cause the gate current to increase as frequency increases. To calculate $f_T$, consider the ac circuit of Fig. 1.37a and the small-signal equivalent of Fig. 1.37b. Since $v_{sb} = v_{ds} = 0$, $g_{mb}$, $r_o$, $C_{sb}$, and $C_{db}$ have no effect on the calculation and are ignored. The small-signal input current $i_i$ is

$$i_i = s(C_{gs} + C_{gb} + C_{gd})v_{gs} \tag{1.203}$$

If the current fed forward through $C_{gd}$ is neglected,

$$i_o \simeq g_m v_{gs} \tag{1.204}$$

Solving (1.203) for $v_{gs}$ and substituting into (1.204) gives

$$\frac{i_o}{i_i} \simeq \frac{g_m}{s(C_{gs} + C_{gb} + C_{gd})} \tag{1.205}$$

To find the frequency response, we set $s = j\omega$. Then

$$\frac{i_o}{i_i} \simeq \frac{g_m}{j\omega(C_{gs} + C_{gb} + C_{gd})} \tag{1.206}$$

The magnitude of the small-signal current gain is unity when

$$\omega = \omega_T = \frac{g_m}{C_{gs} + C_{gb} + C_{gd}} \tag{1.207}$$

Therefore,

$$f_T = \frac{1}{2\pi}\omega_T = \frac{1}{2\pi}\frac{g_m}{C_{gs} + C_{gb} + C_{gd}} \tag{1.208}$$

Assume the intrinsic device capacitance $C_{gs}$ is much greater than $(C_{gb} + C_{gd})$. Then substituting (1.180) and (1.191) into (1.208) gives

$$f_T = 1.5\frac{\mu_n}{2\pi L^2}(V_{GS} - V_t) \tag{1.209}$$

Comparison of this equation with the intrinsic $f_T$ of a bipolar transistor when parasitic depletion-layer capacitance is neglected leads to an interesting result. From (1.128) and (1.130) with $\tau_F \gg (C_{je} + C_\mu)/g_m$,

$$f_T = \frac{1}{2\pi\tau_F} \tag{1.210}$$

Substituting from (1.99) for $\tau_F$ and using the Einstein relationship $D_n/\mu_n = kT/q = V_T$, we find for a bipolar transistor

$$f_T = 2\frac{\mu_n}{2\pi W_B^2}V_T \qquad (1.211)$$

The similarity in form between (1.211) and (1.209) is striking. In both cases, the intrinsic device $f_T$ increases as the inverse square of the critical device dimension across which carriers are in transit. The voltage $V_T = 26$ mV is fixed for a bipolar transistor, but the $f_T$ of an MOS transistor can be increased by operating at high values of $(V_{GS} - V_t)$. Note that the base width $W_B$ in a bipolar transistor is a vertical dimension determined by diffusions or implants and can typically be made much smaller than the channel length $L$ of an MOS transistor, which depends on surface geometry and photolithographic processes. Thus bipolar transistors generally have higher $f_T$ than MOS transistors made with comparable processing. Finally, (1.209) was derived assuming that the MOS transistor exhibits square-law behavior as in (1.157). However, as described in Section 1.7, submicron MOS transistors depart significantly from square-law characteristics, and we find that for such devices $f_T$ is proportional to $L^{-1}$ rather than $L^{-2}$.

■ **EXAMPLE**

Derive the complete small-signal model for an NMOS transistor with $I_D = 100$ μA, $V_{SB} = 1$ V, $V_{DS} = 2$ V. Device parameters are $\phi_f = 0.3$ V, $W = 10$ μm, $L = 1$ μm, $\gamma = 0.5$ V$^{1/2}$, $k' = 200$ μA/V$^2$, $\lambda = 0.02$ V$^{-1}$, $t_{ox} = 100$ angstroms, $\psi_0 = 0.6$ V, $C_{sb0} = C_{db0} = 10$ fF. Overlap capacitance from gate to source and gate to drain is 1 fF. Assume $C_{gb} = 5$ fF.

From (1.166),

$$V_{ov} = V_{GS} - V_t = \sqrt{\frac{2I_D}{k'(W/L)}} = \sqrt{\frac{2 \times 100}{200 \times 10}} \simeq 0.316 \text{ V}$$

Since $V_{DS} > V_{ov}$, the transistor operates in the saturation or active region. From (1.180),

$$g_m = \sqrt{2k'\frac{W}{L}I_D} = \sqrt{2 \times 200 \times 10 \times 100}\ \mu \text{ A/V} \simeq 632\ \mu\text{A/V}$$

From (1.199),

$$g_{mb} = \gamma\sqrt{\frac{k'(W/L)I_D}{2(2\phi_f + V_{SB})}} = 0.5\sqrt{\frac{200 \times 10 \times 100}{2 \times 1.6}} \simeq 125\ \mu\text{A/V}$$

From (1.194),

$$r_o = \frac{1}{\lambda I_D} = \frac{1000}{0.02 \times 100} \text{ k}\Omega = 500 \text{ k}\Omega$$

Using (1.201) with $V_{SB} = 1$ V, we find

$$C_{sb} = \frac{10}{\left(1 + \dfrac{1}{0.6}\right)^{1/2}} \text{ fF} \simeq 6 \text{ fF}$$

The voltage from drain to body is

$$V_{DB} = V_{DS} + V_{SB} = 3 \text{ V}$$

and substitution in (1.202) gives

$$C_{db} = \frac{10}{\left(1 + \dfrac{3}{0.6}\right)^{1/2}} \text{ fF} \simeq 4 \text{ fF}$$

From (1.142), the oxide capacitance per unit area is

$$C_{ox} = \frac{3.9 \times 8.854 \times 10^{-14} \dfrac{\text{F}}{\text{cm}} \times \dfrac{100 \text{ cm}}{10^6 \,\mu\text{m}}}{100 \,\text{Å} \times \dfrac{10^6 \,\mu\text{m}}{10^{10} \,\text{Å}}} \simeq 3.45 \ \frac{\text{fF}}{\mu\text{m}^2}$$

The intrinsic portion of the gate-source capacitance can be calculated from (1.191), giving

$$C_{gs} \simeq \frac{2}{3} \times 10 \times 1 \times 3.45 \text{ fF} \simeq 23 \text{ fF}$$

The addition of overlap capacitance gives

$$C_{gs} \simeq 24 \text{ fF}$$

Finally, since the transistor operates in the saturation or active region, the gate-drain capacitance consists of only overlap capacitance and is

$$C_{gd} = 1 \text{ fF}$$

The complete small-signal equivalent circuit is shown in Fig. 1.38. The $f_T$ of the device can be calculated from (1.208) as

$$f_T = \frac{1}{2\pi} \frac{g_m}{C_{gs} + C_{gb} + C_{gd}} = \frac{1}{2\pi} \times 632 \times 10^{-6} \times \frac{10^{15}}{24 + 5 + 1} \text{ Hz} = 3.4 \text{ GHz}$$

## 1.7 Short-Channel Effects in MOS Transistors

The evolution of integrated-circuit processing techniques has led to continuing reductions in both the horizontal and vertical dimensions of the active devices. (The minimum

**Figure 1.38** Complete small-signal equivalent circuit for an NMOS transistor with $I_D = 100 \,\mu\text{A}$, $V_{SB} = 1$ V, $V_{DS} = 2$ V. Device parameters are $W = 10 \,\mu\text{m}$, $L = 1 \,\mu\text{m}$, $\gamma = 0.5$ V$^{1/2}$, $k' = 200 \,\mu\text{A/V}^2$, $\lambda = 0.02$ V$^{-1}$, $t_{ox} = 100$ Å, $\psi_0 = 0.6$ V, $C_{sb0} = C_{db0} = 10$ fF, $C_{gd} = 1$ fF, and $C_{gb} = 5$ fF.

allowed dimensions of passive devices have also decreased.) This trend is driven primarily by economics in that reducing dimensions increases the number of devices and circuits that can be processed at one time on a given wafer. A second benefit has been that the frequency capability of the active devices continues to increase, as intrinsic $f_T$ values increase with smaller dimensions while parasitic capacitances decrease.

Vertical dimensions such as the base width of a bipolar transistor in production processes may now be on the order of 0.05 μm or less, whereas horizontal dimensions such as bipolar emitter width or MOS transistor gate length may be significantly less than 1 μm. Even with these small dimensions, the large-signal and small-signal models of bipolar transistors given in previous sections remain valid. However, significant short-channel effects become important in MOS transistors at channel lengths of about 1 μm or less and require modifications to the MOS models given previously. The primary effect is to modify the classical MOS square-law transfer characteristic in the saturation or active region to make the device voltage-to-current transfer characteristic more linear. However, even in processes with submicron capability, many of the MOS transistors in a given analog circuit may be deliberately designed to have channel lengths larger than the minimum and may be well approximated by the square-law model.

## 1.7.1 Velocity Saturation from the Horizontal Field

The most important short-channel effect in MOS transistors stems from velocity saturation of carriers in the channel.[27] When an MOS transistor operates in the triode region, the average horizontal electric field along the channel is $V_{DS}/L$. When $V_{DS}$ is small and/or $L$ is large, the horizontal field is low, and the linear relation between carrier velocity and field assumed in (1.148) is valid. At high fields, however, the carrier velocities approach the thermal velocities, and subsequently the slope of the carrier velocity decreases with increasing field. This effect is illustrated in Fig. 1.39, which shows typical measured electron drift velocity $v_d$ versus horizontal electric field strength magnitude $\mathscr{E}$ in an NMOS surface channel. While the velocity at low field values is proportional to the field, the velocity at high field values approaches a constant called the *scattering-limited* velocity $v_{scl}$. A first-order analytical approximation to this curve is

$$v_d = \frac{\mu_n \mathscr{E}}{1 + \mathscr{E}/\mathscr{E}_c} \qquad (1.212)$$

Figure 1.39 Typical measured electron drift velocity $v_d$ versus horizontal electric field $\mathscr{E}$ in an MOS surface channel (solid plot). Also shown (dashed plot) is the analytical approximation of Eq. 1.212 with $\mathscr{E}_c = 1.5 \times 10^6$ V/m and $\mu_n = 0.07$ m²/V-s.

where $\mathscr{E}_c \approx 1.5 \times 10^6$ V/m and $\mu_n \approx 0.07$ m²/V-s is the low-field mobility close to the gate. Equation 1.212 is also plotted in Fig. 1.39. From (1.212), as $\mathscr{E} \to \infty$, $v_d \to v_{scl} = \mu_n \mathscr{E}_c$. At the critical field value $\mathscr{E}_c$, the carrier velocity is a factor of 2 less than the low-field formula would predict. In a device with a channel length $L = 0.5$ μm, we need a voltage drop of only 0.75 V along the channel to produce an average field equal to $\mathscr{E}_c$, and this condition is readily achieved in short-channel MOS transistors. Similar results are found for PMOS devices.

Substituting (1.212) and (1.149) into (1.147) and rearranging gives

$$I_D\left(1 + \frac{1}{\mathscr{E}_c}\frac{dV}{dy}\right) \doteq WQ_I(y)\mu_n\frac{dV}{dy} \tag{1.213}$$

Note that as $\mathscr{E}_c \to \infty$ and velocity saturation becomes negligible, (1.213) approaches the original equation (1.147). Integrating (1.213) along the channel, we obtain

$$\int_0^L I_D\left(1 + \frac{1}{\mathscr{E}_c}\frac{dV}{dy}\right)dy = \int_0^{V_{DS}} WQ_I(y)\mu_n\,dV \tag{1.214}$$

and thus

$$I_D = \frac{\mu_n C_{ox}}{2\left(1 + \dfrac{V_{DS}}{\mathscr{E}_c L}\right)}\cdot\frac{W}{L}[2(V_{GS} - V_t)V_{DS} - V_{DS}^2] \tag{1.215}$$

In the limit as $\mathscr{E}_c \to \infty$, (1.215) is the same as (1.152), which gives the drain current in the triode region without velocity saturation. The quantity $V_{DS}/L$ in (1.215) can be interpreted as the average horizontal electric field in the channel. If this field is comparable to $\mathscr{E}_c$, the drain current for a given $V_{DS}$ is less than the simple expression (1.152) would predict.

Equation 1.215 is valid in the triode region. Let $V_{DS(act)}$ represent the maximum value of $V_{DS}$ for which the transistor operates in the triode region, which is equivalent to the minimum value of $V_{DS}$ for which the transistor operates in the active region. In the active region, the current should be independent of $V_{DS}$ because channel-length modulation is not included here. Therefore, $V_{DS(act)}$ is the value of $V_{DS}$ that sets $\partial I_D/\partial V_{DS} = 0$. From (1.215),

$$\frac{\partial I_D}{\partial V_{DS}} = \frac{k'}{2}\frac{W}{L}\left[\frac{\left(1 + \dfrac{V_{DS}}{\mathscr{E}_c L}\right)[2(V_{GS} - V_t) - 2V_{DS}] - \dfrac{[2(V_{GS} - V_t)V_{DS} - V_{DS}^2]}{\mathscr{E}_c L}}{\left(1 + \dfrac{V_{DS}}{\mathscr{E}_c L}\right)^2}\right] \tag{1.216}$$

where $k' = \mu_n C_{ox}$ as given by (1.153). To set $\partial I_D/\partial V_{DS} = 0$,

$$\left(1 + \frac{V_{DS}}{\mathscr{E}_c L}\right)[2(V_{GS} - V_t) - 2V_{DS}] - \frac{[2(V_{GS} - V_t)V_{DS} - V_{DS}^2]}{\mathscr{E}_c L} = 0 \tag{1.217}$$

Rearranging (1.217) gives

$$\frac{V_{DS}^2}{\mathscr{E}_c L} + 2V_{DS} - 2(V_{GS} - V_t) = 0 \tag{1.218}$$

Solving the quadratic equation gives

$$V_{DS(act)} = V_{DS} = -\mathscr{E}_c L \pm \mathscr{E}_c L\sqrt{1 + \frac{2(V_{GS} - V_t)}{\mathscr{E}_c L}} \tag{1.219}$$

Since the drain-source voltage must be greater than zero,

$$V_{DS(act)} = V_{DS} = \mathscr{E}_c L \left( \sqrt{1 + \frac{2(V_{GS} - V_t)}{\mathscr{E}_c L}} - 1 \right) \tag{1.220}$$

To determine $V_{DS(act)}$ without velocity-saturation effects, let $\mathscr{E}_c \to \infty$ so that the drift velocity is proportional to the electric field, and let $x = (V_{GS} - V_t)/(\mathscr{E}_c L)$. Then $x \to 0$, and a Taylor series can be used to show that

$$\sqrt{1 + 2x} = 1 + x - \frac{x^2}{2} + \cdots \tag{1.221}$$

Using (1.221) in (1.220) gives

$$V_{DS(act)} = (V_{GS} - V_t)\left(1 - \frac{V_{GS} - V_t}{2\mathscr{E}_c L} + \cdots \right) \tag{1.222}$$

When $\mathscr{E}_c \to \infty$, (1.222) shows that $V_{DS(act)} \to (V_{GS} - V_t)$, as expected.[28] This observation is confirmed by plotting the ratio of $V_{DS(act)}$ to the overdrive $V_{ov}$ versus $\mathscr{E}_c L$ in Fig. 1.40. When $\mathscr{E}_c \to \infty$, $V_{DS(act)} \to V_{ov} = V_{GS} - V_t$, as predicted by (1.222). On the other hand, when $\mathscr{E}_c$ is small enough that velocity saturation is significant, Fig. 1.40 shows that $V_{DS(act)} < V_{ov}$.

To find the drain current in the active region with velocity saturation, substitute $V_{DS(act)}$ in (1.220) for $V_{DS}$ in (1.215). After rearranging, the result is

$$I_D = \frac{\mu_n C_{ox}}{2} \frac{W}{L} [V_{DS(act)}]^2 \tag{1.223}$$

Equation 1.223 is in the same form as (1.157), where velocity saturation is neglected, except that $V_{DS(act)}$ is less than $(V_{GS} - V_t)$ when velocity saturation is significant, as shown in Fig. 1.40. Therefore, the current predicted by (1.157) overestimates the current that really flows when the carrier velocity saturates. To examine the limiting case when the velocity is completely saturated, let $\mathscr{E}_c \to 0$. Then (1.212) shows that the drift velocity approaches the scattering-limited velocity $v_d \to v_{scl} = \mu_n \mathscr{E}_c$. Substituting (1.220) into (1.223) gives

$$\lim_{\mathscr{E}_c \to 0} I_D = \mu_n C_{ox} W (V_{GS} - V_t) \mathscr{E}_c = W C_{ox} (V_{GS} - V_t) v_{scl} \tag{1.224}$$

**Figure 1.40** Ratio of the minimum drain-source voltage required for operation in the active region to the overdrive versus the product of the critical field and the channel length. When $\mathscr{E}_c \to \infty$, velocity saturation is not a factor, and $V_{DS(act)} \to V_{ov} = V_{GS} - V_t$, as expected. When velocity saturation is significant, $V_{DS(act)} < V_{ov}$.

In contrast to the square-law behavior predicted by (1.157), (1.224) shows that the drain current is a *linear* function of the overdrive $(V_{GS} - V_t)$ when the carrier velocity saturates. Also, (1.224) shows that the drain current is independent of the channel length when the carrier velocity saturates. In this case, both the charge in the channel and the time required for the charge to cross the channel are proportional to $L$. Since the current is the ratio of the charge in the channel to the time required to cross the channel, the current does not depend on $L$ as long as the channel length is short enough to produce an electric field that is high enough for velocity saturation to occur.[29] In contrast, when the carrier velocity is proportional to the electric field instead of being saturated, the time required for channel charge to cross the channel is proportional to $L^2$ because increasing $L$ both reduces the carrier velocity and increases the distance between the source and the drain. Therefore, when velocity saturation is not significant, the drain current is inversely proportional to $L$, as we have come to expect through (1.157). Finally, (1.224) shows that the drain current in the active region is proportional to the scattering-limited velocity $v_{scl} = \mu_n \mathscr{E}_c$ when the velocity is saturated.

Substituting (1.222) into (1.223) gives

$$
\begin{aligned}
I_D &= \frac{\mu_n C_{ox}}{2} \frac{W}{L} (V_{GS} - V_t)^2 \left(1 - \frac{V_{GS} - V_t}{2\mathscr{E}_c L} + \cdots\right)^2 \\
&= \frac{\mu_n C_{ox}}{2} \frac{W}{L} (V_{GS} - V_t)^2 \left(1 - \frac{x}{2} + \cdots\right)^2 \\
&= \frac{\mu_n C_{ox}}{2} \frac{W}{L} (V_{GS} - V_t)^2 (1 - x + \cdots) \\
&= \frac{\mu_n C_{ox}}{2} \frac{W}{L} (V_{GS} - V_t)^2 \left(1 - \frac{V_{GS} - V_t}{\mathscr{E}_c L} + \cdots\right)
\end{aligned}
\tag{1.225}
$$

where $x = (V_{GS} - V_t)/(\mathscr{E}_c L)$ as defined for (1.221). If $x \ll 1$, $(1 - x) \simeq 1/(1 + x)$, and

$$
I_D \simeq \frac{\mu_n C_{ox}}{2\left(1 + \dfrac{V_{GS} - V_t}{\mathscr{E}_c L}\right)} \frac{W}{L} (V_{GS} - V_t)^2
\tag{1.226}
$$

Equation 1.226 is valid without velocity saturation and at its onset, where $(V_{GS} - V_t) \ll \mathscr{E}_c L$. The effect of velocity saturation on the current in the active region predicted by (1.226) can be modeled with the addition of a resistance in series with the source of an ideal square-law device, as shown in Fig. 1.41. Let $V'_{GS}$ be the gate-source voltage of the ideal square-law transistor. From (1.157),

$$
I_D = \frac{\mu_n C_{ox}}{2} \frac{W}{L} (V'_{GS} - V_t)^2
\tag{1.227}
$$

Let $V_{GS}$ be the sum of $V'_{GS}$ and the voltage drop on $R_{SX}$. Then

$$
V_{GS} = V'_{GS} + I_D R_{SX}
\tag{1.228}
$$

This sum models the gate-source voltage of a real MOS transistor with velocity saturation. Substituting (1.228) into (1.227) gives

$$
I_D = \frac{\mu_n C_{ox}}{2} \frac{W}{L} (V_{GS} - I_D R_{SX} - V_t)^2
$$

Figure 1.41 Model of velocity saturation in an MOSFET by addition of series source resistance to an ideal square-law device.

$$I_D = \frac{\mu_n C_{ox}}{2} \frac{W}{L} \left( (V_{GS} - V_t)^2 - 2(V_{GS} - V_t)I_D R_{SX} + (I_D R_{SX})^2 \right) \quad (1.229)$$

Rearranging (1.229) while ignoring the $(I_D R_{SX})^2$ term gives

$$I_D \simeq \frac{\mu_n C_{ox}}{2\left(1 + \mu_n C_{ox} \dfrac{W}{L} R_{SX}(V_{GS} - V_t)\right)} \frac{W}{L}(V_{GS} - V_t)^2 \quad (1.230)$$

Equation 1.230 has the same form as (1.226) if we identify

$$\mu_n C_{ox} \frac{W}{L} R_{SX} = \frac{1}{\mathscr{E}_c L} \quad (1.231)$$

Rearranging (1.231) gives

$$\boxed{R_{SX} = \frac{1}{\mathscr{E}_c \mu_n C_{ox} W}} \quad (1.232)$$

Thus the influence of velocity saturation on the large-signal characteristics of an MOS transistor can be modeled to first order by a resistor $R_{SX}$ in series with the source of an ideal square-law device. Note that $R_{SX}$ varies inversely with $W$, as does the intrinsic physical series resistance due to the source and drain contact regions. Typically, $R_{SX}$ is larger than the physical series resistance. For $W = 2 \ \mu\text{m}$, $k' = \mu_n C_{ox} = 200 \ \mu\text{A/V}^2$, and $\mathscr{E}_c = 1.5 \times 10^6 \ \text{V/m}$, we find $R_{SX} \simeq 1700 \ \Omega$.

### 1.7.2 Transconductance and Transition Frequency

The values of all small-signal parameters can change significantly in the presence of short-channel effects.[30] One of the most important changes is to the transconductance. Substituting (1.220) into (1.223) and calculating $\partial I_D / \partial V_{GS}$ gives

$$g_m = \frac{\partial I_D}{\partial V_{GS}} = W C_{ox} v_{scl} \frac{\sqrt{1 + \dfrac{2(V_{GS} - V_t)}{\mathscr{E}_c L}} - 1}{\sqrt{1 + \dfrac{2(V_{GS} - V_t)}{\mathscr{E}_c L}}} \quad (1.233)$$

where $v_{scl} = \mu_n \mathscr{E}_c$ as in Fig. 1.39. To determine $g_m$ without velocity saturation, let $E_c \rightarrow \infty$ and $x = (V_{GS} - V_t)/(\mathscr{E}_c L)$. Then substituting (1.221) into (1.233) and rearranging gives

$$\lim_{\mathscr{E}_c \to \infty} g_m = k' \frac{W}{L}(V_{GS} - V_t) \quad (1.234)$$

as predicted by (1.180). In this case, the transconductance increases when the overdrive increases or the channel length decreases. On the other hand, letting $\mathscr{E}_c \to 0$ to determine $g_m$ when the velocity is saturated gives

$$\lim_{\mathscr{E}_c \to 0} g_m = W C_{ox} v_{scl} \tag{1.235}$$

Equation 1.235 shows that further decreases in $L$ or increases in $(V_{GS} - V_t)$ do not change the transconductance when the velocity is saturated.

From (1.223) and (1.233), the ratio of the transconductance to the current can be calculated as

$$\frac{g_m}{I} = \frac{2}{(\mathscr{E}_c L)\sqrt{1 + \dfrac{2(V_{GS} - V_t)}{\mathscr{E}_c L}}\left(\sqrt{1 + \dfrac{2(V_{GS} - V_t)}{\mathscr{E}_c L}} - 1\right)} \tag{1.236}$$

As $\mathscr{E}_c \to 0$, the velocity saturates and

$$\lim_{\mathscr{E}_c \to 0} \frac{g_m}{I} = \frac{1}{V_{GS} - V_t} \tag{1.237}$$

Comparing (1.237) to (1.181) shows that velocity saturation reduces the transconductance-to-current ratio for a given overdrive.

On the other hand, when $x = (V_{GS} - V_t)/(\mathscr{E}_c L) \ll 1$, substituting (1.221) into (1.236) gives

$$\frac{g_m}{I} \simeq \frac{2}{(V_{GS} - V_t)(1 + x)} \tag{1.238}$$

Therefore, as $\mathscr{E}_c \to \infty$, $x \to 0$, and (1.238) collapses to

$$\lim_{\mathscr{E}_c \to \infty} \frac{g_m}{I} = \frac{2}{V_{GS} - V_t} \tag{1.239}$$

as predicted by (1.181). Equation 1.238 shows that if $x < 0.1$, the error in using (1.181) to calculate the transconductance-to-current ratio is less than about 10 percent. Therefore, we will conclude that velocity-saturation effects are insignificant in hand calculations if

$$(V_{GS} - V_t) < 0.1(\mathscr{E}_c L) \tag{1.240}$$

Figure 1.42 plots the transconductance-to-current ratio versus the overdrive for three cases. The highest and lowest ratios come from (1.239) and (1.237), which correspond to asymptotes where velocity saturation is insignificant and dominant, respectively. In practice, the transition between these extreme cases is gradual and described by (1.236), which is plotted in Fig. 1.42 for an example where $\mathscr{E}_c = 1.5 \times 10^6$ V/m and $L = 0.5$ μm.

One reason the change in transconductance caused by velocity saturation is important is because it affects the transition frequency $f_T$. Assuming that $C_{gs} \gg C_{gb} + C_{gd}$, substituting (1.235) into (1.208) shows that

$$f_T = \frac{1}{2\pi} \frac{g_m}{C_{gs}} \propto \frac{W C_{ox} v_{scl}}{W L C_{ox}} \propto \frac{v_{scl}}{L} \tag{1.241}$$

One key point here is that the transition frequency is independent of the overdrive once velocity saturation is reached. In contrast, (1.209) shows that increasing $(V_{GS} - V_t)$ increases $f_T$ before the velocity saturates. Also, (1.241) shows that the transition frequency

Figure 1.42 Transconductance-to-current ratio versus over-drive ($V_{GS} - V_t$) where velocity saturation is insignificant ($\mathscr{E}_c L \to \infty$), dominant ($\mathscr{E}_c L = 0$), and of gradually increasing importance ($\mathscr{E}_c L = 0.75$ V).

is inversely proportional to the channel length when the velocity is saturated. In contrast, (1.209) predicts that $f_T$ is inversely proportional to the square of the channel length before the velocity saturates. As a result, velocity saturation reduces the speed improvement that can be achieved through reductions in the minimum channel length.

### 1.7.3 Mobility Degradation from the Vertical Field

Thus far, we have considered only the effects of the horizontal field due to the $V_{DS}$ along the channel when considering velocity saturation. However, a vertical field originating from the gate voltage also exists and influences carrier velocity. A physical reason for this effect is that increasing the vertical electric field forces the carriers in the channel closer to the surface of the silicon, where surface imperfections impede their movement from the source to the drain, reducing mobility.[31] The vertical field at any point in the channel depends on the gate-channel voltage. Since the gate-channel voltage is not constant from the source to the drain, the effect of the vertical field on mobility should be included within the integration in (1.214) in principle.[32] For simplicity, however, this effect is often modeled after integration by changing the mobility in the previous equations to an effective mobility given by

$$\mu_{\text{eff}} = \frac{\mu_n}{1 + \theta(V_{GS} - V_t)} \tag{1.242}$$

where $\mu_n$ is the mobility with zero vertical field, and $\theta$ is inversely proportional to the oxide thickness. For $t_{ox} = 100$ Å, $\theta$ is typically in the range from 0.1 V$^{-1}$ to 0.4 V$^{-1}$.[33] In practice, $\theta$ is determined by a best fit to measured device characteristics.

## 1.8 Weak Inversion in MOS Transistors

The MOSFET analysis of Section 1.5 considered the normal region of operation for which a well-defined conducting channel exists under the gate. In this region of *strong inversion*, changes in the gate-source voltage are assumed to cause only changes in the channel charge and not in the depletion-region charge. In contrast, for gate-source voltages less than the extrapolated threshold voltage $V_t$ but high enough to create a depletion region at the surface of the silicon, the device operates in *weak inversion*. In the weak-inversion region, the channel charge is much less than the charge in the depletion region, and the drain current arising from the drift of majority carriers is negligible. However, the total drain current in weak inversion is larger than that caused by drift because a gradient in minority-carrier concentration causes a diffusion current to flow. In weak inversion, an $n$-channel MOS transistor operates as an $npn$ bipolar transistor, where the source acts as the emitter, the substrate as the base, and the drain as the collector.[34]

## 1.8.1 Drain Current in Weak Inversion

To analyze this situation, assume that the source and the body are both grounded. Also assume that $V_{DS} > 0$. (If $V_{DS} < 0$, the drain acts as the emitter and the source as the collector.)[35] Then increasing the gate-source voltage increases the surface potential $\psi_s$, which tends to reduce the reverse bias across the source-substrate (emitter-base) junction and to exponentially increase the concentration of electrons in the $p$-type substrate at the source $n_p(0)$. From (1.27),

$$n_p(0) = n_{po} \exp \frac{\psi_s}{V_T} \qquad (1.243)$$

where $n_{po}$ is the equilibrium concentration of electrons in the substrate (base). Similarly, the concentration of electrons in the substrate at the drain $n_p(L)$ is

$$n_p(L) = n_{po} \exp \frac{\psi_s - V_{DS}}{V_T} \qquad (1.244)$$

From (1.31), the drain current due to the diffusion of electrons in the substrate is

$$I_D = qAD_n \frac{n_p(L) - n_p(0)}{L} \qquad (1.245)$$

where $D_n$ is the diffusion constant for electrons, and $A$ is the cross-sectional area in which the diffusion current flows. The area $A$ is the product of the transistor width $W$ and the thickness $X$ of the region in which $I_D$ flows. Substituting (1.243) and (1.244) into (1.245) and rearranging gives

$$I_D = \frac{W}{L} qXD_n n_{po} \exp\left(\frac{\psi_s}{V_T}\right)\left[1 - \exp\left(-\frac{V_{DS}}{V_T}\right)\right] \qquad (1.246)$$

In weak inversion, the surface potential is approximately a linear function of the gate-source voltage.[36] Assume that the charge stored at the oxide-silicon interface is independent of the surface potential. Then, in weak inversion, changes in the surface potential $\Delta\psi_s$ are controlled by changes in the gate-source voltage $\Delta V_{GS}$ through a voltage divider between the oxide capacitance $C_{ox}$ and the depletion-region capacitance $C_{js}$. Therefore,

$$\frac{d\psi_s}{dV_{GS}} = \frac{C_{ox}}{C_{js} + C_{ox}} = \frac{1}{n} = \frac{1}{1 + \chi} \qquad (1.247)$$

in which $n = (1 + C_{js}/C_{ox})$ and $\chi = C_{js}/C_{ox}$, as defined in (1.197). Separating variables in (1.247) and integrating gives

$$\psi_s = \frac{V_{GS}}{n} + k_1 \qquad (1.248)$$

where $k_1$ is a constant. Equation 1.248 is valid only when the transistor operates in weak inversion. When $V_{GS} = V_t$ with $V_{SB} = 0$, $\psi_s = 2\phi_f$ by definition of the threshold voltage. For $V_{GS} > V_t$, the inversion layer holds the surface potential nearly constant and

(1.248) is not valid. Since (1.248) is valid only when $V_{GS} \leq V_t$, (1.248) is rewritten as follows:

$$\psi_s = \frac{V_{GS} - V_t}{n} + k_2 \tag{1.249}$$

where $k_2 = k_1 + V_t/n$. Substituting (1.249) into (1.246) gives

$$I_D = \frac{W}{L} q X D_n n_{po} \exp\left(\frac{k_2}{V_T}\right) \exp\left(\frac{V_{GS} - V_t}{nV_T}\right)\left[1 - \exp\left(-\frac{V_{DS}}{V_T}\right)\right] \tag{1.250}$$

Let

$$I_t = q X D_n n_{po} \exp\left(\frac{k_2}{V_T}\right) \tag{1.251}$$

represent the drain current with $V_{GS} = V_t$, $W/L = 1$, and $V_{DS} \gg V_T$. Then

$$I_D = \frac{W}{L} I_t \exp\left(\frac{V_{GS} - V_t}{nV_T}\right)\left[1 - \exp\left(-\frac{V_{DS}}{V_T}\right)\right] \tag{1.252}$$

Figure 1.43 plots the drain current versus the drain-source voltage for three values of the overdrive, with $W = 20\ \mu\text{m}$, $L = 20\ \mu\text{m}$, $n = 1.5$, and $I_t = 0.1\ \mu\text{A}$. Notice that the drain current is almost constant when $V_{DS} > 3V_T$ because the last term in (1.252) approaches unity in this case. Therefore, unlike in strong inversion, the minimum drain-source voltage required to force the transistor to operate as a current source in weak inversion is independent of the overdrive.[37] Figure 1.43 and Equation 1.252 also show that the drain current is not zero when $V_{GS} \leq V_t$. To further illustrate this point, we show measured NMOS characteristics plotted on two different scales in Fig. 1.44. In Fig. 1.44a, we show $\sqrt{I_D}$ versus $V_{GS}$ in the active region plotted on linear scales. For this device, $W = 20\ \mu\text{m}$, $L = 20\ \mu\text{m}$, and short-channel effects are negligible. (See Problem 1.21 for an example of a case in which short-channel effects are important.) The resulting straight line shows that the device characteristic is close to an ideal square law. Plots like the one in Fig. 1.44a are commonly used to obtain $V_t$ by extrapolation (0.7 V in this case) and also $k'$ from the slope of the curve (54 $\mu\text{A/V}^2$ in this case). Near the threshold voltage, the curve deviates from the straight line representing the square law. This region is weak inversion. The data are plotted a second time in Fig. 1.44b on log-linear scales. The straight line obtained for $V_{GS} < V_t$ fits (1.252) with $n = 1.5$. For $I_D < 10^{-12}$ A, the slope decreases because leakage currents are significant and do not follow (1.252).

**Figure 1.43** Drain current versus drain-source voltage in weak inversion.

Figure 1.44 (*a*) Measured NMOS transfer characteristic in the active region plotted on linear scales as $\sqrt{I_D}$ versus $V_{GS}$, showing the square-law characteristic.

Figure 1.44 (*b*) Data from Fig. 1.44*a* plotted on log-linear scales showing the exponential characteristic in the subthreshold region.

The major use of transistors operating in weak inversion is in very low power applications at relatively low signal frequencies. The limitation to low signal frequencies occurs because the MOSFET $f_T$ becomes very small. This result stems from the fact that the small-signal $g_m$ calculated from (1.252) becomes proportional to $I_D$ and therefore very small in weak inversion, as shown next.

## 1.8.2 Transconductance and Transition Frequency in Weak Inversion

Calculating $\partial I_D / \partial V_{GS}$ from (1.252) and using (1.247) gives

$$g_m = \frac{W}{L}\frac{I_t}{nV_T}\exp\left(\frac{V_{GS}-V_t}{nV_T}\right)\left[1-\exp\left(-\frac{V_{DS}}{V_T}\right)\right] = \frac{I_D}{nV_T} = \frac{I_D}{V_T}\frac{C_{ox}}{C_{js}+C_{ox}} \quad (1.253)$$

The transconductance of an MOS transistor operating in weak inversion is identical to that of a corresponding bipolar transistor, as shown in (1.182), except for the factor of $1/n = C_{ox}/(C_{js} + C_{ox})$. This factor stems from a voltage divider between the oxide and depletion capacitors in the MOS transistor, which models the indirect control of the gate on the surface potential.

From (1.253), the ratio of the transconductance to the current of an MOS transistor in weak inversion is

$$\frac{g_m}{I} = \frac{1}{nV_T} = \frac{1}{V_T}\frac{C_{ox}}{C_{js} + C_{ox}} \tag{1.254}$$

Equation 1.254 predicts that this ratio is independent of the overdrive. In contrast, (1.181) predicts that the ratio of transconductance to current is inversely proportional to the overdrive. Therefore, as the overdrive approaches zero, (1.181) predicts that this ratio becomes infinite. However, (1.181) is valid only when the transistor operates in strong inversion. To estimate the overdrive required to operate the transistor in strong inversion, we will equate the $g_m/I$ ratios calculated in (1.254) and (1.181). The result is

$$V_{ov} = V_{GS} - V_t = 2nV_T \tag{1.255}$$

which is about 78 mV at room temperature with $n = 1.5$. Although this analysis implies that the transition from weak to strong inversion occurs abruptly, a nonzero transition width occurs in practice. Between weak and strong inversion, the transistor operates in a region of *moderate* inversion, where both diffusion and drift currents are significant.[38]

Figure 1.45 plots the transconductance-to-current ratio versus overdrive for an example case with $n = 1.5$. When the overdrive is negative but high enough to cause depletion at the surface, the transistor operates in weak inversion and the transconductance-to-current ratio is constant, as predicted by (1.254). When $V_{GS} - V_t = 0$, the surface potential is $2\psi_f$, which means that the surface concentration of electrons is equal to the bulk concentration of holes. This point is usually defined as the upper bound on the region of weak inversion. When $V_{GS} - V_t > 2nV_T$, the transconductance-to-current ratio is given by (1.181), assuming that velocity saturation is negligible. If velocity saturation is significant, (1.236) should be used instead of (1.181) both to predict the transconductance-to-current ratio and to predict the overdrive required to operate in strong inversion. For $0 \le V_{GS} - V_t \le 2nV_T$, the transistor operates in moderate inversion. Because simple models for moderate inversion are not known in practice, we will ignore this region in

Figure 1.45 Transconductance-to-current ratio versus overdrive.

the remainder of this book and assume that MOS transistors operate in weak inversion for overdrives less than the bound given in (1.255).

Equation 1.208 can be used to find the transition frequency. In weak inversion, $C_{gs} \approx C_{gd} \approx 0$ because the inversion layer contains little charge.[39] However, $C_{gb}$ can be thought of as the series combination of the oxide and depletion capacitors. Therefore,

$$C_{gs} + C_{gb} + C_{gd} \approx C_{gb} = WL\left(\frac{C_{ox}C_{js}}{C_{ox} + C_{js}}\right) \tag{1.256}$$

Substituting (1.253) and (1.256) into (1.208) gives

$$f_T = \frac{1}{2\pi}\omega_T = \frac{1}{2\pi}\frac{\dfrac{I_D}{V_T}\dfrac{C_{ox}}{C_{js} + C_{ox}}}{WL\dfrac{C_{ox}C_{js}}{C_{ox} + C_{js}}} = \frac{1}{2\pi}\frac{I_D}{V_T}\frac{1}{WLC_{js}} \tag{1.257}$$

Let $I_M$ represent the maximum drain current that flows in the transistor in weak inversion. Then

$$I_M = \frac{W}{L}I_t \tag{1.258}$$

where $I_t$ is given in (1.251). Multiplying numerator and denominator in (1.257) by $I_M$ and using (1.258) gives

$$f_T = \frac{1}{2\pi}\frac{\dfrac{W}{L}I_t}{V_T}\frac{1}{WLC_{js}}\frac{I_D}{I_M} = \frac{1}{2\pi}\frac{I_t}{V_T}\frac{1}{C_{js}}\frac{1}{L^2}\frac{I_D}{I_M} \tag{1.259}$$

From (1.251), $I_t \propto D_n$. Using the Einstein relationship $D_n = \mu_n V_T$ gives

$$f_T \propto \frac{D_n}{L^2}\frac{I_D}{I_M} \propto \frac{\mu_n V_T}{L^2}\frac{I_D}{I_M} \tag{1.260}$$

Equation 1.260 shows that the transition frequency for an MOS transistor operating in weak inversion is inversely proportional to the square of the channel length. This result is consistent with (1.209) for strong inversion without velocity saturation. In contrast, when velocity saturation is significant, the transition frequency is inversely proportional to the channel length, as predicted by (1.241). Equation 1.260 also shows that the transition frequency in weak inversion is independent of the overdrive, unlike the case in strong inversion without velocity saturation, but like the case with velocity saturation. Finally, a more detailed analysis shows that the constant of proportionality in (1.260) is approximately unity.[39]

■  **EXAMPLE**

Calculate the overdrive and the transition frequency for an NMOS transistor with $I_D = 1\ \mu A$, $I_t = 0.1\ \mu A$, and $V_{DS} \gg V_T$. Device parameters are $W = 10\ \mu m$, $L = 1\ \mu m$, $n = 1.5$, $k' = 200\ \mu A/V^2$, and $t_{ox} = 100\ \text{Å}$. Assume that the temperature is 27°C.

From (1.166), if the transistor operates in strong inversion,

$$V_{ov} = V_{GS} - V_t = \sqrt{\frac{2I_D}{k'(W/L)}} = \sqrt{\frac{2 \times 1}{200 \times 10}} \approx 32\ \text{mV}$$

Since the value of the overdrive calculated by (1.166) is less than $2nV_T \simeq 78$ mV, the overdrive calculated previously is not valid except to indicate that the transistor does not operate in strong inversion. From (1.252), the overdrive in weak inversion with $V_{DS} \gg V_T$ is

$$V_{ov} = nV_T \ln\left(\frac{I_D}{I_t}\frac{L}{W}\right) = (1.5)(26 \text{ mV}) \ln\left(\frac{1}{0.1}\frac{1}{10}\right) = 0$$

From (1.253),

$$g_m = \frac{1 \ \mu A}{1.5(26 \text{ mV})} \simeq 26 \ \frac{\mu A}{V}$$

From (1.247),

$$C_{js} = (n - 1)C_{ox} = (0.5)C_{ox}$$

From (1.256),

$$C_{gs} + C_{gb} + C_{gd} \simeq C_{gb} = WL\frac{C_{ox}(0.5C_{ox})}{C_{ox} + 0.5C_{ox}} = WL\frac{C_{ox}}{3}$$

$$= \frac{10 \ \mu m^2}{3} \frac{3.9 \times 8.854 \times 10^{-14} \dfrac{F}{cm} \times \dfrac{100 \text{ cm}}{10^6 \mu m}}{100 \ \text{Å} \times \dfrac{10^6 \ \mu m}{10^{10} \text{Å}}}$$

$$\simeq 11.5 \text{ fF}$$

From (1.208),

$$f_T = \frac{1}{2\pi}\omega_T = \frac{1}{2\pi}\frac{26 \ \mu A/V}{11.5 \text{ fF}} \simeq 360 \text{ MHz}$$

Although 360 MHz may seem to be a high transition frequency at first glance, this result should be compared with the result of the example at the end of Section 1.6, where the same transistor operating in strong inversion with an overdrive of 316 mV had a transition frequency of 3.4 GHz.

## 1.9 Substrate Current Flow in MOS Transistors

In Section 1.3.4, the effects of avalanche breakdown on bipolar transistor characteristics were described. As the reverse-bias voltages on the device are increased, carriers traversing the depletion regions gain sufficient energy to create new electron-hole pairs in lattice collisions by a process known as *impact ionization*. Eventually, at sufficient bias voltages, the process results in large avalanche currents. For collector-base bias voltages well below the breakdown value, a small enhanced current flow may occur across the collector-base junction due to this process, with little apparent effect on the device characteristics.

Impact ionization also occurs in MOS transistors but has a significantly different effect on the device characteristics. This difference is because the channel electrons (for the NMOS case) create electron-hole pairs in lattice collisions in the drain depletion region, and some of the resulting holes then flow to the substrate, creating a substrate current. (The electrons created in the process flow out the drain terminal.) The carriers created by impact ionization are therefore not confined within the device as in a bipolar transistor. The effect of this phenomenon can be modeled by inclusion of a controlled current generator

**Figure 1.46** Representation of impact ionization in an MOSFET by a drain-substrate current generator.

$I_{DB}$ from drain to substrate, as shown in Fig. 1.46 for an NMOS device. The magnitude of this substrate current depends on the voltage across the drain depletion region (which determines the energy of the ionizing channel electrons) and also on the drain current (which is the rate at which the channel electrons enter the depletion region). Empirical investigation has shown that the current $I_{DB}$ can be expressed as

$$I_{DB} = K_1(V_{DS} - V_{DS(\text{act})})I_D \exp\left(-\frac{K_2}{V_{DS} - V_{DS(\text{act})}}\right) \qquad (1.261)$$

where $K_1$ and $K_2$ are process-dependent parameters and $V_{DS(\text{act})}$ is the minimum value of $V_{DS}$ for which the transistor operates in the active region.[40] Typical values for NMOS devices are $K_1 = 5 \text{ V}^{-1}$ and $K_2 = 30 \text{ V}$. The effect is generally much less significant in PMOS devices because the holes carrying the charge in the channel are much less efficient in creating electron-hole pairs than energetic electrons.

The major impact of this phenomenon on circuit performance is that it creates a parasitic resistance from drain to substrate. Because the common substrate terminal must always be connected to the most negative supply voltage in the circuit, the substrate of an NMOS device in a $p$-substrate process is an ac ground. Therefore, the parasitic resistance shunts the drain to ac ground and can be a limiting factor in many circuit designs. Differentiating (1.261), we find that the drain-substrate small-signal conductance is

$$g_{db} = \frac{\partial I_{DB}}{\partial V_D} = \frac{I_{DB}}{V_{DS} - V_{DS(\text{act})}}\left(\frac{K_2}{V_{DS} - V_{DS(\text{act})}} + 1\right) \simeq \frac{K_2 I_{DB}}{(V_{DS} - V_{DS(\text{act})})^2} \qquad (1.262)$$

where the gate and the source are assumed to be held at fixed potentials.

■ **EXAMPLE**

Calculate $r_{db} = 1/g_{db}$ for $V_{DS} = 2 \text{ V}$ and 4 V, and compare with the device $r_o$. Assume $I_D = 100 \text{ μA}$, $\lambda = 0.05 \text{ V}^{-1}$, $V_{DS(\text{act})} = 0.3 \text{ V}$, $K_1 = 5 \text{ V}^{-1}$, and $K_2 = 30 \text{ V}$.

For $V_{DS} = 2 \text{ V}$, we have from (1.261)

$$I_{DB} = 5 \times 1.7 \times 100 \times 10^{-6} \times \exp\left(-\frac{30}{1.7}\right) \simeq 1.8 \times 10^{-11} \text{ A}$$

From (1.262),

$$g_{db} \simeq \frac{30 \times 1.8 \times 10^{-11}}{1.7^2} \simeq 1.9 \times 10^{-10} \frac{\text{A}}{\text{V}}$$

and thus

$$r_{db} = \frac{1}{g_{db}} \simeq 5.3 \times 10^9 \text{ Ω} = 5.3 \text{ GΩ}$$

This result is negligibly large compared with

$$r_o = \frac{1}{\lambda I_D} = \frac{1}{0.05 \times 100 \times 10^{-6}} = 200 \text{ k}\Omega$$

However, for $V_{DS} = 4$ V,

$$I_{DB} = 5 \times 3.7 \times 100 \times 10^{-6} \times \exp\left(-\frac{30}{3.7}\right) \approx 5.6 \times 10^{-7} \text{ A}$$

The substrate leakage current is now about 0.5 percent of the drain current. More important, we find from (1.262)

$$g_{db} \approx \frac{30 \times 5.6 \times 10^{-7}}{3.7^2} \approx 1.2 \times 10^{-6} \frac{\text{A}}{\text{V}}$$

and thus

$$r_{db} = \frac{1}{g_{db}} \approx 8.15 \times 10^5 \ \Omega = 815 \text{ k}\Omega$$

This parasitic resistor is now comparable to $r_o$ and can have a dominant effect on high-output-impedance MOS current mirrors, as described in Chapter 4.

# APPENDIX

## A.1.1  SUMMARY OF ACTIVE-DEVICE PARAMETERS

### (a) *npn* Bipolar Transistor Parameters

| Quantity | Formula |
|---|---|
| **Large-Signal Forward-Active Operation** | |
| Collector current | $I_c = I_S \exp \dfrac{V_{be}}{V_T}$ |
| **Small-Signal Forward-Active Operation** | |
| Transconductance | $g_m = \dfrac{qI_C}{kT} = \dfrac{I_C}{V_T}$ |
| Transconductance-to-current ratio | $\dfrac{g_m}{I_C} = \dfrac{1}{V_T}$ |
| Input resistance | $r_\pi = \dfrac{\beta_0}{g_m}$ |
| Output resistance | $r_o = \dfrac{V_A}{I_C} = \dfrac{1}{\eta g_m}$ |
| Collector-base resistance | $r_\mu = \beta_0 r_o$ to $5\beta_0 r_o$ |
| Base-charging capacitance | $C_b = \tau_F g_m$ |
| Base-emitter capacitance | $C_\pi = C_b + C_{je}$ |
| Emitter-base junction depletion capacitance | $C_{je} \approx 2C_{je0}$ |
| Collector-base junction capacitance | $C_\mu = \dfrac{C_{\mu 0}}{\left(1 - \dfrac{V_{BC}}{\psi_{0c}}\right)^{n_c}}$ |

(*continued*)

| Quantity | Formula |
|---|---|
| **Small-Signal Forward-Active Operation** | |
| Collector-substrate junction capacitance | $C_{cs} = \dfrac{C_{cs0}}{\left(1 - \dfrac{V_{SC}}{\psi_{0s}}\right)^{n_s}}$ |
| Transition frequency | $f_T = \dfrac{1}{2\pi}\dfrac{g_m}{C_\pi + C_\mu}$ |
| Effective transit time | $\tau_T = \dfrac{1}{2\pi f_T} = \tau_F + \dfrac{C_{je}}{g_m} + \dfrac{C_\mu}{g_m}$ |
| Maximum gain | $g_m r_o = \dfrac{V_A}{V_T} = \dfrac{1}{\eta}$ |

## (b)  *NMOS* Transistor Parameters

| Quantity | Formula |
|---|---|
| **Large-Signal Operation** | |
| Drain current (active region) | $I_d = \dfrac{\mu C_{ox}}{2}\dfrac{W}{L}(V_{gs} - V_t)^2$ |
| Drain current (triode region) | $I_d = \dfrac{\mu C_{ox}}{2}\dfrac{W}{L}[2(V_{gs} - V_t)V_{ds} - V_{ds}^2]$ |
| Threshold voltage | $V_t = V_{t0} + \gamma\left[\sqrt{2\phi_f + V_{sb}} - \sqrt{2\phi_f}\right]$ |
| Threshold voltage parameter | $\gamma = \dfrac{1}{C_{ox}}\sqrt{2q\epsilon N_A}$ |
| Oxide capacitance | $C_{ox} = \dfrac{\epsilon_{ox}}{t_{ox}} = 3.45 \text{ fF}/\mu\text{m}^2 \text{ for } t_{ox} = 100 \text{ Å}$ |
| **Small-Signal Operation (Active Region)** | |
| Top-gate transconductance | $g_m = \mu C_{ox}\dfrac{W}{L}(V_{GS} - V_t) = \sqrt{2I_D \mu C_{ox}\dfrac{W}{L}}$ |
| Transconductance-to-current ratio | $\dfrac{g_m}{I_D} = \dfrac{2}{V_{GS} - V_t}$ |
| Body-effect transconductance | $g_{mb} = \dfrac{\gamma}{2\sqrt{2\phi_f + V_{SB}}}g_m = \chi g_m$ |
| Channel-length modulation parameter | $\lambda = \dfrac{1}{V_A} = \dfrac{1}{L_{\text{eff}}}\dfrac{dX_d}{dV_{DS}}$ |
| Output resistance | $r_o = \dfrac{1}{\lambda I_D} = \dfrac{L_{\text{eff}}}{I_D}\left(\dfrac{dX_d}{dV_{DS}}\right)^{-1}$ |
| Effective channel length | $L_{\text{eff}} = L_{\text{drwn}} - 2L_d - X_d$ |
| Maximum gain | $g_m r_o = \dfrac{1}{\lambda}\dfrac{2}{V_{GS} - V_t} = \dfrac{2V_A}{V_{GS} - V_t}$ |
| Source-body depletion capacitance | $C_{sb} = \dfrac{C_{sb0}}{\left(1 + \dfrac{V_{SB}}{\psi_0}\right)^{0.5}}$ |

(*continued*)

| Quantity | Formula |
|---|---|
| **Small-Signal Operation (Active Region)** | |
| Drain-body depletion capacitance | $C_{db} = \dfrac{C_{db0}}{\left(1 + \dfrac{V_{DB}}{\psi_0}\right)^{0.5}}$ |
| Gate-source capacitance | $C_{gs} = \dfrac{2}{3} WLC_{ox}$ |
| Transition frequency | $f_T = \dfrac{g_m}{2\pi(C_{gs} + C_{gd} + C_{gb})}$ |

## PROBLEMS

**1.1(a)** Calculate the built-in potential, depletion-layer depths, and maximum field in a plane-abrupt *pn* junction in silicon with doping densities $N_A = 8 \times 10^{15}$ atoms/cm$^3$ and $N_D = 10^{17}$ atoms/cm$^3$. Assume a reverse bias of 5 V.

**(b)** Repeat (a) for zero external bias and 0.3 V forward bias.

**1.2** Calculate the zero-bias junction capacitance for the example in Problem 1.1, and also calculate the value at 5 V reverse bias and 0.3 V forward bias. Assume a junction area of $2 \times 10^{-5}$ cm$^2$.

**1.3** Calculate the breakdown voltage for the junction of Problem 1.1 if the critical field is $\mathcal{E}_{crit} = 4 \times 10^5$ V/cm.

**1.4** If junction curvature causes the maximum field at a practical junction to be 1.5 times the theoretical value, calculate the doping density required to give a breakdown voltage of 150 V with an abrupt *pn* junction in silicon. Assume that one side of the junction is much more heavily doped than the other and $\mathcal{E}_{crit} = 3 \times 10^5$ V/cm.

**1.5** If the collector doping density in a transistor is $6 \times 10^{15}$ atoms/cm$^3$, and is much less than the base doping, find $BV_{CEO}$ for $\beta_F = 200$ and $n = 4$. Use $\mathcal{E}_{crit} = 3 \times 10^5$ V/cm.

**1.6** Repeat Problem 1.5 for a doping density of $10^{15}$ atoms/cm$^3$ and $\beta_F = 400$.

**1.7(a)** Sketch the $I_C$-$V_{CE}$ characteristics in the forward-active region for an *npn* transistor with $\beta_F = 100$ (measured at low $V_{CE}$), $V_A = 50$ V, $BV_{CBO} = 120$ V, and $n = 4$. Use

$$I_C = \left(1 + \frac{V_{CE}}{V_A}\right) \frac{M\alpha_F}{1 - M\alpha_F} I_B$$

where $M$ is given by (1.78). Plot $I_C$ from 0 to 10 mA and $V_{CE}$ from 0 to 50 V. Use $I_B = 1\ \mu$A, 10 $\mu$A, 30 $\mu$A, and 60 $\mu$A.

**(b)** Repeat (a), but sketch $V_{CE}$ from 0 to 10 V.

**1.8** Derive and sketch the complete small-signal equivalent circuit for a bipolar transistor at $I_C = 0.2$ mA, $V_{CB} = 3$ V, $V_{CS} = 4$ V. Device parameters are $C_{je0} = 20$ fF, $C_{\mu0} = 10$ fF, $C_{cs0} = 20$ fF, $\beta_0 = 100$, $\tau_F = 15$ ps, $\eta = 10^{-3}$, $r_b = 200\ \Omega$, $r_c = 100\ \Omega$, $r_{ex} = 4\ \Omega$, and $r_\mu = 5\beta_0 r_o$. Assume $\psi_0 = 0.55$ V for all junctions.

**1.9** Repeat Problem 1.8 for $I_C = 1$ mA, $V_{CB} = 1$ V, and $V_{CS} = 2$ V.

**1.10** Sketch the graph of small-signal, common-emitter current gain versus frequency on log scales from 0.1 MHz to 1000 MHz for the examples of Problems 1.8 and 1.9. Calculate the $f_T$ of the device in each case.

**1.11** An integrated-circuit *npn* transistor has the following measured characteristics: $r_b = 100\ \Omega$, $r_c = 100\ \Omega$, $\beta_0 = 100$, $r_o = 50$ k$\Omega$ at $I_C = 1$ mA, $f_T = 600$ MHz with $I_C = 1$ mA and $V_{CB} = 10$ V, $f_T = 1$ GHz with $I_C = 10$ mA and $V_{CB} = 10$ V, $C_\mu = 0.15$ pF with $V_{CB} = 10$ V, and $C_{cs} = 1$ pF with $V_{CS} = 10$ V. Assume $\psi_0 = 0.55$ V for all junctions, and assume $C_{je}$ is constant in the forward-bias region. Use $r_\mu = 5\beta_0 r_o$.

**(a)** Form the *complete* small-signal equivalent circuit for this transistor at $I_C = 0.1$ mA, 1 mA, and 5 mA with $V_{CB} = 2$ V and $V_{CS} = 15$ V.

**(b)** Sketch the graph of $f_T$ versus $I_C$ for this transistor on log scales from 1 $\mu$A to 10 mA with $V_{CB} = 2$ V.

**1.12** A lateral $pnp$ transistor has an effective base width of 10 μm (1 μm = $10^{-4}$ cm).

**(a)** If the emitter-base depletion capacitance is 2 pF in the forward-bias region and is constant, calculate the device $f_T$ at $I_C = -0.5$ mA. (Neglect $C_\mu$.) Also, calculate the minority-carrier charge stored in the base of the transistor at this current level. *Data* : $D_P = 13$ cm$^2$/s in silicon.

**(b)** If the collector-base depletion layer width changes 0.11 μm per volt of $V_{CE}$, calculate $r_o$ for this transistor at $I_C = -0.5$ mA.

**1.13** If the area of the transistor in Problem 1.11 is effectively doubled by connecting two transistors in parallel, which model parameters in the small-signal equivalent circuit of the composite transistor would differ from those of the original device if the *total* collector current is unchanged? What is the relationship between the parameters of the composite and original devices?

**1.14** An integrated $npn$ transistor has the following characteristics: $\tau_F = 0.25$ ns, small-signal, short-circuit current gain is 9 with $I_C = 1$ mA at $f = 50$ MHz, $V_A = 40$ V, $\beta_0 = 100$, $r_b = 150\ \Omega$, $r_c = 150\ \Omega$, $C_\mu = 0.6$ pF, $C_{cs} = 2$ pF at the bias voltage used. Determine all elements in the small-signal equivalent circuit at $I_C = 2$ mA and sketch the circuit.

**1.15** An NMOS transistor has parameters $W = 10$ μm, $L = 1$ μm, $k' = 194$ μA/V$^2$, $\lambda = 0.024$ V$^{-1}$, $t_{ox} = 80\ \mathring{A}$, $\phi_f = 0.3$ V, $V_{t0} = 0.6$ V, and $N_A = 5 \times 10^{15}$ atoms/cm$^3$. Ignore velocity saturation effects.

**(a)** Sketch the $I_D$-$V_{DS}$ characteristics for $V_{DS}$ from 0 to 3 V and $V_{GS} = 0.5$ V, 1.5 V, and 3 V. Assume $V_{SB} = 0$.

**(b)** Sketch the $I_D$-$V_{GS}$ characteristics for $V_{DS} = 2$ V as $V_{GS}$ varies from 0 to 2 V with $V_{SB} = 0, 0.5$ V, and 1 V.

**1.16** Derive and sketch the complete small-signal equivalent circuit for the device of Problem 1.15 with $V_{GS} = 1$ V, $V_{DS} = 2$ V, and $V_{SB} = 1$ V. Use $\psi_0 = 0.7$ V, $C_{sb0} = C_{db0} = 20$ fF, and $C_{gb} = 5$ fF. Overlap capacitance from gate to source and gate to drain is 2 fF.

**1.17** Use the device data of Problems 1.15 and 1.16 to calculate the frequency of unity current gain of this transistor with $V_{DS} = 3$ V, $V_{SB} = 0$ V, $V_{GS} = 1$ V, 1.5 V, and 2 V.

**1.18** Examine the effect of velocity saturation on MOSFET characteristics by plotting $I_D - V_{DS}$ curves for $V_{GS} = 1$ V, 2 V, and 3 V, and $V_{DS} = 0$ to 3 V in the following cases, and by comparing the results with and without inclusion of velocity saturation effects. Assume $V_{SB} = 0$, $V_{t0} = 0.6$ V, $k' = 194$ μA/V$^2$, $\lambda = 0$, and $\mathscr{E}_c = 1.5 \times 10^6$ V/m.

**(a)** $W = 100$ μm and $L = 10$ μm.

**(b)** $W = 10$ μm and $L = 1$ μm.

**(c)** $W = 5$ μm and $L = 0.5$ μm.

**1.19** Consider an NMOS transistor with $W = 2$ μm, $L = 0.5$ μm, $k' = 194$ μA/V$^2$, $\lambda = 0$, $V_{t0} = 0.6$ V, and $\mathscr{E}_c = 1.5 \times 10^6$ V/m. Compare the drain current predicted by the model of Fig. 1.41 to the drain current predicted by direct calculation using the equations including velocity saturation for $V_{GS}$ from 0 to 3 V. Assume $V_{DS} = 3$ V and $V_{SB} = 0$. For what range of $V_{GS}$ is the model of Fig. 1.41 accurate within 10 percent?

**1.20** Calculate the transconductance of an $n$-channel MOSFET with $W = 10$ μm, $\mu_n = 450$ cm$^2$/(V-s), and $\mathscr{E}_c = 1.5 \times 10^6$ V/m using channel lengths from 10 μm to 0.4 μm. Assume that $t_{ox} = L/50$ and that the device operates in the active region with $V_{GS} - V_t = 0.1$ V. Compare the result to a calculation that ignores velocity saturation. For what range of channel lengths is the model without velocity saturation accurate within 10 percent?

**1.21** Plot $\sqrt{I_D}$ versus $V_{GS}$ for an $n$-channel MOSFET with $W = 1$ μm, $L = 1$ μm, $k' = 54$ μA/V$^2$, $\lambda = 0$, $V_{DS} = 5$ V, $V_{SB} = 0$, $V_{t0} = 0.7$ V, and $\mathscr{E}_c = 1.5 \times 10^6$ V/m. Ignore subthreshold conduction. Compare the plot with Fig. 1.44$a$ and explain the main difference for large $V_{GS}$.

**1.22** Calculate the transconductance of an $n$-channel MOSFET at $I_D = 10$ nA and $V_{DS} = 1$ V, assuming subthreshold operation and $n = 1.5$. Assuming $(C_{gs} + C_{gd} + C_{gb}) = 10$ fF, calculate the corresponding device $f_T$.

# REFERENCES

1. P. E. Gray, D. DeWitt, A. R. Boothroyd, J. F. Gibbons. *Physical Electronics and Circuit Models of Transistors.* Wiley, New York, 1964, p. 20.

2. H. C. Poon and H. K. Gummel. "Modeling of Emitter Capacitance," *Proc. IEEE,* Vol. 57, pp. 2181–2182, December 1969.

3. B. R. Chawla and H. K. Gummel. "Transition Region Capacitance of Diffused pn Junctions," *IEEE Trans. Electron Devices,* Vol. ED-18, pp. 178–195, March 1971.

4. S. L. Miller. "Avalanche Breakdown in Germanium," *Phys. Rev.,* Vol. 99, p. 1234, 1955.

5. A. S. Grove. *Physics and Technology of Semiconductor Devices.* Wiley, New York, 1967, Ch. 6.

6. A. S. Grove. Op. cit., Ch. 4.

7. A. S. Grove. Op. cit., Ch. 7.

8. P. E. Gray et al. Op. cit., p. 10.

9. P. E. Gray et al. Op. cit., p. 129.

10. P. E. Gray et al. Op. cit., p. 180.

11. B. A. McDonald. "Avalanche Degradation of $h_{FE}$," *IEEE Trans. Electron Devices,* Vol. ED-17, pp. 871–878, October 1970.

12. H. DeMan. "The Influence of Heavy Doping on the Emitter Efficiency of a Bipolar Transistor," *IEEE Trans. Electron Devices,* Vol. ED-18, pp. 833–835, October 1971.

13. R. J. Whittier and D. A. Tremere. "Current Gain and Cutoff Frequency Falloff at High Currents," *IEEE Trans. Electron Devices,* Vol. ED-16, pp. 39–57, January 1969.

14. J. L. Moll and I. M. Ross. "The Dependence of Transistor Parameters on the Distribution of Base Layer Resistivity," *Proc. IRE,* Vol. 44, p. 72, 1956.

15. P. E. Gray et al. Op. cit., Ch. 8.

16. R. S. Muller and T. I. Kamins. *Device Electronics for Integrated Circuits.* Second Edition, Wiley, New York, 1986, p. 386.

17. Y. P. Tsividis. *Operation and Modeling of the MOS Transistor.* McGraw-Hill, New York, 1987, p. 141.

18. D. Frohman-Bentchkowsky and A. S. Grove. "Conductance of MOS Transistors in Saturation," *IEEE Trans. Electron Devices,* Vol. ED-16, pp. 108–113, January 1969.

19. S. M. Sze. *Physics of Semiconductor Devices.* Second Edition, Wiley, New York, 1981, pp. 451–452.

20. R. S. Muller and T. I. Kamins. Op. cit., p. 17.

21. Y. P. Tsividis. Op. cit., p. 148.

22. R. S. Muller and T. I. Kamins. Op. cit., pp. 490–496.

23. Y. P. Tsividis. Op. cit., pp. 150–151 and 198–200.

24. R. S. Muller and T. I. Kamins. Op. cit., p. 496.

25. Y. P. Tsividis. Op. cit., p. 151.

26. Y. P. Tsividis. Op. cit., pp. 310–328.

27. R. S. Muller and T. I. Kamins. Op. cit., p. 480.

28. R. S. Muller and T. I. Kamins. Op. cit., p. 482.

29. Y. P. Tsividis. Op. cit., p. 181.

30. Y. P. Tsividis. Op. cit., p. 294.

31. Y. P. Tsividis. Op. cit., p. 142.

32. R. S. Muller and T. I. Kamins. Op. cit., p. 484.

33. Y. P. Tsividis. Op. cit., p. 146.

34. S. M. Sze. Op. cit., p. 446.

35. Y. P. Tsividis. Op. cit., p. 136.

36. Y. P. Tsividis. Op. cit., p. 83.

37. Y. P. Tsividis. Op. cit., p. 139.

38. Y. P. Tsividis. Op. cit., p. 137.

39. Y. P. Tsividis. Op. cit., p. 324.

40. K. Y. Toh, P. K. Ko, and R. G. Meyer. "An Engineering Model for Short-Channel MOS Devices," *IEEE Journal of Solid-State Circuits,* Vol. 23, pp. 950–958, August 1988.

## GENERAL REFERENCES

I. Getreu. *Modelling the Bipolar Transistor.* Tektronix Inc., 1976.

P. E. Gray and C. L. Searle, *Electronic Principles.* Wiley, New York, 1969.

R. S. Muller and T. I Kamins. *Device Electronics for Integrated Circuits.* Wiley, New York, 1986.

Y. P. Tsividis. *Operation and Modeling of the MOS Transistor.* McGraw-Hill, New York, 1987.

# Bipolar, MOS, and BiCMOS Integrated-Circuit Technology

## 2.1 Introduction

For the designer and user of integrated circuits, a knowledge of the details of the fabrication process is important for two reasons. First, IC technology has become pervasive because it provides the economic advantage of the planar process for fabricating complex circuitry at low cost through batch processing. Thus a knowledge of the factors influencing the cost of fabrication of integrated circuits is essential for both the selection of a circuit approach to solve a given design problem by the designer and the selection of a particular circuit for fabrication as a custom integrated circuit by the user. Second, integrated-circuit technology presents a completely different set of cost constraints to the circuit designer from those encountered with discrete components. The optimum choice of a circuit approach to realize a specified circuit function requires an understanding of the degrees of freedom available with the technology and the nature of the devices that are most easily fabricated on the integrated-circuit chip.

At the present time, analog integrated circuits are designed and fabricated in bipolar technology, in MOS technology, and in technologies that combine both types of devices in one process. The necessity of combining complex digital functions on the same integrated circuit with analog functions has resulted in an increased use of digital MOS technologies for analog functions, particularly those functions such as analog-digital conversion required for interfaces between analog signals and digital systems. However, bipolar technology is now used and will continue to be used in a wide range of applications requiring high-current drive capability and the highest levels of precision analog performance.

In this chapter, we first enumerate the basic processes that are fundamental in the fabrication of bipolar and MOS integrated circuits: solid-state diffusion, lithography, epitaxial growth, ion implantation, selective oxidation, and polysilicon deposition. Next, we describe the sequence of steps that are used in the fabrication of bipolar integrated circuits and describe the properties of the passive and active devices that result from the process sequence. Also, we examine several modifications to the basic process. In the next subsection, we consider the sequence of steps in fabricating MOS integrated circuits and describe the types of devices resulting in that technology. This is followed by descriptions of BiCMOS technology, silicon-germanium heterojunction transistors, and interconnect materials under study to replace aluminum wires and silicon-dioxide dielectric. Next, we examine the factors affecting the manufacturing cost of monolithic circuits and, finally, present packaging considerations for integrated circuits.

## 2.2 Basic Processes in Integrated-Circuit Fabrication

The fabrication of integrated circuits and most modern discrete component transistors is based on a sequence of photomasking, diffusion, ion implantation, oxidation, and epitaxial growth steps applied to a slice of silicon starting material called a wafer.[1,2] Before beginning a description of the basic process steps, we will first review the effects produced on the electrical properties of silicon by the addition of impurity atoms.

### 2.2.1 Electrical Resistivity of Silicon

The addition of small concentrations of $n$-type or $p$-type impurities to a crystalline silicon sample has the effect of increasing the number of majority carriers (electrons for $n$-type, holes for $p$-type) and decreasing the number of minority carriers. The addition of impurities is called *doping* the sample. For practical concentrations of impurities, the density of majority carriers is approximately equal to the density of the impurity atoms in the crystal. Thus for $n$-type material,

$$n_n \simeq N_D \tag{2.1}$$

where $n_n$ (cm$^{-3}$) is the equilibrium concentration of electrons and $N_D$ (cm$^{-3}$) is the concentration of $n$-type donor impurity atoms. For $p$-type material,

$$p_p \simeq N_A \tag{2.2}$$

where $p_p$ (cm$^{-3}$) is the equilibrium concentration of holes and $N_A$ (cm$^{-3}$) is the concentration of $p$-type acceptor impurities. Any increase in the equilibrium concentration of one type of carrier in the crystal must result in a decrease in the equilibrium concentration of the other. This occurs because the holes and electrons recombine with each other at a rate that is proportional to the product of the concentration of holes and the concentration of electrons. Thus the number of recombinations per second, $R$, is given by

$$R = \gamma np \tag{2.3}$$

where $\gamma$ is a constant, and $n$ and $p$ are electron and hole concentrations, respectively, in the silicon sample. The generation of the hole-electron pairs is a thermal process that depends only on temperature; the rate of generation, $G$, is not dependent on impurity concentration. In equilibrium, $R$ and $G$ must be equal, so that

$$G = \text{constant} = R = \gamma np \tag{2.4}$$

If no impurities are present, then

$$n = p = n_i(T) \tag{2.5}$$

where $n_i$ (cm$^{-3}$) is the *intrinsic* concentration of carriers in a pure sample of silicon. Equations 2.4 and 2.5 establish that, for any impurity concentration, $\gamma np = \text{constant} = \gamma n_i^2$, and thus

$$np = n_i^2(T) \tag{2.6}$$

Equation 2.6 shows that as the majority carrier concentration is increased by impurity doping, the minority carrier concentration is decreased by the same factor so that product $np$ is constant in equilibrium. For impurity concentrations of practical interest, the majority carriers outnumber the minority carriers by many orders of magnitude.

The importance of minority- and majority-carrier concentrations in the operation of the transistor was described in Chapter 1. Another important effect of the addition of impurities

**Figure 2.1** Hole and electron mobility as a function of doping in silicon[3]

is an increase in the ohmic conductivity of the material itself. This conductivity is given by

$$\sigma = q \ (\mu_n n + \mu_p p) \tag{2.7}$$

where $\mu_n$ (cm²/V-s) is the electron mobility, $\mu_p$ (cm²/V-s) is the hole mobility, and $\sigma$ $(\Omega\text{-cm})^{-1}$ is the electrical conductivity. For an $n$-type sample, substitution of (2.1) and (2.6) in (2.7) gives

$$\sigma = q \left( \mu_n N_D + \mu_p \frac{n_i^2}{N_D} \right) \simeq q \mu_n N_D \tag{2.8}$$

For a $p$-type sample, substitution of (2.2) and (2.6) in (2.7) gives

$$\sigma = q \left( \mu_n \frac{n_i^2}{N_A} + \mu_p N_A \right) \simeq q \mu_p N_A \tag{2.9}$$

The mobility $\mu$ is different for holes and electrons and is also a function of the impurity concentration in the crystal for high impurity concentrations. Measured values of mobility in silicon as a function of impurity concentration are shown in Fig. 2.1. The resistivity $\rho$ $(\Omega\text{-cm})$ is usually specified in preference to the conductivity, and the resistivity of $n$- and $p$-type silicon as a function of impurity concentration is shown in Fig. 2.2. The conductivity and resistivity are related by the simple expression $\rho = 1/\sigma$.

### 2.2.2 Solid-State Diffusion

Solid-state diffusion of impurities in silicon is the movement, usually at high temperature, of impurity atoms from the surface of the silicon sample into the bulk material. During this high-temperature process, the impurity atoms replace silicon atoms in the lattice and are termed *substitutional impurities*. Since the doped silicon behaves electrically as $p$-type or $n$-type material depending on the type of impurity present, regions of $p$-type and $n$-type material can be formed by solid-state diffusion.

The nature of the diffusion process is illustrated by the conceptual example shown in Figs. 2.3 and 2.4. We assume that the silicon sample initially contains a uniform concentration of $n$-type impurity of $10^{15}$ atoms per cubic centimeter. Commonly used $n$-type impurities in silicon are phosphorus, arsenic, and antimony. We further assume that by

**Figure 2.2** Resistivity of p- and n-type silicon as a function of impurity concentration.[4]

**Figure 2.3** An n-type silicon sample with boron deposited on the surface.

some means we deposit atoms of *p*-type impurity on the top surface of the silicon sample. The most commonly used *p*-type impurity in silicon device fabrication is boron. The distribution of impurities prior to the diffusion step is illustrated in Fig. 2.3. The initial placement of the impurity atoms on the surface of the silicon is called the *predeposition step* and can be accomplished by a number of different techniques.

If the sample is now subjected to a high temperature of about 1100°C for a time of about one hour, the impurities *diffuse* into the sample, as illustrated in Fig. 2.4. Within the silicon, the regions in which the *p*-type impurities outnumber the original *n*-type impurities display *p*-type electrical behavior, whereas the regions in which the *n*-type impurities are

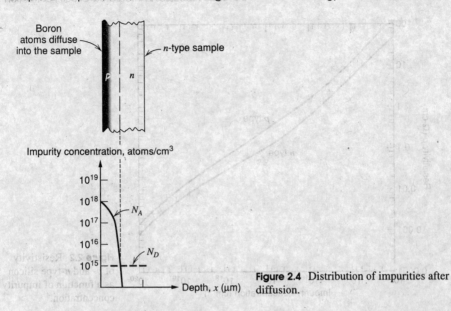

**Figure 2.4**  Distribution of impurities after diffusion.

more numerous display *n*-type electrical behavior. The diffusion process has allowed the formation of a *pn* junction within the continuous crystal of silicon material. The depth of this junction from the surface varies from 0.1 μm to 20 μm for silicon integrated-circuit diffusions (where 1 μm = 1 micrometer = $10^{-6}$ m).

## 2.2.3  Electrical Properties of Diffused Layers

The result of the diffusion process is often a thin layer near the surface of the silicon sample that has been converted from one impurity type to another. Silicon devices and integrated circuits are constructed primarily from these layers. From an electrical standpoint, if the *pn* junction formed by this diffusion is reverse biased, then the layer is electrically isolated from the underlying material by the reverse-biased junction, and the electrical properties of the layer itself can be measured. The electrical parameter most often used to characterize such layers is the *sheet resistance*. To define this quantity, consider the resistance of a uniformly doped sample of length $L$, width $W$, thickness $T$, and *n*-type doping concentration $N_D$, as shown in Fig. 2.5. The resistance is

$$R = \frac{\rho L}{WT} = \frac{1}{\sigma}\frac{L}{WT}$$

**Figure 2.5**  Rectangular sample for calculation of sheet resistance.

Substitution of the expression for conductivity $\sigma$ from (2.8) gives

$$R = \left(\frac{1}{q\mu_n N_D}\right)\frac{L}{WT} = \frac{L}{W}\left(\frac{1}{q\mu_n N_D T}\right) = \frac{L}{W}R_\square \qquad (2.10)$$

Quantity $R_\square$ is the *sheet resistance* of the layer and has units of Ohms. Since the sheet resistance is the resistance of any *square* sheet of material with thickness $T$, its units are often given as *Ohms per square* ($\Omega/\square$) rather than simply Ohms. The sheet resistance can be written in terms of the resistivity of the material, using (2.8), as

$$R_\square = \frac{1}{q\mu_n N_D T} = \frac{\rho}{T} \qquad (2.11)$$

The diffused layer illustrated in Fig. 2.6 is similar to this case except that the impurity concentration is not uniform. However, we can consider the layer to be made up of a parallel combination of many thin conducting sheets. The conducting sheet of thickness $dx$ at depth $x$ has a conductance

$$dG = q\left(\frac{W}{L}\right)\mu_n N_D(x)\ dx \qquad (2.12)$$

To find the total conductance, we sum all the contributions.

$$G = \int_0^{x_j} q\frac{W}{L}\mu_n N_D(x)\ dx = \frac{W}{L}\int_0^{x_j} q\mu_n N_D(x)\ dx \qquad (2.13)$$

Inverting (2.13), we obtain

$$R = \frac{L}{W}\left[\frac{1}{\int_0^{x_j} q\mu_n N_D(x)\ dx}\right] \qquad (2.14)$$

Comparison of (2.10) and (2.14) gives

$$R_\square = \left[\int_0^{x_j} q\mu_n N_D(x)\ dx\right]^{-1} \approx \left[q\bar{\mu}_n\int_0^{x_j} N_D(x)\ dx\right]^{-1} \qquad (2.15)$$

Impurity concentration, atoms/cm$^3$

Net impurity concentration,
$N_D(x) - N_A(x) \approx N_D(x)$

**Figure 2.6** Calculation of the resistance of a diffused layer.

where $\bar{\mu}_n$ is the average mobility. Thus (2.10) can be used for diffused layers if the appropriate value of $R_\square$ is used. Equation 2.15 shows that the sheet resistance of the diffused layer depends on the total number of impurity atoms in the layer per unit area. The depth $x_j$ in (2.13), (2.14), and (2.15) is actually the distance from the surface to the edge of the junction depletion layer, since the donor atoms within the depletion layer do not contribute to conduction. Sheet resistance is a useful parameter for the electrical characterization of diffusion processes and is a key parameter in the design of integrated resistors. The sheet resistance of a diffused layer is easily measured in the laboratory; the actual evaluation of (2.15) is seldom necessary.

▪  **EXAMPLE**

Calculate the resistance of a layer with length 50 μm and width 5 μm in material of sheet resistance 200 Ω/$\square$.
   From (2.10)

$$R = \frac{50}{5} \times 200 \ \Omega = 2 \ k\Omega$$

Note that this region constitutes 10 squares in series, and $R$ is thus 10 times the sheet
▪  resistance.
   In order to use these diffusion process steps to fabricate useful devices, the diffusion must be restricted to a small region on the surface of the sample rather than the entire planar surface. This restriction is accomplished with photolithography.

### 2.2.4 Photolithography

When a sample of crystalline silicon is placed in an oxidizing environment, a layer of silicon dioxide will form at the surface. This layer acts as a barrier to the diffusion of impurities, so that impurities separated from the surface of the silicon by a layer of oxide do not diffuse into the silicon during high-temperature processing. A *pn* junction can thus be formed in a selected location on the sample by first covering the sample with a layer of oxide (called an *oxidation step*), removing the oxide in the selected region, and then performing a predeposition and diffusion step. The selective removal of the oxide in the desired areas is accomplished with photolithography. This process is illustrated by the conceptual example of Fig. 2.7. Again we assume the starting material is a sample of *n*-type silicon. We first perform an oxidation step in which a layer of silicon dioxide ($SiO_2$) is thermally grown on the top surface, usually of thickness of 0.2 μm to 1 μm. The wafer following this step is shown in Fig. 2.7a. Then the sample is coated with a thin layer of photosensitive material called photoresist. When this material is exposed to a particular wavelength of light, it undergoes a chemical change and, in the case of positive photoresist, becomes soluble in certain chemicals in which the unexposed photoresist is insoluble. The sample at this stage is illustrated in Fig. 2.7b. To define the desired diffusion areas on the silicon sample, a photomask is placed over the surface of the sample; this photomask is opaque except for clear areas where the diffusion is to take place. Light of the appropriate wavelength is directed at the sample, as shown in Fig. 2.7c, and falls on the photoresist only in the clear areas of the mask. These areas of the resist are then chemically dissolved in the development step, as shown in Fig. 2.7d. The unexposed areas of the photoresist are impervious to the developer.
   Since the objective is the formation of a region clear of $SiO_2$, the next step is the etching of the oxide. This step can be accomplished by dipping the sample in an etching

**Figure 2.7** Conceptual example of the use of photolithography to form a *pn* junction diode. (*a*) Grow SiO$_2$. (*b*) Apply photoresist. (*c*) Expose through mask. (*d*) Develop photoresist. (*e*) Etch SiO$_2$ and remove photoresist. (*f*) Predeposit and diffuse impurities.

solution, such as hydrofluoric acid, or by exposing it to an electrically produced plasma in a plasma etcher. In either case, the result is that in the regions where the photoresist has been removed, the oxide is etched away, leaving the bare silicon surface.

The remaining photoresist is next removed by a chemical stripping operation, leaving the sample with holes, or *windows,* in the oxide at the desired locations, as shown in Fig. 2.7*e*. The sample now undergoes a predeposition and diffusion step, resulting in the formation of *p*-type regions where the oxide had been removed, as shown in Fig. 2.7*f*. In some instances, the impurity to be locally added to the silicon surface is deposited by using ion implantation (see Section 2.2.6). This method of insertion can often take place through the silicon dioxide so that the oxide-etch step is unnecessary.

The minimum dimension of the diffused region that can be routinely formed with this technique in device production has decreased with time, and at present is approximately 0.2 μm by 0.2 μm. The number of such regions that can be fabricated simultaneously can be calculated by noting that the silicon sample used in the production of integrated circuits is a round slice, typically 4 inches to 12 inches in diameter and 250 μm thick. Thus the number of electrically independent *pn* junctions of dimension 0.2 μm × 0.2 μm spaced 0.2 μm apart that can be formed on one such wafer is on the order of $10^{11}$. In actual integrated circuits, a number of masking and diffusion steps are used to form more complex structures such as transistors, but the key points are that photolithography is capable of defining a large number of devices on the surface of the sample and that all of these devices are batch fabricated at the same time. Thus the cost of the photomasking and diffusion steps applied to the wafer during the process is divided among the devices or circuits on the wafer. This ability to fabricate hundreds or thousands of devices at once is the key to the economic advantage of IC technology.

### 2.2.5 Epitaxial Growth

Early planar transistors and the first integrated circuits used only photomasking and diffusion steps in the fabrication process. However, all-diffused integrated circuits had severe

**Figure 2.8**  Triple-diffused transistor and resulting impurity profile.

limitations compared with discrete component circuits. In a triple-diffused bipolar transistor, as illustrated in Fig. 2.8, the collector region is formed by an $n$-type diffusion into the $p$-type wafer. The drawbacks of this structure are that the series collector resistance is high and the collector-to-emitter breakdown voltage is low. The former occurs because the impurity concentration in the portion of the collector diffusion below the collector-base junction is low, giving the region high resistivity. The latter occurs because the concentration of impurities near the surface of the collector is relatively high, resulting in a low breakdown voltage between the collector and base diffusions at the surface, as described in Chapter 1. To overcome these drawbacks, the impurity concentration should be low at the collector-base junction for high breakdown voltage but high below the junction for low collector resistance. Such a concentration profile cannot be realized with diffusions alone, and the epitaxial growth technique was adopted as a result.

Epitaxial (epi) growth consists of formation of a layer of single-crystal silicon on the surface of the silicon sample so that the crystal structure of the silicon is continuous across the interface. The impurity concentration in the epi layer can be controlled independently and can be greater or smaller than in the substrate material. In addition, the epi layer is often of opposite impurity type from the substrate on which it is grown. The thickness of epi layers used in integrated-circuit fabrication varies from 1 $\mu$m to 20 $\mu$m, and the growth of the layer is accomplished by placing the wafer in an ambient atmosphere containing silicon tetrachloride ($SiCl_4$) or silane ($SiH_4$) at an elevated temperature. A chemical reaction takes place in which elemental silicon is deposited on the surface of the wafer, and the resulting surface layer of silicon is crystalline in structure with few defects if the conditions are carefully controlled. Such a layer is suitable as starting material for the fabrication of bipolar transistors. Epitaxy is also utilized in some CMOS and most BiCMOS technologies.

## 2.2.6 Ion Implantation

Ion implantation is a technique for directly inserting impurity atoms into a silicon wafer.[5,6] The wafer is placed in an evacuated chamber, and ions of the desired impurity species are directed at the sample at high velocity. These ions penetrate the surface of the silicon wafer to an average depth of from less than 0.1 $\mu$m to about 0.6 $\mu$m, depending on the velocity with which they strike the sample. The wafer is then held at a moderate temperature for a period of time (for example, 800°C for 10 minutes) in order to allow the ions to become mobile and fit into the crystal lattice. This is called an *anneal step* and is essential to allow repair of any crystal damage caused by the implantation. The principal advantages of ion implantation over conventional diffusion are (1) that small amounts of impurities can be reproducibly deposited and (2) that the amount of impurity deposited per unit area can be precisely controlled. In addition, the deposition can be made with a high level of uniformity across the wafer. Another useful property of ion-implanted layers is that the peak of the impurity concentration profile can be made to occur below the surface of the silicon, unlike with diffused layers. This allows the fabrication of implanted bipolar structures with properties that are significantly better than those of diffused devices. This technique is also widely applied in MOS technology where small, well-controlled amounts of impurity are required at the silicon surface for adjustment of device thresholds, as described in Section 1.5.1.

## 2.2.7 Local Oxidation

In both MOS and bipolar technologies, the need often arises to fabricate regions of the silicon surface that are covered with relatively thin silicon dioxide, adjacent to areas covered by relatively thick oxide. Typically, the former regions constitute the active-device areas, whereas the latter constitute the regions that electrically isolate the devices from each other. A second requirement is that the transition from thick to thin regions must be accomplished without introducing a large vertical step in the surface geometry of the silicon, so that the metallization and other patterns that are later deposited can lie on a relatively planar surface. Local oxidation is used to achieve this result. The local oxidation process begins with a sample that already has a thin oxide grown on it, as shown in Fig. 2.9a. First a layer of silicon nitride (SiN) is deposited on the sample and subsequently removed with a masking step from all areas where thick oxide is to be grown, as shown in Fig. 2.9b. Silicon nitride acts as a barrier to oxygen atoms that might otherwise reach the Si-SiO$_2$ interface and cause further oxidation. Thus when a subsequent long, high-temperature oxidation step is carried out, a thick oxide is grown in the regions where there is no nitride, but no oxidation takes place under the nitride. The resulting geometry after nitride removal is shown in Fig. 2.9c. Note that the top surface of the silicon dioxide has a smooth transition from thick to thin areas and that the height of this transition is less than the oxide thickness difference because the oxidation in the thick oxide regions consumes some of the underlying silicon.

## 2.2.8 Polysilicon Deposition

Many process technologies utilize layers of polycrystalline silicon that are deposited during fabrication. After deposition of the polycrystalline silicon layer on the wafer, the desired features are defined by using a masking step and can serve as gate electrodes for silicon-gate MOS transistors, emitters of bipolar transistors, plates of capacitors, resistors,

Figure 2.9  Local oxidation process. (*a*) Silicon sample prior to deposition of nitride. (*b*) After nitride deposition and definition. (*c*) After oxidation and nitride removal.

fuses, and interconnect layers. The sheet resistance of such layers can be controlled by the impurity added, much like bulk silicon, in a range from about 20 $\Omega/\square$ up to very high values. The process that is used to deposit the layer is much like that used for epitaxy. However, since the deposition is usually over a layer of silicon dioxide, the layer does not form as a single-crystal extension of the underlying silicon but forms as a granular (or polysilicon) film. Some MOS technologies contain as many as three separate polysilicon layers, separated from one another by layers of $SiO_2$.

## 2.3  High-Voltage Bipolar Integrated-Circuit Fabrication

Integrated-circuit fabrication techniques have changed dramatically since the invention of the basic planar process. This change has been driven by developments in photolithography, processing techniques, and also the trend to reduce power-supply voltages in many systems. Developments in photolithography have reduced the minimum feature size attainable from tens of microns to the submicron level. The precise control allowed by ion implantation has resulted in this technique becoming the dominant means of predepositing impurity atoms. Finally, many circuits now operate from 3 V or 5 V power supplies instead of from the ±15 V supplies used earlier to achieve high dynamic range in stand-alone integrated circuits, such as operational amplifiers. Reducing the operating voltages allows closer spacing between devices in an IC. It also allows shallower structures with higher frequency capability. These effects stem from the fact that the thickness of junction depletion layers is reduced by reducing operating voltages, as described in Chapter 1. Thus the highest-frequency IC processes are designed to operate from 5-V supplies or less and are generally not usable at higher supply voltages. In fact, a fundamental trade-off exists between the frequency capability of a process and its breakdown voltage.

In this section, we examine first the sequence of steps used in the fabrication of high-voltage bipolar integrated circuits using junction isolation. This was the original IC process

**Figure 2.10** Buried-layer diffusion.

and is useful as a vehicle to illustrate the basic methods of IC fabrication. It is still used in various forms to fabricate high-voltage circuits.

The fabrication of a junction-isolated bipolar integrated circuit involves a sequence of from six to eight masking and diffusion steps. The starting material is a wafer of $p$-type silicon, usually 250 $\mu$m thick and with an impurity concentration of approximately $10^{16}$ atoms/cm$^3$. We will consider the sequence of diffusion steps required to form an $npn$ integrated-circuit transistor. The first mask and diffusion step, illustrated in Fig. 2.10, forms a low-resistance $n$-type layer that will eventually become a low-resistance path for the collector current of the transistor. This step is called the *buried-layer diffusion*, and the layer itself is called the *buried layer*. The sheet resistance of the layer is in the range of 20 to 50 $\Omega/\square$, and the impurity used is usually arsenic or antimony because these impurities diffuse slowly and thus do not greatly redistribute during subsequent processing.

After the buried-layer step, the wafer is stripped of all oxide and an epi layer is grown, as shown in Fig. 2.11. The thickness of the layer and its $n$-type impurity concentration determine the collector-base breakdown voltage of the transistors in the circuit since this material forms the collector region of the transistor. For example, if the circuit is to operate at a power-supply voltage of 36 V, the devices generally are required to have $BV_{CEO}$ breakdown voltages above this value. As described in Chapter 1, this implies that the plane breakdown voltage in the collector-base junction must be several times this value because of the effects of collector avalanche multiplication. For $BV_{CEO} = 36$ V, a collector-base plane breakdown voltage of approximately 90 V is required, which implies an impurity concentration in the collector of approximately $10^{15}$ atoms/cm$^3$ and a resistivity of 5 $\Omega$-cm. The thickness of the epitaxial layer then must be large enough to accommodate the depletion layer associated with the collector-base junction. At 36 V, the results of Chapter 1 can be used to show that the depletion-layer thickness is approximately 6 $\mu$m. Since the buried layer diffuses outward approximately 8 $\mu$m during subsequent processing, and the base diffusion will be approximately 3 $\mu$m deep, a total epitaxial layer thickness of 17 $\mu$m is required for a 36-V circuit. For circuits with lower operating voltages, thinner and more heavily doped epitaxial layers are used to reduce the transistor collector series resistance, as will be shown later.

Following the epitaxial growth, an oxide layer is grown on the top surface of the epitaxial layer. A mask step and boron ($p$-type) predeposition and diffusion are performed, resulting in the structure shown in Fig. 2.12. The function of this diffusion is to isolate the collectors of the transistors from each other with reverse-biased $pn$ junctions, and it

**Figure 2.11** Bipolar integrated-circuit wafer following epitaxial growth.

**Figure 2.12** Structure following isolation diffusion.

**Figure 2.13** Structure following base diffusion.

is termed the *isolation diffusion*. Because of the depth to which the diffusion must penetrate, this diffusion requires several hours in a diffusion furnace at temperatures of about 1200°C. The isolated diffused layer has a sheet resistance from 20 $\Omega/\square$ to 40 $\Omega/\square$.

The next steps are the base mask, base predeposition, and base diffusion, as shown in Fig. 2.13. The latter is usually a boron diffusion, and the resulting layer has a sheet resistance of from 100 $\Omega/\square$ to 300 $\Omega/\square$, and a depth of 1 $\mu$m to 3 $\mu$m at the end of the process. This diffusion forms not only the bases of the transistors, but also many of the resistors in the circuit, so that control of the sheet resistance is important.

Following the base diffusion, the emitters of the transistors are formed by a mask step, *n*-type predeposition, and diffusion, as shown in Fig. 2.14. The sheet resistance is between 2 $\Omega/\square$ and 10 $\Omega/\square$, and the depth is 0.5 $\mu$m to 2.5 $\mu$m after the diffusion. This diffusion step is also used to form a low-resistance region, which serves as the contact to the collector region. This is necessary because ohmic contact is difficult to accomplish between aluminum metallization and the high-resistivity epitaxial material directly. The next masking step, the contact mask, is used to open holes in the oxide over the emitter, the base, and the collector of the transistors so that electrical contact can be made to them. Contact windows are also opened for the passive components on the chip. The entire wafer

**Figure 2.14** Structure following emitter diffusion.

**Figure 2.15** Final structure following contact mask and metallization.

is then coated with a thin (about 1 μm) layer of aluminum that will interconnect the circuit elements. The actual interconnect pattern is defined by the last mask step, in which the aluminum is etched away in the areas where the photoresist is removed in the develop step. The final structure is shown in Fig. 2.15. A microscope photograph of an actual structure of the same type is shown in Fig. 2.16. The terraced effect on the surface of the device results from the fact that additional oxide is grown during each diffusion cycle, so that the oxide is thickest over the epitaxial region, where no oxide has been removed, is less thick over the base and isolation regions, which are both opened at the base mask step, and is thinnest over the emitter diffusion. A typical diffusion profile for a high-voltage, deep-diffused analog integrated circuit is shown in Fig. 2.17.

This sequence allows simultaneous fabrication of a large number (often thousands) of complex circuits on a single wafer. The wafer is then placed in an automatic tester, which checks the electrical characteristics of each circuit on the wafer and puts an ink dot on circuits that fail to meet specifications. The wafer is then broken up, by sawing or scribing and breaking, into individual circuits. The resulting silicon chips are called *dice*, and the singular is *die*. Each good die is then mounted in a package, ready for final testing.

**Figure 2.16** Scanning electron microscope photograph of *npn* transistor structure.

**Figure 2.17** Typical impurity concentration for a monolithic $npn$ transistor in a high-voltage, deep-diffused process.

## 2.4 Advanced Bipolar Integrated-Circuit Fabrication

A large fraction of bipolar analog integrated circuits currently manufactured uses the basic technology described in the previous section, or variations thereof. The fabrication sequence is relatively simple and low in cost. However, many of the circuit applications of commercial importance have demanded steadily increasing frequency response capability, which translates directly to a need for transistors of higher frequency-response capability in the technology. The higher speed requirement dictates a device structure with thinner base width to reduce base transit time and smaller dimensions overall to reduce parasitic capacitances. The smaller device dimensions require that the width of the junction depletion layers within the structure be reduced in proportion, which in turn requires the use of lower circuit operating voltages and higher impurity concentrations in the device structure. To meet this need, a class of bipolar fabrication technologies has evolved that, compared to the high-voltage process sequence described in the last section, use much thinner and more heavily doped epitaxial layers, selectively oxidized regions for isolation instead of diffused junctions, and a polysilicon layer as the source of dopant for the emitter. Because of the growing importance of this class of bipolar process, the sequence for such a process is described in this section.

**Figure 2.18** Device cross section following initial buried-layer mask, implant, and epitaxial-layer growth.

The starting point for the process is similar to that for the conventional process, with a mask and implant step resulting in the formation of a heavily-doped $n^+$ buried layer in a $p$-type substrate. Following this step, a thin $n$-type epitaxial layer is grown, about 1 μm in thickness and about 0.5 $\Omega$-cm in resistivity. The result after these steps is shown in cross section in Fig. 2.18.

Next, a selective oxidation step is carried out to form the regions that will isolate the transistor from its neighbors and also isolate the collector-contact region from the rest of the transistor. The oxidation step is as described in Section 2.2.7, except that prior to the actual growth of the thick $SiO_2$ layer, an etching step is performed to remove silicon material from the regions where oxide will be grown. If this is not done, the thick oxide growth results in elevated *humps* in the regions where the oxide is grown. The steps around these humps cause difficulty in coverage by subsequent layers of metal and polysilicon that will be deposited. The removal of some silicon material before oxide growth results in a nearly planar surface after the oxide is grown and removes the step coverage problem in subsequent processing. The resulting structure following this step is shown in Fig. 2.19. Note that the $SiO_2$ regions extend all the way down to the $p$-type substrate, electrically isolating the $n$-type epi regions from one another. These regions are often referred to as *moats*. Because growth of oxide layers thicker than a micron or so requires impractically long times, this method of isolation is practical only for very thin transistor structures.

Next, two mask and implant steps are performed. A heavy $n^+$ implant is made in the collector-contact region and diffused down to the buried layer, resulting in a low-resistance path to the collector. A second mask is performed to define the base region, and a thin-base $p$-type implant is performed. The resulting structure is shown in Fig. 2.20.

A major challenge in fabricating this type of device is the formation of very thin base and emitter structures, and then providing low-resistance ohmic contact to these regions. This is most often achieved using polysilicon as a doping source. An $n^+$ doped layer of polysilicon is deposited and masked to leave polysilicon only in the region directly over the emitter. During subsequent high-temperature processing steps, the dopant (usually

**Figure 2.19** Device cross section following selective etch and oxidation to form thick-oxide moats.

**Figure 2.20** Device cross section following mask, implant, and diffusion of collector $n^+$ region, and mask and implant of base $p$-type region.

**Figure 2.21** Device cross section following poly deposition and mask, base $p$-type implant, and thermal diffusion cycle.

arsenic) diffuses out of the polysilicon and into the crystalline silicon, forming a very thin, heavily doped emitter region. Following the poly deposition, a heavy $p$-type implant is performed, which results in a more heavily doped $\dot{p}$-type layer at all points in the base region except directly under the polysilicon, where the polysilicon itself acts as a mask to prevent the boron atoms from reaching this part of the base region. The structure that results following this step is shown in Fig. 2.21.

This method of forming low-resistance regions to contact the base is called a *self-aligned structure* because the alignment of the base region with the emitter happens automatically and does not depend on mask alignment. Similar processing is used in MOS technology, described later in this chapter.

The final device structure after metallization is shown in Fig. 2.22. Since the moats are made of $SiO_2$, the metallization contact windows can overlap into them, a fact that

**Figure 2.22** Final device cross section. Note that collector and base contact windows can overlap moat regions. Emitter contact for the structure shown here would be made on an extension of the polysilicon emitter out of the device active area, allowing the minimum possible emitter size.

**Figure 2.23** Scanning-electron-microscope photographs of a bipolar transistor in an advanced, polysilicon-emitter, oxide-isolated process. (*a*) After polysilicon emitter definition and first-metal contact to the base and collector. The polysilicon emitter is 1 μm wide. (*b*) After oxide deposition, contact etch, and second-metal interconnect. [QUBic process photograph courtesy of Signetics.]

dramatically reduces the minimum achievable dimensions of the base and collector regions. All exposed silicon and polysilicon is covered with a highly conductive silicide (a compound of silicon and a refractory metal such as tungsten) to reduce series and contact resistance. For minimum-dimension transistors, the contact to the emitter is made by extending the polysilicon to a region outside the device active area and forming a metal contact to the polysilicon there. A photograph of such a device is shown in Fig. 2.23, and a typical impurity profile is shown in Fig. 2.24. The use of the remote emitter contact with polysilicon connection does add some series emitter resistance, so for larger device geometries or cases in which emitter resistance is critical, a larger emitter is used and the contact is placed directly on top of the polysilicon emitter itself. Production IC processes[7,8] based on technologies similar to the one just described yield bipolar transistors having $f_T$ values well in excess of 10 GHz, compared to a typical value of 500 MHz for deep-diffused, high-voltage processes.

## 2.5 Active Devices in Bipolar Analog Integrated Circuits

The high-voltage IC fabrication process described previously is an outgrowth of the one used to make *npn* double-diffused discrete bipolar transistors, and as a result the process inherently produces double-diffused *npn* transistors of relatively high performance. The advanced technology process improves further on all aspects of device performance except for breakdown voltage. In addition to *npn* transistors, *pnp* transistors are also required in many analog circuits, and an important development in the evolution of analog IC technologies was the invention of device structures that allowed the standard technology to produce *pnp* transistors as well. In this section, we will explore the structure and properties of *npn*, lateral *pnp*, and substrate *pnp* transistors. We will draw examples primarily from the high-voltage technology. The available structures in the more advanced technology

**Figure 2.24**  Typical impurity profile in a shallow oxide-isolated bipolar transistor.

are similar, except that their frequency response is correspondingly higher. We will include representative device parameters from these newer technologies as well.

### 2.5.1 Integrated-Circuit *npn* Transistors

The structure of a high-voltage, integrated-circuit *npn* transistor was described in the last section and is shown in plan view and cross section in Fig. 2.25. In the forward-active region of operation, the only electrically active portion of the structure that provides current gain is that portion of the base immediately under the emitter diffusion. The rest of the structure provides a top contact to the three transistor terminals and electrical isolation of the device from the rest of the devices on the same die. From an electrical standpoint, the principal effect of these regions is to contribute parasitic resistances and capacitances that must be included in the small-signal model for the complete device to provide an accurate representation of high-frequency behavior.

An important distinction between integrated-circuit design and discrete-component circuit design is that the IC designer has the capability to utilize a device geometry that is specifically optimized for the particular set of conditions found in the circuit. Thus the circuit-design problem involves a certain amount of device design as well. For example, the need often exists for a transistor with a high current-carrying capability to be used in the output stage of an amplifier. Such a device can be made by using a larger device geometry than the standard one, and the transistor then effectively consists of many standard devices connected in parallel. The larger geometry, however, will display larger

**Figure 2.25** Integrated-circuit *npn* transistor. The mask layers are coded as shown.

base-emitter, collector-base, and collector-substrate capacitance than the standard device, and this must be taken into account in analyzing the frequency response of the circuit. The circuit designer then must be able to determine the effect of changes in device geometry on device characteristics and to estimate the important device parameters when the device structure and doping levels are known. To illustrate this procedure, we will calculate the model parameters of the *npn* device shown in Fig. 2.25. This structure is typical of the devices used in circuits with a 5-$\Omega$-cm, 17-$\mu$m epitaxial layer. The emitter diffusion is 20 $\mu$m $\times$ 25 $\mu$m, the base diffusion is 45 $\mu$m $\times$ 60 $\mu$m, and the base-isolation spacing is 25 $\mu$m. The overall device dimensions are 140 $\mu$m $\times$ 95 $\mu$m. Device geometries intended for lower epi resistivity and thickness can be much smaller; the base-isolation spacing is dictated by the side diffusion of the isolation region plus the depletion layers associated with the base-collector and collector-isolation junctions.

**Saturation Current $I_S$.** In Chapter 1, the saturation current of a graded-base transistor was shown to be

$$I_S = \frac{qA\bar{D}_n n_i^2}{Q_B} \tag{2.16}$$

where $A$ is the emitter-base junction area, $Q_B$ is the total number of impurity atoms per unit area in the base, $n_i$ is the intrinsic carrier concentration, and $\bar{D}_n$ is the effective diffusion constant for electrons in the base region of the transistor. From Fig. 2.17, the quantity $Q_B$ can be identified as the area under the concentration curve in the base region. This could be determined graphically but is most easily determined experimentally from measurements of the base-emitter voltage at a constant collector current. Substitution of (2.16) in (1.35) gives

$$\frac{Q_B}{\bar{D}_n} = A \frac{qn_i^2}{I_C} \exp \frac{V_{BE}}{V_T} \tag{2.17}$$

and $Q_B$ can be determined from this equation.

## ▪ EXAMPLE

A base-emitter voltage of 550 mV is measured at a collector current of 10 $\mu$A on a test transistor with a 100 $\mu$m $\times$ 100 $\mu$m emitter area. Estimate $Q_B$ if $T = 300°$K. From Chapter 1, we have $n_i = 1.5 \times 10^{10}$ cm$^{-3}$. Substitution in (2.17) gives

$$\frac{Q_B}{\bar{D}_n} = (100 \times 10^{-4})^2 \frac{1.6 \times 10^{-19} \times 2.25 \times 10^{20}}{10^{-5}} \exp(550/26)$$

$$= 5.54 \times 10^{11} \text{ cm}^{-4} \text{ s}$$

At the doping levels encountered in the base, an approximate value of $\bar{D}_n$, the electron diffusivity, is

$$\bar{D}_n = 13 \text{ cm}^2 \text{ s}^{-1}$$

Thus for this example,

$$Q_B = 5.54 \times 10^{11} \times 13 \text{ cm}^{-2} = 7.2 \times 10^{12} \text{ atoms/cm}^2$$

Note that $Q_B$ depends on the diffusion profiles and will be different for different types of processes. Generally speaking, fabrication processes intended for lower voltage operation use thinner base regions and display lower values of $Q_B$. Within one nominally fixed process, $Q_B$ can vary by a factor of two or three to one because of diffusion process variations. The principal significance of the numerical value for $Q_B$ is that it allows the calculation of the saturation current $I_S$ for any device structure once the emitter-base junction area is known.

**Series Base Resistance $r_b$.** Because the base contact is physically removed from the active base region, a significant series ohmic resistance is observed between the contact and the active base. This resistance can have a significant effect on the high-frequency gain and on the noise performance of the device. As illustrated in Fig. 2.26$a$, this resistance consists of two parts. The first is the resistance $r_{b1}$ of the path between the base contact and the edge of the emitter diffusion. The second part $r_{b2}$ is that resistance between the edge of

(a)

Figure 2.26  ($a$) Base resistance components for the $npn$ transistor.

**Figure 2.26** (*b*) Calculation of $r_{b1}$. The $r_{b1}$ component of base resistance can be estimated by calculating the resistance of the rectangular block above.

the emitter and the site within the base region at which the current is actually flowing. The former component can be estimated by neglecting fringing and by assuming that this component of the resistance is that of a rectangle of material as shown in Fig. 2.26*b*. For a base sheet resistance of 100 $\Omega/\square$ and typical dimensions as shown in Fig. 2.26*b*, this would give a resistance of

$$r_{b1} = \frac{10 \ \mu m}{25 \ \mu m} 100 \ \Omega = 40 \ \Omega$$

The calculation of $r_{b2}$ is complicated by several factors. First, the current flow in this region is not well modeled by a single resistor because the base resistance is distributed throughout the base region and two-dimensional effects are important. Second, at even moderate current levels, the effect of current crowding[9] in the base causes most of the carrier injection from the emitter into the base to occur near the periphery of the emitter diffusion. At higher current levels, essentially all of the injection takes place at the periphery and the effective value of $r_b$ approaches $r_{b1}$. In this situation, the portion of the base directly beneath the emitter is not involved in transistor action. A typically observed variation of $r_b$ with collector current for the *npn* geometry of Fig. 2.25 is shown in Fig. 2.27. In transistors designed for low-noise and/or high-frequency applications where low $r_b$ is important, an effort is often made to maximize the periphery of the emitter that is adjacent to the base contact. At the same time, the emitter-base junction and collector-base junction areas must be kept small to minimize capacitance. In the case of high-frequency transistors, this usually dictates the use of an emitter geometry that consists of many narrow

**Figure 2.27** Typical variation of effective small-signal base resistance with collector current for integrated-circuit *npn* transistor.

(a)

**Figure 2.28** (a) Components of collector resistance $r_c$.

stripes with base contacts between them. The ease with which the designer can use such device geometries is an example of the flexibility allowed by monolithic IC construction.

**Series Collector Resistance $r_c$.** The series collector resistance is important both in high-frequency circuits and in low-frequency applications where low collector-emitter saturation voltage is required. Because of the complex three-dimensional shape of the collector region itself, only an approximate value for the collector resistance can be obtained by hand analysis. From Fig. 2.28, we see that the resistance consists of three parts: that from the collector-base junction under the emitter down to the buried layer, $r_{c1}$; that of the buried layer from the region under the emitter over to the region under the collector contact, $r_{c2}$; and finally, that portion from the buried layer up to the collector contact, $r_{c3}$. The small-signal series collector resistance in the forward-active region can be estimated by adding the resistance of these three paths.

■ **EXAMPLE**

Estimate the collector resistance of the transistor of Fig. 2.25, assuming the doping profile of Fig. 2.17. We first calculate the $r_{c1}$ component. The thickness of the lightly doped epi layer between the collector-base junction and the buried layer is 6 μm. Assuming that the collector-base junction is at zero bias, the results of Chapter 1 can be used to show that the depletion layer is about 1 μm thick. Thus the undepleted epi material under the base is 5 μm thick.

The effective cross-sectional area of the resistance $r_{c1}$ is larger at the buried layer than at the collector-base junction. The emitter dimensions are 20 μm × 25 μm, while the buried layer dimensions are 41 μm × 85 μm on the mask. Since the buried layer side-diffuses a distance roughly equal to the distance that it out-diffuses, about 8 μm must be added on each edge, giving an effective size of 57 μm × 101 μm. An exact calculation of the ohmic resistance of this three-dimensional region would require a solution of Laplace's equation in the region, with a rather complex set of boundary conditions. Consequently, we will carry out an approximate analysis by modeling the region as a rectangular paral-

(b)

**Figure 2.28** (b) Model for calculation of collector resistance.

lelepiped, as shown in Fig. 2.28b. Under the assumptions that the top and bottom surfaces of the region are equipotential surfaces, and that the current flow in the region takes place only in the vertical direction, the resistance of the structure can be shown to be

$$R = \frac{\rho T}{WL} \frac{\ln\left(\dfrac{a}{b}\right)}{(a - b)} \tag{2.18}$$

where

$T$ = thickness of the region
$\rho$ = resistivity of the material
$W, L$ = width, length of the top rectangle
$a$ = ratio of the width of the bottom rectangle to the width of the top rectangle
$b$ = ratio of the length of the bottom rectangle to the length of the top rectangle

Direct application of this expression to the case at hand would give an unrealistically low value of resistance, because the assumption of one-dimensional flow is seriously violated when the dimensions of the lower rectangle are much larger than those of the top rectangle. Equation 2.18 gives realistic results when the sides of the region form an angle of about 60° or less with the vertical. When the angle of the sides is increased beyond this point, the resistance does not decrease very much because of the long path for current flow between the top electrode and the remote regions of the bottom electrode. Thus the limits of the bottom electrode should be determined either by the edges of the buried layer or by the edges of the emitter plus a distance equal to about twice the vertical thickness $T$ of the region, whichever is smaller. For the case of $r_{c1}$,

$$T = 5 \ \mu m = 5 \times 10^{-4} \ cm$$
$$\rho = 5 \ \Omega\text{-cm}$$

We assume that the effective emitter dimensions are those defined by the mask plus approximately 2 μm of side diffusion on each edge. Thus

$$W = 20 \ \mu m + 4 \ \mu m = 24 \times 10^{-4} \ cm$$
$$L = 25 \ \mu m + 4 \ \mu m = 29 \times 10^{-4} \ cm$$

For this case, the buried-layer edges are further away from the emitter edge than twice the thickness $T$ on all four sides when side diffusion is taken into account. Thus the *effective* buried-layer dimensions that we use in (2.18) are

$$W_{BL} = W + 4T = 24 \ \mu m + 20 \ \mu m = 44 \ \mu m$$
$$L_{BL} = L + 4T = 29 \ \mu m + 20 \ \mu m = 49 \ \mu m$$

and

$$a = \frac{44 \ \mu m}{24 \ \mu m} = 1.83$$
$$b = \frac{49 \ \mu m}{29 \ \mu m} = 1.69$$

Thus from (2.18),

$$r_{c1} = \frac{(5)(5 \times 10^{-4})}{(24 \times 10^{-4})(29 \times 10^{-4})}(0.57) \ \Omega = 204 \ \Omega$$

We will now calculate $r_{c2}$, assuming a buried-layer sheet resistance of 20 $\Omega/\square$. The distance from the center of the emitter to the center of the collector-contact diffusion is 62 $\mu$m, and the width of the buried layer is 41 $\mu$m. The $r_{c2}$ component is thus, approximately,

$$r_{c2} = (20\ \Omega/\square)\left(\frac{L}{W}\right) = 20\ \Omega/\square\left(\frac{62\ \mu m}{41\ \mu m}\right) = 30\ \Omega$$

Here the buried-layer side diffusion was not taken into account because the ohmic resistance of the buried layer is determined entirely by the number of impurity atoms actually diffused [see (2.15)] into the silicon, which is determined by the mask dimensions and the sheet resistance of the buried layer.

For the calculation of $r_{c3}$, the dimensions of the collector-contact $n^+$ diffusion are 18 $\mu$m $\times$ 49 $\mu$m, including side diffusion. The distance from the buried layer to the bottom of the $n^+$ diffusion is seen in Fig. 2.17 to be 6.5 $\mu$m, and thus $T = 6.5\mu$m in this case. On the three sides of the collector $n^+$ diffusion that do not face the base region, the out-diffused buried layer extends only 4 $\mu$m outside the $n^+$ diffusion, and thus the effective dimension of the buried layer is determined by the actual buried-layer edge on these sides. On the side facing the base region, the effective edge of the buried layer is a distance $2T$, or 13 $\mu$m, away from the edge of the $n^+$ diffusion. The effective buried-layer dimensions for the calculation of $r_{c3}$ are thus 35 $\mu$m $\times$ 57 $\mu$m. Using (2.18),

$$r_{c3} = \frac{(5)(6.5 \times 10^{-4})}{(18 \times 10^{-4})(49 \times 10^{-4})}0.66 = 243\ \Omega$$

The total collector resistance is thus

$$r_c = r_{c1} + r_{c2} + r_{c3} = 531\ \Omega$$

The value actually observed in such devices is somewhat lower than this for three reasons. First, we have approximated the flow as one-dimensional, and it is actually three-dimensional. Second, for larger collector-base voltages, the collector-base depletion layer extends further into the epi, decreasing $r_{c1}$. Finally, the value of $r_c$ that is important is often that for a saturated device. In saturation, holes are injected into the epi region under the emitter by the forward-biased, collector-base function, and they modulate the conductivity of the region even at moderate current levels.[10] Thus the collector resistance one measures when the device is in saturation is closer to $(r_{c2} + r_{c3})$, or about 250 to 300 $\Omega$. Thus $r_c$ is smaller in saturation than in the forward-active region.

**Collector-Base Capacitance.** The collector-base capacitance is simply the capacitance of the collector-base junction including both the flat bottom portion of the junction and the sidewalls. This junction is formed by the diffusion of boron into an $n$-type epitaxial material that we will assume has a resistivity of 5 $\Omega$-cm, corresponding to an impurity concentration of $10^{15}$ atoms/cm$^3$. The uniformly doped epi layer is much more lightly doped than the $p$-diffused region, and as a result, this junction is well approximated by a step junction in which the depletion layer lies almost entirely in the epitaxial material. Under this assumption, the results of Chapter 1 regarding step junctions can be applied, and for convenience this relationship has been plotted in nomograph form in Fig. 2.29. This nomograph is a graphical representation of the relation

$$\frac{C_j}{A} = \sqrt{\frac{q\epsilon N_B}{2(\psi_0 + V_R)}}$$

(2.19)

**Figure 2.29** Capacitance and depletion-layer width of an abrupt $pn$ junction as a function of applied voltage and doping concentration on the lightly doped side of the junction[11]

where $N_B$ is the doping density in the epi material and $V_R$ is the reverse bias on the junction. The nomograph of Fig. 2.29 can also be used to determine the junction depletion-region width as a function of applied voltage, since this width is inversely proportional to the capacitance. The width in microns is given on the axis on the right side of the figure.

Note that the horizontal axis in Fig. 2.29 is the *total* junction potential, which is the applied potential plus the built-in voltage $\psi_0$. In order to use the curve, then, the built-in potential must be calculated. While this would be an involved calculation for a diffused junction, the built-in potential is actually only weakly dependent on the details of the diffusion profile and can be assumed to be about 0.55 V for the collector-base junction, 0.52 V for the collector-substrate junction, and about 0.7 V for the emitter-base junction.

■ **EXAMPLE**

Calculate the collector-base capacitance of the device of Fig. 2.25. The zero-bias capacitance per unit area of the collector-base junction can be found from Fig. 2.29 to be approximately $10^{-4}$ pF/$\mu$m$^2$. The total area of the collector-base junction is the sum of the area of the bottom of the base diffusion plus the base sidewall area. From Fig. 2.25, the bottom area is

$$A_{\text{bottom}} = 60 \ \mu\text{m} \times 45 \ \mu\text{m} = 2700 \ \mu\text{m}^2$$

The edges of the base region can be seen from Fig. 2.17 to have the shape similar to one-quarter of a cylinder. We will assume that the region is cylindrical in shape, which yields a sidewall area of

$$A_{\text{sidewall}} = P \times d \times \frac{\pi}{2}$$

where

$P$ = base region periphery
$d$ = base diffusion depth

Thus we have

$$A_{\text{sidewall}} = 3 \ \mu\text{m} \times (60 \ \mu\text{m} + 60 \ \mu\text{m} + 45 \ \mu\text{m} + 45 \ \mu\text{m}) \times \frac{\pi}{2} = 989 \ \mu\text{m}^2$$

and the total capacitance is

$$C_{\mu 0} = (A_{\text{bottom}} + A_{\text{sidewall}})(10^{-4} \ \text{pF}/\mu\text{m}^2) = 0.36 \ \text{pF}$$

**Collector-Substrate Capacitance.** The collector-substrate capacitance consists of three portions: that of the junction between the buried layer and the substrate, that of the sidewall of the isolation diffusion, and that between the epitaxial material and the substrate. Since the substrate has an impurity concentration of about $10^{16} \ \text{cm}^{-3}$, it is more heavily doped than the epi material, and we can analyze both the sidewall and epi-substrate capacitance under the assumption that the junction is a one-sided step junction with the epi material as the lightly doped side. Under this assumption, the capacitance per unit area in these regions is the same as in the collector-base junction.

▪ **EXAMPLE**

Calculate the collector-substrate capacitance of the standard device of Fig. 2.25. The area of the collector-substrate sidewall is

$$A_{\text{sidewall}} = (17 \ \mu\text{m})(140 \ \mu\text{m} + 140 \ \mu\text{m} + 95 \ \mu\text{m} + 95 \ \mu\text{m})\left(\frac{\pi}{2}\right) = 12,550 \ \mu\text{m}^2$$

We will assume that the actual buried layer covers the area defined by the mask, indicated on Fig. 2.25 as an area of 41 $\mu$m $\times$ 85 $\mu$m, plus 8 $\mu$m of side-diffusion on each edge. This gives a total area of 57 $\mu$m $\times$ 101 $\mu$m. The area of the junction between the epi material and the substrate is the total area of the isolated region, minus that of the buried layer.

$$A_{\text{epi-substrate}} = (140 \ \mu\text{m} \times 95 \ \mu\text{m}) - (57 \ \mu\text{m} \times 101 \ \mu\text{m})$$
$$= 7543 \ \mu\text{m}^2$$

The capacitances of the sidewall and epi-substrate junctions are, using a capacitance per unit area of $10^{-4} \text{pF}/\mu\text{m}^2$

$$C_{cs0} \ (\text{sidewall}) = (12,550 \ \mu\text{m}^2)(10^{-4}\text{pF}/\mu\text{m}^2) = 1.26 \ \text{pF}$$
$$C_{cs0}(\text{epi-substrate}) = (7543 \ \mu\text{m}^2)(10^{-4} \ \text{pF}/\mu\text{m}^2) = 0.754 \ \text{pF}$$

For the junction between the buried layer and the substrate, the lightly doped side of the junction is the substrate. Assuming a substrate doping level of $10^{16}$ atoms/cm$^3$, and a built-in voltage of 0.52 V, we can calculate the zero-bias capacitance per unit area as $3.3 \times 10^{-4} \ \text{pF}/\mu\text{m}^2$. The area of the buried layer is

$$A_{BL} = 57 \ \mu\text{m} \times 101 \ \mu\text{m} = 5757 \ \mu\text{m}^2$$

and the zero-bias capacitance from the buried layer to the substrate is thus

$$C_{cs0}(BL) = (5757 \ \mu\text{m}^2)(3.3 \times 10^{-4} \ \text{pF}/\mu\text{m}^2) = 1.89 \ \text{pF}$$

The total zero-bias, collector-substrate capacitance is thus

$$C_{cs0} = 1.26 \text{ pF} + 0.754 \text{ pF} + 1.89 \text{ pF} = 3.90 \text{ pF}$$

**Emitter-Base Capacitance.** The emitter-base junction of the transistor has a doping profile that is not well approximated by a step junction because the impurity concentration on both sides of the junction varies with distance in a rather complicated way. Furthermore, the sidewall capacitance per unit area is not constant but varies with distance from the surface because the base impurity concentration varies with distance. A precise evaluation of this capacitance can be carried out numerically, but a first-order estimate of the capacitance can be obtained by calculating the capacitance of an abrupt junction with an impurity concentration on the lightly doped side that is equal to the concentration in the base at the edge of the junction. The sidewall contribution is neglected.

■ **EXAMPLE**

Calculate the zero-bias, emitter-base junction capacitance of the standard device of Fig. 2.25.

We first estimate the impurity concentration at the emitter edge of the base region. From Fig. 2.17, it can be seen that this concentration is approximately $10^{17}$ atoms/cm$^3$. From the nomograph of Fig. 2.29, this abrupt junction would have a zero-bias capacitance per unit area of $10^{-3}$ pF/$\mu$m$^2$. Since the area of the bottom portion of the emitter-base junction is 25 $\mu$m $\times$ 20 $\mu$m, the capacitance of the bottom portion is

$$C_{\text{bottom}} = (500 \ \mu\text{m}^2)(10^{-3} \text{ pF}/\mu\text{m}^2) = 0.5 \text{ pF}$$

Again assuming a cylindrical cross section, the sidewall area is given by

$$A_{\text{sidewall}} = 2 \ (25 \ \mu\text{m} + 20 \ \mu\text{m})\left(\frac{\pi}{2}\right)(2.5 \ \mu\text{m}) = 353 \ \mu\text{m}^2$$

Assuming that the capacitance per unit area of the sidewall is approximately the same as the bottom,

$$C_{\text{sidewall}} = (353 \ \mu\text{m}^2)(10^{-3} \text{ pF}/\mu\text{m}^2) = 0.35 \text{ pF}$$

The total emitter-base capacitance is

$$C_{je0} = 0.85 \text{ pF}$$

**Current Gain.** As described in Chapter 1, the current gain of the transistor depends on minority-carrier lifetime in the base, which affects the base transport factor, and on the diffusion length in the emitter, which affects the emitter efficiency. In analog IC processing, the base minority-carrier lifetime is sufficiently long that the base transport factor is not a limiting factor in the forward current gain in *npn* transistors. Because the emitter region is heavily doped with phosphorus, the minority-carrier lifetime is degraded in this region, and current gain is limited primarily by emitter efficiency.[12] Because the doping level, and hence lifetime, vary with distance in the emitter, the calculation of emitter efficiency for the *npn* transistor is difficult, and measured parameters must be used. The room-temperature current gain typically lies between 200 and 1000 for these devices. The current gain falls with decreasing temperature, usually to a value of from 0.5 to 0.75 times the room temperature value at $-55°$C.

| Parameter | | Typical Value, 5-Ω-cm, 17-μm epi 44-V Device | Typical Value, 1-Ω-cm, 10-μm epi 20-V Device |
|---|---|---|---|
| $\beta_F$ | | 200 | 200 |
| $B_R$ | | 2 | 2 |
| $V_A$ | | 130 V | 90 V |
| $\eta$ | | $2 \times 10^{-4}$ | $2.8 \times 10^{-4}$ |
| $I_S$ | | $5 \times 10^{-15}$A | $1.5 \times 10^{-15}$ A |
| $I_{CO}$ | | $10^{-10}$A | $10^{-10}$ A |
| $BV_{CEO}$ | | 50 V | 25 V |
| $BV_{CBO}$ | | 90 V | 50 V |
| $BV_{EBO}$ | | 7 V | 7 V |
| $\tau_F$ | | 0.35 ns | 0.25 ns |
| $\tau_R$ | | 400 ns | 200 ns |
| $\beta_0$ | | 200 | 150 |
| $r_b$ | | 200 Ω | 200 Ω |
| $r_c$ (saturation) | | 200 Ω | 75 Ω |
| $r_{ex}$ | | 2 Ω | 2 Ω |
| Base-emitter junction | $C_{je0}$ | 1 pF | 1.3 pF |
| | $\psi_{0e}$ | 0.7 V | 0.7 V |
| | $n_e$ | 0.33 | 0.33 |
| Base-collector junction | $C_{\mu0}$ | 0.3 pF | 0.6 pF |
| | $\psi_{0c}$ | 0.55 V | 0.6 V |
| | $n_c$ | 0.5 | 0.5 |
| Collector-substrate junction | $C_{cs0}$ | 3 pF | 3 pF |
| | $\psi_{0s}$ | 0.52 V | 0.58 V |
| | $n_s$ | 0.5 | 0.5 |

**Figure 2.30** Typical parameters for high-voltage integrated $npn$ transistors with 500 μm$^2$ emitter area. The thick epi device is typical of those used in circuits operating at up to 44 V power-supply voltage, while the thinner device can operate up to about 20 V. While the geometry of the thin epi device is smaller, the collector-base capacitance is larger because of the heavier epi doping. The emitter-base capacitance is higher because the base is shallower, and the doping level in the base at the emitter-base junction is higher.

**Summary of High-Voltage npn Device Parameters.** A typical set of device parameters for the device of Fig. 2.25 is shown in Fig. 2.30. This transistor geometry is typical of that used for circuits that must operate at power supply voltages up to 40 V. For lower operating voltages, thinner epitaxial layers can be used, and smaller device geometries can be used as a result. Also shown in Fig. 2.30 are typical parameters for a device made with 1-Ω-cm epi material, which is 10 μm thick. Such a device is physically smaller and has a collector-emitter breakdown voltage of about 25 V.

**Advanced-Technology Oxide-Isolated npn Bipolar Transistors.** The structure of an advanced oxide-isolated, poly-emitter $npn$ bipolar transistor is shown in plan view and cross section in Fig. 2.31. Typical parameters for such a device are listed in Fig. 2.32. Note the enormous reduction in device size, transit time, and parasitic capacitance compared to the high-voltage, deep-diffused process. These very small devices achieve optimum performance characteristics at relatively low bias currents. The value of $\beta$ for such a device typically peaks at a collector current of about 50 μA. For these advanced-technology tran-

**Figure 2.31** Plan view and cross section of a typical advanced-technology bipolar transistor. Note the much smaller dimensions compared with the high-voltage device.

sistors, the use of ion implantation allows precise control of very shallow emitter (0.1 $\mu$m) and base (0.2 $\mu$m) regions. The resulting base width is of the order of 0.1 $\mu$m, and (1.99) predicts a base transit time about 25 times smaller than the deep-diffused device of Fig. 2.17. This is observed in practice, and the ion-implanted transistor has a peak $f_T$ of about 13 GHz.

## 2.5.2 Integrated-Circuit *pnp* Transistors

As mentioned previously, the integrated-circuit bipolar fabrication process is an outgrowth of that used to build double-diffused epitaxial *npn* transistors, and the technology inherently produces *npn* transistors of high performance. However, *pnp* transistors of comparable performance are not easily produced in the same process, and the earliest analog integrated circuits used no *pnp* transistors. The lack of a complementary device for use in biasing, level shifting, and as load devices in amplifier stages proved to be a severe

| Parameter | Vertical $npn$ Transistor with 2 $\mu m^2$ Emitter Area | Lateral $pnp$ Transistor with 2 $\mu m^2$ Emitter Area |
|---|---|---|
| $\beta_F$ | 120 | 50 |
| $\beta_R$ | 2 | 3 |
| $V_A$ | 35 V | 30 V |
| $I_S$ | $6 \times 10^{-18}$A | $6 \times 10^{-18}$A |
| $I_{CO}$ | 1 pA | 1 pA |
| $BV_{CEO}$ | 8 V | 14 V |
| $BV_{CBO}$ | 18 V | 18 V |
| $BV_{EBO}$ | 6 V | 18 V |
| $\tau_F$ | 10 ps | 650 ps |
| $\tau_R$ | 5 ns | 5 ns |
| $r_b$ | 400 $\Omega$ | 200 $\Omega$ |
| $r_c$ | 100 $\Omega$ | 20 $\Omega$ |
| $r_{ex}$ | 40 $\Omega$ | 10 $\Omega$ |
| $C_{je0}$ | 5 fF | 14 fF |
| $\psi_{0e}$ | 0.8 V | 0.7 V |
| $n_e$ | 0.4 | 0.5 |
| $C_{\mu 0}$ | 5 fF | 15 fF |
| $\psi_{0c}$ | 0.6 V | 0.6 V |
| $n_c$ | 0.33 | 0.33 |
| $C_{cs0}$ $(C_{bs0})$ | 20 fF | 40 fF |
| $\psi_{0s}$ | 0.6 V | 0.6 V |
| $n_s$ | 0.33 | 0.4 |

**Figure 2.32** Typical device parameters for bipolar transistors in a low-voltage, oxide-isolated, ion-implanted process.

limitation on the performance attainable in analog circuits, leading to the development of several $pnp$ transistor structures that are compatible with the standard IC fabrication process. Because these devices utilize the lightly doped $n$-type epitaxial material as the base of the transistor, they are generally inferior to the $npn$ devices in frequency response and high-current behavior, but are useful nonetheless. In this section, we will describe the lateral $pnp$ and substrate $pnp$ structures.

**Lateral pnp Transistors.** A typical lateral $pnp$ transistor structure fabricated in a high-voltage process is illustrated in Fig. 2.33a.[13] The emitter and collector are formed with the same diffusion that forms the base of the $npn$ transistors. The collector is a $p$-type ring around the emitter, and the base contact is made in the $n$-type epi material *outside* the collector ring. The flow of minority carriers across the base is illustrated in Fig. 2.33b. Holes are injected from the emitter, flow parallel to the surface across the $n$-type base region, and ideally are collected by the $p$-type collector before reaching the base contact. Thus the transistor action is *lateral* rather than *vertical* as in the case for $npn$ transistors. The principal drawback of the structure is the fact that the base region is more lightly doped than the collector. As a result, the collector-base depletion layer extends almost entirely into the base. The base region must then be made wide enough so that the depletion layer does not reach the emitter when the maximum collector-emitter voltage is applied. In a typical analog IC process, the width of this depletion layer is 6 $\mu$m to 8 $\mu$m when the collector-emitter voltage is in the 40-V range. Thus the minimum base width for such a device is about 8 $\mu$m, and the minimum base transit time can be estimated from (1.99)

Figure 2.33  (a) Lateral $pnp$ structure fabricated in a high-voltage process.

as

$$\tau_F = \frac{W_B^2}{2D_p} \qquad (2.20)$$

Use of $W_B = 8$ μm and $D_p = 10$ cm²/s (for holes) in (2.20) gives

$$\tau_F = 32 \text{ ns}$$

This corresponds to a peak $f_T$ of 5 MHz, which is a factor of 100 lower than a typical $npn$ transistor in the same process.

The current gain of lateral $pnp$ transistors tends to be low for several reasons. First, minority carriers (holes) in the base are injected downward from the emitter as well as laterally, and some of them are collected by the substrate, which acts as the collector of a parasitic vertical $pnp$ transistor. The buried layer sets up a retarding field that tends to inhibit this process, but it still produces a measurable degradation of $\beta_F$. Second, the emitter of the $pnp$ is not as heavily doped as is the case for the $npn$ devices, and thus the emitter injection efficiency given by (1.51b) is not optimized for the $pnp$ devices. Finally,

**Figure 2.33** (*b*) Minority-carrier flow in the lateral *pnp* transistor.

the wide base of the lateral *pnp* results in both a low emitter injection efficiency and also a low base transport factor as given by (1.51a).

Another drawback resulting from the use of a lightly doped base region is that the current gain of the device falls very rapidly with increasing collector current due to high-level injection. The minority-carrier distribution in the base of a lateral *pnp* transistor in the forward-active region is shown in Fig. 2.34. The collector current per unit of cross-sectional area can be obtained from (1.32) as

$$J_p = qD_p\frac{p_n(0)}{W_B} \tag{2.21}$$

Inverting this relationship, we can calculate the minority-carrier density at the emitter edge of the base as

$$p_n(0) = \frac{J_pW_B}{qD_p} \tag{2.22}$$

As long as this concentration is much less than the majority-carrier density in the base, low-level injection conditions exist and the base minority-carrier lifetime remains constant. However, when the minority-carrier density becomes comparable with the majority-carrier density, the majority-carrier density must increase to maintain charge neutrality in the base. This causes a decrease in $\beta_F$ for two reasons. First, there is a decrease in the effective lifetime of minority carriers in the base since there is an increased number of majority carriers with which recombination can occur. Thus the base transport factor given by (1.51a) decreases. Second, the increase in the majority-carrier density represents an effective increase in base doping density. This causes a decrease in emitter injection efficiency given by (1.51b). Both these mechanisms are also present in *npn* transistors, but occur at much higher current levels due to the higher doping density in the base of the *npn* transistor.

**Figure 2.34** Minority-carrier distribution in the base of a lateral *pnp* transistor in the forward-active region. This distribution is that observed through section *x*-*x'* in Fig. 2.33*b*.

The collector current at which these effects become significant can be calculated for a lateral $pnp$ transistor by equating the minority-carrier concentration given by (2.22) to the equilibrium majority-carrier concentration. Thus

$$\frac{J_p W_B}{q D_p} = n_n \simeq N_D \tag{2.23}$$

where (2.1) has been substituted for $n_n$, and $N_D$ is the donor density in the $pnp$ base ($npn$ collector). From (2.23), we can calculate the collector current for the onset of high-level injection in a $pnp$ transistor as

$$I_C = \frac{q A N_D D_p}{W_B} \tag{2.24}$$

where $A$ is the effective area of the emitter-base junction. Note that this current depends directly on the base doping density in the transistor, and since this is quite low in a lateral $pnp$ transistor, the current density at which this fall-off begins is quite low.

Lateral $pnp$ transistors are also widely used in shallow oxide-isolated bipolar IC technologies. The device structure used is essentially identical to that of Fig. 2.33, except that the device area is orders of magnitude smaller and the junction isolation is replaced by oxide isolation. Typical parameters for such a device are listed in Fig. 2.32. As in the case of $npn$ transistors, we see dramatic reductions in device transit time and parasitic capacitance compared to the high-voltage, thick-epi process. The value of $\beta$ for such a device typically peaks at a collector current of about 50 nA.

■ **EXAMPLE**

Calculate the collector current at which the current gain begins to fall for the $pnp$ structure of Fig. 2.33a. The effective cross-sectional area $A$ of the emitter is the sidewall area of the emitter, which is the $p$-type diffusion depth multiplied by the periphery of the emitter multiplied by $\pi/2$.

$$A = (3 \ \mu m)(30 \ \mu m + 30 \ \mu m + 30 \ \mu m + 30 \ \mu m)\left(\frac{\pi}{2}\right) = 565 \ \mu m^2 = 5.6 \times 10^{-6} \ cm^2$$

The majority-carrier density is $10^{15}$ atoms/cm$^3$ for an epi-layer resistivity of 5 $\Omega$-cm. In addition, we can assume $W_B = 8 \ \mu m$ and $D_p = 10 \ cm^2$/s. Substitution of this data in (2.24) gives

$$I_C = 5.6 \times 10^{-6} \times 1.6 \times 10^{-19} \times 10^{15} \times 10 \frac{1}{8 \times 10^{-4}} A = 11.2 \ \mu A$$

■

The typical lateral $pnp$ structure of Fig. 2.33a shows a low-current beta of approximately 30 to 50, which begins to decrease at a collector current of a few tens of microamperes, and has fallen to less than 10 at a collector current of 1 mA. A typical set of parameters for a structure of this type is shown in Fig. 2.35. Note that in the lateral $pnp$ transistor, the substrate junction capacitance appears between the *base* and the substrate.

**Substrate $pnp$ Transistors.**  One reason for the poor high-current performance of the lateral $pnp$ is the relatively small effective cross-sectional area of the emitter, which results from the lateral nature of the injection. A common application for a $pnp$ transistor is in a Class-B output stage where the device is called on to operate at collector currents in the 10-mA range. A lateral $pnp$ designed to do this would require a large amount of die area. In this application, a different structure is usually used in which the substrate itself is used as the collector instead of a diffused $p$-type region. Such a substrate $pnp$ transistor in a

| Parameter | Typical Value, 5-Ω-cm, 17-μm epi 44-V Device | Typical Value, 1-Ω-cm, 10-μm epi 20-V Device |
|---|---|---|
| $\beta_F$ | 50 | 20 |
| $\beta_R$ | 4 | 2 |
| $V_A$ | 50 V | 50 V |
| $\eta$ | $5 \times 10^{-4}$ | $5 \times 10^{-4}$ |
| $I_S$ | $2 \times 10^{-15}$ A | $2 \times 10^{-15}$ A |
| $I_{CO}$ | $10^{-10}$ A | $5 \times 10^{-9}$ A |
| $BV_{CEO}$ | 60 V | 30 V |
| $BV_{CBO}$ | 90 V | 50 V |
| $BV_{EBO}$ | 90 V | 50 V |
| $\tau_F$ | 30 ns | 20 ns |
| $\tau_R$ | 3000 ns | 2000 ns |
| $\beta_0$ | 50 | 20 |
| $r_b$ | 300 Ω | 150 Ω |
| $r_c$ | 100 Ω | 75 Ω |
| $r_{ex}$ | 10 Ω | 10 Ω |
| Base-emitter junction $\begin{cases} C_{je0} \\ \psi_{0e} \\ n_e \end{cases}$ | 0.3 pF / 0.55 V / 0.5 | 0.6 pF / 0.6 V / 0.5 |
| Base-collector junction $\begin{cases} C_{\mu0} \\ \psi_{0c} \\ n_c \end{cases}$ | 1 pF / 0.55 V / 0.5 | 2 pF / 0.6 V / 0.5 |
| Base-substrate junction $\begin{cases} C_{bs0} \\ \psi_{0s} \\ n_s \end{cases}$ | 3 pF / 0.52 V / 0.5 | 3.5 pF / 0.58 V / 0.5 |

**Figure 2.35** Typical parameters for lateral $pnp$ transistors with 900 μm$^2$ emitter area in a high-voltage, thick-epi process.

high-voltage, thick-epi process is shown in Fig. 2.36a. The $p$-type emitter diffusion for this particular substrate $pnp$ geometry is rectangular with a rectangular hole in the middle. In this hole an $n^+$ region is formed with the $npn$ emitter diffusion to provide a contact for the $n$-type base. Because of the lightly doped base material, the series base resistance can become quite large if the base contact is far removed from the active base region. In this particular structure, the $n^+$ base contact diffusion is actually allowed to come in contact with the $p$-type emitter diffusion, in order to get the low-resistance base contact diffusion as close as possible to the active base. The only drawback of this, in a substrate $pnp$ structure, is that the emitter-base breakdown voltage is reduced to approximately 7 V. If larger emitter-base breakdown is required, then the $p$-emitter diffusion must be separated from the $n^+$ base contact diffusion by a distance of about 10 μm to 15 μm. Many variations exist on the substrate $pnp$ geometry shown in Fig. 2.36a. They can also be realized in thin-epi, oxide-isolated processes.

The minority-carrier flow in the forward-active region is illustrated in Fig. 2.36b. The principal advantage of this device is that the current flow is vertical and the effective cross-sectional area of the emitter is much larger than in the case of the lateral $pnp$ for the same overall device size. The device is restricted to use in emitter-follower configurations, however, since the collector is electrically identical with the substrate that must be tied to

Figure 2.36 (a) Substrate $pnp$ structure in a high-voltage, thick-epi process.

Figure 2.36 (b) Minority-carrier flow in the substrate $pnp$ transistor.

the most negative circuit potential. Other than the better current-handling capability, the properties of substrate $pnp$ transistors are similar to those for lateral $pnp$ transistors since the base width is similar in both cases. An important consideration in the design of substrate $pnp$ structures is that the collector current flows in the $p$-substrate region, which usually has relatively high resistivity. Thus, unless care is taken to provide an adequate low-resistance path for the collector current, a high series collector resistance can result. This resistance can degrade device performance in two ways. First, large collector currents in the $pnp$ can cause enough voltage drop in the substrate region itself that other substrate-epitaxial layer junctions within the circuit can become forward biased. This usually has a catastrophic effect on circuit performance. Second, the effects of the collector-base junction capacitance on the $pnp$ are multiplied by the Miller effect resulting from the large series collector resistance, as described further in Chapter 7. To minimize these effects, the collector contact is usually made by contacting the isolation diffusion immediately adjacent to the substrate $pnp$ itself with metallization. For high-current devices, this isolation diffusion contact is made to surround the device to as great an extent as possible.

The properties of a typical substrate $pnp$ transistor in a high-voltage, thick-epi process are summarized in Fig. 2.37. The dependence of current gain on collector current for a typical $npn$, lateral $pnp$, and substrate $pnp$ transistor in a high-voltage, thick-epi process are shown in Fig. 2.38. The low-current reduction in $\beta$, which is apparent for all three

| Parameter | Typical Value,<br>5-$\Omega$-cm, 17-$\mu$m epi<br>44-V Device<br>5100 $\mu$m$^2$<br>Emitter Area | Typical Value,<br>1-$\Omega$-cm, 10-$\mu$m epi<br>20-V Device<br>5100 $\mu$m$^2$<br>Emitter Area |
|---|---|---|
| $\beta_F$ | 50 | 30 |
| $\beta_R$ | 4 | 2 |
| $V_A$ | 50 V | 30 V |
| $\eta$ | $5 \times 10^{-4}$ | $9 \times 10^{-4}$ |
| $I_S$ | $10^{-14}$ A | $10^{-14}$ A |
| $I_{CO}$ | $2 \times 10^{-10}$A | $2 \times 10^{-10}$ A |
| $BV_{CEO}$ | 60 V | 30 V |
| $BV_{CBO}$ | 90 V | 50 V |
| $BV_{EBO}$ | 7 V or 90 V | 7 V or 50 V |
| $\tau_F$ | 20 ns | 14 ns |
| $\tau_R$ | 2000 ns | 1000 ns |
| $\beta_0$ | 50 | 30 |
| $r_b$ | 150 $\Omega$ | 50 $\Omega$ |
| $r_c$ | 50 $\Omega$ | 50 $\Omega$ |
| $r_{ex}$ | 2 $\Omega$ | 2 $\Omega$ |
| Base-emitter junction { $C_{je0}$ | 0.5 pF | 1 pF |
| $\psi_{0e}$ | 0.55 V | 0.58 V |
| $n_e$ | 0.5 | 0.5 |
| Base-collector junction { $C_{\mu0}$ | 2 pF | 3 pF |
| $\psi_{0c}$ | 0.52 V | 0.58 V |
| $n_c$ | 0.5 | 0.5 |

**Figure 2.37** Typical device parameters for a substrate $pnp$ with 5100 $\mu$m$^2$ emitter area in a high-voltage, thick-epi process.

**Figure 2.38** Current gain as a function of collector current for typical lateral $pnp$, substrate $pnp$, and $npn$ transistor geometries in a high-voltage, thick-epi process.

devices, is due to recombination in the base-emitter depletion region, described in Section 1.3.5.

## 2.6 Passive Components in Bipolar Integrated Circuits

In this section, we describe the structures available to the integrated-circuit designer for realization of resistance and capacitance. Resistor structures include base-diffused, emitter-diffused, ion-implanted, pinch, epitaxial, and pinched epitaxial resistors. Other resistor technologies, such as thin-film resistors, are considered in Section 2.7.3. Capacitance structures include MOS and junction capacitors. Inductors with values larger than a few nanohenries have not proven to be feasible in monolithic technology. However, such small inductors are useful in very-high-frequency integrated circuits.[14,15,16]

### 2.6.1 Diffused Resistors

In an earlier section of this chapter, the sheet resistance of a diffused layer was calculated. Integrated-circuit resistors are generally fabricated using one of the diffused or ion-implanted layers formed during the fabrication process, or in some cases a combination of two layers. The layers available for use as resistors include the base, the emitter, the epitaxial layer, the buried layer, the active-base region layer of a transistor, and the

**Figure 2.39**  Base-diffused resistor structure.

epitaxial layer pinched between the base diffusion and the $p$-type substrate. The choice of layer generally depends on the value, tolerance, and temperature coefficient of the resistor required.

**Base and Emitter Diffused Resistors.**  The structure of a typical base-diffused resistor in a high-voltage process is shown in Fig. 2.39. The resistor is formed from the $p$-type base diffusion for the $npn$ transistors and is situated in a separate isolation region. The epitaxial region into which the resistor structure is diffused must be biased in such a way that the $pn$ junction between the resistor and the epi layer is always reverse biased. For this reason, a contact is made to the $n$-type epi region as shown in Fig. 2.39, and it is connected either to that end of the resistor that is most positive or to a potential that is more positive than either end of the resistor. The junction between these two regions contributes a parasitic capacitance between the resistor and the epi layer, and this capacitance is distributed along the length of the resistor. For most applications, this parasitic capacitance can be adequately modeled by separating it into two lumped portions and placing one lump at each end of the resistor as illustrated in Fig. 2.40.

The resistance of the structure shown in Fig. 2.39 is given by (2.10) as

$$R = \frac{L}{W}R_{\square}$$

where $L$ is the resistor length and $W$ is the width. The base sheet resistance $R_{\square}$ lies in the range 100 to 200 $\Omega/\square$, and thus resistances in the range 50 $\Omega$ to 50 k$\Omega$ are practical using

**Figure 2.40** Lumped model for the base-diffused resistor.

the base diffusion. The resistance contributed by the *clubheads* at each end of the resistor can be significant, particularly for small values of $L/W$. The clubheads are required to allow space for ohmic contact to be made at the ends of the resistor.

Since minimization of die area is an important objective, the width of the resistor is kept as small as possible, the minimum practical width being limited to about 1 $\mu$m by photolithographic considerations. Both the tolerance on the resistor value and the precision with which two identical resistors can be matched can be improved by the use of wider geometries. However, for a given base sheet resistance and a given resistor value, the area occupied by the resistor increases as the *square* of its width. This can be seen from (2.10) since the ratio $L/W$ is constant.

In shallow ion-implanted processes, the ion-implanted base can be used in the same way to form a resistor.

## EXAMPLE

Calculate the resistance and parasitic capacitance of the base-diffused resistor structure shown in Fig. 2.39 for a base sheet resistance of 100 $\Omega/\square$, and an epi resistivity of 2.5 $\Omega$-cm. Neglect end effects. The resistance is simply

$$R = 100 \ \Omega/\square \left( \frac{100 \ \mu m}{10 \ \mu m} \right) = 1 \ k\Omega$$

The capacitance is the total area of the resistor multiplied by the capacitance per unit area. The area of the resistor body is

$$A_1 = (10 \ \mu m)(100 \ \mu m) = 1000 \ \mu m^2$$

The area of the clubheads is

$$A_2 = 2 \ (30 \ \mu m \times 30 \ \mu m) = 1800 \ \mu m^2$$

The total zero-bias capacitance is, from Fig. 2.29,

$$C_{j0} = (10^{-4} \ pF/\mu m^2)(2800 \ \mu m^2) = 0.28 \ pF$$

As a first-order approximation, this capacitance can be divided into two parts, one placed at each end. Note that this capacitance will vary depending on the voltage at the clubhead with respect to the epitaxial pocket.

Emitter-diffused resistors are fabricated using geometries similar to the base resistor, but the emitter diffusion is used to form the actual resistor. Since the sheet resistance of this diffusion is in the 2 to 10 $\Omega/\square$ range, these resistors can be used to advantage where very low resistance values are required. In fact, they are widely used simply to provide a

**Figure 2.41** Pinch resistor structure.

crossunder beneath an aluminum metallization interconnection. The parasitic capacitance can be calculated in a way similar to that for the base diffusion. However, these resistors have different temperature dependence from base-diffused resistors and the two types do not track with temperature.

**Base Pinch Resistors.** A third layer available for use as a resistor is the layer that forms the active base region in the $npn$ transistor. This layer is *pinched* between the $n^+$ emitter and the $n$-type collector regions, giving rise to the term *pinch resistor*. The layer can be electrically isolated by reverse biasing the emitter-base and collector-base junctions, which is usually accomplished by connecting the $n$-type regions to the most positive end of the resistor. The structure of a typical pinch resistor is shown in Fig. 2.41; the $n^+$ diffusion overlaps the $p$-diffusion so that the $n^+$ region is electrically connected to the $n$-type epi region. The sheet resistance is in the 5 kΩ/□ to 15 kΩ/□ range. As a result, this resistor allows the fabrication of large values of resistance. Unfortunately, the sheet resistance undergoes the same process-related variations as does the $Q_B$ of the transistor, which is approximately ±50 percent. Also, because the material making up the resistor itself is relatively lightly doped, the resistance displays a relatively large variation with temperature. Another significant drawback is that the maximum voltage that can be applied across the resistor is limited to around 6 V because of the breakdown voltage between the emitter-diffused top layer and the base diffusion. Nonetheless, this type of resistor has found wide application where the large tolerance and low breakdown voltage are not significant drawbacks.

## 2.6.2 Epitaxial and Epitaxial Pinch Resistors

The limitation of the pinch resistor to low operating voltages disallows its use in circuits where a small bias current is to be derived directly from a power-supply voltage of more than about 7 V using a large-value resistor. The epitaxial layer itself has a sheet resistance much larger than the base diffusion, and the epi layer is often used as a resistor for this application. For example, the sheet resistance of a 17-μm thick, 5-Ω-cm epi layer can be calculated from (2.11) as

$$R_\square = \frac{\rho_{epi}}{T} = \frac{5\ \Omega\text{-cm}}{(17\ \mu\text{m}) \times (10^{-4}\ \text{cm/}\mu\text{m})} = 2.9\ \text{k}\Omega/\square \tag{2.25}$$

Large values of resistance can be realized in a small area using structures of the type shown in Fig. 2.42. Again, because of the light doping in the resistor body, these resistors display a rather large temperature coefficient. A still larger sheet resistance can be obtained by putting a p-type base diffusion over the top of an epitaxial resistor, as shown in Fig. 2.42. The depth of the p-type base and the thickness of the depletion region between the p-type

Substrate

epi-FET with top plate
(two alternate symbols)

Figure 2.42 Epitaxial resistor structure. The p-cap diffusion is optional and forms an epitaxial pinch resistor.

| Resistor Type | Sheet $\rho$ $\Omega/\square$ | Absolute Tolerance (%) | Matching Tolerance (%) | Temperature Coefficient |
|---|---|---|---|---|
| Base diffused | 100 to 200 | ±20 | ±2(5 μm wide) ±0.2(50 μm wide) | (+1500 to +2000) ppm/°C |
| Emitter diffused | 2 to 10 | ±20 | ±2 | +600 ppm/°C |
| Ion implanted | 100 to 1000 | ±3 | ±1(5 μm wide) ±0.1(50 μm wide) | Controllable to ±100ppm/°C |
| Base pinch | 2k to 10k | ±50 | ±10 | +2500 ppm/°C |
| Epitaxial | 2k to 5k | ±30 | ±5 | +3000 ppm/°C |
| Epitaxial pinch | 4k to 10k | ±50 | ±7 | +3000 ppm/°C |
| Thin film | 0.1k to 2k | ± 5 to ± 20 | ± 0.2 to ± 2 | (±10 to ±200) ppm/°C |

**Figure 2.43**  Summary of resistor properties for different types of IC resistors.

base and the $n$-type epi together reduce the thickness of the resistor, increasing its sheet resistance. Such a structure actually behaves as a junction FET, in which the $p$-type gate is tied to the substrate.[17]

The properties of the various diffused and pinch-resistor structures are summarized in Fig. 2.43.

## 2.6.3 Integrated-Circuit Capacitors

Early analog integrated circuits were designed on the assumption that capacitors of usable value were impractical to integrate on the chip because they would take too much area, and external capacitors were used where required. Monolithic capacitors of value larger than a few tens of picofarads are still expensive in terms of die area. As a result, design approaches have evolved for monolithic circuits that allow small values of capacitance to be used to perform functions that previously required large capacitance values. The compensation of operational amplifiers is perhaps the best example of this result, and monolithic capacitors are now widely used in all types of analog integrated circuits. These capacitors fall into two categories. First, $pn$ junctions under reverse bias inherently display depletion capacitance, and in certain circumstances this capacitance can be effectively utilized. The drawbacks of junction capacitance are that the junction must always be kept reverse biased, that the capacitance varies with reverse voltage, and that the breakdown voltage is only about 7 V for the emitter-base junction. For the collector-base junction, the breakdown voltage is higher, but the capacitance per unit area is quite low.

By far the most commonly used monolithic capacitor in bipolar technology is the MOS capacitor structure shown in Fig. 2.44. In the fabrication sequence, an additional mask step is inserted to define a region over an emitter diffusion on which a thin layer of silicon dioxide is grown. Aluminum metallization is then placed over this thin oxide, producing a capacitor between the aluminum and the emitter diffusion, which has a capacitance of $0.3$ fF/$\mu$m$^2$ to $0.5$ fF/$\mu$m$^2$ and a breakdown voltage of 60 V to 100 V. This capacitor is extremely linear and has a low temperature coefficient. A sizable parasitic capacitance

**Figure 2.44** MOS capacitor structure.

$C_{ISO}$ is present between the $n$-type bottom plate and the substrate because of the depletion capacitance of the epi-substrate junction, but this parasitic is unimportant in many applications.

### 2.6.4 Zener Diodes

As described in Chapter 1, the emitter-base junction of the $npn$ transistor structure displays a reverse breakdown voltage of between 6 V and 8 V, depending on processing details. When the total supply voltage is more than this value, the reverse-biased, emitter-base junction is useful as a voltage reference for the stabilization of bias reference circuits, and for such functions as level shifting. The reverse bias $I$-$V$ characteristic of a typical emitter-base junction is illustrated in Fig. 2.45$a$.

An important aspect of the behavior of this device is the temperature sensitivity of the breakdown voltage. The actual breakdown mechanism is dominated by quantum mechanical tunneling through the depletion layer when the breakdown voltage is below about 6 V; it is dominated by avalanche multiplication in the depletion layer at the larger breakdown voltages. Because these two mechanisms have opposite temperature coefficients of breakdown voltage, the actually observed breakdown voltage has a temperature coefficient that varies with the value of breakdown voltage itself, as shown in Fig. 2.45$b$.

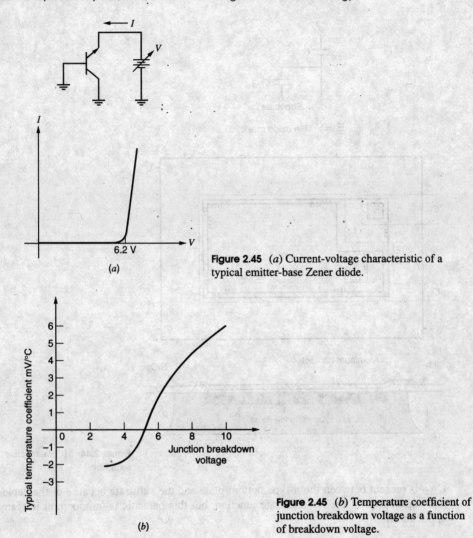

**Figure 2.45** (*a*) Current-voltage characteristic of a typical emitter-base Zener diode.

**Figure 2.45** (*b*) Temperature coefficient of junction breakdown voltage as a function of breakdown voltage.

### 2.6.5 Junction Diodes

Junction diodes can be formed by various connections of the *npn* and *pnp* transistor structures, as illustrated in Fig. 2.46. When the diode is forward biased in the diode connections *a*, *b*, and *d* of Fig. 2.46, the collector-base junction becomes forward biased as well. When this occurs, the collector-base junction injects holes into the epi region that can be collected by the reverse-biased, epi-isolation junction or by other devices in the same isolation region. A similar phenomenon occurs when a transistor enters saturation. As a result, substrate currents can flow that can cause voltage drops in the high-resistivity substrate material, and other epi-isolation junctions within the circuit can become inadvertently forward biased. Thus the diode connections of Fig. 2.46*c* are usually preferable since they keep the base-collector junction at zero bias. These connections have the additional advantage of resulting in the smallest amount of minority charge storage within the diode under forward-bias conditions.

**Figure 2.46** Diode connections for *npn* and *pnp* transistors.

## 2.7 Modifications to the Basic Bipolar Process

The basic high-voltage bipolar IC fabrication process described previously can be modified by the addition of extra processing steps to produce special devices or characteristics.

### 2.7.1 Dielectric Isolation

We first consider a special isolation technique–*dielectric isolation*–that has been used in digital and analog integrated circuits that must operate at very high speed and/or must operate in the presence of large amounts of radiation. The objective of the isolation technique is to electrically isolate the collectors of the devices from each other with a layer of silicon dioxide rather than with a *pn* junction. This layer has much lower capacitance per unit area than a *pn* junction, and as a result, the collector-substrate capacitance of the transistors is greatly reduced. Also, the reverse photocurrent that occurs with junction-isolated devices under intense radiation is eliminated.

The fabrication sequence used for dielectric isolation is illustrated in Figs. 2.47*a-d*. The starting material is a wafer of *n*-type material of resistivity appropriate for the collector region of the transistor. The first step is to etch grooves in the back side of the starting wafer, which will become the isolation regions in the finished circuit. These grooves are about 20 μm deep for typical analog circuit processing. This step, called *moat etch*, can be accomplished with a variety of techniques, including a preferential etch that allows precise definition of the depth of the moats. Next, an oxide is grown on the surface and a thick layer of polycrystalline silicon is deposited on the surface. This layer will be the mechanical support for the finished wafer and thus must be on the order of 200 μm thick. Next, the starting wafer is etched or ground from the top side until it is entirely removed except for the material left in the isolated islands between the moats, as illustrated in Fig. 2.47*c*. After the growth of an oxide, the wafer is ready for the rest of the standard process sequence. Note that the isolation of each device is accomplished by means of an oxide layer.

**Figure 2.47** Fabrication steps in dielectric isolation. (*a*) Moat etch on bottom of starting wafer. (*b*) Deposit polycrystalline silicon support layer. (*c*) Grind off starting wafer and polish. (*d*) Carry out standard process, starting with base mask.

## 2.7.2 Compatible Processing for High-Performance Active Devices

Many specialized circuit applications require a particular type of active device other than the *npn* and *pnp* transistors that result from the standard process schedule. These include high-beta (*superbeta*) *npn* transistors for low-input-current amplifiers, MOSFETs for analog switching and low-input-current amplifiers, and high-speed *pnp* transistors for fast analog circuits. The fabrication of these devices generally requires the addition of one or more mask steps to the basic fabrication process. We now describe these special structures.

**Superbeta Transistors.** One approach to decreasing the input bias current in amplifiers is to increase the current gain of the input stage transistors.[18] Since a decrease in the base width of a transistor improves both the base transport factor and the emitter efficiency (see Section 1.3.1), the current gain increases as the base width is made smaller. Thus the current gain of the devices in the circuit can be increased by simply increasing the emitter diffusion time and narrowing the base width in the resulting devices. However, any increase in the current gain also causes a reduction in the breakdown voltage $BV_{CEO}$ of the transistors. Section 1.3.4 shows that

$$BV_{CEO} = \frac{BV_{CBO}}{\sqrt[n]{\beta}} \qquad (2.26)$$

where $BV_{CBO}$ is the plane breakdown voltage of the collector-base junction. Thus for a given epitaxial layer resistivity and corresponding collector-base breakdown voltage, an increase in beta gives a decrease in $BV_{CEO}$. As a result, using such a process modification to increase the beta of all the transistors in an operational amplifier is not possible because the modified transistors could not withstand the required operating voltage.

The problem of the trade-off between current gain and breakdown voltage can be avoided by fabricating two different types of devices on the same die. The standard device is similar to conventional transistors in structure. By inserting a second diffusion, however, high-beta devices also can be formed. A structure typical of such devices is shown in Fig. 2.48. These devices may be made by utilizing the same base diffusion for both devices and using separate emitter diffusions, or by using two different base diffusions and the same emitter diffusion. Both techniques are used. If the superbeta devices are used only as the input transistors in an operational amplifier, they are not required to have a breakdown voltage of more than about 1 V. Therefore, they can be diffused to extremely narrow base widths, giving current gain on the order of 2000 to 5000. At these base widths, the actual breakdown mechanism is often no longer collector multiplication at all but is due to the depletion layer of the collector-base junction depleting the whole base region and reaching the emitter-base depletion layer. This breakdown mechanism is called *punchthrough*. An application of these devices in op-amp design is described in Section 6.9.2.

**MOS Transistors.** MOS transistors are useful in bipolar integrated-circuit design because they provide high-performance analog switches and low-input-current amplifiers, and particularly because complex digital logic can be realized in a small area using MOS technology. The latter consideration is important since the partitioning of subsystems into analog and digital chips becomes more and more cumbersome as the complexity of the individual chips becomes greater.

Metal-gate $p$-channel MOS transistors can be formed in a standard high-voltage bipolar analog IC process with one extra mask step.[19] If a capacitor mask is included in the

Base width
$W_B \sim 0.1\ \mu m$–$0.2\ \mu m$

Base width
$W_B \approx 0.5\ \mu m$   $1\ \mu m$

Super–$\beta$ transistor,
$\beta \approx 2000$–$5000$

Standard transistor,
$\beta \approx 200$–$500$

**Figure 2.48** Superbeta device structure.

**Figure 2.49** Compatible $p$-channel MOS transistor.

original sequence, then no extra mask steps are required. As illustrated in Fig. 2.49, the source and drain are formed in the epi material using the base diffusion. The capacitor mask is used to define the oxide region over the channel and the aluminum metallization forms the metal gate.

A major development in IC processing in recent years has been the combination on the same chip of high-performance bipolar devices with CMOS devices in a BiCMOS process. This topic is considered in Section 2.11.

**Double-Diffused $pnp$ Transistors.** The limited frequency response of the lateral $pnp$ transistor places a limitation on the high-frequency performance attainable with certain types of analog circuits. While this problem can be circumvented by clever circuit design in many cases, the resulting circuit is often quite complex and costly. An alternative approach is to use a more complex process that produces a high-speed, double-diffused $pnp$ transistor with properties comparable to those of the $npn$ transistor.[20] The process usually utilizes three additional mask steps and diffusions: one to form a lightly doped $p$-type region, which will be the collector of the $pnp$; one $n$-type diffusion to form the base of the $pnp$; and one $p$-type diffusion to form the emitter of the $pnp$. A typical resulting structure

**Figure 2.50** Compatible double-diffused $pnp$ process.

is shown in Fig. 2.50. This process requires 10 masking steps and two epitaxial growth steps. Oxide isolation and poly-emitter technology have been incorporated into more advanced versions of this process.

### 2.7.3 High-Performance Passive Components

Diffused resistors have three drawbacks: They have high temperature coefficients, they have poor tolerance, and they are junction-isolated. The latter means that a parasitic capacitance is associated with each resistor, and exposure to radiation causes photocurrents to flow across the isolating junction. These drawbacks can be overcome by the use of thin-film resistors deposited on the top surface of the die over an insulating layer of oxide. After the resistor material itself is deposited, the individual resistors are defined in a conventional way using a masking step. They are then interconnected with the rest of the circuit using the standard aluminum interconnect process. The most common materials for the resistors are nichrome and tantalum, and a typical structure is shown in Fig. 2.51. The properties of the resulting resistors using these materials are summarized in Fig. 2.52.

## 2.8 MOS Integrated-Circuit Fabrication

Fabrication technologies for MOS integrated circuits span a considerably wider spectrum of complexity and performance than those for bipolar technology. CMOS technologies provide two basic types of transistors: enhancement-mode $n$-channel transistors (which have positive thresholds) and enhancement-mode $p$-channel transistors (which have negative thresholds). The magnitudes of the threshold voltages of these transistors are typically set to be 0.6 V to 0.8 V so that the drain current resulting from subthreshold conduction with zero gate-source voltage is very small. This property gives standard CMOS digital circuits high noise margins and essentially zero static power dissipation. However, such thresholds do not always minimize the *total* power dissipation because significant dynamic power is

**Figure 2.51** Typical thin-film resistor structure.

|  | Nichrome | Tantalum | Cermet (Cr-SiO) |
|---|---|---|---|
| Range of sheet resistance ($\Omega/\square$) | 10 to 1000 | 10 to 1000 | 30 to 2500 |
| Temperature coefficient (ppm/°C) | $\pm 10$ to $\pm 150$ | $\pm 5$ to $\pm 200$ | $\pm 50$ to $\pm 150$ |

**Figure 2.52** Properties of monolithic thin-film resistors.

dissipated by charging and discharging internal nodes during logical transitions, especially for high clock rates and power-supply voltages.[21] To reduce the minimum required supply voltage and the total power dissipation for some applications, low-threshold, enhancement-mode devices or depletion-mode devices are sometimes used instead of or along with the standard-threshold, enhancement-mode devices. For the sake of illustration, we will consider an example process that contains enhancement-mode $n$- and $p$-channel devices along with a depletion-mode $n$-channel device.

CMOS technologies can utilize either a $p$-type or $n$-type substrate, with the complementary device type formed in an implanted well of the opposite impurity type. We will take as an example a process in which the starting material is $p$-type. The starting material is a silicon wafer with a concentration in the range of $10^{14}$ to $10^{15}$ atoms/cm$^3$. In CMOS technology, the first step is the formation of a *well* of opposite impurity-type material where the complementary device will be formed. In this case, the well is $n$-type and is formed by a masking operation and ion implantation of a donor species, typically phosphorus. Subsequent diffusion results in the structure shown in Fig. 2.53. The surface concentration in the well following diffusion is typically between $10^{15}$ and $10^{16}$ atoms/cm$^3$.

Next, a layer of silicon nitride is deposited and defined with a masking operation so that nitride is left only in the areas that are to become active devices. After this masking operation, additional ion implantations are carried out, which increase the surface concentrations in the areas that are not covered by nitride, called the *field regions*. This often involves an extra masking operation so that the surface concentration in the well and that in the substrate areas can be independently controlled by means of separate implants. This increase in surface concentration in the field is necessary because the field regions themselves are MOS transistors with very thick gate oxide. To properly isolate the active devices from one another, the field devices must have a threshold voltage high enough that they never turn on. This can be accomplished by increasing the surface concentration in the field regions. Following the field implants, a local oxidation is performed, which results in the structure shown in Fig. 2.54.

**Figure 2.53** Cross section of sample following implantation and diffusion of the $n$-type well. Subsequent processing will result in formation of an $n$-channel device in the unimplanted $p$-type portions of the substrate and a $p$-type transistor in the $n$-type well region.

**Figure 2.54** Cross section of the sample following field implant steps and field oxidation.

**Figure 2.55** Cross section of the sample following deposition and definition of the polysilicon gate layer. Ion implantations have been performed in the thin-oxide regions to adjust the thresholds of the devices.

After field-oxide growth, the nitride is removed from the active areas, and implantation steps are carried out, which adjust the surface concentrations in what will become the channel of the MOS transistors. Equation 1.139, applied to the doping levels usually found in the active-device areas, gives an $n$-channel threshold of within a few hundred millivolts of zero, and $p$-channel threshold of about $-2$ V. To shift the magnitudes of the device threshold voltages to 0.6 V to 0.8 V, an implantation step that changes the impurity concentration at the surface in the channel regions of the two transistor types is usually included. This shift in threshold can sometimes be accomplished by using a single sheet implant over the entire wafer, which simultaneously shifts the thresholds of both types of devices. More typically, however, two separate masked implants are used, one for each device type. Also, if a depletion-mode $n$-channel device is included in the process, it is defined at this point by a masking operation and subsequent implant to shift the threshold of the selected devices to a negative value so that they are normally on.

Next, a layer of polysilicon is deposited, and the gates of the various devices are defined with a masking operation. The resulting structure is shown in Fig. 2.55. Silicon-gate MOS technology provides three materials that can be used for interconnection: polysilicon, diffusion, and several layers of metal. Unless special provision is made in the process, connections between polysilicon and diffusion layers require a metallization bridge, since the polysilicon layer acts as a mask for the diffused layers. To provide a direct electrical connection between polysilicon and diffusion layers, a buried contact can be included just prior to the polysilicon deposition. This masking operation opens a window in the silicon dioxide under the polysilicon, allowing it to touch the bare silicon surface when it is deposited, forming a direct polysilicon-silicon contact. The depletion device shown in Fig. 2.55 has such a buried contact connecting its source to its gate.

Next, a masking operation is performed such that photoresist covers the $p$-channel devices, and the wafer is etched to remove the oxide from the source and drain areas of the $n$-channel devices. Arsenic or phosphorus is then introduced into these areas, using either diffusion or ion implantation. After a short oxidation, the process is repeated for the $p$-channel source and drain areas, where boron is used. The resulting structure is shown in Fig. 2.56.

At this point in the process, a layer of silicon dioxide is usually deposited on the wafer, using chemical vapor deposition or some other similar technique. This layer is required to reduce the parasitic capacitance of the interconnect metallization and cannot be thermally grown because of the redistribution of the impurities within the device structures that would result during the growth. Following the oxide deposition, the contact windows are formed with a masking operation, and metallization is deposited and defined with a second masking operation. The final structure is shown in Fig. 2.57. A microscope photograph of such a device is shown in Fig. 2.58. Subsequent fabrication steps are as described in Section 2.3 for bipolar technology.

**Figure 2.56** Cross section of the sample following the source drain masking and diffusion operations.

**Figure 2.57** Cross section of the sample after final process step. The enhancement and depletion $n$-channel devices are distinguished from each other by the fact that the depletion device has received a channel implantation of donor impurities to lower its threshold voltage, usually to the range of $-1.5$ V to $-3$ V.

**Figure 2.58** Photomicrograph of a silicon-gate MOS transistor. Visible in this picture are the polysilicon gate, field-oxide region boundary, source and drain metallization, and contact windows. In this particular device, the contact windows have been broken into two smaller rectangular openings rather than a single long one as shown in Fig. 2.59. Large contact windows are frequently implemented with an array of small openings so that all individual contact holes in the integrated circuit have the same nominal geometry. This results in better uniformity of the etch rate of the contact windows and better matching.

## 2.9  Active Devices in MOS Integrated Circuits

The process sequence described in the previous section results in a variety of device types having different threshold voltages, channel mobilities, and parasitic capacitances. In addition, the sequence allows the fabrication of a bipolar emitter follower, using the well as a base. In this section, we explore the properties of these different types of devices.

### 2.9.1  n-Channel Transistors

A typical layout of an n-channel MOS transistor is shown in Fig. 2.59. The electrically active portion of the device is the region under the gate; the remainder of the device area simply provides electrical contact to the terminals. As in the case of integrated bipolar transistors, these areas contribute additional parasitic capacitance and resistance.

In the case of MOS technology, the circuit designer has even greater flexibility than in the bipolar case to tailor the properties of each device to the role it is to play in the individual circuit application. Both the channel width (analogous to the emitter area in bipolar) and the channel length can be defined by the designer. The latter is analogous to the base width of a bipolar device, which is not under the control of the bipolar circuit designer since it is a process parameter and not a mask parameter. In contrast to a bipolar transistor, the transconductance of an MOS device can be made to vary over a wide range

**Figure 2.59** Example layout of an n-channel silicon-gate MOS transistor. The mask layers are coded as shown.

at a fixed drain current by simply changing the device geometry. The same is true of the gate-source voltage. In making these design choices, the designer must be able to relate changes in device geometry to changes in the electrical properties of the device. To illustrate this procedure, we will calculate the model parameters of the device shown in Fig. 2.59. This device has a drawn channel length of 6 μm and channel width of 50 μm. We will assume the process has the parameters that are summarized in Table 2.1. This is typical of processes with minimum allowed gate lengths of 3 μm. Parameters for more advanced processes are given in Tables 2.2, 2.3, and 2.4.

**Threshold Voltage.** In Chapter 1, an MOS transistor was shown to have a threshold voltage of

$$V_t = \phi_{ms} + 2\phi_f + \frac{Q_b}{C_{ox}} - \frac{Q_{ss}}{C_{ox}} \tag{2.27}$$

**Table 2.1** Summary of Process Parameters for a Typical Silicon-Gate $n$-Well CMOS Process with 3 μm Minimum Allowed Gate Length

| Parameter | Symbol | Value $n$-Channel Transistor | Value $p$-Channel Transistor | Units |
|---|---|---|---|---|
| Substrate doping | $N_A, N_D$ | $1 \times 10^{15}$ | $1 \times 10^{16}$ | Atoms/cm$^3$ |
| Gate oxide thickness | $t_{ox}$ | 400 | 400 | Å |
| Metal-silicon work function | $\phi_{ms}$ | $-0.6$ | $-0.1$ | V |
| Channel mobility | $\mu_n, \mu_p$ | 700 | 350 | cm$^2$/V-s |
| Minimum drawn channel length | $L_{drwn}$ | 3 | 3 | μm |
| Source, drain junction depth | $X_j$ | 0.6 | 0.6 | μm |
| Source, drain side diffusion | $L_d$ | 0.3 | 0.3 | μm |
| Overlap capacitance per unit gate width | $C_{ol}$ | 0.35 | 0.35 | fF/μm |
| Threshold adjust implant (box dist) impurity type |  | P | P |  |
| effective depth | $X_i$ | 0.3 | 0.3 | μm |
| effective surface concentration | $N_{si}$ | $2 \times 10^{16}$ | $0.9 \times 10^{16}$ | Atoms/cm$^3$ |
| Nominal threshold voltage | $V_t$ | 0.7 | $-0.7$ | V |
| Polysilicon gate doping concentration | $N_{dpoly}$ | $10^{20}$ | $10^{20}$ | Atoms/cm$^3$ |
| Poly gate sheet resistance | $R_s$ | 20 | 20 | Ω/□ |
| Source, drain-bulk junction capacitances (zero bias) | $C_{j0}$ | 0.08 | 0.20 | fF/μm$^2$ |
| Source, drain-bulk junction capacitance grading coefficient | $n$ | 0.5 | 0.5 |  |
| Source, drain periphery capacitance (zero bias) | $C_{jsw0}$ | 0.5 | 1.5 | fF/μm |
| Source, drain periphery capacitance grading coefficient | $n$ | 0.5 | 0.5 |  |
| Source, drain junction built-in potential | $\psi_0$ | 0.65 | 0.65 | V |
| Surface-state density | $\frac{Q_{ss}}{q}$ | $10^{11}$ | $10^{11}$ | Atoms/cm$^2$ |
| Channel-length modulation parameter | $\left|\frac{dX_d}{dV_{DS}}\right|$ | 0.2 | 0.1 | μm/V |

**Table 2.2** Summary of Process Parameters for a Typical Silicon-Gate $n$-Well CMOS Process with 1.5 $\mu$m Minimum Allowed Gate Length

| Parameter | Symbol | Value $n$-Channel Transistor | Value $p$-Channel Transistor | Units |
|---|---|---|---|---|
| Substrate doping | $N_A, N_D$ | $2 \times 10^{15}$ | $1.5 \times 10^{16}$ | Atoms/cm$^3$ |
| Gate oxide thickness | $t_{ox}$ | 250 | 250 | Å |
| Metal-silicon work function | $\phi_{ms}$ | $-0.6$ | $-0.1$ | V |
| Channel mobility | $\mu_n, \mu_p$ | 650 | 300 | cm$^2$/V-s |
| Minimum drawn channel length | $L_{\text{drwn}}$ | 1.5 | 1.5 | $\mu$m |
| Source, drain junction depth | $X_j$ | 0.35 | 0.4 | $\mu$m |
| Source, drain side diffusion | $L_d$ | 0.2 | 0.3 | $\mu$m |
| Overlap capacitance per unit gate width | $C_{ol}$ | 0.18 | 0.26 | fF/$\mu$m |
| Threshold adjust implant (box dist) | | | | |
|   impurity type | | P | P | |
|   effective depth | $X_i$ | 0.3 | 0.3 | $\mu$m |
|   effective surface concentration | $N_{si}$ | $2 \times 10^{16}$ | $0.9 \times 10^{16}$ | Atoms/cm$^3$ |
| Nominal threshold voltage | $V_t$ | 0.7 | $-0.7$ | V |
| Polysilicon gate doping concentration | $N_{\text{dpoly}}$ | $10^{20}$ | $10^{20}$ | Atoms/cm$^3$ |
| Poly gate sheet resistance | $R_s$ | 20 | 20 | $\Omega/\square$ |
| Source, drain-bulk junction capacitances (zero bias) | $C_{j0}$ | 0.14 | 0.25 | fF/$\mu$m$^2$ |
| Source, drain-bulk junction capacitance grading coefficient | $n$ | 0.5 | 0.5 | |
| Source, drain periphery capacitance (zero bias) | $C_{jsw0}$ | 0.8 | 1.8 | fF/$\mu$m |
| Source, drain periphery capacitance grading coefficient | $n$ | 0.5 | 0.5 | |
| Source, drain junction built-in potential | $\psi_0$ | 0.65 | 0.65 | V |
| Surface-state density | $\dfrac{Q_{ss}}{q}$ | $10^{11}$ | $10^{11}$ | Atoms/cm$^2$ |
| Channel-length modulation parameter | $\left\| \dfrac{dX_d}{dV_{DS}} \right\|$ | 0.12 | 0.06 | $\mu$m/V |

where $\phi_{ms}$ is the metal-silicon work function, $\phi_f$ is the Fermi level in the bulk silicon, $Q_b$ is the bulk depletion layer charge, $C_{ox}$ is the oxide capacitance per unit area, and $Q_{ss}$ is the concentration of surface-state charge. An actual calculation of the threshold is illustrated in the following example.

Often the threshold voltage must be deduced from measurements, and a useful approach to doing this is to plot the square root of the drain current as a function of $V_{GS}$, as shown in Fig. 2.60. The threshold voltage can be determined as the extrapolation of the straight portion of the curve to zero current. The slope of the curve also yields a direct measure of the quantity $\mu_n C_{ox} W/L_{\text{eff}}$ for the device at the particular drain-source voltage at which the measurement is made. The measured curve deviates from a straight line at low currents because of subthreshold conduction and at high currents because of mobility degradation in the channel as the carriers approach scattering-limited velocity.

**Table 2.3** Summary of Process Parameters for a Typical Silicon-Gate $n$-Well CMOS Process with 0.8 $\mu$m Minimum Allowed Gate Length

| Parameter | Symbol | Value $n$-Channel Transistor | Value $p$-Channel Transistor | Units |
|---|---|---|---|---|
| Substrate doping | $N_A, N_D$ | $4 \times 10^{15}$ | $3 \times 10^{16}$ | Atoms/cm$^3$ |
| Gate oxide thickness | $t_{ox}$ | 150 | 150 | Å |
| Metal-silicon work function | $\phi_{ms}$ | $-0.6$ | $-0.1$ | V |
| Channel mobility | $\mu_n, \mu_p$ | 550 | 250 | cm$^2$/V-s |
| Minimum drawn channel length | $L_{drwn}$ | 0.8 | 0.8 | $\mu$m |
| Source, drain junction depth | $X_j$ | 0.2 | 0.3 | $\mu$m |
| Source, drain side diffusion | $L_d$ | 0.12 | 0.18 | $\mu$m |
| Overlap capacitance per unit gate width | $C_{ol}$ | 0.12 | 0.18 | fF/$\mu$m |
| Threshold adjust implant (box dist) | | | | |
|   impurity type | | P | P | |
|   effective depth | $X_i$ | 0.2 | 0.2 | $\mu$m |
|   effective surface concentration | $N_{si}$ | $3 \times 10^{16}$ | $2 \times 10^{16}$ | Atoms/cm$^3$ |
| Nominal threshold voltage | $V_t$ | 0.7 | $-0.7$ | V |
| Polysilicon gate doping concentration | $N_{dpoly}$ | $10^{20}$ | $10^{20}$ | Atoms/cm$^3$ |
| Poly gate sheet resistance | $R_s$ | 10 | 10 | $\Omega/\square$ |
| Source, drain-bulk junction capacitances (zero bias) | $C_{j0}$ | 0.18 | 0.30 | fF/$\mu$m$^2$ |
| Source, drain-bulk junction capacitance grading coefficient | $n$ | 0.5 | 0.5 | |
| Source, drain periphery capacitance (zero bias) | $C_{jsw0}$ | 1.0 | 2.2 | fF/$\mu$m |
| Source, drain periphery capacitance grading coefficient | $n$ | 0.5 | 0.5 | |
| Source, drain junction built-in potential | $\psi_0$ | 0.65 | 0.65 | V |
| Surface-state density | $\dfrac{Q_{SS}}{q}$ | $10^{11}$ | $10^{11}$ | Atoms/cm$^2$ |
| Channel-length modulation parameter | $\left\lvert \dfrac{dX_d}{dV_{DS}} \right\rvert$ | 0.08 | 0.04 | $\mu$m/V |

**Figure 2.60** Typical experimental variation of drain current as a function of the square root of gate-source voltage in the active region.

**Table 2.4** Summary of Process Parameters for a Typical Silicon-Gate $n$-Well CMOS Process with 0.4 $\mu$m Minimum Allowed Gate Length

| Parameter | Symbol | Value $n$-Channel Transistor | Value $p$-Channel Transistor | Units |
|---|---|---|---|---|
| Substrate doping | $N_A, N_D$ | $5 \times 10^{15}$ | $4 \times 10^{16}$ | Atoms/cm$^3$ |
| Gate oxide thickness | $t_{ox}$ | 80 | 80 | Å |
| Metal-silicon work function | $\phi_{ms}$ | $-0.6$ | $-0.1$ | V |
| Channel mobility | $\mu_n, \mu_p$ | 450 | 150 | cm$^2$/V-s |
| Minimum drawn channel length | $L_{drwn}$ | 0.4 | 0.4 | $\mu$m |
| Source, drain junction depth | $X_j$ | 0.15 | 0.18 | $\mu$m |
| Source, drain side diffusion | $L_d$ | 0.09 | 0.09 | $\mu$m |
| Overlap capacitance per unit gate width | $C_{ol}$ | 0.35 | 0.35 | fF/$\mu$m |
| Threshold adjust implant (box dist) impurity type | | P | P | |
| effective depth | $X_i$ | 0.16 | 0.16 | $\mu$m |
| effective surface concentration | $N_{si}$ | $4 \times 10^{16}$ | $3 \times 10^{16}$ | Atoms/cm$^3$ |
| Nominal threshold voltage | $V_t$ | 0.6 | $-0.8$ | V |
| Polysilicon gate doping concentration | $N_{dpoly}$ | $10^{20}$ | $10^{20}$ | Atoms/cm$^3$ |
| Poly gate sheet resistance | $R_s$ | 5 | 5 | $\Omega$/□ |
| Source, drain-bulk junction capacitances (zero bias) | $C_{j0}$ | 0.2 | 0.4 | fF/$\mu$m$^2$ |
| Source, drain-bulk junction capacitance grading coefficient | $n$ | 0.5 | 0.4 | |
| Source, drain periphery capacitance (zero bias) | $C_{jsw0}$ | 1.2 | 2.4 | fF/$\mu$m |
| Source, drain periphery capacitance grading coefficient | $n$ | 0.4 | 0.3 | |
| Source, drain junction built-in potential | $\psi_0$ | 0.7 | 0.7 | V |
| Surface-state density | $\dfrac{Q_{SS}}{q}$ | $10^{11}$ | $10^{11}$ | Atoms/cm$^2$ |
| Channel-length modulation parameter | $\left\| \dfrac{dX_d}{dV_{DS}} \right\|$ | 0.02 | 0.04 | $\mu$m/V |

- **EXAMPLE**

Calculate the zero-bias threshold voltage of the unimplanted and implanted NMOS transistors for the process given in Table 2.1.

Each of the four components in the threshold voltage expression (2.27) must be calculated. The first term is the metal-silicon work function. For an $n$-channel transistor with an $n$-type polysilicon gate electrode, this has a value equal to the difference in the Fermi potentials in the two regions, or approximately $-0.6$ V.

The second term in the threshold voltage equation represents the band bending in the semiconductor that is required to strongly invert the surface. To produce a surface concentration of electrons that is approximately equal to the bulk concentration of holes, the surface potential must be increased by approximately twice the bulk Fermi potential.

The Fermi potential in the bulk is given by

$$\phi_f = \frac{kT}{q} \ln\left(\frac{N_A}{n_i}\right) \tag{2.28}$$

For the unimplanted transistor with the substrate doping given in Table 2.1, this value is 0.27 V. Thus the second term in (2.27) takes on a value of 0.54 V. The value of this term will be the same for the implanted transistor since we are defining the threshold voltage as the voltage that causes the surface concentration of electrons to be the same as that of holes in the bulk material beneath the channel implant. Thus the potential difference between the surface and the bulk silicon beneath the channel implant region that is required to bring this condition about is still given by (2.30), independent of the details of the channel implant.

The third term in (2.27) is related to the charge in the depletion layer under the channel. We first consider the unimplanted device. Using (1.137), with a value of $N_A$ of $10^{15}$ atoms/cm$^3$,

$$Q_{b0} = \sqrt{2\, qN_A\epsilon 2\phi_f} = \sqrt{2\,(1.6 \times 10^{-19})(10^{15})(11.6 \times 8.86 \times 10^{-14})(0.54)}$$
$$= 1.34 \times 10^{-8} \text{ C/cm}^2 \tag{2.29}$$

Also, the capacitance per unit area of the 400-Å gate oxide is

$$C_{ox} = \frac{\epsilon_{ox}}{t_{ox}} = \frac{3.9 \times 8.86 \times 10^{-14} \text{ F/cm}}{400 \times 10^{-8} \text{ cm}} = 8.6 \times 10^{-8}\, \frac{\text{F}}{\text{cm}^2} = 0.86\, \frac{\text{fF}}{\mu\text{m}^2} \tag{2.30}$$

The resulting magnitude of the third term is 0.16 V.

The fourth term in (2.27) is the threshold shift due to the surface-state charge. This positive charge has a value equal to the charge of one electron multiplied by the density of surface states, $10^{11}$ atoms/cm$^2$, from Table 2.1. The value of the surface-state charge term is then

$$\frac{Q_{ss}}{C_{ox}} = \frac{1.6 \times 10^{-19} \times 10^{11}}{8.6 \times 10^{-8}} = 0.19 \text{ V} \tag{2.31}$$

Using these calculations, the threshold voltage for the unimplanted transistor is

$$V_t = -0.6 \text{ V} + 0.54 \text{ V} + 0.16 \text{ V} - 0.19 \text{ V} = -0.09 \text{ V} \tag{2.32}$$

For the implanted transistor, the calculation of the threshold voltage is complicated by the fact that the depletion layer under the channel spans a region of nonuniform doping. A precise calculation of device threshold voltage would require consideration of this nonuniform profile. The threshold voltage can be approximated, however, by considering the implanted layer to be approximated by a box distribution of impurities with a depth $X_i$ and a specified impurity concentration $N_i$. If the impurity profile resulting from the threshold-adjustment implant and subsequent process steps is sufficiently deep so that the channel-substrate depletion layer lies entirely within it, then the effect of the implant is simply to raise the effective substrate doping. For the implant specified in Table 2.1, the average doping in the layer is the sum of the implant doping and the background concentration, or $2.1 \times 10^{16}$ atoms/cm$^3$. This increases the $Q_{b0}$ term in the threshold voltage to 0.71 V and gives device threshold voltage of 0.47 V. The validity of the assumption regarding the boundary of the channel-substrate depletion layer can be checked by using Fig. 2.29. For a doping level of $2.1 \times 10^{16}$ atoms/cm$^3$, a one-sided step junction displays a depletion region width of approximately 0.2 $\mu$m. Since the depth of the layer is 0.3 $\mu$m in this case, the assumption is valid.

Alternatively, if the implantation and subsequent diffusion had resulted in a layer that was very shallow, and was contained entirely within the depletion layer, the effect of the implanted layer would be simply to increase the effective value of $Q_{ss}$ by an amount equal to the effective implant dose over and above that of the unimplanted transistor. The total active impurity dose for the implant given in Table 2.1 is the product of the depth and the impurity concentration, or $6 \times 10^{11}$ atoms/cm$^2$. For this case, the increase in threshold voltage would have been 1.11 V, giving a threshold voltage of 1.02 V.

**Body-Effect Parameter.** For an unimplanted, uniform-channel transistor, the body-effect parameter is given by (1.141).

$$\gamma = \frac{1}{C_{ox}} \sqrt{2q\epsilon N_A} \qquad (2.33)$$

The application of this expression is illustrated in the following example.

■ **EXAMPLE**

Calculate the body-effect parameter for the unimplanted $n$-channel transistor in Table 2.1. Utilizing in (2.33) the parameters given in Table 2.1, we obtain

$$\gamma = \frac{\sqrt{2\,(1.6 \times 10^{-19})(11.6 \times 8.86 \times 10^{-14})(10^{15})}}{8.6 \times 10^{-8}} = 0.21 \; \text{V}^{1/2} \qquad (2.34)$$

■

The calculation of body effect in an implanted transistor is complicated by the fact that the channel is not uniformly doped and the preceding simple expression does not apply. The threshold voltage as a function of body bias voltage can be approximated again by considering the implanted layer to be approximated by a box distribution of impurity of depth $X_i$ and concentration $N_i$. For small values of body bias where the channel-substrate depletion layer resides entirely within the implanted layer, the body effect is that corresponding to a transistor with channel doping $(N_i + N_A)$. For larger values of body bias for which the depletion layer extends into the substrate beyond the implanted distribution, the incremental body effect corresponds to a transistor with substrate doping $N_A$. A typical variation of threshold voltage as a function of substrate bias for this type of device is illustrated in Fig. 2.61.

**Effective Channel Length.** The gate dimension parallel to current flow that is actually drawn on the mask is called the drawn channel length $L_{\text{drwn}}$. This is the length referred to on circuit schematics. Because of exposure variations and other effects, the physical length of the polysilicon strip defining the gate may be somewhat larger or smaller than

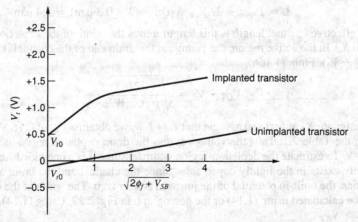

**Figure 2.61** Typical variation of threshold voltage as a function of substrate bias for $n$-channel devices with uniform channel doping (no channel implant) and with nonuniform channel doping resulting from threshold adjustment channel implant.

this value. The actual channel length of the device is the physical length of the polysilicon gate electrode minus the side or lateral diffusions of the source and the drain under the gate. This length will be termed the *metallurgical channel length* and is the distance between the metallurgical source and drain junctions. Assuming that the lateral diffusion of the source and drain are each equal to $L_d$, the metallurgical channel length is $L = (L_{drwn} - 2L_d)$.

When the transistor is biased in the active or saturation region, a depletion region exists between the drain region and the end of the channel. In Chapter 1, the width of this region was defined as $X_d$. Thus for a transistor operating in the active region, the actual effective channel length $L_{eff}$ is given by

$$L_{eff} = L_{drwn} - 2L_d - X_d \tag{2.35}$$

A precise determination of $X_d$ is complicated by the fact that the field distribution in the drain region is two-dimensional and quite complex. The drain depletion width $X_d$ can be approximated by assuming that the electric field in the drain region is one-dimensional and that the depletion width is that of a one-sided step junction with an applied voltage of $V_{DS} - V_{ov}$, where $V_{ov} = V_{GS} - V_t$ is the potential at the drain end of the channel with respect to the source. This assumption is used in the following example.

As shown in Chapter 1, the small-signal output resistance of the transistor is inversely proportional to the effective channel length. Because the performance of analog circuits often depends strongly on the transistor small-signal output resistance, analog circuits often use channel lengths that are longer than the minimum channel length for digital circuits. This statement is particularly true for unimplanted transistors.

▪ **EXAMPLE**

Estimate the effective channel length for the unimplanted and implanted transistors for the process shown in Table 2.1 and the device geometry shown in Fig. 2.59. Assume the device is biased at a drain-source voltage of 5 V and a drain current of 10 μA. Calculate the transconductance and the output resistance. For the calculation of $X_d$, assume that the depletion region between the drain and the end of the channel behaves like a step junction. At the given drain bias voltage, assume that the values of $dX_d/dV_{DS}$ have been deduced from other measurements to be 0.1 μm/V for the unimplanted device and 0.02 μm/V for the implanted device.

The metallurgical channel length is given by

$$L = L_{drwn} - 2L_d = 6 \text{ μm} - (2 \times 0.3 \text{ μm}) = 5.4 \text{ μm} \tag{2.36}$$

The effective channel length is this length minus the width of the depletion region at the drain $X_d$. In the active region, the voltage at the drain end of the channel is approximately $(V_{GS} - V_t)$. From (1.166),

$$V_{GS} - V_t = \sqrt{\frac{2I_D}{\mu_n C_{ox} W/L}} = V_{ov} \tag{2.37}$$

If we ignore $X_d$ at first and assume that $L \simeq L_{eff}$, we obtain a $V_{ov}$ of 0.16 V using the data from the Table 2.1. Thus the voltage across the drain depletion region is approximately 4.84 V. To estimate the depletion-region width, assume it is a one-sided step junction that mainly exists in the lightly doped side. Since the channel and the drain are both n-type regions, the built-in potential of the junction is near zero. The width of the depletion layer can be calculated using (1.14) or the nomograph in Fig. 2.29. Using (1.14), and assuming $N_D \gg N_A$,

$$X_d = \sqrt{\frac{2\epsilon (V_{DS} - V_{ov})}{qN_A}} \tag{2.38}$$

For the unimplanted device, this equation gives a depletion width of 2.4 $\mu$m. For the implanted device, the result is 0.5 $\mu$m, assuming an effective constant channel doping of $2.1 \times 10^{16}$ atoms/cm$^3$. Thus the effective channel lengths of the two devices would be approximately 3.0 $\mu$m and 4.9 $\mu$m, respectively.

From (1.180), the device transconductance is given by

$$g_m = \sqrt{2\mu_n C_{ox}(W/L)I_D} \tag{2.39}$$

Assuming that $\mu_n = 700$ cm$^2$/V-s, we find

$$g_m = \sqrt{2\,(700)(8.6 \times 10^{-8})(50/3.0)(10 \times 10^{-6})} = 141 \ \mu\text{A/V} \tag{2.40}$$

for the unimplanted transistor and

$$g_m = \sqrt{2\,(700)(8.6 \times 10^{-8})(50/4.9)(10 \times 10^{-6})} = 111 \ \mu\text{A/V} \tag{2.41}$$

for the implanted transistor.

The output resistance can be calculated by using (1.163) and (1.194). For the unimplanted device,

$$r_o = \frac{L_{\text{eff}}}{I_D}\left(\frac{dX_d}{dV_{DS}}\right)^{-1} = \left(\frac{3.0 \ \mu\text{m}}{10 \ \mu\text{A}}\right)\frac{1}{0.1 \ \mu\text{m/V}} = 3.0 \ \text{M}\Omega \tag{2.42}$$

For the implanted device,

$$r_o = \left(\frac{4.9 \ \mu\text{m}}{10 \ \mu\text{A}}\right)\frac{1}{0.02 \ \mu\text{m/V}} = 25 \ \text{M}\Omega \tag{2.43}$$

Because the depletion region for unimplanted devices is much wider than for implanted devices, the channel length of unimplanted devices must be made longer than for implanted devices to achieve comparable punch-through voltages and small-signal output resistances under identical bias conditions.

**Effective Channel Width.** The effective channel width of an MOS transistor is determined by the gate dimension parallel to the surface and perpendicular to the channel length over which the gate oxide is thin. Thick field oxide regions are grown at the edges of each transistor by using the local-oxidation process described in Sections 2.2.7 and 2.8. Before the field oxide is grown, nitride is deposited and patterned so that it remains only in areas that should become transistors. Therefore, the width of a nitride region corresponds to the the drawn width of a transistor. To minimize the width variation, the field oxide should grow only vertically; that is, the oxide thickness should increase only in regions were nitride does not cover the oxide. In practice, however, some lateral growth of oxide also occurs near the edges of the nitride during field-oxide growth. As a result, the edges of the field oxide are not vertical, as shown in Figures 2.9 and 2.54. This lateral growth of the oxide reduces the effective width of MOS transistors compared to their drawn widths. It is commonly referred to as the *bird's beak* because the gradually decreasing oxide thickness in the cross sections of Figures 2.9 and 2.54 resembles the corresponding portion of the profile of a bird.

As a result, both the effective lengths and the effective widths of transistors differ from the corresponding drawn dimensions. In analog design, the change in the effective length is usually much more important than the change in the effective width because transistors usually have drawn lengths much less than their drawn widths. As a result, the difference between the drawn and effective width is often ignored. However, this difference is sometimes important, especially when the matching between two ratioed transistors limits the accuracy of a given circuit. This topic is considered in Section 4.2.

**Intrinsic Gate-Source Capacitance.** As described in Chapter 1, the intrinsic gate-source capacitance of the transistor in the active region of operation is given by

$$C_{gs} = \frac{2}{3} W L_{eff} C_{ox} \qquad (2.44)$$

The calculation of this parameter is illustrated in the next example.

**Overlap Capacitance.** Assuming that the source and drain regions each diffuse under the gate by $L_d$ after implantation, the gate-source and gate-drain overlap capacitances are given by

$$C_{ol} = W L_d C_{ox} \qquad (2.45)$$

This parasitic capacitance adds directly to the intrinsic gate-source capacitance. It constitutes the entire drain-gate capacitance in the active region of operation.

**Junction Capacitances.** Source-substrate and drain-substrate capacitances result from the junction-depletion capacitance between the source and drain diffusions and the substrate. A complicating factor in calculating these capacitances is the fact that the substrate doping around the source and drain regions is not constant. In the region of the periphery of the source and drain diffusions that border on the field regions, a relatively high surface concentration exists on the field side of the junction because of the field threshold adjustment implant. Although approximate calculations can be carried out, the zero-bias value and grading parameter of the periphery capacitance are often characterized experimentally by using test structures. The bulk-junction capacitance can be calculated directly by using (1.21) or can be read from the nomograph in Fig. 2.29.

An additional capacitance that must be accounted for is the depletion capacitance between the channel and the substrate under the gate, which we will term $C_{cs}$. Calculation of this capacitance is complicated by the fact that the channel-substrate voltage is not constant but varies along the channel. Also, the allocation of this capacitance to the source and drain varies with operating conditions in the same way as the allocation of $C_{gs}$. A reasonable approach is to develop an approximate total value for this junction capacitance under the gate and allocate it to source and drain in the same ratio as the gate capacitance is allocated. For example, in the active region, a capacitance of two-thirds of $C_{cs}$ would appear in parallel with the source-substrate capacitance and none would appear in parallel with the drain-substrate capacitance.

## EXAMPLE

Calculate the capacitances of an implanted device with the geometry shown in Fig. 2.59. Use the process parameters given in Table 2.1 and assume a drain-source voltage of 5 V, drain current of 10 μA, and no substrate bias voltage. Neglect the capacitance between the channel and the substrate. Assume that $X_d$ is negligibly small.

From (2.44), the intrinsic gate-source capacitance is

$$C_{gs} = \frac{2}{3} W L_{eff} C_{ox} = \left(\frac{2}{3}\right) 50 \text{ μm} \times 5.4 \text{ μm} \times 0.86 \text{ fF/μm}^2 = 155 \text{ fF} \qquad (2.46)$$

From (2.45), the overlap capacitance is given by

$$C_{ol} = W L_d C_{ox} = 50 \text{ μm} \times 0.3 \text{ μm} \times 0.86 \text{ fF/μm}^2 = 12.9 \text{ fF} \qquad (2.47)$$

Thus the total gate-source capacitance is ($C_{gs} + C_{ol}$) or 168 fF. The gate-drain capacitance is equal to the overlap capacitance, or 12.9 fF.

The source- and drain-to-substrate capacitances consist of two portions. The periphery or sidewall part $C_{jsw}$ is associated with that portion of the edge of the diffusion area that is adjacent to the field region. The second portion $C_j$ is the depletion capacitance between the diffused junction and the bulk silicon under the source and drain. For the bias conditions given, the source-substrate junction operates with zero bias and the drain-substrate junction has a reverse bias of 5 V. Using Table 2.1, the periphery portion for the source-substrate capacitance is

$$C_{jsw}(\text{source}) = (50\ \mu m + 9\ \mu m + 9\ \mu m)(0.5\ \text{fF}/\mu m) = 34\ \text{fF} \qquad (2.48)$$

Here, the perimeter is set equal to $W + 2L$ because that is the distance on the surface of the silicon around the part of the source and drain regions that border on field-oxide regions. Since the substrate doping is high along this perimeter to increase the magnitude of the threshold voltage in the field regions, the sidewall capacitance here is dominant. The bulk capacitance is simply the source-diffusion area multiplied by the capacitance per unit area from Table 2.1.

$$C_j(\text{source}) = (50\ \mu m)(9\ \mu m)(0.08\ \text{fF}/\mu m^2) = 36\ \text{fF} \qquad (2.49)$$

The total capacitance from source to bulk is the sum of these two, or

$$C_{sb} = 70\ \text{fF} \qquad (2.50)$$

For the geometry given for this example, the transistor is symmetrical, and the source and drain areas and peripheries are the same. From Table 2.1, both the bulk and periphery capacitances have a grading coefficient of 0.5. As a result, the drain-bulk capacitance is the same as the source-bulk capacitance modified to account for the 5 V reverse bias on the junction. Assuming $\psi_0 = 0.65$ V,

$$C_{db} = \frac{(70\ \text{fF})}{\sqrt{1 + V_{DB}/\psi_0}} = \frac{(70\ \text{fF})}{\sqrt{1 + 5/0.65}} = 24\ \text{fF} \qquad (2.51)$$

### 2.9.2 p-Channel Transistors

The p-channel transistor in most CMOS technologies displays dc and ac properties that are comparable to the n-channel transistor. One difference is that the transconductance parameter $k'$ of a p-channel device is about one-half to one-third that of an n-channel device because holes have correspondingly lower mobility than electrons. As shown in (1.209), this difference in mobility also reduces the $f_T$ of p-channel devices by the same factor. Another difference is that for a CMOS technology with a p-type substrate and n-type wells, the substrate terminal of the p-channel transistors can be electrically isolated since the devices are made in an implanted well. Good use can be made of this fact in analog circuits to alleviate the impact of the high body effect in these devices. For a CMOS process made on an n-type substrate with p-type wells, the p-channel devices are made in the substrate material, which is connected to the highest power-supply voltage, but the n-channel devices can have electrically isolated substrate terminals.

The calculation of device parameters for p-channel devices proceeds exactly as for n-channel devices. An important difference is the fact that for the p-channel transistors the threshold voltage that results if no threshold adjustment implant is used is relatively high, usually in the range of 1 to 3 V. This occurs because the polarities of the $Q_{ss}$ term and the work-function term are such that they tend to increase the p-channel threshold voltages while decreasing the n-channel threshold voltages. Thus the p-type threshold adjustment implant is used to *reduce* the surface concentration by partially compensating the doping of the $n$-type well or substrate. Thus in contrast to the $n$-channel device, the $p$-channel transistor has an effective surface concentration in the channel that is lower than the bulk concentration, and as a result, often displays a smaller incremental body effect for low values of substrate bias and a larger incremental body effect for larger values of substrate bias.

### 2.9.3 Depletion Devices

The properties of depletion devices are similar to those of the enhancement device already considered, except that an implant has been added in the channel to make the threshold negative (for an $n$-channel device). In most respects a depletion device closely resembles an enhancement device with a voltage source in series with the gate lead of value $(V_{tD} - V_{tE})$, where $V_{tD}$ is the threshold voltage of the depletion-mode transistor and $V_{tE}$ is the threshold voltage of the enhancement-mode transistor. Depletion transistors are most frequently used with the gate tied to the source. Because the device is on with $V_{GS} = 0$, if it operates in the active region, it operates like a current source with a drain current of

$$I_{DSS} = I_D\big|_{V_{GS}=0} = \frac{\mu_n C_{ox}}{2} \frac{W}{L} V_{tD}^2 \tag{2.52}$$

An important aspect of depletion-device performance is the variation of $I_{DSS}$ with process variations. These variations stem primarily from the fact that the threshold voltage varies substantially from its nominal value due to processing variations. Since the transistor $I_{DSS}$ varies as the square of the threshold voltage, large variations in $I_{DSS}$ due to process variations often occur. Tolerances of $\pm 40$ percent or more from nominal due to process variations are common. Because $I_{DSS}$ determines circuit bias current and power dissipation, the magnitude of this variation is an important factor. Another important aspect of the behavior of depletion devices stems from the body effect. Because the threshold voltage varies with body bias, a depletion device with $V_{GS} = 0$ and $v_{sb} \neq 0$ displays a finite conductance in the active region even if the effect of channel-length modulation is ignored. In turn, this finite conductance has a strong effect on the performance of analog circuits that use depletion devices as load elements.

### 2.9.4 Bipolar Transistors

Standard CMOS technologies include process steps that can be used to form a bipolar transistor whose collector is tied to the substrate. The substrate, in turn, is tied to one of the power supplies. Fig. 2.62$a$ shows a cross section of such a device. The well region forms the base of the transistor, and the source/drain diffusion of the device in the well forms the emitter. Since the current flow through the base is perpendicular to the surface of the silicon, the device is a vertical bipolar transistor. It is a $pnp$ transistor in processes that utilize $p$-type substrates as in Fig. 2.62$a$ and an $npn$ transistor in processes that use an $n$-type substrate. The device is particularly useful in band-gap references, described in Chapter 4, and in output stages, considered in Chapter 5. The performance of the device is a strong function of well depth and doping but is generally similar to the substrate $pnp$ transistor in bipolar technology, described in Section 2.5.2.

The main limitation of such a vertical bipolar transistor is that its collector is the substrate and is connected to a power supply to keep the substrate $p$-$n$ junctions reverse biased. Standard CMOS processes also provide another bipolar transistor for which the collector need not be connected to a power supply.[22] Figure 2.62$b$ shows a cross section of such a device. As in the vertical transistor, the well region forms the base and a source/drain diffusion forms the emitter. In this case, however, another source/drain diffusion forms the collector $C_1$. Since the current flow through the base is parallel to the surface of the sili-

Figure 2.62 **Figure 2.62** (a) Cross section of a vertical $pnp$ transistor in an $n$-well CMOS process. (b) Cross section of lateral and vertical $pnp$ transistors in an $n$-well CMOS process. (c) Schematic of the bipolar transistors in (b).

con, this device is a lateral bipolar transistor. Again, it is a $pnp$ transistor in processes that utilize $n$-type wells and an $npn$ transistor in processes that use $p$-type wells. The emitter and collector of this lateral device correspond to the source and drain of an MOS transistor. Since the goal here is to build a bipolar transistor, the MOS transistor is deliberately biased to operate in the cutoff region. In Fig. 2.62$b$, for example, the gate of the $p$-channel transistor must be connected to a voltage sufficient to bias it in the cutoff region. A key point here is that the base width of the lateral bipolar device corresponds to the channel length of the MOS device.

One limitation of this structure is that when a lateral bipolar transistor is intentionally formed, a vertical bipolar transistor is also formed. In Fig. 2.62$b$, the emitter and base connections of the vertical transistor are the same as for the lateral transistor, but the collector is the substrate, which is connected to the lowest supply voltage. When the emitter injects minority carriers into the base, some flow parallel to the surface and are collected by the collector of the lateral transistor $C_1$. However, others flow perpendicular to the surface and are collected by the substrate $C_2$. Figure 2.62$c$ models this behavior by showing a transistor symbol with one emitter and one base but two collectors. The current $I_{C1}$ is the collector current of the lateral transistor, and $I_{C2}$ is the collector current of the vertical transistor. Although the base current is small because little recombination and reverse injection occur, the undesired current $I_{C2}$ is comparable to the desired current $I_{C1}$. To minimize the ratio, the collector of the lateral transistor usually surrounds the emitter, and the emitter area as well as the lateral base width are minimized. Even with these techniques, however, the ratio of $I_{C2}/I_{C1}$ is poorly controlled in practice.[22,23] If the total emitter current is held constant as in many conventional circuits, variation of $I_{C2}/I_{C1}$ changes the desired collector current and associated small-signal parameters such as the transconductance. To overcome this problem, the emitter current can be adjusted by negative feedback so that the desired collector current is insensitive to variations in $I_{C2}/I_{C1}$.[24]

Some important properties of the lateral bipolar transistor, including its $\beta_F$ and $f_T$, improve as the base width is reduced. Since the base width corresponds to the channel length of an MOS transistor, the steady reduction in the minimum channel length of scaled MOS technologies is improving the performance and increasing the importance of the available lateral bipolar transistor.

## 2.10  Passive Components in MOS Technology

In this section, we describe the various passive components that are available in CMOS technologies. Resistors include diffused, poly-silicon, and well resistors. Capacitors include poly-poly, metal-poly, metal-silicon, silicon-silicon, and vertical and lateral metal-metal.

### 2.10.1  Resistors

**Diffused Resistors.**  The diffused layer used to form the source and drain of the n-channel and p-channel devices can be used to form a diffused resistor. The resulting resistor structure and properties are very similar to the resistors described in Section 2.6.1 on diffused resistors in bipolar technology. The sheet resistances, layout geometries, and parasitic capacitances are similar.

**Polysilicon Resistors.**  At least one layer of polysilicon is required in silicon-gate MOS technologies to form the gates of the transistors, and this layer is often used to form resistors. The geometries employed are similar to those used for diffused resistors, and the resistor exhibits a parasitic capacitance to the underlying layer much like a diffused resistor. In this case, however, the capacitance stems from the oxide layer under the polysilicon instead of from a reverse-biased $pn$ junction. The nominal sheet resistance of most polysilicon layers that are utilized in MOS processes is on the order of 20 $\Omega/\square$ to 80 $\Omega/\square$ and typically displays a relatively large variation around the nominal value due to process variations. The matching properties of polysilicon resistors are similar to those of diffused resistors. A cross section and plan view of a typical polysilicon resistor are shown in Fig. 2.63a.

The sheet resistance of polysilicon can limit the speed of interconnections, especially in submicron technologies. To reduce the sheet resistance, a silicide layer is sometimes deposited on top of the polysilicon. Silicide is a compound of silicon and a metal, such as tungsten, that can withstand subsequent high-temperature processing with little movement. Silicide reduces the sheet resistance by about an order of magnitude. Also, it has little effect on the oxidation rate of polysilicon and is therefore compatible with conventional CMOS process technologies.[25] Finally, silicide can be used on the source/drain diffusions as well as on the polysilicon.

**Well Resistors.**  In CMOS technologies the well region can be used as the body of a resistor. It is a relatively lightly doped region and when used as a resistor provides a sheet resistance on the order of 10 k$\Omega/\square$. Its properties and geometrical layout are much like the epitaxial

Figure 2.63  (a) Plan view and cross section of polysilicon resistor.

resistor described in Section 2.6.2 and shown in Fig. 2.42. It displays large tolerance, high voltage coefficient, and high temperature coefficient relative to other types of resistors. Higher sheet resistance can be achieved by the addition of the pinching diffusion just as in the bipolar technology case.

**MOS Devices as Resistors.** The MOS transistor biased in the triode region can be used in many circuits to perform the function of a resistor. The drain-source resistance can be calculated by differentiating the equation for the drain current in the triode region with respect to the drain-source voltage. From (1.153),

$$R = \left(\frac{\partial I_D}{\partial V_{DS}}\right)^{-1} = \frac{L}{W}\frac{1}{k'(V_{GS} - V_t - V_{DS})} \tag{2.53}$$

Since $L/W$ gives the number of squares, the second term on the right side of this equation gives the sheet resistance. This equation shows that the effective sheet resistance is a function of the applied gate bias. In practice, this sheet resistance can be much higher than polysilicon or diffused resistors, allowing large amounts of resistance to be implemented in a small area. Also, the resistance can be made to track the transconductance of an MOS transistor operating in the active region, allowing circuits to be designed with properties insensitive to variations in process, supply, and temperature. An example of such a circuit is considered in Section 9.4.3. The principal drawback of this form of resistor is the high degree of nonlinearity of the resulting resistor element; that is, the drain-source resistance is not constant but depends on the drain-source voltage. Nevertheless, it can be used very effectively in many applications.

## 2.10.2 Capacitors in MOS Technology

As a passive component, capacitors play a much more important role in MOS technology than they do in bipolar technology. Because of the fact that MOS transistors have virtually infinite input resistance, voltages stored on capacitors can be sensed with little leakage using MOS amplifiers. As a result, capacitors can be used to perform many functions that are traditionally performed by resistors in bipolar technology.

**Poly-Poly Capacitors.** Many MOS technologies that are used to implement analog functions have two layers of polysilicon. The additional layer provides an efficient capacitor structure, an extra layer of interconnect, and can also be used to implement floating-gate memory cells that are electrically programmable and optically erasable with UV light (EPROM). A typical poly-poly capacitor structure is shown in cross section and plan view in Fig. 2.63b. The plate separation is usually comparable to the gate oxide thickness of the MOS transistors.

An important aspect of the capacitor structure is the parasitic capacitance associated with each plate. The largest parasitic capacitance exists from the bottom plate to the underlying layer, which could be either the substrate or a well diffusion whose terminal is electrically isolated. This bottom-plate parasitic capacitance is proportional to the bottom-plate area and typically has a value from 10 to 30 percent of the capacitor itself.

The top-plate parasitic is contributed by the interconnect metallization or polysilicon that connects the top plate to the rest of the circuit, plus the parasitic capacitance of the transistor to which it is connected. In the structure shown in Fig. 2.63b, the drain-substrate capacitance of an associated MOS transistor contributes to the top-plate parasitic capacitance. The minimum value of this parasitic is technology dependent but is typically on the order of 5 fF to 50 fF.

Other important parameters of monolithic capacitor structures are the tolerance, voltage coefficient, and temperature coefficient of the capacitance value. The tolerance on the absolute value of the capacitor value is primarily a function of oxide-thickness variations and is usually in the 10 percent to 30 percent range. Within the same die, however, the matching of one capacitor to another identical structure is much more precise and can typically be in the range of 0.05 percent to 1 percent, depending on the geometry. Because the plates of the capacitor are a heavily doped semiconductor rather than an ideal conductor, some variation in surface potential relative to the bulk material of the plate occurs as voltage is applied to the capacitor.[26] This effect is analogous to the variation in surface potential that occurs in an MOS transistor when a voltage is applied to the gate. However, since the impurity concentration in the plate is usually relatively high, the variations in surface potential are small. The result of these surface potential variations is a slight variation in capacitance with applied voltage. Increasing the doping in the capacitor plates

First poly layer　SiO₂·　Second poly layer

Si-Substrate

(b)

**Figure 2.63** (b) Plan view and cross section of typical poly-poly capacitor.

reduces the voltage coefficient. For the impurity concentrations that are typically used in polysilicon layers, the voltage coefficient is usually less than 50 ppm/V, [26,27] a level small enough to be neglected in most applications.

A variation in the capacitance value also occurs with temperature variations. This variation stems primarily from the temperature variation of the surface potential in the plates previously described.[26] Also, secondary effects include the temperature variation of the dielectric constant and the expansion and contraction of the dielectric. For heavily doped polysilicon plates, this temperature variation is usually less than 50 ppm/°C.[26,27]

**MOS Transistors as Capacitors.** The MOS transistor itself can be used as a capacitor when biased in the triode region, the gate forming one plate and the source, drain, and channel forming another. Unfortunately, because the underlying substrate is lightly doped, a large amount of surface potential variation occurs with changes in applied voltage and the capacitor displays a high voltage coefficient. In noncritical applications, however, it can be used effectively under two conditions. The circuit must be designed in such a way that the device is biased in the triode region when a high capacitance value is desired, and the high sheet resistance of the bottom plate formed by the channel must be taken into account.

**Other Vertical Capacitor Structures.** In processes with only one layer of polysilicon, alternative structures must be used to implement capacitive elements. One approach involves the insertion of an extra mask to reduce the thickness of the oxide on top of the polysilicon layer so that when the interconnect metallization is applied, a thin-oxide layer exists between the metal layer and the polysilicon layer in selected areas. Such a capacitor has properties that are similar to poly-poly capacitors.

Another capacitor implementation in single-layer polysilicon processing involves the insertion of an extra masking and diffusion operation such that a diffused layer with low sheet resistance can be formed underneath the polysilicon layer in a thin-oxide area. This is not possible in conventional silicon-gate processes because the polysilicon layer is deposited before the source-drain implants or diffusions are performed. The properties of such capacitors are similar to the poly-poly structure, except that the bottom-plate parasitic capacitance is that of a $pn$ junction, which is voltage dependent and is usually larger than in the poly-poly case. Also, the bottom plate has a junction leakage current that is associated with it, which is important in some applications.

To avoid the need for extra processing steps, capacitors can also be constructed using the metal and poly layers with standard oxide thicknesses between layers. For example, in a process with one layer of polysilicon and two layers of metal, the top metal and the poly can be connected together to form one plate of a capacitor, and the bottom metal can be used to form the other plate. A key disadvantage of such structures, however, is that the capacitance per unit area is small because the oxide used to isolate one layer from another is thick. Therefore, such capacitors usually occupy large areas. Furthermore, the thickness of this oxide changes little as CMOS processes evolve with reduced minimum channel length. As a result, the area required by analog circuits using such capacitors undergoes a much smaller reduction than that of digital circuits in new technologies. This characteristic is important because reducing the area of an integrated circuit reduces its cost.

**Lateral Capacitor Structures.** To reduce the capacitor area, and to avoid the need for extra processing steps, lateral capacitors can be used.[28] A lateral capacitor can be formed in one layer of metal by separating one plate from another by spacing $s$, as shown in Fig. 2.64$a$. If $w$ is the width of the metal and $t$ is the metal thickness, the capacitance is $(wt\epsilon/s)$, where $\epsilon$ is the dielectric constant. As technologies evolve to reduced feature sizes, the

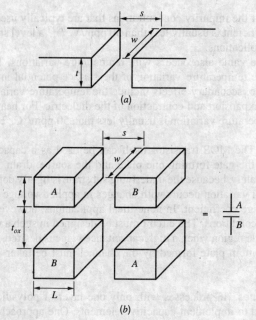

**Figure 2.64** (a) Lateral capacitor in one level of metal. (b) Capacitor using two levels of metal in which both lateral and vertical capacitance contribute to the desired capacitance.

minimum metal spacing shrinks but the thickness changes little; therefore, the die area required for a given lateral capacitance decreases in scaled technologies.[29] Note that the lateral capacitance is proportional to the perimeter of each plate that is adjacent to the other in a horizontal plane. Geometries to increase this perimeter in a given die area have been proposed.[29]

Lateral capacitors can be used in conjunction with vertical capacitors, as shown in Fig. 2.64b.[28] The key point here is that each metal layer is composed of multiple pieces, and each capacitor node is connected in an alternating manner to the pieces in each layer. As a result, the total capacitance includes vertical and lateral components arising between all adjacent pieces. If the vertical and lateral dielectric constants are equal, the total capacitance is increased compared to the case in which the same die area is used to construct only a vertical capacitor when the minimum spacing $s < \sqrt{2t(t_{ox})}$, where $t$ is the metal thickness and $t_{ox}$ is the oxide thickness between metal layers. This concept can be extended to additional pieces in each layer and additional layers.

### 2.10.3 Latchup in CMOS Technology

The device structures that are present in standard CMOS technology inherently comprise a *pnpn* sandwich of layers. For example, consider the typical circuit shown in Fig. 2.65a. It uses one *n*-channel and one *p*-channel transistor and operates as an inverter if the two gates are connected together as the inverter input. Figure 2.65b shows the cross section in an *n*-well process. When the two MOS transistors are fabricated, two parasitic bipolar transistors are also formed: a lateral *npn* and a vertical *pnp*. In this example, the source of the *n*-channel transistor forms the emitter of the parasitic lateral *npn* transistor, the substrate forms the base, and the *n*-well forms the collector. The source of the *p*-channel transistor forms the emitter of a parasitic vertical *pnp* transistor, the *n*-well forms the base, and the *p*-type substrate forms the collector. The electrical connection of these bipolar transistors that results from the layout shown is illustrated in Fig. 2.65c. In normal operation, all the *pn* junctions in the structure are reverse biased. If the two bipolar transistors enter the

**Figure 2.65** (*a*) Schematic of a typical CMOS device pair. (*b*) Cross section illustrating the parasitic bipolar transistors. (*c*) Schematic of the parasitic bipolar transistors.

active region for some reason, however, the circuit can display a large amount of positive feedback, causing both transistors to conduct heavily. This device structure is similar to that of a silicon-controlled rectifier (SCR), a widely used component in power-control applications. In power-control applications, the property of the *pnpn* sandwich to remain in the *on* state with no externally supplied signal is a great advantage. However, the result of this behavior here is usually a destructive breakdown phenomenon called *latchup*.

The positive feedback loop is labeled in Fig. 2.65*c*. Feedback is studied in detail in Chapters 8 and 9. To explain why the feedback around this loop is positive, assume that both transistors are active and that the base current of the *npn* transistor increases by $i$ for some reason. Then the collector current of the *npn* transistor increases by $\beta_{npn}i$. This current is pulled out of the base of the *pnp* transistor if $R_2$ is ignored. As a result, the current flowing out of the collector of the *pnp* transistor increases by $\beta_{npn}\beta_{pnp}i$. Finally, this current flows into the base of the *npn* transistor if $R_1$ is ignored. This analysis shows that the circuit generates a current that flows in the same direction as the initial disturbance; therefore, the feedback is positive. If the gain around the loop is more than unity, the response of the circuit to the initial disturbance continues to grow until one or both of the bipolar transistors saturate. In this case, a large current flows from the positive supply to ground until the power supply is turned off or the circuit burns out. This condition is called *latchup*. If $R_1$ and $R_2$ are large enough that base currents are large compared to the currents in these resistors, the gain around the loop is $\beta_{npn}\beta_{pnp}$. Therefore, latchup can occur if the product of the betas is greater than unity.

For latchup to occur, one of the junctions in the sandwich must become forward biased. In the configuration illustrated in Fig. 2.65, current must flow in one of the resistors between the emitter and the base of one of the two transistors in order for this to occur. This current can come from a variety of causes. Examples are an application of a voltage that is larger than the power-supply voltage to an input or output terminal, improper sequencing of the power supplies, the presence of large dc currents in the substrate or $p$- or $n$-well, or the flow of displacement current in the substrate or well due to fast-changing internal nodes. Latchup is more likely to occur in circuits as the substrate and well concentration is made lighter, as the well is made thinner, and as the device geometries are made smaller. All these trends in process technology tend to increase $R_1$ and $R_2$ in Fig. 2.65$b$. Also, they tend to increase the betas of the two bipolar transistors. These changes increase the likelihood of the occurrence of latchup.

The layout of CMOS-integrated circuits must be carried out with careful attention paid to the prevention of latchup. Although the exact rules followed depend on the specifics of the technology, the usual steps are to keep $R_1$ and $R_2$, as well as the product of the betas, small enough to avoid this problem. The beta of the vertical bipolar transistor is determined by process characteristics, such as the well depth, that are outside the control of circuit designers. However, the beta of the lateral bipolar transistor can be decreased by increasing its base width, which is the distance between the source of the $n$-channel transistor and the $n$-type well. To reduce $R_1$ and $R_2$, many substrate and well contacts are usually used instead of just one each, as shown in the simple example of Fig. 2.65. In particular, *guard rings* of substrate and well contacts are often used just outside and inside the well regions. These rings are formed by using the source/drain diffusion and provide low-resistance connections in the substrate and well to reduce series resistance. Also, special protection structures at each input and output pad are usually included so that excessive currents flowing into or out of the chip are safely shunted.

## 2.11 BiCMOS Technology

In Section 2.3, we showed that to achieve a high collector-base breakdown voltage in a bipolar transistor structure, a thick epitaxial layer is used (17 $\mu$m of 5 $\Omega$-cm material for 36-V operation). This in turn requires a deep $p$-type diffusion to isolate transistors and other devices. On the other hand, if a low breakdown voltage (say about 7 V to allow 5-V supply operation) can be tolerated, then a much more heavily doped (on the order of 0.5 $\Omega$-cm) collector region can be used that is also much thinner (on the order of 1 $\mu$m). Under these conditions, the bipolar devices can be isolated by using the same local-oxidation technique used for CMOS, as described in Section 2.4. This approach has the advantage of greatly reducing the bipolar transistor collector-substrate parasitic capacitance because the heavily doped high-capacitance regions near the surface are now replaced by low-capacitance oxide isolation. The devices can also be packed much more densely on the chip. In addition, CMOS and bipolar fabrication technologies begin to look rather similar, and the combination of high-speed, shallow, ion-implanted bipolar transistors with CMOS devices in a BiCMOS technology becomes feasible (at the expense of several extra processing steps).[30] This technology has performance advantages in digital applications because the high current-drive capability of the bipolar transistors greatly facilitates driving large capacitive loads. Such processes are also attractive for analog applications because they allow the designer to take advantage of the unique characteristics of both types of devices.

We now describe the structure of a typical high-frequency, low-voltage, oxide-isolated BiCMOS process. A simplified cross section of a high-performance process[31] is shown in Fig. 2.66. The process begins with masking steps and the implantation of $n$-type antimony buried layers into a $p$-type substrate wherever an $npn$ bipolar transistor or PMOS device is to be formed. A second implant of $p$-type boron impurities forms a $p$-well wherever an NMOS device is to be formed. This is followed by the growth of about 1 $\mu$m of $n^-$ epi,

**Figure 2.66** Cross section of a high-performance BiCMOS process.

which forms the collectors of the $npn$ bipolar devices and the channel regions of the PMOS devices. During this and subsequent heat cycles, the more mobile boron atoms out-diffuse and the $p$-well extends to the surface, whereas the antimony buried layers remain essentially fixed.

A masking step defines regions where thick field oxide is to be grown and these regions are etched down into the epi layer. Field-oxide growth is then carried out, followed by a planarization step where the field oxide that has grown above the plane of the surface is etched back level with the other regions. This eliminates the lumpy surface shown in Fig. 2.57 and helps to overcome problems of ensuring reliable metal connections over the oxide steps (so-called *step coverage*). Finally, a series of masking steps and $p$- and $n$-type implants are carried out to form bipolar base and emitter regions, low-resistance bipolar collector contact, and source and drain regions for the MOSFETs. In this sequence, gate oxide is grown, polysilicon gates and emitters are formed, and threshold-adjusting implants are made for the MOS devices. Metal contacts are then made to the desired regions, and the chip is coated with a layer of deposited $SiO_2$. A second layer of metal interconnects is formed on top of this oxide with connections where necessary to the first layer of metal below. A further deposited layer of $SiO_2$ is then added with a third layer of metal interconnect and vias to give even more connection flexibility and thus to improve the density of the layout.

## 2.12 Heterojunction Bipolar Transistors

A *heterojunction* is a $pn$ junction made of two different materials. Until this point, all the junctions we have considered have been *homojunctions* because the same material (silicon) has been used to form both the $n$-type and the $p$-type regions. In contrast, a junction between an $n$-type region of silicon and a $p$-type region of germanium or a compound of silicon and germanium forms a heterojunction.

In homojunction bipolar transistors, the emitter doping is selected to be much greater than the base doping to give an emitter injection efficiency $\gamma$ of about unity, as shown by (1.51b). As a result, the base is relatively lightly doped while the emitter is heavily doped in practice. Section 1.4.8 shows that the $f_T$ of bipolar devices is limited in part by $\tau_F$, which is the time required for minority carriers to cross the base. Maximizing $f_T$ is important in some applications such as radio-frequency electronics. To increase $f_T$, the base width can be reduced. If the base doping is fixed to maintain a constant $\gamma$, however, this approach increases the base resistance $r_b$. In turn, this base resistance limits speed because it forms a time constant with capacitance attached to the base node. As a result, a tradeoff exists in standard bipolar technology between high $f_T$ on the one hand and low $r_b$ on the other, and both extremes limit the speed that can be attained in practice.

One way to overcome this tradeoff is to add some germanium to the base of bipolar transistors to form heterojunction transistors. The key idea is that the different materials on the two sides of the junction have different band gaps. In particular, the band gap of silicon is greater than for germanium, and forming a SiGe compound in the base reduces the band gap there. The relatively large band gap in the emitter can be used to increase the potential barrier to holes that can be injected from the base back to the emitter. Therefore, this structure does not require that the emitter doping be much greater than the base doping to give $\gamma \simeq 1$. As a result, the emitter doping can be decreased and the base doping can be increased in a heterojunction bipolar transistor compared to its homojunction counterpart. Increasing the base doping allows $r_b$ to be constant even when the base width is reduced to increase $f_T$. Furthermore, this change also reduces the width of the base-collector depletion region in the base when the transistor operates in the forward active region, thus decreasing the effect of base-width modulation and increasing the early voltage $V_A$. Not only does increasing the base doping have a beneficial effect on performance, but also decreasing the emitter doping increases the width of the base-emitter, space-charge region in the emitter, reducing the $C_{je}$ capacitance and further increasing the maximum speed.

The base region of the heterojunction bipolar transistors can be formed by growing a thin epitaxial layer of SiGe using ultra-high vacuum chemical vapor deposition (UHV/CVD).[32] Since this is an epi layer, it takes on the crystal structure of the silicon in the substrate. Because the lattice constant for germanium is greater than that for silicon, the SiGe layer forms under a compressive strain, limiting the concentration of germanium and the thickness of the layer to avoid defect formation after subsequent high-temperature processing used at the back end of conventional technologies.[33] In practice, with a base thickness of 0.1 μm, the concentration of germanium is limited to about 15 percent so that the layer is unconditionally stable.[34] With only a small concentration of germanium, the change in the band gap and the resulting shift in the potential barrier that limits reverse injection of holes into the emitter is small. However, the reverse injection is an exponential function of this barrier; therefore, even a small change in the barrier greatly reduces the reverse injection and results in these benefits.

In practice, the concentration of germanium in the base need not be constant. In particular, the UHV/CVD process is capable of increasing the concentration of germanium in the base from the emitter end to the collector end. This grading of the germanium concentration results in an electric field that helps electrons move across the base, further reducing $\tau_F$ and increasing $f_T$.

The heterojunction bipolar transistors described above can be included as the bipolar transistors in otherwise conventional BiCMOS processes. The key point is that the device processing sequence retains the well-established properties of silicon integrated-circuit processing because the average concentration of germanium in the base is small.[33] This characteristic is important because it allows the new processing steps to be included as a simple addition to an existing process, reducing the cost of the new technology. For example, a BiCMOS process with a minimum drawn CMOS channel length of 0.3 μm and heterojunction bipolar transistors with a $f_T$ of 50 GHz has been reported.[34] The use of the heterojunction technology increases the $f_T$ by about a factor of two compared to a comparable homojunction technology.

## 2.13 Interconnect Delay

As the minimum feature size allowed in integrated-circuit technologies is reduced, the maximum operating speed and bandwidth have steadily increased. This trend stems partly from the reductions in the minimum base width of bipolar transistors and the minimum channel length of MOS transistors, which in turn increase the $f_T$ of these devices. While scaling has increased the speed of the transistors, however, it is also increasing the delay introduced by the interconnections to the point where it could soon limit the maximum speed of integrated circuits.[35] This delay is increasing as the minimum feature size is reduced because the width of metal lines and spacing between them are both being reduced to increase the allowed density of interconnections. Decreasing the width of the lines increases the number of squares for a fixed length, increasing the resistance. Decreasing the spacing between the lines increases the lateral capacitance between lines. The delay is proportional to the product of the resistance and capacitance. To reduce the delay, alternative materials are being studied for use in integrated circuits.

First, copper is replacing aluminum in metal layers because copper reduces the resistivity of the interconnection by about 40 percent and is less susceptible to electromigration and stress migration than aluminum. Electromigration and stress migration are processes in which the material of a conductor moves slightly while it conducts current and is under tension, respectively. These processes can cause open circuits to appear in metal interconnects and are important failure mechanisms in integrated circuits. Unfortunately, however, copper can not simply be substituted for aluminum with the same fabrication process. Two key problems are that copper diffuses through silicon and silicon dioxide more quickly than aluminum, and copper is difficult to plasma etch.[36] To overcome the diffusion problem, copper must be surrounded by a thin film of another metal that can endure high-temperature processing with little movement. To overcome the etch problem, a damascene process has been developed.[37] In this process, a layer of interconnection is formed by first depositing a layer of oxide. Then the interconnect pattern is etched into the oxide, and the wafer is uniformly coated by a thin diffusion-resistant layer and then copper. The wafer is then polished by a chemical-mechanical process until the surface of the oxide is reached, which leaves the copper in the cavities etched into the oxide. A key advantage of this process is that it results in a planar structure after each level of metalization.

Also, low-permittivity dielectrics are being studied to replace silicon dioxide to reduce the interconnect capacitance. The dielectric constant of silicon dioxide is 3.9 times more than for air. For relative dielectric constants between about 2.5 and 3.0, polymers have been studied. For relative dielectric constants below about 2.0, the proposed materials include foams and gels, which include air.[36] Other important requirements of low-permittivity dielectric materials include low leakage, high breakdown voltage, high thermal conductivity, stability under high-temperature processing, and adhesion to the metal layers.[35] The search for a replacement for silicon dioxide is difficult because it is an excellent dielectric in all these ways.

## 2.14 Economics of Integrated-Circuit Fabrication

The principal reason for the growing pervasiveness of integrated circuits in systems of all types is the reduction in cost attainable through integrated-circuit fabrication. Proper utilization of the technology to achieve this cost reduction requires an understanding of the factors influencing the cost of an integrated circuit in completed, packaged form. In this section, we consider these factors.

### 2.14.1 Yield Considerations in Integrated-Circuit Fabrication

As pointed out earlier in this chapter, integrated circuits are batch-fabricated on single wafers, each containing up to several thousand separate but identical circuits. At the end of the processing sequence, the individual circuits on the wafer are probed and tested prior to the breaking up of the wafer into individual dice. The percentage of the circuits that are electrically functional and within specifications at this point is termed the wafer-sort yield $Y_{ws}$ and is usually in the range of 10 percent to 90 percent. The nonfunctional units can result from a number of factors, but one major source of yield loss is point defects of various kinds that occur during the photoresist and diffusion operations. These defects can result from mask defects, pinholes in the photoresist, airborne particles that fall on the surface of the wafer, crystalline defects in the epitaxial layer, and so on. If such a defect occurs in the active region on one of the transistors or resistors making up the circuit, a nonfunctional unit usually results. The frequency of occurrence per unit of wafer area of such defects

$$Y_{ws} = 0$$

$$Y_{ws} = \frac{10}{16} = 62\%$$

**Figure 2.67** Conceptual example of the effect of die size on yield.

is usually dependent primarily on the particular fabrication process used and not on the particular circuit being fabricated. Generally speaking, the more mask steps and diffusion operations that the wafer is subjected to, the higher will be the density of defects on the surface of the finished wafer.

The existence of these defects limits the size of the circuit that can be economically fabricated on a single die. Consider the two cases illustrated in Fig. 2.67, where two identical wafers with the same defect locations have been used to fabricate circuits of different area. Although the defect locations in both cases are the same, the wafer-sort yield of the large die would be zero. When the die size is cut to one-fourth of the original size, the wafer sort yield is 62 percent. This conceptual example illustrates the effect of die size on wafer-sort yield. Quantitatively, the expected yield for a given die size is a strong function of the complexity of the process, the nature of the individual steps in the process, and perhaps, most importantly, the maturity and degree of development of the process as a whole and the individual steps within it. Since the inception of the planar process, a steady reduction in defect densities has occurred as a result of improved lithography, increased use of low-temperature processing steps such as ion implantation, improved manufacturing environmental control, and so forth. Three typical curves derived from yield data on bipolar and MOS processes are shown in Fig. 2.68. These are representative of yields for processes ranging from a very complex process with many yield-reducing steps to a very simple process

**Figure 2.68** Typically observed yield versus die size for the three different processes, ranging from a very simple, well-developed process (curve A), to a very complex process with many yield-reducing steps (curve C).

carried out in an advanced VLSI fabrication facility. Also, the yield curves can be raised or lowered by more conservative design rules, and other factors. Uncontrolled factors such as testing problems and design problems in the circuit can cause results for a particular integrated circuit to deviate widely from these curves, but still the overall trend is useful.

In addition to affecting yield, the die size also affects the total number of dice that can be fabricated on a wafer of a given size. The total number of usable dice on the wafer, called the

**Figure 2.69** Gross die per wafer for 4-in., 8-in., and 12-in. wafers.

**Figure 2.70** Net good die per wafer for the three processes in Fig. 2.66, assuming a 4-in. wafer. The same curve can be obtained approximately for other wafer sizes by simply scaling the vertical axis by a factor equal to the wafer area.

gross die per wafer $N$, is plotted in Fig. 2.69 as a function of die size for several wafer sizes. The product of the gross die per wafer and the wafer-sort yield gives the net good die per wafer, plotted in Fig. 2.70 for the yield curve of Fig. 2.68, assuming a 4-in wafer.

Once the wafer has undergone the wafer-probe test, it is separated into individual dice by sawing or scribing and breaking. The dice are visually inspected, sorted, and readied for assembly into packages. This step is termed *die fab,* and some loss of good dice occurs in the process. Of the original electrically good dice on the wafer, some will be lost in the die fab process due to breakage and scratching of the surface. The ratio of the electrically good dice following die fab to the number of electrically good dice on the wafer before die fab is called the *die fab yield,* $Y_{df}$. The good dice are then inserted in a package, and the electrical connections to each die are made with bonding wires to the pins on the package. The packaged circuits then undergo a final test, and some loss of functional units usually occurs because of improper bonding and handling losses. The ratio of the number of good units at final test to the number of good dice into assembly is called the *final test yield* $Y_{ft}$.

## 2.14.2 Cost Considerations in Integrated-Circuit Fabrication

The principal direct costs to the manufacturer can be divided into two categories: those associated with fabricating and testing the wafer, called the *wafer fab cost* $C_w$, and those associated with packaging and final testing the individual dice, called the *packaging cost* $C_p$. If we consider the costs incurred by the complete fabrication of one wafer of dice, we first have the wafer cost itself $C_w$. The number of electrically good dice that are packaged from the wafer is $N Y_{ws} Y_{df}$. The total cost $C_t$ incurred once these units have been packaged and tested is

$$C_t = C_w + C_p N Y_{ws} Y_{df} \tag{2.54}$$

The total number of good finished units $N_g$ is

$$N_g = N Y_{ws} Y_{df} Y_{ft} \tag{2.55}$$

Thus the cost per unit is

$$C = \frac{C_t}{N_g} = \frac{C_w}{N Y_{ws} Y_{df} Y_{ft}} + \frac{C_p}{Y_{ft}} \tag{2.56}$$

The first term in the cost expression is wafer fab cost, while the second is associated with assembly and final testing. This expression can be used to calculate the direct cost of the finished product to the manufacturer as shown in the following example.

■ **EXAMPLE**

Plot the direct fabrication cost as a function of die size for the following two sets of assumptions.

(a) Wafer-fab cost of $75.00, packaging and testing costs per die of $0.06, a die-fab yield of 0.9, and a final-test yield of 0.9. Assume yield curve $B$ in Fig. 2.68. This set of conditions might characterize an operational amplifier manufactured on a medium-complexity bipolar process and packaged in an inexpensive 8 or 14 lead package.

From (2.56),

$$C = \frac{\$75.00}{(N Y_{ws})(0.81)} + \frac{0.06}{0.9} = \frac{\$92.59}{N Y_{ws}} + 0.066 \tag{2.57}$$

This cost is plotted versus die size in Fig. 2.71$a$.

(b) A wafer-fab cost of $100.00, packaging and testing costs of $1.00, die-fab yield of

4-inch wafer yield curve B

Package cost limited  → Die cost limited

Figure 2.71 (a) Cost curve for example a.

0.9, and final-test yield of 0.8. Assume yield curve A in Fig. 2.68. This might character-ize a complex analog/digital integrated circuit, utilizing an advanced CMOS process and packaged in a large, multilead package. Again, from (2.56),

$$C = \frac{\$100.00}{(NY_{ws})(0.72)} + \frac{\$1.00}{0.8} = \frac{\$138.89}{NY_{ws}} + \$1.25 \qquad (2.58)$$

■ This cost is plotted versus die size in Fig. 2.71b.

This example shows that most of the cost comes from packaging and testing for small die sizes, whereas most of the cost comes from wafer-fab costs for large die sizes. This relationship is made clearer by considering the cost of the integrated circuit in terms of cost per unit area of silicon in the finished product, as illustrated in Fig. 2.72 for the examples previously given. These curves plot of the ratio of the finished-product cost to the number of square mils of silicon on the die. The minimum cost per unit area of silicon results

4-inch wafer yield curve A

Package cost limited

Die cost limited

Figure 2.71 (b) Cost curve for example b.

**Figure 2.72** Cost of finished product in terms of cost per unit of silicon area for the two examples. Because the package and testing costs are lower in example *a*, the minimum cost point falls at a much smaller die size. The cost per unit of silicon area at large die sizes is smaller for example *b* because process *A* gives higher yield at large die sizes.

midway between the package-cost and die-cost limited regions for each example. Thus the fabrication of excessively large or small dice is uneconomical in terms of utilizing the silicon die area at minimum cost. The significance of these curves is that, for example, if a complex analog/digital system, characterized by example *b* in Fig. 2.72 with a total silicon area of 80,000 square mils is to be fabricated in silicon, it probably would be most economical to build the system on two chips rather than on a single chip. This decision would also be strongly affected by other factors such as the increase in the number of total package pins required for the two chips to be interconnected, the effect on performance of the required interconnections, and the additional printed circuit board space required for additional packages. The shape of the cost curves is also a strong function of the package cost, test cost of the individual product, yield curve for the particular process, and so forth.

The preceding analysis concerned only the direct costs to the manufacturer of the fabrication of the finished product; the actual selling price is much higher and reflects additional research and development, engineering, and selling costs. Many of these costs are fixed, however, so that the selling price of a particular integrated circuit tends to vary inversely with the quantity of the circuits sold by the manufacturer.

## 2.15 Packaging Considerations for Integrated Circuits

The finished cost of an integrated circuit is heavily dependent on the cost of the package in which it is encapsulated. In addition to the cost, the package also strongly affects two other important parameters. The first is the maximum allowable power dissipation in the circuit, and the second is the reliability of the circuit. We will consider these limitations individually.

### 2.15.1 Maximum Power Dissipation

When power is dissipated within a device on the surface of the integrated circuit die, two distinct changes occur. First, the dissipated heat must flow away from the individual

**Figure 2.73**  Electrical analog for the thermal behavior of the die-package structure.

device through the silicon material, which gives rise to temperature gradients across the top surface of the chip. These gradients can strongly affect circuit performance, and their effects are studied further in Chapter 6. Second, the heat must then flow out of the silicon material into the package structure, and then out of the package and to the ambient atmosphere. The flow of heat from the package to the ambient atmosphere can occur primarily by radiation and convection or, if the package is attached to a heat sink, can occur primarily by conduction. This flow of heat to the ambient environment causes the die as a whole to experience an increase in temperature, and in the steady state the average die temperature will be higher than the ambient temperature by an amount proportional to the power dissipation on the chip and the *thermal resistance* of the package.

The steady-state thermal behavior of the die/package structure can be analyzed approximately using the electrical model shown in Fig. 2.73. In this model, current is analogous to a flow of heat, and voltage is analogous to temperature. The current source represents the power dissipation on the integrated circuit die. The voltage drop across the resistance $\theta_{jc}$ represents the temperature drop between the surface of the chip and the outside of the case of the package. Finally, the drop across the resistor $\theta_{ca}$ represents the temperature drop between the outside of the case and the ambient atmosphere. This representation is only approximate since in reality the structure is distributed and neither the top surface of the die nor the outside of the case is isothermal. However, this equivalent circuit is useful for approximate analysis.

The resistance $\theta_{jc}$ is termed the *junction-to-case thermal resistance* of the package. This resistance varies from about 30°C/W for the TO-99 metal package to about 4°C/W for the TO-3 metal power package. These packages are shown in Fig. 2.74 along with the plastic dual-in-line package (DIP). The resistance $\theta_{ca}$ is termed the *case-to-ambient thermal resistance*. For the situation in which no heat sink is used, this resistance is determined primarily by the rate at which heat can be transferred from the outside surface of the package to the surrounding air. This rate is dependent on package size and on the rate of airflow around the package, if any. Because thermal radiation effects are present, the rate of heat transfer is not a linear function of case temperature, but the approximation is usually made that this thermal resistance is linear. For the case in which the surrounding air is still and no heat sink is used, the resistance $\theta_{ca}$ varies from about 100°C/W for the TO-99 to about 40°C/W for the TO-3.

For integrated circuits that dissipate large amounts of power, the use of a heat sink is often necessary to prevent excessive die temperatures. For this situation, the case-to-ambient thermal resistance is determined by the heat sink. Heat sinks for use with integrated circuit packages vary from small finned structures having a thermal resistance of about 30°C/W to massive structures achieving thermal resistances in the range of 2°C/W. Effective utilization of low-thermal-resistance heat sinks requires that the package and

**Figure 2.74** TO-99, TO-3, dual-in-line (DIP) integrated-circuit packages. Dimensions are in inches. The TO-3 is used as shown for three-terminal ICs such as voltage regulators, and in versions with up to 10 leads when required. The basic TO-99 package shape is available in 3, 4, 6, 8, 10, and 12 lead versions. The DIP package is available in 8, 14, 16, 18, and 22 lead versions. It is available in both hermetically sealed ceramic and plastic versions.

heat sink be in intimate thermal contact with each other. For TO-3 packages, special mica washers and heat-sink grease are used to attach the package to the heat sink while maintaining electrical isolation.

The choice of package and heat sink for a particular circuit is dependent on the power to be dissipated in the circuit, the range of ambient temperatures to be encountered, and the maximum allowable chip temperature. These three quantities are related under steady-state conditions by the following expression:

$$T_{chip} = T_{ambient} + (\theta_{jc} + \theta_{ca}) P_d \qquad (2.59)$$

where $T_{ambient}$ is the ambient temperature, $T_{chip}$ is the chip temperature, and $P_d$ is the power dissipation on the chip. For silicon integrated circuits, reliability considerations dictate that the chip temperature be kept below about 150°C, and this temperature is normally taken as the maximum allowable chip temperature. Thus once the maximum ambient temperature is known, the temperature drop across the series combination of $\theta_{jc}$ and $\theta_{ca}$ is specified. Once the power dissipation is known, the maximum allowable thermal resistance of the package and heat sink can be calculated.

■ **EXAMPLE**

What is the maximum permissible power dissipation in a circuit in a TO-99 package in still air when the ambient temperature is 70°C? 125°C?

For the TO-99 in still air, $(\theta_{jc} + \theta_{ca}) = 30°C/W + 100°C/W = 130°C/W$.

From (2.59),

$$T_{chip} = T_{ambient} + (130°C/W)(P_d)$$

For $T_{ambient} = 70°C$,

$$150°C = 70°C + (130°C/Watt) P_{dmax}$$

and thus

$$P_{dmax} = 620 \text{ mW}$$

For $T_{ambient} = 125°C$,

$$150°C = 125°C + (130°C/W) P_{dmax}$$

and thus

$$P_{dmax} = 190 \text{ mW}$$

■

## 2.15.2 Reliability Considerations in Integrated-Circuit Packaging

In applications where field servicing is difficult or impossible, or where device failure has catastrophic consequences, circuit reliability becomes a primary concern. The primary parameter describing circuit reliability is the mean time to failure of a sample of integrated circuits under a specified set of worst-case environmental conditions. The study of the various failure modes that can occur in integrated circuits under such conditions and the means to avoid such failures have evolved into a separate discipline, which is beyond the scope of this book. However, integrated circuit packages can be divided into two distinct groups from a reliability standpoint: those in which the die is in a hermetically sealed cavity and those in which the cavity is not hermetically sealed. The former group includes most of the metal can packages and the ceramic dual-in-line and flat packages. The latter group includes the plastic packages. The plastic packages are less expensive to produce and are as reliable as the hermetic packages under mild environmental conditions. The hermetic packages are generally more expensive to produce, but are more reliable under adverse environmental conditions, particularly in the case of high temperature/high humidity conditions.

## APPENDIX

## A.2.1 SPICE MODEL-PARAMETER FILES

In this section, SPICE model-parameter symbols are compared with the symbols employed in the text for commonly used quantities.

### Bipolar Transistor Parameters

| SPICE Symbol | Text Symbol | Description |
|---|---|---|
| IS | $I_S$ | Transport saturation current |
| BF | $\beta_F$ | Maximum forward current gain |
| BR | $\beta_R$ | Maximum reverse current gain |
| VAF | $V_A$ | Forward Early voltage |
| RB | $r_b$ | Base series resistance |
| RE | $r_{ex}$ | Emitter series resistance |
| RC | $r_c$ | Collector series resistance |
| TF | $\tau_F$ | Forward transit time |
| TR | $\tau_R$ | Reverse transit time |
| CJE | $C_{je0}$ | Zero-bias base-emitter depletion capacitance |
| VJE | $\psi_{0e}$ | Base-emitter junction built-in potential |
| MJE | $n_e$ | Base-emitter junction-capacitance exponent |
| CJC | $C_{\mu 0}$ | Zero-bias base-collector depletion capacitance |
| VJC | $\psi_{0c}$ | Base-collector junction built-in potential |
| MJC | $n_c$ | Base-collector junction-capacitance exponent |
| CJS | $C_{CS0}$ | Zero-bias collector-substrate depletion capacitance |
| VJS | $\psi_{0s}$ | Collector-substrate junction built-in potential |
| MJS | $n_s$ | Collector-substrate junction-capacitance exponent |

*Note:* Depending on which version of SPICE is used, a separate diode may have to be included to model base-substrate capacitance in a lateral *pnp* transistor.

### MOSFET Parameters

| SPICE Symbol | Text Symbol | Description |
|---|---|---|
| VTO | $V_t$ | Threshold voltage with zero source-substrate voltage |
| KP | $k' = \mu C_{ox}$ | Transconductance parameter |
| GAMMA | $\gamma = \dfrac{\sqrt{2q\epsilon N_A}}{C_{ox}}$ | Threshold voltage parameter |
| PHI | $2\phi_f$ | Surface potential |
| LAMBDA | $\lambda = \dfrac{1}{L_{\text{eff}}}\dfrac{dX_d}{dV_{DS}}$ | Channel-length modulation parameter |
| CGSO | $C_{ol}$ | Gate-source overlap capacitance per unit channel width |
| CGDO | $C_{ol}$ | Gate-drain overlap capacitance per unit channel width |

**MOSFET Parameters**

| SPICE Symbol | Text Symbol | Description |
|---|---|---|
| CJ | $C_{j0}$ | Zero-bias junction capacitance per unit area from source and drain bottom to bulk (substrate) |
| MJ | $n$ | Source-bulk and drain-bulk junction capacitance exponent (grading coefficient) |
| CJSW | $C_{jsw0}$ | Zero-bias junction capacitance per unit junction perimeter from source and drain sidewall (periphery) to bulk |
| MJSW | $n$ | Source-bulk and drain-bulk sidewall junction capacitance exponent |
| PB | $\psi_0$ | Source-bulk and drain-bulk junction built-in potential |
| TOX | $t_{ox}$ | Oxide thickness |
| NSUB | $N_A, N_D$ | Substrate doping |
| NSS | $Q_{SS}/q$ | Surface-state density |
| XJ | $X_j$ | Source, drain junction depth |
| LD | $L_d$ | Source, drain lateral diffusion |

## PROBLEMS

**2.1** What impurity concentration corresponds to a 1 Ω-cm resistivity in $p$-type silicon? In $n$-type silicon?

**2.2** What is the sheet resistance of a layer of 1 Ω-cm material that is 5 μm thick?

**2.3** Consider a hypothetical layer of silicon that has an $n$-type impurity concentration of $10^{17}$ cm$^{-3}$ at the top surface, and in which the impurity concentration decreases exponentially with distance into the silicon. Assume that the concentration has decreased to $1/e$ of its surface value at a depth of 0.5 μm, and that the impurity concentration in the sample before the insertion of the $n$-type impurities was $10^{15}$ cm$^{-3}$ $p$-type. Determine the depth below the surface of the $pn$ junction that results and determine the sheet resistance of the $n$-type layer. Assume a constant electron mobility of 800 cm$^2$/V-s. Assume that the width of the depletion layer is negligible.

**2.4** A diffused resistor has a length of 200 μm and a width of 5 μm. The sheet resistance of the base diffusion is 100 Ω/□ and the emitter diffusion is 5 Ω/□. The base pinched layer has a sheet resistance of 5 kΩ/□. Determine the resistance of the resistor if it is an emitter-diffused, base-diffused, or pinch resistor.

**2.5** A base-emitter voltage of from 520 mV to 580 mV is measured on a test $npn$ transistor

structure with 10 μA collector current. The emitter dimensions on the test transistor are 100 μm × 100 μm. Determine the range of values of $Q_B$ implied by this data. Use this information to calculate the range of values of sheet resistance that will be observed in the pinch resistors in the circuit. Assume a constant electron diffusivity, $\bar{D}_n$, of 13 cm$^2$/s, and a constant hole mobility of 150 cm$^2$/V-s. Assume that the width of the depletion layer is negligible.

**2.6** Estimate the series base resistance, series collector resistance $r_c$, base-emitter capacitance, base-collector capacitance, and collector-substrate capacitance of the high-current $npn$ transistor structure shown in Fig. 2.75. This structure is typical of those used as the output transistor in operational amplifiers that must supply up to about 20 mA. Assume a doping profile as shown in Fig. 2.17.

**2.7** If the lateral $pnp$ structure of Fig. 2.33$a$ is fabricated with an epi layer resistivity of 0.5 Ω-cm, determine the value of collector current at which the current gain begins to fall off. Assume a diffusivity for holes of: $\bar{D}_p = 10$ cm$^2$/s. Assume a base width of 8 μm.

**2.8** The substrate $pnp$ of Fig. 2.36$a$ is to be used as a test device to monitor epitaxial layer thickness. Assume that the flow of minority carriers across the base is vertical, and that the width of the emitter-base and collector-base depletion layers is

Distance,
μm

∇ ⇒ Buried layer          ≡ ⇒ Emitter
− ⇒ Isolation             /// ⇒ Contact opening
= ⇒ Base                  — · — ⇒ Metal

**Figure 2.75** Device structure for Problem 2.6.

negligible. Assume that the epi layer resistivity is known to be 2 Ω-cm by independent measurement. The base-emitter voltage is observed to vary from 525 mV to 560 mV over several wafers at a collector current of 10 μA. What range of epitaxial layer thickness does this imply? What is the corresponding range of sheet resistance that will be observed in the epitaxial pinch resistors? Assume a hole diffusivity of 10 cm²/s, and an electron mobility of 800 cm²/V-s. Neglect the depletion layer thickness. Assume a junction depth of 3 μm for the base diffusion.

**2.9** Calculate the total parasitic junction capacitance associated with a 10-kΩ base-diffused resistor if the base sheet resistance is 100 Ω/□ and the resistor width is 6 μm. Repeat for a resistor width of 12 μm. Assume the doping profiles are as shown in Fig. 2.17. Assume the clubheads are 26 μm × 26 μm, and that the junction depth is 3 μm. Account for sidewall effects.

**2.10** For the substrate $pnp$ structure shown in Fig. 2.36a, calculate $I_S$, $C_{je}$, $C_\mu$, and $\tau_F$. Assume the doping profiles are as shown in Fig. 2.17.

**2.11** A base-emitter voltage of 480 mV is measured on a super-$\beta$ test transistor with a

100 μm × 100 μm emitter area at a collector current of 10 μA. Calculate the $Q_B$ and the sheet resistance of the base region. Estimate the punch-through voltage in the following way. When the base depletion region includes the entire base, charge neutrality requires that the number of ionized acceptors in the depletion region in the base be equal to the number of ionized donors in the depletion region on the collector side of the base. [See (1.2).] Therefore, when enough voltage is applied that the depletion region in the base region includes the whole base, the depletion region in the collector must include a number of ionized atoms equal to $Q_B$. Since the density of these atoms is known (equal to $N_D$), the width of the depletion layer in the collector region at punch-through can be determined. If we assume that the doping in the base $N_A$ is much larger than that in the collector $N_D$, then (1.15) can be used to find the voltage that will result in this depletion layer width. Repeat this problem for the standard device, assuming a $V_{BE}$ measured at 560 mV. Assume an electron diffusivity $\bar{D}_n$ of 13 cm²/s, and a hole mobility $\bar{\mu}_p$ of 150 cm²/V-s. Assume the epi doping is $10^{15}$ cm$^{-3}$. Use $\epsilon = 1.04 \times 10^{-12}$ F/cm for the permittivity of silicon. Also, assume $\psi_o$ for the collector-base junction is 0.55 V.

**2.12** An MOS transistor biased in the active region displays a drain current of 100 $\mu$A at a $V_{GS}$ of 1.5 V and a drain current of 10 $\mu$A at a $V_{GS}$ of 0.8 V. Determine the threshold voltage and $\mu_n C_{ox}$(W/L). Neglect subthreshold conduction and assume that the mobility is constant.

**2.13** Calculate the threshold voltage of the p-channel transistors for the process given in Table 2.1. First do the calculation for the unimplanted transistor, then for the case in which the device receives the channel implant specified. Note that this is a p-type implant, so that the effective surface concentration is the difference between the background substrate concentration and the effective concentration in the implant layer.

**2.14** An n-channel implanted transistor from the process described in Table 2.1 displays a measured output resistance of 5 M$\Omega$ at a drain current of 10 $\mu$A, biased in the active region at a $V_{DS}$ of 5 V. The drawn dimensions of the device are 100 $\mu$m by 7 $\mu$m. Find the output resistance of a second device on the same technology that has drawn dimensions of 50 $\mu$m by 12 $\mu$m and is operated at a drain current of 30 $\mu$A and a $V_{DS}$ of 5 V.

**2.15** Calculate the small-signal model parameters of the device shown in Fig. 2.76, including $g_m$, $g_{mb}, r_o, C_{gs}, C_{gd}, C_{sb}$, and $C_{db}$. Assume the transistor is biased at a drain-source voltage of 2 V and a drain current of 20 $\mu$A. Use the process parameters that are specified in Table 2.4. Assume $V_{SB} = 1$ V.

**2.16** The transistor shown in Fig. 2.76 is connected in the circuit shown in Fig. 2.77. The gate is grounded, the substrate is connected to $-1.5$ V, and the drain is open circuited. An ideal current source is tied to the source, and this source has a value of zero for $t < 0$ and 10 $\mu$A for $t > 0$. The source and drain are at an initial voltage of +1.5 V at $t = 0$. Sketch the voltage at the source and drain from $t = 0$ until the drain voltage reaches $-1.5$ V. For simplicity, assume that the source-substrate and drain-substrate capacitances are constant at their zero-bias values. Assume the transistor has a threshold voltage of 0.6 V.

**Figure 2.76** Transistor for Problem 2.15.

**Figure 2.77** Circuit for Problem 2.16.

**2.17** Show that two MOS transistors connected in parallel with channel widths of $W_1$ and $W_2$ and identical channel lengths of $L$ can be modeled as one equivalent MOS transistor whose width is $W_1 + W_2$ and whose length is $L$, as shown in Fig. 2.78. Assume the transistors are identical except for their channel widths.

**2.18** Show that two MOS transistors connected in series with channel lengths of $L_1$ and $L_2$ and

**Figure 2.78** Circuit for Problem 2.17

identical channel widths of $W$ can be modeled as one equivalent MOS transistor whose width is $W$ and whose length is $L_1 + L_2$, as shown in Fig. 2.79. Assume the transistors are identical except for their channel lengths. Ignore the body effect and channel-length modulation.

**Figure 2.79** Circuit for Problem 2.18.

**2.19** An integrated electronic subsystem is to be fabricated, which requires 40,000 square mils of silicon area. Determine whether the system should be put on one or two chips, assuming that the fabrication cost of the two chips is the only consideration.Assume that the wafer-fab cost is $100.00, the packaging and testing costs are $0.60, the die-fab yield is 0.9, and the final-test yield is 0.8. Assume the process used follows curve $B$ in Fig. 2.68. Repeat the problem assuming yield curve $A$, and then yield curve $C$. Assume a 4-in wafer.

**2.20** Determine the direct fabrication cost of an integrated circuit that is 150 mils on a side in size.

Assume a wafer-fab cost of $130.00, a package and testing cost of $0.40, a die-fab yield of 0.8, and a final-test yield of 0.8. Work the problem for yield curves $A$, $B$, and $C$ in Fig. 2.68. Assume a 4-in wafer.

**2.21 (a)** A frequently used empirical approximation for the yield of an IC process as a function of die size is

$$Y_{ws} = \exp(-A/A_0)$$

where $A$ is the die area and $A_0$ is a constant. Using Fig. 2.68, determine approximate values of $A_0$ for each of the three processes shown. Use the point on the curve at which the yield is $e^{-1}$ to determine $A_0$. Plot the yield predicted by this expression and compare with the curves shown in Fig. 2.68.

**(b)** Use the expression derived in (a), together with the gross-die-per-wafer curves shown in Fig. 2.69, to develop an analytical expression for the cost of silicon per unit area as a function of die size, $Y_{df}$, $Y_{ft}$, $C_p$, and $C_w$ for each of the three processes $A$, $B$, and $C$.

**2.22** A TO-99 package is used with a heat sink, providing a thermal resistance from case to ambient of 20°C/W. The junction-to-case thermal resistance of the TO-99 is 30°C/W. Plot the maximum allowable power dissipation in this package as a function of ambient temperature, assuming a maximum die temperature of 150°C.

# REFERENCES

1. A. S. Grove. *Physics and Technology of Semiconductor Devices.* Wiley, New York, 1967.

2. R. S. Muller and T. I. Kamins. *Device Electronics for Integrated Circuits.* Wiley, New York, 1986.

3. E. M. Conwell. "Properties of Silicon and Germanium," *Proc. IRE,* Vol. 46, pp 1281–1300, June 1958.

4. J. C. Irvin. "Resistivity of Bulk Silicon and of Diffused Layers in Silicon," *Bell System Tech. Journal,* Vol. 41, pp. 387–410, March 1962.

5. R. W. Russell and D. D. Culmer. "Ion-Implanted JFET-Bipolar Monolithic Analog Circuits," *Digest of Technical Papers, 1974 International Solid-State Circuits Conference,* Philadelphia, PA, pp. 140–141, February 1974.

6. D. J. Hamilton and W. G. Howard. *Basic Integrated Circuit Engineering.* McGraw-Hill, New York, 1975.

7. Y. Tamaki, T. Shiba, I. Ogiwara, T. Kure, K. Ohyu, and T. Nakamura. "Advanced Device Process Technology for 0.3 μm Self-Aligned Bipolar LSI," *Proceedings of the IEEE Bipolar Circuits and Technology Meeting,* pp. 166–168, September 1990.

8. M. Kurisu, Y. Sasyama, M. Ohuchi, A. Sawairi, M. Sigiyama, H. Takemura, and T. Tashiro. "A Si Bipolar 21 GHz Static Frequency Divider," *Digest of Technical Papers, 1991 International Solid-State Circuits Conference,* pp. 158–159, February 1991.

9. R. M. Burger and R. P. Donovan. *Fundamentals of Silicon Integrated Device Technology.* Vol. 2, pp. 134–136. Prentice-Hall, Englewood Cliffs, NJ, 1968.

10. R. J. Whittier and D. A. Tremere. "Current Gain and Cutoff Frequency Falloff at High

Currents," *IEEE Transactions Electron Devices,* Vol. ED-16, pp. 39–57, January 1969.

11. H. R. Camenzind. *Electronic Integrated Systems Design.* Van Nostrand Reinhold, New York, 1972. Copyright © 1972 Litton Educational Publishing, Inc. Reprinted by permission of Van Nostrand Reinhold Company.

12. H. J. DeMan. "The Influence of Heavy Doping on the Emitter Efficiency of a Bipolar Transistor," *IEEE Transactions on Electron Devices,* Vol. ED-18, pp. 833–835, October 1971.

13. H. C. Lin. *Integrated Electronics.* Holden-Day, San Francisco, 1967.

14. N. M. Nguyen and R. G. Meyer. "Si IC-Compatible Inductors and *LC* Passive Filters," *IEEE Journal of Solid-State Circuits,* Vol. 25, pp. 1028–1031, August 1990.

15. J. Y.-C. Chang, A. A. Abidi, and M. Gaitan. "Large Suspended Inductors on Silicon and Their Use in a 2 μm CMOS RF Amplifier," *IEEE Electron Device Letters,* Vol. 14, pp. 246–248, May 1993.

16. K. Negus, B. Koupal, J. Wholey, K. Carter, D. Millicker, C. Snapp, and N. Marion. "Highly Integrated Transmitter RFIC with Monolithic Narrowband Tuning for Digital Cellular Handsets," *Digest of Technical Papers, 1994 International Solid-State Circuits Conference,* San Francisco, CA, pp. 38–39, February 1994.

17. P. R. Gray and R. G. Meyer. *Analysis and Design of Analog Integrated Circuits,* Third Edition, Wiley, New York, 1993.

18. R. J. Widlar. "Design Techniques for Monolithic Operational Amplifiers," *IEEE Journal of Solid-State Circuits,* Vol. SC-4, pp. 184–191, August 1969.

19. K. R. Stafford, P. R. Gray, and R. A. Blanchard. "A Complete Monolithic Sample/Hold Amplifier," *IEEE Journal of Solid-State Circuits,* Vol. SC-9, pp. 381–387, December 1974.

20. P. C. Davis, S. F. Moyer, and V. R. Saari. "High Slew Rate Monolithic Operational Amplifier Using Compatible Complementary *pnp*'s," *IEEE Journal of Solid-State Circuits,* Vol. SC-9, pp. 340–346, December 1974.

21. A. P. Chandrakasan, S. Sheng, and R. W. Brodersen. "Low-Power CMOS Digital Design," *IEEE Journal of Solid-State Circuits,* Vol. 27, pp. 473–484, April 1992.

22. E. A. Vittoz. "MOS Transistors Operated in the Lateral Bipolar Mode and Their Application in CMOS Technology," *IEEE Journal of Solid-State Circuits,* Vol. SC-18, pp. 273–279, June 1983.

23. W. T. Holman and J. A. Connelly. "A Compact Low-Noise Operational Amplifier for a 1.2 μm Digital CMOS Technology," *IEEE Journal of Solid-State Circuits,* Vol. 30, pp. 710–714, June 1995.

24. C. A. Laber, C. F. Rahim, S. F. Dreyer, G. T. Uehara, P. T. Kwok, and P. R. Gray. "Design Considerations for a High-Performance 3-μm CMOS Analog Standard-Cell Library," *IEEE Journal of Solid-State Circuits,* Vol. SC-22, pp. 181–189, April 1987.

25. B. L. Crowder and S. Zirinsky. "1 μm MOSFET VLSI Technology: Part VII—Metal Silicide Interconnection Technology—A Future Perspective," *IEEE Journal of Solid-State Circuits,* Vol. SC-14, pp. 291–293, April 1979.

26. J. L. McCreary. "Matching Properties, and Voltage and Temperature Dependence of MOS Capacitors," *IEEE Journal of Solid-State Circuits,* Vol. SC-16, pp. 608–616, December 1981.

27. D. J. Allstot and W. C. Black, Jr. "Technological Design Considerations for Monolithic MOS Switched-Capacitor Filtering Systems," *Proceedings of the IEEE,* Vol. 71, pp. 967–986, August 1983.

28. O. E. Akcasu. "High Capacitance Structure in a Semiconductor Device," *U.S. Patent 5,208,725,* May 1993.

29. H. Samavati, A. Hajimiri, A. R. Shahani, G. N. Nasserbakht, and T. H. Lee. "Fractal Capacitors," *IEEE Journal of Solid-State Circuits,* Vol. 33, pp. 2035–2041, December 1998.

30. A. R. Alvarez. *BiCMOS Technology and Applications.* Kluwer Academic Publishers, Dordrecht, The Netherlands, 1989.

31. J. L. de Jong, R. Lane, B. van Schravendijk, and G. Conner. "Single Polysilicon Layer Advanced Super High-speed BiCMOS Technology," *Proceedings of the IEEE Bipolar Circuits and Technology Meeting,* pp. 182–185, September 1989.

32. D. L. Harame, J. H. Comfort, J. D. Cressler, E. F. Crabbé, J. Y.-C. Sun, B. S. Meyerson, and T. Tice. "Si/SiGe Epitaxial-Base Transistors–Part I: Materials, Physics, and Circuits," *IEEE Transactions on Electron Devices,* Vol. 42, pp. 455–468, March 1995.

33. J. D. Cressler, D. L. Harame, J. H. Comfort, J. M. C. Stork, B. S. Meyerson, and T. E. Tice. "Silicon-Germanium Heterojunction Bipolar Technology: The Next Leap in Silicon?" *Digest of Technical Papers, 1994 International Solid-State Circuits Conference,* San Francisco, CA, pp. 24–27, February 1994.

34.  D. L. Harame, J. H. Comfort, J. D. Cressler, E. F. Crabbé, J. Y.-C. Sun, B. S. Meyerson, and T. Tice. "Si/SiGe Epitaxial-Base Transistors—Part II: Process Integration and Analog Applications," *IEEE Transactions on Electron Devices,* Vol. 42, pp. 469–482, March 1995.

35.  M. T. Bohr. "Interconnect Scaling—The Real Limiter to High Performance ULSI," *Technical Digest, International Electron Devices Meeting,* pp. 241–244, December 1995.

36.  C. S. Chang, K. A. Monnig, and M. Melliar-Smith. "Interconnection Challenges and the National Technology Roadmap for Semiconductors," *IEEE International Interconnect Technology Conference,* pp. 3–6, June 1998.

37.  D. Edelstein, J. Heidenreich, R. Goldblatt, W. Cote, C. Uzoh, N. Lustig, P. Roper, T. McDevitt, W. Motsiff, A. Simon, J. Dukovic, R. Wachnik, H. Rathore, R. Schulz, L. Su, S. Luce, and J. Slattery. "Full Copper Wiring in a Sub-0.25 μm CMOS ULSI Technology," *IEEE International Electron Devices Meeting,* pp. 773–776, December 1997.

# Single-Transistor and Multiple-Transistor Amplifiers

The technology used to fabricate integrated circuits presents a unique set of component-cost constraints to the circuit designer. The most cost-effective circuit approach to accomplish a given function may be quite different when the realization of the circuit is to be in monolithic form as opposed to discrete transistors and passive elements.[1] As an illustration, consider the two realizations of a three-stage audio amplifier shown in Figs. 3.1 and 3.2. The first reflects a cost-effective solution in the context of discrete-component circuits, since passive components such as resistors and capacitors are less expensive than the active components, the transistors. Hence, the circuit contains a minimum number of transistors, and the interstage coupling is accomplished with capacitors. However, for the case of monolithic construction, a key determining factor in cost is the die area used. Capacitors of the values used in most discrete-component circuits are not feasible and would have to be external to the chip, increasing the pin count of the package, which increases cost. Therefore, a high premium is placed on eliminating large capacitors, and a dc-coupled circuit realization is very desirable. A second constraint is that the *cheapest* component that can be fabricated in the integrated circuit is the one that occupies the least area, usually a transistor. Thus a circuit realization that contains the minimum possible total resistance while using more active components may be optimum.[2,3] Furthermore, an important application of analog circuits is to provide interfaces between the real world and digital circuits. In building digital integrated circuits, CMOS technologies have become dominant because of their high densities and low power dissipations. To reduce the cost and increase the portability of mixed-analog-and-digital systems, both increased levels of integration and reduced power dissipations are required. As a result, we are interested in building analog interface circuits in CMOS technologies. The circuit of Fig. 3.2 reflects these constraints. It uses a CMOS technology and many more transistors than in Fig. 3.1, has less total resistance, and has no coupling capacitors. A differential pair is used to allow direct coupling between stages, while transistor current sources provide biasing without large amounts of resistance. In practice, feedback would be required around the amplifier shown in Fig. 3.2 but is not shown for simplicity. Feedback is described in Chapter 8.

The next three chapters analyze various circuit configurations encountered in linear integrated circuits. In discrete-component circuits, the number of transistors is usually minimized. The best way to analyze such circuits is usually to regard each individual transistor as a *stage* and to analyze the circuit as a collection of single-transistor stages. A typical monolithic circuit, however, contains a large number of transistors that perform many functions, both passive and active. Thus monolithic circuits are often regarded as a collection of *subcircuits* that perform specific functions, where the subcircuits may contain many transistors. In this chapter, we first consider the dc and low-frequency properties of the simplest subcircuits: common-emitter, common-base, and common-collector single-transistor amplifiers and their counterparts using MOS transistors. We then consider some multi-transistor subcircuits that are useful as amplifying stages. The most widely used of

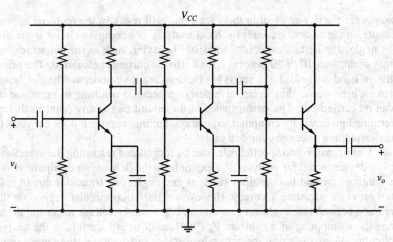

**Figure 3.1** Typical discrete-component realization of an audio amplifier.

**Figure 3.2** Typical CMOS integrated-circuit realization of an audio amplifier.

these multi-transistor circuits are the differential pairs, which are analyzed extensively in this chapter.

## 3.1 Device Model Selection for Approximate Analysis of Analog Circuits

Much of this book is concerned with the salient performance characteristics of a variety of subcircuits commonly used in analog circuits and of complete functional blocks made up of these subcircuits. The aspects of the performance that are of interest include the dc currents and voltages within the circuit, the effect of mismatches in device characteristics on these voltages and currents, the small-signal, low-frequency input and output resistance, and the voltage gain of the circuit. In later chapters, the high-frequency, small-signal behavior of circuits is considered. The subcircuit or circuit under investigation is often one of considerable complexity, and the most important single principle that must be followed to achieve success in the hand analysis of such circuits is *selecting the simplest possible model* for the devices within the circuit that will result in the required accuracy. For example, in the case of dc analysis, hand analysis of a complex circuit is greatly simplified by neglecting certain aspects of transistor behavior, such as the output resistance, which may result in a 10 to 20 percent error in the dc currents calculated. The principal objective of hand analysis, however, is to obtain an intuitive understanding of factors affecting circuit behavior so that an iterative design procedure resulting in improved performance can be carried out. The performance of the circuit can at any point in this cycle be determined precisely by computer simulation, but this approach does not yield the intuitive understanding necessary for design.

Unfortunately, no specific rules can be formulated regarding the selection of the simplest device model for analysis. For example, in the dc analysis of bipolar biasing circuits, assuming constant base-emitter voltages and neglecting transistor output resistances often provides adequate accuracy. However, certain bias circuits depend on the nonlinear relation between the collector current and base-emitter voltage to control the bias current, and the assumption of a constant $V_{BE}$ will result in gross errors in the analyses of these circuits. When analyzing the active-load stages in Chapter 4, the output resistance must be considered to obtain meaningful results. Therefore, a key step in every analysis is to inspect the circuit to determine what aspects of the behavior of the transistors strongly affect the performance of the circuit, and then simplify the model(s) to include only those aspects. This step in the procedure is emphasized in this and the following chapters.

## 3.2 Two-Port Modeling of Amplifiers

The most basic parameter of an amplifier is its gain. Since amplifiers may be connected to a wide variety of sources and loads, predicting the dependence of the gain on the source and load resistance is also important. One way to observe this dependence is to include these resistances in the amplifier analysis. However, this approach requires a completely new amplifier analysis each time the source or load resistance is changed. To simplify this procedure, amplifiers are often modeled as two-port equivalent networks. As shown in Fig. 3.3, two-port networks have four terminals and four port variables (a voltage and a current at each port). A pair of terminals is a port if the current that flows into one terminal is equal to the current that flows out of the other terminal. To model an amplifier, one port represents the amplifier input characteristics and the other represents the output. One variable at each port can be set independently. The other variable at each port is dependent on the two-port network and the independent variables. This dependence is expressed by two equations. We will focus here on the admittance-parameter equations, where the terminal currents are viewed as dependent variables controlled by the independent terminal voltages because we usually model transistors with voltage-controlled current sources. If the network is linear and contains no independent sources, the admittance-parameter equations are:

$$i_1 = y_{11}v_1 + y_{12}v_2 \tag{3.1}$$

$$i_2 = y_{21}v_1 + y_{22}v_2 \tag{3.2}$$

**Figure 3.3**  Two-port-network block diagram.

**Figure 3.4** Admittance-parameter, two-port equivalent circuit.

The voltages and currents in these equations are deliberately written as small-signal quantities because transistors behave in an approximately linear way only for small signals around a fixed operating point. An equivalent circuit for these equations is shown in Fig. 3.4. The parameters can be found and interpreted as follows:

$$y_{11} = \frac{i_1}{v_1} \Big|_{v_2=0} = \text{Input admittance with the output short-circuited} \tag{3.3}$$

$$y_{12} = \frac{i_1}{v_2} \Big|_{v_1=0} = \text{Reverse transconductance with the input short-circuited} \tag{3.4}$$

$$y_{21} = \frac{i_2}{v_1} \Big|_{v_2=0} = \text{Forward transconductance with the output short-circuited} \tag{3.5}$$

$$y_{22} = \frac{i_2}{v_2} \Big|_{v_1=0} = \text{Output admittance with the input short-circuited} \tag{3.6}$$

The $y_{12}$ parameter represents feedback in the amplifier. When the signal propagates back from the output to the input as well as forward from the input to the output, the amplifier is said to be *bilateral*. In many practical cases, especially at low frequencies, this feedback is negligible and $y_{12}$ is assumed to be zero. Then the amplifier is *unilateral* and characterized by the other three parameters. Since the model includes only one transconductance when $y_{12} = 0$, $y_{21}$ is usually referred to simply as the *short-circuit transconductance*, which will be represented by $G_m$ in this book. When an amplifier is unilateral, the calculation of $y_{11}$ is simplified from that given in (3.3) because the connections at the output port do not affect the input admittance when $y_{12} = 0$.

Instead of calculating $y_{11}$ and $y_{22}$, we will often calculate the reciprocals of these parameters, or the input and output impedances $Z_i = 1/y_{11}$ and $Z_o = 1/y_{22}$, as shown in the unilateral two-port model of Fig. 3.5a. Also, instead of calculating the short-circuit transconductance $G_m = y_{21}$, we will sometimes calculate the open-circuit voltage gain $a_v$. This substitution is justified by conversion of the Norton-equivalent output model shown in Fig. 3.5a to the Thévenin-equivalent output model shown in Fig. 3.5b. In general, finding

(a)

(b)

**Figure 3.5** Unilateral two-port equivalent circuits with (a) Norton output model (b) Thévenin output model.

**Figure 3.6** Example of loading at the input and output of an amplifier modeled by a two-port equivalent circuit.

any two of the three parameters including $G_m$, $Z_o$, and $a_v$ specifies the third parameter because

$$a_v = \frac{v_2}{v_1}\bigg|_{i_2=0} = -G_m Z_o \qquad (3.7)$$

Once two of these parameters and the input impedance are known, calculation of the effects of loading at the input and output ports is possible. At low frequencies, the input and output impedances are usually dominated by resistances. Therefore, we will characterize the low-frequency behavior of many amplifiers in this book by finding the input and output resistances, $R_i$ and $R_o$, as well as $G_m$ or $a_v$.

■ **EXAMPLE**

A two-port model of a unilateral amplifier is shown in Fig. 3.6. Assume $R_i = 1\,\text{k}\Omega$, $R_o = 1\,\text{M}\Omega$, and $G_m = 1\,\text{mA/V}$. Let $R_S$ and $R_L$ represent the source resistance of the input generator and load resistance, respectively. Find the low-frequency gain $v_{\text{out}}/v_{\text{in}}$, assuming that the input is an ideal voltage source and the output is unloaded. Repeat, assuming that $R_S = 1\,\text{k}\Omega$ and $R_L = 1\,\text{M}\Omega$.

The open-circuit voltage gain of the two-port amplifier model by itself from $v_1$ to $v_{\text{out}}$ is

$$\frac{v_{\text{out}}}{v_1}\bigg|_{R_L\to\infty} = \frac{v_2}{v_1}\bigg|_{i_2=0} = -G_m R_o = -(1\,\text{mA/V})(1000\,\text{k}\Omega) = -1000$$

Since the source and input resistances form a voltage divider, and since the output resistance appears in parallel with the load resistance, the overall gain from $v_{\text{in}}$ to $v_{\text{out}}$ is

$$\frac{v_{\text{out}}}{v_{\text{in}}} = \frac{v_1}{v_{\text{in}}}\frac{v_{\text{out}}}{v_1} = -\frac{R_i}{R_i + R_S}\, G_m\,(R_o \parallel R_L)$$

With an ideal voltage source at the input and no load at the output, $R_S = 0$, $R_L \to \infty$, and $v_{\text{out}}/v_{\text{in}} = -1000$. With $R_S = 1\,\text{k}\Omega$ and $R_L = 1\,\text{M}\Omega$, the gain is reduced by a factor of four to $v_{\text{out}}/v_{\text{in}} = -0.5(1\,\text{mA/V})(500\,\text{k}\Omega) = -250$.

## 3.3 Basic Single-Transistor Amplifier Stages

Bipolar and MOS transistors are capable of providing useful amplification in three different configurations. In the common-emitter or common-source configuration, the signal is applied to the base or gate of the transistor and the amplified output is taken from the collector or drain. In the common-collector or common-drain configuration, the signal is applied to the base or gate and the output signal is taken from the emitter or source. This configuration is often referred to as the *emitter follower* for bipolar circuits and the *source follower* for MOS circuits. In the common-base or common-gate configuration, the signal is applied to the emitter or the source, and the output signal is taken from the collector or the drain. Each of these configurations provides a unique combination of input resistance, output resistance, voltage gain, and current gain. In many instances, the analysis of complex multistage amplifiers can be reduced to the analysis of a number of single-transistor stages of these types.

We showed in Chapter 1 that the small-signal equivalent circuits for the bipolar and MOS transistors are very similar, with the two devices differing mainly in the values of some of their small-signal parameters. In particular, MOS transistors have essentially infinite input resistance from the gate to the source, in contrast with the finite $r_\pi$ of bipolar transistors. On the other hand, bipolar transistors have a $g_m$ that is usually an order of magnitude larger than that of MOS transistors biased with the same current. These differences often make one or the other device desirable for use in different situations. For example, amplifiers with very high input impedance are more easily realized with MOS transistors than with bipolar transistors. However, the higher $g_m$ of bipolar transistors makes the realization of high-gain amplifiers with bipolar transistors easier than with MOS transistors. In other applications, the exponential large-signal characteristics of bipolar transistors and the square-law characteristics of MOS transistors may each be used to advantage.

As described in Chapter 2, integrated-circuit processes of many varieties now exist. Examples include processes with bipolar or MOS transistors as the only active devices and combined bipolar and CMOS devices in BiCMOS processes. Because the more complex processes involve more masking steps and are thus somewhat more costly to produce, integrated-circuit designers generally use the simplest process available that allows the desired circuit specifications to be achieved. Therefore, designers must appreciate the similarities and differences between bipolar and MOS transistors so that appropriate choices of technology can be made.

### 3.3.1 Common-Emitter Configuration

The resistively loaded common-emitter (CE) amplifier configuration is shown in Fig. 3.7. The resistor $R_C$ represents the collector load resistance. The short horizontal line labeled $V_{CC}$ at the top of $R_C$ implies that a voltage source of value $V_{CC}$ is connected between that point and ground. This symbol will be used throughout the book. We first calculate the dc transfer characteristic of the amplifier as the input voltage is increased in the positive direction from zero. We assume that the base of the transistor is driven by a voltage source of value $V_i$. When $V_i$ is zero, the transistor operates in the cutoff state and no collector

**Figure 3.7** Resistively loaded common-emitter amplifier.

**Figure 3.8** Large-signal equivalent circuit valid when the transistor is in the forward-active region. The saturation current of the equivalent base-emitter diode is $I_S/\beta_F$.

current flows other than the leakage current $I_{CO}$. As the input voltage is increased, the transistor enters the forward-active region, and the collector current is given by

$$I_c = I_S \exp \frac{V_i}{V_T} \qquad (3.8)$$

The equivalent circuit for the amplifier when the transistor operates in the forward-active region was derived in Chapter 1 and is repeated in Fig. 3.8. Because of the exponential relationship between $I_c$ and $V_{be}$, the value of the collector current is very small until the input voltage reaches approximately 0.5 V. As long as the transistor operates in the forward-active region, the base current is equal to the collector current divided by $\beta_F$, or

$$I_b = \frac{I_c}{\beta_F} = \frac{I_S}{\beta_F} \exp \frac{V_i}{V_T} \qquad (3.9)$$

The output voltage is equal to the supply voltage, $V_{CC}$, minus the voltage drop across the collector resistor:

$$V_o = V_{CC} - I_c R_C = V_{CC} - R_C I_S \exp \frac{V_i}{V_T} \qquad (3.10)$$

When the output voltage approaches zero, the collector-base junction of the transistor becomes forward biased and the device enters saturation. Once the transistor becomes saturated, the output voltage and collector current take on nearly constant values:

$$V_o = V_{CE(sat)} \qquad (3.11)$$

$$I_c = \frac{V_{CC} - V_{CE(sat)}}{R_C} \qquad (3.12)$$

The base current, however, continues to increase with further increases in $V_i$. Therefore, the forward current gain $I_c/I_b$ decreases from $\beta_F$ as the transistor leaves the forward-active region of operation and moves into saturation. In practice, the current available from the signal source is limited. When the signal source can no longer increase the base current, $V_i$ is maximum. The output voltage and the base current are plotted as a function of the input voltage in Fig. 3.9. Note that when the device operates in the forward-active region, small changes in the input voltage can give rise to large changes in the output voltage. The circuit thus provides *voltage gain*. We now proceed to calculate the voltage gain in the forward-active region.

While incremental performance parameters such as the voltage gain can be calculated from derivatives of the large-signal analysis, the calculations are simplified by using the small-signal hybrid-$\pi$ model for the transistor developed in Chapter 1. The small-signal

Figure 3.9 Output voltage and base current as a function of $V_i$ for the common-emitter circuit.

equivalent circuit for the common-emitter amplifier is shown in Fig. 3.10. Here we have neglected $r_b$, assuming that it is much smaller than $r_\pi$. We have also neglected $r_\mu$. This equivalent circuit does not include the resistance of the load connected to the amplifier output. The collector resistor $R_C$ is included because it is usually present in some form as a biasing element. Our objective is to characterize the amplifier alone so that the voltage gain can then be calculated under arbitrary conditions of loading at the input and output. Since the common-emitter amplifier is unilateral when $r_\mu$ is neglected, we will calculate the small-signal input resistance, transconductance, and output resistance of the circuit as explained in Section 3.2.

The input resistance is the Thévenin-equivalent resistance seen looking into the input. For the CE amplifier,

$$R_i = \frac{v_i}{i_i} = r_\pi = \frac{\beta_0}{g_m} \tag{3.13}$$

The transconductance $G_m$ is the change in the short-circuit output current per unit change of input voltage and is given by

$$G_m = \left.\frac{i_o}{v_i}\right|_{v_o=0} = g_m \tag{3.14}$$

Figure 3.10 Small-signal equivalent circuit for the CE amplifier.

Equation 3.14 shows that the transconductance of the CE amplifier is equal to the transconductance of the transistor. The output resistance is the Thévenin-equivalent resistance seen looking into the output with the input shorted, or

$$R_o = \left.\frac{v_o}{i_o}\right|_{v_i=0} = R_C \parallel r_o \tag{3.15}$$

The *open-circuit*, or *unloaded*, *voltage gain* is

$$a_v = \left.\frac{v_o}{v_i}\right|_{i_o=0} = -g_m(r_o \parallel R_C) \tag{3.16}$$

If the collector load resistor $R_C$ is made very large, then $a_v$ becomes

$$\lim_{R_C \to \infty} a_v = -g_m r_o = -\frac{I_C}{V_T}\frac{V_A}{I_C} = -\frac{V_A}{V_T} = -\frac{1}{\eta} \tag{3.17}$$

where $I_C$ is the dc collector current at the operating point, $V_T$ is the thermal voltage, $V_A$ is the Early voltage, and $\eta$ is given in (1.114). This gain represents the maximum low-frequency voltage gain obtainable from the transistor. It is independent of the collector bias current for bipolar transistors, and the magnitude is approximately 5000 for typical *npn* devices.

Another parameter of interest is the *short-circuit current gain* $a_i$. This parameter is the ratio of $i_o$ to $i_i$ when the output is shorted. For the CE amplifier,

$$a_i = \left.\frac{i_o}{i_i}\right|_{v_o=0} = \frac{G_m v_i}{\dfrac{v_i}{R_i}} = g_m r_\pi = \beta_0 \tag{3.18}$$

■ **EXAMPLE**

(a) Find the input resistance, output resistance, voltage gain, and current gain of the common-emitter amplifier in Fig. 3.11a. Assume that $I_C = 100\ \mu\text{A}$, $\beta_0 = 100$, $r_b = 0$, and $r_o \to \infty$.

$$R_i = r_\pi = \frac{\beta_0}{g_m} \simeq \frac{100\,(26\ \text{mV})}{100\ \mu\text{A}} = 26\ \text{k}\Omega$$

$$R_o = R_C = 5\ \text{k}\Omega$$

$$a_v = -g_m R_C \simeq -\left(\frac{100\ \mu\text{A}}{26\ \text{mV}}\right)(5\ \text{k}\Omega) \simeq -19.2$$

$$a_i = \beta_0 = 100$$

(b) Calculate the voltage gain of the circuit of Fig. 3.11b. Assume that $V_{BIAS}$ is adjusted so that the dc collector current is maintained at $100\ \mu\text{A}$.

$$v_1 = v_s\left(\frac{R_i}{R_S + R_i}\right)$$

$$v_o = -G_m v_1 (R_o \parallel R_L) = -G_m\left(\frac{R_i}{R_S + R_i}\right)(R_o \parallel R_L)v_s$$

$$\frac{v_o}{v_s} = -\left(\frac{1}{260\ \Omega}\right)\left(\frac{26\ \text{k}\Omega}{26\ \text{k}\Omega + 20\ \text{k}\Omega}\right)\left[\frac{(10\ \text{k}\Omega)(5\ \text{k}\Omega)}{10\ \text{k}\Omega + 5\ \text{k}\Omega}\right] \simeq -7.25$$

**Figure 3.11** (a) Example amplifier circuit. (b) Circuit for calculation of voltage gain with typical source and load resistance values.

## 3.3.2 Common-Source Configuration

The resistively loaded common-source (CS) amplifier configuration is shown in Fig. 3.12a using an $n$-channel MOS transistor. The corresponding small-signal equivalent circuit is shown in Fig. 3.12b. As in the case of the bipolar transistor, the MOS transistor is cutoff for $V_i = 0$ and thus $I_d = 0$ and $V_o = V_{DD}$. As $V_i$ is increased beyond the threshold voltage $V_t$, nonzero drain current flows and the transistor operates in the active region (which is often called saturation for MOS transistors) when $V_o > V_{GS} - V_t$. The large-signal model

**Figure 3.12** (a) Resistively loaded, common-source amplifier. (b) Small-signal equivalent circuit for the common-source amplifier.

(a)

(b)

of Fig. 1.30 can then be used together with (1.157) to derive

$$V_o = V_{DD} - I_d R_D \tag{3.19}$$

$$= V_{DD} - \frac{\mu_n C_{ox}}{2} \frac{W}{L} R_D (V_i - V_t)^2 \tag{3.20}$$

The output voltage is equal to the drain-source voltage and decreases as the input increases. When $V_o < V_{GS} - V_t$, the transistor enters the triode region, where its output resistance becomes low and the small-signal voltage gain drops dramatically. In the triode region, the output voltage can be calculated by using (1.152) in (3.19). These results are illustrated in the plot of Fig. 3.13. The slope of this transfer characteristic at any operating

**Figure 3.13** Output voltage versus input voltage for the common-source circuit.

point is the small-signal voltage gain at that point. The MOS transistor has much lower voltage gain in the active region than does the bipolar transistor; therefore, the active region for the MOS CS amplifier extends over a much larger range of $V_i$ than in the bipolar common-emitter amplifier.

Since the source and body of the MOS transistor both operate at ac ground, $v_{bs} = 0$ in Fig. 1.36; therefore, the $g_{mb}$ generator is omitted in Fig. 3.12b. As a result, this circuit is topologically identical to the small-signal equivalent circuit for the common-emitter amplifier shown in Fig. 3.10. The CS amplifier is unilateral because it contains no feedback. Therefore, the low-frequency behavior of this circuit can be characterized using the transconductance, input resistance, and output resistance as described in Section 3.2.

The transconductance $G_m$ is

$$G_m = \left. \frac{i_o}{v_i} \right|_{v_o = 0} = g_m \tag{3.21}$$

Equation 3.21 shows that the transconductance of the CS amplifier is equal to the transconductance of the transistor, as in a common-emitter amplifier. Since the input of the CS amplifier is connected to the gate of an MOS transistor, the dc input current and its low-frequency, small-signal variation $i_i$ are both assumed to equal zero. Under this assumption, the input resistance $R_i$ is

$$R_i = \frac{v_i}{i_i} \rightarrow \infty \tag{3.22}$$

Another way to see this result is to let $\beta_0 \rightarrow \infty$ in (3.13) because MOS transistors behave like bipolar transistors with infinite $\beta_0$. The output resistance is the Thévenin-equivalent resistance seen looking into the output with the input shorted, or

$$R_o = \left. \frac{v_o}{i_o} \right|_{v_i = 0} = R_D \| r_o \tag{3.23}$$

The *open-circuit*, or *unloaded*, *voltage gain* is

$$a_v = \left. \frac{v_o}{v_i} \right|_{i_o = 0} = -g_m(r_o \| R_D) \tag{3.24}$$

If the drain load resistor $R_D$ is replaced by a current source, $R_D \rightarrow \infty$ and $a_v$ becomes

$$\lim_{R_D \rightarrow \infty} a_v = -g_m r_o \tag{3.25}$$

Equation 3.25 gives the maximum possible voltage gain of a one-stage CS amplifier. This result is identical to the first part of (3.17) for a common-emitter amplifier. In the case of the CS amplifier, however, $g_m$ is proportional to $\sqrt{I_D}$ from (1.180) whereas $r_o$ is inversely proportional to $I_D$ from (1.194). Thus, we find in (3.25) that the maximum voltage gain per stage is proportional to $1/\sqrt{I_D}$. In contrast, the maximum voltage gain in the common-emitter amplifier is independent of current. A plot of the maximum voltage gain versus $I_D$ for a typical MOS transistor is shown in Fig. 3.14. At very low currents, the gain approaches a constant value comparable to that of a bipolar transistor. This region is sometimes called *subthreshold*, where the transistor operates in weak inversion and the square-law characteristic in (1.157) is no longer valid. As explained in Section 1.8, the drain current becomes an exponential function of the gate-source voltage in this region, resembling the collector-current dependence on the base-emitter voltage in a bipolar transistor.

Figure 3.14 Typical variation of maximum MOSFET voltage gain with bias current.

Using (1.194), the limiting gain given by (3.25) can also be expressed as

$$\lim_{R_D \to \infty} a_v = -g_m r_o = -\frac{g_m}{I_D} I_D r_o = -\frac{g_m}{I_D} V_A \qquad (3.26)$$

In the square-law region in Fig. 3.14, substituting (1.181) into (3.26) gives

$$\lim_{R_D \to \infty} a_v = -\frac{V_A}{(V_{GS} - V_t)/2} = -\frac{2V_A}{V_{ov}} \qquad (3.27)$$

where $V_{ov} = V_{GS} - V_t$ is the gate *overdrive*. Since the gate overdrive is typically an order of magnitude larger than the thermal voltage $V_T$, the magnitude of the maximum gain predicted by (3.27) is usually much smaller than that predicted by (3.17) for the bipolar case. Substituting (1.163) into (3.27) gives

$$\lim_{R_D \to \infty} a_v = -\frac{2L_{\text{eff}}}{V_{GS} - V_t} \left( \frac{dX_d}{dV_{DS}} \right)^{-1} \qquad (3.28)$$

■ **EXAMPLE**

Find the voltage gain of the common-source amplifier of Fig 3.12a with $V_{DD} = 5$ V, $R_D = 5$ k$\Omega$, $k' = \mu_n C_{ox} = 100$ $\mu$A/V$^2$, $W = 50$ $\mu$m, $L = 1$ $\mu$m, $V_t = 0.8$ V, $L_d = 0$, $X_d = 0$, and $\lambda = 0$. Assume that the bias value of $V_i$ is 1 V.

To determine whether the transistor operates in the active region, we first find the dc output voltage $V_O = V_{DS}$. If the transistor operates in the active region, (1.157) gives

$$I_D = \frac{k'}{2} \frac{W}{L} (V_{GS} - V_t)^2 = \frac{100}{2} \times 10^{-6} \times \frac{50}{1} (1 - 0.8)^2 = 100 \ \mu A$$

Then

$$V_O = V_{DS} = V_{DD} - I_D R_D = 5 \text{ V} - (0.1 \text{ mA})(5 \text{ k}\Omega) = 4.5 \text{ V}$$

Since $V_{DS} = 4.5$ V $> V_{GS} - V_t = 0.2$ V, the transistor does operate in the active region, as assumed. Then from (1.180),

$$g_m = k' \frac{W}{L}(V_{GS} - V_t) = 100 \times 10^{-6} \times \frac{50}{1}(1 - 0.8) = 1000 \ \frac{\mu A}{V}$$

**Figure 3.15** Typical common-base amplifier.

Then since $\lambda = 0$, $V_A \to \infty$ and (3.24) gives

$$a_v = -g_m R_D = -(1.0 \text{ mA/V}) (5 \text{ k}\Omega) = -5$$

Note that the open-circuit voltage gain here is much less than in the bipolar example in Section 3.3.1 even though the dc bias currents are equal.

### 3.3.3 Common-Base Configuration

In the common-base (CB) configuration,[4] the input signal is applied to the emitter of the transistor, and the output is taken from the collector. The base is tied to ac ground. The common-base connection is shown in Fig. 3.15. While the connection is not as widely used as the common-emitter amplifier, it has properties that make it useful in certain circumstances. In this section, we calculate the small-signal properties of the common-base stage.

The hybrid-$\pi$ model provides an accurate representation of the small-signal behavior of the transistor independent of the circuit configuration. For the common-base stage, however, the hybrid-$\pi$ model is somewhat cumbersome because the dependent current source is connected between the input and output terminals.[4] The analysis of common-base stages can be simplified if the model is modified as shown in Fig. 3.16. The small-signal hybrid-$\pi$ model is shown in Fig. 3.16a. First note that the dependent current source flows from the collector terminal to the emitter terminal. The circuit behavior is unchanged if we replace this single current source with two current sources of the same value, one going from the collector to the base and the other going from the base to the emitter, as shown in Fig. 3.16b. Since the currents fed into and removed from the base are equal, the equations that describe the operation of these circuits are identical. We next note that the controlled current source connecting the base and emitter is controlled by the voltage across its own terminals. Therefore, by the application of Ohm's law to this branch, this dependent current source can be replaced by a resistor of value $1/g_m$. This resistance appears in parallel with $r_\pi$, and the parallel combination of the two is called the emitter resistance $r_e$.

$$r_e = \cfrac{1}{g_m + \cfrac{1}{r_\pi}} = \cfrac{1}{g_m \left(1 + \cfrac{1}{\beta_0}\right)} = \frac{\alpha_0}{g_m} \tag{3.29}$$

The new equivalent circuit is called the *T model* and is shown in Fig. 3.16c. It has terminal properties exactly equivalent to those of the hybrid-$\pi$ model but is often more convenient to use for common-base calculations. For dc and low input frequencies, the capacitors $C_\pi$ and $C_\mu$ appear as high-impedance elements and can be neglected. Assume at first that $r_b = 0$ and $r_o \to \infty$ so that the circuit is unilateral. When $r_\mu$ is also neglected, the model reduces to the simple form shown in Fig. 3.16d. Using the T model under these conditions, the small-signal equivalent circuit of the common-base stage is shown in

**Figure 3.16** Generation of emitter-current-controlled T model from the hybrid-$\pi$. (a) Hybrid-$\pi$ model. (b) The collector current source $g_m v_1$ is changed to two current sources in series, and the point between them attached to the base. This change does not affect the current flowing in the base. (c) The current source between base and emitter is converted to a resistor of value $1/g_m$. (d) T model for low frequencies, neglecting $r_o$, $r_\mu$, and the charge-storage elements.

Fig. 3.17. By inspection of Fig. 3.17, the short-circuit transconductance is

$$G_m = g_m \qquad (3.30)$$

The input resistance is just the resistance $r_e$:

$$R_i = r_e \qquad (3.31)$$

**Figure 3.17** Small-signal equivalent circuit of the common-base stage; $r_o$, $r_b$, and $r_\mu$ are assumed negligible.

The output resistance is given by

$$R_o = R_C \tag{3.32}$$

Using these parameters, the open-circuit voltage gain and the short-circuit current gain are

$$a_v = G_m R_o = g_m R_C \tag{3.33}$$
$$a_i = G_m R_i = g_m r_e = \alpha_0 \tag{3.34}$$

Comparing (3.31) and (3.13) shows that the input resistance of the common-base configuration is a factor of $(\beta_0 + 1)$ less than in the common-emitter configuration. Also, comparing (3.34) and (3.18) shows that the current gain of the common-base configuration is reduced by a factor of $(\beta_0 + 1)$ compared to that of the common-emitter configuration.

Until now, we have assumed that $r_b$ is negligible. In practice, however, the base resistance has a significant effect on the transconductance and the input resistance when the common-base stage is operated at sufficiently high current levels. To recalculate these parameters with $r_b > 0$, assume the transistor operates in the forward-active region and consider the small-signal model shown in Fig. 3.18. Here, the transconductance is

$$G_m = \left.\frac{i_o}{v_i}\right|_{v_o=0} = g_m\left(\frac{v_e}{v_i}\right) \tag{3.35}$$

To find the relationship between $v_e$ and $v_i$, Kirchoff's current law (KCL) and Kirchoff's voltage law (KVL) can be applied at the internal base node (node ①) and around the input loop, respectively. From KCL at node ①,

$$g_m v_e + \frac{v_b}{r_b} - \frac{v_e}{r_e} = 0 \tag{3.36}$$

From KVL around the input loop,

$$v_i = v_e + v_b \tag{3.37}$$

Solving (3.37) for $v_b$, substituting into (3.36), and rearranging gives

$$\frac{v_i}{v_e} = 1 + \frac{g_m}{\beta_0}r_b = 1 + \frac{r_b}{r_\pi} \tag{3.38}$$

Substituting (3.38) into (3.35) gives

$$G_m = \frac{g_m}{1 + \dfrac{r_b}{r_\pi}} \tag{3.39}$$

Similarly, the input resistance in Fig. 3.18 is

$$R_i = \frac{v_i}{i_i} = \frac{v_i}{v_e/r_e} = r_e\left(\frac{v_i}{v_e}\right) \tag{3.40}$$

**Figure 3.18** Small-signal model of the common-base stage with $r_b > 0$.

Substituting (3.38) into (3.40) gives

$$R_i = r_e\left(1 + \frac{r_b}{r_\pi}\right) = \frac{\alpha_0}{g_m}\left(1 + \frac{r_b}{r_\pi}\right) \tag{3.41}$$

Thus if the dc collector current is large enough that $r_\pi$ is comparable with $r_b$, then the effects of base resistance must be included. For example, if $r_b = 100\ \Omega$ and $\beta_0 = 100$, then a collector current of 26 mA makes $r_b$ and $r_\pi$ equal.

The main motivation for using common-base stages is twofold. First, the collector-base capacitance does not cause high-frequency feedback from output to input as in the common-emitter amplifier. As described in Chapter 7, this change can be important in the design of high-frequency amplifiers. Second, as described in Chapter 4, the common-base amplifier can achieve much larger output resistance than the common-emitter stage in the limiting case where $R_C \to \infty$. As a result, the common-base configuration can be used as a current source whose current is nearly independent of the voltage across it.

### 3.3.4 Common-Gate Configuration

In the common-gate configuration, the input signal is applied to the source of the transistor, and the output is taken from the drain while the gate is connected to ac ground. This configuration is shown in Fig. 3.19, and its behavior is similar to that of a common-base stage.

As in the analysis of common-base amplifiers in Section 3.3.3, the analysis of common-gate amplifiers can be simplified if the model is changed from a hybrid-$\pi$ configuration to a T model, as shown in Fig. 3.20. In Fig. 3.20a, the low-frequency hybrid-$\pi$ model is shown. Note that both transconductance generators are now active. If the substrate or body connection is assumed to operate at ac ground, then $v_{bs} = v_{gs}$ because the gate also operates at ac ground. Therefore, in Fig. 3.20b, the two dependent current sources are combined. In Fig. 3.20c, the combined current source from the source to the drain is replaced by two current sources: one from the source to the gate and the other from the gate to the drain. Since equal currents are pushed into and pulled out of the gate, the equations that describe the operation of the circuits in Figs. 3.20b and 3.20c are identical. Finally, because the current source from the source to the gate is controlled by the voltage across itself, it can be replaced by a resistor of value $1/(g_m + g_{mb})$, as in Fig. 3.20d.

If $r_o$ is finite, the circuit of Fig. 3.20d is bilateral because of feedback provided through $r_o$. At first, we will assume that $r_o \to \infty$ so that the circuit is unilateral. Using the T model under these conditions, the small-signal equivalent circuit of the common-gate stage is shown in Fig. 3.21. By inspection of Fig. 3.21,

$$G_m = g_m + g_{mb} \tag{3.42}$$

**Figure 3.19** Common-gate configuration.

(a)

(b)

(c)

(d)

**Figure 3.20** Conversion from hybrid-$\pi$ to T model. (a) Low-frequency hybrid-$\pi$ model. (b) The two dependent sources are combined. (c) The combined source is converted into two sources. (d) The current source between the source and gate is converted into a resistor.

$$R_i = \frac{1}{g_m + g_{mb}} \tag{3.43}$$

$$R_o = R_D \tag{3.44}$$

Using these parameters, the open-circuit voltage gain and the short-circuit current gain are

$$a_v = G_m R_o = (g_m + g_{mb})R_D \tag{3.45}$$

$$a_i = G_m R_i = 1 \tag{3.46}$$

**Figure 3.21**  Small-signal equivalent circuit of the common-gate stage; $r_o$ is assumed negligible.

### 3.3.5 Common-Base and Common-Gate Configurations with Finite $r_o$

In calculating the expressions for $G_m$, $R_i$, and $R_o$ of the common-base and common-gate amplifiers, we have neglected the effects of $r_o$. Since $r_o$ is connected from each amplifier output back to its input, finite $r_o$ causes each circuit to be bilateral, making the input resistance depend on the connection at the amplifier output. Let $R = R_C$ in Fig. 3.17 or $R = R_D$ in Fig. 3.21, depending on which circuit is under consideration. When $R$ becomes large enough that it is comparable with $r_o$, $r_o$ must be included in the small-signal model to accurately predict not only the input resistance, but also the output resistance. On the other hand, since the transconductance is calculated with the output shorted, the relationship between $r_o$ and $R$ has no effect on this calculation, and the effect of finite $r_o$ on transconductance can be ignored if $r_o \gg 1/G_m$.

#### 3.3.5.1 Common-Base and Common-Gate Input Resistance

Figure 3.22$a$ shows a small-signal T model of a common-base or common-gate stage including finite $r_o$, where $R_{i(\text{ideal})}$ is given by (3.31) for a common-base amplifier or by (3.43) for a common-gate amplifier. Also, $R$ represents $R_C$ in Fig. 3.17 or $R_D$ in Fig. 3.21. Connections to the load and the input source are shown in Fig. 3.22$a$ to include their contributions to the input and output resistance, respectively. In Fig. 3.22$a$, the input resistance is $R_i = v_1/i_i$. To find the input resistance, a simplified equivalent circuit such as in Fig. 3.22$b$ is often used. Here, a test voltage source $v_t$ is used to drive the amplifier input, and the resulting test current $i_t$ is calculated. KCL at the output node in Fig. 3.22$b$ gives

$$\frac{v_o}{R \parallel R_L} + \frac{v_o - v_t}{r_o} = G_m v_t \tag{3.47}$$

KCL at the input in Fig. 3.22$b$ gives

$$i_t = \frac{v_t}{R_{i(\text{ideal})}} + \frac{v_t - v_o}{r_o} \tag{3.48}$$

Solving (3.47) for $v_o$ and substituting into (3.48) gives

$$\frac{i_t}{v_t} = \frac{1}{R_{i(\text{ideal})}} + \frac{1}{r_o}\left(1 - \frac{G_m + \dfrac{1}{r_o}}{\dfrac{1}{R \parallel R_L} + \dfrac{1}{r_o}}\right) \tag{3.49}$$

Rearranging (3.49) gives

$$R_i = \frac{v_t}{i_t} = \frac{r_o + R \parallel R_L}{1 - G_m(R \parallel R_L) + \dfrac{r_o + R \parallel R_L}{R_{i(\text{ideal})}}} \tag{3.50}$$

**Common-Base Input Resistance.**  For the common-base amplifier, $G_m = g_m$ from (3.30), and $R_{i(\text{ideal})} = r_e = \alpha_0/g_m$ from (3.31). Substituting (3.30) and (3.31) into (3.50) with

**Figure 3.22** (a) Model of common-base and common-gate amplifiers with finite $r_o$, showing connections to the input source and load. (b) Equivalent circuit for calculation of $R_i$. (c) Equivalent circuit for calculation of $R_o$.

$R = R_C$ and rearranging gives

$$R_i = \frac{v_t}{i_t} = \frac{r_o + R_C \| R_L}{1 + \dfrac{g_m(R_C \| R_L)}{\beta_0} + \dfrac{g_m r_o}{\alpha_0}} = \frac{r_o + R_C \| R_L}{1 + \dfrac{g_m}{\beta_0} \left(R_C \| R_L + (\beta_0 + 1) r_o\right)} \tag{3.51}$$

From (3.51), when $(\beta_0 + 1)r_o \gg R_C \| R_L$,

$$R_i \simeq \frac{r_o + R_C \| R_L}{1 + \dfrac{g_m r_o}{\alpha_0}} \tag{3.52}$$

From (3.52), when $g_m r_o \gg \alpha_0$,

$$R_i \simeq \frac{\alpha_0}{g_m} + \frac{\alpha_0 (R_C \| R_L)}{g_m r_o} = r_e + \frac{\alpha_0 (R_C \| R_L)}{g_m r_o} \tag{3.53}$$

The first term on the right side of (3.53) is the same as in (3.31), where the common-base amplifier was unilateral because infinite $r_o$ was assumed. The second term shows that the input resistance now depends on the connection to the output (because finite $r_o$ provides feedback and makes the amplifier bilateral). The second term is about equal to the resistance at the amplifier output divided by the $G_m r_o$ product. When $r_o \gg (R_C \| R_L)$, the effect of the second term can be neglected.

**Common-Gate Input Resistance.** For the common-gate amplifier, $G_m = (g_m + g_{mb})$ from (3.42) and $R_{i(ideal)} = 1/(g_m + g_{mb})$ from (3.43). Substituting (3.42) and (3.43) into

(3.50) with $R = R_D$ and rearranging gives

$$R_i = \frac{v_t}{i_t} = \frac{r_o + R_D \parallel R_L}{1 + (g_m + g_{mb}) r_o} \tag{3.54}$$

When $(g_m + g_{mb}) r_o \gg 1$,

$$R_i \simeq \frac{1}{g_m + g_{mb}} + \frac{R_D \parallel R_L}{(g_m + g_{mb}) r_o} \tag{3.55}$$

The first term on the right side of (3.55) is the same as in (3.43), where the common-gate amplifier was unilateral because infinite $r_o$ was assumed. The second term is about equal to the resistance at the amplifier output divided by the $G_m r_o$ product and shows the effect of finite $r_o$, which makes the circuit bilateral. When $r_o \gg (R_D \parallel R_L)$, the effect of the second term can be neglected. Neglecting the second term usually causes only a small error when $R_D$ here or $R_C$ in the common-base case is built as a physical resistor even if the amplifier is unloaded ($R_L \rightarrow \infty$). However, when $R_D$ or $R_C$ is replaced by a transistor current source, the effect of the second term can be significant. Chapter 4 describes techniques used to construct transistor current sources that can have very high equivalent resistance.

### 3.3.5.2 Common-Base and Common-Gate Output Resistance

The output resistance in Fig. 3.22a is $R_o = v_o/i_o$ with $v_s = 0$. For this calculation, consider the equivalent circuit shown in Fig. 3.22c, where $v_s = 0$. A test voltage $v_t$ is used to drive the amplifier output, and the resulting test current $i_t$ can be calculated. Since $R$ appears in parallel with the amplifier output, the calculation will be done in two steps. First, the output resistance with $R \rightarrow \infty$ is calculated. Second, this result is placed in parallel with $R$ to give the overall output resistance. From KCL at the input node in Fig. 3.22c,

$$\frac{v_1}{R_S} + \frac{v_1}{R_{i(\text{ideal})}} + \frac{v_1 - v_t}{r_o} = 0 \tag{3.56}$$

With $R \rightarrow \infty$, KCL at the output node gives

$$i_t = -G_m v_1 + \frac{v_t - v_1}{r_o} \tag{3.57}$$

Solving (3.56) for $v_1$ and substituting into (3.57) gives

$$\frac{i_t}{v_t} = \frac{1}{r_o} - \frac{1}{r_o} \left( \frac{G_m + \dfrac{1}{r_o}}{\dfrac{1}{R_S} + \dfrac{1}{R_{i(\text{ideal})}} + \dfrac{1}{r_o}} \right) \tag{3.58}$$

Rearranging (3.58) gives

$$\frac{v_t}{i_t} = \frac{r_o \left( \dfrac{1}{R_S} + \dfrac{1}{R_{i(\text{ideal})}} + \dfrac{1}{r_o} \right)}{\dfrac{1}{R_S} + \dfrac{1}{R_{i(\text{ideal})}} - G_m} \tag{3.59}$$

With finite $R$, the output resistance is

$$R_o = R \parallel \left( \frac{v_t}{i_t} \right) = R \parallel \left[ \frac{r_o \left( \dfrac{1}{R_S} + \dfrac{1}{R_{i(\text{ideal})}} + \dfrac{1}{r_o} \right)}{\dfrac{1}{R_S} + \dfrac{1}{R_{i(\text{ideal})}} - G_m} \right] \tag{3.60}$$

**Common-Base Output Resistance.** For the common-base amplifier, $G_m = g_m$ from (3.30) and $R_{i(\text{ideal})} = r_e = \alpha_0/g_m$ from (3.31). Substituting (3.30) and (3.31) into (3.60) and rearranging gives

$$R_o = R \left\| \left[ \frac{r_o + R_S \left( 1 + \dfrac{g_m r_o}{\alpha_0} \right)}{1 + \dfrac{R_S}{r_\pi}} \right] \right. \tag{3.61}$$

The term in brackets on the right side of (3.61) shows that the output resistance of the common-base amplifier depends on the resistance of the input source $R_S$ when $r_o$ is finite. For example, if the input comes from an ideal voltage source, $R_S = 0$ and

$$R_o = R \parallel r_o \tag{3.62}$$

On the other hand, if the input comes from an ideal current source, $R_S \rightarrow \infty$ and

$$R_o = R \left\| \left[ \left( \frac{1 + g_m r_o}{\alpha_0} \right) r_\pi \right] \right. \tag{3.63}$$

From (3.61), when $R_S \ll r_\pi$,

$$R_o \simeq R \left\| \left[ r_o + R_S \left( \frac{1 + g_m r_o}{\alpha_0} \right) \right] \right. \tag{3.64}$$

From (3.64), when $g_m r_o \gg \alpha_0$ and $g_m R_S \gg \alpha_0$,

$$R_o \simeq R \left\| \left( \frac{g_m r_o}{\alpha_0} R_S \right) \right. \tag{3.65}$$

The term in parentheses in (3.65) is about equal to the input source resistance multiplied by the $G_m r_o$ product. Therefore, (3.65) and (3.53) together show that the common-base amplifier can be thought of as a resistance scaler, where the resistance is scaled up from the emitter to the collector and down from the collector to the emitter by a factor approximately equal to the $G_m r_o$ product in each case.

**Common-Gate Output Resistance.** For the common-gate amplifier, $G_m = (g_m + g_{mb})$ from (3.42) and $R_{i(\text{ideal})} = 1/(g_m + g_{mb})$ from (3.43). Substituting (3.42) and (3.43) into (3.60) and rearranging gives

$$R_o = R \parallel [r_o + R_S (1 + (g_m + g_{mb}) r_o)] \tag{3.66}$$

From (3.66), when $(g_m + g_{mb}) r_o \gg 1$ and $(g_m + g_{mb}) \cdot R_S \gg 1$,

$$R_o \simeq R \parallel ((g_m + g_{mb}) r_o R_S) \tag{3.67}$$

The term in parentheses in (3.67) is equal to the input source resistance multiplied by the $G_m r_o$ product. Therefore, (3.67) and (3.55) together show that the common-gate amplifier is also a resistance scaler, where the resistance is scaled up from the source to the drain and down from the drain to the source by a factor approximately equal to the $G_m r_o$ product in each case.

### 3.3.6 Common-Collector Configuration (Emitter Follower)

The common-collector connection is shown in Fig. 3.23a. The distinguishing feature of this configuration is that the signal is applied to the base and the output is taken from the

**Figure 3.23** (a) Common-collector configuration. (b) Small-signal equivalent circuit of the emitter-follower circuit including $R_L$ and $R_S$.

emitter.[4] From a large-signal standpoint, the output voltage is equal to the input voltage minus the base-emitter voltage. Since the base-emitter voltage is a logarithmic function of the collector current, the base-emitter voltage is almost constant even when the collector current varies. If the base-emitter voltage were exactly constant, the output voltage of the common-collector amplifier would be equal to the input voltage minus a constant offset, and the small-signal gain of the circuit would be unity. For this reason, the circuit is also known as an *emitter follower* because the emitter voltage follows the base voltage. In practice, the base-emitter voltage is not exactly constant if the collector current varies. For example, (1.82) shows that the base-emitter voltage must increase by about 18 mV to double the collector current and by about 60 mV to increase the collector current by a factor of 10 at room temperature. Furthermore, even if the collector current were exactly constant, the base-emitter voltage depends to some extent on the collector-emitter voltage if the Early voltage is finite. These effects are most easily studied using small-signal analysis.

The appropriate small-signal transistor model is the hybrid-$\pi$, and the small-signal equivalent circuit is shown in Fig. 3.23b. When the input voltage $v_s$ increases, the base-emitter voltage of the transistor increases, which increases the output current $i_o$. However, increasing $i_o$ increases the output voltage $v_o$, which decreases the base-emitter voltage by negative feedback. Negative feedback is covered thoroughly in Chapter 8. The key point here is that the common-collector configuration is not unilateral. As a result, the input resistance depends on the load resistor $R_L$ and the output resistance depends on the source resistance $R_S$. Therefore, the characterization of the emitter follower by the corresponding equivalent two-port network is not particularly useful for intuitive understanding. Instead, we will analyze the entire emitter-follower circuit of Fig. 3.23b, including both the source resistance $R_S$ and the load resistor $R_L$. From KCL at the output node, we find

$$\frac{v_s - v_o}{R_S + r_\pi} + \beta_0 \left( \frac{v_s - v_o}{R_S + r_\pi} \right) - \frac{v_o}{R_L} - \frac{v_o}{r_o} = 0 \qquad (3.68)$$

from which we find

$$\frac{v_o}{v_s} = \frac{1}{1 + \dfrac{R_S + r_\pi}{(\beta_0 + 1)(R_L \| r_o)}} \tag{3.69}$$

If the base resistance $r_b$ is significant, it can simply be added to $R_S$ in these expressions. The voltage gain is always less than unity and will be close to unity if $\beta_0 (R_L \| r_o) \gg (R_S + r_\pi)$. In most practical circuits, this condition holds. Note that because we have included the source resistance in this calculation, the value of $v_o/v_s$ is not analogous to $a_v$ calculated for the CE and CB stages. When $r_\pi \gg R_S$, $\beta_0 \gg 1$, and $r_o \gg R_L$, (3.69) can be approximated as

$$\frac{v_o}{v_s} \simeq \frac{g_m R_L}{1 + g_m R_L} \tag{3.70}$$

We calculate the input resistance $R_i$ by removing the input source, driving the input with a test current source $i_t$, and calculating the resulting voltage $v_t$ across the input terminals. The circuit used to do this calculation is shown in Fig. 3.24a. From KCL at the output node,

$$\frac{v_o}{R_L} + \frac{v_o}{r_o} = i_t + \beta_0 i_t \tag{3.71}$$

Then the voltage $v_t$ is

$$v_t = i_t r_\pi + v_o = i_t r_\pi + \frac{i_t + \beta_0 i_t}{\dfrac{1}{R_L} + \dfrac{1}{r_o}} \tag{3.72}$$

and thus

$$R_i = \frac{v_t}{i_t} = r_\pi + (\beta_0 + 1)(R_L \| r_o) \tag{3.73}$$

A general property of emitter followers is that the resistance looking into the base is equal to $r_\pi$ plus $(\beta_0 + 1)$ times the incremental resistance connected from the emitter to small-signal ground. The factor of $\beta_0 + 1$ in (3.73) stems from the current gain of the common-collector configuration from the base to the emitter, which increases the voltage drop on the resistance connected from the emitter to small-signal ground and its contribution to the test voltage $v_t$ in (3.72).

We now calculate the output resistance $R_o$ by removing the load resistance $R_L$ and finding the Thévenin-equivalent resistance looking into the output terminals. We can do this by either inserting a test current and calculating the resulting voltage or applying a test voltage and calculating the current. In this case, the calculation is simpler if a test voltage $v_t$ is applied as shown in Fig. 3.24b. The voltage $v_1$ is given by

$$v_1 = -v_t\left(\frac{r_\pi}{r_\pi + R_S}\right) \tag{3.74}$$

The total output current $i_t$ is thus

$$i_t = \frac{v_t}{r_\pi + R_S} + \frac{v_t}{r_o} + g_m v_t\left(\frac{r_\pi}{r_\pi + R_S}\right) \tag{3.75}$$

**Figure 3.24** (a) Circuit for calculation of the input resistance of the emitter follower. (b) Circuit for calculation of the output resistance of the emitter follower. (c) Example emitter follower.

Therefore,

$$R_o = \frac{v_t}{i_t} = \left(\frac{r_\pi + R_S}{\beta_0 + 1}\right) \| r_o \qquad (3.76)$$

If $\beta_0 \gg 1$ and $r_o \gg (1/g_m) + R_S/(\beta_0 + 1)$,

$$R_o \simeq \frac{1}{g_m} + \frac{R_S}{\beta_0 + 1} \qquad (3.77)$$

Equation 3.77 shows that the resistance at the output is about equal to the resistance in the base lead, divided by $(\beta_0 + 1)$, plus $1/g_m$. In (3.77), $R_S$ is divided by $\beta_0 + 1$ because the base current flows in $R_S$, and the base current is $\beta_0 + 1$ times smaller than the emitter current.

Therefore, the emitter follower has high input resistance, low output resistance, and near-unity voltage gain. It is most widely used as an impedance transformer to reduce loading of a preceding signal source by the input impedance of a following stage. It also finds application as a unity-voltage-gain level shift because the dc output voltage is shifted from the dc input voltage by $V_{BE(\text{on})}$.

■  **EXAMPLE**

Calculate the input resistance, output resistance, and voltage gain of the emitter follower of Fig. 3.24c. Assume that $\beta_0 = 100$, $r_b = 0$, $r_o \to \infty$, and $I_C = 100\ \mu\text{A}$.

$$R_i = r_\pi + R_L(1 + \beta_0) = 26\ \text{k}\Omega + (1\ \text{k}\Omega)(101) = 127\ \text{k}\Omega$$

$$\frac{v_o}{v_s} = \frac{1}{1 + \dfrac{r_\pi + R_S}{(\beta_0 + 1)R_L}} = \frac{1}{1 + \dfrac{26\ \text{k}\Omega + 1\ \text{k}\Omega}{(101)(1\ \text{k}\Omega)}} \approx 0.79$$

$$R_o = \frac{R_S + r_\pi}{1 + \beta_0} = \frac{1\ \text{k}\Omega + 26\ \text{k}\Omega}{101} \approx 270\ \Omega$$

■

### 3.3.7 Common-Drain Configuration (Source Follower)

The common-drain configuration is shown in Fig. 3.25a. The input signal is applied to the gate and the output is taken from the source. From a large-signal standpoint, the output voltage is equal to the input voltage minus the gate-source voltage. The gate-source voltage consists of two parts: the threshold and the overdrive. If both parts are constant, the resulting output voltage is simply offset from the input, and the small-signal gain would be unity. Therefore, the source follows the gate, and the circuit is also known as a *source follower*. In practice, the body effect changes the threshold voltage, and the overdrive depends on the drain current, which changes as the output voltage changes unless $R_L \to \infty$. Furthermore, even if the current were exactly constant, the overdrive depends to some extent on the drain-source voltage unless the Early voltage is infinite. We will use small-signal analysis to study these effects.

The small-signal equivalent circuit is shown in Fig. 3.25b. Since the body terminal is not shown in Fig. 3.25a, we assume that the body is connected to the lowest supply voltage (ground here) to keep the source-body $pn$ junction reverse biased. As a result, $v_{bs}$ changes when the output changes because the source is connected to the output, and the $g_{mb}$ generator is active in general.

From KVL around the input loop,

$$v_i = v_{gs} + v_o \tag{3.78}$$

With the output open circuited, $i_o = 0$, and KCL at the output node gives

$$g_m v_{gs} - g_{mb} v_o - \frac{v_o}{R_L} - \frac{v_o}{r_o} = 0 \tag{3.79}$$

Solving (3.78) for $v_{gs}$, substituting into (3.79), and rearranging gives

$$\left.\frac{v_o}{v_i}\right|_{i_o=0} = \frac{g_m}{g_m + g_{mb} + \dfrac{1}{R_L} + \dfrac{1}{r_o}} = \frac{g_m r_o}{1 + (g_m + g_{mb})r_o + \dfrac{r_o}{R_L}} \tag{3.80}$$

If $R_L \to \infty$, (3.80) simplifies to

$$\lim_{R_L \to \infty} \left.\frac{v_o}{v_i}\right|_{i_o=0} = \frac{g_m r_o}{1 + (g_m + g_{mb})r_o} \tag{3.81}$$

**Figure 3.25** (a) Common-drain configuration. (b) Small-signal equivalent circuit of the common-drain configuration.

Equation 3.81 gives the open-circuit voltage gain of the source follower with the load resistor replaced by an ideal current source. If $r_o$ is finite, this gain is less than unity even if the body effect is eliminated by connecting the source to the body to deactivate the $g_{mb}$ generator. In this case, variation in the output voltage changes the drain-source voltage and the current through $r_o$. From a large-signal standpoint, solving (1.165) for $V_{GS} - V_t$ shows that the overdrive also depends on the drain-source voltage unless the channel-length modulation parameter $\lambda$ is zero. This dependence causes the small-signal gain to be less than unity.

A significant difference between bipolar and MOS followers is apparent from (3.80). If $R_L \to \infty$ and $r_o \to \infty$,

$$\lim_{\substack{R_L \to \infty \\ r_o \to \infty}} \frac{v_o}{v_i} = \frac{g_m}{g_m + g_{mb}} = \frac{1}{1 + \chi} \tag{3.82}$$

Equation 3.82 shows that the source-follower gain is less than unity under these conditions and that the gain depends on $\chi = g_{mb}/g_m$, which is typically in the range of 0.1 to 0.3. In contrast, the gain of an emitter follower would be unity under these conditions. As a result, the source-follower gain is not as well specified as that of an emitter follower when body effect is a factor. Furthermore, (1.200) shows that $\chi$ depends on the source-body voltage which is equal to $V_o$ when the body is connected to ground. Therefore, the gain calculated in (3.82) depends on the output voltage, causing distortion to arise for large-signal changes in the output as shown in Section 5.3.2. To overcome these limitations in practice, the type of source follower (n-channel or p-channel) can be chosen so that it can be fabricated in an isolated well. Then the well can be connected to the source of the transistor, setting $V_{SB} = 0$ and $v_{sb} = 0$. Unfortunately, the parasitic capacitance from the well to the substrate increases the capacitance attached to the source with this connection, reducing the bandwidth of the source follower. The frequency response of source followers is covered in Chapter 7.

The output resistance of the source follower can be calculated from Fig. 3.25$b$ by setting $v_i = 0$ and driving the output with a voltage source $v_o$. Then $v_{gs} = -v_o$ and $i_o$ is

$$i_o = \frac{v_o}{r_o} + \frac{v_o}{R_L} + g_m v_o + g_{mb} v_o \qquad (3.83)$$

Rearranging (3.83) gives

$$R_o = \frac{v_o}{i_o} = \frac{1}{g_m + g_{mb} + \dfrac{1}{r_o} + \dfrac{1}{R_L}} \qquad (3.84)$$

Equation 3.84 shows that the body effect reduces the output resistance, which is desirable because the source follower produces a voltage output. This beneficial effect stems from the nonzero small-signal current conducted by the $g_{mb}$ generator in Fig. 3.25$b$, which increases the output current for a given change in the output voltage. As $r_o \rightarrow \infty$ and $R_L \rightarrow \infty$, this output resistance approaches $1/(g_m + g_{mb})$. The common-gate input resistance given in (3.54) approaches the same limiting value.

As with emitter followers, source followers are used as voltage buffers and level shifters. When used as a level shifter, they are more flexible than emitter followers because the dc value of $V_{GS}$ can be altered by changing the $W/L$ ratio.

### 3.3.8 Common-Emitter Amplifier with Emitter Degeneration

In the common-emitter amplifier considered earlier, the signal is applied to the base, the output is taken from the collector, and the emitter is attached to ac ground. In practice, however, the common-emitter circuit is often used with a nonzero resistance in series with the emitter as shown in Fig. 3.26$a$. The resistance has several effects, including reducing the transconductance, increasing the output resistance, and increasing the input resistance. These changes stem from negative feedback introduced by the emitter resistor $R_E$. When $V_i$ increases, the base-emitter voltage increases, which increases the collector current. As a result, the voltage dropped across the emitter resistor increases, reducing the base-emitter voltage compared to the case where $R_E = 0$. Therefore, the presence of nonzero $R_E$ reduces the base-emitter voltage through a negative-feedback process termed *emitter degeneration*. This circuit is examined from a feedback standpoint in Chapter 8.

In this section, we calculate the input resistance, output resistance, and transconductance of the emitter-degenerated, common-emitter amplifier. To find the input resistance and transconductance, consider the small-signal equivalent circuit shown in Fig. 3.26$b$, and focus on $v_i$, $i_b$, and $i_o$. From KCL at the emitter,

$$\frac{v_e}{R_E} + \frac{v_e + i_o R_C}{r_o} = (\beta_0 + 1) i_b \qquad (3.85)$$

From KCL at the collector,

$$i_o + \frac{v_e + i_o R_C}{r_o} = \beta_0 i_b \qquad (3.86)$$

From KVL around the input loop,

$$i_b = \frac{v_i - v_e}{r_\pi} \qquad (3.87)$$

(a)

**Figure 3.26** (a) Common-emitter amplifier with emitter degeneration. (b) Small-signal equivalent circuit for emitter-degenerated, common-emitter amplifier. (c) Circuit for calculation of output resistance. (d) Small-signal, two-port equivalent of emitter-degenerated CE amplifier.

(b)

(c)

(d)

$$R_i \simeq r_\pi \, (1 + g_m R_E)$$

$$R_o \simeq r_o \, (1 + g_m R_E)$$

$$G_m \simeq \left( \frac{g_m}{1 + g_m R_E} \right)$$

Solving (3.85) for $i_o$, substituting into (3.86) and rearranging gives

$$v_e = i_b \left( \frac{1 + (\beta_0 + 1)\dfrac{r_o}{R_C}}{\dfrac{1}{R_C} + \dfrac{1}{R_E} + \dfrac{r_o}{R_C R_E}} \right) \tag{3.88}$$

Substituting (3.88) into (3.87) and rearranging gives

$$R_i = \frac{v_i}{i_b} = r_\pi + (\beta_0 + 1) R_E \left( \frac{r_o + \dfrac{R_C}{\beta_0 + 1}}{r_o + R_C + R_E} \right) \tag{3.89}$$

If $r_o \gg R_C$ and $r_o \gg R_E$, the last term in parentheses in (3.89) is approximately equal to unity and

$$R_i \simeq r_\pi + (\beta_0 + 1) R_E \tag{3.90}$$

Because the last term in parentheses in (3.89) is less than one, comparing (3.89) and (3.90) shows that finite $r_o$ reduces the input resistance of the common-emitter amplifier with emitter degeneration. This reduction stems from nonzero current that flows in $r_o$ when $r_o$ is finite. If $v_i$ increases, $v_e$ follows $v_i$ because the base-emitter voltage is approximately constant, but the collector voltage $(-i_o R_C)$ decreases by an amount determined by the small-signal gain from the base to the collector. Therefore, the current that flows in $r_o$ from the emitter to the collector increases, increasing the base current and reducing the input resistance. In practice, (3.90) is usually used to calculate the input resistance. The error in the approximation is usually small unless the resistances represented by $R_C$ or $R_E$ are large, such as when implemented with transistors in active-load configurations. Active loads are considered in Chapter 4.

Now we will calculate the transconductance of the stage. First, set $R_C = 0$ in Fig. 3.26b because $G_m = i_o/v_i$ with the output shorted. Substituting (3.87) into (3.85) with $R_C = 0$ and rearranging gives

$$v_e = v_i \left( \frac{\dfrac{(\beta_0 + 1)}{r_\pi}}{\dfrac{1}{R_E} + \dfrac{1}{r_o} + \dfrac{\beta_0 + 1}{r_\pi}} \right) \tag{3.91}$$

Substituting (3.87) and (3.91) into (3.86) with $R_C = 0$ and rearranging gives

$$G_m = \frac{i_o}{v_i} = g_m \left[ \frac{1 - \dfrac{R_E}{\beta_0 r_o}}{1 + g_m R_E \left( 1 + \dfrac{1}{\beta_0} + \dfrac{1}{g_m r_o} \right)} \right] \tag{3.92}$$

In most practical cases, $\beta_0 \gg 1$, $r_o \gg R_E$, and $g_m r_o \gg 1$. Then

$$G_m \simeq \frac{g_m}{1 + g_m R_E} \tag{3.93}$$

Equation 3.93 is usually used to calculate the transconductance of a common-emitter amplifier with emitter degeneration.

The output resistance is calculated using the equivalent circuit of Fig. 3.26c. For the time being, assume that $R_C$ is very large and can be neglected. The test current $i_t$ flows in the parallel combination of $r_\pi$ and $R_E$, so that

$$v_1 = -i_t(r_\pi \parallel R_E) \tag{3.94}$$

The current through $r_o$ is

$$i_1 = i_t - g_m v_1 = i_t + i_t g_m (r_\pi \parallel R_E) \tag{3.95}$$

As a result, the voltage $v_t$ is

$$v_t = -v_1 + i_1 r_o = i_t (r_\pi \parallel R_E) + i_t r_o [1 + g_m (r_\pi \parallel R_E)] \tag{3.96}$$

Thus

$$R_o = \frac{v_t}{i_t} = (r_\pi \parallel R_E) + r_o [1 + g_m (r_\pi \parallel R_E)] \tag{3.97}$$

In this equation, the first term is much smaller than the second. If the first term is neglected, we obtain,

$$R_o \simeq r_o \left(1 + g_m \frac{r_\pi R_E}{r_\pi + R_E}\right) = r_o \left(1 + \frac{g_m R_E}{1 + \frac{R_E}{r_\pi}}\right) = r_o \left(1 + \frac{g_m R_E}{1 + \frac{g_m R_E}{\beta_0}}\right) \tag{3.98}$$

If $g_m R_E \ll \beta_0$, then

$$\boxed{R_o \simeq r_o (1 + g_m R_E)} \tag{3.99}$$

Thus the output resistance is increased by a factor $(1 + g_m R_E)$. This fact makes the use of emitter degeneration desirable in transistor current sources. If the collector load resistor $R_C$ is not large enough to neglect, it must be included in parallel with the expressions in (3.97)–(3.99). A small-signal equivalent circuit, neglecting $R_C$, is shown in Fig. 3.26d. On the other hand, if $g_m R_E \gg \beta_0$, (3.98) shows that

$$R_o \simeq r_o (1 + \beta_0) \tag{3.100}$$

The output resistance is finite even when $R_E \rightarrow \infty$ because nonzero test current flows in $r_\pi$ when $\beta_0$ is finite.

### 3.3.9 Common-Source Amplifier with Source Degeneration

Source degeneration in MOS transistor amplifiers is not as widely used as emitter degeneration in bipolar circuits for at least two reasons. First, the transconductance of MOS transistors is normally much lower than that of bipolar transistors so that further reduction in transconductance is usually undesirable. Second, although degeneration increases the input resistance in the bipolar case, $R_i \rightarrow \infty$ even without degeneration in the MOS case. However, examining the effects of source degeneration is important in part because it is widely used to increase the output resistance of MOS current sources. Also, because small-geometry MOS transistors can be modeled as ideal square-law devices with added source resistors as shown in Section 1.7.1, we will consider the effects of source degeneration below.

A common-source amplifier with source degeneration is shown in Fig. 3.27. Its small-signal equivalent circuit is shown in Fig. 3.28. Because the input is connected to the gate of the MOS transistor, $R_i \rightarrow \infty$. To calculate the transconductance, set $R_D = 0$ because $G_m = i_o/v_i$ with the output shorted. Also, since a connection to the body is not shown in

**Figure 3.27** Common-source amplifier with source degeneration.

**Figure 3.28** Small-signal equivalent of the source-degenerated, common-source amplifier.

Fig. 3.27, we assume that the body is connected to the lowest power-supply voltage, which is ground. Therefore, the dc body voltage is constant and $v_b = 0$. From KCL at the source with $R_D = 0$,

$$\frac{v_s}{R_S} + \frac{v_s}{r_o} = g_m (v_i - v_s) + g_{mb} (0 - v_s) \qquad (3.101)$$

From KCL at the drain with $R_D = 0$,

$$i_o + \frac{v_s}{r_o} = g_m (v_i - v_s) + g_{mb} (0 - v_s) \qquad (3.102)$$

Solving (3.101) for $v_s$, substituting into (3.102), and rearranging gives

$$G_m = \frac{i_o}{v_i} = \frac{g_m}{1 + (g_m + g_{mb}) R_S + \dfrac{R_S}{r_o}} \qquad (3.103)$$

If $r_o \gg R_S$,

$$G_m \simeq \frac{g_m}{1 + (g_m + g_{mb}) R_S} \qquad (3.104)$$

For large $R_S$, (3.104) shows that the value of $G_m$ approaches $1/[(1 + \chi) R_S]$. Even in this limiting case, the transconductance of the common-source amplifier with degeneration is dependent on an active-device parameter $\chi$. Since $\chi$ is typically in the range of 0.1 to 0.3, the body effect causes the transconductance in this case to deviate from $1/R_S$ by about 10 to 20 percent. In contrast, (3.92) indicates that the value of $G_m$ for a common-emitter amplifier with degeneration approaches $\beta_0/[(\beta_0 + 1) R_E]$ for large $R_E$, assuming that $r_o \gg R_E$ and $g_m r_o \gg 1$. If $\beta_0 > 100$, the transconductance of this bipolar amplifier is within 1 percent of $1/R_E$. Therefore, the transconductance of a common-source amplifier with degeneration is usually much more dependent on active-device parameters than in its bipolar counterpart.

**Figure 3.29** Circuit for calcula
tion of output resistance.

The output resistance of the circuit can be calculated from the equivalent circuit of Fig. 3.29, where $R_D$ is neglected. Since the entire test current flows in $R_S$,

$$v_s = i_t R_S \tag{3.105}$$

Then

$$v_t = v_s + i_1 r_o = v_s + r_o \left[ i_t - g_m (0 - v_s) - g_{mb} (0 - v_s) \right] \tag{3.106}$$

Substituting (3.105) into (3.106) and rearranging gives

$$R_o = \frac{v_t}{i_t} = R_S + r_o \left[ 1 + (g_m + g_{mb}) R_S \right] \tag{3.107}$$

This equation shows that as $R_S$ is made arbitrarily large, the value of $R_o$ continues to increase. In contrast, (3.100) shows that $R_o$ in the common-emitter amplifier with degeneration approaches a maximum value of about $(\beta_0 + 1) \, r_o$ as $R_E \to \infty$.

## 3.4 Multiple-Transistor Amplifier Stages

Most integrated-circuit amplifiers consist of a number of stages, each of which provides voltage gain, current gain, and/or impedance-level transformation from input to output. Such circuits can be analyzed by considering each transistor to be a *stage* and analyzing the circuit as a collection of individual transistors. However, certain combinations of transistors occur so frequently that these combinations are usually characterized as *subcircuits* and regarded as a single stage. The usefulness of these topologies varies considerably with the technology being used. For example, the Darlington two-transistor connection is widely used in bipolar integrated circuits to improve the effective current gain and input resistance of a single bipolar transistor. Since the current gain and input resistance are infinite with MOS transistors however, this connection finds little use in pure MOS integrated circuits. On the other hand, the cascode connection achieves a very high output resistance and is useful in both bipolar and MOS technologies.

### 3.4.1 The CC-CE, CC-CC and Darlington Configurations

The common-collector–common-emitter (CC-CE), common-collector–common-collector (CC-CC), and Darlington[5] configurations are all closely related. They incorporate an additional transistor to boost the current gain and input resistance of the basic bipolar transistor. The common-collector–common-emitter configuration is shown in Fig. 3.30a. The biasing current source $I_{BIAS}$ is present to establish the quiescent dc operating current in the emitter-follower transistor $Q_1$; this current source may be absent in some cases or may be replaced by a resistor. The common-collector–common-collector configuration is

Figure 3.30  (a) Common-collector–common-emitter cascade. (b) Common-collector–common-collector cascade.

illustrated in Fig. 3.30b. In both of these configurations, the effect of transistor $Q_1$ is to increase the current gain through the stage and to increase the input resistance. For the purpose of the low-frequency, small-signal analysis of circuits, the two transistors $Q_1$ and $Q_2$ can be thought of as a single composite transistor, as illustrated in Fig. 3.31. The small-signal equivalent circuit for this composite device is shown in Fig. 3.32, assuming that the effects of the $r_o$ of $Q_1$ are negligible. We will now calculate effective values for the $r_\pi$, $g_m$, $\beta_0$, and $r_o$ of the composite device, and we will designate these composite parameters with a superscript $c$. We will also denote the terminal voltages and currents of the composite device with a superscript $c$. We assume that $\beta_0$ is constant.

The effective value of $r_\pi$, $r_\pi^c$, is the resistance seen looking into the composite base $B^c$ with the composite emitter $E^c$ grounded. Referring to Fig. 3.32, we see that the resistance looking into the base of $Q_2$ with $E^c$ grounded is simply $r_{\pi 2}$. Thus (3.73) for the input resistance of the emitter follower can be used. Substituting $r_{\pi 2}$ for $R_L$ and allowing

Figure 3.31  The composite transistor representation of the CC-CE and CC-CC connections.

Figure 3.32  Small-signal equivalent circuit for the CC-CE and CC-CC connected transistors.

$r_o \to \infty$ gives

$$r_\pi^c = r_{\pi 1} + (\beta_0 + 1) \, r_{\pi 2} \qquad (3.108)$$

The effective transconductance of the configuration $g_m^c$ is the change in the collector current of $Q_2$, $i_c^c$, for a unit change in $v_{be}^c$ with $C^c$ and $E^c$ grounded. To calculate this transconductance, we first find the change in $v_2$ that occurs for a unit change in $v_{be}^c$. Equation 3.69 can be used directly, giving

$$\frac{v_2}{v_{be}^c} = \frac{1}{1 + \left( \dfrac{r_{\pi 1}}{(\beta_0 + 1) \, r_{\pi 2}} \right)} \qquad (3.109)$$

Also

$$i_c^c = g_m^c v_{be}^c = g_{m2} v_2 = \frac{g_{m2} v_{be}^c}{1 + \left( \dfrac{r_{\pi 1}}{(\beta_0 + 1) \, r_{\pi 2}} \right)} \qquad (3.110)$$

Thus

$$g_m^c = \frac{i_c^c}{v_{be}^c} = \frac{g_{m2}}{1 + \left( \dfrac{\cdot \, r_{\pi 1}}{(\beta_0 + 1) \, r_{\pi 2}} \right)} \qquad (3.111)$$

For the special case in which the biasing current source $I_{BIAS}$ is zero, the emitter current of $Q_1$ is equal to the base current of $Q_2$. Thus the ratio of $r_{\pi 1}$ to $r_{\pi 2}$ is $(\beta_0 + 1)$, and (3.111) reduces to

$$g_m^c = \frac{g_{m2}}{2} \qquad (3.112)$$

The effective current gain $\beta^c$ is the ratio

$$\beta^c = \frac{i_c^c}{i_b^c} = \frac{i_{c2}}{i_{b1}} \qquad (3.113)$$

The emitter current of $Q_1$ is given by

$$i_{e1} = (\beta_0 + 1) \, i_{b1} \qquad (3.114)$$

Since $i_{e1} = i_{b2}$,

$$i_{c2} = i_c^c = \beta_0 i_{b2} = \beta_0 (\beta_0 + 1) \, i_{b1} = \beta_0 (\beta_0 + 1) \, i_b^c \qquad (3.115)$$

Therefore,

$$\beta^c = \beta_0 (\beta_0 + 1) \qquad (3.116)$$

Equation 3.116 shows that the current gain of the composite transistor is approximately equal to $\beta_0^2$. Also, by inspection of Fig. 3.32, assuming $r_\mu$ is negligible, we have

$$r_o^c = r_{o2} \qquad (3.117)$$

The small-signal, two-port network equivalent for the CC-CE connection is shown in Fig. 3.33, where the collector resistor $R_C$ has not been included. This small-signal equivalent can be used to represent the small-signal operation of the composite device, simplifying the analysis of circuits containing this structure.

$$R_i^c = r_\pi^c = r_{\pi 1} + (\beta_0 + 1) \, r_{\pi 2}$$

$$G_m^c = g_m^c = \frac{g_{m2}}{1 + \left[ \dfrac{r_{\pi 1}}{(\beta_0 + 1) \, r_{\pi 2}} \right]}$$

$$R_o^c = r_o^c = r_{o2}$$

**Figure 3.33** Two-port representation, CC-CE connection.

The Darlington configuration, illustrated in Fig. 3.34, is a composite two-transistor device in which the collectors are tied together and the emitter of the first device drives the base of the second. A biasing element of some sort is used to control the emitter current of $Q_1$. The result is a three-terminal composite transistor that can be used in place of a single transistor in common-emitter, common-base, and common-collector configurations. When used as an emitter follower, the device is identical to the CC-CC connection already described. When used as a common-emitter amplifier, the device is very similar to the CC-CE connection, except that the collector of $Q_1$ is connected to the output instead of to the power supply. One effect of this change is to reduce the effective output resistance of the device because of feedback through the $r_o$ of $Q_1$. Also, this change increases the input capacitance because of the connection of the collector-base capacitance of $Q_1$ from the input to the output. Because of these drawbacks, the CC-CE connection is normally preferable in integrated small-signal amplifiers. The term *Darlington* is often used to refer to both the CC-CE and CC-CC connections.

As mentioned previously, Darlington-type connections are used to boost the effective current gain of bipolar transistors and have no significant application in pure-MOS circuits. In BiCMOS technologies, however, a potentially useful connection is shown in Fig. 3.35, where an MOS transistor is used for $Q_1$. This configuration not only realizes the infinite input resistance and current gain of the MOS transistor, but also the large transconductance of the bipolar transistor.

■ **EXAMPLE**

Find the effective $r_\pi^c$, $\beta^c$, and $g_m^c$ for the composite transistor shown in Fig. 3.31. For both devices, assume that $\beta_0 = 100$, $r_b = 0$, and $r_o \to \infty$. For $Q_2$, assume that $I_C = 100 \, \mu A$ and that $I_{BIAS} = 10 \, \mu A$.

**Figure 3.34** The Darlington configuration.

**Figure 3.35** Compound Darlington connection available in BiCMOS technology.

The base current of $Q_2$ is 100 $\mu$A/100 = 1 $\mu$A. Thus the emitter current of $Q_1$ is 11 $\mu$A. Then

$$r_{\pi 1} = \frac{\beta_0}{g_m} = \frac{100}{11\ \mu\text{A}/26\ \text{mV}} = 236\ \text{k}\Omega$$

$$g_{m1} = (2.36\ \text{k}\Omega)^{-1}$$

$$r_{\pi 2} = 26\ \text{k}\Omega$$

$$g_{m2} = (260\ \Omega)^{-1}$$

$$r_\pi^c = 236\ \text{k}\Omega + (101)(26\ \text{k}\Omega) = 2.8\ \text{M}\Omega$$

$$\beta^c = (101)(100) = 10,100$$

$$g_m^c = g_{m2}\,(0.916) = (283\ \Omega)^{-1}$$

Thus the composite transistor has much higher input resistance and current gain than a single transistor.

### 3.4.2 The Cascode Configuration

The cascode configuration was first invented for vacuum-tube circuits.[6,7] With vacuum tubes, the terminal that emits electrons is the *cathode*, the terminal that controls current flow is the *grid*, and the terminal that collects electrons is the *anode*. The *cascode* is a cascode of common-cathode and common-grid stages joined at the anode of the first stage and the cathode of the second stage. The cascode configuration is important mostly because it increases output resistance and reduces unwanted capacitive feedback in amplifiers, allowing operation at higher frequencies than would otherwise be possible. The high output resistance attainable is particularly useful in desensitizing bias references from variations in power-supply voltage and in achieving large amounts of voltage gain. These applications are described further in Chapter 4. The topic of frequency response is covered in Chapter 7. Here, we will focus on the low-frequency, small-signal properties of the cascode configuration.

#### 3.4.2.1 The Bipolar Cascode

In bipolar form, the cascode is a common-emitter–common-base (CE-CB) amplifier, as shown in Fig. 3.36. We will assume here that $r_b$ in both devices is zero. Although the base resistances have a negligible effect on the low-frequency performance, the effects of nonzero $r_b$ are important in the high-frequency performance of this combination. These effects are considered in Chapter 7.

**Figure 3.36** The cascode amplifier using bipolar transistors.

The small-signal equivalent for the bipolar cascode circuit is shown in Fig. 3.37. Since we are considering the low-frequency performance, we neglect the capacitances in the model of each transistor. We will determine the input resistance, output resistance, and transconductance of the cascode circuit. By inspection of Fig. 3.37, the input resistance is simply

$$R_i = r_{\pi 1} \tag{3.118}$$

Since the current gain from the emitter to the collector of $Q_2$ is nearly unity, the transconductance of the circuit from input to output is

$$G_m \simeq g_{m1} \tag{3.119}$$

The output resistance can be calculated by shorting the input $v_i$ to ground and applying a test signal at the output. Then $v_1 = 0$ in Fig. 3.37 and the $g_{m1}v_1$ generator is inactive. The circuit is then identical to that of Fig. 3.26c for a bipolar transistor with emitter degeneration. Therefore, using (3.98) with $R_E = r_{o1}$ shows that the output resistance is

$$R_o \simeq r_{o2}\left(1 + \frac{g_{m2}r_{o1}}{1 + \frac{g_{m2}r_{o1}}{\beta_0}}\right) \tag{3.120}$$

If $g_{m2}r_{o1} \gg \beta_0$ and $\beta_0 \gg 1$,

$$R_o \simeq \beta_0 r_{o2} \tag{3.121}$$

Therefore, the CE-CB connection displays an output resistance that is larger by a factor of about $\beta_0$ than the CE stage alone. If this circuit is operated with a hypothetical collector load that has infinite incremental resistance, the voltage gain is

$$A_v - \frac{v_o}{v_i} = -G_m R_o \simeq -g_{m1}r_{o2}\beta_0 = -\frac{\beta_0}{\eta} \tag{3.122}$$

**Figure 3.37** Small-signal equivalent circuit for the bipolar-transistor cascode connection.

Thus the magnitude of the maximum available voltage gain is higher by a factor $\beta_0$ than for the case of a single transistor. For a typical $npn$ transistor, the ratio of $\beta_0/\eta$ is approximately $2 \times 10^5$. In this analysis, we have neglected $r_\mu$. As described in Chapter 1, the value of $r_\mu$ for integrated-circuit $npn$ transistors is usually much larger than $\beta_0 r_o$, and then $r_\mu$ has little effect on $R_o$. For lateral $pnp$ transistors, however, $r_\mu$ is comparable with $\beta_0 r_o$ and decreases $R_o$ somewhat.

### 3.4.2.2 The MOS Cascode

In MOS form, the cascode is a common-source–common-gate (CS-CG) amplifier, as shown in Fig. 3.38. The small-signal equivalent circuit is shown in Fig. 3.39. Since the input is connected to the gate of $M_1$, the input resistance is

$$R_i \to \infty \tag{3.123}$$

To find the transconductance, set $R = 0$ to short the output and calculate the current $i_o$. From KCL at the output,

$$i_o + g_{m2}v_{ds1} + g_{mb2}v_{ds1} + \frac{v_{ds1}}{r_{o2}} = 0 \tag{3.124}$$

From KCL at the source of $M_2$,

$$g_{m1}v_i + g_{m2}v_{ds1} + g_{mb2}v_{ds1} + \frac{v_{ds1}}{r_{o1}} + \frac{v_{ds1}}{r_{o2}} = 0 \tag{3.125}$$

Solving (3.125) for $v_{ds1}$, substituting into (3.124), and rearranging gives

$$G_m = \frac{i_o}{v_i}\bigg|_{v_o=0} = g_{m1}\left(1 - \frac{1}{1 + (g_{m2} + g_{mb2})\,r_{o1} + \dfrac{r_{o1}}{r_{o2}}}\right) \simeq g_{m1} \tag{3.126}$$

Figure 3.38  Cascode amplifier using MOSFETs.

Figure 3.39  Small-signal equivalent circuit for the MOS-transistor cascode connection.

Equation 3.126 shows that the transconductance of the simple cascode is less than $g_{m1}$. If $(g_{m2} + g_{mb2}) r_{o1} \gg 1$, however, the difference is small, and the main point here is that the cascode configuration has little effect on the transconductance. This result stems from the observation that $R_{i2}$, the resistance looking in the source of $M_2$, is much less than $r_{o1}$. From (3.54) and (3.55) with $R = R_D \parallel R_L$,

$$R_{i2} = \frac{r_{o2} + R}{1 + (g_{m2} + g_{mb2}) r_{o2}} \simeq \frac{1}{g_{m2} + g_{mb2}} + \frac{R}{(g_{m2} + g_{mb2}) r_{o2}} \qquad (3.127)$$

In finding the transconductance, we set $R = 0$ so that $v_o = 0$. Then $R_{i2} \simeq 1/(g_m + g_{mb})$, and most of the $g_{m1} v_i$ current flows in the source of $M_2$ because $R_{i2} \ll r_{o1}$. Finally, the current gain from the source to the drain of $M_2$ is unity. Therefore, most of the $g_{m1} v_i$ current flows in the output, and $G_m \simeq g_{m1}$, as shown in (3.126).

To find the output resistance, set $v_i = 0$, which deactivates the $g_{m1}$ generator in Fig. 3.39 and reduces the model for common-source transistor $M_1$ to simply $r_{o1}$. Therefore, the output resistance of the cascode can be found by substituting $R_S = r_{o1}$ in (3.66), which was derived for a common-gate amplifier. To focus on the output resistance of the cascode itself, let $R \to \infty$. The result is

$$R_o = r_{o1} + r_{o2} + (g_{m2} + g_{mb2}) r_{o1} r_{o2} \simeq (g_{m2} + g_{mb2}) r_{o1} r_{o2} \qquad (3.128)$$

Equation 3.128 shows that the MOS cascode increases the output resistance by a factor of about $(g_m + g_{mb}) r_o$ compared to a common-source amplifier.

The increase in the output resistance can be predicted in another way that provides insight into the operation of the cascode. Let $i_o$ represent the current that flows in the output node in Fig. 3.39 when the output is driven by voltage $v_o$. Since $v_{ds1} = i_o r_{o1}$ when $v_i = 0$, the output resistance is

$$R_o = \frac{v_o}{i_o}\bigg|_{v_i=0} = \frac{v_o}{(v_{ds1}/r_{o1})}\bigg|_{v_i=0} = r_{o1} \left(\frac{v_{ds1}}{v_o}\right)^{-1}\bigg|_{v_i=0} \qquad (3.129)$$

To find the ratio $v_{ds1}/v_o$, consider the modified small-signal circuits shown in Fig. 3.40. In Fig. 3.40a, $R \to \infty$ so we can concentrate on the output resistance of the cascode circuit itself. Also, the $g_{m1} v_i$ generator is eliminated because $v_i = 0$, and the two generators $g_{m2} v_{ds1}$ and $g_{mb2} v_{ds1}$ have been combined into one equivalent generator $(g_{m2} + g_{mb2}) v_{ds1}$. In Fig. 3.40b, the $(g_{m2} + g_{mb2}) v_{ds1}$ generator from the source to the drain of $M_2$ has been replaced by two equal-valued generators: one from ground to the drain of $M_2$ and the other from the source of $M_2$ to ground. This replacement is similar to the substitution made in Fig. 3.20 to convert the hybrid-$\pi$ model to a T model for a common-gate amplifier. Because the equations that describe the operation of the circuits in Fig. 3.40a and Fig. 3.40b are identical, the circuit in Fig. 3.40b is equivalent to that in Fig. 3.40a. Finally, in Fig. 3.40c, the current source from the source of $M_2$ to ground, which is controlled by the voltage across itself, is replaced by an equivalent resistor of value $1/(g_{m2} + g_{mb2})$. The current $(g_{m2} + g_{mb2}) v_{ds1}$ in Fig. 3.40c flows into the test source $v_o$. The two resistors in Fig. 3.40c form a voltage divider, giving

$$\frac{v_{ds1}}{v_o} = \frac{\left(\dfrac{1}{g_{m2} + g_{mb2}}\right) \parallel r_{o1}}{\left[\left(\dfrac{1}{g_{m2} + g_{mb2}}\right) \parallel r_{o1}\right] + r_{o2}} \simeq \frac{1}{(g_{m2} + g_{mb2}) r_{o2}} \qquad (3.130)$$

Substituting (3.130) into (3.129) and rearranging gives the same result as in (3.128). In (3.130), the term $1/(g_{m2} + g_{mb2})$ represents the resistance looking into the source of

**Figure 3.40** Construction of a cascode model to find $v_{ds1}/v_o$. (a) The dependent sources are combined. (b) The combined source is converted into two sources. (c) The current source between the source of $M_2$ and ground is converted into a resistor.

the common-gate transistor $M_2$ when the output in Fig. 3.39 is voltage driven. The key point here is that the output resistance of the cascode can be increased by reducing the input resistance of the common-gate transistor under these conditions because this change reduces both $v_{ds1}$ and $i_o$.

Unlike in the bipolar case, the maximum value of the output resistance in the MOS cascode does not saturate at a level determined by $\beta_0$; therefore, further increases in the output resistance can be obtained by using more than one level of cascoding. This approach is used in practice. Ultimately, the maximum output resistance is limited by impact ionization as described in Section 1.9 or by leakage current in the reverse-biased junction diode at the output. Also, the number of levels of cascoding is limited by the power-supply voltage and signal-swing requirements. Each additional level of cascoding places one more transistor in series with the input transistor between the power supply and ground. To operate all the transistors in the active region, the drain-source voltage of each transistor must be greater than its overdrive $V_{GS} - V_t$. Since the cascode transistors operate in series with the input transistor, additional levels of cascoding use some of the available power-supply voltage, reducing the amount by which the output can vary before pushing one or more transistors into the triode region. This topic is considered further in Chapter 4.

In BiCMOS technologies, cascodes are sometimes used with the MOS transistor $M_2$ in Fig. 3.38 replaced by a bipolar transistor, such as $Q_2$ in Fig. 3.36. This configuration has the infinite input resistance given by $M_1$. Also, the resistance looking into the emitter of the common-base stage $Q_2$ when the output is grounded is $R_{i2} \simeq 1/g_{m2}$ in this configuration. Since the transconductance for a given bias current of bipolar transistors is usually much greater than for MOS transistors, the BiCMOS configuration is often used to reduce the load resistance presented to $M_1$ and to improve the high-frequency properties of the cascode amplifier. The frequency response of a cascode amplifier is described in Chapter 7.

■ **EXAMPLE**

Calculate the transconductance and output resistance of the cascode circuit of Fig. 3.38. Assume that both transistors operate in the active region with $g_m = 1$ mA/V, $\chi = 0.1$, and $r_o = 20$ k$\Omega$.

From (3.126),

$$G_m = \left(1 \frac{mA}{V}\right)\left(1 - \frac{1}{1 + (1.1)(20) + 1}\right) = 960 \frac{\mu A}{V}$$

From (3.128),

$$R_o = 20 \text{ k}\Omega + 20 \text{ k}\Omega + (1.1)(20) 20 \text{ k}\Omega = 480 \text{ k}\Omega$$

The approximations in (3.126) and (3.128) give $G_m \approx 1$ mA/V and $R_o \approx 440$ k$\Omega$. These approximations deviate from the exact results by about 4 percent and 8 percent, respectively, and are usually close enough for hand calculations.

### 3.4.3 The Active Cascode

As mentioned in the previous section, increasing the number of levels of cascoding increases the output resistance of MOS amplifiers. In practice, however, the power-supply voltage and signal-swing requirements limit the number of levels of cascoding that can be applied. One way to increase the output resistance of the MOS cascode circuit without increasing the number of levels of cascoding is to use the active-cascode circuit, as shown in Fig. 3.41.[8,9]

This circuit uses an amplifier in a negative feedback loop to control the voltage from the gate of $M_2$ to ground. If the amplifier gain $a$ is infinite, the negative feedback loop adjusts the gate of $M_2$ until the voltage difference between the two amplifier inputs is zero. In other words, the drain-source voltage of $M_1$ is driven to equal $V_{BIAS}$. If the drain-source voltage of $M_1$ is constant, the change in the drain current in response to changes in the output voltage $V_o$ is zero, and the output resistance is infinite. In practice, the amplifier gain $a$ is finite, which means that the drain-source voltage of $M_1$ is not exactly constant and the output resistance is finite. The effect of negative feedback on output resistance is considered quantitatively in Chapter 8. In this section, we will derive the small-signal properties of the active-cascode circuit by comparing its small-signal model to that of the simple cascode described in the previous section.

**Figure 3.41** Active cascode amplifier using MOSFETs.

**Figure 3.42** Small-signal equivalent circuit for the active-cascode connection with MOS transistors.

Qualitatively, when the output voltage increases, the drain current of $M_2$ increases, which increases the drain current and drain-source voltage of $M_1$. This voltage increase is amplified by $-a$, causing the voltage from the gate of $M_2$ to ground to fall. The falling gate voltage of $M_2$ acts to reduce the change in its drain current, increasing the output resistance compared to a simple cascode, where the voltage from the gate of $M_2$ to ground is held constant.

Figure 3.42 shows the low-frequency, small-signal equivalent circuit. The body-effect transconductance generator for $M_1$ is inactive because $v_{bs1} = 0$. The gate-source voltage of $M_2$ is

$$v_{gs2} = v_{g2} - v_{s2} = v_{g2} - v_{ds1} = -(a)\,v_{ds1} - v_{ds1} = -(a + 1)\,v_{ds1} \quad (3.131)$$

In contrast, $v_{gs2} = -v_{ds1}$ in a simple cascode because the voltage from the gate of $M_2$ to ground is constant in Fig. 3.38. Therefore, if $a > 0$, the factor $(a + 1)$ in (3.131) amplifies the gate-source voltage of $M_2$ compared to the case of a simple cascode. This amplification is central to the characteristics of the active-cascode circuit. Since the small-signal diagrams of the simple and active-cascode circuits are identical except for the value of $v_{gs2}$, and since $v_{gs2}$ is only used to control the current flowing in the $g_{m2}$ generator, the active-cascode circuit can be analyzed using the equations for the simple cascode with $g_{m2}$ replaced by $(a + 1)\,g_{m2}$. In other words, the active cascode behaves as if it were a simple cascode with an enhanced value of $g_{m2}$.

To find the transconductance of the active cascode, $g_{m2}\,(a+1)$ replaces $g_{m2}$ in (3.126), giving

$$G_m = g_{m1}\left(1 - \frac{1}{1 + [g_{m2}\,(a + 1) + g_{mb2}]\,r_{o1} + \dfrac{r_{o1}}{r_{o2}}}\right) \quad (3.132)$$

Again, $G_m \simeq g_{m1}$ under most conditions; therefore, the active-cascode structure is generally not used to modify the transconductance.

The active cascode reduces $R_{i2}$, the resistance looking into the source of $M_2$, compared to the simple cascode, which reduces the $v_{ds1}/v_o$ ratio given in (3.130) and increases the output resistance. Substituting (3.130) into (3.129) with $g_{m2}\,(a+1)$ replacing $g_{m2}$ gives

$$R_o = r_{o1} + r_{o2} + [g_{m2}\,(a + 1) + g_{mb2}]\,r_{o1}r_{o2} \simeq [g_{m2}\,(a + 1) + g_{mb2}]\,r_{o1}r_{o2} \quad (3.133)$$

This result can also be derived by substituting $g_{m2}(a+1)$ for $g_{m2}$ in (3.128). Equation 3.133 shows that the active-cascode configuration increases the output resistance by a factor of about $[g_m(a+1) + g_{mb}]\,r_o$ compared to a common-source amplifier.

A key limitation of the active-cascode circuit is that the output impedance is increased only at frequencies where the amplifier that drives the gate of $M_2$ provides some gain. In practice, the gain of this amplifier falls with increasing frequency, reducing the potential benefits of the active-cascode circuits in high-frequency applications. A potential problem with the active-cascode configuration is that the negative feedback loop through $M_2$ may not be stable in all cases.

### 3.4.4 The Super Source Follower

Equation 3.84 shows that the output resistance of a source follower is approximately $1/(g_m + g_{mb})$. Because MOS transistors usually have much lower transconductance than their bipolar counterparts, this output resistance may be too high for some applications, especially when a resistive load must be driven. One way to reduce the output resistance is to increase the transconductance by increasing the $W/L$ ratio of the source follower and its dc bias current. However, this approach requires a proportionate increase in the area and power dissipation to reduce $R_o$. To minimize the area and power dissipation required to reach a given output resistance, the super source follower configuration shown in Fig. 3.43 is sometimes used. This circuit uses negative feedback through $M_2$ to reduce the output resistance. Negative feedback is studied quantitatively in Chapter 8. From a qualitative standpoint, when the input voltage is constant and the output voltage increases, the magnitude of the drain current of $M_1$ also increases, in turn increasing the gate-source voltage of $M_2$. As a result, the drain current of $M_2$ increases, reducing the output resistance by increasing the total current that flows into the output node under these conditions.

From a dc standpoint, the bias current in $M_2$ is the difference between $I_1$ and $I_2$; therefore, $I_1 > I_2$ is required for proper operation. This information can be used to find the small-signal parameters of both transistors. The small-signal equivalent circuit is shown in Fig. 3.44. The body-effect transconductance generator for $M_2$ is inactive because $v_{bs2} = 0$. Also, the polarities of the voltage-controlled current sources for $n$- and $p$-channel devices are identical. Finally, the output resistances of current sources $I_1$ and $I_2$ are represented by $r_1$ and $r_2$, respectively. If the current sources are ideal, $r_1 \to \infty$ and $r_2 \to \infty$. In practice, these resistances are large but finite. Techniques to build high-resistance current sources are considered in Chapter 4.

To find the output resistance, set $v_i = 0$ and calculate the current $i_o$ that flows in the output node when the output is driven by a voltage $v_o$. From KCL at the output under these

**Figure 3.43** Super-source-follower configuration.

**Figure 3.44** Small-signal equivalent circuit of the super-source follower.

conditions,

$$i_o = \frac{v_o}{r_1} + \frac{v_o}{r_{o2}} + g_{m2}v_2 + \frac{v_2}{r_2} \qquad (3.134)$$

From KCL at the drain of $M_1$ with $v_i = 0$,

$$\frac{v_2}{r_2} - g_{m1}v_o - g_{mb1}v_o + \frac{v_2 - v_o}{r_{o1}} = 0 \qquad (3.135)$$

Solving (3.135) for $v_2$, substituting into (3.134), and rearranging gives

$$R_o = \frac{v_o}{i_o}\bigg|_{v_i=0} = r_1 \parallel r_{o2} \parallel \left( \frac{r_{o1} + r_2}{[1 + (g_{m1} + g_{mb1})\, r_{o1}](1 + g_{m2}r_2)} \right) \qquad (3.136)$$

Assume $I_1$ and $I_2$ are ideal current sources so that $r_1 \to \infty$ and $r_2 \to \infty$. If $r_{o2} \to \infty$, and if $(g_{m1} + g_{mb1})\, r_{o1} \gg 1$,

$$R_o \simeq \frac{1}{g_{m1} + g_{mb1}} \left( \frac{1}{g_{m2}r_{o1}} \right) \qquad (3.137)$$

Comparing (3.84) and (3.137) shows that the negative feedback through $M_2$ reduces the output resistance by a factor of about $g_{m2}r_{o1}$.

Now we will calculate the open-circuit voltage gain of the super-source follower. With the output open circuited, KCL at the output node gives

$$\frac{v_o}{r_1} + \frac{v_o}{r_{o2}} + g_{m2}v_2 + \frac{v_2}{r_2} = 0 \qquad (3.138)$$

From KCL at the drain of $M_1$,

$$\frac{v_2}{r_2} + g_{m1}(v_i - v_o) - g_{mb1}v_o + \frac{v_2 - v_o}{r_{o1}} = 0 \qquad (3.139)$$

Solving (3.138) for $v_2$, substituting into (3.139), and rearranging gives

$$\frac{v_o}{v_i}\bigg|_{i_o=0} = \frac{g_{m1}r_{o1}}{1 + (g_{m1} + g_{mb1})\, r_{o1} + \dfrac{(r_2 + r_{o1})}{(r_1 \parallel r_{o2})(1 + g_{m2}r_2)}} \qquad (3.140)$$

With ideal current sources,

$$\lim_{\substack{r_1 \to \infty \\ r_2 \to \infty}} \frac{v_o}{v_i}\bigg|_{i_o=0} = \frac{g_{m1}\, r_{o1}}{1 + (g_{m1} + g_{mb1})\, r_{o1} + \dfrac{1}{g_{m2}r_{o2}}} \qquad (3.141)$$

Comparing (3.141) and (3.81) shows that the deviation of this gain from unity is greater than with a simple source follower. If $g_{m2}r_{o2} \gg 1$, however, the difference is small and the main conclusion is that the super-source-follower configuration has little effect on the open-circuit voltage gain.

As mentioned earlier, the super-source follower is sometimes used in MOS technologies to reduce the source-follower output resistance. It is also used in bipolar technologies in output stages to reduce the current conducted in a weak lateral $pnp$ transistor. This application is described in Chapter 5. The main potential problem with the super-source-follower configuration is that the negative feedback loop through $M_2$ may not be stable in all cases, especially when driving a capacitive load. The stability of feedback amplifiers is considered in Chapter 9.

## 3.5 Differential Pairs

The differential pair is another example of a circuit that was first invented for use with vacuum tubes.[10] The original circuit uses two vacuum tubes whose cathodes are connected together. Modern differential pairs use bipolar or MOS transistors coupled at their emitters or sources, respectively, and are perhaps the most widely used two-transistor subcircuits in monolithic analog circuits. The usefulness of the differential pair stems from two key properties. First, cascades of differential pairs can be directly connected to one another without interstage coupling capacitors. Second, the differential pair is primarily sensitive to the difference between two input voltages, allowing a high degree of rejection of signals common to both inputs.[11,12] In this section, we consider the properties of emitter-coupled pairs of bipolar transistors and source-coupled pairs of MOS transistors in detail.

### 3.5.1 The dc Transfer Characteristic of an Emitter-Coupled Pair

The simplest form of an emitter-coupled pair is shown in Fig. 3.45. The biasing circuit in the lead connected to the emitters of $Q_1$ and $Q_2$ can be a transistor current source, which is called a *tail* current source, or a simple resistor. If a simple resistor $R_{TAIL}$ is used alone, $I_{TAIL} = 0$ in Fig. 3.45. Otherwise, $I_{TAIL}$ and $R_{TAIL}$ together form a Norton-equivalent model of the tail current source.

**Figure 3.45** Emitter-coupled pair circuit diagram.

The large-signal behavior of the emitter-coupled pair is important in part because it illustrates the limited range of input voltages over which the circuit behaves almost linearly. Also, the large-signal behavior shows that the amplitude of analog signals in bipolar circuits can be limited without pushing the transistors into saturation, where the response time would be increased because of excess charge storage in the base region. For simplicity in the analysis, we assume that the output resistance of the tail current source $R_{\text{TAIL}} \to \infty$, that the output resistance of each transistor $r_o \to \infty$, and that the base resistance of each transistor $r_b = 0$. These assumptions do not strongly affect the low-frequency, large-signal behavior of the circuit. From KVL around the input loop,

$$V_{i1} - V_{be1} + V_{be2} - V_{i2} = 0 \tag{3.142}$$

Assume the collector resistors are small enough that the transistors do not operate in saturation if $V_{i1} \leq V_{CC}$ and $V_{i2} \leq V_{CC}$. If $V_{be1} \gg V_T$ and $V_{be2} \gg V_T$, the Ebers-Moll equations show that

$$V_{be1} = V_T \ln \frac{I_{c1}}{I_{S1}} \tag{3.143}$$

$$V_{be2} = V_T \ln \frac{I_{c2}}{I_{S2}} \tag{3.144}$$

Assume the transistors are identical so that $I_{S1} = I_{S2}$. Then combining (3.142), (3.143), and (3.144), we find

$$\frac{I_{c1}}{I_{c2}} = \exp\left(\frac{V_{i1} - V_{i2}}{V_T}\right) = \exp\left(\frac{V_{id}}{V_T}\right) \tag{3.145}$$

where $V_{id} = V_{i1} - V_{i2}$. Since we have assumed that the transistors are identical, $\alpha_{F1} = \alpha_{F2} = \alpha_F$. Then KCL at the emitters of the transistors shows

$$-(I_{e1} + I_{e2}) = I_{\text{TAIL}} = \frac{I_{c1} + I_{c2}}{\alpha_F} \tag{3.146}$$

Combining (3.145) and (3.146), we find that

$$I_{c1} = \frac{\alpha_F I_{\text{TAIL}}}{1 + \exp\left(-\dfrac{V_{id}}{V_T}\right)} \tag{3.147}$$

$$I_{c2} = \frac{\alpha_F I_{\text{TAIL}}}{1 + \exp\left(\dfrac{V_{id}}{V_T}\right)} \tag{3.148}$$

These two currents are shown as a function of $V_{id}$ in Fig. 3.46. When the magnitude of $V_{id}$ is greater than about $3V_T$, which is approximately 78 mV at room temperature, the collector currents are almost independent of $V_{id}$ because one of the transistors turns off and the other conducts all the current that flows. Furthermore, the circuit behaves in an approximately linear fashion only when the magnitude of $V_{id}$ is less than about $V_T$. We can now compute the output voltages as

$$V_{o1} = V_{CC} - I_{c1}R_C \tag{3.149}$$

$$V_{o2} = V_{CC} - I_{c2}R_C \tag{3.150}$$

The output signal of interest is often the difference between $V_{o1}$ and $V_{o2}$, which we define as $V_{od}$. Then

$$V_{od} = V_{o1} - V_{o2} = \alpha_F I_{\text{TAIL}} R_C \tanh\left(\frac{-V_{id}}{2V_T}\right) \tag{3.151}$$

**Figure 3.46** Emitter-coupled pair collector currents as a function of differential input voltage.

**Figure 3.47** Emitter-coupled pair, differential output voltage as a function of differential input voltage.

This function is plotted in Fig. 3.47. Here a significant advantage of differential amplifiers is apparent: When $V_{id}$ is zero, $V_{od}$ is zero if $Q_1$ and $Q_2$ are identical and if identical resistors are connected to the collectors of $Q_1$ and $Q_2$. This property allows direct coupling of cascaded stages without offsets.

### 3.5.2 The dc Transfer Characteristic with Emitter Degeneration

To increase the range of $V_{id}$ over which the emitter-coupled pair behaves approximately as a linear amplifier, emitter-degeneration resistors are frequently included in series with the emitters of the transistors, as shown in Fig. 3.48. The analysis of this circuit proceeds in the same manner as without degeneration, except that the voltage drop across these resistors must be included in the KVL equation corresponding to (3.142). A transcendental equation results from this analysis and a closed-form solution like that of (3.151) does not exist, but the effect of the resistors may be understood intuitively from the examples plotted in Fig. 3.49. For large values of emitter-degeneration resistors, the linear range of operation is extended by an amount approximately equal to $I_{TAIL}R_E$. This result stems from the observation that all of $I_{TAIL}$ flows in one of the degeneration resistors when one transistor turns off. Therefore, the voltage drop is $I_{TAIL}R_E$ on one resistor and zero on the other, and the value of $V_{id}$ required to turn one transistor off is changed by the difference of the voltage drops on these resistors. Furthermore, since the voltage gain is the slope of

**Figure 3.48** Circuit diagram of emitter-coupled pair with emitter degeneration.

**Figure 3.49** Output voltage as a function of input voltage, emitter-coupled pair with emitter degeneration.

the transfer characteristic, the voltage gain is reduced by approximately the same factor that the input range is increased. In operation, the emitter resistors introduce local negative feedback in the differential pair. This topic is considered in Chapter 8.

### 3.5.3 The dc Transfer Characteristic of a Source-Coupled Pair

Consider the $n$-channel MOS-transistor source-coupled pair shown in Fig. 3.50. The following analysis applies equally well to a corresponding $p$-channel source-coupled pair with appropriate sign changes. In monolithic form, a transistor current source, called a *tail* current source, is usually connected to the sources of $M_1$ and $M_2$. In that case, $I_{TAIL}$ and $R_{TAIL}$ together form a Norton-equivalent model of the tail current source.

For this large-signal analysis, we assume that the output resistance of the tail current source is $R_{TAIL} \rightarrow \infty$. Also, we assume that the output resistance of each transistor $r_o \rightarrow \infty$. Although these assumptions do not strongly affect the low-frequency, large-signal behavior of the circuit, they could have a significant impact on the small-signal behavior. Therefore, we will reconsider these assumptions when we analyze the circuit from a small-

Figure 3.50  $n$-channel MOSFET source-coupled pair.

signal standpoint. From KVL around the input loop,

$$V_{i1} - V_{gs1} + V_{gs2} - V_{i2} = 0 \tag{3.152}$$

We assume that the drain resistors are small enough that neither transistor operates in the triode region if $V_{i1} \le V_{DD}$ and $V_{i2} \le V_{DD}$. Furthermore, we assume that the drain current of each transistor is related to its gate-source voltage by the approximate square-law relationship given in (1.157). If the transistors are identical, applying (1.157) to each transistor and rearranging gives

$$V_{gs1} = V_t + \sqrt{\frac{2I_{d1}}{k'\,(W/L)}} \tag{3.153}$$

and

$$V_{gs2} = V_t + \sqrt{\frac{2I_{d2}}{k'\,(W/L)}} \tag{3.154}$$

Substituting (3.153) and (3.154) into (3.152) and rearranging gives

$$V_{id} = V_{i1} - V_{i2} = \frac{\sqrt{I_{d1}} - \sqrt{I_{d2}}}{\sqrt{\dfrac{k'}{2}\dfrac{W}{L}}} \tag{3.155}$$

From KCL at the source of $M_1$ and $M_2$,

$$I_{d1} + I_{d2} = I_{\text{TAIL}} \tag{3.156}$$

Solving (3.156) for $I_{d2}$, substituting into (3.155), rearranging, and using the quadratic formula gives

$$I_{d1} = \frac{I_{\text{TAIL}}}{2} \pm \frac{k'}{4}\frac{W}{L}V_{id}\sqrt{\frac{4I_{\text{TAIL}}}{k'\,(W/L)} - V_{id}^2} \tag{3.157}$$

Since $I_{d1} > I_{TAIL}/2$ when $V_{id} > 0$, the potential solution where the second term is subtracted from the first in (3.157) cannot occur in practice. Therefore,

$$I_{d1} = \frac{I_{TAIL}}{2} + \frac{k'}{4}\frac{W}{L}V_{id}\sqrt{\frac{4I_{TAIL}}{k'(W/L)} - V_{id}^2} \tag{3.158}$$

Substituting (3.158) into (3.156) gives

$$I_{d2} = \frac{I_{TAIL}}{2} - \frac{k'}{4}\frac{W}{L}V_{id}\sqrt{\frac{4I_{TAIL}}{k'(W/L)} - V_{id}^2} \tag{3.159}$$

Equations 3.158 and 3.159 are valid when both transistors operate in the active or saturation region. Since we have assumed that neither transistor operates in the triode region, the limitation here stems from turning off one of the transistors. When $M_1$ turns off, $I_{d1} = 0$ and $I_{d2} = I_{TAIL}$. On the other hand, $I_{d1} = I_{TAIL}$ and $I_{d2} = 0$ when $M_2$ turns off. Substituting these values in (3.155) shows that both transistors operate in the active region if

$$|V_{id}| \le \sqrt{\frac{2I_{TAIL}}{k'(W/L)}} \tag{3.160}$$

Since $I_{d1} = I_{d2} = I_{TAIL}/2$ when $V_{id} = 0$, the range in (3.160) can be rewritten as

$$|V_{id}| \le \sqrt{2}\left(\sqrt{\frac{2I_{d1}}{k'(W/L)}}\right)\Bigg|_{V_{id}=0} = \sqrt{2}\,(V_{ov})\,\big|_{V_{id}=0} \tag{3.161}$$

Equation 3.161 shows that the range of $V_{id}$ for which both transistors operate in the active region is proportional to the overdrive calculated when $V_{id} = 0$. This result is illustrated in Fig. 3.51. The overdrive is an important quantity in MOS circuit design, affecting not only the input range of differential pairs, but also other characteristics including the speed, offset, and output swing of MOS amplifiers. Since the overdrive of an MOS transistor depends on its current and $W/L$ ratio, the range of a source-coupled pair can be adjusted to suit a given application by adjusting the value of the tail current and/or the

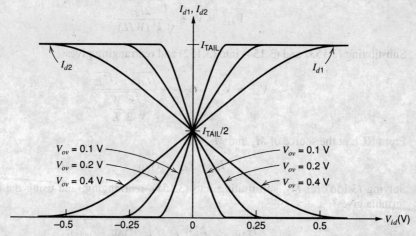

**Figure 3.51**  dc transfer characteristic of the MOS source-coupled pair. The parameter is the overdrive $V_{ov} = V_{GS} - V_t$ determined when $V_{id} = 0$.

aspect ratio of the input devices. In contrast, the input range of the bipolar emitter-coupled pair is about $\pm 3V_T$, independent of bias current or device size. In fact, the source-coupled pair behaves somewhat like an emitter-coupled pair with emitter-degeneration resistors that can be selected to give a desired input voltage range.

In many practical cases, the key output of the differential pair is not $I_{d1}$ or $I_{d2}$ alone but the difference between these quantities. Subtracting (3.159) from (3.158) gives

$$\Delta I_d = I_{d1} - I_{d2} = \frac{k'}{2}\frac{W}{L}V_{id}\sqrt{\frac{4I_{\text{TAIL}}}{k'\,(W/L)} - V_{id}^2} \qquad (3.162)$$

We can now compute the differential output voltage as

$$V_{od} = V_{o1} - V_{o2} = V_{DD} - I_{d1}R_D - V_{DD} + I_{d2}R_D = -(\Delta I_d)\,R_D \qquad (3.163)$$

Since $\Delta I_d = 0$ when $V_{id} = 0$, (3.163) shows that $V_{od} = 0$ when $V_{id} = 0$ if $M_1$ and $M_2$ are identical and if identical resistors are connected to the drains of $M_1$ and $M_2$. This property allows direct coupling of cascaded MOS differential pairs, as in the bipolar case.

### 3.5.4 Introduction to the Small-Signal Analysis of Differential Amplifiers

The features of interest in the performance of differential pairs are often the small-signal properties for dc differential input voltages near zero volts. In the next two sections, we assume that the dc differential input voltage is zero and calculate the small-signal parameters. If the parameters are constant, the small-signal model predicts that the circuit operation is linear. The results of the small-signal analysis are valid for signals that are small enough to cause insignificant nonlinearity.

In previous sections, we have considered amplifiers with two input terminals ($V_i$ and ground) and two output terminals ($V_o$ and ground). Small-signal analysis of such circuits leads to one equation for each circuit, such as

$$v_o = Av_i \qquad (3.164)$$

Here, $A$ is the small-signal voltage gain under given loading conditions. In contrast, differential pairs have three input terminals ($V_{i1}$, $V_{i2}$, and ground) and three output terminals ($V_{o1}$, $V_{o2}$, and ground). Therefore, direct small-signal analysis of differential pairs leads to two equations for each circuit (one for each output), where each output depends on each input:

$$v_{o1} = A_{11}v_{i1} + A_{12}v_{i2} \qquad (3.165)$$
$$v_{o2} = A_{21}v_{i1} + A_{22}v_{i2} \qquad (3.166)$$

Here, four voltage gains, $A_{11}$, $A_{12}$, $A_{21}$, and $A_{22}$, specify the small-signal operation of the circuit under given loading conditions. These gains can be interpreted as

$$A_{11} = \left.\frac{v_{o1}}{v_{i1}}\right|_{v_{i2}=0} \qquad (3.167)$$

$$A_{12} = \left.\frac{v_{o1}}{v_{i2}}\right|_{v_{i1}=0} \qquad (3.168)$$

$$A_{21} = \left.\frac{v_{o2}}{v_{i1}}\right|_{v_{i2}=0} \qquad (3.169)$$

$$A_{22} = \left.\frac{v_{o2}}{v_{i2}}\right|_{v_{i1}=0} \qquad (3.170)$$

Although direct small-signal analysis of differential pairs can be used to calculate these four gain values in a straightforward way, the results are difficult to interpret because differential pairs usually are not used to react to $v_{i1}$ or $v_{i2}$ alone. Instead, differential pairs are used most often to sense the difference between the two inputs while trying to ignore the part of the two inputs that is common to each. Desired signals will be forced to appear as differences in differential circuits. In practice, undesired signals will also appear. For example, *mixed-signal* integrated circuits use both analog and digital signal processing, and the analog signals are vulnerable to corruption from noise generated by the digital circuits and transmitted through the common substrate. The hope in using differential circuits is that undesired signals will appear equally on both inputs and be rejected.

To highlight this behavior, we will define new differential and common-mode variables at the input and output as follows. The differential input, to which differential pairs are sensitive, is

$$v_{id} = v_{i1} - v_{i2} \qquad (3.171)$$

The common-mode or average input, to which differential pairs are insensitive, is

$$v_{ic} = \frac{v_{i1} + v_{i2}}{2} \qquad (3.172)$$

These equations can be inverted to give $v_{i1}$ and $v_{i2}$ in terms of $v_{id}$ and $v_{ic}$:

$$v_{i1} = v_{ic} + \frac{v_{id}}{2} \qquad (3.173)$$

$$v_{i2} = v_{ic} - \frac{v_{id}}{2} \qquad (3.174)$$

The physical significance of these new variables can be understood by using (3.173) and (3.174) to redraw the input connections to a differential amplifier as shown in Fig. 3.52. The common-mode input is the input component that appears equally in $v_{i1}$ and $v_{i2}$. The differential input is the input component that appears between $v_{i1}$ and $v_{i2}$.

New output variables are defined in the same way. The differential output is

$$v_{od} = v_{o1} - v_{o2} \qquad (3.175)$$

The common-mode or average output is

$$v_{oc} = \frac{v_{o1} + v_{o2}}{2} \qquad (3.176)$$

(a)

(b)

**Figure 3.52** A differential amplifier with its inputs (*a*) shown as independent of each other and (*b*) redrawn in terms of the differential and common-mode components.

Solving these equations for $v_{o1}$ and $v_{o2}$, we obtain

$$v_{o1} = v_{oc} + \frac{v_{od}}{2} \qquad (3.177)$$

$$v_{o2} = v_{oc} - \frac{v_{od}}{2} \qquad (3.178)$$

We have now defined two new input variables and two new output variables. By substituting the expressions for $v_{i1}$, $v_{i2}$, $v_{o1}$, and $v_{o2}$ in terms of the new variables back into (3.165) and (3.166), we find

$$v_{od} = \left(\frac{A_{11} - A_{12} - A_{21} + A_{22}}{2}\right)v_{id} + \left(A_{11} + A_{12} - A_{21} - A_{22}\right)v_{ic} \qquad (3.179)$$

$$v_{oc} = \left(\frac{A_{11} - A_{12} + A_{21} - A_{22}}{4}\right)v_{id} + \left(\frac{A_{11} + A_{12} + A_{21} + A_{22}}{2}\right)v_{ic} \qquad (3.180)$$

Defining four new gain factors that are equal to the coefficients in these equations, (3.179) and (3.180) can be rewritten as

$$v_{od} = A_{dm}v_{id} + A_{cm-dm}v_{ic} \qquad (3.181)$$

$$v_{oc} = A_{dm-cm}v_{id} + A_{cm}v_{ic} \qquad (3.182)$$

The *differential-mode* gain $A_{dm}$ is the change in the differential output per unit change in differential input:

$$A_{dm} = \left.\frac{v_{od}}{v_{id}}\right|_{v_{ic}=0} = \frac{A_{11} - A_{12} - A_{21} + A_{22}}{2} \qquad (3.183)$$

The *common-mode* gain $A_{cm}$ is the change in the common-mode output voltage per unit change in the common-mode input:

$$A_{cm} = \left.\frac{v_{oc}}{v_{ic}}\right|_{v_{id}=0} = \frac{A_{11} + A_{12} + A_{21} + A_{22}}{2} \qquad (3.184)$$

The *differential-mode-to-common-mode* gain $A_{dm-cm}$ is the change in the common-mode output voltage per unit change in the differential-mode input:

$$A_{dm-cm} = \left.\frac{v_{oc}}{v_{id}}\right|_{v_{ic}=0} = \frac{A_{11} - A_{12} + A_{21} - A_{22}}{4} \qquad (3.185)$$

The *common-mode-to-differential-mode* gain $A_{cm-dm}$ is the change in the differential-mode output voltage per unit change in the common-mode input:

$$A_{cm-dm} = \left.\frac{v_{od}}{v_{ic}}\right|_{v_{id}=0} = A_{11} + A_{12} - A_{21} - A_{22} \qquad (3.186)$$

The purpose of a differential amplifier is to sense changes in its differential input while rejecting changes in its common-mode input. The desired output is differential, and its variation should be proportional to the variation in the differential input. Variation in the common-mode output is undesired because it must be rejected by another differential stage to sense the desired differential signal. Therefore, an important design goal in differential amplifiers is to make $A_{dm}$ large compared to the other three gain coefficients in (3.181) and (3.182).

In differential amplifiers with perfect symmetry, each component on the side of one output corresponds to an identical component on the side of the other output. With such *perfectly balanced* amplifiers, when $v_{i1} = -v_{i2}$, $v_{o1} = -v_{o2}$. In other words, when the input is purely differential ($v_{ic} = 0$), the output of a perfectly balanced differential amplifier is purely differential ($v_{oc} = 0$), and thus $A_{dm-cm} = 0$. Similarly, pure common-mode inputs (for which $v_{id} = 0$) produce pure common-mode outputs and $A_{cm-dm} = 0$ in perfectly balanced differential amplifiers. Even with perfect symmetry, however, $A_{cm} \neq 0$ is possible. Therefore, the ratio $A_{dm}/A_{cm}$ is one figure of merit for a differential amplifier, giving the ratio of the desired differential-mode gain to the undesired common-mode gain. In this book, we will define the magnitude of this ratio as the common-mode-rejection ratio, CMRR:

$$\text{CMRR} \equiv \left| \frac{A_{dm}}{A_{cm}} \right| \tag{3.187}$$

Furthermore, since differential amplifiers are not perfectly balanced in practice, $A_{dm-cm} \neq 0$ and $A_{cm-dm} \neq 0$. The ratios $A_{dm}/A_{cm-dm}$ and $A_{dm}/A_{dm-cm}$ are two other figures of merit that characterize the performance of differential amplifiers. Of these, the first is particularly important because ratio $A_{dm}/A_{cm-dm}$ determines the extent to which the differential output is produced by the desired differential input instead of by the undesired common-mode input. This ratio is important because once a common-mode input is converted to a differential output, the result is treated as the *desired* signal by subsequent differential amplifiers. In fact, in multistage differential amplifiers, the common-mode-to-differential-mode gain of the first stage is usually an important factor in the overall CMRR. In Section 3.5.5, we consider perfectly balanced differential amplifiers from a small-signal standpoint; in Section 3.5.6.9, imperfectly balanced differential amplifiers from the same standpoint.

### 3.5.5 Small-Signal Characteristics of Balanced Differential Amplifiers

In this section, we will study perfectly balanced differential amplifiers. Therefore, $A_{cm-dm} = 0$ and $A_{dm-cm} = 0$ here, and our goal is to calculate $A_{dm}$ and $A_{cm}$. Although calculating $A_{dm}$ and $A_{cm}$ from the entire small-signal equivalent circuit of a differential amplifier is possible, these calculations are greatly simplified by taking advantage of the symmetry that exists in perfectly balanced amplifiers. In general, we first find the response of a given circuit to pure differential and pure common-mode inputs separately. Then the results can be superposed to find the total solution. Since superposition is valid only for linear circuits, the following analysis is strictly valid only from a small-signal standpoint and approximately valid only for signals that cause negligible nonlinearity. In previous sections, we carried out large-signal analyses of differential pairs and assumed that the Norton-equivalent resistance of the tail current source was infinite. Since this resistance has a considerable effect on the small-signal behavior of differential pairs, however, we now assume that this resistance is finite.

Because the analysis here is virtually the same for both bipolar and MOS differential pairs, the two cases will be considered together. Consider the bipolar emitter-coupled pair of Fig. 3.45 and the MOS source-coupled pair of Fig. 3.50 from a small-signal standpoint. Then $V_{i1} = v_{i1}$ and $V_{i2} = v_{i2}$. These circuits are redrawn in Fig. 3.53a and Fig. 3.53b with the common-mode input voltages set to zero so we can consider the effect of the differential-mode input by itself. The small-signal equivalent circuit for both cases is shown in Fig. 3.54 with $R$ used to replace $R_C$ in Fig. 3.53a and $R_D$ in 3.53b. Note that the small-signal equivalent circuit neglects finite $r_o$ in both cases. Also, in the MOS case, nonzero $g_{mb}$ is ignored and $r_\pi \rightarrow \infty$ because $\beta_0 \rightarrow \infty$.

Figure 3.53 (a) Emitter-coupled pair with pure differential input. (b) Source-coupled pair with pure differential input.

Figure 3.54 Small-signal equivalent circuit for differential pair with pure differential-mode input.

**Figure 3.55** Differential-mode circuit with the tail current source grounded. Because of the symmetry of the circuit, $i_x = 0$.

Because the circuit in Fig. 3.54 is perfectly balanced, and because the inputs are driven by equal and opposite voltages, the voltage across $R_{TAIL}$ does not vary at all. Another way to see this result is to view the two lower parts of the circuit as voltage followers. When one side pulls up, the other side pulls down, resulting in a constant voltage across the tail current source by superposition. Since the voltage across $R_{TAIL}$ experiences no variation, the behavior of the small-signal circuit is unaffected by the placement of a short circuit across $R_{TAIL}$, as shown in Fig. 3.55. After placing this short circuit, we see that the two sides of the circuit are not only identical, but also independent because they are joined at a node that operates as a small-signal ground. Therefore, the response to small-signal differential inputs can be determined by analyzing one side of the original circuit with $R_{TAIL}$ replaced by a short circuit. This simplified circuit, shown in Fig. 3.56, is called the *differential-mode* half circuit and is useful for analysis of both the low- and high-frequency performance of all types of differential amplifiers. By inspection of Fig. 3.56, we recognize this circuit as the small-signal equivalent of a common-emitter or common-source amplifier. Therefore,

$$\frac{v_{od}}{2} = -g_m R \frac{v_{id}}{2} \tag{3.188}$$

and

$$A_{dm} = \left. \frac{v_{od}}{v_{id}} \right|_{v_{ic}=0} = -g_m R \tag{3.189}$$

To include the output resistance of the transistor in the above analysis, $R$ in (3.189) should be replaced by $R \parallel r_o$. Finally, note that neglecting $g_{mb}$ from this analysis for MOS source-coupled pairs has no effect on the result because the voltage from the source to the body of the input transistors is the same as the voltage across the tail current source, which is constant with a pure differential input.

**Figure 3.56** Differential-mode half circuit.

**Figure 3.57** (a) Emitter-coupled pair with pure common-mode input. (b) Source-coupled pair with pure common-mode input.

The circuits in Fig. 3.45 and Fig. 3.50 are now reconsidered from a small-signal, common-mode standpoint. Setting $V_{i1} = V_{i2} = v_{ic}$, the circuits are redrawn in Fig. 3.57a and Fig. 3.57b. The small-signal equivalent circuit is shown in Fig. 3.58, but with the modification that the resistor $R_{TAIL}$ has been split into two parallel resistors, each of value twice the original. Also $R$ has been used to replace $R_C$ in Fig. 3.57a and $R_D$ in 3.57b. Again $r_o$ is neglected in both cases, and $g_{mb}$ is neglected in the MOS case, where $r_\pi \to \infty$ because $\beta_0 \to \infty$.

**Figure 3.58**  Small-signal equivalent circuit, pure common-mode input.

Because the circuit in Fig. 3.58 is divided into two identical halves, and because each half is driven by the same voltage $v_{ic}$, no current $i_x$ flows in the lead connecting the half circuits. The circuit behavior is thus unchanged when this lead is removed as shown in Fig. 3.59. As a result, we see that the two halves of the circuit in Fig. 3.58 are not only identical, but also independent because they are joined by a branch that conducts no small-signal current. Therefore, the response to small-signal, common-mode inputs can be determined by analyzing one half of the original circuit with an open circuit replacing the branch that joins the two halves of the original circuit. This simplified circuit, shown in Fig. 3.60, is called the *common-mode* half circuit. By inspection of Fig. 3.60, we recognize this circuit as a common-emitter or common-source amplifier with degeneration. Then

$$v_{oc} = -G_m R v_{ic} \qquad (3.190)$$

and

$$A_{cm} = \left.\frac{v_{oc}}{v_{ic}}\right|_{v_{id}=0} = -G_m R \qquad (3.191)$$

where $G_m$ is the transconductance of a common-emitter or common-source amplifier with degeneration and will be considered quantitatively below. Since degeneration reduces the transconductance, and since degeneration occurs only in the common-mode case, (3.189) and (3.191) show that $|A_{dm}| > |A_{cm}|$; therefore, the differential pair is more sensitive to differential inputs than to common-mode inputs. In other words, the tail current source provides local negative feedback to common-mode inputs (or local common-mode feedback). Negative feedback is studied in Chapter 8.

**Figure 3.59**  Modified common-mode equivalent circuit.

**Figure 3.60** Common-mode half circuit.

**Bipolar Emitter-Coupled Pair.** For the bipolar case, substituting (3.93) for $G_m$ with $R_E = 2R_{TAIL}$ into (3.191) and rearranging gives

$$A_{cm} \simeq -\frac{g_m R}{1 + g_m(2R_{TAIL})} = -\frac{g_m R}{1 + 2g_m R_{TAIL}} \qquad (3.192)$$

To include the effect of finite $r_o$ in the above analysis, $R$ in (3.192) should be replaced by $R \parallel R_o$, where $R_o$ is the output resistance of a common-emitter amplifier with emitter degeneration of $R_E = 2R_{TAIL}$, given in (3.97) or (3.98). This substitution ignores the effect of finite $r_o$ on $G_m$, which is shown in (3.92) and is usually negligible.

The CMRR is found by substituting (3.189) and (3.192) into (3.187), which gives

$$\text{CMRR} = 1 + 2g_m R_{TAIL} \qquad (3.193)$$

This expression applies to the particular case of a single-stage, emitter-coupled pair. It shows that increasing the output resistance of the tail current source $R_{TAIL}$ improves the common-mode-rejection ratio. This topic is considered in Chapter 4.

Since bipolar transistors have finite $\beta_0$, and since differential amplifiers are often used as the input stage of instrumentation circuits, the input resistance of emitter-coupled pairs is also an important design consideration. The differential input resistance $R_{id}$ is defined as the ratio of the small-signal differential input voltage $v_{id}$ to the small-signal input current $i_b$ when a pure differential input voltage is applied. By inspecting Fig. 3.56, we find that

$$\frac{v_{id}}{2} = i_b r_\pi \qquad (3.194)$$

Therefore, the differential input resistance of the emitter-coupled pair is

$$R_{id} = \frac{v_{id}}{i_b}\bigg|_{v_{ic}=0} = 2r_\pi \qquad (3.195)$$

Thus the differential input resistance depends on the $r_\pi$ of the transistor, which increases with increasing $\beta_0$ and decreasing collector current. High input resistance is therefore obtained when an emitter-coupled pair is operated at low bias current levels. Techniques to achieve small bias currents are considered in Chapter 4.

The common-mode input resistance $R_{ic}$ is defined as the ratio of the small-signal, common-mode input voltage $v_{ic}$ to the small-signal input current $i_b$ in one terminal when a pure common-mode input is applied. Since the common-mode half circuit in Fig. 3.60 is the same as that for a common-emitter amplifier with emitter degeneration, substituting $R_E = 2R_{TAIL}$ into (3.90) gives $R_{ic}$ as

$$R_{ic} = \frac{v_{ic}}{i_b}\bigg|_{v_{id}=0} = r_\pi + (\beta_0 + 1)(2R_{TAIL}) \qquad (3.196)$$

**Figure 3.61** (a) General low-frequency, small-signal, $\pi$-equivalent input circuit for the differential amplifier. (b) T-equivalent input circuit.

The small-signal input current that flows when both common-mode and differential-mode input voltages are applied can be found by superposition and is given by

$$i_{b1} = \frac{v_{id}}{R_{id}} + \frac{v_{ic}}{R_{ic}} \qquad (3.197)$$

$$i_{b2} = -\frac{v_{id}}{R_{id}} + \frac{v_{ic}}{R_{ic}} \qquad (3.198)$$

where $i_{b1}$ and $i_{b2}$ represent the base currents of $Q_1$ and $Q_2$, respectively.

The input resistance can be represented by the $\pi$ equivalent circuit of Fig. 3.61a or by the T-equivalent circuit of Fig. 3.61b. For the $\pi$ model, the common-mode input resistance is exactly $R_{ic}$ independent of $R_x$. To make the differential-mode input resistance exactly $R_{id}$, the value of $R_x$ should be more than $R_{id}$ to account for nonzero current in $R_{ic}$. On the other hand, for the T model, the differential-mode input resistance is exactly $R_{id}$ independent of $R_y$, and the common-mode input resistance is $R_{ic}$ if $R_y$ is chosen to be less than $R_{ic}/2$ as shown. The approximations in Fig. 3.61 are valid if $R_{ic}$ is much larger than $R_{id}$.

**MOS Source-Coupled Pair.** For the MOS case, substituting (3.104) for $G_m$ with $g_{mb} = 0$ and $R_S = 2R_{TAIL}$ into (3.191) and rearranging gives

$$A_{cm} \simeq -\frac{g_m R}{1 + g_m (2R_{TAIL})} = -\frac{g_m R}{1 + 2g_m R_{TAIL}} \qquad (3.199)$$

Although (3.199) and the common-mode half circuit in Fig. 3.60 ignore the body-effect transconductance $g_{mb}$, the common-mode gain depends on $g_{mb}$ in practice because the body effect changes the source-body voltage of the transistors in the differential pair. Since nonzero $g_{mb}$ was included in the derivation of the transconductance of the common-source amplifier with degeneration, a simple way to include the body effect here is to allow nonzero $g_{mb}$ when substituting (3.104) into (3.191). The result is

$$A_{cm} \simeq -\frac{g_m R}{1 + (g_m + g_{mb})(2R_{TAIL})} = -\frac{g_m R}{1 + 2(g_m + g_{mb})R_{TAIL}} \qquad (3.200)$$

To include the effect of finite $r_o$ in the above analysis, $R$ in (3.199) and (3.200) should be replaced by $R \parallel R_o$, where $R_o$ is the output resistance of a common-source amplifier with source degeneration of $R_S = 2R_{TAIL}$, given in (3.107). This substitution ignores the effect of finite $r_o$ on $G_m$, which is shown in (3.103) and is usually negligible.

The CMRR is found by substituting (3.189) and (3.200) into (3.187), which gives

$$\text{CMRR} \simeq 1 + 2(g_m + g_{mb}) R_{TAIL} \qquad (3.201)$$

Equation 3.201 is valid for a single-stage, source-coupled pair and shows that increasing $R_{TAIL}$ increases the CMRR. This topic is studied in Chapter 4.

### 3.5.6 Device Mismatch Effects in Differential Amplifiers

An important aspect of the performance of differential amplifiers is the minimum dc and ac differential voltages that can be detected. The presence of component mismatches within the amplifier itself and drifts of component values with temperature produce dc differential voltages at the output that are indistinguishable from the dc component of the signal being amplified. Also, such mismatches and drifts cause nonzero common-mode-to-differential-mode gain as well as nonzero differential-to-common-mode gain to arise. Nonzero $A_{cm-dm}$ is especially important because it converts common-mode inputs to differential outputs, which are treated as the desired signal by subsequent stages. In many analog systems, these types of errors pose the basic limitation on the resolution of the system, and hence consideration of mismatch-induced effects is often central to the design of analog circuits.

#### 3.5.6.1 Input Offset Voltage and Current

For differential amplifiers, the effect of mismatches on dc performance is most conveniently represented by two quantities, the input offset voltage and the input offset current. These quantities represent the input-referred effect of all the component mismatches within the amplifier on its dc performance.[11,12] As illustrated in Fig. 3.62, the dc behavior of the amplifier containing the mismatches is identical to an ideal amplifier with no mismatches but with the input offset voltage source added in series with the input and the input offset current source in shunt across the input terminals. Both quantities are required to represent the effect of mismatch in general so that the model is valid for any source resistance. For example, if the input terminals are driven by an ideal voltage source with zero resistance, the input offset current does not contribute to the amplifier output, and the offset voltage generator is needed to model the effect of mismatch. On the other hand, if the input terminals are driven by an ideal current source with infinite resistance, the input offset voltage does not contribute to the amplifier output, and the offset current generator is needed to model the effect of mismatch. These quantities are usually a function of both temperature and common-mode input voltage. In the next several sections, we calculate the input offset voltage and current of the emitter-coupled pair and the source-coupled pair.

**Figure 3.62** Equivalent input offset voltage ($V_{OS}$) and current ($I_{OS}$) for a differential amplifier. (a) Actual circuit containing mismatches. (b) Equivalent dc circuit with identically matched devices and the offset voltage and current referred to the input.

### 3.5.6.2 Input Offset Voltage of the Emitter-Coupled Pair

The predominant sources of offset error in the emitter-coupled pair are the mismatches in the base width, base doping level, and collector doping level of the transistors, mismatches in the effective emitter area of the transistors, and mismatches in the collector load resistors. To provide analytical results simple enough for intuitive interpretation, the analysis will be carried out assuming a uniform-base transistor. The results are similar for the nonuniform case, although the analytical procedure is more tedious. In most instances the dc base current is low enough that the dc voltage drop in $r_b$ is negligible, so we neglect $r_b$.

Consider Fig. 3.45 with dc signals so that $V_{i1} = V_{I1}$, $V_{i2} = V_{I2}$, $V_{o1} = V_{O1}$, and $V_{o2} = V_{O2}$. Let $V_{ID} = V_{I1} - V_{I2}$. Also, assume that the collector resistors may not be identical. Let $R_{C1}$ and $R_{C2}$ represent the values of the resistors attached to $Q_1$ and $Q_2$, respectively. From KVL around the input loop,

$$V_{ID} - V_{BE1} + V_{BE2} = 0 \tag{3.202}$$

Therefore,

$$V_{ID} = V_T \ln \frac{I_{C1}}{I_{S1}} - V_T \ln \frac{I_{C2}}{I_{S2}} = V_T \ln \frac{I_{C1}}{I_{C2}} \frac{I_{S2}}{I_{S1}} \tag{3.203}$$

The factors determining the saturation current $I_S$ of a bipolar transistor are described in Chapter 1. There it was shown that if the impurity concentration in the base region is uniform, these saturation currents can be written

$$I_{S1} = \frac{qn_i^2 \bar{D}_n}{N_A W_{B1}(V_{CB})} A_1 = \frac{qn_i^2 \bar{D}_n}{Q_{B1}(V_{CB})} A_1 \tag{3.204}$$

$$I_{S2} = \frac{qn_i^2 \bar{D}_n}{N_A W_{B2}(V_{CB})} A_2 = \frac{qn_i^2 \bar{D}_n}{Q_{B2}(V_{CB})} A_2 \tag{3.205}$$

where $W_B(V_{CB})$ is the base width as a function of $V_{CB}$, $N_A$ is the acceptor density in the base, and $A$ is the emitter area. We denote the product $N_A W_B(V_{CB})$ as $Q_B(V_{CB})$, the total base impurity doping per unit area.

The input offset voltage $V_{OS}$ is equal to the value of $V_{ID} = V_{I1} - V_{I2}$ that must be applied to the input to drive the differential output voltage $V_{OD} = V_{O1} - V_{O2}$ to zero. For $V_{OD}$ to be zero, $I_{C1} R_{C1} = I_{C2} R_{C2}$; therefore,

$$\frac{I_{C1}}{I_{C2}} = \frac{R_{C2}}{R_{C1}} \tag{3.206}$$

Substituting (3.204), (3.205), and (3.206) into (3.203) gives

$$V_{OS} = V_T \ln \left[ \left( \frac{R_{C2}}{R_{C1}} \right) \left( \frac{A_2}{A_1} \right) \left( \frac{Q_{B1}(V_{CB})}{Q_{B2}(V_{CB})} \right) \right] \tag{3.207}$$

This expression relates the input offset voltage to the device parameters and $R_C$ mismatch. Usually, however, the argument of the log function is very close to unity and the equation can be interpreted in a more intuitively satisfying way. In the following section we perform an approximate analysis, valid if the mismatches are small.

### 3.5.6.3 Offset Voltage of the Emitter-Coupled Pair: Approximate Analysis

In cases of practical interest involving offset voltages and currents, the mismatch between any two nominally matched circuit parameters is usually small compared with the absolute value of that parameter. This observation leads to a procedure by which the individual contributions to offset voltage can be considered separately and summed.

First, define new parameters to describe the mismatch in the components, using the relations

$$\Delta X = X_1 - X_2 \tag{3.208}$$

$$X = \frac{X_1 + X_2}{2} \tag{3.209}$$

Thus $\Delta X$ is the difference between two parameters, and $X$ is the average of the two nominally matched parameters. Note that $\Delta X$ can be positive or negative. Next invert (3.208) and (3.209) to give

$$X_1 = X + \frac{\Delta X}{2} \tag{3.210}$$

$$X_2 = X - \frac{\Delta X}{2} \tag{3.211}$$

These relations can be applied to the collector resistances, the emitter areas, and the base doping parameters in (3.207) to give

$$V_{OS} = V_T \ln\left[\left(\frac{R_C - \frac{\Delta R_C}{2}}{R_C + \frac{\Delta R_C}{2}}\right)\left(\frac{A - \frac{\Delta A}{2}}{A + \frac{\Delta A}{2}}\right)\left(\frac{Q_B + \frac{\Delta Q_B}{2}}{Q_B - \frac{\Delta Q_B}{2}}\right)\right] \tag{3.212}$$

With the assumptions that $\Delta R_C \ll R_C$, $\Delta A \ll A$, and $\Delta Q_B \ll Q_B$, (3.212) can be simplified to

$$V_{OS} \simeq V_T \ln\left[\left(1 - \frac{\Delta R_C}{R_C}\right)\left(1 - \frac{\Delta A}{A}\right)\left(1 + \frac{\Delta Q_B}{Q_B}\right)\right]$$

$$\simeq V_T\left[\ln\left(1 - \frac{\Delta R_C}{R_C}\right) + \ln\left(1 - \frac{\Delta A}{A}\right) + \ln\left(1 + \frac{\Delta Q_B}{Q_B}\right)\right] \tag{3.213}$$

If $x \ll 1$, a Taylor series can be used to show that

$$\ln(1 + x) = x - \frac{x^2}{2} + \frac{x^3}{3} - \cdots \tag{3.214}$$

Applying (3.214) to each logarithm in (3.213) and ignoring terms higher than first order in the expansions gives

$$V_{OS} \simeq V_T\left(-\frac{\Delta R_C}{R_C} - \frac{\Delta A}{A} + \frac{\Delta Q_B}{Q_B}\right) \tag{3.215}$$

Thus, under the assumptions made, we have obtained an approximate expression for the input offset voltage, which is the linear superposition of the effects of the different components. It can be shown that this can always be done for small component mismatches. Note that the signs of the individual terms of (3.215) are not particularly significant, since the mismatch factors can be positive or negative depending on the direction of the random parameter variation. The worst-case offset occurs when the terms have signs such that the individual contributions add.

Equation 3.215 relates the offset voltage to mismatches in the resistors and in the structural parameters $A$ and $Q_B$ of the transistors. For the purpose of predicting the offset voltage from device parameters that are directly measurable electrically, we rewrite (3.215) to express the offset in terms of the resistor mismatch and the mismatch in the saturation currents of the transistors:

$$V_{OS} \simeq V_T \left( -\frac{\Delta R_C}{R_C} - \frac{\Delta I_S}{I_S} \right) \qquad (3.216)$$

where

$$\frac{\Delta I_S}{I_S} = \frac{\Delta A}{A} - \frac{\Delta Q_B}{Q_B} \qquad (3.217)$$

is the offset voltage contribution from the transistors themselves, as reflected in the mismatch in saturation current. Mismatch factors $\Delta R_C / R_C$ and $\Delta I_S / I_S$ are actually random parameters that take on a different value for each circuit fabricated, and the distribution of the observed values is described by a probability distribution. For large samples the distribution tends toward a normal, or Gaussian, distribution with zero mean. Typically observed standard deviations for the preceding mismatch parameters for small-area diffused devices are

$$\sigma_{\Delta R/R} = 0.01 \qquad \sigma_{\Delta I_S/I_S} = 0.05 \qquad (3.218)$$

In the Gaussian distribution, 68 percent of the samples have a value within $\pm \sigma$ of the mean value. If we assume that the mean value of the distribution is zero, then 68 percent of the resistor pairs in a large sample will match within 1 percent, and 68 percent of the transistor pairs will have saturation currents that match within 5 percent for the distributions described by (3.218). These values can be heavily influenced by device geometry and processing. If we pick one sample from each distribution so that the parameter mismatch is equal to the corresponding standard deviation, and if the mismatch factors are chosen in the direction so that they add, the resulting offset from (3.216) would be

$$V_{OS} \simeq (26 \text{ mV})(0.01 + 0.05) \simeq 1.5 \text{ mV} \qquad (3.219)$$

Large ion-implanted devices with careful layout can achieve $V_{OS} \simeq 0.1$ mV. A parameter of more interest to the circuit designer than the offset of one sample is the standard deviation of the total offset voltage. Since the offset is the sum of two uncorrelated random parameters, the standard deviation of the sum is equal to the square root of the sum of the squares of the standard deviation of the two mismatch contributions, or

$$\sigma_{V_{OS}} = V_T \sqrt{(\sigma_{\Delta R/R})^2 + (\sigma_{\Delta I_S/I_S})^2} \qquad (3.220)$$

The properties of the Gaussian distribution are summarized in Appendix A.3.1.

### 3.5.6.4 Offset Voltage Drift in the Emitter-Coupled Pair

When emitter-coupled pairs are used as low-level dc amplifiers where the offset voltage is critical, provision is sometimes made to manually adjust the input offset voltage to zero with an external potentiometer. When this adjustment is done, the important parameter becomes not the offset voltage itself, but the variation of this offset voltage with temperature, often referred to as *drift*. For most practical circuits, the sensitivity of the input offset voltage to temperature is not zero, and the wider the excursion of temperature experienced by the circuit, the more error the offset voltage drift will contribute. This parameter is easily calculated for the emitter-coupled pair by differentiating (3.207) as follows

$$\frac{dV_{OS}}{dT} = \frac{V_{OS}}{T} \qquad (3.221)$$

using $V_T = kT/q$ and assuming the ratios in (3.207) are independent of temperature. Thus the drift and offset are proportional for the emitter-coupled pair. This relationship is observed experimentally. For example, an emitter-coupled pair with a measured offset voltage of 2 mV would display a drift of $2\ mV/300°K$ or $6.6\ \mu V/°C$ under the assumptions we have made.

Equation 3.221 appears to show that the drift also would be nulled by externally adjusting the offset to zero. This observation is only approximately true because of the way in which the nulling is accomplished.[13] Usually an external potentiometer is placed in parallel with a portion of one of the collector load resistors in the pair. The temperature coefficient of the nulling potentiometer generally does not match that of the diffused resistors, so a resistor-mismatch temperature coefficient is introduced that can make the drift worse than it was without nulling. Voltage drifts in the $1\ \mu V/°C$ range can be obtained with careful design.

### 3.5.6.5 Input Offset Current of the Emitter-Coupled Pair

The input offset current $I_{OS}$ is measured with the inputs connected only to current sources and is the difference in the base currents that must be applied to drive the differential output voltage $V_{OD} = V_{O1} - V_{O2}$ to zero. Since the base current of each transistor is equal to the corresponding collector current divided by beta, the offset current is

$$I_{OS} = \frac{I_{C1}}{\beta_{F1}} - \frac{I_{C2}}{\beta_{F2}} \tag{3.222}$$

when $V_{OD} = 0$. As before, we can write

$$I_{C1} = I_C + \frac{\Delta I_C}{2} \qquad I_{C2} = I_C - \frac{\Delta I_C}{2} \tag{3.223}$$

$$\beta_{F1} = \beta_F + \frac{\Delta\beta_F}{2} \qquad \beta_{F2} = \beta_F - \frac{\Delta\beta_F}{2} \tag{3.224}$$

Inserting (3.223) and (3.224) into (3.222), the offset current becomes

$$I_{OS} = \left( \frac{I_C + \dfrac{\Delta I_C}{2}}{\beta_F + \dfrac{\Delta\beta_F}{2}} - \frac{I_C - \dfrac{\Delta I_C}{2}}{\beta_F - \dfrac{\Delta\beta_F}{2}} \right) \tag{3.225}$$

Neglecting higher-order terms, this becomes

$$I_{OS} \approx \frac{I_C}{\beta_F} \left( \frac{\Delta I_C}{I_C} - \frac{\Delta\beta_F}{\beta_F} \right) \tag{3.226}$$

For $V_{OD}$ to be zero, $I_{C1}R_{C1} = I_{C2}R_{C2}$; therefore, from (3.206), the mismatch in collector currents is

$$\frac{\Delta I_C}{I_C} = -\frac{\Delta R_C}{R_C} \tag{3.227}$$

Equation 3.227 shows that the fractional mismatch in the collector currents must be equal in magnitude and opposite in polarity from the fractional mismatch in the collector resistors to force $V_{OD} = 0$. Substituting (3.227) into (3.226) gives

$$I_{OS} \approx -\frac{I_C}{\beta_F} \left( \frac{\Delta R_C}{R_C} + \frac{\Delta\beta_F}{\beta_F} \right) \tag{3.228}$$

A typically observed beta mismatch distribution displays a deviation of about 10 percent. Assuming a beta mismatch of 10 percent and a mismatch in collector resistors of

1 percent, we obtain

$$I_{OS} \simeq -\frac{I_C}{\beta_F}\left(\frac{\Delta R_C}{R_C} + \frac{\Delta\beta_F}{\beta_F}\right) = -\frac{I_C}{\beta_F}(0.11) = -0.11\,(I_B) \tag{3.229}$$

In many applications, the input offset current as well as the input current itself must be minimized. A good example is the input stage of operational amplifiers. Various circuit and technological approaches to reduce these currents are considered in Chapter 6.

### 3.5.6.6 Input Offset Voltage of the Source-Coupled Pair

As mentioned earlier in the chapter, MOS transistors inherently provide higher input resistance and lower input bias current than bipolar transistors when the MOS gate is used as the input. This observation also applies to differential-pair amplifiers. The input offset current of an MOS differential pair is the difference between the two gate currents and is essentially zero because the gates of the input transistors are connected to silicon dioxide, which is an insulator. However, MOS transistors exhibit lower transconductance than bipolar transistors at the same current, resulting in poorer input offset voltage and common-mode rejection ratio in MOS differential pairs than in the case of bipolar transistors. In this section we calculate the input offset voltage of the source-coupled MOSFET pair.

Consider Fig. 3.50 with dc signals so that $V_{i1} = V_{I1}$, $V_{i2} = V_{I2}$, $V_{o1} = V_{O1}$, and $V_{o2} = V_{O2}$. Let $V_{ID} = V_{I1} - V_{I2}$. Also, assume that the drain resistors may not be identical. Let $R_{D1}$ and $R_{D2}$ represent the values of the resistors attached to $M_1$ and $M_2$, respectively. KVL around the input loop gives

$$V_{ID} - V_{GS1} + V_{GS2} = 0 \tag{3.230}$$

Solving (1.157) for the gate-source voltage and substituting into (3.230) gives

$$V_{ID} = V_{GS1} - V_{GS2}$$

$$= V_{t1} + \sqrt{\frac{2I_{D1}}{k'\,(W/L)_1}} - V_{t2} - \sqrt{\frac{2I_{D2}}{k'\,(W/L)_2}} \tag{3.231}$$

As in the bipolar case, the input offset voltage $V_{OS}$ is equal to the value of $V_{ID} = V_{I1} - V_{I2}$ that must be applied to the input to drive the differential output voltage $V_{OD} = V_{O1} - V_{O2}$ to zero. For $V_{OD}$ to be zero, $I_{D1}R_{D1} = I_{D2}R_{D2}$; therefore,

$$V_{OS} = V_{t1} - V_{t2} + \sqrt{\frac{2I_{D1}}{k'\,(W/L)_1}} - \sqrt{\frac{2I_{D2}}{k'\,(W/L)_2}} \tag{3.232}$$

subject to the constraint that $I_{D1}R_{D1} = I_{D2}R_{D2}$.

### 3.5.6.7 Offset Voltage of the Source-Coupled Pair: Approximate Analysis

The mismatch between any two nominally matched circuit parameters is usually small compared with the absolute value of that parameter in practice. As a result, (3.232) can be rewritten in a way that allows us to understand the contributions of each mismatch to the overall offset.

Defining difference and average quantities in the usual way, we have

$$\Delta I_D = I_{D1} - I_{D2} \tag{3.233}$$

$$I_D = \frac{I_{D1} + I_{D2}}{2} \tag{3.234}$$

$$\Delta(W/L) = (W/L)_1 - (W/L)_2 \tag{3.235}$$

$$(W/L) = \frac{(W/L)_1 + (W/L)_2}{2} \tag{3.236}$$

$$\Delta V_t = V_{t1} - V_{t2} \tag{3.237}$$

$$V_t = \frac{V_{t1} + V_{t2}}{2} \tag{3.238}$$

$$\Delta R_L = R_{L1} - R_{L2} \tag{3.239}$$

$$R_L = \frac{R_{L1} + R_{L2}}{2} \tag{3.240}$$

Rearranging (3.233) and (3.234) as well as (3.235) and (3.236) gives

$$I_{D1} = I_D + \frac{\Delta I_D}{2} \qquad I_{D2} = I_D - \frac{\Delta I_D}{2} \tag{3.241}$$

$$(W/L)_1 = (W/L) + \frac{\Delta(W/L)}{2} \qquad (W/L)_2 = (W/L) - \frac{\Delta(W/L)}{2} \tag{3.242}$$

Substituting (3.237), (3.241), and (3.242) into (3.232) gives

$$V_{OS} = \Delta V_t + \sqrt{\frac{2\,(I_D + \Delta I_D/2)}{k'\,[(W/L) + \Delta(W/L)/2]}} - \sqrt{\frac{2\,(I_D - \Delta I_D/2)}{k'\,[(W/L) - \Delta(W/L)/2]}} \tag{3.243}$$

Rearranging (3.243) gives

$$V_{OS} = \Delta V_t + (V_{GS} - V_t)\left( \sqrt{\frac{1 + \Delta I_D/2I_D}{1 + \frac{\Delta(W/L)}{2\,(W/L)}}} - \sqrt{\frac{1 - \Delta I_D/2I_D}{1 - \frac{\Delta(W/L)}{2\,(W/L)}}} \right) \tag{3.244}$$

If the mismatch terms are small, the argument of each square root in (3.244) is approximately unity. Using $\sqrt{x} \approx (1 + x)/2$ when $x \approx 1$ for the argument of each square root in (3.244), we have

$$V_{OS} \simeq \Delta V_t + \frac{(V_{GS} - V_t)}{2}\left( \frac{1 + \Delta I_D/2I_D}{1 + \frac{\Delta(W/L)}{2\,(W/L)}} - \frac{1 - \Delta I_D/2I_D}{1 - \frac{\Delta(W/L)}{2\,(W/L)}} \right) \tag{3.245}$$

Carrying out the long divisions in (3.245) and ignoring terms higher than first order gives

$$V_{OS} \simeq \Delta V_t + \frac{(V_{GS} - V_t)}{2}\left( \frac{\Delta I_D}{I_D} - \frac{\Delta(W/L)}{(W/L)} \right) \tag{3.246}$$

When the differential input voltage is $V_{OS}$, the differential output voltage is zero; therefore, $I_{D1}R_{L1} = I_{D2}R_{L2}$, and

$$\frac{\Delta I_D}{I_D} = -\frac{\Delta R_L}{R_L} \tag{3.247}$$

In other words, the mismatch in the drain currents must be equal and opposite the mismatch of the load resistors to set $V_{OD} = 0$. Substituting (3.247) into (3.246) gives

$$V_{OS} = \Delta V_t + \frac{(V_{GS} - V_t)}{2}\left( -\frac{\Delta R_L}{R_L} - \frac{\Delta(W/L)}{(W/L)} \right) \tag{3.248}$$

The first term on the right side of (3.248) stems from threshold mismatch. This mismatch component is present in MOS devices but not in bipolar transistors. This component results in a constant offset component that is bias-current independent. Threshold mismatch is a strong function of process cleanliness and uniformity and can be substantially improved by the use of careful layout. Measurements indicate that large-geometry structures are capable of achieving threshold-mismatch distributions with standard deviations on the order of 2 mV in a modern silicon-gate MOS process. This offset component alone limits the minimum offset in the MOS case and is an order of magnitude larger than the total differential-pair offset in modern ion-implanted bipolar technologies.

The second term on the right side of (3.248) shows that another component of the offset scales with the overdrive $V_{ov} = (V_{GS} - V_t)$ and is related to a mismatch in the load elements or in the device $W/L$ ratio. In the bipolar emitter-coupled pair offset, the corresponding mismatch terms were multiplied by $V_T$, typically a much smaller number than $V_{ov}/2$. Thus source-coupled pairs of MOS transistors display higher input offset voltage than bipolar pairs for the same level of geometric mismatch or process gradient even when threshold mismatch is ignored. The key reason for this limitation is that the ratio of the transconductance to the bias current is much lower with MOS transistors than in the bipolar case. The quantities $V_T$ in (3.216) and $(V_{GS} - V_t)/2 = V_{ov}/2$ in (3.248) are both equal to $I_{BIAS}/g_m$ for the devices in question. This quantity is typically in the range 100 mV to 500 mV for MOS transistors instead of 26 mV for bipolar transistors.◄

### 3.5.6.8 Offset Voltage Drift in the Source-Coupled Pair

Offset voltage drift in MOSFET source-coupled pairs does not show the high correlation with offset voltage observed in bipolar pairs. The offset consists of several terms that have different temperature coefficients. Both $V_t$ and $V_{ov}$ have a strong temperature dependence, affecting $V_{GS}$ in opposite directions. The temperature dependence of $V_{ov}$ stems primarily from the mobility variation, which gives a negative temperature coefficient to the drain current, while the threshold voltage depends on the Fermi potential. As shown in Section 1.5.4, the latter decreases with temperature and contributes a positive temperature coefficient to the drain current. The drift due to the $\Delta V_t$ term in $V_{OS}$ may be quite large if this term itself is large. These two effects can be made to cancel at one value of $I_D$, which is a useful phenomenon for temperature-stable biasing of single-ended amplifiers. In differential amplifiers, however, this phenomenon is not greatly useful because differential configurations already give first-order cancellation of $V_{GS}$ temperature variations.

### 3.5.6.9 Small-Signal Characteristics of Unbalanced Differential Amplifiers[11]

As mentioned in Section 3.5.4, the common-mode-to-differential-mode gain and differential-mode-to-common-mode gain of unbalanced differential amplifiers are nonzero. The direct approach to calculation of these cross-gain terms requires analysis of the entire small-signal diagram. In perfectly balanced differential amplifiers, the cross-gain terms are zero, and the differential-mode and common-mode gains can be found by using two *independent* half circuits, as shown in Section 3.5.5. With imperfect matching, exact half-circuit analysis is still possible if the half circuits are *coupled* instead of independent. Furthermore, if the mismatches are small, a modified version of half-circuit analysis gives results that are approximately valid. This modified half-circuit analysis not only greatly simplifies the required calculations, but also gives insight about how to reduce $A_{cm-dm}$ and $A_{dm-cm}$ in practice.

First consider a pair of mismatched resistors $R_1$ and $R_2$ shown in Fig. 3.63. Assume that the branch currents are $i_1$ and $i_2$, respectively. From Ohm's law, the differential and

**Figure 3.63** A pair of mismatched resistors.

common-mode voltages across the resistors can be written as

$$v_d = v_1 - v_2 = i_1 R_1 - i_2 R_2 \tag{3.249}$$

and

$$v_c = \frac{v_1 + v_2}{2} = \frac{i_1 R_1 + i_2 R_2}{2} \tag{3.250}$$

Define $i_d = i_1 - i_2$, $i_c = (i_1 + i_2)/2$, $\Delta R = R_1 - R_2$, and $R = (R_1 + R_2)/2$. Then (3.249) and (3.250) can be rewritten as

$$v_d = \left(i_c + \frac{i_d}{2}\right)\left(R + \frac{\Delta R}{2}\right) - \left(i_c - \frac{i_d}{2}\right)\left(R - \frac{\Delta R}{2}\right) = i_d R + i_c (\Delta R) \tag{3.251}$$

and

$$v_c = \frac{\left(i_c + \frac{i_d}{2}\right)\left(R + \frac{\Delta R}{2}\right) + \left(i_c - \frac{i_d}{2}\right)\left(R - \frac{\Delta R}{2}\right)}{2} = i_c R + \frac{i_d (\Delta R)}{4} \tag{3.252}$$

These equations can be used to draw differential and common-mode half circuits for the pair of mismatched resistors. Since the differential half circuit should give half the differential voltage dropped across the resistors, the two terms on the right-hand side of (3.251) are each divided by two and used to represent one component of a branch voltage of $v_d/2$. The differential half circuit is shown in Fig. 3.64a. The first component of the branch voltage is the voltage dropped across $R$ and is half the differential current times the average resistor value. The second component is the voltage across the dependent voltage source controlled by the current flowing in the common-mode half circuit and is proportional to half the mismatch in the resistor values. The common-mode half circuit is constructed from (3.252) and is shown in Fig. 3.64b. Here the total branch voltage $v_c$ is the sum of the voltages across a resistor and a dependent voltage source controlled by the current flowing in the differential half circuit. In the limiting case where $\Delta R = 0$, the voltage across each

(a)

(b)

**Figure 3.64** (a) Differential and (b) common-mode half circuits for a pair of mismatched resistors.

**Figure 3.65** A pair of mismatched voltage-controlled current sources.

dependent source in Fig. 3.64 is zero, and each half circuit collapses to simply a resistor of value $R$. Therefore, the half circuits are independent in this case, as expected. In practice, however, $\Delta R \neq 0$, and Fig. 3.64 shows that the differential voltage depends not only on the differential current, but also on the common-mode current. Similarly, the common-mode voltage depends in part on the differential current. Thus the behavior of a pair of mismatched resistors can be represented exactly by using coupled half circuits.

Next consider a pair of mismatched voltage-controlled current sources as shown in Fig. 3.65. Assume that the control voltages are $v_1$ and $v_2$, respectively. Then the differential and common-mode currents can be written as

$$
\begin{aligned}
i_d &= i_1 - i_2 = g_{m1}v_1 - g_{m2}v_2 \\
&= \left(g_m + \frac{\Delta g_m}{2}\right)\left(v_c + \frac{v_d}{2}\right) - \left(g_m - \frac{\Delta g_m}{2}\right)\left(v_c - \frac{v_d}{2}\right) \\
&= g_m v_d + \Delta g_m v_c
\end{aligned}
\tag{3.253}
$$

and

$$
\begin{aligned}
i_c &= \frac{i_1 + i_2}{2} = \frac{g_{m1}v_1 + g_{m2}v_2}{2} \\
&= \frac{\left(g_m + \dfrac{\Delta g_m}{2}\right)\left(v_c + \dfrac{v_d}{2}\right) + \left(g_m - \dfrac{\Delta g_m}{2}\right)\left(v_c - \dfrac{v_d}{2}\right)}{2} \\
&= g_m v_c + \frac{\Delta g_m v_d}{4}
\end{aligned}
\tag{3.254}
$$

where $v_d = v_1 - v_2$, $v_c = (v_1 + v_2)/2$, $\Delta g_m = g_{m1} - g_{m2}$, and $g_m = (g_{m1} + g_{m2})/2$. The corresponding differential and common-mode half circuits each use two voltage-controlled current sources, as shown in Fig. 3.66. In each case, one dependent source voltages across a resistor and a dependent voltage source controlled by the current flowing in the differential half circuit. In the limiting case where $\Delta R = 0$, the voltage across each

**Figure 3.66** (a) Differential and (b) common-mode half circuits for a pair of mismatched voltage-controlled current sources.

(a)                    (b)

is proportional to the average transconductance and the other to half the mismatch in the transconductances. With perfect matching, the mismatch terms are zero, and the two half circuits are independent. With imperfect matching, however, the mismatch terms are nonzero. In the differential half circuit, the mismatch current source is controlled by the common-mode control voltage. In the common-mode half circuit, the mismatch current source is controlled by half the differential control voltage. Thus, as for mismatched resistors, the behavior of a pair of mismatched voltage-controlled current sources can be represented exactly by using coupled half circuits.

With these concepts in mind, construction of the differential and common-mode half circuits of unbalanced differential amplifiers is straightforward. In the differential half circuit, mismatched resistors are replaced by the circuit shown in Fig. 3.64a, and mismatched voltage-controlled current sources are replaced by the circuit in Fig. 3.66a. Similarly, the circuits shown in Fig. 3.64b and Fig. 3.66b replace mismatched resistors and voltage-controlled current sources in the common-mode half circuit. Although mismatches change the differential and common-mode components of signals that appear at various points in the complete unbalanced amplifier, the differential components are still equal and opposite while the common-mode components are identical by definition. Therefore, small-signal short and open circuits induced by the differential and common-mode signals are unaffected by these replacements.

For example, the differential and common-mode half circuits of the unbalanced differential amplifier shown in Fig. 3.67 are shown in Fig. 3.68. KCL at the output of the differential half circuit in Fig. 3.68a gives

$$\frac{i_{Rd}}{2} + g_m \frac{v_{id}}{2} + \frac{\Delta g_m}{2} v = 0 \tag{3.255}$$

KCL at the output of the common-mode half circuit in Fig. 3.68b gives

$$g_m v + \frac{\Delta g_m}{2} \frac{v_{id}}{2} + i_{Rc} = 0 \tag{3.256}$$

Also, KVL around the input loop in the common-mode half circuit gives

$$v = v_{ic} - v_{tail} = v_{ic} + 2 i_{Rc} r_{tail} \tag{3.257}$$

Substituting (3.257) into (3.256) and rearranging gives

$$i_{Rc} = -\frac{g_m v_{ic} + \frac{\Delta g_m}{2} \frac{v_{id}}{2}}{1 + 2 g_m r_{tail}} \tag{3.258}$$

Figure 3.67 The small-signal diagram of an unbalanced differential amplifier.

(a)

(b)

**Figure 3.68** (a) Differential and (b) common-mode half circuits of the differential amplifier shown in Fig. 3.67.

Substituting (3.257) and (3.258) into (3.255) and rearranging gives

$$\frac{i_{Rd}}{2} = \frac{v_{id}}{2}\left(-g_m + \frac{\Delta g_m r_{\text{tail}}\dfrac{\Delta g_m}{2}}{1 + 2g_m r_{\text{tail}}}\right) + v_{ic}\left(-\frac{\Delta g_m}{2} + \frac{\Delta g_m r_{\text{tail}}g_m}{1 + 2g_m r_{\text{tail}}}\right) \quad (3.259)$$

From KVL in the $R$ branch in the differential half circuit in Fig. 3.68a,

$$\frac{v_{od}}{2} = i_{Rc}\frac{\Delta R}{2} + \frac{i_{Rd}}{2}R \quad (3.260)$$

Substituting (3.258) and (3.259) into (3.260) and rearranging gives

$$v_{od} = A_{dm}v_{id} + A_{cm-dm}v_{ic} \quad (3.261)$$

where $A_{dm}$ and $A_{cm-dm}$ are

$$A_{dm} = \frac{v_{od}}{v_{id}}\bigg|_{v_{ic}=0} = -g_m R + \frac{\Delta g_m r_{\text{tail}}\dfrac{\Delta g_m}{2}R - \dfrac{\Delta g_m}{2}\dfrac{\Delta R}{2}}{1 + 2g_m r_{\text{tail}}} \quad (3.262)$$

$$A_{cm-dm} = \frac{v_{od}}{v_{ic}}\bigg|_{v_{id}=0} = -\left(\frac{g_m \Delta R + \Delta g_m R}{1 + 2g_m r_{\text{tail}}}\right) \quad (3.263)$$

From KVL in the $R$ branch in the common-mode half circuit in Fig. 3.68b,

$$v_{oc} = \frac{i_{Rd}}{2}\frac{\Delta R}{2} + i_{Rc}R \quad (3.264)$$

Substituting (3.258) and (3.259) into (3.264) and rearranging gives

$$v_{oc} = A_{dm-cm}v_{id} + A_{cm}v_{ic} \qquad (3.265)$$

where $A_{dm-cm}$ and $A_{cm}$ are

$$A_{dm-cm} = \left.\frac{v_{oc}}{v_{id}}\right|_{v_{ic}=0}$$

$$= -\frac{1}{4}\left[g_m\Delta R + \frac{\Delta g_m R - g_m\Delta R\left(2g_m r_{\text{tail}}\left(\dfrac{\Delta g_m}{2g_m}\right)^2\right)}{1 + 2g_m r_{\text{tail}}}\right] \qquad (3.266)$$

$$A_{cm} = \left.\frac{v_{oc}}{v_{ic}}\right|_{v_{id}=0} = -\left(\frac{g_m R + \dfrac{\Delta g_m}{2}\dfrac{\Delta R}{2}}{1 + 2g_m r_{\text{tail}}}\right) \qquad (3.267)$$

The calculations in (3.255) through (3.267) are based on the half circuits in Fig. 3.68 and give *exactly* the same results as an analysis of the entire differential amplifier shown in Fig. 3.67. Because the half circuits are coupled, however, exact half-circuit analysis requires the simultaneous consideration of both half circuits, which is about as complicated as the direct analysis of the entire original circuit.

In practice, the mismatch terms are usually a small fraction of the corresponding average values. As a result, the dominant contributions to the differential signals that control the mismatch generators in the common-mode half circuit stem from differential inputs. Similarly, the dominant part of the common-mode signals that control the mismatch generators in the differential half circuit arise from common-mode inputs. Therefore, we will assume that the signals controlling the mismatch generators can be found approximately by analyzing each half circuit independently without mismatch. The signals that control the mismatch generators in Fig. 3.68 are $i_{Rc}$, $i_{Rd}/2$, $v$, and $v_{id}/2$. We will find approximations to these quantities, $\hat{i}_{Rc}$, $\hat{i}_{Rd}/2$, $\hat{v}$, and $\hat{v}_{id}/2$ using the half circuits shown in Fig. 3.69, where the inputs are the same as in Fig. 3.68 but where the mismatch terms are set equal to zero. By ignoring the second-order interactions in which the mismatch generators influence the values of the control signals, this process greatly simplifies the required calculations, as shown next.

**Figure 3.69** (a) Differential and (b) common-mode half circuits of the differential amplifier shown in Fig. 3.67 with mismatch terms set equal to zero.

From inspection of the differential half circuit in Fig. 3.69a,

$$\frac{\hat{v}_{id}}{2} = \frac{v_{id}}{2} \tag{3.268}$$

and

$$\frac{\hat{i}_{Rd}}{2} = -g_m \frac{v_{id}}{2} \tag{3.269}$$

From the common-mode half circuit in Fig. 3.69b,

$$\hat{v} = v_{ic} - g_m \hat{v} \left(2r_{\text{tail}}\right) = \frac{v_{ic}}{1 + 2g_m r_{\text{tail}}} \tag{3.270}$$

Therefore,

$$\hat{i}_{Rc} = -\frac{g_m v_{ic}}{1 + 2g_m r_{\text{tail}}} \tag{3.271}$$

Now reconsider the differential half circuit with mismatch shown in Fig. 3.68a. Assume that $i_{Rc} \simeq \hat{i}_{Rc}$ and $v \simeq \hat{v}$. Then

$$v_{od} \simeq -\frac{\Delta R}{2}\left(\frac{g_m v_{ic}}{1 + 2g_m r_{\text{tail}}}\right) - g_m \frac{v_{id}}{2} R - \frac{\Delta g_m}{2} \frac{v_{ic}}{1 + 2g_m r_{\text{tail}}} R \tag{3.272}$$

From (3.272),

$$A_{dm} = \left.\frac{v_{od}}{v_{id}}\right|_{v_{ic}=0} \simeq -g_m R \tag{3.273}$$

and

$$A_{cm-dm} = \left.\frac{v_{od}}{v_{ic}}\right|_{v_{id}=0} \simeq -\left(\frac{g_m \Delta R + \Delta g_m R}{1 + 2g_m r_{\text{tail}}}\right) \tag{3.274}$$

Equation 3.274 shows that the ratio $A_{dm}/A_{cm-dm}$ is approximately proportional to $1 + 2g_m r_{\text{tail}}$. Also, (3.274) agrees exactly with (3.263) in this case because the $g_m$ generator in Fig. 3.68a is controlled by a purely differential signal. In other examples, the common-mode-to-differential-mode gain calculated in this way will be only approximately correct.

Now reconsider the common-mode half circuit with mismatch shown in Fig. 3.68b and assume that $i_{Rd} \simeq \hat{i}_{Rd}$. From KCL at the tail node,

$$v_{\text{tail}} \simeq \left(g_m v + \frac{\Delta g_m}{2} \frac{v_{id}}{2}\right) 2r_{\text{tail}} \tag{3.275}$$

Then

$$v = v_{ic} - v_{\text{tail}} \simeq \frac{v_{ic} - \dfrac{\Delta g_m}{2} \dfrac{v_{id}}{2}\left(2r_{\text{tail}}\right)}{1 + 2g_m r_{\text{tail}}} \tag{3.276}$$

From KCL at the output node in Fig. 3.68b,

$$\frac{v_{oc} - \dfrac{i_{Rd}}{2} \dfrac{\Delta R}{2}}{R} + g_m v + \frac{\Delta g_m}{2} \frac{v_{id}}{2} = 0 \tag{3.277}$$

Assume that $i_{Rd} \simeq \hat{i}_{Rd}$. Substituting (3.269) and (3.276) into (3.277) and rearranging gives

$$v_{oc} \simeq -\frac{1}{4}\left(g_m \Delta R + \frac{\Delta g_m R}{1 + 2g_m r_{\text{tail}}}\right) v_{id} - \frac{g_m R}{1 + 2g_m r_{\text{tail}}} v_{ic} \tag{3.278}$$

From (3.278),

$$A_{dm-cm} = \frac{v_{oc}}{v_{id}}\bigg|_{v_{ic}=0} \simeq -\frac{1}{4}\left(g_m\Delta R + \frac{\Delta g_m R}{1 + 2g_m r_{\text{tail}}}\right) \tag{3.279}$$

and

$$A_{cm} = \frac{v_{oc}}{v_{ic}}\bigg|_{v_{id}=0} \simeq -\frac{g_m R}{1 + 2g_m r_{\text{tail}}} \tag{3.280}$$

These equations show that increasing the degeneration to common-mode inputs represented by the quantity $1 + 2g_m r_{\text{tail}}$ reduces the magnitude of $A_{cm-dm}$, $A_{dm-cm}$, and $A_{cm}$. As $r_{\text{tail}} \to \infty$ in this case, $A_{cm-dm} \to 0$ and $A_{cm} \to 0$. On the other hand, $A_{dm-cm}$ does not approach zero when $r_{\text{tail}}$ becomes infinite. Instead,

$$\lim_{r_{\text{tail}}\to\infty} A_{dm-cm} \simeq -\frac{g_m\Delta R}{4} \tag{3.281}$$

With finite and mismatched transistor output resistances, $A_{cm-dm}$ also approaches a nonzero value as $r_{\text{tail}}$ becomes infinite. Therefore, $r_{\text{tail}}$ should be viewed as an important parameter because it reduces the sensitivity of differential pairs to common-mode inputs and helps reduce the effects of mismatch. However, even an ideal tail current source does not overcome all the problems introduced by mismatch. In Chapter 4, we will consider transistor current sources for which $r_{\text{tail}}$ can be quite large.

## ■ EXAMPLE

Consider the unbalanced differential amplifier in Fig. 3.67. Assume that

$$g_{m1} = 1.001 \text{ mA/V} \quad g_{m2} = 0.999 \text{ mA/V}$$
$$R_1 = 101 \text{ k}\Omega \quad R_2 = 99 \text{ k}\Omega \quad r_{\text{tail}} = 1 \text{ M}\Omega$$

Find $A_{dm}$, $A_{cm}$, $A_{cm-dm}$, and $A_{dm-cm}$.

Calculating average and mismatch quantities gives

$$g_m = \frac{g_{m1} + g_{m2}}{2} = 1 \frac{\text{mA}}{\text{V}} \quad \Delta g_m = g_{m1} - g_{m2} = 0.002 \frac{\text{mA}}{\text{V}}$$

$$R = \frac{R_1 + R_2}{2} = 100 \text{ k}\Omega \quad \Delta R = R_1 - R_2 = 2 \text{ k}\Omega$$

From (3.269)

$$\frac{i_{Rd}}{2} = -1 \frac{\text{mA}}{\text{V}} \frac{v_{id}}{2} = -\frac{v_{id}}{2 \text{ k}\Omega}$$

From (3.271)

$$\frac{i_{Rc}}{2} = -\frac{1 \frac{\text{mA}}{\text{V}} v_{ic}}{1 + 2 (1)(1000)} = -\frac{v_{ic}}{2001 \text{ k}\Omega}$$

From (3.273), (3.274), (3.279), and (3.280),

$$A_{dm} \simeq -1 (100) = -100$$

$$A_{cm-dm} \simeq -\frac{1 (2) + 0.002 (100)}{1 + 2 (1)(1000)} \simeq -0.0011$$

$$A_{dm-cm} \simeq -\frac{1}{4}\left(1\,(2) + \frac{0.002\,(100)}{1 + 2\,(1)(1000)}\right) \simeq -0.5$$

$$A_{cm} \simeq -\frac{1\,(100)}{1 + 2\,(1)(1000)} \simeq -0.05$$

■

## APPENDIX

### A.3.1 ELEMENTARY STATISTICS AND THE GAUSSIAN DISTRIBUTION

From the standpoint of a circuit designer, many circuit parameters are best regarded as random variables whose behavior is described by a probability distribution. This view is particularly important in the case of a parameter such as offset voltage. Even though the offset may be zero with perfectly matched components, random variations in resistors and transistors cause a spread of offset voltage around the mean value, and the size of this spread determines the fraction of circuits that meet a given offset specification.

Several factors cause the parameters of an integrated circuit to show random variations. One of these factors is the randomness of the edge definition when regions are defined to form resistors and active devices. In addition, random variations across the wafer in the diffusion of impurities can be a significant factor. These processes usually give rise to a *Gaussian* distribution (sometimes called a *normal* distribution) of the parameters. A Gaussian distribution of a parameter $x$ is specified by a probability density function $p(x)$ given by

$$p(x) = \frac{1}{\sqrt{2\pi}\sigma}\exp\left[-\frac{(x-m)^2}{2\sigma^2}\right] \tag{3.282}$$

where $\sigma$ is the standard deviation of the distribution and $m$ is the mean or average value of $x$. The significance of this function is that, for one particular circuit chosen at random from a large collection of circuits, the probability of the parameter having values between $x$ and $(x + dx)$ is given by $p(x)dx$, which is the *area under the curve $p(x)$* in the range $x$ to $(x + dx)$. For example, the probability that $x$ has a value less than $X$ is obtained by integrating (3.282) to give

$$P(x < X) = \int_{-\infty}^{X} p(x)\,dx \tag{3.283}$$

$$= \int_{-\infty}^{X} \frac{1}{\sqrt{2\pi}\sigma}\exp\left[-\frac{(x-m)^2}{2\sigma^2}\right]dx \tag{3.284}$$

In a large sample, the *fraction of circuits* where $x$ is less than $X$ will be given by the probability $P(x < X)$, and thus this quantity has real practical significance. The probability density function $p(x)$ in (3.282) is sketched in Fig. 3.70 and shows a characteristic bell shape. The peak value of the distribution occurs when $x = m$, where $m$ is the mean value of $x$. The standard deviation $\sigma$ is a measure of the *spread* of the distribution, and large values of $\sigma$ give rise to a broad distribution. The distribution extends over $-\infty < x < \infty$, as shown by (3.282), but most of the area under the curve is found in the range $x = m \pm 3\sigma$, as will be seen in the following analysis.

The development thus far has shown that the probability of the parameter $x$ having values in a certain range is just equal to the area under the curve of Fig. 3.70 in that range.

**Figure 3.70** Probability density function $p(x)$ for a Gaussian distribution with mean value $m$ and standard deviation $\sigma$. $p(x) = \exp[-(x - m)^2/(2\sigma^2)]/(\sqrt{2\pi}\sigma)$

Since $x$ must lie somewhere in the range $\pm\infty$, the total area under the curve must be unity, and integration of (3.282) will show that this is so. The most common specification of interest to circuit designers is the fraction of a large sample of circuits that lies inside a band around the mean. For example, if a circuit has a gain $x$ that has a Gaussian distribution with mean value 100, what fraction of circuits have gain values in the range 90 to 110? This fraction can be found by evaluating the probability that $x$ takes on values in the range $x = m \pm 10$ where $m = 100$. This probability could be found from (3.282) if $\sigma$ is known by integrating as follows:

$$P(m - 10 < x < m + 10) = \int_{m-10}^{m+10} \frac{1}{\sqrt{2\pi}\sigma} \exp\left[-\frac{(x - m)^2}{2\sigma^2}\right] dx \quad (3.285)$$

This equation gives the area under the Gaussian curve in the range $x = m \pm 10$.

To simplify calculations of the kind described above, values of the integral in (3.285) have been calculated and tabulated. To make the tables general, the range of integration is normalized to $\sigma$ to give

$$P(m - k\sigma < x < m + k\sigma) = \int_{m-k\sigma}^{m+k\sigma} \frac{1}{\sqrt{2\pi}\sigma} \exp\left[-\frac{(x - m)^2}{2\sigma^2}\right] dx \quad (3.286)$$

Values of this integral for various values of $k$ are tabulated in Fig. 3.71. This table shows that $P = 0.683$ for $k = 1$ and thus 68.3 percent of a large sample of a Gaussian distribution lies within a range $x = m \pm \sigma$. For $k = 3$, the value of $P = 0.997$ and thus 99.7 percent of a large sample lies within a range $x = m \pm 3\sigma$.

Circuit parameters such as offset or gain often can be expressed as a linear combination of other parameters as shown in (3.216) and (3.248) for offset voltage. If all the parameters are independent random variables with Gaussian distributions, the standard deviations and means can be related as follows. Assume that the random variable $x$ can be expressed in terms of random variables $a$, $b$, and $c$ using

$$x = a + b - c \quad (3.287)$$

Then it can be shown that

$$m_x = m_a + m_b - m_c \qquad (3.288)$$

$$\sigma_x^2 = \sigma_a^2 + \sigma_b^2 + \sigma_c^2 \qquad (3.289)$$

where $m_x$ is the mean value of $x$ and $\sigma_x$ is the standard deviation of $x$. Equation 3.289 shows that the square of the standard deviation of $x$ is the sum of the square of the standard deviations of $a$, $b$, and $c$. This result extends to any number of variables.

These results were treated in the context of the random variations found in circuit parameters. The Gaussian distribution is also useful in the treatment of random noise, as described in Chapter 11.

■    **EXAMPLE**

The offset voltage of a circuit has a mean value of $m = 0$ and a standard deviation of $\sigma = 2$ mV. What fraction of circuits will have offsets with magnitudes less than 4 mV?

A range of offset of $\pm 4$ mV corresponds to $\pm 2\sigma$. From Fig. 3.71, we find that the area under the Gaussian curve in this range is 0.954, and thus 95.4 percent of circuits will have
■    offsets with magnitudes less than 4 mV.

| $k$ | Area under the Gaussian curve in the range $m \pm k\sigma$ |
|-----|------|
| 0.2 | 0.159 |
| 0.4 | 0.311 |
| 0.6 | 0.451 |
| 0.8 | 0.576 |
| 1.0 | 0.683 |
| 1.2 | 0.766 |
| 1.4 | 0.838 |
| 1.6 | 0.890 |
| 1.8 | 0.928 |
| 2.0 | 0.954 |
| 2.2 | 0.972 |
| 2.4 | 0.984 |
| 2.6 | 0.991 |
| 2.8 | 0.995 |
| 3.0 | 0.997 |

**Figure 3.71** Values of the integral in (3.286) for various values of $k$. This integral gives the area under the Gaussian curve of Fig. 3.70 in the range $x = \pm k\sigma$.

# PROBLEMS

For the *npn* bipolar transistors in these problems, use the high-voltage bipolar device parameters given in Fig. 2.30, unless otherwise specified.

**3.1** Determine the input resistance, transconductance, and output resistance of the CE ampli-

fier of Fig. 3.7 if $R_C = 20$ k$\Omega$ and $I_C = 250$ $\mu$A. Assume that $r_b = 0$.

**3.2** A CE transistor is to be used in the amplifier of Fig. 3.72 with a source resistance $R_S$ and collector resistor $R_C$. First, find the overall small-signal gain $v_o/v_i$ as a function of $R_S$, $R_C$, $\beta_0$, $V_A$, and the collector current $I_C$. Next, determine the value of dc collector bias current $I_C$ that maximizes the small-signal voltage gain. Explain qualitatively why the gain falls at very high and very low collector currents. Do not neglect $r_o$ in this problem. What is the voltage gain at the optimum $I_C$? Assume that $r_b = 0$.

**Figure 3.72**  Circuit for Problem 3.2.

**3.3** Assume that $R_S = R_C = 50$ k$\Omega$ in Problem 3.2, and calculate the optimum $I_C$. What is the dc voltage drop across $R_C$? What is the voltage gain?

**3.4** For the common-source amplifier of Fig. 3.12, calculate the small-signal voltage gain and the bias values of $V_i$ and $V_o$ at the edge of the triode region. Also calculate the bias values of $V_i$ and $V_o$ where the small-signal voltage gain is unity with the transistor operating in the active region. What is the maximum voltage gain of this stage? Assume $V_{DD} = 3$ V, $R_D = 5$ k$\Omega$, $\mu_n C_{ox} = 200$ $\mu$A/V$^2$, $W = 10$ $\mu$m, $L = 1$ $\mu$m, $V_t = 0.6$ V, and $\lambda = 0$. Check your answer with SPICE.

**3.5** Determine the input resistance, transconductance, and output resistance of the CB amplifier of Fig. 3.15 if $I_C = 250$ $\mu$A and $R_C = 10$ k$\Omega$. Neglect $r_b$ and $r_o$.

**3.6** Assume that $R_C$ is made large compared with $r_o$ in the CB amplifier of Fig. 3.15. Use the equivalent circuit of Fig. 3.17 and add $r_o$ between the input (emitter terminal) and the output (collector terminal) to calculate the output resistance when

(a) The amplifier is driven by an ideal current source.

(b) The amplifier is driven by an ideal voltage source. Neglect $r_b$.

**3.7** Determine the input resistance of the CG amplifier of Fig. 3.19 if the transistor operates in the active region with $I_D = 100$ $\mu$A. Let

$R_D = 10$ k$\Omega$, $\mu_n C_{ox} = 200$ $\mu$A/V$^2$, $\lambda = 0.01$ V$^{-1}$, $W = 100$ $\mu$m, and $L = 1$ $\mu$m. Ignore the body effect. Repeat with $R_D = 1$ M$\Omega$. If the 100 $\mu$A current flows through $R_D$ in this case, a power-supply voltage of at least 100 V would be required. To overcome this problem, assume that an ideal 100-$\mu$A current source is placed in parallel with $R_D$ here.

**3.8** Determine the input resistance, voltage gain $v_o/v_s$, and output resistance of the CC amplifier of Fig. 3.23a if $R_S = 5$ k$\Omega$, $R_L = 500$ $\Omega$, and $I_C = 1$ mA. Neglect $r_b$ and $r_o$. Do not include $R_S$ in calculating the input resistance. In calculating the output resistance, however, include $R_L$. Include both $R_S$ and $R_L$ in the gain calculation.

**3.9** For the common-drain amplifier of Fig. 3.73, assume $W/L = 10$ and $\lambda = 0$. Use Table 2.2 for other parameters. Find the dc output voltage $V_O$ and the small-signal gain $v_o/v_i$ under the following conditions:

(a) Ignoring the body effect and with $R \rightarrow \infty$

(b) Including the body effect and with $R \rightarrow \infty$

(c) Including the body effect and with $R = 100$ k$\Omega$

(d) Including the body effect and with $R = 10$ k$\Omega$

**Figure 3.73**  Circuit for Problem 3.9.

**3.10** Determine the dc collector currents in $Q_1$ and $Q_2$, and then the input resistance and voltage gain for the Darlington emitter follower of Fig. 3.74. Neglect $r_\mu$, $r_b$, and $r_o$. Assume that $V_{BE(on)} = 0.7$ V. Check your answer with SPICE and also use SPICE to determine the output resistance of the stage.

**3.11** Calculate the output resistance $r_o^c$ of the common-emitter Darlington transistor of Fig. 3.75 as a function of $I_{BIAS}$. Do not neglect either $r_{o1}$ or $r_{o2}$ in this calculation, but you may neglect $r_b$ and $r_\mu$. If $I_{C2} = 1$ mA, what is $r_o^c$ for $I_{BIAS} = 1$ mA? For $I_{BIAS} = 0$?

**Figure 3.74**  Circuit for Problem 3.10.

**Figure 3.75**  Circuit for Problem 3.11.

**3.12**  A BiCMOS Darlington is shown in Fig. 3.76. The bias voltage $V_B$ is adjusted for a dc output voltage of 2 V. Calculate the bias currents in both devices and then calculate the small-signal voltage gain $v_o/v_i$ of the circuit. For the MOS transistor, assume $W = 10$ μm, $L = 1$ μm, $\mu_n C_{ox} = 200$ μA/V$^2$, $V_t = 0.6$ V, $\gamma = 0.25$ V$^{1/2}$, $\phi_f = 0.3$ V, and $\lambda = 0$. For the bipolar transistor, assume $I_S = 10^{-16}$ A, $\beta_F = 100$, $r_b = 0$, and $V_A \to \infty$. Use SPICE to check your result. Then add $\lambda = 0.05$ V$^{-1}$, $r_b = 100$ Ω, and $V_A = 20$ V and compare the original result to the result with this new transistor data. Finally, use SPICE to compute the dc transfer characteristic of the circuit.

**3.13**  Determine the input resistance, transconductance, output resistance, and maximum open-circuit voltage gain for the CE-CB circuit of Fig. 3.36 if $I_{C1} = I_{C2} = 250$ μA.

**3.14**  Determine the input resistance, transconductance, output resistance, and maximum open-circuit voltage gain for the CS-CG circuit of Fig. 3.38 if $I_{D1} = I_{D2} = 250$ μA. Assume $W/L = 100$, $\lambda = 0.1$ V$^{-1}$, and $\chi = 0.1$. Use Table 2.2 for other parameters.

**3.15**  Find the output resistance for the active-cascode circuit of Fig. 3.77 excluding resistor $R$.

**Figure 3.76**  BiCMOS Darlington circuit for Problem 3.12.

Assume that all the transistors operate in the active region with dc drain currents of 100 μA. Use the transistor parameters in Table 2.4. Ignore the body effect. Assume $W = 10$ μm, $L_{drwn} = 0.4$ μm, and $X_d = 0.1$ μm for all transistors. Check your answer with SPICE.

**Figure 3.77**  Active-cascode circuit for Problem 3.15.

**3.16**  Find the short-circuit transconductance of the super-source follower shown in Fig. 3.43. Assume $I_1 = 200$ μA, $I_2 = 100$ μA, $W_1 = 30$ μm, and $W_2 = 10$ μm. Also, assume that both transistors operate in the active region, and ignore the body effect. Use the transistor parameters in Table 2.4. Assume $L_{drwn} = 0.4$ μm and $X_d = 0.1$μm for all transistors.

**3.17**  A BiCMOS amplifier is shown in Fig. 3.78. Calculate the small-signal voltage gain $v_o/v_i$. Assume $I_S = 10^{-16}$ A, $\beta_F = 100$, $r_b = 0$, $V_A \to \infty$, $\mu_n C_{ox} = 200$ μA/V$^2$, $V_t = 0.6$ V, and $\lambda = 0$. Check your answer with SPICE and then use SPICE to investigate the effects of velocity saturation by including source degeneration in the

Figure 3.78  BiCMOS amplifier for Problem 3.17.

MOS transistors as shown in Fig. 1.41 using $\mathscr{E}_c = 1.5 \times 10^6$ V/m.

**3.18** Determine the differential-mode gain, common-mode gain, differential-mode input resistance, and common-mode input resistance for the circuit of Fig. 3.45 with $I_{TAIL} = 20$ μA, $R_{TAIL} = 10$ MΩ, $R_C = 100$ kΩ, and $V_{EE} = V_{CC} = 5$ V. Neglect $r_b$, $r_o$, and $r_\mu$. Calculate the CMRR. Check with SPICE and use SPICE to investigate the effects of adding nonzero $r_b$ and finite $V_A$ as given in Fig. 2.30.

**3.19** Repeat Problem 3.18, but with the addition of emitter-degeneration resistors of value 4 kΩ each.

**3.20** Determine the overall input resistance, voltage gain, and output resistance of the CC-CB

$V_{CC} = +15$ V

Figure 3.79  Circuit for Problem 3.20.

connection of Fig. 3.79. Neglect $r_o$, $r_\mu$, and $r_b$. Note that the addition of a 10-k Ω resistor in the collector of $Q_1$ would not change the results, so that the results of the emitter-coupled pair analysis can be used.

**3.21** Use half-circuit concepts to determine the differential-mode and common-mode gain of the circuit shown in Fig. 3.80. Neglect $r_o$, $r_\mu$, and $r_b$. Calculate the differential-mode and common-mode input resistance.

Figure 3.80  Circuit for Problem 3.21.

**3.22** Consider the circuit of Fig. 3.80 except replace both $npn$ transistors with $n$-channel MOS transistors. Neglect the body effect, and assume $\lambda = 0$. Use half-circuit concepts to determine the differential-mode and common-mode gain of this modified circuit.

**3.23**  Design an emitter-coupled pair of the type shown in Fig. 3.53a. Assume $I_{TAIL} = 0$ and select values of $R_C$ and $R_{TAIL}$ to give a differential input resistance of 2 MΩ, a differential voltage gain of 500, and a CMRR of 500. What are the minimum values of $V_{CC}$ and $V_{EE}$ that will yield this performance while keeping the transistors biased in the forward-active region under zero-signal conditions? Assume that the dc common-mode input voltage is zero. Neglect $r_b$, $r_\mu$, and $r_o$.

**3.24**  Determine the required bias current and device sizes to design a source-coupled pair to have the following two characteristics. First, the small-signal transconductance with zero differential input voltage should be 1.0 mA/V. Second, a differential input voltage of 0.2 V should result in a differential output current of 85 percent of the maximum value. Assume that the devices are *n*-channel transistors that are made with the technology summarized in Table 2.4. Use a drawn device channel length of 1 μm. Neglect channel-length modulation, and assume $X_d = 0$.

**3.25**  For the circuit of Fig. 3.45, determine the input offset voltage if the transistor base widths mismatch by 10 percent but otherwise the circuit is balanced. Let $R_{TAIL} \to \infty$.

**3.26**  Determine the input offset voltage of the source-coupled pair in Fig. 3.50 for which $I_{TAIL} = 50$ μA. The drawn device dimensions are $W = 10$ μm and $L = 1$ μm. Use the process parameters given in Table 2.4. Assume that the worst-case $W/L$ mismatch is 2 percent and the device thresholds are identical. Also assume that $X_d = 0$, $R_{TAIL} \to \infty$ and the load resistors are identical.

**3.27**  Use half-circuit analysis to determine $A_{dm}$, $A_{cm}$, $A_{cm-dm}$, and $A_{dm-cm}$ for a resistively loaded differential pair with mismatched resistive loads, $R_1$ and $R_2$. Assume that $R_1 = 10.1$ kΩ and $R_2 = 9.9$ kΩ. Also assume that $g_{m1} = g_{m2} = 1$ mA/V, $r_{o1} \to \infty$, and $r_{o2} \to \infty$. Finally, assume that the equivalent resistance of the tail current source $r_{tail} = 1$ MΩ.

**3.28**  Repeat Problem 3.27 but with matched loads and mismatched transistor output resistances. Assume $R_1 = R_2 = 10$ kΩ, $r_{o1} = 505$ kΩ, and $r_{o2} = 495$ kΩ. What happens when $r_{tail} \to \infty$?

# BIBLIOGRAPHY

1. R. J. Widlar. "Some Circuit Design Techniques for Linear Integrated Circuits," *IEEE Transactions on Circuit Theory*, Vol. CT-12, pp. 586–590, December 1965.

2. H. R. Camenzind and A. B. Grebene. "An Outline of Design Techniques for Linear Integrated Circuits," *IEEE Journal of Solid-State Circuits*, Vol. SC-4, pp. 110–122, June 1969.

3. J. Giles. *Fairchild Semiconductor Linear Integrated Circuits Applications ∙Handbook*. Fairchild Semiconductor, 1967.

4. C. L. Searle, A. R. Boothroyd, E. J. Angelo, P. E. Gray, and D. O. Pederson. *Elementary Circuit Properties of Transistors*. Wiley, New York, 1964, Chapter 7.

5. S. Darlington. "Semiconductor Signal Translating Device," U.S. Patent 2,663,806, May 1952.

6. F. V. Hunt and R. W. Hickman. "On Electronic Voltage Stabilizers," *Review of Scientific Instruments*, Vol. 10, pp. 6–21, January 1939.

7. H. Wallman, A. B. Macnee, and C. P. Gadsden. "A Low-Noise Amplifier," *Proceedings of the I.R.E.*, Vol. 36, pp. 700–708, June 1948.

8. B. J. Hosticka. "Improvement of the Gain of MOS Amplifiers," *IEEE Journal of Solid-State Circuits*, Vol. SC-14, pp. 1111–1114, December 1979.

9. E. Säckinger and W. Guggenbühl. "A High-Swing, High-Impedance MOS Cascode Circuit," *IEEE Journal of Solid-State Circuits*, Vol. 25, pp. 289–298, February 1990.

10. A. D. Blumlein. "Improvements in or relating to Thermionic Valve Amplifying Circuit Arrangements," British Patent 482,740, July, 1936.

11. R. D. Middlebrook. *Differential Amplifiers*. Wiley, New York, 1963.

12. L. J. Giacoletto. *Differential Amplifiers*. Wiley, New York, 1970.

13. G. Erdi. "A Low-Drift, Low-Noise Monolithic Operational Amplifier for Low Level Signal Processing," *Fairchild Semiconductor Applications Brief*. No. 136, July 1969.

# Current Mirrors, Active Loads, and References

## 4.1 Introduction

Current mirrors made by using active devices have come to be widely used in analog integrated circuits both as biasing elements and as load devices for amplifier stages. The use of current mirrors in biasing can result in superior insensitivity of circuit performance to variations in power supply and temperature. Current mirrors are frequently more economical than resistors in terms of the die area required to provide bias current of a certain value, particularly when the required value of bias current is small. When used as a load element in transistor amplifiers, the high incremental resistance of the current mirror results in high voltage gain at low power-supply voltages.

The first section of this chapter describes the general properties of current mirrors and compares various bipolar and MOS mirrors to each other using these properties. The next section deals with the use of current mirrors as load elements in amplifier stages. The last section shows how current mirrors are used to construct references that are insensitive to variations in supply and temperature. Finally, the appendix analyzes the effects of device mismatch.

## 4.2 Current Mirrors

### 4.2.1 General Properties

A current mirror is an element with at least three terminals, as shown in Fig. 4.1. The common terminal is connected to a power supply, and the input current source is connected to the input terminal. Ideally, the output current is equal to the input current multiplied by a desired current gain. If the gain is unity, the input current is reflected to the output, leading to the name *current mirror*. Under ideal conditions, the current-mirror gain is independent of input frequency, and the output current is independent of the voltage between the output and common terminals. Furthermore, the voltage between the input and common terminals is ideally zero because this condition allows the entire supply voltage to appear across the input current source, simplifying its transistor-level design. More than one input and/or output terminals are sometimes used.

In practice, real transistor-level current mirrors suffer many deviations from this ideal behavior. For example, the gain of a real current mirror is never independent of the input frequency. The topic of frequency response is covered in Chapter 7, and mainly dc and low-frequency ac signals are considered in the rest of this chapter. Deviations from ideality that will be considered in this chapter are listed below.

1. One of the most important deviations from ideality is the variation of the current-mirror output current with changes in voltage at the output terminal. This effect is

(a)

(b)

**Figure 4.1** Current-mirror block diagrams referenced to (a) ground and (b) the positive supply.

characterized by the small-signal output resistance, $R_o$, of the current mirror. A Norton-equivalent model of the output of the current mirror includes $R_o$ in parallel with a current source controlled by the input current. The output resistance directly affects the performance of many circuits that use current mirrors. For example, the common-mode rejection ratio of the differential amplifier depends directly on this resistance, as does the gain of the active-load circuits. Increasing the output resistance reduces the dependence of the output current on the output voltage and is therefore desirable. Generally speaking, the output resistance increases in practical circuits when the output current decreases. Unfortunately, decreasing the output current also decreases the maximum operating speed. Therefore, when comparing the output resistance of two current mirrors, they should be compared at identical output currents.

2. Another important error source is the gain error, which is the deviation of the gain of a current mirror from its ideal value. The gain error is separated into two parts: (1) the systematic gain error and (2) the random gain error. The systematic gain error, $\epsilon$, is the gain error that arises even when all matched elements in the mirror are perfectly matched and will be calculated for each of the current mirrors presented in this section. The random gain error is the gain error caused by unintended mismatches between matched elements.

3. When the input current source is connected to the input terminal of a real current mirror, it creates a positive voltage drop, $V_{IN}$, that reduces the voltage available across the input current source. Minimizing $V_{IN}$ is important because it simplifies the design of the input current source, especially in low-supply applications. To reduce $V_{IN}$, current mirrors sometimes have more than one input terminal. In that case, we will calculate an input voltage for each input terminal. An example is the MOS high-swing cascode current mirror considered in Section 4.2.5.

4. A positive output voltage, $V_{OUT}$, is required in practice to make the output current depend mainly on the input current. This characteristic is summarized by the minimum voltage across the output branch, $V_{OUT(min)}$, that allows the output device(s) to operate in the active region. Minimizing $V_{OUT(min)}$ maximizes the range of output voltages for which the current-mirror output resistance is almost constant, which is important in applications where current mirrors are used as active loads in amplifiers (especially with low power-supply voltages). This topic is covered in Section 4.3. When current mirrors have more than one output terminal, each output must be biased above its $V_{OUT(min)}$ to make the corresponding output current depend mainly on the input current.

In later sections, the performance of various current mirrors will be compared to each other through these four parameters: $R_o$, $\epsilon$, $V_{IN}$, and $V_{OUT(min)}$.

## 4.2.2 Simple Current Mirror

### 4.2.2.1 Bipolar
The simplest form of a current mirror consists of two transistors. Fig. 4.2 shows a bipolar version of this mirror. Transistor $Q_1$ is diode connected, forcing its collector-base voltage to zero. In this mode, the collector-base junction is off in the sense that no injection takes place there, and $Q_1$ operates in the forward-active region. Assume that $Q_2$ also operates in the forward-active region and that both transistors have infinite output resistance. Then $I_{OUT}$ is controlled by $V_{BE2}$, which is equal to $V_{BE1}$ by KVL. A KVL equation is at the heart of the operation of all current mirrors. Neglecting junction leakage currents,

$$V_{BE2} = V_T \ln \frac{I_{C2}}{I_{S2}} = V_{BE1} = V_T \ln \frac{I_{C1}}{I_{S1}} \tag{4.1}$$

where $V_T = kT/q$ is the thermal voltage and $I_{S1}$ and $I_{S2}$ are the transistor saturation currents. From (4.1),

$$I_{C2} = \frac{I_{S2}}{I_{S1}} I_{C1} \tag{4.2}$$

If the transistors are identical, $I_{S1} = I_{S2}$ and (4.2) shows that the current flowing in the collector of $Q_1$ is mirrored to the collector of $Q_2$. KCL at the collector of $Q_1$ yields

$$I_{IN} - I_{C1} - \frac{I_{C1}}{\beta_F} - \frac{I_{C2}}{\beta_F} = 0 \tag{4.3}$$

**Figure 4.2** A simple bipolar current mirror.

Therefore, with identical transistors,

$$I_{OUT} = I_{C2} = I_{C1} = \frac{I_{IN}}{1 + \dfrac{2}{\beta_F}} \tag{4.4}$$

If $\beta_F$ is large, the base currents are small and

$$I_{OUT} = I_{C1} \simeq I_{IN} \tag{4.5}$$

Thus for identical devices $Q_1$ and $Q_2$, the gain of the current mirror is approximately unity. This result holds for both dc and low-frequency ac currents. Above the 3-dB frequency of the mirror, however, the base current increases noticeably because the impedance of the base-emitter capacitance decreases, reducing the gain of the current mirror. Frequency response is studied in Chapter 7. The rest of this section considers dc currents only.

In practice, the devices need not be identical. Then from (4.2) and (4.3),

$$I_{OUT} = \frac{I_{S2}}{I_{S1}} I_{C1} = \left(\frac{I_{S2}}{I_{S1}} I_{IN}\right)\left(\frac{1}{1 + \dfrac{1 + (I_{S2}/I_{S1})}{\beta_F}}\right) \tag{4.6}$$

When $I_{S2} = I_{S1}$, (4.6) is the same as (4.4). Since the saturation current of a bipolar transistor is proportional to its emitter area, the first term in (4.6) shows that the gain of the current mirror can be larger or smaller than unity because the emitter areas can be ratioed. If the desired current-mirror gain is a rational number, $M/N$, the area ratio is usually set by connecting $M$ identical devices called *units* in parallel to form $Q_2$ and $N$ units in parallel to form $Q_1$ to minimize mismatch arising from lithographic effects in forming the emitter regions. However, area ratios greater than about five to one consume a large die area dominated by the area of the larger of the two devices. Thus other methods described in later sections are preferred for the generation of large current ratios. The last term in (4.6) accounts for error introduced by finite $\beta_F$. Increasing $I_{S2}/I_{S1}$ increases the magnitude of this error by increasing the base current of $Q_2$ compared to that of $Q_1$.

In writing (4.1) and (4.2), we assumed that the collector currents of the transistors are independent of their collector-emitter voltages. If a transistor is biased in the forward-active region, its collector current actually increases slowly with increasing collector-emitter voltage. Fig. 4.3 shows an output characteristic for $Q_2$. The output resistance of the current mirror at any given operating point is the reciprocal of the slope of the output characteristic at that point. In the forward-active region,

$$R_o = r_{o2} = \frac{V_A}{I_{C2}} \tag{4.7}$$

**Figure 4.3** *npn* output characteristic.

The point where $V_{CE2} = V_{CE1}$ and $V_{BE2} = V_{BE1}$ is labeled on the characteristic. Because the collector current is controlled by the base-emitter and collector-emitter voltages, $I_{C2} = (I_{S2}/I_{S1})I_{C1}$ at this point. If the slope of the characteristic in saturation is constant, the variation in $I_{C2}$ for changes in $V_{CE2}$ can be predicted by a straight line that goes through the labeled point. As described in Chapter 1, extrapolation of the output characteristic in the forward-active region back to the $V_{CE2}$ axis gives an intercept at $-V_A$, where $V_A$ is the Early voltage. If $V_A \gg V_{CE1}$, the slope of the straight line is about equal to $(I_{S2}/I_{S1})(I_{C1}/V_A)$. Therefore,

$$I_{OUT} = \frac{I_{S2}}{I_{S1}}I_{C1}\left(1 + \frac{V_{CE2} - V_{CE1}}{V_A}\right) = \frac{\dfrac{I_{S2}}{I_{S1}}I_{IN}\left(1 + \dfrac{V_{CE2} - V_{CE1}}{V_A}\right)}{1 + \dfrac{1 + (I_{S2}/I_{S1})}{\beta_F}} \tag{4.8}$$

Since the ideal gain of the current mirror is $I_{S2}/I_{S1}$, the systematic gain error, $\epsilon$, of the current mirror can be calculated from (4.8).

$$\epsilon = \left(\frac{1 + \dfrac{V_{CE2} - V_{CE1}}{V_A}}{1 + \dfrac{1 + (I_{S2}/I_{S1})}{\beta_F}}\right) - 1 \simeq \frac{V_{CE2} - V_{CE1}}{V_A} - \frac{1 + (I_{S2}/I_{S1})}{\beta_F} \tag{4.9}$$

The first term in (4.9) stems from finite output resistance and the second term from finite $\beta_F$. If $V_{CE2} > V_{CE1}$, the polarities of the two terms are opposite. Since the two terms are independent, however, cancellation is unlikely in practice. The first term dominates when the difference in the collector-emitter voltages and $\beta_F$ are large. For example, with identical transistors and $V_A = 130$ V, if the collector-emitter voltage of $Q_1$ is held at $V_{BE(on)}$, and if the collector-emitter voltage of $Q_2$ is 30 V, then the systematic gain error $(30 - 0.6)/130 - 2/200 \simeq 0.22$. Thus for a circuit operating at a power-supply voltage of 30 V, the current-mirror currents can differ by more than 20 percent from those values calculated by assuming that the transistor output resistance and $\beta_F$ are infinite. Although the first term in (4.9) stems from finite output resistance, it does not depend on $r_{o2}$ directly but instead on the collector-emitter and Early voltages. The Early voltage is independent of the bias current, and

$$V_{IN} = V_{CE1} = V_{BE1} = V_{BE(on)} \tag{4.10}$$

Since $V_{BE(on)}$ is proportional to the natural logarithm of the collector current, $V_{IN}$ changes little with changes in bias current. Therefore, changing the bias current in a current mirror changes systematic gain error mainly through changes in $V_{CE2}$.

Finally, the minimum output voltage required to keep $Q_2$ in the forward-active region is

$$V_{OUT(min)} = V_{CE2(sat)} \tag{4.11}$$

### 4.2.2.2 MOS

Figure 4.4 shows an MOS version of the simple current mirror. The drain-gate voltage of $M_1$ is zero; therefore, the channel does not exist at the drain, and the transistor operates in the saturation or active region if the threshold is positive. Although the principle of operation for MOS transistors does not involve forward biasing any diodes, $M_1$ is said to be *diode connected* in an analogy to the bipolar case. Assume that $M_2$ also operates in the active region and that both transistors have infinite output resistance. Then $I_{D2}$ is controlled by $V_{GS2}$, which is equal to $V_{GS1}$ by KVL. A KVL equation is at the heart of

**Figure 4.4** A simple MOS current mirror.

the operation of all current mirrors. As described in Section 1.5.3, the gate-source voltage of a given MOS transistor is usually separated into two parts: the threshold $V_t$ and the overdrive $V_{ov}$. Assuming square-law behavior as in (1.157), the overdrive for $M_2$ is

$$V_{ov2} = V_{GS2} - V_t = \sqrt{\frac{2I_{D2}}{k'(W/L)_2}}$$ (4.12)

Since the transconductance parameter $k'$ is proportional to mobility, and since mobility falls with increasing temperature, the overdrive rises with temperature. In contrast, Section 1.5.4 shows that the threshold falls with increasing temperature. From KVL and (1.157),

$$V_{GS2} = V_t + \sqrt{\frac{2I_{D2}}{k'(W/L)_2}} = V_{GS1} = V_t + \sqrt{\frac{2I_{D1}}{k'(W/L)_1}}$$ (4.13)

Equation 4.13 shows that the overdrive of $M_2$ is equal to that of $M_1$.

$$V_{ov2} = V_{ov1} = V_{ov}$$ (4.14)

If the transistors are identical, $(W/L)_2 = (W/L)_1$, and therefore

$$I_{OUT} = I_{D2} = I_{D1}$$ (4.15)

Equation 4.15 shows that the current that flows in the drain of $M_1$ is mirrored to the drain of $M_2$. Since $\beta_F \to \infty$ for MOS transistors, (4.15) and KCL at the drain of $M_1$ yield

$$I_{OUT} = I_{D1} = I_{IN}$$ (4.16)

Thus for identical devices operating in the active region with infinite output resistance, the gain of the current mirror is unity. This result holds when the gate currents are zero; that is, (4.16) is at least approximately correct for dc and low-frequency ac currents. As the input frequency increases, however, the gate currents of $M_1$ and $M_2$ increase because each transistor has a nonzero gate-source capacitance. The part of the input current that flows into the gate leads does not flow into the drain of $M_1$ and is not mirrored to $M_2$; therefore, the gain of the current mirror decreases as the frequency of the input current increases. The rest of this section considers dc currents only.

In practice, the devices need not be identical. Then from (4.13) and (4.16),

$$I_{OUT} = \frac{(W/L)_2}{(W/L)_1} I_{D1} = \frac{(W/L)_2}{(W/L)_1} I_{IN}$$ (4.17)

Equation 4.17 shows that the gain of the current mirror can be larger or smaller than unity because the transistor sizes can be ratioed. To ratio the transistor sizes, either the widths or the lengths can be made unequal in principle. In practice, however, the lengths of $M_1$ and $M_2$ are rarely made unequal. The lengths that enter into (4.17) are the effective channel lengths given by (2.35). Equation 2.35 shows that the effective channel length of a given transistor differs from its drawn length by offset terms stemming from the depletion region at the drain and lateral diffusion at the drain and source. Since the offset terms are independent of the drawn length, a ratio of two effective channel lengths is equal to the drawn ratio only if the drawn lengths are identical. As a result, a ratio of unequal channel lengths depends on process parameters that may not be well controlled in practice. Similarly, Section 2.9.1 shows that the effective width of a given transistor differs from the drawn width because of lateral oxidation resulting in a *bird's beak*. Therefore, a ratio of unequal channel widths will also be process dependent. In many applications, however, the shortest channel length allowed in a given technology is selected for most transistors to maximize speed and minimize area. In contrast, the drawn channel widths are usually many times larger than the minimum dimensions allowed in a given technology. Therefore, to minimize the effect of the offset terms when the current-mirror gain is designed to differ from unity, the widths are ratioed rather than the lengths in most practical cases. If the desired current-mirror gain is a rational number, $M/N$, the ratio is usually set by connecting $M$ identical devices called *units* in parallel to form $M_2$ and $N$ units in parallel to form $M_1$ to minimize mismatch arising from lithographic effects in forming the gate regions. As in the bipolar case, ratios greater than about five to one consume a large die area dominated by the area of the larger of the two devices. Thus other methods described in later sections are preferred for the generation of large current ratios.

In writing (4.13) and (4.15), we assumed that the drain currents of the transistors are independent of their drain-source voltages. If a transistor is biased in the active region, its drain current actually increases slowly with increasing drain-source voltage. Figure 4.5 shows an output characteristic for $M_2$. The output resistance of the current mirror at any given operating point is the reciprocal of the slope of the output characteristic at that point. In the active region,

$$R_o = r_{o2} = \frac{V_A}{I_{D2}} = \frac{1}{\lambda I_{D2}} \tag{4.18}$$

The point where $V_{DS2} = V_{DS1}$ and $V_{GS2} = V_{GS1}$ is labeled on the characteristic. Because the drain current is controlled by the gate-source and drain-source voltages, $I_{D2} = [(W/L)_2/(W/L)_1]I_{D1}$ at this point. If the slope of the characteristic in saturation is constant, the variation in $I_{D2}$ for changes in $V_{DS2}$ can be predicted by a straight line that goes

**Figure 4.5** Output characteristic of simple MOS current mirror.

through the labeled point. As described in Chapter 1, extrapolation of the output characteristic in the active region back to the $V_{DS2}$ axis gives an intercept at $-V_A = -1/\lambda$, where $V_A$ is the Early voltage. If $V_A \gg V_{DS1}$, the slope of the straight line is about equal to $[(W/L)_2/(W/L)_1][I_{D1}/V_A]$. Therefore,

$$I_{OUT} = \frac{(W/L)_2}{(W/L)_1} I_{IN} \left(1 + \frac{V_{DS2} - V_{DS1}}{V_A}\right) \tag{4.19}$$

Since the ideal gain of the current mirror is $(W/L)_2/(W/L)_1$, the systematic gain error, $\epsilon$, of the current mirror can be calculated from (4.19).

$$\epsilon = \frac{V_{DS2} - V_{DS1}}{V_A} \tag{4.20}$$

For example, if the drain-source voltage of $M_1$ is held at 1.2 V, and if the drain-source voltage of $M_2$ is 5 V, then the systematic gain error is $(5 - 1.2)/10 \simeq 0.38$ with $V_A = 10$ V. Thus for a circuit operating at a power-supply voltage of 5 V, the current-mirror currents can differ by more than 35 percent from those values calculated by assuming that the transistor output resistance is infinite. Although $\epsilon$ stems from finite output resistance, it does not depend on $r_{o2}$ directly but instead on the drain-source and Early voltages. Since the Early voltage is independent of the bias current, this observation shows that changing the input bias current in a current mirror changes systematic gain error mainly through changes to the drain-source voltages.

For the simple MOS current mirror, the input voltage is

$$V_{IN} = V_{GS1} = V_t + V_{ov1} = V_t + V_{ov} \tag{4.21}$$

With square-law behavior, the overdrive in (4.21) is proportional to the square root of the input current. In contrast, (4.10) shows that the entire $V_{IN}$ in a simple bipolar mirror is proportional to the natural logarithm of the input current. Therefore, for a given change in the input current, the variation in $V_{IN}$ in a simple MOS current mirror is generally larger than in its bipolar counterpart.

Finally, the minimum output voltage required to keep $M_2$ in the active region is

$$V_{OUT(min)} = V_{ov2} = V_{ov} = \sqrt{\frac{2I_{OUT}}{k'(W/L)_2}} \tag{4.22}$$

Equation 4.22 predicts that $V_{OUT(min)}$ depends on the transistor geometry and can be made arbitrarily small in a simple MOS mirror, unlike in the bipolar case. However, if the overdrive predicted by (4.22) is less than $2nV_T$, where $n$ is defined in (1.247) and $V_T$ is a thermal voltage, the result is invalid except to indicate that the transistors operate in weak inversion. At room temperature with $n = 1.5$, $2nV_T \simeq 78$ mV. If the transistors operate in weak inversion,

$$V_{OUT(min)} \simeq 3V_T \tag{4.23}$$

as shown in Fig. 1.43[1].

### 4.2.3 Simple Current Mirror with Beta Helper

#### 4.2.3.1 Bipolar

In addition to the variation in output current due to finite output resistance, the second term in (4.9) shows that the collector current $I_{C2}$ differs from the input current because of finite

**Figure 4.6** Simple current mirror with beta helper.

$\beta_F$. To reduce this source of error, an additional transistor can be added, as shown in Fig. 4.6. If $Q_1$ and $Q_3$ are identical, the emitter current of transistor $Q_2$ is

$$I_{E2} = -\frac{I_{C1}}{\beta_F} - \frac{I_{C3}}{\beta_F} = -\frac{2}{\beta_F}I_{C1} \tag{4.24}$$

where $I_E$, $I_C$, and $I_B$ are defined as positive when flowing into the transistor, and where we have neglected the effects of finite output resistance. The base current of transistor $Q_2$ is equal to

$$I_{B2} = -\frac{I_{E2}}{\beta_F + 1} = \frac{2}{\beta_F(\beta_F + 1)}I_{C1} \tag{4.25}$$

Finally, KCL at the collector of $Q_1$ gives

$$I_{IN} - I_{C1} - \frac{2}{\beta_F(\beta_F + 1)}I_{C1} = 0 \tag{4.26}$$

Since $I_{C1}$ and $I_{C3}$ are equal when $Q_1$ and $Q_3$ are identical,

$$I_{OUT} = I_{C3} = \frac{I_{IN}}{1 + \dfrac{2}{\beta_F(\beta_F + 1)}} \approx I_{IN}\left(1 - \frac{2}{\beta_F(\beta_F + 1)}\right) \tag{4.27}$$

Equation 4.27 shows that the systematic gain error from finite $\beta_F$ has been reduced by a factor of $[\beta_F + 1]$, which is the current gain of emitter follower $Q_2$. As a result, $Q_2$ is often referred to as a *beta helper*.

Although the beta helper has little effect on the output resistance and the minimum output voltage of the current mirror, it increases the input voltage by the base-emitter voltage of $Q_2$:

$$V_{IN} = V_{BE1(on)} + V_{BE2(on)} \tag{4.28}$$

If multiple emitter followers are cascaded to further reduce the gain error arising from finite $\beta_F$, $V_{IN}$ increases by an extra base-emitter voltage for each additional emitter follower, posing one limit to the use of cascaded emitter followers.

Current mirrors often use a beta helper when they are constructed with *pnp* transistors because the value of $\beta_F$ for *pnp* transistors is usually less than for *npn* transistors. Another application of the beta-helper configuration is in current mirrors with multiple outputs. An example with two independent outputs is shown in Fig. 4.7. At first, ignore $Q_2$ and imagine that $Q_1$ is simply diode connected. Also, let $R_1 = R_3 = R_4 = 0$ here. (The effects of nonzero resistances will be considered in Section 4.2.4.) Then the gain from the input to

**Figure 4.7** Simple current mirror with beta helper, multiple outputs, and emitter degeneration.

each output is primarily determined by the area ratios $I_{S3}/I_{S1}$ and $I_{S4}/I_{S1}$. Because the bases of three instead of two transistors are connected together, the total base current is increased here, which increases the gain error from the input to either output arising from finite $\beta_F$. Furthermore, the gain errors worsen as the number of independent outputs increases. Since the beta helper, $Q_2$, reduces the gain error from the input to each output by a factor of $[\beta_F + 1]$, it is often used in bipolar current mirrors with multiple outputs.

#### 4.2.3.2 MOS
Since $\beta_F \to \infty$ for an MOS transistor, beta helpers are not used in simple MOS current mirrors to reduce the systematic gain error. However, a beta-helper configuration can increase the bandwidth of MOS and bipolar current mirrors.

### 4.2.4 Simple Current Mirror with Degeneration

#### 4.2.4.1 Bipolar
The performance of the simple bipolar transistor current mirror of Fig. 4.6 can be improved by the addition of emitter degeneration as shown in Fig. 4.7 for a current mirror with two independent outputs. The purpose of the emitter resistors is twofold. First, Appendix A.4.1 shows that the matching between $I_{IN}$ and outputs $I_{C3}$ and $I_{C4}$ can be greatly improved by using emitter degeneration. Second, as shown in Section 3.3.8, the use of emitter degeneration boosts the output resistance of each output of the current mirror. Transistors $Q_1$ and $Q_2$ combine to present a very low resistance at the bases of $Q_3$ and $Q_4$. Therefore, from (3.99), the small-signal output resistance seen at the collectors of $Q_3$ and $Q_4$ is

$$R_o \simeq r_o(1 + g_m R_E) \tag{4.29}$$

if $r_\pi \gg R_E$. Taking $Q_3$ as an example and using $g_{m3} = I_{C3}/V_T$, we find

$$R_o \simeq r_{o3}\left(1 + \frac{I_{C3}R_3}{V_T}\right) \tag{4.30}$$

This increase in the output resistance for a given output current also decreases the component of systematic gain error that stems from finite output resistance by the same factor. From (4.9) and (4.30) with infinite $\beta_F$,

$$\epsilon \simeq \frac{V_{CE2} - V_{CE1}}{V_A\left(1 + \dfrac{I_{C3}R_3}{V_T}\right)} \tag{4.31}$$

The quantity $I_{C3}R_3$ is just the dc voltage drop across $R_3$. If this quantity is 260 mV, for example, then $R_o$ is about $10r_o$ at room temperature, and $\epsilon$ is reduced by a factor of about eleven. Unfortunately, this improvement in $R_o$ is limited by corresponding increases in the input and minimum output voltages of the mirror:

$$V_{IN} \simeq V_{BE1(on)} + V_{BE2(on)} + I_{IN}R_1 \qquad (4.32)$$

and

$$V_{OUT(min)} = V_{CE3(sat)} + I_{C3}R_3 \qquad (4.33)$$

The emitter areas of $Q_1$, $Q_3$, and $Q_4$ may be matched or ratioed. For example, if we want $I_{OUT1} = I_{IN}$ and $I_{OUT2} = 2I_{IN}$, we would make $Q_3$ identical to $Q_1$, and $Q_4$ consist of two copies of $Q_1$ connected in parallel so that $I_{S4} = 2I_{S1}$. In addition, we could make $R_3 = R_1$, and $R_4$ consist of two copies of $R_1$ connected in parallel so that $R_4 = R_1/2$. Note that all the dc voltage drops across $R_1$, $R_3$, and $R_4$ would then be equal. Using KVL around the loop including $Q_1$ and $Q_4$ and neglecting base currents, we find

$$I_{C1}R_1 + V_T \ln \frac{I_{C1}}{I_{S1}} = I_{C4}R_4 + V_T \ln \frac{I_{C4}}{I_{S4}} \qquad (4.34)$$

from which

$$I_{OUT2} = I_{C4} = \frac{1}{R_4}\left(I_{IN}R_1 + V_T \ln \frac{I_{IN}}{I_{C4}}\frac{I_{S4}}{I_{S1}}\right) \qquad (4.35)$$

Since $I_{S4} = 2I_{S1}$, the solution to (4.35) is

$$I_{OUT2} = \frac{R_1}{R_4}I_{IN} = 2I_{IN} \qquad (4.36)$$

because the last term in (4.35) goes to zero. If we make the voltage drops $I_{IN}R_1$ and $I_{C4}R_4$ much greater than $V_T$, the current-mirror gain to the $Q_4$ output is determined primarily by the resistor ratio $R_4/R_1$, and only to a secondary extent by the emitter area ratio, because the natural log term in (4.35) varies slowly with its argument.

### 4.2.4.2 MOS

Source degeneration is rarely used in MOS current mirrors because, in effect, MOS transistors are inherently controlled resistors. Thus, matching in MOS current mirrors is improved simply by increasing the gate areas of the transistors.[2,3,4] Furthermore, the output resistance can be increased by increasing the channel length. To increase the output resistance while keeping the current and $V_{GS} - V_t$ constant, the $W/L$ ratio must be held constant. Therefore, the channel width must be increased as much as the length, and the price paid for the improved output resistance is that increased chip area is consumed by the current mirror.

### 4.2.5 Cascode Current Mirror

#### 4.2.5.1 Bipolar

Section 3.4.2 shows that the cascode connection achieves a very high output resistance. Since this is a desirable characteristic for a current mirror, exploring the use of cascodes for high-performance current mirrors is natural. A bipolar-transistor current mirror based on the cascode connection is shown in Fig. 4.8. Transistors $Q_3$ and $Q_1$ form a simple current mirror, and emitter resistances can be added to improve the matching. Transistor

**Figure 4.8** Cascode current mirror with bipolar transistors.

$Q_2$ acts as the common-base part of the cascode and transfers the collector current of $Q_1$ to the output while presenting a high output resistance. Transistor $Q_4$ acts as a diode level shifter and biases the base of $Q_2$ so that $Q_1$ operates in the forward-active region with $V_{CE1} \simeq V_{CE3} = V_{BE3(on)}$. If we assume that the small-signal resistances of diodes $Q_3$ and $Q_4$ are small, a direct application of (3.98) with $R_E \equiv r_{o1}$ concludes that

$$R_o = r_{o2}\left(1 + \frac{g_{m2}r_{o1}}{1 + \frac{g_{m2}r_{o1}}{\beta_0}}\right) \simeq \beta_0 r_{o2} \tag{4.37}$$

because $g_{m2}r_{o1} \simeq g_{m1}r_{o1} \gg \beta_0$. This calculation assumes that almost all of the small-signal current that flows into the collector of $Q_2$ flows out its base because the small-signal resistance connected to the emitter of $Q_2$ is much greater than that connected to its base. A key problem with this calculation, however, is that it ignores the effect of the simple current mirror formed by $Q_3$ and $Q_1$. Let $i_{b2}$ and $i_{e2}$ represent increases in the base and emitter currents flowing out of $Q_2$ caused by increasing output voltage. Then the simple mirror forces $i_{e2} \simeq i_{b2}$. As a result, the variation in the collector current of $Q_2$ splits into two equal parts and half flows in $r_{\pi2}$. A small-signal analysis shows that $R_o$ in (4.37) is reduced by half to

$$R_o \simeq \frac{\beta_0 r_{o2}}{2} \tag{4.38}$$

Thus, the cascode configuration boosts the output resistance by approximately $\beta_0/2$. For $\beta_0 = 100$, $V_A = 130$ V, and $I_{C2} = 1$ mA,

$$R_o = \frac{\beta_0 V_A}{2I_{C2}} = \frac{100(130)}{2 \text{ mA}} = 6.5 \text{ M}\Omega \tag{4.39}$$

In this calculation of output resistance, we have neglected the effects of $r_\mu$. Although this assumption is easy to justify in the case of the simple current mirror, it must be re-examined here because the output resistance is so high. The collector-base resistance $r_\mu$ results from modulation of the base-recombination current as a consequence of the Early effect, as described in Chapter 1. For a transistor whose base current is composed entirely of base-recombination current, the percentage change in base current when $V_{CE}$ is changed at a constant $V_{BE}$ would equal that of the collector current, and $r_\mu$ would be equal to $\beta_0 r_o$.

In this case, the effect of $r_\mu$ would be to reduce the output resistance of the cascode current mirror given in (4.38) by a factor of 1.5.

In actual integrated-circuit $npn$ transistors, however, only a small percentage of the base current results from recombination in the base. Since only this component is modulated by the Early effect, the observed values of $r_\mu$ are a factor of 10 or more larger than $\beta_0 r_o$. Therefore, $r_\mu$ has a negligible effect here with $npn$ transistors. On the other hand, for lateral $pnp$ transistors, the feedback resistance $r_\mu$ is much smaller than for $npn$ transistors because most of the base current results from base-region recombination. The actual value of this resistance depends on a number of process and device-geometry variables, but observed values range from 2 to 5 times $\beta_0 r_o$. Therefore, for a cascode current mirror constructed with lateral $pnp$ transistors, the effect of $r_\mu$ on the output resistance can be significant. Furthermore, when considering current mirrors that give output resistances higher than $\beta_0 r_o$, the effects of $r_\mu$ must be considered.

In the cascode current mirror, the base of $Q_1$ is connected to a low-resistance point because $Q_3$ is diode connected. As a result, feedback from $r_{\mu 1}$ is greatly attenuated and has negligible effect on the output resistance. On the other hand, if the resistance from the base of $Q_1$ to ground is increased while all other parameters are held constant, local feedback from $r_{\mu 1}$ significantly affects the base-emitter voltage of $Q_1$ and reduces the output resistance. In the limit where the resistance from the base of $Q_1$ to ground becomes infinite, $Q_1$ acts as if it were diode connected. Local feedback is considered in Chapter 8.

The input voltage of the cascode current mirror is

$$V_{IN} = V_{BE3} + V_{BE4} = 2V_{BE(on)} \tag{4.40}$$

Although $V_{IN}$ is higher here than in (4.10) for a simple current mirror, the increase becomes a limitation only if the power-supply voltage is reduced to nearly two diode drops.

The minimum output voltage for which the output resistance is given by (4.38) must allow both $Q_1$ and $Q_2$ to be biased in the forward-active region. Since $V_{CE1} \simeq V_{CE3} = V_{BE(on)}$,

$$V_{OUT(min)} = V_{CE1} + V_{CE2(sat)} \simeq V_{BE(on)} + V_{CE2(sat)} \tag{4.41}$$

Comparing (4.41) and (4.11) shows that the minimum output voltage for a cascode current mirror is higher than for a simple current mirror by a diode drop. This increase poses an important limitation on the minimum supply voltage when the current mirror is used as an active load for an amplifier.

Since $V_{CE1} \simeq V_{CE3}$, $I_{C1} \simeq I_{C3}$, and the systematic gain error arising from finite transistor output resistance is almost zero. A key limitation of the cascode current mirror, however, is that the systematic gain error arising from finite $\beta_F$ is worse than for a simple current mirror. From KCL at the collector of $Q_3$,

$$I_{E4} = I_{C3} + \frac{2I_{C3}}{\beta_F} \tag{4.42}$$

From KCL at the collector of $Q_4$,

$$I_{IN} = I_{E4} + \frac{I_{C2}}{\beta_F} \tag{4.43}$$

The collector current of $Q_2$ is

$$I_{C2} = \frac{\beta_F}{\beta_F + 1} I_{C3} \tag{4.44}$$

Substituting (4.42) and (4.44) into (4.43) gives

$$I_{IN} = I_{C3} + \frac{2I_{C3}}{\beta_F} + \frac{I_{C3}}{\beta_F + 1} \tag{4.45}$$

Rearranging (4.45) to find $I_{C3}$ and substituting back into (4.44) gives

$$I_{OUT} = I_{C2} = \left(\frac{\beta_F}{\beta_F + 1}\right)\left(\frac{I_{IN}}{1 + \dfrac{2}{\beta_F} + \dfrac{1}{\beta_F + 1}}\right) \tag{4.46}$$

Equation 4.46 can be rearranged to give

$$I_{OUT} = I_{IN}\left(1 - \frac{4\beta_F + 2}{\beta_F^2 + 4\beta_F + 2}\right) \tag{4.47}$$

Equation 4.47 shows that the systematic gain error is

$$\epsilon = -\frac{4\beta_F + 2}{\beta_F^2 + 4\beta_F + 2} \tag{4.48}$$

When $\beta_F \gg 1$, (4.48) simplifies to

$$\epsilon \simeq -\frac{4}{\beta_F + 4} \tag{4.49}$$

In contrast, the systematic gain error stemming from finite $\beta_F$ in a simple current mirror with identical transistors is about $-2/\beta_F$, which is less in magnitude than (4.49) predicts for a cascode current mirror if $\beta_F > 4$. This limitation of a cascode current mirror is overcome by the Wilson current mirror described in Section 4.2.6.

### 4.2.5.2 MOS

The cascode current mirror is widely used in MOS technology, where it does not suffer from finite $\beta_F$ effects. Figure 4.9 shows the simplest form. From (3.107), the small-signal output resistance is

$$R_o = r_{o2}[1 + (g_{m2} + g_{mb2})r_{o1}] + r_{o1} \tag{4.50}$$

As shown in the previous section, the bipolar cascode current mirror cannot realize an output resistance larger than $\beta_0 r_o/2$ because $\beta_0$ is finite and nonzero small-signal base current flows in the cascode transistor. In contrast, the MOS cascode is capable of realizing arbitrarily high output resistance by increasing the number of stacked cascode devices because $\beta_0 \to \infty$ for MOS transistors. However, the MOS substrate leakage current described in Section 1.9 can create a resistive shunt to ground from the output node, which can dominate the output resistance for $V_{OUT} > V_{OUT(min)}$.[5]

■    **EXAMPLE**

Find the output resistance of the double-cascode current mirror shown in Fig. 4.10. Assume all the transistors operate in the active region with $I_D = 10\ \mu A$, $V_A = 50\ V$, and $g_m r_o = 50$. Neglect body effect.

The output resistance of each transistor is

$$r_o = \frac{V_A}{I_D} = \frac{50\ V}{10\ \mu A} = 5\ M\Omega$$

(a)

$M_1$ active, $M_2$ in triode region

Both $M_1$ and $M_2$ in triode region

(b)

**Figure 4.9** (a) Cascode current mirror using MOS transistors. (b) I-V characteristic.

**Figure 4.10** Example of a double-cascode current mirror.

From (4.50), looking into the drain of $M_2$:

$$R_{o2} = r_{o2}(1 + g_{m2}r_{o1}) + r_{o1} \qquad (4.51)$$

Similarly, looking into the drain of $M_3$:

$$R_o = r_{o3}[1 + g_{m3}R_{o2}] + R_{o2} \qquad (4.52)$$

Each cascode stage increases the output resistance by a factor of about $(1 + g_m r_o)$. Therefore,

$$R_o \simeq r_o(1 + g_m r_o)^2 \simeq 5(51)^2 \text{ M}\Omega \simeq 13 \text{ G}\Omega \qquad (4.53)$$

With such a large output resistance, other parasitic leakage paths, such as the substrate leakage path, could be comparable to this resistance in practice.

From KVL in Fig. 4.9,

$$V_{DS1} = V_{GS3} + V_{GS4} - V_{GS2} \qquad (4.54)$$

Since $V_{DS3} = V_{GS3}$, (4.54) shows that $V_{DS1} = V_{DS3}$ when $V_{GS2} = V_{GS4}$. Under this condition, the systematic gain error of the cascode current mirror is zero because $M_1$ and $M_3$ are identically biased, and because $\beta_F \to \infty$ for MOS transistors. In practice, $V_{GS2}$ is not exactly equal to $V_{GS4}$ even with perfect matching unless $V_{OUT} = V_{IN}$ because of channel-length modulation. As a result, $V_{DS1} \simeq V_{DS3}$ and

$$\epsilon \simeq 0 \qquad (4.55)$$

The input voltage of the MOS cascode current mirror in Fig. 4.9 is

$$\begin{aligned} V_{IN} &= V_{GS3} + V_{GS4} \\ &= V_{t3} + V_{ov3} + V_{t4} + V_{ov4} \end{aligned} \qquad (4.56)$$

The input voltage here includes two gate-source drops, each composed of threshold and overdrive components. Ignoring the body effect and assuming the transistors all have equal overdrives,

$$V_{IN} = 2V_t + 2V_{ov} \qquad (4.57)$$

Also, adding extra cascode levels increases the input voltage by another threshold and another overdrive component for each additional cascode. Furthermore, the body effect increases the threshold of all transistors with $V_{SB} > 0$. Together, these facts increase the difficulty of designing the input current source for low power-supply voltages.

When $M_1$ and $M_2$ both operate in the active region, $V_{DS1} \simeq V_{DS3} = V_{GS3}$. For $M_2$ to operate in the active region, $V_{DS2} > V_{ov2}$ is required. Therefore, the minimum output voltage for which $M_1$ and $M_2$ operate in the active region is

$$\begin{aligned} V_{OUT(min)} &= V_{DS1} + V_{ov2} \\ &\simeq V_{GS3} + V_{ov2} = V_t + V_{ov3} + V_{ov2} \end{aligned} \qquad (4.58)$$

If the transistors all have equal overdrives,

$$V_{OUT(min)} \simeq V_t + 2V_{ov} \qquad (4.59)$$

On the other hand, $M_2$ operates in the triode region if $V_{OUT} < V_{OUT(min)}$, and both $M_1$ and $M_2$ operate in the triode region if $V_{OUT} < V_{ov1}$. These results are shown graphically in Fig. 4.9b.

Although the overdrive term in (4.59) can be made small by using large values of $W$ for a given current, the threshold term represents a significant loss of voltage swing when the current mirror is used as an active load in an amplifier. The threshold term in (4.59)

$$V_{ov} = \sqrt{\frac{2\,I_{IN}}{\mu_n C_{ox} W/L}}$$

Figure 4.11  (a) MOS cascode current mirror with improved biasing for maximum voltage swing. (b) Practical implementation. (c) I-V characteristic.

stems from the biasing of the drain-source voltage of $M_1$ so that

$$V_{DS1} = V_{IN} - V_{GS2} \tag{4.60}$$

Ignoring the body effect and assuming that $M_1$-$M_4$ all operate in the active region with equal overdrives,

$$V_{DS1} = V_t + V_{ov} \tag{4.61}$$

Therefore, the drain-source voltage of $M_1$ is a threshold larger than necessary to operate $M_1$ in the active region. To reduce $V_{DS1}$, the voltage from the gate of $M_2$ to ground can be level shifted down by a threshold as shown in Fig. 4.11a. In practice, a source follower is used to implement the level shift, as shown in Fig. 4.11b.[6] Transistor $M_5$ acts as the source follower and is biased by the output of the simple current mirror $M_3$ and $M_6$. Because the gate-source voltage of $M_5$ is greater than its threshold by the overdrive, however, the drain-source voltage of $M_1$ would be zero with equal thresholds and overdrives on all transistors.

To bias $M_1$ at the boundary between the active and triode regions,

$$V_{DS1} = V_{ov} \tag{4.62}$$

is required. Therefore, the overdrive on $M_4$ is doubled by reducing its $W/L$ by a factor of four to satisfy (4.62). As a result, the threshold term in (4.59) is eliminated and

$$V_{OUT(min)} \simeq 2V_{ov} \tag{4.63}$$

Because the minimum output voltage does not contain a threshold component, the range of output voltages for which $M_1$ and $M_2$ both operate in the active region is significantly improved. Therefore, the current mirror in Fig. 4.11 places much less restriction on the range of output voltages that can be achieved in an amplifier using this current mirror as an active load than the mirror in Fig. 4.9. For this reason, the mirror in Fig. 4.11 is called a *high-swing* cascode current mirror. This type of level shifting to reduce $V_{OUT(min)}$ can also be applied to bipolar circuits.

The output resistance of the high-swing cascode current mirror is the same as in (4.50) when both $M_1$ and $M_2$ operate in the active region. However, the input voltage and the systematic gain error are worsened compared to the cascode current mirror without level shift. The input voltage is still given by (4.56), but the overdrive component of the gate-source voltage of $M_4$ has increased by a factor of two because its $W/L$ has been reduced by a factor of four. Therefore,

$$V_{IN} = 2V_t + 3V_{ov} \tag{4.64}$$

Since $M_3$ and $M_1$ form a simple current mirror with unequal drain-source voltages, the systematic gain error is

$$\epsilon = \frac{V_{DS1} - V_{DS3}}{V_A} \simeq \frac{V_{ov1} - (V_t + V_{ov1})}{V_A} = -\frac{V_t}{V_A} \tag{4.65}$$

The negative sign in (4.65) shows that $I_{OUT} < I_{IN}$. For example, if $I_{IN} = 100 \ \mu A$, $V_t = 1$ V, and $V_A = 10$ V, $\epsilon \simeq -0.1$, which means that $I_{OUT} \simeq 90 \ \mu A$.

In practice, $(W/L)_4 < (1/4)(W/L)$ is usually selected for two reasons. First, MOS transistors display an indistinct transition from the triode to active regions. Therefore, increasing the drain-source voltage of $M_1$ by a few hundred millivolts above $V_{ov1}$ is usually required to realize the incremental output resistance predicted by (4.50). Second, although the body effect was not considered in this analysis, it tends to reduce the drain-source voltage on $M_1$, which is determined by the following KVL loop

$$V_{DS1} = V_{GS3} + V_{GS4} - V_{GS5} - V_{GS2} \tag{4.66}$$

Each of the gate-source voltage terms in (4.66) contains a threshold component. Since the source-body voltage of $M_5$ is higher than that of $M_4$, $V_{t5} > V_{t4}$. Also, $V_{t2} > V_{t3}$ because the source-body voltage of $M_2$ is higher than that of $M_3$. Simulations with high-accuracy models are usually required to find the optimum $(W/L)_4$.

One drawback of the current mirror in Fig. 4.11 is that the input current is mirrored to a new branch to do the level shift. Combining the input branches eliminates the possibility of mismatch between the two branch currents and may reduce the power dissipation. In a single combined input branch, some element must provide a voltage drop equal to the desired difference between the gate voltages of $M_1$ and $M_2$. To bias $M_1$ at the edge of the active region, the required voltages from the gates $M_1$ and $M_2$ to ground are $V_t + V_{ov}$ and $V_t + 2V_{ov}$, respectively. Therefore, the desired difference in the gate voltages is $V_{ov}$. This voltage difference can be developed across the drain to the source of a transistor deliberately operated in the triode region, as shown in Fig. 4.12a.[7] Since $M_6$ is diode connected, it operates in the active region as long as the input current and threshold are

**Figure 4.12** (a) Circuit that forces $M_5$ to operate in the triode region. (b) Sooch cascode current mirror using the circuit in (a).

positive. However, since the gate-source voltage of $M_6$ is equal to the gate-drain voltage of $M_5$, a channel exists at the drain of $M_5$ when it exists at the source of $M_6$. In other words, $M_6$ forces $M_5$ to operate in the triode region.

To use the circuit in Fig. 4.12a in a current mirror, we would like to choose the aspect ratios of the transistors so that the drain source voltage of $M_5$ is $V_{ov}$. Since $M_6$ operates in the active region,

$$I_{IN} = \frac{k'}{2}\left(\frac{W}{L}\right)_6 (V_{GS6} - V_t)^2 \tag{4.67}$$

Since $M_5$ operates in the triode region,

$$I_{IN} = \frac{k'}{2}\left(\frac{W}{L}\right)_5 \left(2(V_{GS5} - V_t)V_{DS5} - (V_{DS5})^2\right) \tag{4.68}$$

The goal is to set

$$V_{DS5} = V_{ov} \tag{4.69}$$

when

$$V_{GS6} = V_t + V_{ov} \tag{4.70}$$

From (4.69) and (4.70),

$$V_{GS5} = V_{GS6} + V_{DS5} = V_t + 2V_{ov} \qquad (4.71)$$

Substituting (4.68) - (4.71) into (4.67) gives

$$\frac{k'}{2}\left(\frac{W}{L}\right)_6 (V_{ov})^2 = \frac{k'}{2}\left(\frac{W}{L}\right)_5 \left(2(2V_{ov})V_{ov} - (V_{ov})^2\right) \qquad (4.72)$$

Equation 4.72 can be simplified to

$$\left(\frac{W}{L}\right)_5 = \frac{1}{3}\left(\frac{W}{L}\right)_6 \qquad (4.73)$$

The circuit of Fig. 4.12$a$ is used in the current mirror of Fig. 4.12$b$,[7] which is called the *Sooch* cascode current mirror after its inventor. At first, ignore transistor $M_4$ and assume that $M_3$ is simply diode connected. The difference between the voltages to ground from the gates of $M_1$ and $M_2$ is set by the drain-source voltage of $M_5$. By choosing equal aspect ratios for all devices except $M_5$, whose aspect ratio is given by (4.73), the drain-source voltage of $M_5$ is $V_{ov}$ and $M_1$ is biased at the edge of the active region. The output resistance, minimum output voltage, input voltage, and systematic gain error are the same as in (4.50), (4.63), (4.64), and (4.65) respectively.

Now we will consider the effect of transistor $M_4$. The purpose of $M_4$ is to set the drain-source voltage of $M_3$ equal to that of $M_1$. Without $M_4$, these drain-source voltages differ by a threshold, causing nonzero systematic gain error. With $M_4$,

$$V_{DS3} = V_{G2} - V_{GS4} \qquad (4.74)$$

where

$$V_{G2} = V_{GS3} + V_{DS5} \qquad (4.75)$$

Ignoring channel-length modulation,

$$V_{G2} = (V_t + V_{ov}) + V_{ov} = V_t + 2V_{ov} \qquad (4.76)$$

Ignoring the body effect and assuming that $M_4$ operates in the active region,

$$V_{GS4} = V_t + V_{ov} \qquad (4.77)$$

Then substituting (4.76) and (4.77) into (4.74) gives

$$V_{DS3} = V_{ov} \qquad (4.78)$$

If $M_2$ also operates in the active region under these conditions, $V_{DS3} = V_{DS1}$. As a result, the systematic gain error is

$$\epsilon = 0 \qquad (4.79)$$

Therefore, the purpose of $M_4$ is to equalize the drain-source voltages of $M_3$ and $M_1$ to reduce the systematic gain error.

For $M_4$ to operate in the active region, $V_{DS4} > V_{ov}$ is required. Since

$$V_{DS4} = V_{GS3} - V_{DS3} = (V_t + V_{ov}) - V_{ov} = V_t \qquad (4.80)$$

Equation 4.80 shows that $M_4$ operates in the active region if $V_t > V_{ov}$. Although this condition is usually satisfied, a low threshold and/or high overdrive may cause $M_4$ to operate in the triode region. If this happens, the gate-source voltage of $M_4$ depends strongly on its drain-source voltage, increasing the systematic gain error. Since increasing temperature causes the threshold to decrease, but the overdrive to increase, checking the region of

operation of $M_4$ in simulation at the maximum expected operating temperature
in practice.

The main limitation of the high-swing cascode current mirrors just presented, is
the input voltage is large. In Fig. 4.11, the input voltage is the sum of the gate-source
voltages of $M_3$ and $M_4$ and is given by (4.64) ignoring body effect. In Fig. 4.12, the input
voltage is

$$
\begin{aligned}
V_{IN} &= V_{GS3} + V_{DS5} + V_{GS6} \\
&= V_t + V_{ov} + V_{ov} + V_t + V_{ov} \\
&= 2V_t + 3V_{ov}
\end{aligned}
\tag{4.81}
$$

Equation 4.81 shows that the input voltage of the high-swing cascode current mirror in
Fig. 4.12 is the same as in (4.64) for Fig. 4.11. The large input voltages may limit the minimum power-supply voltage because a transistor-level implementation of the input current
source requires some nonzero drop for proper operation. With threshold voltages of about
1 V, the cascode current mirrors in Figs. 4.11 and 4.12 can operate properly for power-
supply voltages greater than about 3 V. Below about 2 V, however, reduced thresholds or a
new configuration is required. Reducing the magnitude of the threshold for all transistors
increases the difficulty in turning off transistors that are used as switches. This problem
can be overcome by using low-threshold devices in the current mirror and high-threshold
devices as switches, but this solution increases process complexity and cost. Therefore,
circuit techniques to reduce the input voltage are important to minimize cost.

To reduce the input voltage, the input branch can be split into two branches, as shown
in Fig. 4.13. If $M_1$ and $M_2$ are biased in the active region, the output resistance is still
given by (4.50). Also, the minimum output voltage for which (4.50) applies is still given
by (4.63). Furthermore, if $M_4$ operates in the active region, the drain-source voltage of $M_3$
is equal to that of $M_1$, and the systematic gain error is still zero as in (4.79).

Since the mirror in Fig. 4.13 has two input branches, an input voltage can be calculated
for each:

$$
V_{IN1} = V_{DS5} + V_{GS6} = V_t + 2V_{ov}
\tag{4.82}
$$

$$
V_{IN2} = V_{GS3} = V_t + V_{ov}
\tag{4.83}
$$

Both $V_{IN1}$ and $V_{IN2}$ are less than the input voltage given in (4.64) for Fig. 4.12b by more
than a threshold, allowing the input current sources to operate properly with power-supply
voltages greater than about 2 V, assuming thresholds of about 1 V.

**Figure 4.13** MOS high-swing current mirror with two input branches.

13, the drain-source voltage of $M_5$ is only used to bias the source. Therefore, $M_5$ and $M_6$ can be collapsed into one diode-connected transistor whose source is grounded. Call this replacement transistor $M_7$. The aspect ratio of $M_7$ should be smaller than the aspect ratios of $M_1$-$M_4$ to maintain the bias conditions as in Fig. 13. In practice, the aspect ratio of $M_7$ is further reduced to bias $M_1$ past the edge of the active region and to overcome a mismatch in the thresholds of $M_7$ and $M_2$ caused by body effect.

### 4.2.6 Wilson Current Mirror

#### 4.2.6.1 Bipolar

The main limitation of the bipolar cascode current mirror is that the systematic gain error stemming from finite $\beta_F$ was large, as given in (4.49). To overcome this limitation, the Wilson current mirror can be used as shown in Fig. 4.14a.[8] This circuit uses negative feedback through $Q_1$, activating $Q_3$ to reduce the base-current error and raise the output resistance. (See Chapter 8.)

From a qualitative standpoint, the difference between the input current and $I_{C3}$ flows into the base of $Q_2$. This base current is multiplied by $(\beta_F + 1)$ and flows in the diode-connected transistor $Q_1$, which causes current of the same magnitude to flow in $Q_3$. A feedback path is thus formed that regulates $I_{C3}$ so that it is nearly equal to the input current, reducing the systematic gain error caused by finite $\beta_F$. Similarly, when the output voltage increases, the collector current of $Q_2$ also increases, in turn increasing the collector current of $Q_1$. As a result, the collector current of $Q_3$ increases, which reduces the base current of $Q_2$. The decrease in the base current of $Q_2$ caused by negative feedback reduces the original change in the collector current of $Q_2$ and increases the output resistance.

To find the output resistance of the Wilson current mirror when all transistors operate in the active region, we will analyze the small-signal model shown in Fig. 4.14b, in which a test current source $i_t$ is applied at the output. Transistors $Q_1$ and $Q_3$ form a simple current mirror. Since $Q_1$ is diode connected, the small-signal resistance from the base of $Q_1$ to ground is $(1/g_{m1})\|r_{\pi1}\|r_{\pi3}\|r_{o1}$. Assume that an unknown current $i_1$ flows in this resistance. When $g_{m1}r_{\pi1} \gg 1$, $g_{m1}r_{\pi3} \gg 1$, and $g_{m1}r_{o1} \gg 1$, this resistance is approximately equal to $1/g_{m1}$. Transistor $Q_3$ could be modeled as a voltage-controlled current source of value $g_{m3}v_{\pi3}$ in parallel with $r_{o3}$. Since $v_{\pi3} = v_{\pi1} \simeq i_1/g_{m1}$, the voltage-controlled current source in the model for $Q_3$ can be replaced by a current-controlled current source of value $(g_{m3}/g_{m1})(i_1) = 1(i_1)$, as shown in Fig. 4.14b. This model represents the behavior of the simple current mirror directly: The input current $i_1$ is mirrored to the output by the current-controlled current source.

(a)                                                              (b)

**Figure 4.14** (a) Bipolar Wilson current mirror. (b) Small-signal model.

Using this model, the resulting voltage $v_t$ is

$$v_t = \frac{i_1}{g_{m1}} + (i_t - g_{m2}v_{\pi2})r_{o2} \tag{4.84}$$

To find the relationship between $i_1$ and $v_{\pi2}$, note that the voltage across $r_{o3}$ is $(i_1/g_{m1} + v_{\pi2})$ and use KCL at node ② in Fig. 4.14b to show that

$$\frac{v_{\pi2}}{r_{\pi2}} + i_1 + \frac{\dfrac{i_1}{g_{m1}} + v_{\pi2}}{r_{o3}} = 0 \tag{4.85}$$

Rearranging (4.85) gives

$$v_{\pi2} = -i_1 r_{\pi2} \left( \frac{1 + \dfrac{1}{g_{m1}r_{o3}}}{1 + \dfrac{r_{\pi2}}{r_{o3}}} \right) \tag{4.86}$$

To find the relationship between $i_1$ and $i_t$, use KCL at node ① in Fig. 4.14b to show that

$$i_t = i_1 - \frac{v_{\pi2}}{r_{\pi2}} \tag{4.87}$$

Substituting (4.86) into (4.87) and rearranging gives

$$i_1 = \frac{i_t}{1 + \left( \dfrac{1 + \dfrac{1}{g_{m1}r_{o3}}}{1 + \dfrac{r_{\pi2}}{r_{o3}}} \right)} \tag{4.88}$$

Substituting (4.88) into (4.86) and rearranging gives

$$v_{\pi2} = -i_t r_{\pi2} \left( \frac{1 + \dfrac{1}{g_{m1}r_{o3}}}{2 + \dfrac{r_{\pi2}}{r_{o3}} + \dfrac{1}{g_{m1}r_{o3}}} \right) \tag{4.89}$$

Substituting (4.88) and (4.89) into (4.84) and rearranging gives

$$R_o = \frac{v_t}{i_t} = \frac{1}{g_{m1}\left[ 1 + \left( \dfrac{1 + \dfrac{1}{g_{m1}r_{o3}}}{1 + \dfrac{r_{\pi2}}{r_{o3}}} \right) \right]} + r_{o2} + \frac{g_{m2}r_{\pi2}r_{o2}\left( 1 + \dfrac{1}{g_{m1}r_{o3}} \right)}{2 + \dfrac{r_{\pi2}}{r_{o3}} + \dfrac{1}{g_{m1}r_{o3}}} \tag{4.90}$$

If $r_{o3} \rightarrow \infty$, the small-signal current that flows in the collector of $Q_3$ is equal to $i_1$ and (4.90) reduces to

$$R_o = \frac{1}{g_{m1}(2)} + r_{o2} + \frac{g_{m2}r_{\pi2}r_{o2}}{2} \approx \frac{\beta_0 r_{o2}}{2} \tag{4.91}$$

This result is the same as (4.38) for the cascode current mirror. In the cascode current mirror, the small-signal current that flows in the base of $Q_2$ is mirrored through $Q_3$ to $Q_1$ so that the small-signal base and emitter currents leaving $Q_2$ are approximately equal. On the other hand, in the Wilson current mirror, the small-signal current that flows in the emitter of $Q_2$ is mirrored through $Q_1$ to $Q_3$ and then flows in the base of $Q_2$. Although the cause and effect relationship here is opposite of that in a cascode current mirror, the output resistance is unchanged because the small-signal base and emitter currents leaving $Q_2$ are still forced to be equal. Therefore, the small-signal collector current of $Q_2$ that flows because of changes in the output voltage still splits into two equal parts with half flowing in $r_{\pi 2}$.

For the purpose of dc analysis, we assume that $V_A \rightarrow \infty$ and that the transistors are identical. Then the input voltage is

$$V_{IN} = V_{CE3} = V_{BE1} + V_{BE2} = 2V_{BE(on)} \tag{4.92}$$

which is the same as in (4.40) for a cascode current mirror. Also, the minimum output voltage for which both transistors in the output branch operate in the forward-active region is

$$V_{OUT(min)} = V_{CE1} + V_{CE2(sat)} = V_{BE(on)} + V_{CE2(sat)} \tag{4.93}$$

The result in (4.93) is the same as in (4.41) for a cascode current mirror.

To find the systematic gain error, start with KCL at the collector of $Q_1$ to show that

$$-I_{E2} = I_{C1} + I_{B1} + I_{B3} = I_{C1}\left(1 + \frac{1}{\beta_F}\right) + \frac{I_{C3}}{\beta_F} \tag{4.94}$$

Since we assumed that the transistors are identical and $V_A \rightarrow \infty$,

$$I_{C3} = I_{C1} \tag{4.95}$$

Substituting (4.95) into (4.94) gives

$$-I_{E2} = I_{C1}\left(1 + \frac{2}{\beta_F}\right) \tag{4.96}$$

Using (4.96), the collector current of $Q_2$ is then

$$I_{C2} = -I_{E2}\left(\frac{\beta_F}{1 + \beta_F}\right) = I_{C1}\left(1 + \frac{2}{\beta_F}\right)\left(\frac{\beta_F}{1 + \beta_F}\right) \tag{4.97}$$

Rearranging (4.97) we obtain

$$I_{C1} = I_{C2}\left[\frac{1}{\left(1 + \dfrac{2}{\beta_F}\right)\left(\dfrac{\beta_F}{1 + \beta_F}\right)}\right] \tag{4.98}$$

From KCL at the base of $Q_2$,

$$I_{C3} = I_{IN} - \frac{I_{C2}}{\beta_F} \tag{4.99}$$

Inserting (4.98) and (4.99) into (4.95), we find that

$$I_{OUT} = I_{C2} = I_{IN}\left(1 - \frac{2}{\beta_F^2 + 2\beta_F + 2}\right) = \frac{I_{IN}}{1 + \dfrac{2}{\beta_F(\beta_F + 2)}} \tag{4.100}$$

In the configuration shown in Fig. 4.14a, the systematic gain error arising from finite output resistance is not zero because $Q_3$ and $Q_1$ operate with collector-emitter voltages that differ by the base-emitter voltage of $Q_2$. With finite $V_A$ and finite $\beta_F$,

$$
\begin{aligned}
I_{OUT} &\simeq I_{IN}\left(1 - \frac{2}{\beta_F^2 + 2\beta_F + 2}\right)\left(1 + \frac{V_{CE1} - V_{CE3}}{V_A}\right) \\
&\simeq I_{IN}\left(1 - \frac{2}{\beta_F^2 + 2\beta_F + 2}\right)\left(1 - \frac{V_{BE2}}{V_A}\right)
\end{aligned}
$$
(4.101)

Therefore, the systematic gain error is

$$
\epsilon \simeq -\left(\frac{2}{\beta_F^2 + 2\beta_F + 2} + \frac{V_{BE2}}{V_A}\right)
$$
(4.102)

Comparing (4.102) to (4.49) shows two key points. First, the systematic gain error arising from finite $\beta_F$ in a Wilson current mirror is much less than in a cascode current mirror. Second, the systematic gain error arising from finite output resistance is worse in the Wilson current mirror shown in Fig. 4.14a than in the cascode current mirror shown in Fig. 4.9. However, this limitation is not fundamental because it can be overcome by introducing a new diode-connected transistor between the collector of $Q_3$ and the base of $Q_2$ to equalize the collector-emitter voltages of $Q_3$ and $Q_1$.

#### 4.2.6.2 MOS

Wilson current mirrors are also used in MOS technology, as shown in Fig. 4.15. Ignoring $M_4$, the circuit operation is essentially identical to the bipolar case with $\beta_F \to \infty$. One way to calculate the output resistance is to let $r_{\pi2} \to \infty$ in (4.90), which gives

$$
R_o = \frac{1}{g_{m1}} + r_{o2} + g_{m2}r_{o2}\left(1 + \frac{1}{g_{m1}r_{o3}}\right)r_{o3} \simeq (1 + g_{m2}r_{o3})r_{o2}
$$
(4.103)

Since the calculation in (4.103) is based on the small-signal model for the bipolar Wilson current mirror in Fig. 4.14b, it ignores the body effect in transistor $M_2$. Repeating the analysis with a body-effect generator in parallel with $r_{o2}$ gives

$$
R_o \simeq (2 + g_{m2}r_{o3})r_{o2}
$$
(4.104)

The body effect on $M_2$ has little effect on (4.104) because $M_1$ is diode connected and therefore the voltage from the source of $M_2$ to ground is almost constant.

Figure 4.15 Improved MOS Wilson current mirror with an additional device such that the drain voltages of $M_1$ and $M_3$ are equal.

Although $\beta_F \to \infty$ for MOS transistors, the systematic gain error is not zero without $M_4$ because the drain-source voltage of $M_3$ differs from that of $M_1$ by the gate-source voltage of $M_2$. Therefore, without $M_4$,

$$\epsilon = \frac{V_{DS1} - V_{DS3}}{V_A} = -\frac{V_{GS2}}{V_A} \qquad (4.105)$$

Transistor $M_4$ is inserted in series with $M_3$ to equalize the drain-source voltages of $M_3$ and $M_1$ so that

$$\epsilon \simeq 0 \qquad (4.106)$$

With $M_4$, the output resistance is still given by (4.104) if all transistors operate in the active region. Also, insertion of $M_4$ does not change either the minimum output voltage for which (4.104) applies or the input voltage. Ignoring body effect and assuming equal overdrives on all transistors, the minimum output voltage is

$$V_{\text{OUT(min)}} = V_{GS1} + V_{ov2} = V_t + 2V_{ov} \qquad (4.107)$$

Under the same conditions, the input voltage is

$$V_{\text{IN}} = V_{GS1} + V_{GS2} = 2V_t + 2V_{ov} \qquad (4.108)$$

## 4.3 Active Loads

### 4.3.1 Motivation

In differential amplifiers of the type described in Chapter 3, resistors are used as the load elements. For example, consider the differential amplifier shown in Fig. 3.45. For this circuit, the differential-mode (dm) voltage gain is

$$A_{dm} = -g_m R_C \qquad (4.109)$$

Large gain is often desirable because it allows negative feedback to make the gain with feedback insensitive to variations in the parameters that determine the gain without feedback. This topic is covered in Chapter 8. In Chapter 9, we will show that the required gain should be obtained in as few stages as possible to minimize potential problems with instability. Therefore, maximizing the gain of each stage is important.

Multiplying the numerator and denominator of (4.109) by $I$ gives

$$A_{dm} = -\frac{I(R_C)}{I/g_m} \qquad (4.110)$$

With bipolar transistors, let $I$ represent the collector current $I_C$ of each transistor in the differential pair. From (1.91), (4.110) can be rewritten as

$$A_{dm} = -\frac{I_C R_C}{V_T} \qquad (4.111)$$

To achieve large voltage gain, (4.111) shows that the $I_C R_C$ product must be made large, which in turn requires a large power-supply voltage. Furthermore, large values of resistance are required when low current is used to limit the power dissipation. As a result, the required die area for the resistors can be large.

A similar situation occurs in MOS amplifiers with resistive loads. Let $I$ represent the drain current $I_D$ of each transistor in the differential pair, and let the resistive loads be $R_D$.

From (1.157) and (1.180), (4.110) can be rewritten as

$$A_{dm} = -\frac{I_D R_D}{(V_{GS} - V_t)/2} = -\frac{2 I_D R_D}{V_{ov}} \tag{4.112}$$

Equation 4.112 shows that the $I_D R_D$ product must be increased to increase the gain with constant overdrive. As a result, a large power supply is usually required for large gain, and large resistance is usually required to limit power dissipation. Also, since the overdrive is usually much larger than the thermal voltage, comparing (4.111) and (4.112) shows that the gain of an MOS differential pair is usually much less than the gain of its bipolar counterpart with equal resistive drops. This result stems from the observation that bipolar transistors provide much more transconductance for a given current than MOS transistors provide.

If the power-supply voltage is only slightly larger than the drop on the resistors, the range of common-mode input voltages for which the input transistors would operate in the active region would be severely restricted in both bipolar and MOS amplifiers. To overcome this problem and provide large gain without large power-supply voltages or resistances, the $r_o$ of a transistor can be used as a load element.[9] Since the load element in such a circuit is a transistor instead of a resistor, the load element is said to be *active* instead of *passive*.

### 4.3.2 Common-Emitter/Common-Source Amplifier with Complementary Load

A common-emitter amplifier with *pnp* current-mirror load is shown in Fig. 4.16a. The common-source counterpart with a *p*-channel MOS current-mirror load is shown in Fig. 4.16b. In both cases, there are two output variables: the output voltage, $V_{out}$, and the output current, $I_{out}$. The relationship between these variables is governed by both the input transistor and the load transistor. From the standpoint of the input transistor $T_1$,

$$I_{out} = I_{c1} \quad or \quad I_{out} = I_{d1} \tag{4.113}$$

and

$$V_{out} = V_{ce1} \quad or \quad V_{out} = V_{ds1} \tag{4.114}$$

Equations (4.113) and (4.114) show that the output I-V characteristics of $T_1$ can be used directly in the analysis of the relationship between the output variables. Since the input voltage is the base-emitter voltage of $T_1$ in Fig. 4.16a and the gate-source voltage of $T_1$ in Fig. 4.16b, the input voltage is the parameter that determines the particular curve

Figure 4.16 (a) Common-emitter amplifier with active load. (b) Common-source amplifier with active load.

**Figure 4.17** (a) I-V characteristics of the input transistor. (b) I-V characteristic of the active load. (c) I-V characteristics with load characteristic superimposed. (d) dc transfer characteristic of common-emitter or common-source amplifier with current-mirror load.

in the family of output characteristics under consideration at any point, as shown in Fig. 4.17a.

In contrast, the base-emitter or gate-source voltage of the load transistor $T_2$ is fixed by diode-connected transistor $T_3$. Therefore, only one curve in the family of output I-V characteristics needs to be considered for the load transistor, as shown in Fig. 4.17b. From the standpoint of the load transistor,

$$I_{out} = -I_{c2} \quad \text{or} \quad I_{out} = -I_{d2} \tag{4.115}$$

and

$$V_{out} = V_{CC} + V_{ce2} \quad \text{or} \quad V_{out} = V_{DD} + V_{ds2} \tag{4.116}$$

Equation 4.115 shows that the output characteristic of the load transistor should be mirrored along the horizontal axis to plot in the same quadrant as the output characteristics of the input transistor. Equation 4.116 shows that the load curve should be shifted to the right by an amount equal to the power-supply voltage.

We now consider the dc transfer characteristic of the circuits. Initially, assume that $V_i = 0$. Then the input transistor is turned off, and the load is saturated in the bipolar case and linear in the MOS case, corresponding to point ① in Fig. 4.17c. As $V_i$ is increased, the input transistor eventually begins to conduct current but the load remains saturated or linear until point ② is reached. Here the load enters the active region and a small further increase in $V_i$ moves the operating point through point ③ to point ④, where the input transistor saturates in the bipolar case or enters the linear region in the MOS case. The change in $V_i$ required to move from point ② to point ④ is small because the slopes of the output I-V characteristics in the active region are small for both transistors. The transfer curve ($V_{out}$ as a function of $V_i$) is sketched in Fig. 4.17d.

A key point of this analysis is that the slope of the output characteristic is not constant, which is important because the slope is the gain of the amplifier. Since the gain of the amplifier depends on the input voltage, the amplifier is nonlinear in general, causing distortion to appear in the amplifier output. For low $V_i$, the output is high and the gain is low because the load transistor does not operate in the active region. Similarly, for large $V_i$, the output is low and the gain is low because the input transistor does not operate in the active region. To minimize distortion while providing gain, the amplifier should be operated in the intermediate region of $V_i$, where all transistors operate in the active region. The range of outputs for which all transistors operate in the active region should be maximized to use the power-supply voltage to the maximum extent. The active loads in Fig. 4.16 maintain high incremental output resistance as long as the drop across the load is more than $V_{OUT(min)}$ of the current mirror, which is $|V_{CE2(sat)}|$ in the bipolar case and $|V_{ov2}|$ in the MOS case here. Therefore, minimizing $V_{OUT(min)}$ of the mirror maximizes the range of outputs over which the amplifier provides high and nearly constant gain. In contrast, an ideal passive load requires a large voltage drop to give high gain, as shown in (4.111) and (4.112). As a result, the range of outputs for which the gain is high and nearly constant is much less than with an active load.

The gain at any output voltage can be found by finding the slope in Fig. 4.17d. In general, this procedure requires writing equations for the various curves in all of Fig. 4.17. Although this process is required to study the nonlinear behavior of the circuits, it is so complicated analytically that it is difficult to carry out for more than just a couple of transistors at a time. Furthermore, after completing such a large-signal analysis, the results are often so complicated that the effects of the key parameters are difficult to understand, increasing the difficulty of designing with these results. Since we are ultimately interested in being able to analyze and design circuits with a large number of transistors, we will concentrate on the small-signal analysis, which is much simpler to carry out and interpret than the large-signal analysis. Unfortunately, the small-signal analysis provides no information about nonlinearity because it assumes that all transistor parameters are constant.

The primary characteristics of interest in the small-signal analysis here are the voltage gain and output resistance when both devices operate in the active region. The small-signal equivalent circuit is shown in Fig. 4.18. It is drawn for the bipolar case but applies for the MOS case as well when $r_{\pi 1} \to \infty$ and $r_{\pi 2} \to \infty$ because $\beta_0 \to \infty$. Since $I_{REF}$ in Fig. 4.16 is assumed constant, the large-signal base-emitter or gate-source voltage of the load transistor is constant. Therefore, the small-signal base-emitter or gate-source voltage of the load transistor, $v_2$, is zero. As a result, the small-signal voltage-controlled current $g_{m2}v_2 = 0$. To find the output resistance of the amplifier, we set the input to zero. Therefore, $v_1 = 0$ and $g_{m1}v_1 = 0$, and the output resistance is

$$R_o = r_{o1} \| r_{o2} \qquad (4.117)$$

Equation 4.117 together with (1.112) and (1.194) show that the output resistance is inversely proportional to the current in both the bipolar and MOS cases.

Since $v_2 = 0$, $g_{m1}v_1$ flows in $r_{o1} \| r_{o2}$ and

$$A_v = -g_{m1}(r_{o1} \| r_{o2}) \qquad (4.118)$$

**Figure 4.18** Small-signal equivalent circuit for common-emitter amplifier with active load.

Substituting (1.91) and (1.112) into (4.118) gives for the bipolar case,

$$A_v = -\frac{1}{\dfrac{V_T}{V_{A1}} + \dfrac{V_T}{V_{A2}}} \tag{4.119}$$

Equation 4.119 shows that the gain is independent of the current in the bipolar case because the transconductance is proportional to the current while the output resistance is inversely proportional to the current. Typical values for this voltage gain are in the 1000 to 2000 range. Therefore, the actively loaded bipolar stage provides very high voltage gain.

In contrast, (1.180) shows that the transconductance is proportional to the square root of the current in the MOS case assuming square-law operation. Therefore, the gain in (4.118) is inversely proportional to the square root of the current. With channel lengths less than 1 μm, however, the drain current is almost linearly related to the gate-source voltage, as shown in (1.224). Therefore, the transconductance is almost constant, and the gain is inversely proportional to the current with very short channel lengths. Furthermore, typical values for the voltage gain in the MOS case are between 10 and 100, which is much less than with bipolar transistors.

### 4.3.3 Common-Emitter/Common-Source Amplifier with Depletion Load

Actively loaded gain stages using MOS transistors can be realized in processes that include only $n$-channel or only $p$-channel transistors if depletion devices are available. A depletion transistor is useful as a load element because it behaves like a current source when the transistor operates in the active region with the gate shorted to the source.

The $I$-$V$ characteristic of an $n$-channel MOS depletion-load transistor is illustrated in Fig. 4.19. Neglecting body effect, the device exhibits a very high output resistance (equal to the device $r_o$) as long as the device operates in the active region. When the body effect is included, the resistance seen across the device drops to approximately $1/g_{mb}$. A complete gain stage is shown in Fig. 4.20 together with its dc transfer characteristic. The small-signal equivalent model when both transistors operate in the active region is shown in

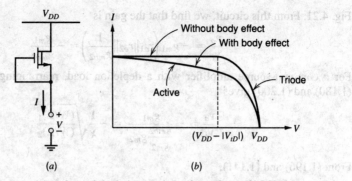

**Figure 4.19** (a) n-channel depletion-mode load transistor. (b) I-V characteristic.

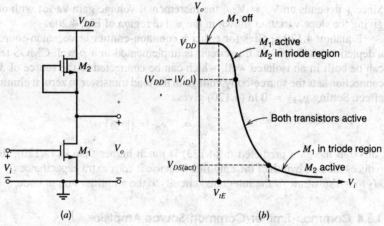

**Figure 4.20** (a) Common-source amplifier with depletion-mode transistor load. (b) dc transfer characteristic.

**Figure 4.21** Small-signal equivalent circuit of the common-source amplifier with depletion load, including the body effect in the load and the channel-length modulation in the load and the common-source device.

Fig. 4.21. From this circuit, we find that the gain is

$$\frac{v_o}{v_i} = -g_{m1}\left(r_{o1}\|r_{o2}\|\frac{1}{g_{mb2}}\right) \simeq -\frac{g_{m1}}{g_{mb2}} \qquad (4.120)$$

For a common-source amplifier with a depletion load, rearranging (4.120) and using (1.180) and (1.200) gives

$$\frac{v_o}{v_i} \simeq -\frac{g_{m1}}{\dfrac{g_{mb2}}{g_{m2}}g_{m2}} = -\frac{1}{\chi}\sqrt{\frac{(W/L)_1}{(W/L)_2}} \qquad (4.121)$$

From (1.196) and (1.141),

$$\frac{1}{\chi} = 2\sqrt{2\phi_f}C_{ox}\sqrt{\frac{1 + V_{SB}/(2\phi_f)}{2q\epsilon N_A}} \qquad (4.122)$$

Since $\chi$ depends on $V_o = V_{SB}$, the incremental voltage gain varies with output voltage, giving the slope variation shown in the active region of Fig. 4.20b.

Equation 4.120 applies for either a common-emitter or common-source driver with a depletion MOS load. If this circuit is implemented in a p-well CMOS technology, $M_2$ can be built in an isolated well, which can be connected to the source of $M_2$. Since this connection sets the source-body voltage in the load transistor to zero, it eliminates the body effect. Setting $g_{mb2} = 0$ in (4.120) gives

$$\frac{v_o}{v_i} = -g_{m1}(r_{o1}\|r_{o2}) \qquad (4.123)$$

Although the gain predicted in (4.123) is much higher than in (4.120), this connection reduces the bandwidth of the amplifier because it adds extra capacitance (from the well of $M_2$ to the substrate of the integrated circuit) to the amplifier output node.

### 4.3.4 Common-Emitter/Common-Source Amplifier with Diode-Connected Load

In this section, we examine the common-emitter/source amplifier with diode-connected load as shown in MOS form in Fig. 4.22. Since the load is diode connected, the load resistance is no more than the reciprocal of the transconductance of the load. As a result, the gain of this circuit is low, and it is often used in wideband amplifiers that require low gain.

For input voltages that are less than one threshold voltage, transistor $M_1$ is off and no current flows in the circuit. When the input voltage exceeds a threshold, transistor $M_1$ turns on, and the circuit provides amplification. Assume that both transistors operate in the active region. From (1.157), the drain currents of $M_1$ and $M_2$ are

$$I_1 = \frac{k'}{2}\left(\frac{W}{L}\right)_1(V_{gs1} - V_{t1})^2 \qquad (4.124)$$

and

$$I_2 = \frac{k'}{2}\left(\frac{W}{L}\right)_2(V_{gs2} - V_{t2})^2 \qquad (4.125)$$

From KVL in Fig. 4.22,

$$V_o = V_{DD} - V_{gs2} \qquad (4.126)$$

**Figure 4.22** (a) Common-source amplifier with enhancement-mode load. (b) I-V characteristic of load transistor. (c) Transfer characteristic of the circuit.

Solving (4.125) for $V_{gs2}$ and substituting into (4.126) gives

$$V_o = V_{DD} - V_{t2} - \sqrt{\frac{2I_2}{k'(W/L)_2}} \tag{4.127}$$

Since $I_2 = I_1$, (4.127) can be rewritten as

$$V_o = V_{DD} - V_{t2} - \sqrt{\frac{2I_1}{k'(W/L)_2}} \tag{4.128}$$

Substituting (4.124) into (4.128) with $V_{gs1} = V_i$ gives

$$V_o = V_{DD} - V_{t2} - \sqrt{\frac{(W/L)_1}{(W/L)_2}}(V_i - V_{t1}) \tag{4.129}$$

Equation 4.129 shows that the slope of the transfer characteristic is the square root of the aspect ratios, assuming that the thresholds are constant. Since the slope of the transfer characteristic is the gain of the amplifier, the gain is constant and the amplifier is linear for a wide range of inputs if the thresholds are constant. This amplifier is useful in implementing broadband, low-gain amplifiers with high linearity.

Equation 4.129 holds when both transistors operate in the active region and when channel-length modulation and body effect are negligible. In practice, the requirement that both transistors operate in the active region leads to an important performance limitation

**Figure 4.23** Small-signal equivalent circuit for the common-source amplifier with enhancement-mode load, including output resistance and body effect in the load.

in enhancement-load inverters. The load device remains in the active region only if the drain-source voltage of the load is at least a threshold voltage. For output voltages more positive than $V_{DD} - V_{t2}$, the load transistor enters the cutoff region and carries no current. Therefore, the amplifier is incapable of producing an output more positive than one threshold voltage below the positive supply. Also, in practice, channel-length modulation and body effect reduce the gain as shown in the following small-signal analysis.

The small-signal voltage gain can be determined by using the small-signal equivalent circuit of Fig. 4.23, in which both the body effect and the output resistance of the two transistors have been included. From KCL at the output node,

$$g_{m1}v_i + \frac{v_o}{r_{o1}} + \frac{v_o}{r_{o2}} + g_{m2}v_o + g_{mb2}v_o = 0 \tag{4.130}$$

Rearranging (4.130) gives

$$\frac{v_o}{v_i} = -g_{m1}\left(\frac{1}{g_{m2}}\|\frac{1}{g_{mb2}}\|r_{o1}\|r_{o2}\right)$$

$$= -\frac{g_{m1}}{g_{m2}}\left(\frac{1}{1 + \dfrac{g_{mb2}}{g_{m2}} + \dfrac{1}{g_{m2}r_{o1}} + \dfrac{1}{g_{m2}r_{o2}}}\right) \tag{4.131}$$

If $g_{m2}/g_{mb2} \gg 1$, $g_{m2}r_{o1} \gg 1$, and $g_{m2}r_{o2} \gg 1$,

$$\frac{v_o}{v_i} \approx -\frac{g_{m1}}{g_{m2}} = -\sqrt{\frac{(W/L)_1}{(W/L)_2}} \tag{4.132}$$

as in (4.129). For practical device geometries, this relationship limits the maximum voltage gain to values on the order of 10 to 20.

The bipolar counterpart of the circuit in Fig. 4.22 is a common-emitter amplifier with a diode-connected load. The magnitude of its gain would be approximately equal to the ratio of the transconductances, which would be unity. However, the current that would flow in this circuit would be extremely large for inputs greater than $V_{be(on)}$ because the collector current in a bipolar transistor is an exponential function of its base-emitter voltage. To limit the current but maintain unity gain, equal-value resistors can be placed in series with the emitter of each transistor. Alternatively, the input transistors can be replaced by a differential pair, where the current is limited by the tail current source. In this case, emitter degeneration is used in the differential pair to increase the range of inputs for which all transistors operate in the active region, as in Fig. 3.49. In contrast, source degeneration is rarely used in MOS differential pairs because their transconductance and linear range can be controlled through the device aspect ratios.

## 4.3.5 Differential Pair with Current-Mirror Load

### 4.3.5.1 Large-Signal Analysis

A straightforward application of the active-load concept to the differential pair would yield the circuit shown in Fig. 4.24a. Assume at first that all $n$-channel transistors are identical and that all $p$-channel transistors are identical. Then the differential-mode half circuit for this differential pair is just a common-source amplifier with an active-load, as in Fig. 4.16b. Thus the differential-mode voltage gain is large when all the transistors are biased in the active region. The circuit as it stands, however, has the drawback that the quiescent value of the common-mode output voltage is very sensitive to changes in the drain currents of

**Figure 4.24** (a) Differential pair with active load. (b) Common-mode half circuit for differential pair with active load.

$M_3$, $M_4$, $M_7$, and $M_8$. As a result, some transistors may operate in or near the triode region, reducing the differential gain or the range of outputs for which the differential gain is high.

This fact is illustrated by the dc common-mode half-circuit shown in Fig. 4.24b. In the common-mode half circuit, the combination of $M_1$, $M_6$, and $M_8$ form a cascode current mirror, which is connected to the simple current mirror formed by $M_3$ and $M_5$. If all transistors operate in the active region, $M_3$ pushes down a current about equal to $I_{REF1}$, and $M_8$ pulls down a current about equal to $I_{REF2}$. KCL requires that the current in $M_3$ must be equal to the current in $M_8$. If $I_{REF2} = I_{REF1}$, KCL can be satisfied while all transistors operate in the active region. In practice, however, $I_{REF2}$ is not exactly equal to $I_{REF1}$, and the current mirrors contain nonzero mismatch, causing changes in the common-mode output to satisfy KCL. Since the output resistance of each current mirror is high, the required change in the common-mode output voltage can be large even for a small mismatch in reference currents or transistors, and one or more transistors can easily move into or near the triode region. For example, suppose that the current pushed down by $M_3$ when it operates in the active region is more than the current pulled down by $M_8$ when it operates in the active region. Then the common-mode output voltage must rise to reduce the current in $M_3$. If the common-mode output voltage rises within $V_{ov3}$ of $V_{DD}$, $M_3$ operates in the triode region. Furthermore, even if all the transistors continue to be biased in the active region, any change in the common-mode output voltage from its desired value reduces the range of outputs for which the differential gain is high.

Since $M_1$ and $M_2$ act as cascodes for $M_7$ and $M_8$, shifts in the common-mode input voltage have little effect on the common-mode output unless the inputs become low enough that $M_7$ and $M_8$ are forced to operate in the triode region. Therefore, feedback to the inputs of the circuit in Fig. 4.24a is not usually adequate to overcome the common-mode bias problem. Instead, this problem is usually overcome in practice through the use of a separate common-mode feedback circuit, which either adjusts the sum of the currents in $M_3$ and $M_4$ to be equal to the sum of the currents in $M_7$ and $M_8$ or vice versa for a given common-mode output voltage. This topic is covered in Chapter 12.

An alternative approach that avoids the need for common-mode feedback is shown in Fig. 4.25. For simplicity in the bipolar circuit shown in Fig. 4.25a, assume that $\beta_F \rightarrow \infty$. The circuit in Fig. 4.25b is the MOS counterpart of the bipolar circuit in Fig. 4.25a because each npn and pnp transistor has been replaced by n-channel and p-channel MOS transistors, respectively. Then under ideal conditions in both the bipolar and MOS circuits, the active load is a current mirror that forces the current in its output transistor $T_4$ to equal the current in its input transistor $T_3$. Since the sum of the currents in both transistors of the active load must equal $I_{TAIL}$ by KCL, $I_{TAIL}/2$ flows in each of side of the active load. Therefore, these circuits eliminate the common-mode bias problem by allowing the currents in the active load to be set by the tail current source. Furthermore, these circuits each provide a single output with much better rejection of common-mode input signals than a standard resistively loaded differential pair with the output taken off one side only. Although these circuits can be analyzed from a large-signal standpoint, we will concentrate on the small-signal analysis for simplicity.

### 4.3.5.2 Small-Signal Analysis

We will analyze the low-frequency small-signal behavior of the bipolar circuit shown in Fig. 4.25a because these results cover both the bipolar and MOS cases by letting $\beta_0 \rightarrow \infty$ and $r_\pi \rightarrow \infty$. Key parameters of interest in this circuit include the small-signal transconductance and output resistance. (The product of these two quantities gives the small-signal voltage gain with no load.) Since only one transistor in the active load is diode connected, the circuit is not symmetrical and a half-circuit approach is not useful. Therefore, we will analyze the small-signal model of this circuit directly. Assume that all transistors operate

**Figure 4.25** (a) Emitter-coupled pair with current-mirror load. (b) Source-coupled pair with current-mirror load (MOS counterpart).

in the active region with $r_\mu \to \infty$ and $r_b = 0$. Let $r_{\text{tail}}$ represent the output resistance of the tail current source $I_{\text{TAIL}}$. The resulting small-signal circuit is shown in Fig. 4.26a.

Since $T_3$ and $T_4$ form a current mirror, we expect the mirror output current to be approximately equal to the mirror input current. Therefore, we will write

$$g_{m4}v_3 = i_3(1 - \epsilon_m) \qquad (4.133)$$

where $\epsilon_m$ is the systematic gain error of the current mirror calculated from small-signal parameters. Let $r_3$ represent the total resistance connected between the base or gate of $T_3$ and the power supply. Then $r_3$ is the parallel combination of $1/g_{m3}$, $r_{\pi3}$, $r_{\pi4}$, and $r_{o3}$. Under the simplifying assumptions that $\beta_0 \gg 1$ and $g_m r_o \gg 1$, this parallel combination is approximately equal to $1/g_{m3}$. Then the drop across $r_{\pi4}$ is

$$v_3 = i_3 r_3 \simeq \frac{i_3}{g_{m3}} \qquad (4.134)$$

**Figure 4.26** (a) Small-signal equivalent circuit, differential pair with current-mirror load. (b) Simplified drawing of small-signal model of differential pair with current-mirror load.

We will also assume that the two transistors in the differential pair match perfectly and operate with equal dc currents, as do the two transistors in the current-mirror load. Then $g_{m(dp)} = g_{m1} = g_{m2}$, $g_{m(mir)} = g_{m3} = g_{m4}$, $r_{\pi(dp)} = r_{\pi1} = r_{\pi2}$, $r_{\pi(mir)} = r_{\pi3} = r_{\pi4}$, $r_{o(dp)} = r_{o1} = r_{o2}$, and $r_{o(mir)} = r_{o3} = r_{o4}$. From (4.134), the resulting voltage-controlled current $g_{m4}v_3$ is

$$g_{m4}v_3 = g_{m(mir)}v_3 \simeq g_{m(mir)}\frac{i_3}{g_{m(mir)}} = i_3 \qquad (4.135)$$

Equations 4.133 and 4.135 show that $\epsilon_m \simeq 0$ and thus the active load acts as a current mirror in a small-signal sense, as expected. Using (4.133), the small-signal circuit is redrawn in Fig. 4.26b with the output grounded to find the transconductance. Note that $r_{o4}$ is omitted because it is attached to a small-signal ground on both ends.

From KCL at node ①,

$$(v_{i1} - v_1 + v_{i2} - v_1)\left(\frac{1}{r_{\pi(dp)}} + g_{m(dp)}\right) + \frac{v_3 - v_1}{r_{o(dp)}} - \frac{v_1}{r_{o(dp)}\|r_{\text{tail}}} = 0 \quad (4.136)$$

where $v_1$ and $v_3$ are the voltages to ground from nodes ① and ③. To complete an exact small-signal analysis, KCL equations could also be written at nodes ② and ③, and these KCL equations plus (4.136) could be solved simultaneously. However, this procedure is complicated algebraically and leads to an equation that is difficult to interpret. To simplify the analysis, we will assume at first that $r_{\text{tail}} \to \infty$ and $r_{o(dp)} \to \infty$ since the transistors are primarily controlled by their base-emitter or gate-source voltages. Then from (4.136)

$$v_1 = \frac{v_{i1} + v_{i2}}{2} = v_{ic} \quad (4.137)$$

where $v_{ic}$ is the common-mode component of the input. Let $v_{id} = v_{i1} - v_{i2}$ represent the differential-mode component of the input. Then $v_{i1} = v_{ic} + v_{id}/2$ and $v_{i2} = v_{ic} - v_{id}/2$, and the small-signal collector or drain currents

$$i_1 = g_{m(dp)}(v_{i1} - v_1) = \frac{g_{m(dp)}v_{id}}{2} \quad (4.138)$$

and

$$i_2 = g_{m(dp)}(v_{i2} - v_1) = -\frac{g_{m(dp)}v_{id}}{2} \quad (4.139)$$

With a resistive load and a single-ended output, only $i_2$ flows in the output. Therefore, the transconductance for a differential-mode (dm) input with a passive load is

$$G_m[dm] = \left.\frac{i_{\text{out}}}{v_{id}}\right|_{v_{\text{out}}=0} = -\frac{i_2}{v_{id}} = \frac{g_{m(dp)}}{2} \quad (4.140)$$

On the other hand, with the active loads in Fig. 4.25, not only $i_2$ but also most of $i_3$ flows in the output because of the action of the current mirror, as shown by (4.135). Therefore, the output current in Fig. 4.26b is

$$i_{\text{out}} = -(1 - \epsilon_m)i_3 - i_2 \quad (4.141)$$

Assume at first that the current mirror is ideal so that $\epsilon_m = 0$. Then since $i_3 = -i_1$, substituting (4.138) and (4.139) in (4.141) gives

$$i_{\text{out}} = g_{m(dp)}v_{id} \quad (4.142)$$

Therefore, with an active load,

$$G_m[dm] = \left.\frac{i_{\text{out}}}{v_{id}}\right|_{v_{\text{out}}=0} = g_{m(dp)} \quad (4.143)$$

Equation 4.143 applies for both the bipolar and MOS amplifiers shown in Fig. 4.25. Comparing (4.140) and (4.143) shows that the current-mirror load doubles the differential transconductance compared to the passive-load case. This result stems from the fact that the current mirror creates a second signal path to the output. (The first path is through the differential pair.) Although frequency response is not analyzed in this chapter, note that the two signal paths usually have different frequency responses, which is often important in high-speed applications.

**Figure 4.27** Circuit for calculation of the output resistance of the differential pair with current-mirror load.

The key assumptions that led to (4.142) and (4.143) are that the current mirror is ideal so $\epsilon_m = 0$ and that $r_{\text{tail}} \to \infty$ and $r_{o(dp)} \to \infty$. Under these assumptions, the output current is independent of the common-mode input. In practice, none of these assumptions is exactly true, and the output current depends on the common-mode input. However, this dependence is small because the active load greatly enhances the common-mode rejection ratio of this stage, as shown in Section 4.3.5.3.

Another important parameter of the differential pair with active load is the output resistance. The output resistance is calculated using the circuit of Fig. 4.27, in which a test voltage source $v_t$ applied at the output while the inputs are connected to small-signal ground. The resulting current $i_t$ has four components. The current in $r_{o4}$ is

$$i_{t1} = \frac{v_t}{r_{o4}} \tag{4.144}$$

The resistance in the emitter or source lead of $T_2$ is $r_{\text{tail}}$ in parallel with the resistance seen looking into the emitter or source of $T_1$, which is approximately $1/g_{m1}$. Thus, using (3.99) for a transistor with degeneration, we find that the effective output resistance looking into the collector or drain of $T_2$ is

$$R_{o2} \simeq r_{o2}\left(1 + g_{m2}\frac{1}{g_{m1}}\right) = 2r_{o2} \tag{4.145}$$

Hence

$$i_{t2} + i_{t4} \simeq \frac{v_t}{2r_{o2}} \tag{4.146}$$

If $r_{\text{tail}} \gg 1/g_{m1}$, this current flows into the emitter or source of $T_1$, and is mirrored to the output with a gain of approximately unity to produce

$$i_{t3} \simeq i_{t2} + i_{t4} \simeq \frac{v_t}{2r_{o2}} \tag{4.147}$$

Thus

$$i_t = i_{t1} + i_{t2} + i_{t3} + i_{t4} \simeq v_t\left(\frac{1}{r_{o4}} + \frac{1}{r_{o2}}\right) \tag{4.148}$$

Since $r_{o2} = r_{o(dp)}$ and $r_{o4} = r_{o(mir)}$,

$$R_o = \left.\frac{v_t}{i_t}\right|_{\substack{v_{i1}=0 \\ v_{i2}=0}} \simeq \frac{1}{\dfrac{1}{r_{o(dp)}} + \dfrac{1}{r_{o(mir)}}} = r_{o(dp)} \| r_{o(mir)} \qquad (4.149)$$

The result in (4.149) applies for both the bipolar and MOS amplifiers shown in Fig. 4.25. In multistage bipolar amplifiers, the low-frequency gain of the loaded circuit is likely to be reduced by the input resistance of the next stage because the output resistance is high. In contrast, low-frequency loading is probably not an issue in multistage MOS amplifiers because the next stage has infinite input resistance if the input is the gate of an MOS transistor.

Finally, although the source-coupled pair has infinite input resistance, the emitter-coupled pair has finite input resistance because $\beta_0$ is finite. If the effects of the $r_o$ of $T_2$ and $T_4$ are neglected, the differential input resistance of the actively loaded emitter-coupled pair is simply $2r_{\pi(dp)}$ as in the resistively loaded case. In practice, however, the asymmetry of the circuit together with the high voltage gain cause feedback to occur through the output resistance of $T_2$ to node ①. This feedback causes the input resistance to differ slightly from $2r_{\pi(dp)}$.

In summary, the actively loaded differential pair is capable of providing differential-to-single-ended conversion, that is, the conversion from a differential voltage to a voltage referenced to the ground potential. The high output resistance of the circuit requires that the next stage must have high input resistance if the large gain is to be realized. A small-signal two-port equivalent circuit for the stage is shown in Fig. 4.28.

### 4.3.5.3 Common-Mode Rejection Ratio

In addition to providing high voltage gain, the circuits in Fig. 4.25 provide conversion from a differential input signal to an output signal that is referenced to ground. Such a conversion is required in all differential-input, single-ended output amplifiers.

The simplest differential-to-single-ended converter is a resistively loaded differential pair in which the output is taken from only one side, as shown in Fig. 4.29a. In this case, $A_{dm} > 0$, $A_{cm} < 0$, and the output is

$$v_o = -\frac{v_{od}}{2} + v_{oc} = -\frac{A_{dm}v_{id}}{2} + A_{cm}v_{ic} \qquad (4.150)$$

$$= -\frac{A_{dm}}{2}\left(v_{id} - \frac{2A_{cm}}{A_{dm}}v_{ic}\right) = -\frac{A_{dm}}{2}\left(v_{id} + 2\left|\frac{A_{cm}}{A_{dm}}\right|v_{ic}\right) \qquad (4.151)$$

$$= -\frac{A_{dm}}{2}\left(v_{id} + \frac{2v_{ic}}{\text{CMRR}}\right) \qquad (4.152)$$

$R_i = 2r_\pi$
$G_m[dm] = g_m$
$R_o = r_{o(dp)} \| r_{o(mir)}$

**Figure 4.28** Two-port representation of small-signal properties of differential pair with current-mirror load. The effects of asymmetrical input resistance have been neglected.

**Figure 4.29** Differential-to-single-ended conversion using (a) resistively loaded differential pairs and (b) actively loaded differential pairs.

Thus, common-mode signals at the input will cause changes in the output voltage. The common-mode rejection ratio (CMRR) is

$$\text{CMRR} = \left| \frac{A_{dm}}{A_{cm}} \right| = \left| \frac{G_m[dm]R_o}{G_m[cm]R_o} \right| = \left| \frac{G_m[dm]}{G_m[cm]} \right| \qquad (4.153)$$

where the common-mode (cm) transconductance is

$$G_m[cm] = \left. \frac{i_{\text{out}}}{v_{ic}} \right|_{v_{\text{out}}=0} \qquad (4.154)$$

Since the circuits in Fig. 4.29a are symmetrical, a common-mode half circuit can be used to find $G_m[cm]$. The common-mode half circuit is a common-emitter/source amplifier with degeneration. From (3.93) and (3.104),

$$G_m[cm] = -\frac{i_2}{v_{ic}} \simeq -\frac{g_{m(dp)}}{1 + g_{m(dp)}(2r_{tail})} \qquad (4.155)$$

where $g_{m(dp)} = g_{m1} = g_{m2}$ and $r_{tail}$ represents the output resistance of the tail current source $T_5$. The negative sign appears in (4.155) because the output current is defined as positive when it flows from the output terminal into the small-signal ground to be consistent with the differential case, as in Fig. 4.26b. Equation 4.155 applies for both the bipolar and MOS cases if the base current is ignored in the bipolar case, the body effect is ignored in the MOS case, and $r_{o1}$ and $r_{o2}$ are ignored in both cases. Substituting (4.140) and (4.155) into (4.153) gives

$$CMRR = \frac{1 + 2g_{m(dp)}r_{tail}}{2} \simeq g_{m(dp)}r_{tail} = g_{m1}r_{o5} \qquad (4.156)$$

Equation 4.156 shows that the common-mode rejection ratio here is about half that in (3.193) because the outputs in Fig. 4.29 are taken only from one side of each differential pair instead of from both sides, reducing the differential-mode gain by a factor of two. The result in (4.156) applies for both the bipolar and MOS amplifiers shown in Fig. 4.29a. Because $g_m r_o$ is much higher for bipolar transistors than MOS transistors, the CMRR of a bipolar differential pair with resistive load is much higher than that of its MOS counterpart.

On the other hand, the active-load stages shown in Fig 4.29b have common-mode rejection ratios much superior to those of the corresponding circuits in Fig. 4.29a. Assume that the outputs in Fig. 4.29b are connected to small-signal ground to allow calculation of the common-mode transconductance. The small-signal model is the same as shown in Fig. 4.26b with $v_{i1} = v_{i2} = v_{ic}$. For simplicity, let $\beta_0 \to \infty$ and $r_\pi \to \infty$ at first. As with a resistive load, changes in the common-mode input will cause changes in the tail bias current $i_{tail}$ because the output resistance of $T_5$ is finite. If we assume that the currents in the differential-pair transistors are controlled only by the base-emitter or gate-source voltages, the change in the current in $T_1$ and $T_2$ is

$$i_1 = i_2 = \frac{i_{tail}}{2} \qquad (4.157)$$

If $\epsilon_m = 0$, the gain of the current mirror is unity. Then substituting (4.157) into (4.141) with $i_3 = -i_1$ gives

$$i_{out} = -i_3 - i_2 = i_1 - i_2 = 0 \qquad (4.158)$$

As a result,

$$G_m[cm] = \frac{i_{out}}{v_{ic}}\Bigg|_{v_{out}=0} = 0 \qquad (4.159)$$

Therefore,

$$CMRR \to \infty \qquad (4.160)$$

The common-mode rejection ratio in (4.160) is infinite because the change in the current in $T_4$ cancels that in $T_2$ even when $r_{tail}$ is finite under these assumptions.

The key assumptions that led to (4.160) are that $r_{o(dp)} \to \infty$ so $i_1 = i_2$ and that the current mirror is ideal so $\epsilon_m = 0$. In practice, the currents in the differential-pair transistors are not only controlled by their base-emitter or gate-source voltages, but also to some extent by their collector-emitter or drain-source voltages. As a result, $i_1$ is not exactly equal to $i_2$ because of finite $r_{o(dp)}$ in $T_1$ and $T_2$. Furthermore, the gain of the current mirror is not exactly unity, which means that $\epsilon_m$ is not exactly zero in practice because of finite $r_{o(mir)}$ in $T_3$ and $T_4$. Finite $\beta_0$ also affects the systematic gain error of the current mirror when bipolar transistors are used. For these reasons, the common-mode rejection ratio is finite in practice. However, the use of the active load greatly improves the common-mode rejection ratio compared to the resistive load case, as we will show next.

Suppose that

$$i_1 = i_2(1 - \epsilon_d) \tag{4.161}$$

where $\epsilon_d$ can be thought of as the gain error in the differential pair. Substituting (4.161) into (4.141) with $i_3 = -i_1$ gives

$$i_{\text{out}} = i_1(1 - \epsilon_m) - i_2 = i_2\big((1 - \epsilon_d)(1 - \epsilon_m) - 1\big) \tag{4.162}$$

Rearranging (4.162) gives

$$i_{\text{out}} = -i_2(\epsilon_d + \epsilon_m - \epsilon_d\epsilon_m) \tag{4.163}$$

If $\epsilon_d \ll 1$ and $\epsilon_m \ll 1$, the product term $\epsilon_d\epsilon_m$ is a second-order error and can be neglected. Therefore,

$$i_{\text{out}} \simeq -i_2(\epsilon_d + \epsilon_m) \tag{4.164}$$

Substituting (4.164) into (4.154) gives

$$G_m[cm] \simeq -\left(\frac{i_2}{v_{ic}}\right)(\epsilon_d + \epsilon_m) \tag{4.165}$$

Equation 4.165 applies for the active-load circuits shown in Fig. 4.29b; however, the first term has approximately the same value as in the passive-load case. Therefore, we will substitute (4.155) into (4.165), which gives

$$G_m[cm] \simeq -\left(\frac{g_{m(dp)}}{1 + g_{m(dp)}(2r_{\text{tail}})}\right)(\epsilon_d + \epsilon_m) \tag{4.166}$$

Substituting (4.166) and (4.143) into (4.153) gives

$$\text{CMRR} = \left|\frac{G_m[dm]}{G_m[cm]}\right| \simeq \frac{1 + 2g_{m(dp)}r_{\text{tail}}}{(\epsilon_d + \epsilon_m)} \tag{4.167}$$

Comparing (4.167) and (4.156) shows that the active load improves the common-mode rejection ratio by a factor of $2/(\epsilon_d + \epsilon_m)$. The factor of 2 in the numerator of this expression stems from the increase in the differential transconductance, and the denominator stems from the decrease in the common-mode transconductance.

To find $\epsilon_d$, we will refer to Fig. 4.26b with $v_{i1} = v_{i2} = v_{ic}$. First, we write

$$i_1 = g_{m(dp)}(v_{ic} - v_1) + \frac{v_3 - v_1}{r_{o(dp)}} \tag{4.168}$$

and

$$i_2 = g_{m(dp)}(v_{ic} - v_1) - \frac{v_1}{r_{o(dp)}} \tag{4.169}$$

Substituting (4.134) and $i_3 = -i_1$ into (4.168) gives

$$i_1 \simeq g_{m(dp)}(v_{ic} - v_1) - \frac{v_1}{r_{o(dp)}} - \frac{i_1}{g_{m(mir)}r_{o(dp)}} \tag{4.170}$$

Equation 4.170 can be rearranged to give

$$\left(\frac{1 + g_{m(mir)}r_{o(dp)}}{g_{m(mir)}r_{o(dp)}}\right)i_1 \simeq g_{m(dp)}(v_{ic} - v_1) - \frac{v_1}{r_{o(dp)}} \tag{4.171}$$

Substituting (4.169) into (4.171) gives

$$i_1 \simeq \left(\frac{g_{m(mir)}r_{o(dp)}}{1 + g_{m(mir)}r_{o(dp)}}\right)i_2 \tag{4.172}$$

Substituting (4.161) into (4.172) gives

$$\epsilon_d \simeq \frac{1}{1 + g_{m(mir)}r_{o(dp)}} \tag{4.173}$$

To find $\epsilon_m$, we will again refer to Fig. 4.26b with $v_{i1} = v_{i2} = v_{ic}$. In writing (4.134), we assumed that $r_3 \simeq 1/g_{m3}$. We will now reconsider this assumption and write

$$r_3 = \frac{1}{g_{m3}}\|r_{\pi3}\|r_{\pi4}\|r_{o3} \tag{4.174}$$

We will still assume that the two transistors in the differential pair match perfectly and operate with equal dc currents, as do the two transistors in the active load. Then (4.174) can be rewritten as

$$r_3 = \frac{r_{\pi(mir)}r_{o(mir)}}{r_{\pi(mir)} + 2r_{o(mir)} + g_{m(mir)}r_{\pi(mir)}r_{o(mir)}} \tag{4.175}$$

Substituting (4.175) into (4.135) gives

$$g_{m4}v_3 = g_{m4}i_3r_3 = \frac{g_{m(mir)}r_{\pi(mir)}r_{o(mir)}i_3}{r_{\pi(mir)} + 2r_{o(mir)} + g_{m(mir)}r_{\pi(mir)}r_{o(mir)}} \tag{4.176}$$

Substituting (4.133) into (4.176) gives

$$\epsilon_m = \frac{r_{\pi(mir)} + 2r_{o(mir)}}{r_{\pi(mir)} + 2r_{o(mir)} + g_{m(mir)}r_{\pi(mir)}r_{o(mir)}} \tag{4.177}$$

For bipolar transistors, $r_\pi$ is usually much less than $r_o$; therefore,

$$\epsilon_m[bip] = \frac{2 + \frac{r_{\pi(mir)}}{r_{o(mir)}}}{2 + \frac{r_{\pi(mir)}}{r_{o(mir)}} + g_{m(mir)}r_{\pi(mir)}} \simeq \frac{1}{1 + \frac{g_{m(mir)}r_{\pi(mir)}}{2}} = \frac{1}{1 + \frac{\beta_0}{2}} \tag{4.178}$$

Since $r_\pi \rightarrow \infty$ for MOS transistors,

$$\epsilon_m[MOS] = \frac{1}{1 + g_{m(mir)}r_{o(mir)}} \tag{4.179}$$

For the bipolar circuit in Fig. 4.29b, substituting (4.173) and (4.178) into (4.167) gives

$$CMRR \simeq \frac{1 + 2g_{m(dp)}r_{tail}}{\left(\dfrac{1}{1 + g_{m(mir)}r_{o(dp)}} + \dfrac{1}{1 + \dfrac{g_{m(mir)}r_{\pi(mir)}}{2}}\right)} \tag{4.180}$$

If $(g_{m(mir)}r_{o(dp)}) \gg 1$ and $(g_{m(mir)}r_{\pi(mir)}/2) \gg 1$, (4.180) can be simplified to give

$$\text{CMRR} \simeq (1 + 2g_{m(dp)}r_{\text{tail}})g_{m(mir)}\left(r_{o(dp)}\|\frac{r_{\pi(mir)}}{2}\right)$$

$$\simeq (2g_{m(dp)}r_{\text{tail}})g_{m(mir)}\left(r_{o(dp)}\|\frac{r_{\pi(mir)}}{2}\right) \tag{4.181}$$

Comparing (4.181) and (4.156) shows that the active load increases the common-mode rejection ratio by a factor of about $2g_{m(mir)}\left(r_{o(dp)}\|(r_{\pi(mir)}/2)\right)$ for the bipolar circuit in Fig. 4.29b compared to its passive-load counterpart in Fig. 4.29a.

On the other hand, for the MOS circuit in Fig. 4.29b, substituting (4.173) and (4.179) into (4.167) gives

$$\text{CMRR} \simeq \frac{1 + 2g_{m(dp)}r_{\text{tail}}}{\left(\dfrac{1}{1 + g_{m(mir)}r_{o(dp)}} + \dfrac{1}{1 + g_{m(mir)}r_{o(mir)}}\right)} \tag{4.182}$$

If $(g_{m(mir)}r_{o(dp)}) \gg 1$ and $(g_{m(mir)}r_{o(mir)}) \gg 1$, (4.182) can be simplified to give

$$\text{CMRR} \simeq (1 + 2g_{m(dp)}r_{\text{tail}})g_{m(mir)}(r_{o(dp)}\|r_{o(mir)})$$

$$\simeq (2g_{m(dp)}r_{\text{tail}})g_{m(mir)}(r_{o(dp)}\|r_{o(mir)}) \tag{4.183}$$

Comparing (4.183) and (4.156) shows that the active load increases the common-mode rejection ratio by a factor of about $2g_{m(mir)}(r_{o(dp)}\|r_{o(mir)})$ for the MOS circuit in Fig. 4.29b compared to its passive-load counterpart in Fig. 4.29a.

For these calculations, perfect matching was assumed so that $g_{m1} = g_{m2}, g_{m3} = g_{m4}$, $r_{o1} = r_{o2}$, and $r_{o3} = r_{o4}$. In practice, however, nonzero mismatch occurs. With mismatch in a MOS differential pair using a current-mirror load, the differential-mode transconductance is

$$G_m[dm] \simeq g_{m1-2}\left[\frac{1 - \left(\dfrac{\Delta g_{m1-2}}{2g_{m1-2}}\right)^2}{1 + \left(\dfrac{\Delta g_{m3-4}}{2g_{m3-4}}\right)}\right] \tag{4.184}$$

where $\Delta g_{m1-2} = g_{m1} - g_{m2}$, $g_{m1-2} = (g_{m1} + g_{m2})/2$, $\Delta g_{m3-4} = g_{m3} - g_{m4}$, and $g_{m3-4} = (g_{m3} + g_{m4})/2$. See Problem 4.18. The approximation in (4.184) is valid to the extent that $g_m r_o \gg 1$ for each transistor and $(g_{m1} + g_{m2})r_{\text{tail}} \gg 1$ for the tail current source. Equation 4.184 shows that the mismatch between $g_{m1}$ and $g_{m2}$ has only a minor effect on $G_m[dm]$. This result stems from the fact that the small-signal voltage across the tail current source, $v_{\text{tail}}$, is zero with a purely differential input only when $g_{m1} = g_{m2}$, assuming $r_{o1} \to \infty$ and $r_{o2} \to \infty$. For example, increasing $g_{m1}$ compared to $g_{m2}$ tends to increase the small-signal drain current $i_1$ if $v_{gs1}$ is constant. However, this change also increases $v_{\text{tail}}$, which reduces $v_{gs1}$ for a fixed $v_{id}$. The combination of these two effects causes $i_1$ to be insensitive to $g_{m1} - g_{m2}$. On the other hand, mismatch between $g_{m3}$ and $g_{m4}$ directly modifies the contribution of $i_1$ through the current mirror to the output current. Therefore, (4.184) shows that $G_m[dm]$ is most sensitive to the mismatch between $g_{m3}$ and $g_{m4}$.

With mismatch in a MOS differential pair using a current-mirror load, the common-mode transconductance is

$$G_m[cm] \simeq -\frac{1}{2r_{\text{tail}}}(\epsilon_d + \epsilon_m) \tag{4.185}$$

where $\epsilon_d$ is the gain error in the source-coupled pair with a pure common-mode input defined in (4.161) and $\epsilon_m$ is the gain error in the current mirror defined in (4.133). From Problem 4.19,

$$\epsilon_d \approx \frac{1}{g_{m3}r_{o(dp)}} - \frac{\Delta g_{m1-2}}{g_{m1-2}}\left(1 + \frac{2r_{tail}}{r_{o(dp)}}\right) - \frac{2r_{tail}}{r_{o(dp)}}\frac{\Delta r_{o(dp)}}{r_{o(dp)}} \quad (4.186)$$

Each term in (4.186) corresponds to one source of gain error by itself, and interactions between terms are ignored. The first term in (4.186) is consistent with (4.173) when $g_{m3}r_{o(dp)} \gg 1$ and stems from the observation that the drain of $T_1$ is not connected to a small-signal ground during the calculation of $G_m[dm]$, unlike the drain of $T_2$. The second term in (4.186) stems from mismatch between $g_{m1}$ and $g_{m2}$ alone. The third term in (4.186) stems from the mismatch between $r_{o1}$ and $r_{o2}$ alone. The contribution of this mismatch to $G_m[cm]$ is significant because the action of the current mirror nearly cancels the contributions of the input $g_m$ generators to $G_m[cm]$ under ideal conditions, causing $G_m[cm] \approx 0$ in (4.166). In contrast, $G_m[dm]$ is insensitive to the mismatch between $r_{o1}$ and $r_{o2}$ because the dominant contributions to $G_m[dm]$ arising from the input $g_m$ generators do not cancel at the output. From Problem 4.19,

$$\epsilon_m = \frac{1}{1 + g_{m3}r_{o3}} + \frac{(g_{m3} - g_{m4})r_{o3}}{1 + g_{m3}r_{o3}} \approx \frac{1}{g_{m3}r_{o3}} + \frac{\Delta g_{m3-4}}{g_{m3-4}} \quad (4.187)$$

Each term in (4.187) corresponds to one source of gain error by itself, and interactions between terms are ignored. The first term in (4.187), which is consistent with (4.179) when $g_{m3}r_{o3} \gg 1$, stems from the observation that the small-signal input resistance of the current mirror is not exactly $1/g_{m3}$ but $(1/g_{m3})\|r_{o3}$. The second term in (4.187) stems from mismatch between $g_{m3}$ and $g_{m4}$ alone. The CMRR with mismatch is the ratio of $G_m[dm]$ in (4.184) to $G_m[cm]$ in (4.185), using (4.186) and (4.187) for $\epsilon_d$ and $\epsilon_m$, respectively. Since the common-mode transconductance is very small without mismatch (as a result of the behavior of the current-mirror load), mismatch usually reduces the CMRR by increasing $|G_m[cm]|$.

## 4.4 Voltage and Current References

### 4.4.1 Low-Current Biasing

#### 4.4.1.1 Bipolar Widlar Current Source

In ideal operational amplifiers, the current is zero in each of the two input leads. However, the input current is not zero in real op amps with bipolar input transistors because $\beta_F$ is finite. Since the op-amp inputs are usually connected to a differential pair, the tail current must usually be very small in such op amps to keep the input current small. Typically, the tail current is on the order of 5 $\mu$A. Bias currents of this magnitude are also required in a variety of other applications, especially where minimizing power dissipation is important. The simple current mirrors shown in Fig. 4.30 are usually not optimum for such small currents. For example, using a simple bipolar current mirror as in Fig. 4.30$a$ and assuming a maximum practical emitter area ratio between transistors of ten to one, the mirror would need an input current of 50 $\mu$A for an output current of 5 $\mu$A. If the power-supply voltage in Fig. 4.30$a$ is 5 V, and if $V_{BE(on)} = 0.7$ V, $R = 86$ k$\Omega$ would be required. Resistors of this magnitude are costly in terms of die area. Currents of such low magnitude can be obtained

**Figure 4.30** Simple two-transistor current mirrors where the input current is set by the supply voltage and a resistor using (*a*) bipolar and (*b*) MOS transistors.

with moderate values of resistance, however, by modifying the simple current mirror so that the transistors operate with unequal base-emitter voltages. In the Widlar current source of Fig. 4.31*a*, resistor $R_2$ is inserted in series with the emitter of $Q_2$, and transistors $Q_1$ and $Q_2$ operate with unequal base emitter voltages if $R_2 \neq 0$.[10,11] This circuit is referred to as a current source rather than a current mirror because the output current in Fig. 4.31*a* is much less dependent on the input current and the power-supply voltage than in the simple current mirror of Fig. 4.30*a*, as shown in Section 4.4.2. We will now calculate the output current of the Widlar current source.

If $I_{IN} > 0$, $Q_1$ operates in the forward-active region because it is diode connected. Assume that $Q_2$ also operates in the forward active region. KVL around the base-emitter loop gives

$$V_{BE1} - V_{BE2} - \frac{\beta_F + 1}{\beta_F} I_{OUT} R_2 = 0 \qquad (4.188)$$

**Figure 4.31** Widlar current sources: (*a*) bipolar and (*b*) MOS.

If we assume that $V_{BE1} \doteq V_{BE2} = V_{BE(on)} = 0.7$ V in (4.188), we would predict that $I_{OUT} = 0$. Although $I_{OUT}$ is small in practice, it is greater than zero under the usual bias conditions, which means that the standard assumption about $V_{BE(on)}$ is invalid here. In contrast, the standard assumption is usually valid in calculating $I_{IN}$ because small variations in $V_{BE1}$ have little effect on $I_{IN}$ if $V_{CC} \gg V_{BE1}$. When one base-emitter voltage is subtracted from another, however, small differences between them are important. If $V_A \rightarrow \infty$, (4.188) can be rewritten using (1.35) as

$$V_T \ln \frac{I_{C1}}{I_{S1}} - V_T \ln \frac{I_{OUT}}{I_{S2}} - \frac{\beta_F + 1}{\beta_F} I_{OUT} R_2 = 0 \tag{4.189}$$

If $\beta_F \rightarrow \infty$, (4.189) simplifies to

$$V_T \ln \frac{I_{IN}}{I_{S1}} - V_T \ln \frac{I_{OUT}}{I_{S2}} - I_{OUT} R_2 = 0 \tag{4.190}$$

For identical transistors, $I_{S1}$ and $I_{S2}$ are equal, and (4.190) becomes

$$V_T \ln \frac{I_{IN}}{I_{OUT}} = I_{OUT} R_2 \tag{4.191}$$

This transcendental equation can be solved by trial and error to find $I_{OUT}$ if $R_2$ and $I_{IN}$ are known, as in typical analysis problems. Because the logarithm function compresses changes in its argument, attention can be focused on the linear term in (4.191), simplifying convergence of the trial-and-error process. In design problems, however, the desired $I_{IN}$ and $I_{OUT}$ are usually known, and (4.191) provides the required value of $R_2$.

■ **EXAMPLE**

In the circuit of Fig. 4.31a, determine the proper value of $R_2$ to give $I_{OUT} = 5\,\mu A$. Assume that $V_{CC} = 5$ V, $R_1 = 4.3$ kΩ, $V_{BE(on)} = 0.7$ V, and $\beta_F \rightarrow \infty$.

$$I_{IN} = \frac{5\text{ V} - 0.7\text{ V}}{4.3\text{ k}\Omega} = 1\text{ mA}$$

$$V_T \ln \frac{I_{IN}}{I_{OUT}} = 26\text{ mV} \ln \left( \frac{1\text{ mA}}{5\,\mu A} \right) = 137\text{ mV}$$

Thus from (4.191)

$$I_{OUT} R_2 = 137\text{ mV}$$

and

$$R_2 = \frac{137\text{ mV}}{5\,\mu A} = 27.4\text{ k}\Omega$$

■ The total resistance in the circuit is 31.7 kΩ.

■ **EXAMPLE**

In the circuit of Fig. 4.31a, assume that $I_{IN} = 1$ mA, $R_2 = 5$ kΩ, and $\beta_F \rightarrow \infty$. Find $I_{OUT}$. From (4.191),

$$V_T \ln \frac{1\text{ mA}}{I_{OUT}} - 5\text{ k}\Omega(I_{OUT}) = 0$$

Try

$$I_{OUT} = 15\ \mu A$$

$$108\ mV - 75\ mV \neq 0$$

The linear term $I_{OUT}R_2$ is too small; therefore, $I_{OUT} > 15\ \mu A$ should be tried. Try

$$I_{OUT} = 20\ \mu A$$

$$101.7\ mV - 100\ mV \simeq 0$$

Therefore, the output current is close to $20\ \mu A$. Notice that while the linear term increased by 25 mV from the first to the second trial, the logarithm term decreased by only about 6 mV because the logarithm function compresses changes in its argument.

### 4.4.1.2 MOS Widlar Current Source

The Widlar configuration can also be used in MOS technology, as shown in Fig. 4.31b.

If $I_{IN} > 0$, $M_1$ operates in the active region because it is diode connected. Assume that $M_2$ also operates in the forward active region. KVL around the gate-source loop gives

$$V_{GS1} - V_{GS2} - I_{OUT}R_2 = 0 \tag{4.192}$$

If we ignore the body effect, the threshold components of the gate-source voltages cancel and (4.192) simplifies to

$$I_{OUT}R_2 + V_{ov2} - V_{ov1} = 0 \tag{4.193}$$

If the transistors operate in strong inversion and $V_A \rightarrow \infty$,

$$I_{OUT}R_2 + \sqrt{\frac{2I_{OUT}}{k'(W/L)_2}} - V_{ov1} = 0 \tag{4.194}$$

This quadratic equation can be solved for $\sqrt{I_{OUT}}$.

$$\sqrt{I_{OUT}} = \frac{-\sqrt{\dfrac{2}{k'(W/L)_2}} \pm \sqrt{\dfrac{2}{k'(W/L)_2} + 4R_2V_{ov1}}}{2R_2} \tag{4.195}$$

where $V_{ov1} = \sqrt{2I_{IN}/[k'(W/L)_1]}$. From (1.157),

$$\sqrt{I_{OUT}} = \sqrt{\frac{k'(W/L)_2}{2}}\ (V_{GS2} - V_t) \tag{4.196}$$

Equation 4.196 applies only when $M_2$ operates in the active region, which means that $V_{GS2} > V_t$. As a result, $\sqrt{I_{OUT}} > 0$ and the potential solution where the second term in the numerator of (4.195) is subtracted from the first, cannot occur in practice. Therefore,

$$\sqrt{I_{OUT}} = \frac{-\sqrt{\dfrac{2}{k'(W/L)_2}} + \sqrt{\dfrac{2}{k'(W/L)_2} + 4R_2V_{ov1}}}{2R_2} \tag{4.197}$$

Equation 4.197 shows that a closed-form solution for the output current can be written for a Widlar current source that uses MOS transistors operating in strong inversion, unlike the bipolar case where trial and error is required to find $I_{OUT}$.

■ **EXAMPLE**

In Fig. 4.31$b$, find $I_{OUT}$ if $I_{IN} = 100\ \mu\text{A}$, $R_2 = 4\ \text{k}\Omega$, $k' = 200\ \mu\text{A}/V^2$, and $(W/L)_1 = (W/L)_2 = 25$. Assume the temperature is 27°C and that $n = 1.5$ in (1.247). Then $R_2 = 0.004\ \text{M}\Omega$, $V_{ov1} = \sqrt{200/(200 \times 25)}\ \text{V} = 0.2\ \text{V}$,

$$\sqrt{I_{OUT}} = \frac{-\sqrt{\dfrac{2}{200(25)}} + \sqrt{\dfrac{2}{200(25)} + 4(0.004)(0.2)}}{2(0.004)}\ \sqrt{\mu\text{A}} = 5\ \sqrt{\mu\text{A}}$$

and $I_{OUT} = 25\ \mu\text{A}$. Also,

$$V_{ov2} = V_{ov1} - I_{OUT}R_2 = 0.2 - 25 \times 0.004 = 0.1\ \text{V} > 2nV_T \simeq 78\ \text{mV}$$

■ Therefore, both transistors operate in strong inversion, as assumed.

### 4.4.1.3 Bipolar Peaking Current Source

The Widlar source described in Section 4.4.1.1 allows currents in the microamp range to be realized with moderate values of resistance. Biasing integrated-circuit stages with currents on the order of nanoamps is often desirable. To reach such low currents with moderate values of resistance, the circuit shown in Fig. 4.32 can be used.[12,13,14] Neglecting base currents, we have

$$V_{BE1} - I_{IN}R = V_{BE2} \tag{4.198}$$

If $V_A \to \infty$, (4.198) can be rewritten using (1.35) as

$$V_T \ln \frac{I_{IN}}{I_{S1}} - V_T \ln \frac{I_{OUT}}{I_{S2}} = I_{IN}R \tag{4.199}$$

If $Q_1$ and $Q_2$ are identical, (4.199) can be rewritten as

$$I_{OUT} = I_{IN} \exp\left(-\frac{I_{IN}R}{V_T}\right) \tag{4.200}$$

Equation 4.200 is useful for analysis of a given circuit. For design with identical $Q_1$ and $Q_2$, (4.199) can be rewritten as

$$R = \frac{V_T}{I_{IN}} \ln \frac{I_{IN}}{I_{OUT}} \tag{4.201}$$

**Figure 4.32** Bipolar peaking current source.

**Figure 4.33** Transfer characteristics of the bipolar peaking current source with $T = 27°C$.

For example, for $I_{IN} = 10$ μA and $I_{OUT} = 100$ nA, (4.201) can be used to show that $R \simeq 12$ kΩ.

A plot of $I_{OUT}$ versus $I_{IN}$ from (4.200) is shown in Fig. 4.33. When the input current is small, the voltage drop on the resistor is small, and $V_{BE2} \simeq V_{BE1}$ so $I_{OUT} \simeq I_{IN}$. As the input current increases, $V_{BE1}$ increases in proportion to the logarithm of the input current while the drop on the resistor increases linearly with the input current. As a result, increases in the input current eventually cause the base-emitter voltage of $Q_2$ to decrease. The output current reaches a maximum when $V_{BE2}$ is maximum. The name *peaking current source* stems from this behavior, and the location and magnitude of the peak both depend on $R$.

### 4.4.1.4 MOS Peaking Current Source

The peaking-current configuration can also be used in MOS technology, as shown in Fig. 4.34. If $I_{IN}$ is small and positive, the voltage drop on $R$ is small and $M_1$ operates in the active region. Assume that $M_2$ also operates in the active region. KVL around the gate-source loop gives

$$V_{GS1} - I_{IN}R - V_{GS2} = 0 \tag{4.202}$$

Since the sources of $M_1$ and $M_2$ are connected together, the thresholds cancel and (4.202) simplifies to

$$V_{ov2} = V_{ov1} - I_{IN}R \tag{4.203}$$

**Figure 4.34** MOS peaking current source.

From (1.157),

$$I_{OUT} = \frac{k'(W/L)_2}{2}(V_{ov2})^2 = \frac{k'(W/L)_2}{2}(V_{ov1} - I_{IN}R)^2 \tag{4.204}$$

where $V_{ov1} = \sqrt{2I_{IN}/[k'(W/L)_1]}$. Equation 4.204 assumes that the transistors operate in strong inversion. In practice, the input current is usually small enough that the overdrive of $M_1$ is less than $2nV_T$, where $n$ is defined in (1.247) and $V_T$ is a thermal voltage. Equation 4.203 shows that the overdrive of $M_2$ is even smaller than that of $M_1$. Therefore, both transistors usually operate in weak inversion, where the drain current is an exponential function of the gate-source voltage as shown in (1.252). If $V_{DS1} > 3V_T$, applying (1.252) to $M_1$ and substituting into (4.202) gives

$$V_{GS2} - V_t \simeq nV_T \ln\left(\frac{I_{IN}}{(W/L)_1 I_t}\right) - I_{IN}R \tag{4.205}$$

Then if the transistors are identical and $V_{DS2} > 3V_T$, substituting (4.205) into (1.252) gives

$$I_{OUT} \simeq \frac{W}{L}I_t \exp\left(\frac{V_{GS2} - V_t}{nV_T}\right) \simeq I_{IN} \exp\left(-\frac{I_{IN}R}{nV_T}\right) \tag{4.206}$$

where $I_t$ is given by (1.251) and represents the drain current of $M_2$ with $V_{GS2} = V_t$, $W/L = 1$, and $V_{DS} \gg V_T$. Comparing (4.206) with (4.200) shows that the output current in an MOS peaking current source where both transistors operate in weak inversion is the same as in the bipolar case except that $1.3 \leq n \leq 1.5$ in the MOS case and $n = 1$ in the bipolar case.

Plots of (4.206) and (4.204) are shown in Fig. 4.35 for $n = 1.5$, $T = 27°C$, $R = 10 \text{ k}\Omega$, $k' = 200 \text{ }\mu A/V^2$, and $(W/L)_2 = (W/L)_1 = 25$. In both cases, when the input current is small, the voltage drop on the resistor is small, and $I_{OUT} \simeq I_{IN}$. As the input current increases, $V_{GS1}$ increases more slowly than the drop on the resistor. As a result, increases in the input current eventually cause the gate-source voltage of $M_2$ to decrease. The output current reaches a maximum when $V_{GS2}$ is maximum. As in the bipolar case, the name *peaking current source* stems from this behavior, and the location and magnitude of the peak both depend on $R$. Because the overdrives on both transistors are usually very small, the strong-inversion equation (4.204) usually underestimates the output current.

Figure 4.35 Transfer characteristics of the MOS peaking current source assuming both transistors operate in weak inversion or in strong inversion.

### 4.4.2 Supply-Insensitive Biasing

Consider the simple current mirror of Fig. 4.30a, where the input current source has been replaced by a resistor. Ignoring the effects of finite $\beta_F$ and $V_A$, (4.5) shows that the output current is

$$I_{OUT} \simeq I_{IN} = \frac{V_{CC} - V_{BE(on)}}{R} \tag{4.207}$$

If $V_{CC} \gg V_{BE(on)}$, this circuit has the drawback that the output current is proportional to the power-supply voltage. For example, if $V_{BE(on)} = 0.7$ V, and if this current mirror is used in an operational amplifier that has to function with power-supply voltages ranging from 3 V to 10 V, the bias current would vary over a four-to-one range, and the power dissipation would vary over a thirteen-to-one range.

One measure of this aspect of bias-circuit performance is the fractional change in the bias current that results from a given fractional change in supply voltage. The most useful parameter for describing the variation of the output current with the power-supply voltage is the sensitivity $S$. The sensitivity of any circuit variable $y$ to a parameter $x$ is defined as follows:

$$S_x^y = \lim_{\Delta x \to 0} \frac{\Delta y/y}{\Delta x/x} = \frac{x}{y} \frac{\partial y}{\partial x} \tag{4.208}$$

Applying (4.208) to find the sensitivity of the output current to small variations in the power-supply voltage gives

$$S_{V_{SUP}}^{I_{OUT}} = \frac{V_{SUP}}{I_{OUT}} \frac{\partial I_{OUT}}{\partial V_{SUP}} \tag{4.209}$$

The supply voltage $V_{SUP}$ is usually called $V_{CC}$ in bipolar circuits and $V_{DD}$ in MOS circuits. If $V_{CC} \gg V_{BE(on)}$ in Fig. 4.30a, and if $V_{DD} \gg V_{GS1}$ in Fig. 4.30b,

$$S_{V_{SUP}}^{I_{OUT}} \simeq 1 \tag{4.210}$$

Equation 4.210 shows that the output currents in the simple current mirrors in Fig. 4.30 depend strongly on the power-supply voltages. Therefore, this configuration should not be used when supply insensitivity is important.

#### 4.4.2.1 Widlar Current Sources

For the case of the bipolar Widlar source in Fig. 4.31a, the output current is given implicitly by (4.191). To determine the sensitivity of $I_{OUT}$ to the power-supply voltage, this equation is differentiated with respect to $V_{CC}$:

$$V_T \frac{\partial}{\partial V_{CC}} \ln \frac{I_{IN}}{I_{OUT}} = R_2 \frac{\partial I_{OUT}}{\partial V_{CC}} \tag{4.211}$$

Differentiating yields

$$V_T \left( \frac{I_{OUT}}{I_{IN}} \right) \left( \frac{1}{I_{OUT}} \frac{\partial I_{IN}}{\partial V_{CC}} - \frac{I_{IN}}{I_{OUT}^2} \frac{\partial I_{OUT}}{\partial V_{CC}} \right) = R_2 \frac{\partial I_{OUT}}{\partial V_{CC}} \tag{4.212}$$

Solving this equation for $\partial I_{OUT}/\partial V_{CC}$, we obtain

$$\frac{\partial I_{OUT}}{\partial V_{CC}} = \left( \frac{1}{1 + \dfrac{I_{OUT} R_2}{V_T}} \right) \frac{I_{OUT}}{I_{IN}} \frac{\partial I_{IN}}{\partial V_{CC}} \tag{4.213}$$

Substituting (4.213) into (4.209) gives

$$S_{V_{CC}}^{I_{OUT}} = \left( \frac{1}{1 + \dfrac{I_{OUT}R_2}{V_T}} \right) \frac{V_{CC}}{I_{IN}} \frac{\partial I_{IN}}{\partial V_{CC}} = \left( \frac{1}{1 + \dfrac{I_{OUT}R_2}{V_T}} \right) S_{V_{CC}}^{I_{IN}} \qquad (4.214)$$

If $V_{CC} \gg V_{BE(on)}$, $I_{IN} \simeq V_{CC}/R_1$ and the sensitivity of $I_{IN}$ to $V_{CC}$ is approximately unity, as in the simple current mirror of Fig. 4.30$a$. For the example in Section 4.4.1.1 where $I_{IN} = 1$ mA, $I_{OUT} = 5$ $\mu$A, and $R_2 = 27.4$ k$\Omega$, (4.214) gives

$$S_{V_{CC}}^{I_{OUT}} = \frac{V_{CC}}{I_{OUT}} \frac{\partial I_{OUT}}{\partial V_{CC}} \simeq \frac{1}{1 + \dfrac{137 \text{ mV}}{26 \text{ mV}}} \simeq 0.16 \qquad (4.215)$$

Thus for this case, a 10 percent power-supply voltage change results in only 1.6 percent change in $I_{OUT}$.

For the case of the MOS Widlar source in Fig. 4.31$b$, the output current is given by (4.197). Differentiating with respect to $V_{DD}$ gives

$$\frac{1}{2\sqrt{I_{OUT}}} \frac{\partial I_{OUT}}{\partial V_{DD}} = \frac{1}{4R_2} \frac{1}{\sqrt{\dfrac{2}{k'(W/L)_2} + 4R_2 V_{ov1}}} 4R_2 \frac{\partial V_{ov1}}{\partial V_{DD}} \qquad (4.216)$$

where

$$\frac{\partial V_{ov1}}{\partial V_{DD}} = \sqrt{\frac{2}{k'(W/L)_1}} \frac{1}{2\sqrt{I_{IN}}} \frac{\partial I_{IN}}{\partial V_{DD}} = \frac{V_{ov1}}{2I_{IN}} \frac{\partial I_{IN}}{\partial V_{DD}} \qquad (4.217)$$

Substituting (4.216) and (4.217) into (4.209) gives

$$S_{V_{DD}}^{I_{OUT}} = \frac{V_{ov1}}{\sqrt{V_{ov2}^2 + 4I_{OUT}R_2 V_{ov1}}} S_{V_{DD}}^{I_{IN}} \qquad (4.218)$$

Since $I_{OUT}$ is usually much less than $I_{IN}$, $V_{ov2}$ is usually small and $I_{OUT}R_2 \simeq V_{ov1}$ and (4.218) simplifies to

$$S_{V_{DD}}^{I_{OUT}} \simeq \frac{V_{ov1}}{\sqrt{4V_{ov1}^2}} S_{V_{DD}}^{I_{IN}} = 0.5 S_{V_{DD}}^{I_{IN}} \qquad (4.219)$$

If $V_{DD} \gg V_{GS1}$, $I_{IN} \simeq V_{DD}/R_1$ and the sensitivity of $I_{IN}$ to $V_{DD}$ is approximately unity, as in the simple current mirror of Fig. 4.30$b$. Thus for this case, a 10 percent power-supply voltage change results in a 5 percent change in $I_{OUT}$.

### 4.4.2.2 Current Sources Using Other Voltage Standards

The level of power-supply independence provided by the bipolar and MOS Widlar current sources is not adequate for many types of analog circuits. Much lower sensitivity can be obtained by causing bias currents in the circuit to depend on a voltage standard other than the supply voltage. Bias reference circuits can be classified according to the voltage standard by which the bias currents are established. The most convenient standards are the base-emitter or threshold voltage of a transistor, the thermal voltage, or the breakdown voltage of a reverse-biased $pn$ junction (a Zener diode). Each of these standards can be used to reduce supply sensitivity, but the drawback of the first three standards is that the

**Figure 4.36** (a) Base-emitter referenced current source. (b) Threshold referenced current source.

reference voltage is quite temperature dependent. Both the base-emitter and threshold voltages have negative temperature coefficients of magnitude 1 to 2 mV/°C, and the thermal voltage has a positive temperature coefficient of $k/q \simeq 86\ \mu$V/°C. The Zener diode has the disadvantage that at least 7 to 10 V of supply voltage are required because standard integrated-circuit processes produce a minimum breakdown voltage of about 6 V across the most highly doped junctions (usually $npn$ transistor emitter-base junctions). Furthermore, $pn$ junctions produce large amounts of voltage noise under the reverse-breakdown conditions encountered in a bias reference circuit. Noise in avalanche breakdown is considered further in Chapter 11.

We now consider bias reference circuits based on the base-emitter or gate-source voltage. The circuit in simplest form in bipolar technology is shown in Fig. 4.36a. This circuit is similar to a Wilson current mirror where the diode-connected transistor is replaced by a resistor. For the input current to flow in $T_1$, transistor $T_2$ must supply enough current into $R_2$ so that the base-emitter voltage of $T_1$ is

$$V_{BE1} = V_T\ \ln \frac{I_{IN}}{I_{S1}} \tag{4.220}$$

If we neglect base currents, $I_{OUT}$ is equal to the current flowing through $R_2$. Since the voltage drop on $R_2$ is $V_{BE1}$, the output current is proportional to this base-emitter voltage. Thus, neglecting base currents, we have

$$I_{OUT} = \frac{V_{BE1}}{R_2} = \frac{V_T}{R_2}\ \ln \frac{I_{IN}}{I_{S1}} \tag{4.221}$$

Differentiating (4.221) and substituting into (4.209) gives

$$S_{V_{CC}}^{I_{OUT}} = \frac{V_T}{I_{OUT}R_2} S_{V_{CC}}^{I_{IN}} = \frac{V_T}{V_{BE(on)}} S_{V_{CC}}^{I_{IN}} \tag{4.222}$$

If $V_{CC} \gg 2V_{BE(on)}$, $I_{IN} \simeq V_{CC}/R_1$ and the sensitivity of $I_{IN}$ to $V_{CC}$ is approximately unity. With $V_{BE(on)} = 0.7$ V,

$$S_{V_{CC}}^{I_{OUT}} = \frac{0.026\ \text{V}}{0.7\ \text{V}} \simeq 0.037 \tag{4.223}$$

Thus for this case, a 10 percent power-supply voltage change results in a 0.37 percent change in $I_{OUT}$. The result is significantly better than for a bipolar Widlar current source. The MOS counterpart of the base-emitter reference is shown in Fig. 4.36$b$. Here

$$I_{OUT} = \frac{V_{GS1}}{R_2} = \frac{V_t + V_{ov1}}{R_2} \doteq \frac{V_t + \sqrt{\dfrac{2I_{IN}}{k'(W/L)_1}}}{R_2} \qquad (4.224)$$

The case of primary interest is when the overdrive of $T_1$ is small compared to the threshold voltage. This case can be achieved in practice by choosing sufficiently low input current and large $(W/L)_1$. In this case, the output current is determined mainly by the threshold voltage and $R_2$. Therefore, this circuit is known as a *threshold-referenced* bias circuit. Differentiating (4.224) with respect to $V_{DD}$ and substituting into (4.209) gives

$$S^{I_{OUT}}_{V_{DD}} = \frac{V_{ov1}}{2I_{OUT}R_2}S^{I_{IN}}_{V_{DD}} = \frac{V_{ov1}}{2V_{GS1}}\cdot S^{I_{IN}}_{V_{DD}} \qquad (4.225)$$

For example, if $V_t = 1$ V, $V_{ov1} = 0.1$ V, and $S^{I_{IN}}_{V_{DD}} \simeq 1$

$$S^{I_{OUT}}_{V_{DD}} \simeq \frac{0.1}{2(1.1)} \approx 0.045 \qquad (4.226)$$

These circuits are not fully supply independent because the base-emitter or gate-source voltages of $T_1$ change slightly with power-supply voltage. This change occurs because the collector or drain current of $T_1$ is approximately proportional to the supply voltage. The resulting supply sensitivity is often a problem in bias circuits whose input current is derived from a resistor connected to the supply terminal, since this configuration causes the currents in some portion of the circuit to change with the supply voltage.

#### 4.4.2.3 Self Biasing
Power-supply sensitivity can be greatly reduced by the use of the so-called *bootstrap* bias technique, also referred to as *self biasing*. Instead of developing the input current by connecting a resistor to the supply, the input current is made to depend directly on the output current of the current source itself. The concept is illustrated in block-diagram form in Fig. 4.37$a$. Assuming that the feedback loop formed by this connection has a stable operating point, the currents flowing in the circuit are much less sensitive to power-supply voltage than in the resistively biased case. The two key variables here are the input current, $I_{IN}$,

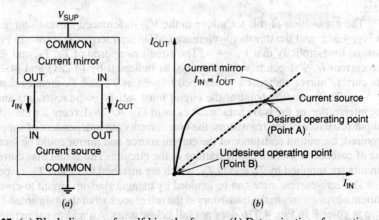

**Figure 4.37** ($a$) Block diagram of a self-biased reference. ($b$) Determination of operating point.

and the output current, $I_{OUT}$. The relationship between these variables is governed by both the current source and the current mirror. From the standpoint of the current source, the output current is almost independent of the input current for a wide range of input currents as shown in Fig. 4.37$b$. From the standpoint of the current mirror, $I_{IN}$ is set equal to $I_{OUT}$, assuming that the gain of the current mirror is unity. The operating point of the circuit must satisfy both constraints and hence is at the intersection of the two characteristics. In the plot of Fig. 4.37$b$, two intersections or potential operating points are shown. Point $A$ is the desired operating point, and point $B$ is an undesired operating point because $I_{OUT} = I_{IN} = 0$.

If the output current in Fig. 4.37$a$ increases for any reason, the current mirror increases the input current by the same amount because the gain of the current mirror is assumed to be unity. As a result, the current source increases the output current by an amount that depends on the gain of the current source. Therefore, the loop responds to an initial change in the output current by further changing the output current in a direction that reinforces the initial change. In other words, the connection of a current source and a current mirror as shown in Fig. 4.37$a$ forms a positive feedback loop, and the gain around the loop is the gain of the current source. In Chapter 9, we will show that circuits with positive feedback are stable if the gain around the loop is less than unity. At point $A$, the gain around the loop is quite small because the output current of the current source is insensitive to changes in the input current around point $A$. On the other hand, at point $B$, the gain around the feedback loop is deliberately made greater than unity so that the two characteristics shown in Fig. 4.37$b$ intersect at a point away from the origin. As a result, this simplified analysis shows that point $B$ is an unstable operating point in principle, and the circuit would ideally tend to drive itself out of this state.

In practice, however, point $B$ is frequently a stable operating point because the currents in the transistors at this point are very small, often in the picoampere range. At such low current levels, leakage currents and other effects reduce the current gain of both bipolar and MOS transistors, usually causing the gain around the loop to be less than unity. As a result, actual circuits of this type are usually unable to drive themselves out of the zero-current state. Thus, unless precautions are taken, the circuit may operate in the zero-current condition. For these reasons, self-biased circuits often have a stable state in which zero current flows in the circuit even when the power-supply voltage is nonzero. This situation is analogous to a gasoline engine that is not running even though it has a full tank of fuel. An electrical or mechanical device is required to start the engine. Similarly, a start-up circuit is usually required to prevent the self-biased circuit from remaining in the zero-current state.

The application of this technique to the $V_{BE}$-referenced current source is illustrated in Fig. 4.38$a$, and the threshold-referenced MOS counterpart is shown in Fig. 4.38$b$. We assume for simplicity that $V_A \rightarrow \infty$. The circuit composed of $T_1$, $T_2$, and $R$ dictates that the current $I_{OUT}$ depends weakly on $I_{IN}$, as indicated by (4.221) and (4.224). Second, the current mirror composed of matched transistors $T_4$ and $T_5$ dictates that $I_{IN}$ is equal to $I_{OUT}$. The operating point of the circuit must satisfy both constraints and hence is at the intersection of the two characteristics as in Fig. 4.37$b$. Except for the effects of finite output resistance of the transistors, the bias currents are independent of supply voltage. If required, the output resistance of the current source and mirror could be increased by the use of cascode or Wilson configurations in the circuits. The actual bias currents for other circuits are supplied by $T_6$ and/or $T_3$, which are matched to $T_5$ and $T_1$, respectively.

The zero-current state can be avoided by using a start-up circuit to ensure that some current always flows in the transistors in the reference so that the gain around the feedback loop at point $B$ in Fig. 4.37$b$ does not fall below unity. An additional requirement is that

**Figure 4.38** (a) Self-biasing $V_{BE}$ reference. (b) Self-biasing $V_t$ reference.

the start-up circuit must not interfere with the normal operation of the reference once the desired operating point is reached. The $V_{BE}$-referenced current source with a typical start-up circuit used in bipolar technologies is illustrated in Fig. 4.39a. We first assume that the circuit is in the undesired zero-current state. If this were true, the base-emitter voltage of $T_1$ would be zero. The base-emitter voltage $T_2$ would be tens of millivolts above ground, determined by the leakage currents in the circuit. However, the voltage on the left-hand end of $D_1$ is four diode drops above ground, so that a voltage of at least three diode drops would appear across $R_x$, and a current would flow through $R_x$ into the $T_1$-$T_2$ combination. This action would cause current to flow in $T_4$ and $T_5$, avoiding the zero-current state.

The bias reference circuit then drives itself toward the desired stable state, and we require that the start-up circuit not affect the steady-state current values. This can be accomplished by causing $R_x$ to be large enough that when the steady-state current is established in $T_1$, the voltage drop across $R_x$ is large enough to reverse bias $D_1$. In the steady state, the collector-emitter voltage of $T_1$ is two diode drops above ground, and the left-hand end of $D_1$ is four diode drops above ground. Thus if we make $I_{IN}R_x$ equal to two diode drops, $D_1$ will have zero voltage across it in the steady state. As a result, the start-up circuit composed of $R_s$, $D_2$–$D_5$, and $D_1$ is, in effect, disconnected from the circuit for steady-state operation.

Floating diodes are not usually available in MOS technologies. The threshold-referenced current source with a typical start-up circuit used in MOS technologies is illustrated in Fig. 4.39b. If the circuit is in the undesired zero-current state, the gate-source voltage of $T_1$ would be less than a threshold voltage. As a result, $T_7$ is off and $T_8$ operates in the triode region, pulling the gate-source voltage of $T_9$ up to $V_{DD}$. Therefore, $T_9$ is on and pulls down on the gates of $T_4$ and $T_5$. This action causes current to flow in $T_4$ and $T_5$, avoiding the zero-current state.

In steady state, the gate-source voltage of $T_7$ rises to $I_{OUT}R$, which turns on $T_7$ and reduces the gate-source voltage of $T_9$. In other words, $T_7$ and $T_8$ form a CMOS inverter

(a)

(b)

**Figure 4.39** (a) Self-biasing $V_{BE}$ reference with start-up circuit. (b) Self-biasing $V_t$ reference with start-up circuit.

whose output falls when the reference circuit turns on. Since the start-up circuit should not interfere with normal operation of the reference in steady state, the inverter output should fall low enough to turn $T_9$ off in steady state. Therefore, the gate-source voltage of $T_9$ must fall below a threshold voltage when the inverter input rises from zero to $I_{OUT}R$. In practice, this requirement is satisfied by choosing the aspect ratio of $T_7$ to be much larger than that of $T_8$.

Another important aspect of the performance of biasing circuits is their dependence on temperature. This variation is most conveniently expressed in terms of the fractional change in output current per degree centigrade of temperature variation, which we call the fractional temperature coefficient $TC_F$:

$$TC_F = \frac{1}{I_{OUT}} \frac{\partial I_{OUT}}{\partial T} \tag{4.227}$$

For the $V_{BE}$-referenced circuit of Fig. 4.38a,

$$I_{OUT} = \frac{V_{BE1}}{R} \tag{4.228}$$

$$\frac{\partial I_{OUT}}{\partial T} = \frac{1}{R} \frac{\partial V_{BE1}}{\partial T} - \frac{V_{BE1}}{R^2} \frac{\partial R}{\partial T} \tag{4.229}$$

$$= I_{OUT} \left( \frac{1}{V_{BE1}} \frac{\partial V_{BE1}}{\partial T} - \frac{1}{R} \frac{\partial R}{\partial T} \right) \tag{4.230}$$

Therefore,

$$TC_F = \frac{1}{I_{OUT}} \frac{\partial I_{OUT}}{\partial T} = \frac{1}{V_{BE1}} \frac{\partial V_{BE1}}{\partial T} - \frac{1}{R} \frac{\partial R}{\partial T} \tag{4.231}$$

Thus the temperature dependence of the output current is related to the difference between the resistor temperature coefficient and that of the base-emitter junction. Since the former has a positive and the latter a negative coefficient, the net $TC_F$ is quite large.

■ **EXAMPLE**

Design a bias reference as shown in Fig. 4.38a to produce 100 μA output current. Find the $TC_F$. Assume that for $T_1$, $I_S = 10^{-14}$ A. Assume that $\partial V_{BE}/\partial T = -2$mV/°C and that $(1/R)(\partial R/\partial T) = +1500$ ppm/°C.

The current in $T_1$ will be equal to $I_{OUT}$, so that

$$V_{BE1} = V_T \ln \frac{100 \ \mu A}{10^{-14} \ A} = 598 \ mV$$

Thus from (4.228),

$$R = \frac{598 \ mV}{0.1 \ mA} = 5.98 \ k\Omega$$

From (4.231),

$$TC_F \approx \frac{-2 \ mV/°C}{598 \ mV} - 1.5 \times 10^{-3} \approx -3.3 \times 10^{-3} - 1.5 \times 10^{-3}$$

and thus

$$TC_F \approx -4.8 \times 10^{-3}/°C = -4800 \ ppm/°C$$

■ The term ppm is an abbreviation for parts per million and implies a multiplier of $10^{-6}$.

For the threshold-referenced circuit of Fig. 4.38b,

$$I_{OUT} = \frac{V_{GS1}}{R} \approx \frac{V_t}{R} \tag{4.232}$$

Differentiating (4.232) and substituting into (4.227) gives

$$TC_F = \frac{1}{I_{OUT}} \frac{\partial I_{OUT}}{\partial T} \approx \frac{1}{V_t} \frac{\partial V_t}{\partial T} - \frac{1}{R} \frac{\partial R}{\partial T} \tag{4.233}$$

**Figure 4.40** Example of a $V_{BE}$-referenced self-biased circuit in CMOS technology.

Since the threshold voltage of an MOS transistor and the base-emitter voltage of a bipolar transistor both change at about $-2$ mV/°C, (4.233) and (4.231) show that the temperature dependence of the threshold-referenced current source in Fig. 4.38$b$ is about the same as the $V_{BE}$-referenced current source in Fig. 4.38$a$.

$V_{BE}$-referenced bias circuits are also used in CMOS technology. An example is shown in Fig. 4.40, where the $pnp$ transistor is the parasitic device inherent in $p$-substrate CMOS technologies. A corresponding circuit utilizing $npn$ transistors can be used in $n$-substrate CMOS technologies. The feedback circuit formed by $M_2$, $M_3$, $M_4$, and $M_5$ forces the current in transistor $Q_1$ to be the same as in resistor $R$. Assuming matched devices, $V_{GS2} = V_{GS3}$ and thus

$$I_{OUT} = \frac{V_{BE1}}{R} \tag{4.234}$$

An alternate source for the voltage reference is the thermal voltage $V_T$. The difference in junction potential between two junctions operated at different current densities can be shown to be proportional to $V_T$. This voltage difference must be converted to a current to provide the bias current. For the Widlar source shown in Fig. 4.31$a$, (4.190) shows that the voltage across the resistor $R_2$ is

$$I_{OUT}R_2 = V_T \ln \frac{I_{IN}}{I_{OUT}} \frac{I_{S2}}{I_{S1}} \tag{4.235}$$

Thus if the ratio of the input to the output current is held constant, the voltage across $R_2$ is indeed proportional to $V_T$. This fact is utilized in the self-biased circuit of Fig. 4.41. Here $Q_3$ and $Q_4$ are selected to have equal areas. Therefore, if we assume that $\beta_F \to \infty$ and $V_A \to \infty$, the current mirror formed by $Q_3$ and $Q_4$ forces the collector current of $Q_1$ to equal that of $Q_2$. Figure 4.41 also shows that $Q_2$ has two emitters and $Q_1$ has one emitter, which indicates that the emitter area of $Q_2$ is twice that of $Q_1$ in this example. This selection is made to force the gain around the positive feedback loop at point $B$ in Fig. 4.37$b$ to be more than unity so that point $B$ is an unstable operating point and a stable nonzero operating point exists at point $A$. As in other self-biased circuits, a start-up circuit is required to make sure that enough current flows to force operation at point $A$ in Fig. 4.37$b$ in practice. Under these conditions, $I_{S2} = 2I_{S1}$ and the voltage across $R_2$ is

$$I_{OUT}R_2 = V_T \ln \frac{I_{IN}}{I_{OUT}} \frac{I_{S2}}{I_{S1}} = V_T \ln 2 \tag{4.236}$$

Figure 4.41 Bias current source using the thermal voltage.

Therefore, the output current is

$$I_{OUT} = \frac{V_T}{R_2} \ln 2 \qquad (4.237)$$

The temperature variation of the output current can be calculated as follows. From (4.237)

$$\frac{\partial I_{OUT}}{\partial T} = (\ln 2) \frac{R_2 \frac{\partial V_T}{\partial T} - V_T \frac{\partial R_2}{\partial T}}{R_2^2}$$

$$= \frac{V_T}{R_2} (\ln 2) \left( \frac{1}{V_T} \frac{\partial V_T}{\partial T} - \frac{1}{R_2} \frac{\partial R_2}{\partial T} \right) \qquad (4.238)$$

Substituting (4.237) in (4.238) gives

$$TC_F = \frac{1}{I_{OUT}} \frac{\partial I_{OUT}}{\partial T} = \frac{1}{V_T} \frac{\partial V_T}{\partial T} - \frac{1}{R_2} \frac{\partial R_2}{\partial T} \qquad (4.239)$$

This circuit produces much smaller temperature coefficient of the output $V_{BE}$ reference because the fractional sensitivities of both $V_T$ and that of a diffused resistor $R_2$ are positive and tend to cancel in (4.239). We have chosen a transistor area ratio of two to one as an example. In practice, this ratio is often chosen to minimize the total area required for the transistors and for resistor $R_2$.

■ **EXAMPLE**

Design a bias reference of the type shown in Fig. 4.41 to produce an output current of 100 μA. Find the $TC_F$ of $I_{OUT}$. Assume the resistor temperature coefficient $(1/R)(\partial R/\partial T) = +1500$ ppm/°C.

From (4.237)

$$R_2 = \frac{V_T (\ln 2)}{I_{OUT}} = \frac{(26 \text{ mV})(\ln 2)}{100 \text{ μA}} \approx 180 \text{ Ω}$$

From (4.239)

$$\frac{1}{I_{OUT}}\frac{\partial I_{OUT}}{\partial T} = \frac{1}{V_T}\frac{\partial V_T}{\partial T} - 1500 \times 10^{-6} = \frac{1}{V_T}\frac{V_T}{T} - 1500 \times 10^{-6}$$

$$= \frac{1}{T} - 1500 \times 10^{-6}$$

Assuming operation at room temperature, $T = 300°K$ and

$$\frac{1}{I_{OUT}}\frac{\partial I_{OUT}}{\partial T} \simeq 3300 \times 10^{-6} - 1500 \times 10^{-6} = 1800 \text{ ppm/°C}$$

■    $V_T$-referenced bias circuits are also commonly used in CMOS technology. A simple example is shown in Fig. 4.42, where bipolar transistors $Q_1$ and $Q_2$ are parasitic devices inherent in $p$-substrate CMOS technologies. Here the emitter areas of these transistors differ by a factor $n$, and the feedback loop forces them to operate at the same bias current. As a result, the difference between the two base-emitter voltages must appear across resistor $R$. The resulting current is

$$I_{OUT} = \frac{V_T \ln(n)}{R} \tag{4.240}$$

In the circuit of Fig. 4.42, small differences in the gate-source voltages of $M_3$ and $M_4$ result in large variations in the output current because the voltage drop across $R$ is only on the order of 100 mV. Such gate-source voltage differences can result from device mismatches or from channel-length modulation in $M_3$ and $M_4$ because they have different drain-source voltages. Practical implementations of this circuit typically utilize large geometry devices for $M_3$ and $M_4$ to minimize offsets and cascode or Wilson current sources to minimize channel-length modulation effects. A typical example of a practical circuit is shown in Fig. 4.43. In general, cascoding is often used to improve the performance of reference circuits in all technologies. The main limitation of the application of cascoding is that it increases the minimum required power-supply voltage to operate all transistors in the active region.

Figure 4.42 Example of a CMOS $V_T$-referenced self-biased circuit.

**Figure 4.43** Example of a CMOS $V_T$-referenced self-biased reference circuit with cascoded devices to improve power-supply rejection and initial accuracy.

### 4.4.3 Temperature-Insensitive Biasing

As illustrated by the examples in Section 4.4.2, the base-emitter-voltage- and thermal-voltage-referenced circuits have rather high temperature coefficients of output current. Although the temperature sensitivity is reduced considerably in the thermal-voltage circuit, even its temperature coefficient is not low enough for many applications. Thus we are led to examine other possibilities for the realization of a biasing circuit with low temperature coefficient.

#### 4.4.3.1 Band-Gap-Referenced Bias Circuits in Bipolar Technology

Since the bias sources referenced to $V_{BE(\text{on})}$ and $V_T$ have opposite $TC_F$, the possibility exists for referencing the output current to a composite voltage that is a weighted sum of $V_{BE(\text{on})}$ and $V_T$. By proper weighting, zero temperature coefficient should be attainable.

In the biasing sources described so far, we have concentrated on the problem of obtaining a *current* with low temperature coefficient. In practice, requirements often arise for low-temperature-coefficient voltage bias or reference *voltages*. The voltage reference for a voltage regulator is a good example. The design of these two types of circuits is similar except that in the case of the current source, a temperature coefficient must be intentionally introduced into the voltage reference to compensate for the temperature coefficient of the resistor that will define the current. In the following description of the band-gap reference, we assume for simplicity that the objective is a *voltage* source of low temperature coefficient.

First consider the hypothetical circuit of Fig. 4.44. An output voltage is developed that is equal to $V_{BE(\text{on})}$ plus a constant $M$ times $V_T$. To determine the required value for $M$, we must determine the temperature coefficient of $V_{BE(\text{on})}$. Neglecting base current,

$$V_{BE(\text{on})} = V_T \ln \frac{I_1}{I_S} \tag{4.241}$$

**Figure 4.44** Hypothetical band-gap reference circuit.

As shown in Chapter 1, the saturation current $I_S$ can be related to the device structure by

$$I_S = \frac{qA n_i^2 \bar{D}_n}{Q_B} = B n_i^2 \bar{D}_n = B' n_i^2 T \bar{\mu}_n \qquad (4.242)$$

where $n_i$ is the intrinsic minority-carrier concentration, $Q_B$ is the total base doping per unit area, $\bar{\mu}_n$ is the average electron mobility in the base, $A$ is the emitter-base junction area, and $T$ is the temperature. Here, the constants $B$ and $B'$ involve only temperature-independent quantities. The Einstein relation $\mu_n = (q/kT)D_n$ was used to write $I_S$ in terms of $\bar{\mu}_n$ and $n_i^2$. The quantities in (4.242) that are temperature dependent are given by[15]

$$\bar{\mu}_n = CT^{-n} \qquad (4.243)$$

$$n_i^2 = DT^3 \exp\left(-\frac{V_{G0}}{V_T}\right) \qquad (4.244)$$

where $V_{G0}$ is the band-gap voltage of silicon extrapolated to 0°K. Here again $C$ and $D$ are temperature-independent quantities whose exact values are unimportant in the analysis. The exponent $n$ in the expression for base-region electron mobility $\bar{\mu}_n$ is dependent on the doping level in the base. Combining (4.241), (4.242), (4.243), and (4.244) yields

$$V_{BE(on)} = V_T \ln\left(I_1 T^{-\gamma} E \exp \frac{V_{G0}}{V_T}\right) \qquad (4.245)$$

where $E$ is another temperature-independent constant and

$$\gamma = 4 - n \qquad (4.246)$$

In actual band-gap circuits, the current $I_1$ is not constant but varies with temperature. We assume for the time being that this temperature variation is known and that it can be written in the form

$$I_1 = GT^\alpha \qquad (4.247)$$

where $G$ is another temperature-independent constant. Combining (4.245) and (4.247) gives

$$V_{BE(\text{on})} = V_{G0} - V_T[(\gamma - \alpha)\ln T - \ln(EG)] \tag{4.248}$$

From Fig. 4.44, the output voltage is

$$V_{\text{OUT}} = V_{BE(\text{on})} + MV_T \tag{4.249}$$

Substitution of (4.248) into (4.249) gives

$$V_{\text{OUT}} = V_{G0} - V_T(\gamma - \alpha)\ln T + V_T[M + \ln(EG)] \tag{4.250}$$

This expression gives the output voltage as a function of temperature in terms of the circuit parameters $G$, $\alpha$, and $M$, and the device parameters $E$ and $\gamma$. Our objective is to make $V_{\text{OUT}}$ independent of temperature. To this end, we take the derivative of $V_{\text{OUT}}$ with respect to temperature to find the required values of $G$, $\gamma$, and $M$ to give zero $TC_F$. Differentiating (4.250) gives

$$0 = \frac{dV_{\text{OUT}}}{dT}\bigg|_{T=T_0} = \frac{V_{T0}}{T_0}[M + \ln(EG)] - \frac{V_{T0}}{T_0}(\gamma - \alpha)\ln T_0 - \frac{V_{T0}}{T_0}(\gamma - \alpha) \tag{4.251}$$

where $T_0$ is the temperature at which the $TC_F$ of the output is zero and $V_{T0}$ is the thermal voltage $V_T$ evaluated at $T_0$. Equation 4.251 can be rearranged to give

$$[M + \ln(EG)] = (\gamma - \alpha)\ln T_0 + (\gamma - \alpha) \tag{4.252}$$

This equation gives the required values of circuit parameters $M$, $\alpha$, and $G$ in terms of the device parameters $E$ and $\gamma$. In principle, these values could be calculated directly from (4.252). However, further insight is gained by back-substituting (4.252) into (4.250). The result is

$$V_{\text{OUT}} = V_{G0} + V_T(\gamma - \alpha)\left(1 + \ln\frac{T_0}{T}\right) \tag{4.253}$$

Thus the temperature dependence of the output voltage is entirely described by the single parameter $T_0$, which in turn is determined by the constants $M$, $E$, and $G$.

Using (4.253), the output voltage at the zero $TC_F$ temperature ($T = T_0$) is given by

$$V_{\text{OUT}}\big|_{T=T_0} = V_{G0} + V_{T0}(\gamma - \alpha) \tag{4.254}$$

For example, to achieve zero $TC_F$ at 27°C, assuming that $\gamma = 3.2$ and $\alpha = 1$,

$$V_{\text{OUT}}\big|_{T=T_0=25°C} = V_{G0} + 2.2V_{T0} \tag{4.255}$$

The band-gap voltage of silicon is $V_{G0} = 1.205$ V so that

$$V_{\text{OUT}}\big|_{T=T_0=25°C} = 1.205 \text{ V} + (2.2)(0.026 \text{ V}) = 1.262 \text{ V} \tag{4.256}$$

Therefore, the output voltage for zero temperature coefficient is close to the band-gap voltage of silicon, which explains the name given to these bias circuits.

Differentiating (4.253) with respect to temperature yields

$$\frac{dV_{\text{OUT}}}{dT} = \frac{1}{T}\left[V_T(\gamma - \alpha)\left(1 + \ln\frac{T_0}{T}\right)\right] - \frac{V_T}{T}(\gamma - \alpha)$$

$$= (\gamma - \alpha)\frac{V_T}{T}\left(\ln\frac{T_0}{T}\right) \tag{4.257}$$

**Figure 4.45** Variation of band-gap reference output voltage with temperature.

Equation 4.257 gives the slope of the output as a function of temperature. A typical family of output-voltage-variation characteristics is shown in Fig. 4.45 for different values of $T_0$ for the special case in which $\alpha = 0$ and $I_1$ is temperature independent. The slope of each curve is zero at $T = T_0$. When $T < T_0$, the slope is positive because the argument of the logarithm in (4.257) is more than unity. Similarly, the slope is negative when $T > T_0$. For values of $T$ near $T_0$,

$$\ln\frac{T_0}{T} = \ln\left(1 + \frac{T_0 - T}{T}\right) \simeq \frac{T_0 - T}{T} \qquad (4.258)$$

and we have

$$\frac{dV_{\text{OUT}}}{dT} \simeq (\gamma - \alpha)\frac{V_T}{T}\left(\frac{T_0 - T}{T}\right) \qquad (4.259)$$

As shown by (4.257) and (4.259), the temperature coefficient of the output is zero only at one temperature $T = T_0$. This result stems from the addition of a weighted thermal voltage to a base-emitter voltage as in Fig. 4.44. Since the temperature coefficient of base-emitter voltage is not exactly constant, the gain $M$ can be chosen to set the temperature coefficient of the output to zero only at one temperature. In other words, the thermal voltage generator is used to cancel the linear dependence of the base-emitter voltage with temperature. After this cancellation, the changing outputs in Fig. 4.45 stem from the nonlinear dependence of the base-emitter voltage with temperature. Band-gap references that compensate for this nonlinearity are said to be *curvature compensated*.[16,17,18]

■  **EXAMPLE**

A band-gap reference is designed to give a nominal output voltage of 1.262 V, which gives zero $TC_F$ at 27°C. Because of component variations, the actual room temperature output voltage is 1.280 V. Find the temperature of actual zero $TC_F$ of $V_{\text{OUT}}$. Also, write an equation for $V_{\text{OUT}}$ as a function of temperature  and calculate the $TC_F$ at room temperature. Assume that $\gamma = 3.2$ and $\alpha = 1$.

From (4.253) at $T = 27°C = 300°K$,

$$1.280 \text{ V} = 1.205 + (0.026 \text{ V})(2.2)\left(1 + \ln \frac{T_0}{300°K}\right)$$

and thus

$$T_0 = 300°K\left(\exp \frac{18 \text{ mV}}{57 \text{ mV}}\right) = 411°K$$

Therefore, the $TC_F$ will be zero at $T_0 = 411°K = 138°C$, and we can express $V_{OUT}$ as

$$V_{OUT} = 1.205 \text{ V} + 57 \text{ mV}\left(1 + \ln \frac{411°K}{T}\right)$$

From (4.259) with $T = 300°K$ and $T_0 = 411°K$,

$$\frac{dV_{OUT}}{dT} \simeq (2.2)\frac{26 \text{ mV}}{300°K}\left(\frac{411 - 300}{300}\right) \simeq 70 \text{ } \mu\text{V/°K} = 70 \text{ } \mu\text{V/°C}$$

Therefore, the $TC_F$ at room temperature is

$$TC_F = \frac{1}{V_{OUT}}\frac{dV_{OUT}}{dT} \simeq \frac{70 \text{ } \mu\text{V/°C}}{1.280 \text{ V}} \simeq 55 \text{ ppm/°C}$$

■

To reduce the $TC_F$, the constant $M$ in (4.249)–(4.252) is often trimmed at one temperature so that the band-gap output is set to a desired target voltage.[19] In principle, the target voltage is given by (4.253). In practice, however, significant inaccuracy in (4.253) stems from an approximation in (4.244).[20] As a result, the target voltage is usually determined experimentally by measuring the $TC_F$ directly for several samples of each band-gap reference in a given process.[21,22] This procedure reduces the $TC_F$ at the reference temperature to a level of about 10 ppm/ °C.

A key parameter of interest in reference sources is the variation of the output that is encountered over the entire temperature range. Since the $TC_F$ expresses the temperature sensitivity only at one temperature, a different parameter must be used to characterize the behavior of the circuit over a broad temperature range. An effective temperature coefficient can be defined for a voltage reference as

$$TC_{F(\text{eff})} = \frac{1}{V_{OUT}}\left(\frac{V_{MAX} - V_{MIN}}{T_{MAX} - T_{MIN}}\right) \tag{4.260}$$

where $V_{MAX}$ and $V_{MIN}$ are the largest and smallest output voltages observed over the temperature range, and $T_{MAX} - T_{MIN}$ is the temperature excursion. $V_{OUT}$ is the nominal output voltage. By this standard, $TC_{F(\text{eff})}$ over the $-55$ to $125°C$ range for case (b) of Fig. 4.45 is 44 ppm/°C. If the temperature range is restricted to 0 to 70°C, $TC_{F(\text{eff})}$ improves to 17 ppm/°C. Thus over a restricted temperature range, this reference is comparable with the standard cell in temperature stability once the zero $TC_F$ temperature has been set at room temperature. Saturated standard cells (precision batteries) have a $TC_F$ of about $\pm30$ ppm/°C.

Practical realizations of band-gap references in bipolar technologies take on several forms.[15,19,23] One such circuit is illustrated in Fig. 4.46a.[15] This circuit uses a feedback loop to establish an operating point in the circuit such that the output voltage is equal to a $V_{BE(\text{on})}$ plus a voltage proportional to the difference between two base-emitter voltages. The operation of the feedback loop is best understood by reference to Fig. 4.46b, in which a portion of the circuit is shown. We first consider the variation of the output voltage $V_2$ as the input voltage $V_1$ is varied from zero in the positive direction. Initially, with $V_1 = 0$, devices $Q_1$ and $Q_2$ do not conduct and $V_2 = 0$. As $V_1$ is increased, $Q_1$ and $Q_2$ do not conduct significant current until the input voltage reaches about 0.6 V. When $V_1 < 0.6$V, $V_2 = V_1$ since the voltage drop on $R_2$ is zero. When $V_1$ exceeds 0.6 V, however, $Q_1$ begins to conduct current, corresponding to point ① in Fig. 4.46b. The magnitude of the current in $Q_1$ is roughly equal to $(V_1 - 0.6 \text{ V})/R_1$. For small values of this current, $Q_1$ and $Q_2$ carry the same current because the drop across $R_3$ is negligible at low currents. Since $R_2$ is much larger than $R_1$, the voltage drop across $R_2$ is much larger than $(V_1 - 0.6 \text{ V})$, and transistor $Q_2$ saturates, corresponding to point ② in Fig. 4.46b. Because of the presence of $R_3$, the collector current that *would* flow in $Q_2$ if it were in the forward-active region has an approximately logarithmic dependence on $V_1$, exactly as in the Widlar source. Thus as $V_1$ is further increased, a point is reached at which $Q_2$ comes out of saturation because $V_1$ increases faster than the voltage drop across $R_2$. This point is labeled point ③ in Fig. 4.46b.

Now consider the complete circuit of Fig. 4.46a. If transistor $Q_3$ is initially turned off, transistor $Q_4$ will drive $V_1$ in the positive direction. This process will continue until enough voltage is developed at the base of $Q_3$ to produce a collector current in $Q_3$ approximately equal to $I$. Thus the circuit stabilizes with voltage $V_2$ equal to one diode drop, the base-emitter voltage of $Q_3$, which can occur at point ① or point ④ in Fig. 4.46b. Appropriate start-up circuitry must be included to ensure operation at point ④.

Assuming that the circuit has reached a stable operating point at point ④, the output voltage $V_{OUT}$ is the sum of the base-emitter voltage of $Q_3$ and the voltage drop across $R_2$. The drop across $R_2$ is equal to the voltage drop across $R_3$ multiplied by $R_2/R_3$ because the collector current of $Q_2$ is approximately equal to its emitter current. The voltage drop across $R_3$ is equal to the difference in base-emitter voltages of $Q_1$ and $Q_2$. The ratio of currents in $Q_1$ and $Q_2$ is set by the ratio of $R_2$ to $R_1$.

A drawback of this reference is that the current $I$ is set by the power supply and may vary with power-supply variations. A self-biased band-gap reference circuit is shown in Fig. 4.46c. Assume that a stable operating point exists for this circuit and that the op amp is ideal. Then the differential input voltage of the op amp must be zero and the voltage drops across resistors $R_1$ and $R_2$ are equal. Thus the ratio of $R_2$ to $R_1$ determines the ratio of $I_1$ to $I_2$. These two currents are the collector currents of the two diode-connected transistors $Q_2$ and $Q_1$, assuming base currents are negligible. The voltage across $R_3$ is

$$V_{R3} = \Delta V_{BE} = V_{BE1} - V_{BE2} = V_T \ln \frac{I_1}{I_2} \frac{I_{S2}}{I_{S1}} = V_T \ln \frac{R_2}{R_1} \frac{I_{S2}}{I_{S1}} \qquad (4.261)$$

Since the same current that flows in $R_3$ also flows in $R_2$, the voltage across $R_2$ must be

$$V_{R2} = \frac{R_2}{R_3} V_{R3} = \frac{R_2}{R_3} \Delta V_{BE} = \frac{R_2}{R_3} V_T \ln \frac{R_2}{R_1} \frac{I_{S2}}{I_{S1}} \qquad (4.262)$$

This equation shows that the voltage across $R_2$ is proportional to absolute temperature (PTAT) because of the temperature dependence of the thermal voltage. Since the op amp forces the voltages across $R_1$ and $R_2$ to be equal, the currents $I_1$ and $I_2$ are both proportional to temperature if the resistors have zero temperature coefficient. Thus for this reference, $\alpha = 1$ in (4.247). The output voltage is the sum of the voltage across $Q_2$, $R_3$, and $R_2$:

$$V_{OUT} = V_{BE2} + V_{R3} + V_{R2} = V_{BE2} + \left(1 + \frac{R_2}{R_3}\right)\Delta V_{BE}$$

$$= V_{BE2} + \left(1 + \frac{R_2}{R_3}\right)V_T \ln \frac{R_2}{R_1} \frac{I_{S2}}{I_{S1}} = V_{BE2} + MV_T \qquad (4.263)$$

Figure 4.46  (a) Widlar band-gap reference. (b) Band-gap subcircuit. (c) Improved band-gap reference.

The circuit thus behaves as a band-gap reference, with the value of $M$ set by the ratios of $R_2/R_3$, $R_2/R_1$, and $I_{S2}/I_{S1}$.

### 4.4.3.2 Band-Gap-Referenced Bias Circuits in CMOS Technology

Band-gap-referenced biasing also can be implemented using the parasitic bipolar devices inherent in CMOS technology. For example, in a $n$-well process, substrate $pnp$ transistors can be used to replace the $npn$ transistors in Fig. 4.46c, as shown in Fig. 4.47. Assume that the CMOS op amp has infinite gain but nonzero input-referred offset voltage $V_{OS}$. (The input-referred offset voltage of an op amp is defined as the differential input voltage required to drive the output to zero.) Because of the threshold mismatch and the low transconductance per current of CMOS transistors, the offset of op amps in CMOS technologies is usually larger than in bipolar technologies. With the offset voltage, the voltage across $R_3$ is

$$V_{R3} = V_{EB1} - V_{EB2} + V_{OS} = \Delta V_{EB} + V_{OS} \tag{4.264}$$

**Figure 4.47** A bandgap reference in $n$-well CMOS.

The emitter-base voltages are used here because the base-emitter voltages of the $pnp$ transistors operating in the forward-active region are negative. Then the voltage across $R_2$ is

$$V_{R2} = \frac{R_2}{R_3} V_{R3} = \frac{R_2}{R_3}(V_{EB1} - V_{EB2} + V_{OS}) = \frac{R_2}{R_3}(\Delta V_{EB} + V_{OS}) \qquad (4.265)$$

and the output voltage is[18]

$$V_{OUT} = V_{EB2} + V_{R3} + V_{R2}$$
$$= V_{EB2} + \left(1 + \frac{R_2}{R_3}\right)(\Delta V_{EB} + V_{OS}) \qquad (4.266)$$

Since the difference in the base-emitter voltages is proportional to the thermal voltage, comparing (4.266) with $V_{OS} = 0$ to (4.249) shows that the gain $M$ here is proportional to $(1 + R_2/R_3)$. Rearranging (4.266) gives

$$V_{OUT} = V_{EB2} + \left(1 + \frac{R_2}{R_3}\right)(\Delta V_{EB}) + V_{OS(out)} \qquad (4.267)$$

where the output-referred offset is

$$V_{OS(out)} = \left(1 + \frac{R_2}{R_3}\right)V_{OS} \qquad (4.268)$$

Equations 4.267 and 4.268 show that the output contains an offset voltage that is a factor of $(1 + R_2/R_3)$ times bigger than the input-referred offset voltage. Therefore, the same gain that is applied to the difference in the base-emitter voltages is also applied to the input-referred offset voltage.

Assume that the offset voltage is independent of temperature. To set $TC_F$ of the output equal to zero, the gain must be changed so that temperature coefficients of the $V_{EB}$ and $\Delta V_{EB}$ terms cancel. Since the offset is assumed to be temperature independent, this cancellation occurs when the output is equal to the target, where zero offset was assumed, plus the output-referred offset. If the gain is trimmed at $T = T_0$ to set the output to a target voltage assuming the offset is zero, (4.267) shows that the gain is too small if the offset voltage is positive and that the gain is too big if the offset voltage is negative. Since the gain is applied to the PTAT term, the resulting slope of the output versus temperature is negative when the offset is positive and the gain is too small. On the other hand, this slope is positive when the offset is negative and the gain is too big.

We will now calculate the magnitude of the slope of the output versus temperature at $T = T_0$. With zero offset and a target that assumes zero offset, trimming $R_2$ and/or $R_3$ to set the output in (4.267) to the target forces the slope of the $\Delta V_{EB}$ term to cancel the slope of the $V_{EB}$ term. With nonzero offset but the same target, the factor $(1 + R_2/R_3)$ differs from its ideal value after trimming by $-V_{OS(out)}/\Delta V_{EB}$. Since this error is multiplied by $\Delta V_{EB}$ in (4.267), the resulting slope of the output versus temperature is

$$\left.\frac{dV_{OUT}}{dT}\right|_{T=T_0} = -\left(\frac{V_{OS(out)}}{\Delta V_{EB}}\right)\frac{d\Delta V_{EB}}{dT} \tag{4.269}$$

Since $\Delta V_{EB}$ is proportional to the thermal voltage $V_T$,

$$\Delta V_{EB} = HV_T \tag{4.270}$$

where $H$ is a temperature-independent constant. Substituting (4.270) into (4.269) gives

$$\left.\frac{dV_{OUT}}{dT}\right|_{T=T_0} = -\frac{V_{OS(out)}}{HV_T}\left.\frac{HV_T}{T}\right|_{T=T_0} = -\frac{V_{OS(out)}}{T_0} \tag{4.271}$$

Therefore, when the gain is trimmed at one temperature to set the band-gap output to a desired target voltage, variation in the op-amp offset causes variation in the output temperature coefficient. In practice, the op-amp offset is usually the largest source of nonzero temperature coefficient.[18] Equation 4.271 shows that the temperature coefficient at $T = T_0$ is proportional to the output-referred offset under these circumstances. Furthermore, (4.268) shows that the output-referred offset is equal to the gain that is applied to the $\Delta V_{EB}$ term times the input-referred offset. Therefore, minimizing this gain minimizes the variation in the temperature coefficient at the output. Since the reference output at $T = T_0$ for zero $TC_F$ is approximately equal to the band-gap voltage, the required gain can be minimized by maximizing the $\Delta V_{EB}$ term.

To maximize the $\Delta V_{EB}$ term, designers generally push a large current into a small transistor and a small current into a large transistor, as shown in Fig. 4.48. Ignoring base currents,

$$\Delta V_{EB} = V_{EB1} - V_{EB2} = V_T \ln\left(\frac{I_1}{I_2}\frac{I_{S2}}{I_{S1}}\right) \tag{4.272}$$

Equation 4.272 shows that maximizing the product of the ratios $I_1/I_2$ and $I_{S2}/I_{S1}$ maximizes $\Delta V_{EB}$. In Fig. 4.48, $I_1 > I_2$ is emphasized by drawing the symbol for $I_1$ larger than the symbol for $I_2$. Similarly, the emitter area of $Q_2$ is larger than that of $Q_1$ to make $I_{S2} > I_{S1}$, and this relationship is shown by drawing the symbol of $Q_2$ larger than the symbol of $Q_1$.[24] In practice, these ratios are often each set to be about equal to ten, and the resulting $\Delta V_{EB} \simeq 120$ mV at room temperature. Because the logarithm function compresses its argument, however, a limitation of this approach arises. For example, if the argument is increased by a factor of ten, $\Delta V_{EB}$ increases by only $V_T \ln(10) \simeq 60$ mV. Therefore, to

**Figure 4.48** A circuit that increases $\Delta V_{EB}$ by increasing $I_1/I_2$ and $I_{S2}/I_{S1}$.

**Figure 4.49** A circuit that cascades emitter followers to double $\Delta V_{EB}$ if $I_{S3} = I_{S1}$ and $I_{S4} = I_{S2}$.

double $\Delta V_{EB}$ to 240 mV, $(I_1/I_2)(I_{S2}/I_{S1})$ must be increased by a factor of 100 to 10,000. On the other hand, if $Q_1$ and the transistors that form $I_2$ are minimum-sized devices when $(I_1/I_2)(I_{S2}/I_{S1}) = 100$, the required die area would be dominated by the biggest devices ($Q_2$ and/or the transistors that form $I_1$). Therefore, increasing $(I_1/I_2)(I_{S2}/I_{S1})$ from 100 to 10,000 would increase the die area by about a factor of 100 but only double $\Delta V_{EB}$.

To overcome this limitation, stages that each contribute to $\Delta V_{EB}$ can be cascaded.[25] For example, consider Fig. 4.49, where two emitter-follower stages are cascaded. Here

$$\Delta V_{EB} = V_{EB3} - V_{EB4} + V_{EB1} - V_{EB2} \qquad (4.273)$$

Assume the new devices in Fig. 4.49 are identical to the corresponding original devices in Fig. 4.48 so that $I_3 = I_1$, $I_4 = I_2$ $I_{S3} = I_{S1}$, and $I_{S4} = I_{S2}$. Then ignoring base currents

$$\Delta V_{EB} = 2(V_{EB1} - V_{EB2}) = 2V_T \ln\left(\frac{I_1}{I_2}\frac{I_{S2}}{I_{S1}}\right) \qquad (4.274)$$

**Figure 4.50** Example of a $V_{BE}$-referenced self-biased reference circuit in CMOS technology.

Thus cascading two identical emitter followers doubles $\Delta V_{EB}$ while only doubling the required die area.

The effect of the offset in a band-gap reference can also be reduced by using offset cancellation. An example of offset cancellation in a CMOS band-gap reference with curvature correction in addition to an analysis of other high-order effects arising from finite $\beta_F$, $\beta_F$ mismatch, $\beta_F$ variation with temperature, nonzero base resistance, and nonzero temperature coefficient in the resistors is presented in Ref. 18.

A high-performance CMOS band-gap reference is shown in Fig. 4.50, where cascoded current mirrors are used to improve supply rejection. A $V_T$-dependent current from $M_{11}$ develops a $V_T$-dependent voltage across resistor $xR$. A proper choice of the ratio $x$ can give a band-gap voltage at $V_{OUT}$. If desired, a temperature-independent output current can be realized by choosing $x$ to give an appropriate temperature coefficient to $V_{OUT}$ to cancel the temperature coefficient of resistor $R_2$.

# APPENDIX

## A.4.1 MATCHING CONSIDERARTION IN CURRENT MIRRORS

In many types of circuits, an objective of current-mirror design is generation of two or more current sources whose values are identical. This objective is particularly important in the design of digital-to-analog converters, operational amplifiers, and instrumentation amplifiers. We first examine the factors affecting matching in active current mirrors in bipolar technologies and then in MOS technologies.

### A.4.1.1 BIPOLAR

Consider the bipolar current mirror with two outputs in Fig. 4.51. If the resistors and transistors are identical and the collector voltages are the same, the collector currents will match precisely. However, mismatch in the transistor parameters $\alpha_F$ and $I_S$ and in the emitter resistors will cause the currents to be unequal. For $Q_3$,

$$V_T \ln \frac{I_{C3}}{I_{S3}} + \frac{I_{C3}}{\alpha_{F3}} R_3 = V_B \tag{4.275}$$

**Figure 4.51** Matched bipolar current sources.

For $Q_4$,

$$V_T \ln \frac{I_{C4}}{I_{S4}} + \frac{I_{C4}}{\alpha_{F4}} R_4 = V_B \tag{4.276}$$

Subtraction of these two equations gives

$$V_T \ln \frac{I_{C3}}{I_{C4}} - V_T \ln \frac{I_{S3}}{I_{S4}} + \frac{I_{C3}}{\alpha_{F3}} R_3 - \frac{I_{C4}}{\alpha_{F4}} R_4 = 0 \tag{4.277}$$

We now define *average* and *mismatch* parameters as follows:

$$I_C = \frac{I_{C3} + I_{C4}}{2} \tag{4.278}$$

$$\Delta I_C = I_{C3} - I_{C4} \tag{4.279}$$

$$I_S = \frac{I_{S3} + I_{S4}}{2} \tag{4.280}$$

$$\Delta I_S = I_{S3} - I_{S4} \tag{4.281}$$

$$R = \frac{R_3 + R_4}{2} \tag{4.282}$$

$$\Delta R = R_3 - R_4 \tag{4.283}$$

$$\alpha_F = \frac{\alpha_{F3} + \alpha_{F4}}{2} \tag{4.284}$$

$$\Delta \alpha_F = \alpha_{F3} - \alpha_{F4} \tag{4.285}$$

These relations can be inverted to give the original parameters in terms of the average and mismatch parameters. For example,

$$I_{C3} = I_C + \frac{\Delta I_C}{2} \tag{4.286}$$

$$I_{C4} = I_C - \frac{\Delta I_C}{2} \tag{4.287}$$

This set of equations for the various parameters is now substituted into (4.277). The result is

$$V_T \ln \left( \frac{I_C + \dfrac{\Delta I_C}{2}}{I_C - \dfrac{\Delta I_C}{2}} \right) - V_T \ln \left( \frac{I_S + \dfrac{\Delta I_S}{2}}{I_S - \dfrac{\Delta I_S}{2}} \right)$$

$$+ \frac{\left( I_C + \dfrac{\Delta I_C}{2} \right) \left( R + \dfrac{\Delta R}{2} \right)}{\alpha_F + \dfrac{\Delta \alpha_F}{2}} - \frac{\left( I_C - \dfrac{\Delta I_C}{2} \right) \left( R - \dfrac{\Delta R}{2} \right)}{\alpha_F - \dfrac{\Delta \alpha_F}{2}} = 0 \tag{4.288}$$

The first term in this equation can be rewritten as

$$V_T \ln \left( \frac{I_C + \dfrac{\Delta I_C}{2}}{I_C - \dfrac{\Delta I_C}{2}} \right) = V_T \ln \left( \frac{1 + \dfrac{\Delta I_C}{2 I_C}}{1 - \dfrac{\Delta I_C}{2 I_C}} \right) \tag{4.289}$$

If $\Delta I_C / 2I_C \ll 1$, this term can be rewritten as

$$V_T \ln \left( \frac{1 + \frac{\Delta I_C}{2I_C}}{1 - \frac{\Delta I_C}{2I_C}} \right) \simeq V_T \ln \left[ \left( 1 + \frac{\Delta I_C}{2I_C} \right) \left( 1 + \frac{\Delta I_C}{2I_C} \right) \right] \tag{4.290}$$

$$\simeq V_T \ln \left[ 1 + \frac{\Delta I_C}{I_C} + \left( \frac{\Delta I_C}{2I_C} \right)^2 \right] \tag{4.291}$$

$$\simeq V_T \ln \left( 1 + \frac{\Delta I_C}{I_C} \right) \tag{4.292}$$

where the squared term is neglected. The logarithm function has the infinite series

$$\ln(1 + x) = x - \frac{x^2}{2} + \dots \tag{4.293}$$

If $x \ll 1$,

$$\ln(1 + x) \simeq x \tag{4.294}$$

To simplify (4.292) when $\Delta I_C / I_C \ll 1$, let $x = \Delta I_C / I_C$. Then

$$V_T \ln \left( \frac{I_C + \frac{\Delta I_C}{2}}{I_C - \frac{\Delta I_C}{2}} \right) \simeq V_T \frac{\Delta I_C}{I_C} \tag{4.295}$$

Applying the same approximations to the other terms in (4.288), we obtain

$$\frac{\Delta I_C}{I_C} \simeq \left( \frac{1}{1 + \frac{g_m R}{\alpha_F}} \right) \frac{\Delta I_S}{I_S} + \frac{\frac{g_m R}{\alpha_F}}{1 + \frac{g_m R}{\alpha_F}} \left( -\frac{\Delta R}{R} + \frac{\Delta \alpha_F}{\alpha_F} \right) \tag{4.296}$$

We will consider two important limiting cases. First, since $g_m = I_C / V_T$, when $g_m R \ll 1$, the voltage drop on an emitter resistor is much smaller than the thermal voltage. In this case, the second term in (4.296) is small and the mismatch is mainly determined by the transistor $I_S$ mismatch in the first term. Observed mismatches in $I_S$ typically range from $\pm 10$ to $\pm 1$ percent depending on geometry. Second, when $g_m R \gg 1$, the voltage drop on an emitter resistor is much larger than the thermal voltage. In this case, the first term in (4.296) is small and the mismatch is mainly determined by the resistor mismatch and transistor $\alpha_F$ mismatch in the second term. Resistor mismatch typically ranges from $\pm 2$ to $\pm 0.1$ percent depending on geometry, and $\alpha_F$ matching is in the $\pm 0.1$ percent range for *npn* transistors. Thus for *npn* current sources, the use of emitter resistors offers significantly improved current matching. On the other hand, for *pnp* current sources, the $\alpha_F$ mismatch is larger due to the lower $\beta_F$, typically around $\pm 1$ percent. Therefore, the advantage of emitter degeneration is less significant with *pnp* than *npn* current sources.

## A.4.1.2 MOS

Matched current sources are often required in MOS analog integrated circuits. The factors affecting this mismatch can be calculated using the circuit of Fig. 4.52. The two transistors $M_1$ and $M_2$ will have mismatches in their $W/L$ ratios and threshold voltages. The drain

**Figure 4.52** Matched MOS current sources.

currents are given by

$$I_{D1} = \frac{1}{2}\mu_n C_{ox}\left(\frac{W}{L}\right)_1 (V_{GS} - V_{t1})^2 \tag{4.297}$$

$$I_{D2} = \frac{1}{2}\mu_n C_{ox}\left(\frac{W}{L}\right)_2 (V_{GS} - V_{t2})^2 \tag{4.298}$$

Defining average and mismatch quantities, we have

$$I_D = \frac{I_{D1} + I_{D2}}{2} \tag{4.299}$$

$$\Delta I_D = I_{D1} - I_{D2} \tag{4.300}$$

$$\frac{W}{L} = \frac{1}{2}\left[\left(\frac{W}{L}\right)_1 + \left(\frac{W}{L}\right)_2\right] \tag{4.301}$$

$$\Delta \frac{W}{L} = \left(\frac{W}{L}\right)_1 - \left(\frac{W}{L}\right)_2 \tag{4.302}$$

$$V_t = \frac{V_{t1} + V_{t2}}{2} \tag{4.303}$$

$$\Delta V_t = V_{t1} - V_{t2} \tag{4.304}$$

Substituting these expressions into (4.297) and (4.298) and neglecting high-order terms, we obtain

$$\frac{\Delta I_D}{I_D} = \frac{\Delta \frac{W}{L}}{\frac{W}{L}} - \frac{\Delta V_t}{(V_{GS} - V_t)/2} \tag{4.305}$$

The current mismatch consists of two components. The first is geometry dependent and contributes a fractional current mismatch that is independent of bias point. The second is dependent on threshold voltage mismatch and increases as the overdrive ($V_{GS} - V_t$) is reduced. This change occurs because as the overdrive is reduced, the fixed threshold mismatch progressively becomes a larger fraction of the total gate drive that is applied to the transistors and therefore contributes a progressively larger percentage error to the current mismatch. In practice, these observations are important because they affect the techniques used to distribute bias signals on integrated circuits.

Consider the current mirror shown in Fig. 4.53, which has one input and two outputs. At first, assume that $R_{S1} = R_{S2} = 0$. Also, assume that the input current is generated by a

**Figure 4.53** Current mirror with two outputs used to compare voltage- and current-routing techniques.

circuit with desirable properties. For example, a self-biased band-gap reference might be used to make $I_{IN}$ insensitive to changes in the power supply and temperature. Finally, assume that each output current is used to provide the required bias in one analog circuit on the integrated circuit (IC). For example, $M_2$ and $M_3$ could each act as the tail current source of a differential pair.

One way to build the circuit in Fig. 4.53 is to place $M_1$ on the IC near the input current source $I_{IN}$, while $M_2$ and $M_3$ are placed near the circuits that they bias, respectively. Since the gate-source voltage of $M_1$ must be routed to $M_2$ and $M_3$ here, this case is referred to as an example of the *voltage routing* of bias signals. An advantage of this approach is that by routing only two nodes (the gate and the source of $M_1$) around the IC, any number of output currents can be produced. Furthermore the gains from the input to each output of the current mirror are not affected by the number of outputs in MOS technologies because $\beta_F \rightarrow \infty$. (In bipolar technologies, $\beta_F$ is finite, and the gain error increases as the number of outputs increase, but a beta-helper configuration can be used to reduce such errors as described in Section 4.2.3.)

Unfortunately, voltage routing has two important disadvantages. First, the input and output transistors in the current mirror may be separated by distances that are large compared to the size of the IC, increasing the potential mismatches in (4.305). In particular, the threshold voltage typically displays considerable gradient with distance across a wafer. Therefore, when the devices are physically separated by large distances, large current mismatch can result from biasing current sources sharing the same gate-source bias, especially when the overdrive is small. The second disadvantage of voltage routing is that the output currents are sensitive to variations in the supply resistances $R_{S1}$ and $R_{S2}$. Although these resistances were assumed to be zero above, they are nonzero in practice because of imperfect conduction in the interconnect layers and their contacts. Since $I_{OUT2}$ flows in $R_{S2}$ and $(I_{OUT1} + I_{OUT2})$ flows in $R_{S1}$, nonzero resistances cause $V_{GS2} < V_{GS1}$ and $V_{GS3} < V_{GS1}$ when $I_{OUT1} > 0$ and $I_{OUT2} > 0$. Therefore, with perfectly matched transistors, the output currents are less than the input current, and the errors in the output currents can be predicted by an analysis similar to that presented in Section 4.4.1 for Widlar current sources. The key point here is that $R_{S1}$ and $R_{S2}$ increase as the distances between the input and output transistors increase, increasing the errors in the output currents. As a result of both of these disadvantages, the output currents may have considerable variation from one IC to another with voltage routing, increasing the difficulty of designing the circuits biased by $M_2$ and $M_3$ to meet the required specifications even if $I_{IN}$ is precisely controlled.

To overcome these problems, the circuit in Fig. 4.53 can be built so that $M_1$–$M_3$ are close together physically, and the current outputs $I_{OUT1}$ and $I_{OUT2}$ are routed as required on the IC. This case is referred to as an example of the *current routing* of bias signals. Current routing reduces the problems with mismatch and supply resistance by reducing the distances between the input and output transistors in the current mirror in Fig. 4.53

**Figure 4.54** Bias-distribution circuit using both current routing and voltage routing.

compared to voltage routing. One disadvantage of current routing is that it requires one node to be routed for each bias signal. Therefore, when the number of bias outputs is large, the die area required for the interconnect to distribute the bias currents can be much larger than that required with voltage routing. Another disadvantage of current routing is that it can increase the parasitic capacitance on the drains of $M_2$ and $M_3$. If these nodes are connected to circuits that process high-frequency signals, increased parasitic capacitance can reduce performance in some ways. For example, if $M_2$ and $M_3$ act as the tail current sources of differential pairs, increased parasitic capacitance will increase the common-mode gain and reduce the common-mode rejection ratio of each differential pair at high frequencies.

In practice, many ICs use a combination of current- and voltage-routing techniques. For example, Fig. 4.54 shows a circuit with five current mirrors, where the input and output currents are still referenced as in Fig. 4.53. If the current routing bus in Fig. 4.54 travels over a large distance, the parasitic capacitances on the drains of $M_2$ and $M_3$ may be large. However, the parasitic capacitances on the drains of $M_7$ and $M_{11}$ are minimized by using voltage routing within each current mirror. Although simple current mirrors are shown in Fig. 4.54, cascoding is often used in practice to reduce gain errors stemming from a finite Early voltage. In ICs using both current and voltage routing, currents are routed globally and voltages locally, where the difference between global and local routing depends on distance. When the distance is large enough to significantly worsen mismatch or supply-resistance effects, the routing is *global*. Otherwise, it is *local*. An effective combination of these bias distribution techniques is to divide an IC into blocks, where bias currents are routed between blocks and bias voltages within the blocks.

## A.4.2 INPUT OFFSET VOLTAGE OF DIFFERENTIAL PAIR WITH ACTIVE LOAD

### A.4.2.1 BIPOLAR

For the resistively loaded emitter-coupled pair, we showed in Chapter 3 that the input offset voltage arises primarily from mismatches in $I_S$ in the input transistors and from mismatches in the collector load resistors. In the active-load case, the input offset voltage results from nonzero base current of the load devices and mismatches in the input transistors and load devices. Refer to Fig. 4.25a. Assume the inputs are grounded. If the matching is perfect and if $\beta_F \to \infty$ in $T_3$ and $T_4$,

$$V_{OUT} = V_{CC} - |V_{BE3}| \tag{4.306}$$

Equation 4.306 holds because only this output voltage forces $V_{CE3} = V_{CE4}$, where $I_{C1} = I_{C2}$ and $V_{BE1} = V_{BE2}$, which is required by KVL when $V_{I1} = V_{I2}$.

The differential input required to drive the output to the value given by (4.306) is the input-referred offset voltage. With finite $\beta_F$ in the active-load transistors and/or device mismatch, the offset is usually nonzero. In the active-load, KVL shows that

$$V_{BE3} = V_{BE4} \tag{4.307}$$

Solving (1.58) for $V_{BE3}$ and $V_{BE4}$ and substituting in (4.307) gives

$$\frac{I_{C3}}{I_{S3}}\left(\frac{1}{1 + \dfrac{V_{CE3}}{V_{A3}}}\right) = \frac{I_{C4}}{I_{S4}}\left(\frac{1}{1 + \dfrac{V_{CE4}}{V_{A4}}}\right) \tag{4.308}$$

Assume that the Early voltages of $T_3$ and $T_4$ are identical. Since $V_{CE3} = V_{CE4}$ when (4.306) is satisfied, (4.308) can be simplified to

$$I_{C4} = I_{C3}\left(\frac{I_{S4}}{I_{S3}}\right) \tag{4.309}$$

Since $I_{C2} = -I_{C4}$, (4.309) can be written as

$$I_{C2} = -I_{C3}\left(\frac{I_{S4}}{I_{S3}}\right) \tag{4.310}$$

From KCL at the collector of $T_3$,

$$I_{C1} = -I_{C3}\left[1 + \left(\frac{2}{\beta_F}\right)\right] \tag{4.311}$$

where $\beta_F$ is the ratio of the collector to base current in the active-load devices. From KVL in the input loop,

$$V_{ID} = V_{I1} - V_{I2} = V_{BE1} - V_{BE2} \tag{4.312}$$

Then the input offset voltage, $V_{OS}$, is the value of $V_{ID}$ for which the output voltage is given by (4.306). If the Early voltages of $T_1$ and $T_2$ are identical, solving (1.58) for $V_{BE1}$ and $V_{BE2}$ and substituting into (4.312) gives

$$V_{OS} = V_{ID} = V_T \ln\left(\frac{I_{C1}}{I_{C2}}\frac{I_{S2}}{I_{S1}}\right) \tag{4.313}$$

because $V_{CE1} = V_{CE2}$ when (4.306) is satisfied. Substituting (4.310) and (4.311) in (4.313) gives

$$V_{OS} = V_T \ln\left[\frac{I_{S3}}{I_{S4}}\frac{I_{S2}}{I_{S1}}\left(1 + \frac{2}{\beta_F}\right)\right] \tag{4.314}$$

If the mismatches are small, this expression can be approximated as

$$V_{OS} \approx V_T\left(\frac{\Delta I_{SP}}{I_{SP}} - \frac{\Delta I_{SN}}{I_{SN}} + \frac{2}{\beta_F}\right) \tag{4.315}$$

using the technique described in Section 3.5.6.3, where

$$\Delta I_{SP} = I_{S3} - I_{S4} \tag{4.316}$$

$$I_{SP} = \frac{I_{S3} + I_{S4}}{2} \tag{4.317}$$

$$\Delta I_{SN} = I_{S1} - I_{S2} \tag{4.318}$$

$$I_{SN} = \frac{I_{S1} + I_{S2}}{2} \tag{4.319}$$

In the derivation of (4.315), we assumed that the Early voltages of matched transistors are identical. In practice, mismatch in Early voltages also contributes to the offset, but the effect is usually negligible when the transistors are biased with collector-emitter voltages much less than their Early voltages.

Assuming a worst-case value for $\Delta I_S / I_S$ of $\pm 5$ percent and a *pnp* beta of 20, the worst-case offset voltage is

$$V_{OS} \simeq V_T(0.05 + 0.05 + 0.1) = 0.2 V_T \simeq 5\,\text{mV} \tag{4.320}$$

To find the worst-case offset, we have added the mismatch terms for the *pnp* and *npn* transistors in (4.320) instead of subtracting them as shown in in (4.315) because the mismatch terms are random and independent of each other in practice. Therefore, the polarity of the mismatch terms is unknown in general. Comparing (4.320) to (3.219) shows that the actively loaded differential pair has significantly higher offset than the resistively loaded case under similar conditions. The offset arising here from mismatch in the load devices can be reduced by inserting resistors in series with the emitters of $T_3$ and $T_4$ as shown in Section A.4.1. To reduce the offset arising from finite $\beta_F$ in the load devices, the current mirror in the load can use a beta helper transistor as described in Section 4.2.3.

### A.4.2.2 MOS

The offset in the CMOS differential pair with active load shown in Fig. 4.25b is similar to the bipolar case. If the matching is perfect with the inputs grounded,

$$V_{\text{OUT}} = V_{DD} - |V_{GS3}| \tag{4.321}$$

Equation 4.321 holds because only this output voltage forces $V_{DS3} = V_{DS4}$, where $I_1 = I_2$ and $V_{GS1} = V_{GS2}$, which is required by KVL when $V_{I1} = V_{I2}$.

The differential input required to drive the output to the value given by (4.321) is the input-referred offset voltage. With device mismatch, the offset is usually nonzero.

$$V_{ID} = V_{GS1} - V_{GS2} = V_{t1} + V_{ov1} - V_{t2} - V_{ov2} \tag{4.322}$$

Assume that the Early voltages of $T_1$ and $T_2$ are identical. Since $V_{DS1} = V_{DS2} = V_{DSN}$ when $V_{ID} = V_{OS}$, applying (1.165) to $V_{ov1}$ and $V_{ov2}$ in (4.322) gives

$$V_{OS} = V_{t1} - V_{t2} + \sqrt{\frac{1}{1 + \lambda_N V_{DSN}}} \left( \sqrt{\frac{2I_1}{k'(W/L)_1}} - \sqrt{\frac{2I_2}{k'(W/L)_2}} \right) \tag{4.323}$$

If the mismatches are small, this expression can be approximated as

$$V_{OS} \simeq V_{t1} - V_{t2} + \frac{V_{ovN}}{2} \left( \frac{\Delta I_N}{I_N} - \frac{\Delta (W/L)_N}{(W/L)_N} \right) \tag{4.324}$$

using the technique described in Section 3.5.6.7, where

$$V_{ovN} = \sqrt{\frac{2I_N}{k'(W/L)_N(1 + \lambda_N V_{DSN})}} \tag{4.325}$$

$$\Delta I_N = I_1 - I_2 \tag{4.326}$$

$$I_N = \frac{I_1 + I_2}{2} \tag{4.327}$$

$$\Delta(W/L)_N = (W/L)_1 - (W/L)_2 \tag{4.328}$$

$$(W/L)_N = \frac{(W/L)_1 + (W/L)_2}{2} \tag{4.329}$$

Since $I_1 = -I_3$ and $I_2 = -I_4$

$$\frac{\Delta I_N}{I_N} = \frac{\Delta I_P}{I_P} \tag{4.330}$$

where

$$\Delta I_P = I_3 - I_4 \tag{4.331}$$

$$I_P = \frac{I_3 + I_4}{2} \tag{4.332}$$

To find $\Delta I_P/I_P$, we will use KVL in the gate-source loop in the load as follows

$$0 = V_{GS3} - V_{GS4} = V_{t3} + V_{ov3} - V_{t4} - V_{ov4} \tag{4.333}$$

Since $T_3$ and $T_4$ are p-channel transistors, their overdrives are negative. Assume that the Early voltages of $T_3$ and $T_4$ are identical. Since $V_{DS3} = V_{DS4} = V_{DSP}$ when $V_{ID} = V_{OS}$ (4.333) can be rewritten as

$$0 = V_{t3} - V_{t4} - \sqrt{\frac{1}{1 + |\lambda_P V_{DSP}|}} \left( \sqrt{\frac{2|I_3|}{k'(W/L)_3}} - \sqrt{\frac{2|I_4|}{k'(W/L)_4}} \right) \tag{4.334}$$

In (4.334), absolute value functions have been used so that the arguments of the square-root functions are positive. If the mismatches are small, this expression can be approximated as

$$\frac{\Delta I_P}{I_P} \simeq \frac{V_{t3} - V_{t4}}{\frac{|V_{ovP}|}{2}} + \frac{\Delta(W/L)_P}{(W/L)_P} \tag{4.335}$$

using the technique described in Section 3.5.6.7, where

$$|V_{ovP}| = \sqrt{\frac{2|I_P|}{k'(W/L)_P(1 + |\lambda_P V_{DSP}|)}} \tag{4.336}$$

$$\Delta(W/L)_P = (W/L)_3 - (W/L)_4 \tag{4.337}$$

$$(W/L)_P = \frac{(W/L)_3 + (W/L)_4}{2} \tag{4.338}$$

Substituting (4.335) and (4.330) into (4.324) gives

$$V_{OS} \simeq V_{t1} - V_{t2} + \frac{V_{ovN}}{2} \left( \frac{V_{t3} - V_{t4}}{\frac{|V_{ovP}|}{2}} + \frac{\Delta(W/L)_P}{(W/L)_P} - \frac{\Delta(W/L)_N}{(W/L)_N} \right) \tag{4.339}$$

Comparing (4.339) to (4.315) shows that the MOS differential pair with active load includes terms to account for threshold mismatch but excludes a term to account for finite beta in the active load because $\beta_F \rightarrow \infty$ in MOS transistors.

▪ **EXAMPLE**

Find the input-referred offset voltage of the circuit in Fig. 4.25$b$ using the transistor parameters in the table below.

| Transistor | $V_t$ (V) | $W$ ($\mu$m) | $L$ ($\mu$m) | $k'$ ($\mu$A/V$^2$) |
|------------|-----------|--------------|--------------|---------------------|
| $T_1$ | 0.705 | 49 | 1 | 100 |
| $T_2$ | 0.695 | 51 | 1 | 100 |
| $T_3$ | -0.698 | 103 | 1 | 50 |
| $T_4$ | -0.702 | 97 | 1 | 50 |

Assume that $I_{\text{TAIL}} = 200\ \mu$A and that $\lambda_N V_{DSN} \ll 1$ and $|\lambda_P V_{DSP}| \ll 1$. From (4.327) and KCL,

$$I_N = \frac{I_1 + I_2}{2} = \frac{I_{\text{TAIL}}}{2} = 100\ \mu\text{A} \qquad (4.340)$$

Substituting (4.340) and (4.329) into (4.325) gives

$$V_{ovN} \simeq \sqrt{\frac{200}{100(49 + 51)/2}}\ \text{V} = 0.2\ \text{V} \qquad (4.341)$$

Similarly, from (4.332) and KCL

$$I_P = \frac{I_3 + I_4}{2} = -\frac{I_{\text{TAIL}}}{2} = -100\ \mu\text{A} \qquad (4.342)$$

Substituting (4.342) and (4.338) into (4.336) gives

$$|V_{ovP}| \simeq \sqrt{\frac{200}{50(103 + 97)/2}}\ \text{V} = 0.2\ \text{V} \qquad (4.343)$$

Substituting (4.337) and (4.328) into (4.339) gives

$$V_{OS} \simeq 0.705\ \text{V} - 0.695\ \text{V}$$
$$+ 0.1\left(\frac{-0.698 + 0.702}{0.1} + \frac{103 - 97}{(103 + 97)/2} - \frac{49 - 51}{(49 + 51)/2}\right)\text{V}$$
$$\simeq 0.01\ \text{V} + 0.1(0.04 + 0.06 + 0.04)\ \text{V} = 0.024\ \text{V} \qquad (4.344)$$

In this example, the mismatches have been chosen so that the individual contributions to the offset add constructively to give the worst-case offset.

# PROBLEMS

For the bipolar transistors in these problems, use the high-voltage device parameters given in Fig. 2.30 and Fig. 2.35, unless otherwise specified. Assume that $r_b = 0$ and $r_\mu \rightarrow \infty$.

in all problems. Assume all bipolar transistors operate in the forward-active region, and neglect base currents in bias calculations unless otherwise specified.

**4.1** Determine the output current and output resistance of the bipolar current mirror shown in Fig. 4.55. Find the output current if $V_{OUT} = 1$ V, 5 V, and 30 V. Ignore the effects of nonzero base currents. Compare your answer with a SPICE simulation.

$V_{CC} = 15$ V

$R = 10$ kΩ

$I_{OUT}$

$V_{OUT}$

$Q_1$  $Q_2$    $Q_3$  $Q_4$  $Q_5$

**Figure 4.55** Circuit for Problem 4.1.

**4.2** Repeat Problem 4.1 including the effects of nonzero base currents.

**4.3** Design a simple MOS current mirror of the type shown in Fig. 4.4 to meet the following constraints:

(a) Transistor $M_2$ must operate in the active region for values of $V_{OUT}$ to within 0.2 V of ground.

(b) The output current must be 50 μA.

(c) The output current must change less than 1 percent for a change in output voltage of 1 V.

Make $M_1$ and $M_2$ identical. You are to minimize the total device area within the given constraints. Here the device area will be taken to be the total gate area ($W \times L$ product). Assume $X_d = 0$ and take other device data from Table 2.4.

**4.4** Calculate an analytical expression for the small-signal output resistance $R_o$ of the bipolar cascode current mirror of Fig. 4.8. Assume that the input current source is not ideal and that the nonideality is modeled by placing a resistor $R_1$ in parallel with $I_{IN}$. Show that for large $R_1$, the output resistance approaches $\beta_0 r_o/2$. Calculate the value of $R_o$ if $V_{CC} = 5$ V, $I_{IN} = 0$, and $R_1 = 10$ kΩ, and estimate the value of $V_{OUT}$ below which $R_o$ will begin to decrease substantially. Use SPICE to check your calculations and also to investigate the $\beta_F$ sensitivity by varying $\beta_F$ by $-50$ percent and examining

$I_{OUT}$. Use SPICE to plot the large-signal $I_{OUT}$-$V_{OUT}$ characteristic.

**4.5** Calculate the output resistance of the circuit of Fig. 4.9, assuming that $I_{IN} = 100$ μA and the devices have drawn dimensions of 100 μm/1 μm. Use the process parameters given in Table 2.4, and assume for all devices that $X_d = 0$. Also, ignore the body effect for simplicity. Compare your answer with a SPICE simulation and also use SPICE to plot the $I_{OUT}$-$V_{OUT}$ characteristic for $V_{OUT}$ from 0 to 3 V.

**4.6** Using the data given in the example of Section 1.9, include the effects of substrate leakage in the calculation of the output resistance for the circuit of Problem 4.5. Let $V_{OUT} = 2$ V and 3 V.

**4.7** Design the circuit of Fig. 4.11b to satisfy the constraints in Problem 4.3 except the output resistance objective is that the output current change less than 0.02 percent for a 1 V change in the output voltage. Ignore the body effect for simplicity. Make all devices identical except for $M_4$. Use SPICE to check your design and also to plot the $I_{OUT}$-$V_{OUT}$ characteristic for $V_{OUT}$ from 0 to 3 V.

**4.8** For the circuit of Fig. 4.56, assume that $(W/L)_8 = (W/L)$. Ignoring the body effect, find $(W/L)_6$ and $(W/L)_7$ so that $V_{DS6} = V_{DS7} = V_{ov8}$. Draw the schematic of a double-cascode current mirror that uses the circuit of Fig. 4.56 to bias both cascode devices in the output branch. For this current mirror, calculate the output resistance, the minimum output voltage for which all three transistors in the output branch operate in the active region, the total voltage across all the devices in the input branch, and the systematic gain error.

$V_{DD}$

$I_{IN}$

$M_8$

$M_7$

$M_6$

**Figure 4.56** Circuit for Problem 4.8.

**4.9** Calculate the output resistance of the Wilson current mirror shown in Fig. 4.57. What is the percentage change in $I_{OUT}$ for a 5-V change in $V_{OUT}$? Compare your answer with a SPICE simulation using a full device model. Use SPICE to check the $\beta_F$ sensitivity by varying $\beta_F$ by $-50$ percent and examining $I_{OUT}$. Also, use SPICE to plot the large-signal $I_{OUT}$-$V_{OUT}$ characteristic for $V_{OUT}$ from 0 to 15 V.

+15 V

13.7 kΩ

$I_{OUT}$

$Q_2$

$V_{OUT}$

$Q_1$

$Q_3$

**Figure 4.57** Circuit for Problem 4.9.

**4.10** Calculate the small-signal voltage gain of the common-source amplifier with active load in Fig. 4.16b. Assume that $V_{DD} = 3$ V and that all the transistors operate in the active region. Do the calculations for values of $I_{REF}$ of 1 mA, 100 μA, 10 μA, and 1 μA. Assume that the drawn dimensions of each transistor are $W = 100$ μm and $L = 1$ μm. Assume $X_d = 0$ and use Table 2.4 for other parameters.

**(a)** At first, assume the transistors operate in strong inversion in all cases.

**(b)** Repeat part (a) including the effects of weak inversion by using (1.253) with $n = 1.5$ to calculate the transconductance of $M_1$. Assume that a transistor operates in weak inversion when its overdrive is less than $2nV_T$, as given in (1.255).

**(c)** Use SPICE to check your calculations for both parts (a) and (b).

**4.11** Calculate the small-signal voltage gain of a common-source amplifier with depletion load in Fig. 4.20, including both the body effect and channel-length modulation. Assume that $V_{DD} = 3$ V and that the dc input voltage is adjusted so that the dc output voltage is 1 V. Assume that $M_1$ has drawn dimensions of $W = 100$ μm and $L = 1$ μm. Also, assume that $M_2$ has drawn dimensions of $W = 10$ μm and $L = 1$ μm. For both transistors, assume that $X_d = 0$. Use Table 2.4 for other parameters of both transistors.

**4.12** Determine the unloaded voltage gain $v_o/v_i$ and output resistance for the circuit of Fig. 4.58. Check with SPICE and also use SPICE to plot out the large-signal $V_O$-$V_I$ transfer characteristic for $V_{SUP} = 2.5$ V. Use SPICE to determine the CMRR if the current-source output resistance is 1 MΩ.

**4.13** Repeat Problem 4.12, but now assuming that 2-kΩ resistors are inserted in series with the emitters of $Q_3$ and $Q_4$.

**4.14** Repeat Problem 4.12 except replace $Q_1$ and $Q_2$ with n-channel MOS transistors $M_1$ and $M_2$. Also, replace $Q_3$ and $Q_4$ with p-channel MOS transistors $M_3$ and $M_4$. Assume $W_n = 50$ μm and $W_p = 100$ μm. For all transistors, assume

$+V_{SUP}$

$Q_3$          $Q_4$

$V_o = V_O + v_o$

$Q_1$          $Q_2$

$V_i = V_I + v_i$

100 μA

$-V_{SUP}$

**Figure 4.58** Circuit for Problem 4.12.

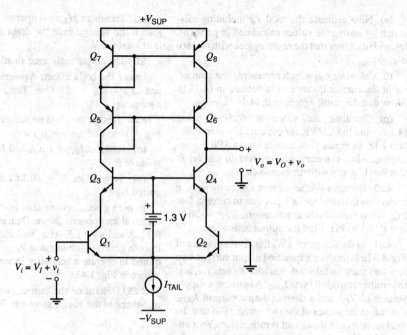

**Figure 4.59** Cascode active-load circuit for Problem 4.16.

$L_{drwn} = 1\ \mu m$ and $X_d = 0$. Use Table 2.3 for other parameters.

**4.15** Repeat Problem 4.14, but now assuming that 2 kΩ resistors are inserted in series with the sources of $M_3$ and $M_4$. Ignore the body effect.

**4.16** Determine the unloaded voltage gain $v_o/v_i$ and output resistance for the circuit of Fig. 4.59. Neglect $r_\mu$. Verify with SPICE and also use SPICE to plot the large-signal $V_O$-$V_I$ transfer characteristic for $V_{SUP} = 2.5$ V.

**4.17** Repeat Problem 4.16 except replace the *npn* and *pnp* transistors with *n*-channel and *p*-channel MOS transistors, respectively. Assume $W_n = 50\ \mu m$ and $W_p = 100\ \mu m$. For all transistors, assume $L_{drwn} = 1\ \mu m$ and $X_d = 0$. Let $I_{TAIL} = 100\ \mu A$. Ignore the body effect. Use Table 2.3 for other parameters.

**4.18** Find $G_m[dm]$ of a source-coupled pair with a current-mirror load with nonzero mismatch (Fig. 4.29b) and show that it is approximately given by (4.184). Calculate the value of $G_m[dm]$ using the following data:

|            | $T_1$ | $T_2$ | $T_3$ | $T_4$ | $T_5$ |
|------------|-------|-------|-------|-------|-------|
| $g_m$ (mA/V) | 1.05 | 0.95 | 1.1 | 0.9 | 2.0 |
| $r_o$ (MΩ) | 0.95 | 1.05 | 1.0 | 1.0 | 0.5 |

Compare your answer with a SPICE simulation. Also, compare your answer to the result that would apply without mismatch.

**4.19** Although $G_m[cm]$ of a differential pair with a current-mirror load can be calculated exactly from a small-signal diagram where mismatch is allowed, the calculation is complicated because the mismatch terms interact, and the results are difficult to interpret. In practice, the mismatch terms are often a small fraction of the corresponding average values, and the interactions between mismatch terms are often negligible. Using the following steps as a guide, calculate an approximation to $G_m[cm]$ including the effects of mismatch.

(a) Derive the ratio $i_2/v_{ic}$ included in (4.165) and show that this ratio is approximately $1/2r_{tail}$ as shown in (4.185) if $\epsilon_d \ll 2$, $g_{m2}r_{o2} \gg 1$, and $2g_{m2}r_{tail} \gg 1$.

(b) Use (4.173) to calculate $\epsilon_d$ with perfect matching, where $\epsilon_d$ represents the gain error of the differential pair with a pure common-mode input and is defined in (4.161).

(c) Calculate $\epsilon_d$ if $1/g_{m3} = 0$ and if the only mismatch is $g_{m1} \neq g_{m2}$.

(d) Calculate $\epsilon_d$ if $1/g_{m3} = 0$ and if the only mismatch is $r_{o1} \neq r_{o2}$.

**(e)** Now estimate the total $\epsilon_d$ including mismatch by adding the values calculated in parts (b), (c), and (d). Show that the result agrees with (4.186) if $g_{m3}r_{o(dp)} \gg 1$.

**(f)** Calculate $\epsilon_m$, which represents the gain error of the current mirror and is defined in (4.133). Show that the result agrees with (4.187).

**(g)** Calculate the value of $G_m[cm]$ using (4.185) and the CMRR for the data given in Problem 4.18. Compare your answer with a SPICE simulation. Also, compare your answer to the result that would apply without mismatch.

**4.20** Design a Widlar current source using $npn$ transistors that produces a 5-$\mu$A output current. Use Fig. 4.31a with identical transistors, $V_{CC} = 30$ V, and $R_1 = 30$ k$\Omega$. Find the output resistance.

**4.21** In the design of a Widlar current source of Fig. 4.31a to produce a specified output current, two resistors must be selected. Resistor $R_1$ sets $I_{IN}$, and the emitter resistor $R_2$ sets $I_{OUT}$. Assuming a supply voltage of $V_{CC}$ and a desired output current $I_{OUT}$, determine the values of the two resistors so that the total resistance in the circuit is minimized. Your answer should be given as expressions for $R_1$ and $R_2$ in terms of $V_{CC}$ and $I_{OUT}$. What values would these expressions give for Problem 4.20? Are these values practical?

**4.22** Determine the output current in the circuit of Fig. 4.60.

**Figure 4.60** Circuit for Problem 4.22.

**4.23** Design a MOS Widlar current source using the circuit shown in Fig. 4.31b to meet the following constraints with $V_{DD} = 3$ V:

**(a)** The input current should be 100 $\mu$A, and the output current should be 10 $\mu$A.

**(b)** $V_{ov1} = 0.2$ V.

**(c)** Transistor $M_2$ must operate in the active region if the voltage from the drain of $M_2$ to ground is at least 0.2 V.

**(d)** The output resistance should be 50 M$\Omega$.

Ignore the body effect. Assume $L_{drwn} = 1$ $\mu$m and $X_d = L_d = 0$. Use Table 2.4 for other parameters.

**4.24** Design the MOS peaking current source in Fig. 4.34 so that $I_{OUT} = 0.1$ $\mu$A.

**(a)** First, let $I_{IN} = 1$ $\mu$A and find the required value of $R$.

**(b)** Second, let $R = 10$ k$\Omega$ and find the required $I_{IN}$.

In both cases, assume that both transistors are identical and operate in weak inversion with $I_t = 0.1$ $\mu$A and $n = 1.5$. Also, find the minimum $W/L$ in both cases, assuming that $V_{GS} - V_t < 0$ is required to operate a transistor in weak inversion as shown in Fig. 1.45.

**4.25** Determine the output current and output resistance of the circuit shown in Fig. 4.61.

**Figure 4.61** Circuit for Problem 4.25.

**4.26** Determine the value of sensitivity $S$ of output current to supply voltage for the circuit of Fig. 4.62, where $S = (V_{CC}/I_{OUT})(\partial I_{OUT}/\partial V_{CC})$.

**4.27** In the analysis of the hypothetical reference of Fig. 4.44, the current $I_1$ was assumed proportional to temperature. Assume instead that this current is derived from a diffused resistor, and thus has a $TC_F$ of $-1500$ ppm/°C. Determine the new value of $V_{OUT}$ required to achieve zero $TC_F$ at 25°C. Neglect base current.

Figure 4.62   Circuit for Problem 4.26.

**4.28** The circuit of Fig. 4.46c is to be used as a band-gap reference. If the op amp is ideal, its differential input voltage and current are both zero and

$$V_{OUT} = (V_{BE1} + I_1 R_1) = (V_{BE1} + I_2 R_2)$$

$$V_{OUT} = V_{BE1} + R_2 \left( \frac{V_{BE1} - V_{BE2}}{R_3} \right)$$

Assume that $I_1$ is to be made equal to 200 μA, and that $(V_{BE1} - V_{BE2})$ is to be made equal to 100 mV. Determine $R_1$, $R_2$, and $R_3$ to realize zero $TC_F$ of $V_{OUT}$ at 25°C. Neglect base currents.

**4.29** A band-gap reference like that of Fig. 4.47 is designed to have nominally zero $TC_F$ at 25°C. Due to process variations, the saturation current $I_S$ of the transistors is actually twice the nominal

value. Assume $V_{OS} = 0$. What is $dV_{OUT}/dT$ at 25°C? Neglect base currents.

**4.30** Simulate the band-gap reference from Problem 4.29 on SPICE. Assume that the amplifier is just a voltage-controlled voltage source with an open-loop gain of 10,000 and that the resistor values are independent of temperature. Also assume that $I_{S1} = 1.25 \times 10^{-17}$ A and $I_{S2} = 1 \times 10^{-16}$ A. In SPICE, adjust the closed-loop gain of the amplifier (by choosing suitable resistor values) so that the output $TC_F$ is zero at 25°C. What is the resulting target value of $V_{OUT}$? Now double $I_{S1}$ and $I_{S2}$. Use SPICE to adjust the gain so that $V_{OUT}$ is equal to the target at 25°C. Find the new $dV_{OUT}/dT$ at 25°C with SPICE. Compare this result with the calculations from Problem 4.29.

**4.31** Repeat Problem 4.29 assuming that the values of $I_S$, $R_2$, and $R_1$ are nominal but that $R_3$ is 1 percent low. Assume $V_{BE(on)} = 0.6$ V.

**4.32** A band-gap reference circuit is shown in Fig. 4.63. Assume that $\beta_F \to \infty$, $V_A \to \infty$, $I_{S1} = 1 \times 10^{-15}$ A, and $I_{S2} = 8 \times 10^{-15}$ A. Assume the op amp is ideal except for a possibly nonzero offset voltage $V_{OS}$, which is modeled by a voltage source in Fig. 4.63.

(a) Suppose that $R_2$ is trimmed to set $V_{OUT}$ equal to the target voltage for which $dV_{OUT}/dT = 0$ at $T = 25$°C when $V_{OS} = 0$. Find $dV_{OUT}/dT$ at $T = 25$°C when $V_{OS} = 30$ mV.

(b) Under the conditions in part (a), is $dV_{OUT}/dT$ positive or negative? Explain.

**4.33** For the circuit of Fig. 4.64, find the value of $W/L$ for which $dV_{GS}/dT = 0$ at 25°C. Assume that the threshold voltage falls 2 mV for each 1°C increase in temperature. Also, assume that the

Figure 4.63   Band-gap reference circuit for Problem 4.32.

mobility temperature dependence is given by (4.243) with $n = 1.5$. Finally, use Table 2.4 for other parameters at 25°C, and let $I = 200$ μA.

**Figure 4.64**  Circuit for Problem 4.33.

**4.34**  Calculate the bias current of the circuit shown in Fig. 4.65 as a function of $R$, $\mu_n C_{ox}$, $(W/L)_1$, and $(W/L)_2$. Comment on the temperature behavior of the bias current. For simplicity, assume that $X_d = L_d = 0$ and ignore the body effect. Assume $M_4$ is identical to $M_3$.

**Figure 4.65**  Circuit for Problem 4.34.

**4.35**  The circuit of Fig. 4.65 produces a supply-insensitive current. Calculate the ratio of small-signal variations in $I_{BIAS}$ to small-signal variations in $V_{DD}$ at low frequencies. Ignore the body effect but include finite transistor $r_o$ in this calculation.

**4.36**  For the bias circuit shown in Fig. 4.66, determine the bias current. Assume that $X_d = L_d = 0$. Neglect base currents and the body

effect. Comment on the temperature dependence of the bias current. Assume a channel mobility and oxide thickness from Table 2.4. Compare your calculations to a SPICE simulation using a full circuit model from Table 2.4, and also use SPICE to determine the supply-voltage sensitivity of $I_{BIAS}$.

**Figure 4.66**  Circuit for Problem 4.36.

**4.37**  A pair of bipolar current sources is to be designed to produce output currents that match with ±1 percent. If resistors display a worst-case mismatch of ±0.5 percent, and transistors a worst-case $V_{BE}$ mismatch of 2 mV, how much voltage must be dropped across the emitter resistors?

**4.38**  Determine the worst-case input offset voltage for the circuit of Fig. 4.58. Assume the worst-case $I_S$ mismatches in the transistors are ±5 percent and $\beta_F = 15$ for the *pnp* transistors. Assume the dc output voltage is $V_{SUP} - |V_{BE(on)}|$.

**4.39**  Repeat Problem 4.38, but assume that 2-kΩ resistors are placed in series with the emitters of $Q_3$ and $Q_4$. Assume the worst-case resistor mismatch is ±0.5 percent and the worst-case *pnp* $\beta_F$ mismatch is ±10 percent.

**4.40**  Repeat Problem 4.38 but replace the bipolar transistors with MOS transistors as in Problem 4.14. Assume the worst-case $W/L$ mismatches in the transistors are ±5 percent and the worst-case $V_t$ mismatches are ±10 mV. Assume the dc output voltage to ground is $V_{SUP} - |V_{GS3}|$. Also, assume that $(W/L)_1 + (W/L)_2 = 20$ and $(W/L)_3 + (W/L)_4 = 60$. Use Table 2.4 to calculate the transconductance parameters.

# REFERENCES

1. Y. P. Tsividis. *Operation and Modeling of the MOS Transistor,* McGraw Hill, New York, 1987, p. 139.

2. J.-B. Shyu, G. C. Temes, and F. Krummenacher. "Random Error Effects in Matched MOS Capacitors and Current Sources," *IEEE Journal of Solid-State Circuits,* Vol. SC-19, pp. 948–955, December 1984.

3. K. R. Lakshmikumar, R. A. Hadaway, and M. A. Copeland. "Characterisation and Modeling of Mismatch in MOS Transistors for Precision Analog Design," *IEEE Journal of Solid-State Circuits,* Vol. SC-21, pp. 1057–1066, December 1986.

4. M. J. M. Pelgrom, A. C. J. Duinmaijer, and A. P. G. Welbers. "Matching Properties of MOS Transistors," *IEEE Journal of Solid-State Circuits,* Vol. 24, pp. 1433–1440, October 1989.

5. W.-J. Hsu, B. J. Sheu, and S. M. Gowda. "Design of Reliable VLSI Circuits Using Simulation Techniques," *IEEE Journal of Solid-State Circuits,* Vol. 26, pp. 452–457, March 1991.

6. T. C. Choi, R. T. Kaneshiro, R. W. Brodersen, P. R. Gray, W. B. Jett, and M. Wilcox. "High-Frequency CMOS Switched-Capacitor Filters for Communications Application," *IEEE Journal of Solid-State Circuits,* Vol. SC-18, pp. 652–664, December 1983.

7. N. S. Sooch. "MOS Cascode Current Mirror," U.S. Patent 4,550,284, October 1985.

8. G. R. Wilson. "A Monolithic Junction FET—n-p-n Operational Amplifier," *IEEE Journal of Solid-State Circuits,* Vol. SC-3, pp. 341–348, December 1968.

9. D. Fullagar. "A New-Performance Monolithic Operational Amplifier," *Fairchild Semiconductor Applications Brief,* May 1968.

10. R. J. Widlar. "Some Circuit Design Techniques for Linear Integrated Circuits," *IEEE Transactions on Circuit Theory,* Vol. CT-12, pp. 586–590, December 1965.

11. R. J. Widlar. "Design Techniques for Monolithic Operational Amplifiers," *IEEE Journal of Solid-State Circuits,* Vol. SC-4, pp. 184–191, August 1969.

12. M. Nagata. "Constant Current Circuits," Japanese Patent 628,228, May 6, 1971.

13. T. M. Frederiksen. "Constant Current Source," U.S. Patent 3,659,121, April 25, 1972.

14. C. Y. Kwok. "Low-Voltage Peaking Complementary Current Generator," *IEEE Journal of Solid-State Circuits,* Vol. SC-20, pp. 816–818, June 1985.

15. R. J. Widlar. "New Developments in IC Voltage Regulators," *IEEE Journal of Solid-State Circuits,* Vol. SC-6, pp. 2–7, February 1971.

16. C. R. Palmer and R. C. Dobkin. "A Curvature Corrected Micropower Voltage Reference," *International Solid-State Circuits Conference,* pp. 58–59, February 1981.

17. G. C. M. Meijer, P. C. Schmale, and K. van Zalinge. "A New Curvature-Corrected Bandgap Reference," *IEEE Journal of Solid-State Circuits,* Vol. SC-17, pp. 1139–1143, December 1982.

18. B.-S. Song and P. R. Gray. "A Precision Curvature-Compensated CMOS Bandgap Reference," *IEEE Journal of Solid-State Circuits,* Vol. SC-18, pp. 634–643, December 1983.

19. A. P. Brokaw. "A Simple Three-Terminal IC Bandgap Reference," *IEEE Journal of Solid-State Circuits,* Vol. SC-9, pp. 388–393, December 1974.

20. Y. P. Tsividis. "Accurate Analysis of Temperature Effects in $I_C - V_{BE}$ Characteristics with Application to Bandgap Reference Sources," *IEEE Journal of Solid-State Circuits,* Vol. SC-15, pp. 1076–1084, December 1980.

21. A. P. Brokaw. Private Communication.

22. R. A. Pease. Private Communication.

23. K. E. Kuijk. "A Precision Reference Voltage Source," *IEEE Journal of Solid-State Circuits,* Vol. SC-8, pp. 222–226, June 1973.

24. T. R. Viswanathan. Private Communication.

25. E. A. Vittoz and O. Neyroud. "A Low-Voltage CMOS Bandgap Reference," *IEEE Journal of Solid-State Circuits,* Vol. SC-14, pp. 573–577, June 1979.

# Output Stages

## 5.1 Introduction

The output stage of an amplifier must satisfy a number of special requirements. One of the most important requirements is to deliver a specified amount of signal power to a load with acceptably low levels of signal distortion. Another common objective of output-stage design is to minimize the output impedance so that the voltage gain is relatively unaffected by the value of load impedance. A well-designed output stage should achieve these performance specifications while consuming low quiescent power and, in addition, should not be a major limitation on the frequency response of the amplifier.

In this chapter, several output-stage configurations will be considered to satisfy the above requirements. The simplest output-stage configurations are the emitter and source followers. More complex output stages employing multiple output devices are also treated, and comparisons are made of power-output capability and efficiency.

Because of their excellent current-handling capability, bipolar transistors are the preferred devices for use in output stages. Although parasitic bipolar transistors can be used in some CMOS output stages, output stages in CMOS technologies are usually constructed without bipolar transistors and are also described in this chapter.

## 5.2 The Emitter Follower as an Output Stage

An emitter-follower output stage is shown in Fig. 5.1. To simplify the analysis, positive and negative bias supplies of equal magnitude $V_{CC}$ are assumed, although these supplies may have different values in practice. When output voltage $V_o$ is zero, output current $I_o$ is also zero. The emitter-follower output device $Q_1$ is biased to a quiescent current $I_Q$ by current source $Q_2$. The output stage is driven by voltage $V_i$, which has a quiescent dc value of $V_{be1}$ for $V_o = 0$ V. The bias components $R_1$, $R_3$, and $Q_3$ can be those used to bias other stages in the circuit. Since the quiescent current $I_Q$ in $Q_2$ will usually be larger than the reference current $I_R$, resistor $R_2$ is usually smaller than $R_1$ to accommodate this difference.

This circuit topology can also be implemented in CMOS technologies using an MOS current source for bias and the parasitic bipolar-transistor emitter follower available in standard CMOS processes. Because any large current flow to the substrate can initiate the *pnpn* latch-up phenomenon described in Chapter 2, however, this configuration should be used carefully in CMOS technologies with lightly doped substrates. Extensive substrate taps in the vicinity of the emitter follower are essential to collect the substrate current flow.

### 5.2.1 Transfer Characteristics of the Emitter-Follower

The circuit of Fig. 5.1 must handle large signal amplitudes; that is, the current and voltage swings resulting from the presence of signals may be a large fraction of the bias values. As a result, the small-signal analyses that have been used extensively up to this point

**Figure 5.1** Emitter-follower output stage with current-mirror bias.

must be used with care in this situation. For this reason, we first determine the dc transfer characteristic of the emitter follower. This characteristic allows calculation of the gain of the circuit and also gives important information on the *linearity* and thus on the *distortion* performance of the stage.

Consider the circuit of Fig. 5.1. The large-signal transfer characteristic can be derived as follows:

$$V_i = V_{be1} + V_o \tag{5.1}$$

In this case, the base-emitter voltage $V_{be1}$ of $Q_1$ cannot be assumed constant but must be expressed in terms of the collector current $I_{c1}$ of $Q_1$ and the saturation current $I_S$. If the load resistance $R_L$ is small compared with the output resistance of the transistors,

$$V_{be1} = \frac{kT}{q} \ln\left(\frac{I_{c1}}{I_S}\right) \tag{5.2}$$

if $Q_1$ is in the forward-active region. Also

$$I_{c1} = I_Q + \frac{V_o}{R_L} \tag{5.3}$$

if $Q_2$ is in the forward-active region and $\beta_F$ is assumed large. Substitution of (5.3) and (5.2) in (5.1) gives

$$V_i = \frac{kT}{q} \ln\left(\frac{I_Q + \dfrac{V_o}{R_L}}{I_S}\right) + V_o \tag{5.4}$$

Equation 5.4 is a nonlinear equation relating $V_o$ and $V_i$ if both $Q_1$ and $Q_2$ are in the forward-active region.

The transfer characteristic from (5.4) has been plotted in Fig. 5.2. First, consider the case where $R_L$ is large, which is labeled $R_{L1}$. In this case, the first term on the right-hand side of (5.4), which represents the base-emitter voltage $V_{be1}$ of $Q_1$, is almost constant as $V_o$ changes. This result stems from the observation that the current in the load is small for a large $R_L$; therefore, the current in $Q_1$ and $V_{be1}$ are both almost constant as $V_o$ changes in this case. As a result, the center part of the transfer characteristic for $R_L = R_{L1}$ is nearly

**Figure 5.2** Transfer characteristic of the circuit of Fig. 5.1 for a low ($R_{L2}$) and a high ($R_{L1}$) value of load resistance.

a straight line with unity slope that is offset on the $V_i$ axis by $V_{BE1}$, the quiescent value of $V_{be1}$. This near-linear region depends on both $Q_1$ and $Q_2$ being in the forward-active region. However, as $V_i$ is made large positive or negative, one of these devices *saturates* and the transfer characteristic abruptly changes slope.

Consider $V_i$ made large and positive. Output voltage $V_o$ follows $V_i$ until $V_o = V_{CC} - V_{CE1(sat)}$ at which point $Q_1$ saturates. The collector–base junction of $Q_1$ is then forward biased and large currents flow from base to collector. In practice, the transistor base resistance (and any source resistance present) limit the current in the forward-biased collector–base junction and prevent the voltage at the internal transistor base from rising appreciably higher. Further increases in $V_i$ thus produce little change in $V_o$ and the characteristic flattens out, as shown in Fig. 5.2. The value of $V_i$ required to cause this behavior is slightly larger than the supply voltage because $V_{be1}$ is larger than the saturation voltage $V_{CE(sat)}$. Consequently, the preceding stage often limits the maximum positive output voltage in a practical circuit because a voltage larger than $V_{CC}$ usually cannot be generated at the base of the output stage. (The portion of the curve for $V_i$ large positive where $Q_1$ is saturated actually has a positive slope if the effect of the collector series resistance $r_c$ of $Q_1$ is included. In any event, this portion of the transfer characteristic must be avoided, because the saturation of $Q_1$ results in large nonlinearity and a major reduction of power gain.)

Now consider $V_i$ made large and negative. The output voltage follows the input until $V_o = -V_{CC} + V_{CE2(sat)}$, at which point $Q_2$ saturates. (The voltage drop across $R_2$ is assumed small and is neglected. It could be lumped in with the saturation voltage $V_{CE2(sat)}$ of $Q_2$ if necessary.) When $Q_2$ saturates, another discontinuity in the transfer curve occurs, and the slope abruptly decreases. For acceptable distortion performance in the circuit, the voltage swing must be limited to the region between these two break points. As mentioned above, the driver stage supplying $V_i$ usually cannot produce values of $V_i$ that have a magnitude exceeding $V_{CC}$ (if it is connected to the same supply voltages) and the driver itself then sets the upper limit.

Next consider the case where $R_L$ in Fig. 5.1 has a relatively small value. Then when $V_o$ is made large and negative, the first term in (5.4) can become large. In particular, this term approaches minus infinity when $V_o$ approaches the critical value

$$V_o = -I_Q R_L \tag{5.5}$$

In this situation, the current drawn from the load $(-V_o/R_L)$ is equal to the current $I_Q$, and device $Q_1$ cuts off, leaving $Q_2$ to draw the current $I_Q$ from the load. Further decreases in $V_i$ produce no change in $V_o$, and the transfer characteristic is the one labeled $R_{L2}$ in Fig. 5.2. The transfer characteristic for positive $V_i$ is similar for both cases.

For the case $R_L = R_{L2}$, the stage will produce severe waveform distortion if $V_i$ is a sinusoid with amplitude exceeding $I_Q R_{L2}$. Consider the two sinusoidal waveforms in Fig. 5.3a. Waveform ① has an amplitude $V_1 < I_Q R_{L2}$ and waveform ② has an amplitude $V_2 > I_Q R_{L2}$. If these signals are applied as inputs at $V_i$ in Fig. 5.1 (together with a bias voltage), the output waveforms that result are as shown in Fig. 5.3b for $R_L = R_{L2}$. For the smaller input signal, the circuit acts as a near-linear amplifier and the output is near sinusoidal. The output waveform distortion, which is apparent for the larger input, is termed "clipping" and must be avoided in normal operation of the circuit as a linear output stage. For a given $I_Q$ and $R_L$, the onset of clipping limits the maximum signal that can be handled. Note that if $I_Q R_L$ is larger than $V_{CC}$, the situation shown for $R_L = R_{L1}$ in Fig. 5.2 holds, and the output voltage can swing almost to the positive and negative supply voltages before excessive distortion occurs.

## 5.2.2 Power Output and Efficiency

Further insight into the operation of the circuit of Fig. 5.1 can be obtained from Fig. 5.4 where three different load lines are drawn on the $I_c - V_{ce}$ characteristics of $Q_1$. The equation for the load lines can be written from Fig. 5.1 and is

$$V_{ce1} = V_{CC} - (I_{c1} - I_Q)R_L \tag{5.6}$$

Figure 5.3 (a) ac input signals applied to the circuit of Fig. 5.1. (b) ac output waveforms corresponding to the inputs in (a) with $R_L = R_{L2}$.

**Figure 5.4** Load lines in the $I_{c1} - V_{ce1}$ plane for emitter follower $Q_1$ of Fig. 5.1.

when both $Q_1$ and $Q_2$ are in the forward-active region. The values of $V_{ce1}$ and $I_{c1}$ are related by (5.6) for any value of $V_i$ and the line includes the quiescent point $Q$, where $I_{c1} = I_Q$ and $V_{ce1} = V_{CC}$. Equation 5.6 is plotted in Fig. 5.4 for load resistances $R_{L1}$, $R_{L2}$, and $R_{L3}$ and the device operating point moves up and down these lines as $V_i$ varies. As $V_i$ increases and $V_{ce1}$ decreases, $Q_1$ eventually saturates, as was illustrated in Fig. 5.2. As $V_i$ decreases and $V_{ce1}$ increases, there are two possibilities as described above. If $R_L$ is large ($R_{L1}$), $V_o$ decreases and $V_{ce1}$ increases until $Q_2$ saturates. Thus the maximum possible value that $V_{ce1}$ can attain is $[2V_{CC} - V_{CE2(sat)}]$ and this value is marked on Fig. 5.4. However, if $R_L$ is small ($R_{L2}$), the maximum negative value of $V_o$ as illustrated in Fig. 5.2 is $-I_Q R_{L2}$ and the maximum possible value of $V_{ce1}$ is $(V_{CC} + I_Q R_{L2})$.

Thus far no mention has been made of the maximum voltage limitations of the output stage. As described in Chapter 1, avalanche breakdown of a bipolar transistor occurs for $V_{ce} = BV_{CEO}$ in the common-emitter configuration, which is the worst case for breakdown voltage. In a conservative design, the value of $V_{ce}$ in the circuit of Fig. 5.1 should always be less than $BV_{CEO}$ by an appropriate safety margin. In the preceding analysis, the maximum value that $V_{ce1}$ can attain in this circuit for *any* load resistance was calculated as approximately $2V_{CC}$, and thus $BV_{CEO}$ must be greater than this value.

Consider now the power relationships in the circuit. When sinusoidal signals are present, the power dissipated in various elements varies with time. We are concerned both with the *instantaneous* power dissipated and with the *average* power dissipated. Instantaneous power is important when considering transistor dissipation with low-frequency or dc signals. The junction temperature of the transistor will tend to rise and fall with the instantaneous power dissipated in the device, limiting the maximum allowable instantaneous power dissipation for safe operation of any device.

*Average* power levels are important because the power delivered to a load is usually specified as an *average* value. Also note that if an output stage handles only high-frequency signals, the transistor junction temperature will not vary appreciably over a cycle and the *average* device power dissipation will then be the limiting quantity.

Consider the output signal power that can be delivered to load $R_L$ when a *sinusoidal* input is applied at $V_i$. Assuming that $V_o$ is approximately sinusoidal, the *average* output power delivered to $R_L$ is

$$P_L = \frac{1}{2}\hat{V}_o\hat{I}_o \tag{5.7}$$

where $\hat{V}_o$ and $\hat{I}_o$ are the amplitudes (zero to peak) of the output sinusoidal voltage and current. As described previously, the maximum output signal amplitude that can be attained before clipping occurs depends on the value of $R_L$. If $P_L|_{max}$ is the maximum value of $P_L$ that can be attained before clipping occurs with sinusoidal signals, then

$$P_L|_{max} = \frac{1}{2}\hat{V}_{om}\hat{I}_{om} \tag{5.7a}$$

where $\hat{V}_{om}$ and $\hat{I}_{om}$ are the maximum values of $\hat{V}_o$ and $\hat{I}_o$ that can be attained before clipping.

Consider the case of the large load resistance, $R_{L1}$. Figures 5.2 and 5.4 show that clipping occurs symmetrically in this case, and we have

$$\hat{V}_{om} = V_{CC} - V_{CE(sat)} \tag{5.8}$$

assuming equal saturation voltages in $Q_1$ and $Q_2$. The corresponding sinusoidal output current amplitude is $\hat{I}_{om} = \hat{V}_{om}/R_{L1}$. The maximum average power that can be delivered to $R_{L1}$ is calculated by substituting these values in (5.7a). This value of power can be interpreted geometrically as the area of the triangle $A$ in Fig. 5.4 since the base of the triangle equals $\hat{V}_{om}$ and its height is $\hat{I}_{pm}$. As $R_{L1}$ is increased, the maximum average output power that can be delivered diminishes because the triangle becomes smaller. The maximum output voltage amplitude remains essentially the same but the current amplitude decreases as $R_{L1}$ increases.

If $R_L = R_{L2}$ in Fig. 5.4, the maximum output voltage swing before clipping occurs is

$$\hat{V}_{om} = I_Q R_{L2} \tag{5.9}$$

The corresponding current amplitude is $\hat{I}_{om} = I_Q$. Using (5.7a), the maximum average output power $P_L|_{max}$ that can be delivered is given by the area of triangle $B$, shown in Fig. 5.4. As $R_{L2}$ is decreased, the maximum average power that can be delivered is diminished.

An examination of Fig. 5.4 shows that the power-output capability of the stage is maximized for $R_L = R_{L3}$, which can be calculated from (5.6) and Fig. 5.4 as

$$R_{L3} = \frac{V_{CC} - V_{CE(sat)}}{I_Q} \tag{5.10}$$

This load line gives the triangle of largest area $(C)$ and thus the largest average output power. In this case, $\hat{V}_{om} = [V_{CC} - V_{CE(sat)}]$ and $\hat{I}_{om} = I_Q$. Using (5.7a), we have

$$P_L|_{max} = \frac{1}{2}\hat{V}_{om}\hat{I}_{om} = \frac{1}{2}[V_{CC} - V_{CE(sat)}]I_Q \tag{5.11}$$

To calculate the *efficiency* of the circuit, the power drawn from the supply voltages must now be calculated. The current drawn from the positive supply is the collector current of $Q_1$, which is assumed sinusoidal with an average value $I_Q$. The current flowing in the negative supply is constant and equal to $I_Q$ (neglecting bias current $I_R$). Since the supply voltages are constant, the *average power* drawn from the supplies is constant and *independent* of the presence of sinusoidal signals in the circuit. The total power drawn

from the two supplies is thus

$$P_{supply} = 2V_{CC}I_Q \qquad (5.12)$$

The *power conversion efficiency* ($\eta_C$) of the circuit at an arbitrary output power level is defined as the ratio of the average power delivered to the load to the average power drawn from the supplies.

$$\eta_C = \frac{P_L}{P_{supply}} \qquad (5.13)$$

Since the power drawn from the supplies is constant in this circuit, the efficiency increases as the output power increases. Also, since the previous analysis shows that the power-output capability of the circuit depends on the value of $R_L$, the efficiency also depends on $R_L$. The best efficiency occurs for $R_L = R_{L3}$ since this value gives maximum average power output. If $R_L = R_{L3}$ and $\hat{V}_o = \hat{V}_{om}$, then substitution of (5.11) and (5.12) in (5.13) gives for the maximum possible efficiency

$$\eta_{max} = \frac{1}{4}\left(1 - \frac{V_{CE(sat)}}{V_{CC}}\right) \qquad (5.14)$$

Thus if $V_{CE(sat)} \ll V_{CC}$, the maximum efficiency of the stage is 1/4 or 25 percent.

Another important aspect of circuit performance is the power dissipated in the active device. The current and voltage waveforms in $Q_1$ at maximum signal swing and with $R_L = R_{L3}$ are shown in Fig. 5.5 (assuming $V_{CE(sat)} \simeq 0$ for simplicity) together with their product, which is the *instantaneous* power dissipation in the transistor. The curve of instantaneous power dissipation in $Q_1$ as a function of time varies at twice the signal frequency and has an average value of one-half the quiescent value. This result can be shown

(a)

(b)

(c)

**Figure 5.5** Waveforms for the transistor $Q_1$ of Figure 5.1 at full output with $R_L = R_{L3}$. (a) Collector-emitter voltage waveform. (b) Collector current waveform. (c) Collector power dissipation waveform.

analytically as follows. The instantaneous power dissipation in $Q_1$ is

$$P_{c1} = V_{ce1}I_{c1} \tag{5.15}$$

At maximum signal swing with a sinusoidal signal, $P_{c1}$ can be expressed as (from Fig. 5.5)

$$P_{c1} = V_{CC}(1 + \sin \omega t)I_Q(1 - \sin \omega t) = \frac{V_{CC}I_Q}{2}(1 + \cos 2\omega t) \tag{5.15a}$$

The average value of $P_{c1}$ from (5.15a) is $V_{CC}I_Q/2$. Thus at maximum output the *average* power dissipated in $Q_1$ is half its quiescent value, and the average device temperature when delivering power with $R_L = R_{L3}$ is *less than* its quiescent value.

Further information on the power dissipated in $Q_1$ can be obtained by plotting curves of constant device dissipation in the $I_c - V_{ce}$ plane. Equation 5.15 indicates that such curves are hyperbolas, which are plotted in Fig. 5.6 for constant transistor instantaneous power dissipation values $P_1, P_2$, and $P_3$ (where $P_1 < P_2 < P_3$). The power hyperbola of value $P_2$ passes through the quiescent point $Q$, and the equation of this curve can be calculated from (5.15) as

$$I_{c1} = \frac{P_2}{V_{ce1}} \tag{5.16}$$

The slope of the curve is

$$\frac{dI_{c1}}{dV_{ce1}} = -\frac{P_2}{V_{ce1}^2}$$

and substitution of (5.16) in this equation gives

$$\frac{dI_{c1}}{dV_{ce1}} = -\frac{I_{c1}}{V_{ce1}} \tag{5.17}$$

At the quiescent point $Q$, we have $I_{c1} = I_Q$ and $V_{ce1} = V_{CC}$. Thus the slope is

$$\left.\frac{dI_{c1}}{dV_{ce1}}\right|_Q = -\frac{I_Q}{V_{CC}} \tag{5.18}$$

From (5.6), the slope of the load line with $R_L = R_{L3}$ is $-(1/R_{L3})$. Using (5.10) for $R_{L3}$ gives

$$-\frac{1}{R_{L3}} \simeq -\frac{I_Q}{V_{CC}} \tag{5.19}$$

Comparing (5.18) with (5.19) shows that the load line with $R_L = R_{L3}$ is tangent to the power hyperbola passing through the quiescent point, since both curves have the same slope at that point. This result is illustrated in Fig. 5.6. As the operating point leaves the quiescent point and moves on the load line with $R_L = R_{L3}$, the load line then intersects constant-power hyperbolas representing lower power values; therefore, the instantaneous device power dissipation *decreases*. This point of view is consistent with the power waveform shown in Fig. 5.5.

The load line for $R_L \to \infty$ (open-circuit load) is also shown in Fig. 5.6. In that case, the transistor collector current does not vary over a period but is constant. For values of $V_{ce1}$ greater than the quiescent value, the instantaneous device power dissipation increases. The maximum possible value of $V_{ce1}$ is $(2V_{CC} - V_{CE2(sat)})$. At this value, the instantaneous power dissipation in $Q_1$ is approximately $2V_{CC}I_Q$ if $V_{CE2(sat)} \ll V_{CC}$. This dissipation is twice the quiescent value of $V_{CC}I_Q$, and this possibility should be taken into account when considering the power-handling requirements of $Q_1$. At the other extreme of the swing where $V_{ce1} \simeq 0$, the power dissipation in $Q_2$ is also $2V_{CC}I_Q$.

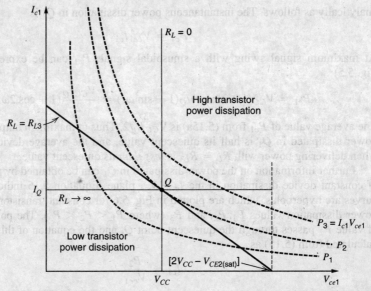

**Figure 5.6** Hyperbolas of constant instantaneous transistor power dissipation $P_1$, $P_2$, and $P_3$ in the $I_{c1} - V_{ce1}$ plane for emitter follower $Q_1$ of Fig. 5.1. Load lines are included for $R_L = 0$, $R_L = R_{L3}$, and $R_L \to \infty$. Note that $P_1 < P_2 < P_3$.

A situation that is potentially even more damaging can occur if the load is short circuited. In that case, the load line is vertical through the quiescent point, as shown in Fig. 5.6. With large input signals, the collector current (and thus the device power dissipation) of $Q_1$ can become quite large. The limit on collector current is set by the ability of the driver to supply the base current to $Q_1$, and also by the high-current fall-off in $\beta_F$ of $Q_1$, described in Chapter 1. In practice, these limits may be sufficient to prevent burnout of $Q_1$, but current-limiting circuitry may be necessary. An example of such protection is given in Section 5.4.6.

A useful general result can be derived from the calculations above involving load lines and constant-power hyperbolas. Figure 5.6 shows that the maximum instantaneous device power dissipation for $R_L = R_{L3}$ occurs at the quiescent point $Q$ (since $P_1 < P_2 < P_3$), which is the *midpoint* of the load line if $V_{CE2(sat)} \ll V_{CC}$. (The midpoint of the load line is assumed to be midway between its intersections with the $I_e$ and $V_{ce}$ axes.) It can be seen from (5.17) that *any* load line tangent to a power hyperbola makes contact with the hyperbola at the midpoint of the load line. Consequently, the midpoint is the point of maximum instantaneous device power dissipation with *any* load line. For example, in Fig. 5.4 with $R_L = R_{L2}$, the maximum instantaneous device power dissipation occurs at the midpoint of the load line where $V_{ce1} = \frac{1}{2}(V_{CC} + I_Q R_{L2})$.

An output stage of the type described in this section, where the output device always conducts appreciable current, is called a *Class A* output stage. This type of operation can be realized with different transistor configurations but always has a maximum efficiency of 25 percent.

Finally, the emitter follower in this analysis was assumed to have a current source $I_Q$ in its emitter as a bias element. In practice, the current source is sometimes replaced by a resistor connected to the negative supply, and such a configuration will give some deviations from the above calculations. In particular, the output power available from the circuit will be reduced.

■   **EXAMPLE**

An output stage such as shown in Fig. 5.1 has the following parameters: $V_{CC} = 10$ V, $R_3 = 5$ kΩ, $R_1 = R_2 = 0$, $V_{CE(sat)} = 0.2$ V, $R_L = 1$ kΩ. Assume that the dc input voltage is adjusted so that the dc output voltage is 0 volts.

(a)  Calculate the maximum average output power that can be delivered to $R_L$ before clipping occurs, and the corresponding efficiency. What is the maximum possible efficiency with this stage and what value of $R_L$ is required to achieve this efficiency? Assume the signals are sinusoidal.

(b)  Calculate the maximum possible instantaneous power dissipation in $Q_1$. Also calculate the average power dissipation in $Q_1$ when $\hat{V}_o = 1.5$ V and the output voltage is sinusoidal.

The solution proceeds as follows.

(a)  The bias current $I_Q$ is first calculated.

$$I_Q = I_R = \frac{V_{CC} - V_{BE3}}{R_3} = \frac{10 - 0.7}{5} \text{ mA} = 1.86 \text{ mA}$$

The product, $I_Q R_L$, is given by

$$I_Q R_L = 1.86 \times 1 = 1.86 \text{ V}$$

Since the dc output voltage is assumed to be 0 volts, and since $I_Q R_L$ is less than $V_{CC}$, the maximum sinusoidal output voltage swing is limited to 1.86 V by clipping on negative voltage swings and the situation corresponds to $R_L = R_{L2}$ in Fig. 5.4. The maximum output voltage and current swings are thus $\hat{V}_{om} = 1.86$ V and $\hat{I}_{om} = 1.86$ mA. The maximum average output power available from the circuit for sinusoidal signals can be calculated from (5.7a) as

$$P_L|_{max} = \frac{1}{2}\hat{V}_{om}\hat{I}_{om} = \frac{1}{2} \times 1.86 \times 1.86 \text{ mW} = 1.73 \text{ mW}$$

The power drawn from the supplies is calculated from (5.12) as

$$P_{supply} = 2V_{CC}I_Q = 2 \times 10 \times 1.86 \text{ mW} = 37.2 \text{ mW}$$

The efficiency of the circuit at the output power level calculated above can be determined from (5.13)

$$\eta_C = \frac{P_L|_{max}}{P_{supply}} = \frac{1.73}{37.2} = 0.047$$

The efficiency of 4.7 percent is quite low and is due to the limitation on the negative voltage swing.

The maximum possible efficiency with this stage occurs for $R_L = R_{L3}$ in Fig. 5.4, and $R_{L3}$ is given by (5.10) as

$$R_{L3} = \frac{V_{CC} - V_{CE(sat)}}{I_Q} = \frac{10 - 0.2}{1.86} \text{ kΩ} = 5.27 \text{ kΩ}$$

In this instance, the maximum average power that can be delivered to the load before clipping occurs is found from (5.11) as

$$P_L|_{max} = \frac{1}{2}[V_{CC} - V_{CE(sat)}]I_Q = \frac{1}{2}(10 - 0.2)1.86 \text{ mW} = 9.11 \text{ mW}$$

The corresponding efficiency using (5.14) is

$$\eta_{max} = \frac{1}{4}\left[1 - \frac{V_{CE(sat)}}{V_{CC}}\right] = \frac{1}{4}\left(1 - \frac{0.2}{10}\right) = 0.245$$

This result is close to the theoretical maximum of 25 percent.

(b) The maximum possible instantaneous power dissipation in $Q_1$ occurs at the midpoint of the load line. Reference to Fig. 5.4 and the load line $R_L = R_{L2}$ shows that this occurs for

$$V_{ce1} = \frac{1}{2}(V_{CC} + I_Q R_L) = \frac{1}{2}(10 + 1.86) = 5.93 \text{ V}$$

The corresponding collector current in $Q_1$ is $I_{c1} = 5.93/R_L = 5.93$ mA since $R_L = 1$ k$\Omega$. Thus the maximum instantaneous power dissipation in $Q_1$ is

$$P_{c1} = I_{c1} V_{ce1} = 35.2 \text{ mW}$$

This power dissipation occurs for $V_{ce1} = 5.93$ V, which represents a signal swing beyond the linear limits of the circuit [clipping occurs when the output voltage reaches $-1.86$ V as calculated in (a)]. However, this condition could easily occur if the circuit is overdriven by a large input signal.

The average power dissipation in $Q_1$ can be calculated by noting that for sinusoidal signals, the average power drawn from the two supplies is constant and independent of the presence of signals. Since the power input to the circuit from the supplies is constant, the *total* average power dissipated in $Q_1$, $Q_2$, and $R_L$ must be constant and independent of the presence of sinusoidal signals. The average power dissipated in $Q_2$ is constant because $I_Q$ is constant, and thus the average power dissipated in $Q_1$ and $R_L$ together is constant. Thus as $\hat{V}_o$ is increased, the average power dissipated in $Q_1$ *decreases* by the same amount as the average power in $R_L$ *increases*. With no input signal, the quiescent power dissipated in $Q_1$ is

$$P_{CQ} = V_{CC} I_Q = 10 \times 1.86 \text{ mW} = 18.6 \text{ mW}$$

For $\hat{V}_o = 1.5$ V, the average power delivered to the load is

$$P_L = \frac{1}{2}\frac{\hat{V}_o^2}{R_L} = \frac{1}{2}\frac{2.25}{1} \text{ mW} = 1.13 \text{ mW}$$

Thus the *average* power dissipated in $Q_1$ when $\hat{V}_o = 1.5$ V with a sinusoidal signal is

$$P_{av} = P_{CQ} - P_L = 17.5 \text{ mW}$$

### 5.2.3 Emitter-Follower Drive Requirements

The calculations above have been concerned with the performance of the emitter-follower output stage when driven by a sinusoidal input voltage. The stage preceding the output stage is called the driver stage, and in practice it may introduce additional limitations on the circuit performance. For example, it was shown that to drive the output voltage $V_o$ of the emitter follower to its maximum positive value required an input voltage slightly greater than the supply voltage. Since the driver stage is connected to the same supplies as the output stage in most cases, the driver stage generally cannot produce voltages greater than the supply, further reducing the possible output voltage swing.

The above limitations stem from the observation that the emitter follower has a voltage gain of unity and thus the driver stage must handle the same voltage swing as the output. However, the driver can be a much *lower power* stage than the output stage because the current it must deliver is the base current of the emitter follower, which is about $1/\beta_F$ times the emitter current. Consequently, the driver bias current can be much lower than the output-stage bias current, and a smaller geometry can be used for the driver device. Although it has only unity voltage gain, the emitter follower has substantial *power gain*, which is a requirement of any output stage.

**Figure 5.7** Low-frequency, small-signal equivalent circuit for the emitter follower of Fig. 5.1.

### 5.2.4 Small-Signal Properties of the Emitter Follower

A simplified low-frequency, small-signal equivalent circuit of the emitter follower of Fig. 5.1 is shown in Fig. 5.7. As described in Chapter 7, the emitter follower is an extremely wideband circuit and rarely is a source of frequency limitation in the small-signal gain of an amplifier. Thus the equivalent circuit of Fig. 5.7 is useful over a wide frequency range and an analysis of this circuit shows that the voltage gain $A_v$ and the output resistance $R_o$ can be expressed approximately for $\beta_0 \gg 1$ as

$$A_v = \frac{v_o}{v_i} \simeq \frac{R_L}{R_L + \dfrac{1}{g_m} + \dfrac{R_S}{\beta_0}} \tag{5.20}$$

$$R_o = \frac{1}{g_m} + \frac{R_S}{\beta_0} \tag{5.21}$$

These quantities are small-signal quantities, and since $g_m = qI_C/kT$ is a function of bias point, both $A_v$ and $R_o$ are functions of $I_C$. Since the emitter follower is being considered here for use as an output stage where the signal swing may be large, (5.20) and (5.21) must be applied with caution. However, for small-to-moderate signal swings, these equations may be used to estimate the average gain and output resistance of the stage if quiescent bias values are used for transistor parameters in the equations. Equation 5.20 can also be used as a means of estimating the nonlinearity[1] in the stage by recognizing that it gives the *incremental slope* of the large-signal characteristic of Fig. 5.2 at any point. If this equation is evaluated at the extremes of the signal swing, an estimate of the curvature of the characteristic is obtained, as illustrated in the following example.

■ **EXAMPLE**

Calculate the incremental slope of the transfer characteristic of the circuit of Fig. 5.1 as the quiescent point and at the extremes of the signal swing with a peak sinusoidal output of 0.6 V. Use data as in the previous example and assume that $R_S = 0$.

From (5.20) the small-signal gain with $R_S = 0$ is

$$A_v = \frac{R_L}{R_L + \dfrac{1}{g_m}} \tag{5.22}$$

Since $I_Q = 1.86$ mA, $1/g_m = 14\ \Omega$ at the quiescent point and the quiescent gain is

$$A_{vQ} = \frac{1000}{1000 + 14} = 0.9862$$

Since the output voltage swing is 0.6 V, the output current swing is

$$\hat{I}_o = \frac{\hat{V}_o}{R_L} = \frac{0.6}{1000} = 0.6 \text{ mA}$$

Thus at the positive signal peak, the transistor collector current is

$$I_Q + \hat{I}_o = 1.86 + 0.6 = 2.46 \text{ mA}$$

At this current, $1/g_m = 10.6 \ \Omega$ and use of (5.22) gives the small-signal gain as

$$A_v^+ = \frac{1000}{1010.6} = 0.9895$$

This gain is 0.3 percent more than the quiescent value. At the negative signal peak, the transistor collector current is

$$I_Q - \hat{I}_o = 1.86 - 0.6 = 1.26 \text{ mA}$$

At this current, $1/g_m = 20.6 \ \Omega$ and use of (5.22) gives the small-signal gain as

$$A_v^- = \frac{1000}{1020.6} = 0.9798$$

This gain is 0.7 percent less than the quiescent value. Although the collector-current signal amplitude is one-third of the bias current in this example, the small-signal gain variation is extremely small. This circuit thus has a high degree of linearity. Since the nonlinearity is small, the resulting distortion can be determined from the three values of the small-signal gain calculated in this example. See Problem 5.8.

## 5.3 The Source Follower as an Output Stage

The small-signal properties of the source follower are calculated in Chapter 3. Since this circuit has low output resistance, it is often used as an output stage. The large signal properties of the source follower are considered next.

### 5.3.1 Transfer Characteristics of the Source Follower

A source-follower output stage is shown in Fig. 5.8 with equal magnitude positive and negative power supplies for simplicity. The large-signal transfer characteristic can be derived as follows:

$$V_i = V_o + V_{gs1} = V_o + V_{t1} + V_{ov1} \qquad (5.23)$$

Figure 5.8 Source-follower output stage with current-mirror bias.

If the threshold and overdrive terms are exactly constant, the output voltage follows the input voltage with a constant difference. In practice, however, the body effect changes the threshold voltage. Also, the overdrive is not constant mainly because the drain current is not constant. Substituting (1.140) with $V_{sb} = V_o + V_{DD}$ and (1.166) with $I_{d1} = I_Q + V_o/R_L$ into (5.23) gives

$$V_i = V_o + V_{t0} + \gamma\left(\sqrt{2\phi_f + V_o + V_{DD}} - \sqrt{2\phi_f}\right) + \sqrt{\frac{2\left(I_Q + \dfrac{V_o}{R_L}\right)}{k'(W/L)_1}} \qquad (5.24)$$

This equation is valid provided that $M_1$ and $M_2$ operate in the active region with output resistances much larger than $R_L$.

The transfer characteristic is plotted in Fig. 5.9. It intersects the $x$ axis at the input-referred offset voltage, which is

$$V_i\big|_{V_o=0} = V_{t0} + \gamma\left(\sqrt{2\phi_f + V_{DD}} - \sqrt{2\phi_f}\right) + \sqrt{\frac{2I_Q}{k'(W/L)_1}} . \qquad (5.25)$$

The slope at this point is the incremental gain calculated in (3.80). With $r_o \to \infty$, the slope is

$$\frac{v_o}{v_i} = \frac{g_m R_L}{1 + (g_m + g_{mb})R_L} \qquad (5.26)$$

When $R_L \to \infty$,

$$\frac{v_o}{v_i} = \frac{g_m}{g_m + g_{mb}} = \frac{1}{1 + \chi} \qquad (5.27)$$

Since $\chi$ is typically in the range of 0.1 to 0.3, the slope typically ranges from about 0.7 to 0.9. In contrast, the slope of the emitter-follower transfer characteristic is unity under these conditions. Furthermore, (1.200) shows that $\chi$ depends on the source-body voltage, which is $V_o + V_{DD}$ in Fig. 5.8. Therefore, the slope calculated in (5.27) changes as $V_o$ changes even when $M_1$ operates in the active region, causing distortion. Fig. 5.9 ignores this variation in the slope, but it is considered in Section 5.3.2.

When the output voltage rises within an overdrive of the positive supply, $M_1$ enters the triode region, dramatically reducing the slope of the transfer characteristic. The overdrive

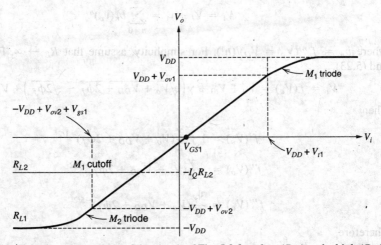

**Figure 5.9** Transfer characteristic of the circuit of Fig. 5.8 for a low ($R_{L2}$) and a high ($R_{L1}$) value of load resistance.

at this break point is calculated using the total drain current, which exceeds $I_Q$ if $R_L$ is finite. Therefore, the location of the break point depends on $R_L$, but this effect is not shown in Fig. 5.9. Unlike in the emitter follower, the output can pull up asymptotically to the supply voltage with unlimited input voltage. In practice, however, the input must be larger than $V_{DD}$ by at least the threshold voltage to bias $M_1$ in the triode region. If the input voltage is limited to $V_{DD}$, $M_1$ never reaches the triode region.

For negative input voltages, the minimum value of the output voltage depends on $R_L$, as in the emitter follower. If $I_Q R_L > V_{DD}$, the slope of the transfer characteristic is approximately constant until $M_2$ enters the triode region, which happens when

$$V_o = -V_{DD} + V_{ov2} = -V_{DD} + \sqrt{\frac{2I_Q}{k'(W/L)_2}} \qquad (5.28)$$

This case is labeled as $R_{L1}$ in Fig. 5.9. On the other hand, if $I_Q R_L < V_{DD}$, the slope is almost constant until $M_1$ turns off. The corresponding minimum output voltage is

$$V_o = -I_Q R_L \qquad (5.29)$$

This case is labeled as $R_{L2}$ in Fig. 5.9. From a design standpoint, $I_Q R_L$ is usually set larger than $V_{DD}$, so that the situation shown for $R_L = R_{L1}$ in Fig. 5.9 holds. Under this condition, the output voltage can swing almost to the positive and negative supply voltages before excessive distortion occurs.

### 5.3.2 Distortion in the Source Follower

The transfer function of the source-follower stage was calculated in (5.23), where $V_i$ is expressed as a function of $V_o$. The calculation of signal distortion from a nonlinear transfer function will now be illustrated using the source-follower stage as an example.

Using a Taylor series, the input voltage can be written as

$$V_i = V_I + v_i = \sum_{n=0}^{\infty} \frac{f^{(n)}(V_o = V_O)(V_o - V_O)^n}{n!} \qquad (5.30)$$

where $f^{(n)}$ represents the $n^{th}$ derivative of $f$. Since $v_o = V_o - V_O$, (5.30) can be re-written as

$$V_i = V_I + v_i = \sum_{n=0}^{\infty} b_n(v_o)^n \qquad (5.31)$$

where $b_n = f^{(n)}(V_o = V_O)/(n!)$. For simplicity, assume that $R_L \to \infty$. From (1.140) and (5.23),

$$V_i = f(V_o) = V_o + V_{t0} + \gamma \left( \sqrt{V_o + V_{DD} + 2\phi_f} - \sqrt{2\phi_f} \right) + V_{ov1} \qquad (5.32)$$

Then

$$f'(V_o) = 1 + \frac{\gamma}{2}(V_o + V_{DD} + 2\phi_f)^{-1/2} \qquad (5.33)$$

$$f''(V_o) = -\frac{\gamma}{4}(V_o + V_{DD} + 2\phi_f)^{-3/2} \qquad (5.34)$$

$$f'''(V_o) = \frac{3\gamma}{8}(V_o + V_{DD} + 2\phi_f)^{-5/2} \qquad (5.35)$$

Therefore,

$$b_0 = f(V_o = V_O) = V_O + V_{t0} + \gamma \left( \sqrt{V_O + V_{DD} + 2\phi_f} - \sqrt{2\phi_f} \right) + V_{ov1} \qquad (5.36)$$

$$b_1 = f'(V_o = V_O) = 1 + \frac{\gamma}{2}(V_O + V_{DD} + 2\phi_f)^{-1/2} \tag{5.37}$$

$$b_2 = \frac{f''(V_o = V_O)}{2} = -\frac{\gamma}{8}(V_O + V_{DD} + 2\phi_f)^{-3/2} \tag{5.38}$$

$$b_3 = \frac{f'''(V_o = V_O)}{3!} = \frac{\gamma}{16}(V_O + V_{DD} + 2\phi_f)^{-5/2} \tag{5.39}$$

Since the constant $b_0$ is the dc input voltage $V_I$, (5.31) can be rewritten as

$$v_i = \sum_{n=1}^{\infty} b_n(v_o)^n = b_1 v_o + b_2 v_o^2 + b_3 v_o^3 + \dots \tag{5.40}$$

To find the distortion, we would like to rearrange this equation into the following form

$$v_o = \sum_{n=1}^{\infty} a_n(v_i)^n = a_1 v_i + a_2 v_i^2 + a_3 v_i^3 + \dots \tag{5.41}$$

Substituting (5.41) into (5.40) gives

$$v_i = b_1(a_1 v_i + a_2 v_i^2 + a_3 v_i^3 + \dots) + b_2(a_1 v_i + a_2 v_i^2 + a_3 v_i^3 + \dots)^2$$
$$+ b_3(a_1 v_i + a_2 v_i^2 + a_3 v_i^3 + \dots)^3 + \dots$$
$$= b_1 a_1 v_i + (b_1 a_2 + b_2 a_1^2)v_i^2 + (b_1 a_3 + 2b_2 a_1 a_2 + b_3 a_1^3)v_i^3 + \dots \tag{5.42}$$

Matching coefficients in (5.42) shows that

$$1 = b_1 a_1 \tag{5.43}$$

$$0 = b_1 a_2 + b_2 a_1^2 \tag{5.44}$$

$$0 = b_1 a_3 + 2b_2 a_1 a_2 + b_3 a_1^3 \tag{5.45}$$

From (5.43),

$$a_1 = \frac{1}{b_1} \tag{5.46}$$

Substituting (5.46) into (5.44) and rearranging gives

$$a_2 = -\frac{b_2}{b_1^3} \tag{5.47}$$

Substituting (5.46) and (5.47) into (5.45) and rearranging gives

$$a_3 = \frac{2b_2^2}{b_1^5} - \frac{b_3}{b_1^4} \tag{5.48}$$

For the source follower, substituting (5.37) into (5.46) gives

$$a_1 = \frac{1}{1 + \frac{\gamma}{2}(V_O + V_{DD} + 2\phi_f)^{-1/2}} \tag{5.49}$$

Substituting (5.37) and (5.38) into (5.47) and rearranging gives

$$a_2 = \frac{\frac{\gamma}{8}(V_O + V_{DD} + 2\phi_f)^{-3/2}}{\left(1 + \frac{\gamma}{2}(V_O + V_{DD} + 2\phi_f)^{-1/2}\right)^3} \tag{5.50}$$

Substituting (5.37), (5.38), and (5.39) into (5.48) and rearranging gives

$$a_3 = -\frac{\frac{\gamma}{16}(V_O + V_{DD} + 2\phi_f)^{-5/2}}{\left(1 + \frac{\gamma}{2}(V_O + V_{DD} + 2\phi_f)^{-1/2}\right)^5} \tag{5.51}$$

Equations 5.41, 5.49, 5.50, and 5.51 can be used to calculate the distortion of the source-follower stage. For small values of $v_i$ such that $a_2 v_i^2 \ll a_1 v_i$, the first term on the right-hand side of (5.41) dominates and the circuit is essentially linear. However, as $v_i$ becomes comparable to $a_1/a_2$, other terms become significant and distortion products are generated, as is illustrated next. A common method of describing the nonlinearity of an amplifier is the specification of *harmonic distortion*, which is defined for a single sinusoidal input applied to the amplifier. Thus let

$$v_i = \hat{v}_i \sin \omega t \tag{5.52}$$

Substituting (5.52) into (5.41) gives

$$\begin{aligned} v_o &= a_1 \hat{v}_i \sin \omega t + a_2 \hat{v}_i^2 \sin^2 \omega t + a_3 \hat{v}_i^3 \sin^3 \omega t + \dots \\ &= a_1 \hat{v}_i \sin \omega t + \frac{a_2 \hat{v}_i^2}{2}(1 - \cos 2\omega t) + \frac{a_3 \hat{v}_i^3}{4}(3 \sin \omega t - \sin 3\omega t) + \dots \end{aligned} \tag{5.53}$$

Equation 5.53 shows that the output voltage contains frequency components at the fundamental frequency, $\omega$ (the input frequency), and also at harmonic frequencies $2\omega$, $3\omega$, and so on. The latter terms represent *distortion products* that are not present in the input signal. Second-harmonic distortion $HD_2$ is defined as the ratio of the amplitude of the output-signal component at frequency $2\omega$ to the amplitude of the first harmonic (or fundamental) at frequency $\omega$. For small distortion, the term $(3/4)a_3\hat{v}_i^3 \sin \omega t$ in (5.53) is small compared to $a_1\hat{v}_i \sin \omega t$, and the amplitude of the fundamental is approximately $a_1\hat{v}_i$. Again for small distortion, higher-order terms in (5.53) may be neglected and

$$HD_2 = \frac{a_2 \hat{v}_i^2}{2} \frac{1}{a_1 \hat{v}_i} = \frac{1}{2}\frac{a_2}{a_1}\hat{v}_i \tag{5.54}$$

Under these assumptions, $HD_2$ varies *linearly* with the peak signal level $\hat{v}_i$. The value of $HD_2$ can be expressed in terms of known parameters by substituting (5.49) and (5.50) in (5.54) to give

$$HD_2 = \frac{\gamma}{16}\frac{(V_O + V_{DD} + 2\phi_f)^{-3/2}(\hat{v}_i)}{\left(1 + \frac{\gamma}{2}(V_O + V_{DD} + 2\phi_f)^{-1/2}\right)^2} \tag{5.55}$$

If $\gamma \ll 2\sqrt{V_O + V_{DD} + 2\phi_f}$, then

$$HD_2 \simeq \frac{\gamma}{16}(V_O + V_{DD} + 2\phi_f)^{-3/2}\hat{v}_i \tag{5.56}$$

This equation shows that the second-harmonic distortion can be reduced by increasing the dc output voltage $V_O$. This result is reasonable because this distortion stems from the body effect. Therefore, increasing $V_O$ decreases the variation of the source-body voltage compared to its dc value caused by an input with fixed peak amplitude.[2] Equation 5.56 also shows that the second-harmonic distortion is approximately proportional to $\gamma$, neglecting the effect of $\gamma$ on $V_O$.

Similarly, third-harmonic distortion $HD_3$ is defined as the ratio of the output signal component at frequency $3\omega$ to the first harmonic. From (5.53) and assuming small distortion,

$$HD_3 = \frac{a_3 \hat{v}_i^3}{4} \frac{1}{a_1 \hat{v}_i} = \frac{1}{4} \frac{a_3}{a_1} \hat{v}_i^2 \tag{5.57}$$

Under these assumptions, $HD_3$ varies as the *square* of the signal amplitude. The value of $HD_3$ can be expressed in terms of known parameters by substituting (5.49) and (5.51) in (5.57) to give

$$HD_3 = -\frac{\gamma}{64} \frac{(V_O + V_{DD} + 2\phi_f)^{-5/2}(\hat{v}_i^2)}{\left(1 + \frac{\gamma}{2}(V_O + V_{DD} + 2\phi_f)^{-1/2}\right)^4} \tag{5.58}$$

Since the distortion calculated above stems from the body effect, it can be eliminated by placing the source follower in an isolated well and connecting the source to the well. However, this approach specifies the type of source-follower transistor because it must be opposite the type of the doping in the well. Also, this approach adds the well-substrate parasitic capacitance to the output load of the source follower, reducing its bandwidth.

■ **EXAMPLE**

Calculate second- and third-harmonic distortion in the circuit of Fig. 5.8 for a peak sinusoidal input voltage $\hat{v}_i = 0.5$ V. Assume that $V_I = 0$, $V_{DD} = 2.5$ V, $I_Q = 1$ mA, and $R_L \to \infty$. Also, assume that $(W/L)_1 = 1000$, $k' = 200\ \mu\text{A/V}^2$, $V_{t0} = 0.7$ V, $\phi_f = 0.3$ V, and $\gamma = 0.5$ V$^{1/2}$.

First, the dc output voltage $V_O$ is

$$V_O = V_I - V_{t0} - \gamma\left(\sqrt{V_O + V_{DD} + 2\phi_f} - \sqrt{2\phi_f}\right) - V_{ov1} \tag{5.59}$$

Rearranging (5.59) gives

$$(V_O + V_{DD} + 2\phi_f) + \gamma\sqrt{V_O + V_{DD} + 2\phi_f}$$
$$- V_I + V_{ov1} + V_{t0} - \gamma\sqrt{2\phi_f} - V_{DD} - 2\phi_f = 0 \tag{5.60}$$

This quadratic equation can be solved for $\sqrt{V_O + V_{DD} + 2\phi_f}$. Since the result must be positive,

$$\sqrt{V_O + V_{DD} + 2\phi_f} =$$
$$-\frac{\gamma}{2} + \sqrt{\left(\frac{\gamma}{2}\right)^2 + V_I - V_{ov1} - V_{t0} + \gamma\sqrt{2\phi_f} + V_{DD} + 2\phi_f} \tag{5.61}$$

Squaring both sides and rearranging gives

$$V_O = -V_{DD} - 2\phi_f$$
$$+ \left(-\frac{\gamma}{2} + \sqrt{\left(\frac{\gamma}{2}\right)^2 + V_I - V_{ov1} - V_{t0} + \gamma\sqrt{2\phi_f} + V_{DD} + 2\phi_f}\right)^2 \tag{5.62}$$

In this example,

$$V_{ov1} = \sqrt{\frac{2I_Q}{k'(W/L)_1}} = \sqrt{\frac{2(1000)}{200(1000)}} \text{ V} = 0.1 \text{ V} \tag{5.63}$$

Since $V_{DD} + 2\phi_f = 3.1$ V and $V_I - V_{ov1} - V_{t0} = -0.8$ V,

$$V_O = -3.1 \text{ V} + \left(-0.25 + \sqrt{(0.25)^2 - 0.8 + 0.5\sqrt{0.6} + 3.1}\right)^2 \text{ V}$$

$$= -1.117 \text{ V}$$

Therefore,

$$V_O + V_{DD} + 2\phi_f = (-1.117 + 2.5 + 0.6) \text{ V} = 1.983 \text{ V}$$

From (5.55),

$$HD_2 = \frac{0.5}{16} \frac{(1.983)^{-3/2}(0.5)}{\left(1 + \frac{0.5}{2}(1.983)^{-1/2}\right)^2} = 0.0040 \tag{5.64}$$

From (5.58),

$$HD_3 = -\frac{0.5}{64} \frac{(1.983)^{-5/2}(0.5)^2}{\left(1 + \frac{0.5}{2}(1.983)^{-1/2}\right)^4} = -1.8 \times 10^{-4} \tag{5.65}$$

■ Thus the second-harmonic distortion is 0.40 percent and the third-harmonic distortion is 0.018 percent. In practice, the second-harmonic distortion is usually dominant.[3]

## 5.4 Class B Push–Pull Output Stage[4,5]

The major disadvantage of Class A output stages is that large power dissipation occurs even for no ac input. In many applications of power amplifiers, the circuit may spend long periods of time in a *standby* condition with no input signal, or with intermittent inputs as in the case of voice signals. Power dissipated in these standby periods is wasted, which is important for two reasons. First, in battery-operated equipment, supply power must be conserved to extend the battery life. Second, any power wasted in the circuit is dissipated in the active devices, increasing their operating temperatures and thus the chance of failure. Furthermore, the power dissipated in the devices affects the physical size of device required, and larger devices are more expensive in terms of silicon area.

A Class B output stage alleviates this problem by having essentially zero power dissipation with zero input signal. *Two* active devices are used to deliver the power instead of one, and each device conducts for alternate half cycles. This behavior is the origin of the name *push–pull*. Another advantage of Class B output stages is that the efficiency is much higher than for a Class A output stage (ideally 78.6 percent at full output power).

A typical integrated-circuit realization of the Class B output stage is shown in Fig. 5.10 in bipolar technology. This circuit uses both *pnp* and *npn* devices and is known as a *complementary* output stage. The *pnp* transistor is usually a substrate *pnp*. Note that the load resistance $R_L$ is connected to the emitters of the active devices; therefore, the devices act as emitter followers.

**Figure 5.10** Simple integrated-circuit Class B output stage.

## 5.4.1 Transfer Characteristic of the Class B Stage

The transfer characteristic of the circuit of Fig. 5.10 is shown in Fig. 5.11. For $V_i$ equal to zero, $V_o$ is also zero and both devices are off with $V_{be} = 0$. As $V_i$ is made positive, the base-emitter voltage of $Q_1$ increases until it reaches the value $V_{BE(on)}$, when appreciable current will start to flow in $Q_1$. At this point, $V_o$ is still approximately zero, but further increases in $V_i$ will cause similar increases in $V_o$ because $Q_1$ acts as an emitter follower. When $V_i > 0$, $Q_2$ is off with a *reverse* bias of $V_{BE(on)}$ across its base-emitter junction. As $V_i$ is made even more positive, $Q_1$ eventually saturates (for $V_i = V_{CC} + V_{be1} - V_{CE1(sat)}$), and the characteristic flattens out as for the conventional emitter follower considered earlier.

As $V_i$ is taken negative from $V_i = 0$, a similar characteristic is obtained except that $Q_2$ now acts as an emitter follower for $V_i$ more negative than $-V_{BE(on)}$. In this region, $Q_1$ is held in the off condition with a reverse bias of $V_{BE(on)}$ across its base-emitter junction.

The characteristic of Fig. 5.11 shows a notch (or *deadband*) of $2V_{BE(on)}$ in $V_i$ centered around $V_i = 0$. This deadband is common in Class B output stages and gives rise to *crossover* distortion, which is illustrated in Fig. 5.12, where the output waveforms from the circuit are shown for various amplitude input sinusoidal signals. In this circuit, the distortion is high for small input signals with amplitudes somewhat larger than $V_{BE(on)}$.

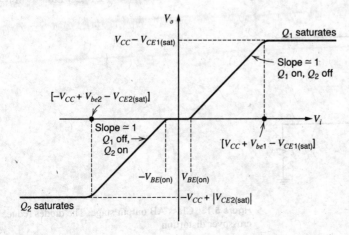

**Figure 5.11** Transfer characteristic of the Class B output stage of Fig. 5.10.

**Figure 5.12** Output waveforms for various amplitude input signals applied to the Class B circuit of Fig. 5.10.

The effect of this source of distortion diminishes as the input signal becomes larger and the deadband represents a smaller fraction of the signal amplitude. Eventually, for very large signals, saturation of $Q_1$ and $Q_2$ occurs and distortion rises sharply again due to clipping. This behavior is characteristic of Class B output stages and is why distortion figures are often quoted for both low and high output power operation.

The crossover distortion described above can be reduced by using *Class AB* operation of the circuit. In this scheme, the active devices are biased so that each conducts a small quiescent current for $V_i = 0$. Such biasing can be achieved as shown in Fig. 5.13, where the current source $I_Q$ forces bias current in diodes $Q_3$ and $Q_4$. Since the diodes are connected in parallel with the base-emitter junctions of $Q_1$ and $Q_2$, the output transistors are biased on with a current that is dependent on the area ratios of $Q_1$, $Q_2$, $Q_3$, and $Q_4$. A

**Figure 5.13** Class AB output stage. The diodes reduce crossover distortion.

**Figure 5.14** Transfer characteristic of the circuit of Fig. 5.13.

typical transfer characteristic for this circuit is shown in Fig. 5.14, and the deadband has been effectively eliminated. The remaining nonlinearities due to crossover in conduction from $Q_1$ to $Q_2$ can be reduced by using negative feedback, as described in Chapter 8.

The operation of the circuit in Fig. 5.13 is quite similar to that of Fig. 5.11. As $V_i$ is taken negative from its quiescent value, emitter follower $Q_2$ forces $V_o$ to follow. The load current flows through $Q_2$, whose base-emitter voltage will increase slightly. Since the diodes maintain a constant total bias voltage across the base-emitter junctions of $Q_1$ and $Q_2$, the base-emitter voltage of $Q_1$ will decrease by the same amount that $Q_2$ increased. Thus during the negative output voltage excursion, $Q_1$ stays on but conducts little current and plays no part in delivering output power. For $V_i$ taken positive, the opposite occurs, and $Q_1$ acts as the emitter follower delivering current to $R_L$ with $Q_2$ conducting only a very small current. In this case, the current source $I_Q$ supplies the base-current drive to $Q_1$.

In the derivation of the characteristics of Figures 5.11 and 5.14, we assumed that the magnitude of the input voltage $V_i$ was unlimited. In the characteristic of Fig. 5.11, the magnitude of $V_i$ required to cause saturation of $Q_1$ or $Q_2$ exceeds the supply voltage $V_{CC}$. However, as in the case of the single emitter follower described earlier, practical driver stages generally cannot produce values of $V_i$ exceeding $V_{CC}$ if they are connected to the same supply voltages as the output stage. For example, the current source $I_Q$ in Fig. 5.13 is usually realized with a *pnp* transistor and thus the voltage at the base of $Q_1$ cannot exceed $(V_{CC} - V_{CE(\text{sat})})$, at which point saturation of the current-source transistor occurs. Consequently, the positive and negative limits of $V_o$ where clipping occurs are generally somewhat less than shown in Fig. 5.11 and Fig. 5.14, and the limitation usually occurs in the driver stage. This point will be investigated further when practical output stages are considered in later sections.

### 5.4.2 Power Output and Efficiency of the Class B Stage

The method of operation of a Class B stage can be further appreciated by plotting the collector current waveforms in the two devices, as in Fig. 5.15, where crossover distortion is ignored. Note that each transistor conducts current to $R_L$ for half a cycle.

The collector current waveforms of Fig. 5.15 also represent the waveforms of the current drawn from the two supplies. If the waveforms are assumed to be half-sinusoids, then the average current drawn from the $+V_{CC}$ supply is

$$I_{\text{supply}} = \frac{1}{T}\int_0^T I_{c1}(t)dt = \frac{1}{T}\int_0^{T/2} \frac{\hat{V}_o}{R_L}\sin\left(\frac{2\pi t}{T}\right)dt = \frac{1}{\pi}\frac{\hat{V}_o}{R_L} = \frac{1}{\pi}\hat{I}_o \qquad (5.66)$$

**Figure 5.15** Voltage and current waveforms for a Class B output stage. (a) Input voltage. (b) Output voltage. (c) $Q_1$ collector current. (d) $Q_2$ collector current.

where $T$ is the period of the input signal. Also, $\hat{V}_o$ and $\hat{I}_o$ are the zero-to-peak amplitudes of the output sinusoidal voltage and current. Since each supply delivers the same current magnitude, the total average power drawn from the two supplies is

$$P_{\text{supply}} = 2V_{CC}I_{\text{supply}} = \frac{2}{\pi}\frac{V_{CC}}{R_L}\hat{V}_o \tag{5.67}$$

where (5.66) has been substituted. Unlike in the Class A case, the average power drawn from the supplies *does vary* with signal level for a Class B stage, and is directly proportional to $\hat{V}_o$.

The average power delivered to $R_L$ is given by

$$P_L = \frac{1}{2}\frac{\hat{V}_o^2}{R_L} \tag{5.68}$$

From the definition of circuit efficiency in (5.13),

$$\eta_C = \frac{P_L}{P_{\text{supply}}} = \frac{\pi}{4}\frac{\hat{V}_o}{V_{CC}} \tag{5.69}$$

where (5.67) and (5.68) have been substituted. Equation 5.69 shows that $\eta$ for a Class B stage is independent of $R_L$ but increases linearly as the output voltage amplitude $\hat{V}_o$ increases.

The maximum value that $\hat{V}_o$ can attain before clipping occurs with the characteristic of Fig. 5.14 is $\hat{V}_{om} = (V_{CC} - V_{CE(sat)})$ and thus the maximum average signal power that can be delivered to $R_L$ for sinusoidal signals can be calculated from (5.68) as

$$P_L\big|_{max} = \frac{1}{2}\frac{[V_{CC} - V_{CE(sat)}]^2}{R_L} \tag{5.70}$$

From (5.69), the corresponding maximum efficiency is

$$\eta_{max} = \frac{\pi}{4}\left(\frac{V_{CC} - V_{CE(sat)}}{V_{CC}}\right) \tag{5.71}$$

If $V_{CE(sat)}$ is small compared with $V_{CC}$, the circuit has a maximum efficiency of 0.786 or 78.6 percent. This maximum efficiency is much higher than the value of 25 percent achieved in Class A circuits. In addition, the standby power dissipation is essentially zero in the Class B circuit. These advantages explain the widespread use of Class B and Class AB output stages.

The load line for one device in a Class B stage is shown in Fig. 5.16. For values of $V_{ce}$ less than the quiescent value (which is $V_{CC}$), the load line has a slope of $(-1/R_L)$. For values of $V_{ce}$ greater than $V_{CC}$, the load line lies along the $V_{ce}$ axis because the device under consideration turns off and the other device conducts. As a result, the $V_{ce}$ of the device under consideration increases while its collector current is zero. The maximum value of $V_{ce}$ is $(2V_{CC} - V_{CE(sat)})$. As in the case of a Class A stage, a geometrical interpretation of the average power $P_L$ delivered to $R_L$ can be obtained by noting that $P_L = \frac{1}{2}\hat{I}_o\hat{V}_o$, where $\hat{I}_o$ and $\hat{V}_o$ are the peak sinusoidal current and voltage delivered to $R_L$. Thus $P_L$ is the area of the triangle in Fig. 5.16 between the $V_{ce}$ axis and the portion of the load line traversed by the operating point.

Consider the instantaneous power dissipated in one device:

$$P_c = V_{ce}I_c \tag{5.72}$$

**Figure 5.16** Load line for one device in a Class B stage.

But

$$V_{ce} = V_{CC} - I_c R_L \qquad (5.73)$$

Substitution of (5.73) in (5.72) gives

$$P_c = I_c(V_{CC} - I_c R_L) = I_c V_{CC} - I_c^2 R_L \qquad (5.74)$$

Differentiation of (5.74) shows that $P_c$ reaches a peak for

$$I_c = \frac{V_{CC}}{2R_L} \qquad (5.75)$$

This peak lies on the load line midway between the $I_c$ and $V_{ce}$ axis intercepts and agrees with the result derived earlier for the Class A stage. As in that case, the load line in Fig. 5.16 is tangent to a power hyperbola at the point of peak dissipation. Thus, in a Class B stage, maximum instantaneous device dissipation occurs for an output voltage equal to about half the maximum swing. Since the quiescent device power dissipation is zero, the operating temperature of a Class B device always *increases* when nonzero signal is applied.

The instantaneous device power dissipation as a function of time is shown in Fig. 5.17, where collector current, collector-emitter voltage, and their product are displayed for one device in a Class B stage at maximum output. (Crossover distortion is ignored, and $V_{CE(\mathrm{sat})} = 0$ is assumed.) When the device conducts, the power dissipation varies at twice the signal frequency. The device power dissipation is zero for the half cycle when the device is cut off. For an open-circuited load, the load line in Fig. 5.16 lies along the $V_{ce}$ axis and the device has zero dissipation. As in the case of Class A stage, the load line in Fig. 5.16 becomes vertical through the quiescent point for a short-circuited load, and the

(a)

(b)

(c)

**Figure 5.17** Waveforms at maximum output for one device in a Class B stage. (a) Collector current waveform. (b) Collector voltage waveform. (c) Collector power dissipation waveform.

instantaneous device power dissipation can then become excessive. Methods of protection against such a possibility are described in Section 5.4.6.

■ **EXAMPLE**

A Class B stage of the type shown in Fig. 5.10 drives a load $R_L = 500 \, \Omega$. If the positive and negative supplies have magnitudes of 15 V, calculate the maximum average power that is delivered to $R_L$ for $\hat{V}_o = 14.4$ V, the corresponding efficiency, and the maximum instantaneous device dissipation. Assume that $V_o$ is sinusoidal.

From (5.66), the average of supply current is

$$I_{supply} = \frac{1}{\pi} \frac{\hat{V}_o}{R_L} = \frac{1}{\pi} \frac{14.4}{500} = 9.17 \text{ mA}$$

Use of (5.67) gives the average power drawn from the supplies as

$$P_{supply} = I_{supply} \times 2V_{CC} = 9.17 \times 30 \text{ mW} = 275 \text{ mW}$$

From (5.68), the average power delivered to $R_L$ is

$$P_L = \frac{1}{2} \frac{\hat{V}_o^2}{R_L} = \frac{1}{2} \frac{14.4^2}{500} = 207 \text{ mW}$$

From (5.13), the corresponding efficiency is

$$\eta_C = \frac{P_L}{P_{supply}} = \frac{207}{275} = 75.3 \text{ percent}$$

This result is close to the theoretical maximum of 78.6 percent. From (5.75), the maximum instantaneous device power dissipation occurs when

$$I_c = \frac{V_{CC}}{2R_L} = \frac{15 \text{ V}}{1000 \, \Omega} = 15 \text{ mA}$$

The corresponding value of $V_{ce}$ is $V_{CC}/2 = 7.5$ V and thus the maximum instantaneous device dissipation is

$$P_c = I_c V_{ce} = 15 \times 7.5 \text{ mW} = 112.5 \text{ mW}$$

By conservation of power, the *average* power dissipated per device is

$$P_{av} = \frac{1}{2}(P_{supply} - P_L) = \frac{1}{2}(275 - 207) \text{ mW} = 34 \text{ mW}$$

■

### 5.4.3 Practical Realizations of Class B Complementary Output Stages[6]

The practical aspects of Class B output-stage design will now be illustrated by considering two examples. One of the simplest realizations is the output stage of the 709 op amp, and a simplified schematic of this is shown in Fig. 5.18. Transistor $Q_3$ acts as a common-emitter driver stage for output devices $Q_1$ and $Q_2$.

The transfer characteristic of this stage can be calculated as follows. In the quiescent condition, $V_o = 0$ and $V_1 = 0$. Since $Q_1$ and $Q_2$ are then off, there is no base current in these devices. Therefore, for $V_{CC} = 10$ V, the bias current in $Q_3$ is

$$I_{C3} = \frac{V_{CC} - V_1}{R_1} = \frac{V_{CC}}{R_1} = \frac{10 \text{ V}}{20 \text{ k}\Omega} = 0.50 \text{ mA}$$

**Figure 5.18** Simplified schematic of the output stage of the 709 op amp.

The limiting values that $V_o$ can take are determined by the *driver stage*. When $V_i$ is taken large positive, $V_1$ decreases until $Q_3$ saturates, at which point the negative voltage limit $V_o^-$ is reached:

$$V_o^- = -V_{CC} + V_{CE3(\text{sat})} - V_{be2} \tag{5.76}$$

For values of $V_1$ between $(-V_{CC} + V_{CE3(\text{sat})})$ and $(-V_{BE(\text{on})})$, both $Q_3$ and $Q_2$ are in the forward-active region, and $V_o$ follows $V_1$ with $Q_2$ acting as an emitter follower.

As $V_i$ is taken negative, the current in $Q_3$ decreases and $V_1$ rises, turning $Q_1$ on. The positive voltage limit $V_o^+$ is reached when $Q_3$ cuts off and the base of $Q_1$ is simply fed from the positive supply via $R_1$. Then

$$V_{CC} = I_{b1}R_1 + V_{be1} + V_o^+ \tag{5.77}$$

If $\beta_{F1}$ is large then

$$V_o^+ = I_{c1}R_L = \beta_{F1}I_{b1}R_L$$

where $\beta_{F1}$ is the current gain of $Q_1$. Thus

$$I_{b1} = \frac{V_o^+}{\beta_{F1}R_L} \tag{5.78}$$

Substituting (5.78) in (5.77) and rearranging gives

$$V_o^+ = \frac{V_{CC} - V_{be1}}{1 + \dfrac{R_1}{\beta_{F1}R_L}} \tag{5.79}$$

For $R_L = 10 \text{ k}\Omega$ and $\beta_{F1} = 100$, (5.79) gives

$$V_o^+ = 0.98(V_{CC} - V_{be1})$$

In this case, the limit on $V_o$ is similar for positive and negative swings. However, if $R_L = 1 \text{ k}\Omega$ and $\beta_{F1} = 100$, (5.79) gives

$$V_o^+ = 0.83(V_{CC} - V_{be1})$$

For this lower value of $R_L$, the maximum positive value of $V_o$ is reduced, and clipping on a sine wave occurs first for $V_o$ going positive.

**Figure 5.19** SPICE-generated transfer characteristic for the circuit of Fig. 5.18 with $V_{CC} = 10$ V and $R_L = 1$ k$\Omega$ and 10 k$\Omega$.

Computer-generated transfer curves using SPICE for this circuit with $V_{CC} = 10$ V are shown in Fig. 5.19 for $R_L = 1$ k$\Omega$ and $R_L = 10$ k$\Omega$. ($\beta_F = 100$ is assumed for all devices.) The reduced positive voltage capability for $R_L = 1$ k$\Omega$ is apparent, as is the deadband present in the transfer characteristic. The curvature in the characteristic is due to the exponential nonlinearity of the driver $Q_3$. In practice, the transfer characteristic may be even more nonlinear than shown in Fig. 5.19 because $\beta_F$ for the $npn$ transistor $Q_1$ is generally larger than $\beta_F$ for the $pnp$ transistor $Q_2$, causing the positive and negative sections of the characteristic to differ significantly. This behavior can be seen by calculating the small-signal gain $\Delta V_o/\Delta V_i$ for positive and negative $V_o$. In the actual 709 integrated circuit, negative feedback is applied around this output stage to reduce these nonlinearities in the transfer characteristic.

A second example of a practical Class B output stage is shown Fig. 5.20, where SPICE-calculated bias currents are included. This circuit is a simplified schematic of the 741 op amp output circuitry. The output devices $Q_{14}$ and $Q_{20}$ are biased to a collector current of about 0.17 mA by the diodes $Q_{18}$ and $Q_{19}$. The value of the bias current in $Q_{14}$ and $Q_{20}$ depends on the effective area ratio between diodes $Q_{18}$ and $Q_{19}$ and the output devices. ($Q_{18}$ and $Q_{19}$ are implemented with transistors in practice.) The output stage is driven by lateral $pnp$ emitter-follower $Q_{23}$, which is driven by common-emitter stage $Q_{17}$ biased to 0.68 mA by current source $Q_{13B}$.

The diodes in Fig. 5.20 essentially eliminate crossover distortion in the circuit, which can be seen in the SPICE-generated transfer characteristic of Fig. 5.21. The linearity of this stage is further improved by the fact that the output devices are driven from a low resistance provided by the emitter follower $Q_{23}$. Consequently, differences in $\beta_F$ between $Q_{14}$ and $Q_{20}$ produce little effect on the transfer characteristic because small-signal gain $\Delta V_o/\Delta V_1 \simeq 1$ for *any* practical value of $\beta_F$ with either $Q_{14}$ or $Q_{20}$ conducting.

The limits on the output voltage swing shown in Fig. 5.21 can be determined as follows. As $V_i$ is taken positive, the voltage $V_1$ at the base of $Q_{23}$ goes negative, and voltages $V_2$ and $V_o$ follow with $Q_{20}$ drawing current from $R_L$. When $Q_{17}$ saturates, the output

Figure 5.20  (a) Simplified schematic of the 741 op amp output stage. (b) Schematic of the 741 output stage showing the detail of $Q_{18}$ and $Q_{19}$.

voltage limit for negative excursions is reached at

$$V_o^- = -V_{CC} + V_{CE17(sat)} - V_{be23} - V_{be20} \tag{5.80}$$

This limit is about 1.4 V more positive than the negative supply. Thus $V_o^-$ is limited by saturation in $Q_{17}$, which is the stage *preceding* driver stage $Q_{23}$.

As $V_i$ is taken negative from its quiescent value (where $V_o = 0$), voltage $V_1$ rises and voltages $V_2$ and $V_o$ follow with $Q_{14}$ delivering current to the load. The positive output

**Figure 5.21** SPICE-generated transfer curve for the circuit of Fig. 5.20a with $V_{CC} = 15$ V and $R_L = 1$ kΩ.

voltage limit $V_o^+$ is reached when current source $Q_{13A}$ saturates and

$$V_o^+ = V_{CC} + V_{CE13A(sat)} - V_{be14} \qquad (5.81)$$

This limit is about 0.8 V below the positive supply because $V_{CE13A(sat)} \approx -0.1$ V for the *pnp* device. Thus $V_o^+$ is also limited by the driver stage.

The power requirements of the driver circuits in a configuration such as shown in Fig. 5.20 require some consideration. The basic requirement of the driver is to supply sufficient drive to the output stage so that it can supply the desired power to $R_L$. As $V_o$ is taken negative, $Q_{23}$ draws current from the base of $Q_{20}$ with essentially no limit. In fact, the circuit must be protected in case of a short-circuited load. Otherwise in this case, a large input signal could cause $Q_{23}$ and $Q_{20}$ to conduct such heavy currents that they burn out. As explained before, the negative voltage limit is reached when $Q_{17}$ saturates and can no longer drive the base of $Q_{23}$ negative.

As $V_o$ is taken positive (by $V_i$ going negative and $V_1$ going positive), $Q_{23}$ conducts less, and current source $Q_{13A}$ supplies base current to $Q_{14}$. The maximum output current is limited by the current of 0.22 mA available for driving $Q_{14}$. As $V_1$, $V_2$, and $V_o$ go positive, the current in $Q_{14}$ increases, and the current in $Q_{13A}$ is progressively diverted to the base of $Q_{14}$. The maximum possible output current delivered by $Q_{14}$ is thus

$$I_o = \beta_{F14} \times 0.22 \text{ mA}$$

If $\beta_{F14} = 100$, the maximum output current is 22 mA. The driver stage may thus limit the maximum positive current available from the output stage. However, this output current level is only reached if $R_L$ is small enough so that $Q_{13A}$ does not saturate on the positive voltage excursion.

The stage preceding the driver in this circuit is $Q_{17}$. As mentioned above, the negative voltage limit of $V_o$ is reached when $Q_{17}$ saturates. The bias current of 0.68 mA in $Q_{17}$ is much greater than the base current of $Q_{23}$, and thus $Q_{23}$ produces very little loading on $Q_{17}$. Consequently, voltage $V_1$ at the base of $Q_{23}$ can be driven to within $V_{CE(\text{sat})}$ of either supply voltage with only a very small fractional change in the collector current of $Q_{17}$.

Finally, we will now examine the detail of the fabrication of diodes $Q_{18}$ and $Q_{19}$ in the 741. The actual circuit is shown in Fig. 5.20b with the output protection circuitry omitted. Diode $Q_{19}$ conducts only a current equal to the base current of $Q_{18}$ plus the bleed current in pinch resistor $R_{10}$. Transistor $Q_{18}$ thus conducts most of the bias current of current source $Q_{13A}$. This arrangement is used for two reasons. First, the basic aim of achieving a voltage drop equal to two base-emitter voltages is achieved. Since $Q_{18}$ and $Q_{19}$ have common collectors, however, they can be placed in the same isolation region, reducing die area. Second, since $Q_{19}$ conducts only a small current, the bias voltage produced by $Q_{18}$ and $Q_{19}$ across the bases of $Q_{14}$ and $Q_{20}$ is less than would result from a connection as shown in Fig. 5.20a. This observation is important because output transistors $Q_{14}$ and $Q_{20}$ generally have emitter areas larger than the standard device geometry (typically four times larger or more) so that they can maintain high $\beta_F$ while conducting large output currents. Thus in the circuit of Fig. 5.20a, the bias current in $Q_{14}$ and $Q_{20}$ would be about four times the current in $Q_{18}$ and $Q_{19}$, which would be excessive in a 741-type circuit. However, the circuit of Fig. 5.20b can be designed to bias $Q_{14}$ and $Q_{20}$ to a current comparable to the current in the diodes, even though the output devices have a large area. The basic reason for this result is that the small bias current in $Q_{19}$ in Fig. 5.20b gives it a smaller base-emitter voltage than for the same device in Fig. 5.20a, reducing the total bias voltage between the bases of $Q_{14}$ and $Q_{20}$.

The results described above can be illustrated quantitatively by calculating the bias currents in $Q_{14}$ and $Q_{20}$ of Fig. 5.20b. From KVL,

$$V_{BE19} + V_{BE18} = V_{BE14} + |V_{BE20}|$$

and thus

$$V_T \ln \frac{I_{C19}}{I_{S19}} + V_T \ln \frac{I_{C18}}{I_{S18}} = V_T \ln \frac{I_{C14}}{I_{S14}} + V_T \ln \left| \frac{I_{C20}}{I_{S20}} \right| \qquad (5.82)$$

If we assume that the circuit is biased for $V_o = 0$ V and also that $\beta_{F14} \gg 1$ and $\beta_{F20} \gg 1$, then $|I_{C14}| = |I_{C20}|$ and (5.82) becomes

$$\frac{I_{C19}I_{C18}}{I_{S18}I_{S19}} = \frac{I_{C14}^2}{I_{S14}I_{S20}}$$

from which

$$I_{C14} = -I_{C20} = \sqrt{I_{C19}I_{C18}} \sqrt{\frac{I_{S14}I_{S20}}{I_{S18}I_{S19}}} \qquad (5.83)$$

Equation 5.83 may be used to calculate the output bias current in circuits of the type shown in Fig. 5.20b. The output-stage bias current from (5.83) is proportional to $\sqrt{I_{C18}}$ and $\sqrt{I_{C19}}$. For this specific example, the collector current in $Q_{19}$ is approximately equal to the current in $R_{10}$ if $\beta_F$ is large and thus

$$I_{C19} \approx \frac{V_{BE18}}{R_{10}} \approx \frac{0.6}{40} \text{ mA} = 15 \text{ }\mu\text{A}$$

If the base currents of $Q_{14}$ and $Q_{20}$ are neglected, the collector current of $Q_{18}$ is

$$I_{C18} \simeq |I_{C13A}| - I_{C19} = (220 - 15)\mu\text{A} \doteq 205 \, \mu\text{A}$$

To calculate the output-stage bias currents from (5.83), values for the various reverse saturation currents are required. These values depend on the particular IC process used, but typical values are $I_{S18} = I_{S19} = 2 \times 10^{-15}$ A, $I_{S14} = 4I_{S18} = 8 \times 10^{-15}$ A, and $I_{S20} = 4 \times 10^{-15}$ A. Substitution of these data in (5.83) gives $I_{C14} = -I_{C20} = 0.16$ mA.

■ **EXAMPLE**

For the output stage of Fig. 5.20a, calculate bias currents in all devices for $V_o = +10$ V. Assume that $V_{CC} = 15$ V, $R_L = 2$ kΩ, and $\beta_F = 100$. For simplicity, assume all devices have equal area and for each device

$$|I_C| = 10^{-14} \exp \left| \frac{V_{be}}{V_T} \right| \tag{5.84}$$

Assuming that $Q_{14}$ supplies the load current for positive output voltages, we have

$$I_{c14} = \frac{V_o}{R_L} = \frac{10 \text{ V}}{2 \text{ k}\Omega} = 5 \text{ mA}$$

Substitution in (5.84) and rearranging gives

$$V_{be14} = (26 \text{ mV}) \ln \left( \frac{5 \times 10^{-3}}{10^{-14}} \right) = 700 \text{ mV}$$

Also

$$I_{b14} = \frac{I_{c14}}{\beta_{F14}} = \frac{5 \text{ mA}}{100} = 0.05 \text{ mA}$$

Thus

$$I_{c19} \simeq I_{c18} \simeq -I_{c23} = (0.22 - 0.05) \text{ mA} = 0.17 \text{ mA}$$

Substitution in (5.84) and rearranging gives

$$V_{be19} = V_{be18} = -V_{be23} = (26 \text{ mV}) \ln \left( \frac{0.17 \times 10^{-3}}{10^{-14}} \right) = 613 \text{ mV}$$

Thus

$$V_{be20} = -(V_{be19} + V_{be18} - V_{be14}) = -525 \text{ mV}$$

Use of (5.84) gives

$$I_{c20} = -5.9 \, \mu\text{A}$$

and the collector current in $Q_{20}$ is quite small as predicted. Finally

$$I_{c17} = 0.68 \text{ mA} - \frac{I_{c23}}{\beta_{F23}} = \left( 0.68 - \frac{0.17}{100} \right) \text{ mA} = 0.68 \text{ mA}$$

and also

$$V_2 = V_o - |V_{be20}| = (10 - 0.525) \text{ V} = 9.475 \text{ V}$$

and

$$V_1 = V_2 - |V_{be23}| = (9.475 - 0.613) \text{ V} = 8.862 \text{ V}$$

### 5.4.4 All-*npn* Class B Output Stage[7,8,9]

The Class B circuits described above are adequate for many integrated-circuit applications where the output power to be delivered to the load is of the order of several hundred milliwatts or less. However, if output-power levels of several watts or more are required, these circuits are inadequate because the substrate *pnp* transistors used in the output stage have a limited current-carrying capability. This limit stems from the fact that the doping levels in the emitter, base, and collector of these devices are not optimized for *pnp* structures because the *npn* devices in the circuit have conflicting requirements.

A circuit design that uses high-power *npn* transistors in both halves of a Class B configuration is shown in Fig. 5.22. In this circuit, common-emitter transistor $Q_1$ delivers power to the load during the negative half-cycle, and emitter follower $Q_2$ delivers power during the positive half-cycle.

To examine the operation of this circuit, consider $V_i$ taken negative from its quiescent value so that $Q_1$ is off and $I_{c1} = 0$. Then diodes $D_1$ and $D_2$ must both be off and all of the collector current of $Q_3$ is delivered to the base of $Q_2$. The output voltage then has its maximum positive value $V_o^+$. If $R_L$ is big enough, $Q_3$ saturates and

$$V_o^+ = V_{CC} - |V_{CE3(\text{sat})}| - V_{be2} \qquad (5.85)$$

To attain this maximum positive value, transistor $Q_3$ must saturate in this extreme condition. In contrast, $Q_2$ in this circuit cannot saturate because the collector of $Q_2$ is connected to the positive supply and the base voltage of $Q_2$ cannot exceed the positive supply voltage. The condition for $Q_3$ to be saturated is that the nominal collector bias current $I_{Q3}$ in $Q_3$ (when $Q_3$ is *not* saturated) should be larger than the required base current of $Q_2$ when $V_o = V_o^+$. Thus we require

$$I_{Q3} > I_{b2} \qquad (5.86)$$

Since $Q_2$ supplies the current to $R_L$ for $V_o > 0$, we have

$$V_o^+ = -I_{e2}R_L = (\beta_2 + 1)I_{b2}R_L \qquad (5.87)$$

**Figure 5.22** All-*npn* Class B output stage.

Substitution of (5.87) and (5.85) in (5.86) gives the requirement on the bias current of $Q_3$ as

$$I_{Q3} > \frac{V_{CC} - V_{CE3(\text{sat})} - V_{be2}}{(\beta_2 + 1)R_L} \tag{5.88}$$

Equation 5.88 also applies to the circuit of Fig. 5.20a. It gives limits on $I_{C3}$, $\beta_2$, and $R_L$ for $V_o$ to be able to swing close to the positive supply. If $I_{Q3}$ is less than the value given by (5.88), $V_o$ will begin clipping at a positive value *less than* that given by (5.85) and $Q_3$ will never saturate.

Now consider $V_i$ made positive to turn $Q_1$ on and produce nonzero $I_{c1}$. Since the base of $Q_2$ is more positive than its emitter, diode $D_1$ will turn on in preference to $D_2$, which will be off with zero volts across its junction. The current $I_{c1}$ will flow through $D_1$ and will be drawn from $Q_3$, which is assumed saturated at first. As $I_{c1}$ increases, $Q_3$ will eventually come out of saturation, and voltage $V_2$ at the base of $Q_2$ will then be pulled down. Since $Q_2$ acts as an emitter follower, $V_o$ will follow $V_2$ down. This behavior occurs during the positive half of the cycle, and $Q_1$ acts as a driver with $Q_2$ as the output device.

When $V_o$ is reduced to 0 V, the load current is zero and $I_{c2} = 0$. This point corresponds to $I_{c1} = |I_{C3}|$, and all of the bias current in $Q_3$ passes through $D_1$ to $Q_1$. If $I_{c1}$ is increased further, $V_o$ stays constant at 0 V while $V_2$ is reduced to 0 V also. Therefore, $V_1$ is negative by an amount equal to the diode voltage drop of $D_1$, and thus power diode $D_2$ turns on. Since the current in $D_1$ is essentially fixed by $Q_3$, further increases in $I_{c1}$ cause increasing current to flow through $D_2$. The negative half of the cycle consists of $Q_1$ acting as the output device and feeding $R_L$ through $D_2$. The maximum negative voltage occurs when $Q_1$ saturates and is

$$V_o^- = -V_{CC} + V_{CE1(\text{sat})} + V_{d2} \tag{5.89}$$

where $V_{d2}$ is the forward voltage drop across $D_2$.

The sequence just described gives rise to a highly nonlinear transfer characteristic, as shown in Fig. 5.23, where $V_o$ is plotted as a function of $I_{c1}$ for convenience. When $V_o$ is

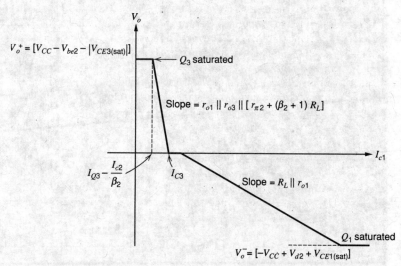

**Figure 5.23** Transfer characteristic of the circuit of Fig. 5.22 from $I_{c1}$ to $V_o$.

positive, the current $I_{c1}$ feeds into the base of $Q_2$ and the small-signal gain is

$$\frac{\Delta V_o}{\Delta I_{c1}} \simeq \frac{\Delta V_2}{\Delta I_{c1}} = r_{o1} \parallel r_{o3} \parallel [r_{\pi2} + (\beta_2 + 1)R_L]$$

where the impedance of $D_1$ is assumed negligible. That is, the impedance at the base of $Q_2$ is equal to the parallel combination of the output resistances of $Q_1$ and $Q_3$ and the input resistance of emitter follower $Q_2$.

When $V_o$ in Fig. 5.22 is negative, $I_{c1}$ feeds $R_L$ directly and the small-signal gain is

$$\frac{\Delta V_o}{\Delta I_{c1}} \simeq r_{o1} \parallel R_L$$

where the impedance of $D_2$ is assumed negligible.

Note the small deadband in Fig. 5.23 where diode $D_2$ turns on. This deadband can be eliminated by adding a second diode in series with $D_1$. In practice, negative feedback must be used around this circuit to linearize the transfer characteristic, and such feedback will reduce any crossover effects. The transfer characteristic of the circuit from $V_i$ to $V_o$ is even more nonlinear than shown in Fig. 5.23 because it includes the exponential nonlinearity of $Q_1$.

In integrated-circuit fabrication of the circuit of Fig. 5.22, devices $Q_1$ and $Q_2$ are identical large-power transistors. In high-power circuits (delivering several watts or more), they may occupy 50 percent of the whole die. Diode $D_2$ is a large-power diode that also occupies considerable area. These features are illustrated in Fig. 5.24, which is a die photo of the 791 high-power op amp. This circuit can dissipate 10 W of power and can deliver 15 W of output power into an 8-$\Omega$ load. The large power transistors in the output stage can be seen on the right-hand side of the die.

Finally, the power and efficiency results derived previously for the complementary Class B stage apply equally to the all-$npn$ Class B stage if allowance is made for the voltage drop in $D_2$. Thus the ideal maximum efficiency is 79 percent.

**Figure 5.24** Die photo of the 791 high-power op amp.

### 5.4.5 Quasi-Complementary Output Stages[10]

The all-*npn* stage described above is one solution to the problem of the limited power-handling capability of the substrate *pnp*. Another solution is shown in Fig. 5.25, where a *composite pnp* has been made from a lateral *pnp* $Q_3$ and a high-power *npn* transistor $Q_4$. This circuit is called a quasi-complementary output stage.

The operation of the circuit of Fig. 5.25 is almost identical to that of Fig. 5.20. The pair $Q_3$-$Q_4$ is equivalent to a *pnp* transistor as shown in Fig. 5.26, and the collector current of $Q_3$ is

$$I_{C3} = -I_S \exp\left(-\frac{V_{BE}}{V_T}\right) \tag{5.90}$$

The composite collector current $I_C$ is the emitter current of $Q_4$, which is

$$I_C = (\beta_{F4} + 1)I_{C3} = -(\beta_{F4} + 1)I_S \exp\left(-\frac{V_{BE}}{V_T}\right) \tag{5.91}$$

The composite device thus shows the standard relationship between $I_C$ and $V_{BE}$ for a *pnp* transistor. However, most of the current is carried by the high-power *npn* transistor. Note

**Figure 5.25** Quasi-complementary Class B output stage.

**Figure 5.26** Equivalence of the composite connection and a *pnp* transistor.

that the magnitude of the saturation voltage of the composite device is $(|V_{CE3(\text{sat})}| + V_{BE4})$. This magnitude is higher than normal because saturation occurs when $Q_3$ saturates, and $V_{BE4}$ must be added to this voltage.

The major problem with the configuration of Fig. 5.25 is potential instability of the local feedback loop formed by $Q_3$ and $Q_4$, particularly with capacitive loads on the amplifier. The stability of feedback loops is considered in Chapter 9.

The quasi-complementary Class B stage can also be effectively implemented in BiCMOS technology. In the circuit of Fig. 5.25, the compound bipolar device $Q_3$-$Q_4$ can be replaced by the MOS-bipolar combination[11] of Fig. 5.27, where $Q_4$ is a large-area high-current bipolar device. The overall transfer characteristic is

$$I_D = (\beta_{F4} + 1)I_{D3} = -(\beta_{F4} + 1)\frac{\mu_n C_{ox}}{2} \left(\frac{W}{L}\right)_3 (V_{GS} - V_t)^2 \qquad (5.92)$$

Equation 5.92 shows that the composite PMOS device appears to have a $W/L$ ratio $(\beta_{F4} + 1)$ times larger than the physical PMOS device $M_3$. With this circuit, one of the diodes $Q_5$ or $Q_6$ in Fig. 5.25 would now be replaced by a diode-connected PMOS transistor to set up a temperature-stable standby current in the output stage. A bias bleed resistor can be connected from the base to the emitter of $Q_4$ to optimize the bias current in $M_3$ and to speed up the turn-off of $Q_4$ in high-frequency applications by allowing reverse base current to remove the base charge. Such a resistor can also be connected from the base to the emitter of $Q_4$ in Fig. 5.25.

## 5.4.6 Overload Protection

The most common type of overload protection in integrated-circuit output stages is short-circuit current protection. As an example, consider the 741 output stage shown in Fig. 5.28 with partial short-circuit protection included. Initially assume that $R_6 = 0$ and ignore $Q_{15}$. The maximum positive drive delivered to the output stage occurs for $V_i$ large positive. If $R_L = 0$ then $V_o$ is held at zero volts and $V_a$ in Fig. 5.28 is equal to $V_{be14}$. Thus, as $V_i$ is taken positive, $Q_{23}$, $Q_{18}$, and $Q_{19}$ will cut off and all of the current of $Q_{13A}$ is fed to $Q_{14}$. If this is a high-$\beta_F$ device, then the output current can become destructively large:

$$I_{c14} = \beta_{F14}|I_{C13A}| \qquad (5.93)$$

If

$$\beta_{F14} = 500$$

then

$$I_{c14} = 500 \times 0.22 = 110 \text{ mA}$$

Figure 5.27  Compound high-current PMOS connection.

**Figure 5.28** Schematic of the 741 op amp showing partial short-circuit protection.

If $V_{CC} = 15$ V, this current level gives a power dissipation in $Q_{14}$ of

$$P_{c14} = V_{ce}I_c = 15 \times 110 \text{ mW} = 1.65 \text{ W}$$

which is sufficient to destroy the device. Thus the current under short-circuit conditions must be limited, and this objective is achieved using $R_6$ and $Q_{15}$ for positive $V_o$.

The short-circuit protection operates by sensing the output current with resistor $R_6$ of about 25 Ω. The voltage developed across $R_6$ is the base-emitter voltage of $Q_{15}$, which is normally off. When the current through $R_6$ reaches about 20 mA (the maximum safe level), $Q_{15}$ begins to conduct appreciably and diverts any further drive away from the base of $Q_{14}$. The drive current is thus harmlessly passed to the output instead of being multiplied by the $\beta_F$ of $Q_{14}$.

The operation of this circuit can be seen by calculating the transfer characteristic of $Q_{14}$ when driving a short-circuit load. This can be done using Fig. 5.29.

$$I_i = I_{b14} + I_{c15} \tag{5.94}$$

$$I_{c15} = I_{S15} \exp \frac{V_{be15}}{V_T} \tag{5.95}$$

Also

$$V_{be15} \simeq I_{c14}R \tag{5.96}$$

From (5.94)

$$I_{b14} = I_i - I_{c15}$$

But

$$I_{c14} = \beta_{F14}I_{b14} = \beta_{F14}(I_i - I_{c15}) \tag{5.97}$$

**Figure 5.29** Equivalent circuit for the calculation of the effect of $Q_{15}$ on the transfer characteristic of $Q_{14}$ in Fig. 5.28 when $R_L \simeq 0$.

Substitution of (5.95) and (5.96) in (5.97) gives

$$I_{c14} + \beta_{F14}I_{S15} \exp \frac{I_{c14}R}{V_T} = \beta_{F14}I_i \tag{5.98}$$

The second term on the left side of (5.98) stems from $Q_{15}$. If this term is negligible, then $I_{c14} = \beta_{F14}I_i$ as expected. The transfer characteristic of the stage is plotted from (5.98) in Fig. 5.30, using $\beta_{F14} = 500$, $I_{S15} = 10^{-14}$ A, and $R = 25\ \Omega$. For a maximum drive of $I_i = 0.22$ mA, the value of $I_{c14}$ is effectively limited to 24 mA. For values of $I_{c14}$ below 20 mA, $Q_{15}$ has little effect on circuit operation.

Similar protection for negative output voltages in Fig. 5.29 is achieved by sensing the voltage across $R_7$ and diverting the base drive away from one of the preceding stages.

## 5.5 CMOS Class AB Output Stages

The classical Class AB topology of Fig. 5.13 can also be implemented in standard CMOS technology. However, the output swing of the resulting circuit is usually much worse than in the bipolar case. Although the swing can be improved using a common-source configuration, this circuit suffers from poor control of the quiescent current in the output devices. These issues are described below.

**Figure 5.30** Transfer characteristic of the circuit of Fig. 5.29 with and without protection transistor $Q_{15}$ ($\beta_{F14} = 500$).

### 5.5.1 Common-Drain Configuration

Figure 5.31 shows the common-drain class-AB output configuration. From KVL,

$$V_{SG5} + V_{GS4} = V_{gs1} + V_{sg2} \tag{5.99}$$

Ignoring the body effect, $V_{SG5} + V_{GS4}$ is constant if the bias current from $M_3$ is constant. Under these conditions, increasing $V_{gs1}$ decreases $V_{sg2}$ and vice versa.

For simplicity, assume at first that a short circuit is connected from the drain of $M_4$ to the drain of $M_5$. Then $V_{SG5} + V_{GS4} = 0$ and $V_{gs1} = V_{gs2}$ from (5.99). For $M_1$ to conduct nonzero drain current, $V_{gs1} > V_{t1}$ is required. Similarly, $V_{gs2} < V_{t2}$ is required for $M_2$ to conduct nonzero drain current. With standard enhancement-mode devices, $V_{t1} > 0$ and $V_{t2} < 0$. Therefore, $M_1$ and $M_2$ do not both conduct simultaneously under these conditions, which is a characteristic of a Class-B output stage. When $V_o > 0$, $M_1$ operates as a source follower and $M_2$ is off. Similarly, $M_2$ operates as a source follower and $M_1$ is off when $V_o < 0$.

In Fig. 5.31, however, $V_{SG5} + V_{GS4} > 0$ and both $M_1$ and $M_2$ are biased to conduct nonzero drain current when $V_o = 0$, which is a characteristic of a Class-AB output stage. If $V_{t1} = V_{t4}$ and $V_{t2} = V_{t5}$, using (1.157) in (5.99) with $I_{D5} = -I_{D4}$ gives

$$\sqrt{\frac{2I_{D4}}{k_p'(W/L)_5}} + \sqrt{\frac{2I_{D4}}{k_n'(W/L)_4}} = \sqrt{\frac{2I_{d1}}{k_n'(W/L)_1}} + \sqrt{\frac{2|I_{d2}|}{k_p'(W/L)_2}} \tag{5.100}$$

If $V_o = 0$, then $I_{d2} = -I_{d1}$ and (5.100) can be rearranged to give

$$I_{D1} = I_{D4} \frac{\left(\dfrac{1}{k_n'(W/L)_4} + \dfrac{1}{k_p'(W/L)_5}\right)}{\left(\dfrac{1}{k_n'(W/L)_1} + \dfrac{1}{k_p'(W/L)_2}\right)} \tag{5.101}$$

where $I_{D1} = I_{d1}$ with $V_o = 0$. The key point of this equation is that the quiescent current in the output transistors is well controlled with respect to the bias current that flows in the diode-connected transistors, as in the bipolar case.

**Figure 5.31** Complementary source-follower CMOS output stage based on traditional bipolar implementation.

An important problem with this circuit is that its output swing can be much less than the corresponding bipolar circuit with equal supply voltages. For $V_o > 0$, $V_{gs1} > V_{t1}$ and $M_1$ acts as a source follower. Therefore,

$$V_o = V_{DD} - V_{sd3} - V_{gs1} \tag{5.102}$$

The minimum $V_{sd3}$ required to operate $M_3$ as a current source is $|V_{ov3}| = |V_{GS3} - V_{t3}|$. From (5.102), the maximum output voltage $V_o^+$ is

$$V_o^+ = V_{DD} - |V_{ov3}| - V_{gs1} \tag{5.103}$$

The minimum output voltage can be found by similar reasoning. (See Problem 5.21.) Although (5.103) appears to be quite similar to (5.81) if $V_{CC}$ in Fig. 5.20 is equal to $V_{DD}$ in Fig. 5.31, the limit in (5.103) is usually much less than in (5.81) for three reasons. First, the gate-source voltage includes a threshold component that is absent in the base-emitter voltage. Second, the body effect increases the threshold voltage $V_{t1}$ as $V_o$ increases. Finally, the overdrive part of the gate-source voltage rises more steeply with increasing current than the entire base-emitter voltage because the overdrive is proportional to the square root of the current and the base-emitter voltage is proportional to the logarithm of the current. In practice, the output voltage swing can be increased by increasing the $W/L$ ratios of the output devices to reduce their overdrives. However, the required transistor sizes are sometimes so large that the parasitic capacitances associated with the output devices can dominate the overall performance at high frequencies. Thus the circuit of Fig. 5.31 is generally limited to much smaller currents than its bipolar equivalent.

▪ **EXAMPLE**

An output stage such as shown in Fig. 5.31 is required to produce a maximum output voltage of 0.7 V with $R_L = 35\ \Omega$ and $V_{DD} = V_{SS} = 1.5\ \text{V}$. Using the transistor parameters in Table 2.4, find the required $W/L$ of $M_1$. Assume $|V_{ov3}| = 100\ \text{mV}$, and ignore the body effect.

From (5.103),

$$V_{gs1} = V_{DD} - |V_{ov3}| - V_o^+ = (1.5 - 0.1 - 0.7)\ \text{V} = 0.7\ \text{V}$$

Since Table 2.4 gives $V_{t1} = 0.6\ \text{V}$,

$$V_{ov1} = V_{gs1} - V_{t1} = (0.7 - 0.6)\ \text{V} = 0.1\ \text{V}$$

With $V_o = 0.7\ \text{V}$, the current in the load is $(0.7\ \text{V})/(35\ \Omega) = 20\ \text{mA}$. If $I_{d2} = 0$ under these conditions, $I_{d1} = 20\ \text{mA}$. Rearranging (1.157) gives

$$\left(\frac{W}{L}\right)_1 = \frac{2I}{k_n' V_{ov1}{}^2} = \frac{2(20000)}{194(0.1)^2} \approx 20,000 \tag{5.104}$$

▪ which is a very large transistor.

### 5.5.2 Common-Source Configuration with Error Amplifiers

Another alternative is the use of quasi-complementary configurations. In this case, a common-source transistor together with an error amplifier replaces an output source-follower device. A circuit with this substitution for both output transistors is shown conceptually in Fig. 5.32.[12,13,14] The combination of the error amplifier and the common-source

Figure 5.32 A complementary Class AB output stage using embedded common-source output devices.

device mimics the behavior of a source follower with high dc transconductance. The function of the amplifiers is to sense the voltage difference between the input and the output of the stage and drive the gates of the output transistors so as to make the difference as small as possible. This operation can be viewed as negative feedback. A key advantage of the use of negative feedback here is that it reduces the output resistance. Since negative feedback is covered in Chapter 8, we will analyze this structure with straightforward circuit analysis.

To find the output resistance, consider the small-signal model of this output stage shown in Fig. 5.33. The current $i_t$ is

$$i_t = \frac{v_t}{r_{o1}} + \frac{v_t}{r_{o2}} + g_{m1}Av_t + g_{m2}Av_t \tag{5.105}$$

Rearranging this equation to solve for $v_t/i_t$ gives

$$R_o = \frac{v_t}{i_t}\bigg|_{v_i=0} = \frac{1}{(g_{m1} + g_{m2})A} \parallel r_{o1} \parallel r_{o2} \tag{5.106}$$

This equation shows that increasing the gain $A$ of the error amplifiers reduces $R_o$ and that $R_o$ is much less than the drain-source resistance of $M_1$ or $M_2$ because of the negative feedback.

To find the transfer characteristic, consider the dc model of the output stage shown in Fig. 5.34. The model includes the input-referred offset voltages of the error amplifiers as

Figure 5.33 Small-signal model of the output stage in Fig. 5.32 used to find $R_o$.

**Figure 5.34** A dc model of the output stage in Fig. 5.32 used to find the transfer characteristic.

voltage sources. Assume $k'_p(W/L)_1 = k'_n(W/L)_2 = k'(W/L)$ and $-V_{t1} = V_{t2} = V_t$. Also assume that the error amplifiers are designed so that $-I_{D1} = I_{D2} = I_Q$ when $V_i = 0$, $V_{OSP} = 0$, and $V_{OSN} = 0$. Under these conditions, $V_o = 0$ and

$$V_{gs1} = -V_t - V_{ov} \tag{5.107}$$

$$V_{gs2} = V_t + V_{ov} \tag{5.108}$$

where

$$V_{ov} = \sqrt{\frac{2I_Q}{k'(W/L)}} \tag{5.109}$$

With nonzero input and offsets, the output may not be zero. As a result, the differential input to the top error amplifier changes from zero to $V_o - (V_i - V_{OSP})$. Similarly, the differential input to the bottom error amplifier changes from zero to $V_o - (V_i - V_{OSN})$. Assuming that the output of each error amplifier changes by its gain $A$ times the change in its input,

$$V_{gs1} = -V_t - V_{ov} + A[V_o - (V_i - V_{OSP})] \tag{5.110}$$

$$V_{gs2} = V_t + V_{ov} + A[V_o - (V_i - V_{OSN})] \tag{5.111}$$

If $M_1$ and $M_2$ operate in the active region,

$$I_{d1} = -\frac{k'_p}{2}\left(\frac{W}{L}\right)_1 (V_{gs1} - V_{t1})^2 = -\frac{k'}{2}\frac{W}{L}(V_{gs1} + V_t)^2 \tag{5.112}$$

$$I_{d2} = \frac{k'_n}{2}\left(\frac{W}{L}\right)_2 (V_{gs2} - V_{t2})^2 = \frac{k'}{2}\frac{W}{L}(V_{gs2} - V_t)^2 \tag{5.113}$$

Also,

$$I_o = \frac{V_o}{R_L} \tag{5.114}$$

From KCL at the output,

$$I_o + I_{d1} + I_{d2} = 0 \tag{5.115}$$

Substituting (5.110)–(5.114) into (5.115) and rearranging gives

$$V_o = \frac{V_i - \dfrac{V_{OSP} + V_{OSN}}{2}}{1 + \dfrac{1}{k'\dfrac{W}{L}A[2V_{ov} - A(V_{OSP} - V_{OSN})]R_L}} \tag{5.116}$$

If $V_{OSP} = V_{OSN} = 0$,

$$V_o = \frac{V_i}{1 + \dfrac{1}{k'\dfrac{W}{L}A2V_{ov}R_L}} = \frac{V_i}{1 + \dfrac{1}{2Ag_mR_L}} \simeq V_i\left(1 - \frac{1}{2Ag_mR_L}\right) \quad (5.117)$$

where $g_m = k'(W/L)V_{ov}$ as shown in (1.180). The term $(2Ag_mR_L)$ is the gain around the feedback loop or the *loop gain* and is usually chosen to be high enough to make the slope of the transfer characteristic to be unity within an allowable gain error. (The concept of loop gain is described in Chapter 8.) The gain error here is approximately $1/(2Ag_mR_L)$. The key point is that the error is reduced if $A$, $g_m$, or $R_L$ are increased.

With nonzero offsets, (5.116) shows that the circuit also displays an offset error. If $A(V_{OSP} - V_{OSN}) \ll 2V_{ov}$ and $2Ag_mR_L \gg 1$,

$$V_o \simeq \frac{V_i - \dfrac{V_{OSP} + V_{OSN}}{2}}{1 + \dfrac{1}{k'\dfrac{W}{L}A2V_{ov}R_L}} = \frac{V_i - \dfrac{V_{OSP} + V_{OSN}}{2}}{1 + \dfrac{1}{2Ag_mR_L}} \simeq V_i - \frac{V_{OSP} + V_{OSN}}{2} \quad (5.118)$$

Therefore, the input offset voltage of the buffer is about $-(V_{OSP} + V_{OSN})/2$.

Equation 5.116 is valid as long as both $M_1$ and $M_2$ operate in the active region. If the magnitude of the output voltage is large enough, however, one of the two output transistors turns off. For example, when $V_i$ increases, $V_o$ also increases but the gain is slightly less than unity. As a result, the differential inputs to the error amplifiers both decrease, decreasing $V_{gs1}$ and $V_{gs2}$. In turn, these changes increase $|I_{d1}|$ but reduce $I_{d2}$, and $M_2$ turns off for large enough $V_i$. To find the portion of the transfer characteristic with $M_1$ in the active region but $M_2$ off, the above analysis can be repeated with $I_{d2} = 0$. See Problem 5.23.

The primary motivation for using the quasi-complementary configuration is to increase the output swing. If the output transistors are not allowed to operate in the triode region, the output voltage can pull within an overdrive of either supply. This result is an improvement compared to the limit given in (5.103) for the common-drain output stage mostly because the threshold voltages of the output transistors do not limit the output swing in the common-source configuration.

Although quasi-complementary circuits improve the output swing, they suffer from two main problems. First, the error amplifiers must have large bandwidth to prevent crossover distortion problems for high input frequencies. Unfortunately, increasing the bandwidth of the error amplifiers worsens the stability margins, especially in the presence of large capacitive loads. As a result, these circuits present difficult design problems in compensation. The topics of stability and compensation are covered in Chapter 9. Second, nonzero offset voltages in the error amplifiers change the quiescent current flowing in the output transistors. From a design standpoint, the quiescent current is chosen to be barely high enough to limit crossover distortion to an acceptable level. Although further increases in the quiescent current reduce the crossover distortion, such increases also increase the power dissipation and reduce the output swing. Therefore, proper control of the quiescent current with nonzero offsets is also a key design constraint.

One way to control the quiescent current is to sense and feedback a copy of the current.[12] This method is not considered further here. Another way to limit the variation in the quiescent current is to design the error amplifiers to have low gain.[13,14] The concept is that the quiescent current is controlled by the gate-source voltages on the output transistors, which in turn are controlled by the outputs of the error amplifiers. Therefore, reducing the error-amplifier gain reduces the variation of gate-source voltages and the quiescent current for a given variation in the offset voltages.

To study this situation quantitatively, define the quiescent current in the output devices as the common-mode component of the current flowing from $V_{DD}$ to $-V_{SS}$ with $V_i = 0$. Then

$$I_Q = \frac{I_{D2} - I_{D1}}{2} \tag{5.119}$$

Subtraction is used in the above equation because the drain current of each transistor is defined as positive when it flows into the transistor. Substituting (5.110)–(5.113) into (5.119) gives

$$I_Q = \frac{k'}{4}\frac{W}{L}\left((V_{ov} + A[V_o + V_{OSN}])^2 + (-V_{ov} + A[V_o + V_{OSP}])^2\right) \tag{5.120}$$

Since $V_o = 0$ if $V_{OSP} = V_{OSN} = 0$, (5.120) shows that

$$I_Q\Big|_{\substack{V_{OSP}=0\\V_{OSN}=0}} = \frac{k'}{4}\frac{W}{L}\left((V_{ov})^2 + (-V_{ov})^2\right) = \frac{k'}{2}\frac{W}{L}(V_{ov})^2 \tag{5.121}$$

From (5.118) with $V_i = 0$,

$$V_o + V_{OSP} \simeq \frac{V_{OSP} - V_{OSN}}{2} \tag{5.122}$$

$$V_o + V_{OSN} \simeq -\frac{V_{OSP} - V_{OSN}}{2} \tag{5.123}$$

Substituting (5.122) and (5.123) into (5.120) gives

$$I_Q = \frac{k'}{2}\frac{W}{L}\left(V_{ov} - A\left[\frac{V_{OSP} - V_{OSN}}{2}\right]\right)^2 \tag{5.124}$$

Define $\Delta I_Q$ as the change in $I_Q$ caused by nonzero offsets; that is,

$$\Delta I_Q = I_Q\Big|_{\substack{V_{OSP}=0\\V_{OSN}=0}} - I_Q \tag{5.125}$$

Substituting (5.124) and (5.121) into (5.125) gives

$$\Delta I_Q = \frac{k'}{2}\frac{W}{L}A(V_{OSP} - V_{OSN})\left[V_{ov} - A\left(\frac{V_{OSP} - V_{OSN}}{4}\right)\right] \tag{5.126}$$

To evaluate the magnitude of $\Delta I_Q$, we will compare it to the quiescent current with zero offsets by dividing (5.126) by (5.121). The result is

$$\frac{\Delta I_Q}{I_Q}\Big|_{\substack{V_{OSP}=0\\V_{OSN}=0}} = A\left(\frac{V_{OSP} - V_{OSN}}{V_{ov}}\right)\left[1 - A\left(\frac{V_{OSP} - V_{OSN}}{4V_{ov}}\right)\right] \tag{5.127}$$

If $A(V_{OSP} - V_{OSN}) \ll 4V_{ov}$,

$$\frac{\Delta I_Q}{I_Q}\Big|_{\substack{V_{OSP}=0\\V_{OSN}=0}} \simeq A\left(\frac{V_{OSP} - V_{OSN}}{V_{ov}}\right) \tag{5.128}$$

Therefore, to keep the fractional change in the quiescent current less than a given amount, the maximum error-amplifier gain is

$$A < \left( \frac{V_{ov}}{V_{OSP} - V_{OSN}} \right) \left( \frac{\Delta I_Q}{I_Q} \bigg|_{\substack{V_{OSP}=0 \\ V_{OSN}=0}} \right) \tag{5.129}$$

For example, if $V_{ov} = 200$ mV, $V_{OSP} - V_{OSN} = 5$ mV, and up to 20 percent variation in the quiescent current is allowed, (5.129) shows that the error amplifier gain should be less than about 8.[13,14]

Figure 5.35 shows a schematic of the top error amplifier and $M_1$ from Fig. 5.32.[14] A complementary structure used to drive $M_2$ is not shown. The difference between $V_i$ and $V_o$ is sensed by the differential pair $M_{11}$ and $M_{12}$, which is biased by the tail current source $I_{TAIL}$. The load of the differential pair consists of two parts: current mirror $M_{13}$ and $M_{14}$ and common-drain transistors $M_{15}$ and $M_{16}$. The purpose of the common-drain transistors is to reduce the output resistance of the error amplifier to set its gain to a well-defined low value. The gates of the common-drain transistors are biased by a negative feedback loop including $M_{13}$, $M_{17}$, $I_{BIAS}$, and $M_{15}$. This circuit adjusts the voltage at the gate of $M_{15}$ so that $M_{17}$ operates in the active region and conducts $I_{BIAS}$. Although negative feedback is studied in Chapter 8, the basic idea can be understood here as follows. If $|I_{D17}|$ is less than $I_{BIAS}$, current source $I_{BIAS}$ pulls the gate voltage of $M_{15}$ down. Since $M_{15}$ operates as a source follower, the source of $M_{15}$ is pulled down, increasing $|I_{D13}|$. Because $M_{13}$ and $M_{17}$ together form a current mirror, $|I_{D17}|$ also increases until $|I_{D17}| = I_{BIAS}$. Similar reasoning shows that this equality is established when $|I_{D17}|$ is initially greater than $I_{BIAS}$. If $M_{15}$ and $M_{17}$ are enhancement-mode devices, $M_{17}$ operates in the active region because $V_{GD17} = V_{SG15} = |V_{t15}| + |V_{ov15}| > 0 > V_{t17}$; therefore, the channel does not exist at the drain of $M_{17}$.

Since $M_{13}$ and $M_{17}$ form a current mirror,

$$I_{D13} = I_{D17} \frac{(W/L)_{13}}{(W/L)_{17}} = -I_{BIAS} \frac{(W/L)_{13}}{(W/L)_{17}} \tag{5.130}$$

**Figure 5.35** Schematic of the top error amplifier and output transistor $M_1$.

Since $M_{13}$ and $M_{14}$ also form a current mirror, and since $(W/L)_{14} = (W/L)_{13}$,

$$I_{D14} = I_{D13} = -I_{BIAS}\frac{(W/L)_{13}}{(W/L)_{17}} \tag{5.131}$$

With $V_i = V_o$,

$$I_{D11} = I_{D12} = \frac{I_{TAIL}}{2} \tag{5.132}$$

From KCL,

$$I_{D16} = I_{D14} + I_{D11} \tag{5.133}$$

Substituting (5.131) and (5.132) into (5.133) gives

$$I_{D16} = -I_{BIAS}\frac{(W/L)_{13}}{(W/L)_{17}} + \frac{I_{TAIL}}{2} \tag{5.134}$$

Since $I_{D15} = I_{D16}$ when $I_{D11} = I_{D12}$,

$$V_{SD14} = V_{SD13} = V_{SG13} = V_{SG1} \tag{5.135}$$

Therefore, ignoring channel-length modulation,

$$I_{D1} = I_{D13}\frac{(W/L)_1}{(W/L)_{13}} \tag{5.136}$$

Substituting (5.130) into (5.136) and rearranging gives

$$I_{D1} = -I_{BIAS}\frac{(W/L)_1}{(W/L)_{17}} \tag{5.137}$$

This equation shows that the drain current in $M_1$ is controlled by $I_{BIAS}$ and a ratio of transistor sizes if the offset voltage of the error amplifier is zero so that $V_o = 0$ when $V_i = 0$. In practice, $(W/L)_1 \gg (W/L)_{17}$ so that little power is dissipated in the bias circuits.

Another design consideration comes out of these equations. To keep the gain of the error amplifier low under all conditions, $M_{16}$ must never cut off. Therefore, from (5.133), $|I_{D14}|$ should be greater than the maximum value of $I_{D11}$. Since the maximum value of $I_{D11}$ is $I_{TAIL}$, (5.131) and (5.133) show that

$$|I_{D14}| = I_{BIAS}\frac{(W/L)_{13}}{(W/L)_{17}} > I_{TAIL} \tag{5.138}$$

To find the gain of the error amplifier, the key observation is that the small-signal resistance from the drain of $M_{13}$ to ground is zero, ignoring channel-length modulation. This result stems from the operation of the same negative feedback loop that biases the gate of $M_{15}$. If the small-signal voltage at the drain of $M_{13}$ changes, the negative feedback loop works to undo the change. For example, suppose that the drain voltage of $M_{13}$ increases. This change reduces the gate voltage of $M_{15}$ because $M_{17}$ operates as a common-source amplifier. Then the drain voltage of $M_{13}$ falls because $M_{15}$ operates as a source follower. Ignoring channel-length modulation, the drain voltage of $M_{13}$ must be held exactly constant because $i_{d17} = 0$ if $I_{BIAS}$ is constant. Therefore, the small-signal resistance at the input of the current mirror $M_{13}$ and $M_{14}$ is zero. As a result, none of the small-signal drain current from $M_{12}$ flows into the source of $M_{15}$. Instead, it is all mirrored to the output of the error amplifier by $M_{13}$ and $M_{14}$. Furthermore, the small-signal drain current from $M_{11}$ flows directly to the output of the error amplifier. Therefore, the short-circuit transconductance of the error amplifier is the same with or without the common-drain transistors $M_{15}$ and $M_{16}$. Without these transistors, the error amplifier is simply a differential pair with a current-mirror load. From (4.143),

$$G_m = g_{m11} = g_{m12} \qquad (5.139)$$

Ignoring channel-length modulation, the output resistance is set by common-drain transistor $M_{16}$. From (3.84),

$$R_o = \frac{1}{g_{m16} + g_{mb16}} \qquad (5.140)$$

Therefore, the gain of the error amplifier is

$$A = G_m R_o = \frac{g_{m11}}{g_{m16} + g_{mb16}} \qquad (5.141)$$

### 5.5.3 Alternative Configurations

The main potential advantage of the common-source output stage described in the last section is that it can increase the output swing compared to the common-drain case. However, the common-source configuration suffers from an increase in harmonic distortion, especially at high frequencies, for two main reasons. First, the bandwidth of the error amplifiers is usually limited, to avoid stability problems. Second, the gain of these amplifiers is limited to establish adequate control on the quiescent output current.

#### 5.5.3.1 Combined Common-Drain Common-Source Configuration

One way to overcome this problem is to use a combination of the common-drain and common-source configurations shown in Fig. 5.31 and Fig. 5.32.[15] The combined schematic is shown in Fig. 5.36. The key aspect of this circuit is that it uses two buffers connected to the output: a Class-AB common-drain buffer ($M_1$-$M_2$) and a Class-B quasi-complementary common-source buffer ($M_{11}$-$M_{12}$ and the error amplifiers $A$). The common-source buffer is dominant when the output swing is maximum, but off with zero output. On the other hand, the common-drain buffer controls the quiescent output current and improves the frequency response, as described next.

From KVL,

$$V_o = V_1 + V_{gs4} - V_{gs1} \qquad (5.142)$$

**Figure 5.36** Combined common-drain, common-source output stage.

If $V_{t1} = V_{t4}$, this equation can be rewritten as

$$V_o = V_1 + V_{ov4} - V_{ov1} \tag{5.143}$$

Therefore, when $V_i$ is adjusted so that $V_1 = 0$, $M_1$-$M_5$ force $V_o = 0$ if $V_{ov1} = V_{ov4}$. From (1.166), $V_{ov1} = V_{ov4}$ if

$$\frac{I_{D1}}{(W/L)_1} = \frac{I_{D4}}{(W/L)_4} \tag{5.144}$$

Substituting (5.101) into (5.144) and rearranging shows that $V_{ov1} = V_{ov4}$ if

$$\frac{(W/L)_1}{(W/L)_2} = \frac{(W/L)_4}{(W/L)_5} \tag{5.145}$$

We will assume that this condition holds so that $V_o = 0$ when $V_1 = 0$. In this case, $M_{11}$ and $M_{12}$ are designed to be cut off. This characteristic stems from small offsets designed into the error amplifiers. These offsets are shown as voltage sources $V_{OS}$ in Fig. 5.36 and can be introduced by intentionally mismatching the input differential pair in each error amplifier. With $V_1 = V_o = 0$ and $V_{OS} > 0$, the error amplifiers are designed to give $V_{gs11} > V_{t11}$ and $V_{gs12} < V_{t12}$ so that $M_{11}$ and $M_{12}$ are off. As a result, the quiescent output current is controlled by the common-drain stage and its biasing circuit $M_1$-$M_5$, as shown in (5.101).

As $V_i$ decreases from the value that forces $V_1 = 0$, $V_1$ increases and $V_o$ follows but with less than unity gain if $R_L$ is finite. Therefore $V_1 - V_o$ increases, and both $V_{gs11}$ and $V_{gs12}$ decrease, eventually turning on $M_{11}$ but keeping $M_{12}$ off. After $M_{11}$ turns on, both $I_{d1}$ and $|I_{d11}|$ increase as $V_o$ rises until $V_{gs1} - V_{t1}$ reaches its maximum value. Such a maximum occurs when the output swing from the common-source stage is greater than that of the common-drain stage. As $V_o$ rises beyond this point, $|I_{d11}|$ increases but $I_{d1}$ decreases, and the common-source stage becomes dominant.

From (5.103), the output swing allowed by the common-drain stage in Fig. 5.31 is limited in part by $V_{gs1}$, which includes a threshold component. On the other hand, the output swing limitation of common-source stage in Fig. 5.32 does not include a threshold term, and this circuit can swing within an overdrive of the positive supply. So with proper design, we expect the common-source stage to have a larger output swing than the common-drain stage. When the two circuits are combined as in Fig. 5.36, however, the output swing is limited by the driver stage that produces $V_1$. Define $V_1^+$ as the maximum value of $V_1$ for which $M_3$ operates in the active region. Then

$$V_1^+ = V_{DD} - |V_{ov3}| - V_{gs4} \tag{5.146}$$

Since $V_1$ is the input to the common-source stage, the maximum output $V_o^+$ can be designed to be

$$V_o^+ \simeq V_1^+ = V_{DD} - |V_{ov3}| - V_{gs4} \tag{5.147}$$

Comparing (5.147) with (5.103) shows that the positive swing of the combined output stage in Fig. 5.36 exceeds that of the common-drain output stage in Fig. 5.31 provided that $V_{gs4} < V_{gs1}$ when $V_o = V_o^+$. This condition is usually satisfied because $I_{d4} \ll I_{d1}$ when the output is maximum with finite $R_L$. Therefore, the circuit in Fig. 5.36 can be designed to increase the output swing.

Since the common-source stage in Fig. 5.36 is not responsible for establishing the quiescent output current, the gain of the error amplifiers in Fig. 5.36 is not limited as in (5.129). In practice, the error amplifiers are often designed as one-stage amplifiers with a gain related to the product of $g_m$ and $r_o$ that can be achieved in a given technology. This increase in gain reduces the harmonic distortion because it reduces the error between the input and the output of the common-source stage.

Finally, we will consider the frequency response of the circuit in Fig. 5.36 qualitatively. The circuit has two paths from $V_1$ to the output. The path through the common-source transistors $M_{11}$ and $M_{12}$ may be slow because of the need to limit the bandwidth of the error amplifiers to guarantee that the circuit is stable. (Stability is studied in Chapter 9.) On the other hand, the path through the common-drain transistors $M_1$ and $M_2$ is fast because source followers are high-bandwidth circuits, as shown in Chapter 7. Since the circuit sums the current from the common-drain and common-source stages in the load to produce the output voltage, the fast path will dominate for high-frequency signals. This technique is called *feedforward*, and other instances are described in Chapter 9. It causes the circuit to take on the characteristics of the source followers for high frequencies, reducing the phase shift that would otherwise be introduced by the slow error amplifiers. As a result, the design required to guarantee stability is simplified,[15] and the harmonic distortion for high-frequency signals is reduced.

### 5.5.3.2 Combined Common-Drain Common-Source Configuration with High Swing

Although the swing of the circuit in Fig. 5.36 is improved compared to the circuit in Fig. 5.31, it can be improved even further. As shown in (5.147), the main limitation to the positive swing in Fig. 5.36 stems from $V_{gs4}$. This voltage includes a threshold component, which increases with increasing $V_1$ and $V_o$ because of the body effect. Similarly, the negative swing is limited by $V_{gs5}$, whose threshold component increases in magnitude as $V_1$ and $V_o$ decrease. In practice, these terms alone reduce the available output swing by about 1.5 V to 2 V.

Figure 5.37 shows a circuit that overcomes this limitation.[16] The circuit is the same as in Fig. 5.36 except that one extra branch is included. The new branch consists of transistors $M_7$ and $M_8$ and operates in parallel with the branch containing $M_3$-$M_6$ to produce voltage $V_1$. The swing of $V_1$ in Fig. 5.36 is limited by the threshold voltages of $M_4$ and $M_5$ as described above. In contrast, the new branch in Fig. 5.37 can drive $V_1$ within an overdrive of either supply while $M_7$ and $M_8$ operate in the active region. Since the output swing in Fig. 5.36 is limited by the swing of $V_1$, improving the swing of $V_1$ as in Fig. 5.37 also improves the output swing.

**Figure 5.37** Combined common-drain, common-source output stage with improved swing.

**Figure 5.38** Output stage with a Class AB common-source buffer and a Class B common-source buffer.

### 5.5.3.3 Parallel Common-Source Configuration

Another circuit that overcomes the problem described in the introduction of Section 5.5.3 is shown in Fig. 5.38.[17] Like the circuit in Fig. 5.37, this circuit combines two buffers in parallel at the output. The error amplifiers with gain $A_1$ along with $M_1$ and $M_2$ form one buffer, which controls the operation of the output stage with $V_i = 0$. The error amplifiers with gain $A_2$ together with $M_{11}$ and $M_{12}$ form the other buffer, which dominates the operation of the output stage for large-magnitude output voltages.

This behavior stems from small offset voltages intentionally built into the $A_1$ amplifiers. These offsets are shown as voltage sources $V_{OS}$ in Fig. 5.38 and are introduced in practice by intentionally mismatching the input differential pairs in the $A_1$ amplifiers. At first, assume that these offsets have little effect on the drain currents of $M_1$ and $M_2$ because $A_1$ is intentionally chosen to be small. Therefore, $M_1$ and $M_2$ operate in the active region when $V_i = 0$, and the buffer that includes these transistors operates in a Class-AB mode. On the other hand, the offsets force $M_{11}$ and $M_{12}$ to operate in cutoff when $V_i = 0$ because the gates of these transistors are driven by the outputs of the $A_2$ amplifiers, which in turn are driven by the differential outputs of the $A_1$ amplifiers. In particular, the product $V_{OS}A_1A_2$ is chosen by design to be big enough to force $V_{gs11} > V_{t11}$ and $V_{gs12} < V_{t12}$ so that $M_{11}$ and $M_{12}$ are off when $V_i = 0$. As a result, the quiescent output current of this output stage is controlled by $M_1$, $M_2$, and the $A_1$ amplifiers.

Figure 5.39 shows a schematic of the top $A_1$ amplifier and $M_1$ from Fig. 5.38.[17] A complementary configuration is used for the bottom $A_1$ amplifier but is not shown for simplicity. The difference between $V_i$ and $V_o$ is sensed by the differential pair $M_3$ and $M_4$. The load of the differential pair consists of two parts: diode-connected transistors $M_5$ and $M_6$ and current sources $I_{BIAS}$, which are implemented by the outputs of $p$-channel current mirrors in practice. The purpose of the diode-connected transistors is to limit the gain of the error amplifier to a small value so that the output quiescent current is well controlled. Ignoring channel-length modulation, the gain of this error amplifier is

$$A_1 = \frac{g_{m3}}{g_{m5}} \tag{5.148}$$

where $A_1$ is the gain from the differential input to the differential output of the error amplifier. This equation shows that the gain is determined by the ratios of the transconductance of a differential-pair transistor to that of a load transistor. Substituting (1.180) into (5.148)

**Figure 5.39** Schematic of the top $A_1$ amplifier and output transistor $M_1$.

for each transistor, and rearranging gives

$$A_1 = \sqrt{\frac{k'_n}{k'_p} \frac{(W/L)_3}{(W/L)_5} \frac{I_{D3}}{|I_{D5}|}} \qquad (5.149)$$

This equation shows that the gain is determined by the product of the ratios of the transconductance parameters, the transistor sizes, and the bias currents. From KCL at the drain of $M_5$,

$$-I_{D5} = I_{D3} - I_{BIAS} \qquad (5.150)$$

where $I_{D3} > I_{BIAS}$. Substituting (5.150) into (5.149) gives

$$A_1 = \sqrt{\frac{k'_n}{k'_p} \frac{(W/L)_3}{(W/L)_5} \left( \frac{I_{D3}}{I_{D3} - I_{BIAS}} \right)} \qquad (5.151)$$

This equation shows that the purpose of the $I_{BIAS}$ current sources is to allow the bias current in a transistor in the differential pair to exceed that in a diode-connected load. As a result, the term in parentheses in (5.151) is greater than unity and contributes to the required gain.

Now consider the effect of the offset $V_{OS}$ in Fig. 5.38. In practice, the offset is implemented in Fig. 5.39 by choosing the width of $M_3$ to be less than the width of $M_4$ by about 20 percent.[17] Assume that $V_o = 0$ when $V_i = 0$. Increasing $V_{OS}$ reduces $I_{D3}$, making $|I_{D5}|$ less than the value given in (5.150). Since $M_5$ and $M_1$ form a current mirror, a positive offset reduces $|I_{D1}|$. Under the assumption that $V_o = 0$ when $V_i = 0$, the differential pair in the error amplifier operates with $V_{gs3} = V_{gs4}$. Therefore, if $V_{t3} = V_{t4}$, $V_{ov3} = V_{ov4}$. From (1.166),

$$\frac{I_{D3}}{(W/L)_3} = \frac{I_{D4}}{(W/L)_4} \qquad (5.152)$$

Substituting $I_{D3} + I_{D4} = I_{TAIL}$ into (5.152) and rearranging gives

$$I_{D3} = \frac{(W/L)_3}{(W/L)_3 + (W/L)_4} I_{TAIL} \qquad (5.153)$$

when $V_o = V_i = 0$. Similarly, a positive offset in the bottom $A_1$ amplifier as labeled in Fig. 5.38 reduces $I_{D2}$. If the tail and bias current in the top $A_1$ amplifier are identical to the corresponding values in the bottom $A_1$ amplifier, and if the fractional mismatches in the differential pairs are identical, the reductions in $|I_{D1}|$ and $I_{D2}$ caused by the mismatches intentionally introduced into the differential pairs are equal and $V_o = 0$ when $V_i = 0$ is assumed. In other words, the offset of the entire output stage shown in Fig. 5.38 is zero even with nonzero $V_{OS}$ in the error amplifiers.

Because a design goal is to bias $M_1$ in the active region when $V_i = 0$, the offset must be chosen to be small enough that $I_{D3} > 0$ when $V_o = V_i = 0$. Also, the error amplifiers contain some unintentional mismatches stemming from random effects in practice. Because another design goal is to bias $M_{11}$ in cutoff, the random component must not be allowed to be larger than the systematic offset in magnitude and opposite in polarity. Therefore, $V_{OS}$ is chosen to be bigger than the expected random offset.

Since the quiescent output current is controlled by the $A_1$ error amplifiers along with $M_1$ and $M_2$, the gain of the $A_2$ error amplifiers driving $M_{11}$ and $M_{12}$ need not be small. With large $A_2$, $M_{11}$ or $M_{12}$ becomes the dominant output device for large output magnitudes if the aspect ratios of $M_{11}$ and $M_{12}$ are at least as big as $M_1$ and $M_2$, respectively. Furthermore, increasing $A_2$ has the advantage of increasing the loop gain when $M_{11}$ or $M_{12}$ turns on. This loop gain is related to the product of $A_2$, $g_{m11}$ or $g_{m12}$, and $R_L$. Increasing the loop gain reduces the error between the input and output, as shown in Chapter 8. If $M_{11}$ conducts, increasing $A_2$ allows the output stage to drive reduced loads with constant $g_{m11}$ and error. If the load is fixed, increasing $A_2$ allows the transconductance to be reduced, which in turn allows $(W/L)_{11}$ to be reduced. One potential concern here is that reducing the transistor sizes also reduces the range of outputs for which the devices operate in the active region. If $M_{11}$ operates in the triode region, its drain-source resistance $r_{o11}$ is finite, and the loop gain is proportional to the product $A_2 g_{m11}(r_{o11} \| R_L)$. Thus, operation of $M_{11}$ in the triode region increases the error by reducing $g_{m11}$ and $r_{o11}$. However, increasing $A_2$ compensates for this effect. Therefore, a key advantage of the output-stage configuration shown in Fig. 5.38 is that it allows the output swing with a given level of nonlinearity to be increased by allowing the dominant transistor to operate in the triode region.

The $A_1$ and $A_2$ amplifiers together form the two-stage error amplifiers that drive $M_{11}$ and $M_{12}$. The $A_2$ amplifiers operate on the differential outputs of the $A_1$ amplifiers. Since the common-mode components of the outputs of the $A_1$ amplifiers are well controlled by diode-connected loads, differential pairs are not required at the inputs of the $A_2$ amplifiers. Figure 5.40 shows a schematic of the top $A_2$ amplifier.[17] A complementary configuration used for the bottom $A_2$ amplifier is not shown for simplicity. The inputs are applied to the gates of common-source transistors $M_{21}$ and $M_{22}$. The cascode current mirror $M_{23}$-$M_{26}$ then converts the differential signal into a single-ended output. Because the output resistance of the cascode-current mirror is large compared to the output resistance of the common-source transistor $M_{22}$,

$$A_2 \simeq g_{m22} r_{o22} \tag{5.154}$$

and $A_2 \simeq 70$ in Ref.17.

To determine the range of input voltages for which $M_{11}$ and $M_{12}$ are both off, let $V_{g11}$ represent the voltage from the gate of $M_{11}$ to ground. Assuming that the gains $A_1$ and $A_2$ are constant,

$$V_{g11} = [V_o - (V_i - V_{OS})]A_1 A_2 + K \tag{5.155}$$

where $K$ is a constant. If the differential input voltage to the top $A_2$ amplifier shown in Fig. 5.40 is zero, $V_{g11} = -V_{SS} + V_{t25} + V_{ov25}$ so that $I_{d21} = I_{d22}$. Substituting this

Figure 5.40 Schematic of the top. $A_2$ amplifier.

boundary condition into (5.155) gives $K = -V_{SS} + V_{t25} + V_{ov25}$; therefore,

$$V_{g11} = [V_o - (V_i - V_{OS})]A_1 A_2 - V_{SS} + V_{t25} + V_{ov25} \qquad (5.156)$$

Also, (5.117) with $g_m = g_{m1} = g_{m2}$ gives $V_o$ in terms of $V_i$ for the output stage in Fig. 5.38 as long as the random offset is negligible, both $M_1$ and $M_2$ operate in the active region, and $M_{11}$ and $M_{12}$ are off. Since the gates of $M_1$ and $M_2$ are each driven by only one output of the corresponding $A_1$ amplifiers, $A = A_1/2$. With these substitutions, (5.117) gives

$$V_o = \frac{V_i}{1 + \dfrac{1}{A_1 g_{m1} R_L}} \qquad (5.157)$$

To turn $M_{11}$ on, $V_{g11} < V_{DD} - |V_{t11}|$. Substituting this condition and (5.157) into (5.156) gives

$$V_{i(min)} = V_{OS}(1 + A_1 g_{m1} R_L) - \frac{(V_{DD} + V_{SS} - |V_{t11}| - V_{t25} - V_{ov25})(1 + A_1 g_{m1} R_L)}{A_1 A_2} \qquad (5.158)$$

where $V_{i(min)}$ is the minimum value of $V_i$ for which $M_{11}$ conducts nonzero drain current. To interpret this result, let $A_2 \rightarrow \infty$. Then to turn $M_{11}$ on, the required differential input voltage of the top $A_2$ amplifier $V_{2t} = 0$. Therefore, the required differential input of the top $A_1$ amplifier is zero; that is,

$$V_o = V_i - V_{OS} \qquad (5.159)$$

This equation and (5.157) are both plotted in Fig. 5.41. As the input voltage increases, the output voltage follows with a slope less than unity if $R_L$ is finite, as shown by the solid plot. Therefore, as $V_i$ increases, $V_i - V_o$ also increases. To turn $M_{11}$ barely on, this difference must be equal to $V_{OS}$ so that the circuit operates at the intersection of the two lines in Fig. 5.41. Substituting (5.157) into (5.159) gives

$$V_{i(min)} = V_{OS}(1 + A_1 g_{m1} R_L) \qquad (5.160)$$

This equation agrees with the result that would be obtained by allowing $A_2 \rightarrow \infty$ in (5.158). The term in parentheses in (5.160) is equal to the reciprocal of the difference in the slopes of the two lines in Fig. 5.41.

**Figure 5.41** Graphical interpretation of $V_{i(min)}$, which is the minimum $V_i$ needed to turn on $M_{11}$ in Fig. 5.38.

■ **EXAMPLE**

Find the minimum input voltage in Fig. 5.38 for which $M_{11}$ turns on, assuming at first that $A_2 \to \infty$ and then that $A_2 = 70$. Let $V_{OS} = 10\,\text{mV}$, $A_1 = 8$, $g_{m1} = 5\,\text{mA/V}$, $R_L = 60\,\Omega$, $V_{DD} = V_{SS} = 2.5\,\text{V}$, $V_{t11} = -0.7\,\text{V}$, $V_{t25} = 0.7\,\text{V}$, and $V_{ov25} = 0.1\,\text{V}$.

From (5.160),

$$V_{i(min)} = 10\,\text{mV}[1 + 8(0.005)(60)] = 34\,\text{mV}$$

when $A_2 \to \infty$. On the other hand, when $A_2 = 70$, (5.158) shows that

$$V_{i(min)} = 10\,\text{mV}[1 + 8(0.005)(60)] - \frac{3.5[1 + 8(0.005)(60)]}{8(70)} \approx 0.13\,\text{mV}$$

This example shows that the minimum input voltage required to turn on $M_{11}$ is reduced from the value given in (5.160) when $A_2$ is finite, because the fractional term in (5.158) is positive.

The key point of this analysis is that $M_{11}$ and $M_{12}$ in Fig. 5.38 remain off for only a small range of input voltages. Therefore, the nonlinearity introduced by turning on $M_{11}$ or $M_{12}$ occurs when $|V_i|$ is small. As a result, this circuit is well suited for the ISDN (Integrated Service Digital Network) line-driving application for which it was designed because the required four-level output code does not include zero, avoiding distortion that would be introduced by turning $M_{11}$ and $M_{12}$ on or off[17] if a zero-level output pulse were required.

## PROBLEMS

**5.1** A circuit as shown in Fig. 5.1 has $V_{CC} = 15\,\text{V}$, $R_1 = R_2 = 0$, $R_3 = 5\,\text{k}\Omega$, $R_L = 2\,\text{k}\Omega$, $V_{CE(sat)} = 0.2\,\text{V}$, and $V_{BE(on)} = 0.7\,\text{V}$. All device areas are equal.

**(a)** Sketch the transfer characteristic from $V_i$ to $V_o$.

**(b)** Repeat (a) if $R_L = 10\,\text{k}\Omega$.

**(c)** Sketch the waveform of $V_o$ if a sinusoidal input voltage with an amplitude (zero to peak) of 10 V is applied at $V_i$ in (a) and (b) above.

**(d)** Use SPICE to verify (a), (b), and (c) and also to determine second and third harmonic distortion in $V_o$ for the conditions in (c).

**5.2 (a)** For the circuit of Problem 5.1, sketch load lines in the $I_c$-$V_{ce}$ plane for $R_L = 2\,\text{k}\Omega$ and $R_L = 10\,\text{k}\Omega$.

**(b)** Calculate the maximum average sinusoidal output power that can be delivered to $R_L$ (both values) before clipping occurs in (a) above. Sketch corresponding waveforms for $I_{c1}$, $V_{ce1}$, and $P_{c1}$.

**(c)** Calculate the circuit efficiency for each value of $R_L$ in (b). (Neglect power dissipated in $Q_3$ and $R_3$.)

**(d)** Select $R_L$ for maximum efficiency in this circuit and calculate the corresponding average output power with sinusoidal signals.

**5.3 (a)** Prove that any load line tangent to a power hyperbola makes contact with the hyperbola at the midpoint of the load line.

**(b)** Calculate the maximum possible instantaneous power dissipation in $Q_1$ for the circuit of Problem 5.1 with $R_L = 2$ k$\Omega$ and $R_L = 10$ k$\Omega$.

**(c)** Calculate the *average* power dissipated in $Q_1$ for the circuit of Problem 5.1 with $R_L = 2$ k$\Omega$ and $R_L = 10$ k$\Omega$. Assume that $V_o$ is sinusoidal with an amplitude equal to the maximum possible before clipping occurs.

**5.4** If $\beta_F = 100$ for $Q_1$ in Problem 5.1, calculate the average signal power delivered to $Q_1$ by its driver stage if $V_o$ is sinusoidal with an amplitude equal to the maximum possible before clipping occurs. Repeat for $R_L = 10$ k$\Omega$. Thus calculate the power gain of the circuit.

**5.5** Calculate the incremental slope of the transfer characteristic of the circuit of Problem 5.1 at the quiescent point and at the extremes of the signal swing with a peak sinusoidal output of 1 V and $R_L = 2$ k$\Omega$.

**5.6 (a)** For the circuit of Problem 5.1, draw load lines in the $I_c$-$V_{ce}$ plane for $R_L = 0$ and $R_L \rightarrow \infty$. Use an $I_c$ scale from 0 to 30 mA. Also draw constant power hyperbolas for $P_c = 0.1$ W, $0.2$ W, and $0.3$ W. What is the maximum possible instantaneous power dissipation in $Q_1$ for the above values of $R_L$? Assume that the driver stage can supply a maximum base current to $Q_1$ of $0.3$ mA and $\beta_F = 100$ for $Q_1$.

**(b)** If the maximum allowable instantaneous power dissipation in $Q_1$ is $0.2$ W, calculate the minimum allowable value of $R_L$. (A graphical solution is the easiest.)

**5.7** Calculate the incremental slope of the transfer characteristic of the circuit of Fig. 5.8 at the quiescent point and at the extremes of the signal swing with $v_i = \hat{v}_i \sin \omega t$ and $\hat{v}_i = 0.5$ V:

**(a)** Let $A_v^+ = A_v$ when $v_i$ is maximum.

**(b)** Let $A_{vQ} = A_v$ when $v_i = 0$.

**(c)** Let $A_v^- = A_v$ when $v_i$ is minimum.
Assume that $V_I = 0$, $V_{DD} = 2.5$V, $I_Q = 1$ mA, and $R_L \rightarrow \infty$. Also, assume that $(W/L)_1 = 1000$, $k' = 200$ $\mu$A/V$^2$, $V_{t0} = 0.7$ V, $\phi_f = 0.3$ V, and $\gamma = 0.5$ V$^{1/2}$.

**5.8** When the distortion is small, the second and third harmonic-distortion terms of an amplifier can be calculated from the small-signal gains at the quiescent and extreme operating points. Starting with the power series given in (5.41),

**(a)** Calculate an expression for the small-signal gain $A_v = dv_o/dv_i$.

**(b)** Let $v_i = \hat{v}_i \sin \omega t$ as in (5.52), and derive expressions for $A_v^+$, $A_{vQ}$, and $A_v^-$ as defined in Problem 5.7.

**(c)** Define two normalized differential gain error terms as

    **(i)** $E^+ = (A_v^+ - A_{vQ})/A_{vQ}$

    **(ii)** $E^- = (A_v^- - A_{vQ})/A_{vQ}$
and calculate expressions for $(E^+ + E^-)$ and $(E^+ - E^-)$.

**(d)** Compare the results of part (c) with (5.54) and (5.57) to calculate $HD_2$ and $HD_3$ in terms of $E^+$ and $E^-$.

**(e)** Use the results of part (d) and Problem 5.7 to calculate $HD_2$ and $HD_3$ for the circuit of Fig. 5.8 under the conditions given in Problem 5.7. Compare the results to the results of the Example in Section 5.3.2.

**5.9** Calculate second-harmonic distortion in the common-source amplifier with a depletion load shown in Fig. 4.20a for a peak sinusoidal input voltage $\hat{v}_i = 0.01$ V and $V_{DD} = 3$ V. Assume that the dc input voltage is adjusted so that the dc output voltage is 1 V. For simplicity, assume that the two transistors have identical parameters except for unequal threshold voltages. Let $W/L = 100$, $k' = 200$ $\mu$A/V$^2$, and $\lambda = 0$. Assume $V_{t1}|_{V_{SB1}=0} = 0.6$ V, $V_{t2}|_{V_{SB2}=0} = -0.6$ V, $\phi_f = 0.3$ V, and $\gamma = 0.5$ V$^{1/2}$. Use SPICE to verify the result.

**5.10** The circuit of Fig. 5.10 has $V_{CC} = 15$ V, $R_L = 2$ k$\Omega$, $V_{BE(on)} = 0.6$ V, and $V_{CE(sat)} = 0.2$ V.

**(a)** Sketch the transfer characteristic from $V_i$ to $V_o$ assuming that the transistors turn on abruptly for $V_{be} = V_{BE(on)}$.

**(b)** Sketch the output voltage waveform and the collector current waveform in each device for a sinusoidal input voltage of amplitude 1 V, 10 V, 20 V.

**(c)** Check (a) and (b) using SPICE with $I_S = 10^{-16}$ A, $\beta_F = 100$, $r_b = 100$ $\Omega$, and $r_c = 20$ $\Omega$ for each device. Use SPICE to determine second and third harmonic distortion in $V_o$ for the conditions in (b).

**5.11** For the circuit of Fig. 5.10, assume that $V_{CC} = 12$ V, $R_L = 1$ k$\Omega$, and $V_{CE(sat)} = 0.2$ V. Assume that there is sufficient sinusoidal input voltage available at $V_i$ to drive $V_o$ to its limits of clipping. Calculate the maximum average power that can be delivered to $R_L$ before clipping occurs, the corresponding efficiency, and the maximum instantaneous device dissipation. Neglect crossover distortion.

**5.12** For the circuit of Problem 5.10, calculate and sketch the waveforms of $I_{c1}$, $V_{ce1}$, and $P_{c1}$ for device $Q_1$ over one cycle. Do this for output voltage amplitudes (zero to peak) of 11.5 V, 6 V, and 3 V. Neglect crossover distortion and assume sinusoidal signals.

**5.13** In the circuit of Fig. 5.13, $V_{CC} = 12$ V, $I_Q = 0.1$ mA, $R_L = 1$ k$\Omega$, and for all devices $I_S = 10^{-15}$ A, $\beta_F = 150$. Calculate the value of $V_i$ and the current in each device for $V_o = 0$, $\pm 5$ V, and $\pm 10$ V. Then sketch the transfer characteristic from $V_o = 10$ V to $V_o = -10$ V.

**5.14** For the output stage of Fig. 5.18, assume that $V_{CC} = 15$ V and for all devices $V_{CE(sat)} = 0.2$ V, $V_{BE(on)} = 0.7$ V, and $\beta_F = 50$.

**(a)** Calculate the maximum positive and negative limits of $V_o$ for $R_L = 10$ k$\Omega$ and $R_L = 2$ k$\Omega$.

**(b)** Calculate the maximum average power that can be delivered to $R_L$ before clipping occurs for $R_L = 10$ k$\Omega$ and $R_L = 2$ k$\Omega$. Calculate the corresponding circuit efficiency (for the output devices only) and the average power dissipated per output device. Neglect crossover distortion and assume sinusoidal signals.

**5.15** For the output stage of Fig. 5.20a, assume that $V_{CC} = 15$ V, $\beta_F(pnp) = 50$, $\beta_F(npn) = 200$, and for all devices $V_{BE(on)} = 0.7$ V, $V_{CE(sat)} = 0.2$ V, $I_S = 10^{-14}$ A. Assume that the magnitude of the collector current in $Q_{13A}$ is 0.2 mA.

**(a)** Calculate the maximum positive and negative limits of $V_o$ for $R_L = 10$ k$\Omega$, $R_L = 1$ k$\Omega$, and $R_L = 200$ $\Omega$.

**(b)** Calculate the maximum average power that can be delivered to $R_L = 1$ k$\Omega$ before clipping occurs, and the corresponding circuit efficiency (for the output devices only). Also calculate the peak instantaneous power dissipation in each output device. Assume sinusoidal signals.

**5.16(a)** For the circuit of Problem 5.15, calculate the maximum possible average output power than can be delivered to a load $R_L$ if the instantaneous power dissipation per device must be less than 100 mW. Also specify the corresponding value of $R_L$ and the circuit efficiency (for the output devices only). Assume sinusoidal signals.

**(b)** Repeat (a) if the maximum instantaneous power dissipation per device is 200 mW.

**5.17** For the circuit of Problem 5.15, calculate bias currents in $Q_{23}$, $Q_{20}$, $Q_{19}$, $Q_{18}$, and $Q_{14}$ for $V_o = -10$ V with $R_L = 1$ k$\Omega$. Use $I_S = 10^{-14}$ A for all devices.

**5.18** An all-*npn* Darlington output stage is shown in Fig. 5.42. For all devices $V_{BE(on)} = 0.7$ V, $V_{CE(sat)} = 0.2$ V, $\beta_F = 100$. The magnitude of the collector current in $Q_3$ is 2 mA.

**(a)** If $R_L = 8$ $\Omega$, calculate the maximum positive and negative limits of $V_o$.

**(b)** Calculate the power dissipated in the circuit for $V_o = 0$ V.

**Figure 5.42** All-*npn* Darlington output stage.

(c) Calculate the maximum average power that an be delivered to $R_L = 8\ \Omega$ before clipping oc-:urs and the corresponding efficiency of the *complete* circuit. Also calculate the maximum instantaneous power dissipated in each output transistor. Assume that feedback is used around the circuit so that $V_o$ is approximately sinusoidal.

(d) Use SPICE to plot the dc transfer characteristic from $V_i$ to $V_o$ as $V_o$ is varied over the complete output voltage range with $R_L = 8\ \Omega$. For $Q_1$, $Q_5$, and $D_1$ assume $I_S = 10^{-15}$ A, $r_b = 1\ \Omega$, $r_c = 0.2\ \Omega$, $\beta_F = 100$, and $V_A = 30$ V. Assume $Q_4$, $Q_2$, $D_2$, and $D_3$ are 1/100 the size of the large devices. For $Q_3$ assume $r_c = 50\ \Omega$ and $V_A = 30$ V.

**5.19** For the circuit of Fig. 5.25, assume that $V_{CC} = 15$ V, $\beta_F(pnp) = 30$, $\beta_F(npn) = 150$, $I_S(npn) = 10^{-14}$ A, $I_S(pnp) = 10^{-15}$ A, and for all devices $V_{BE(on)} = 0.7$ V, $V_{CE(sat)} = 0.2$ V. Assume that $Q_5$ and $Q_6$ are $npn$ devices and the collector current in $Q_7$ is 0.15 mA.

(a) Calculate the maximum positive and negative limits of $V_o$ for $R_L = 1\ \mathrm{k}\Omega$.

(b) Calculate quiescent currents in $Q_1$-$Q_7$ for $V_o = 0$ V.

(c) Calculate the maximum average output power (sine wave) that can be delivered to $R_L$ if the maximum instantaneous dissipation in any device is 100 mW. Calculate the corresponding value of $R_L$, and the peak currents in $Q_3$ and $Q_4$.

**5.20** A BiCMOS Class AB output stage is shown in Fig. 5.43. Device parameters are $\beta_F(npn) = 80$, $\beta_F(pnp) = 20$, $V_{BE(on)} = 0.8$ V, $\mu_p C_{ox} = 26\ \mu\mathrm{A/V}^2$, and $V_t = -0.7$ V.

(a) Calculate bias currents in all devices for $V_o = 0$.

(b) Calculate the positive and negative limits of $V_o$ for $R_L = 200\ \Omega$. Thus calculate the maximum average power that can be delivered to $R_L$ before clipping occurs.

(c) Use SPICE to check (a) and also to plot the complete dc transfer characteristic of the circuit from $V_i$ to $V_o$. Also plot the waveforms of $I_{c1}$, $I_{c2}$, and $I_{d2}$ for a sinusoidal output voltage at $V_o$ of 2 V and then 4 V zero-to-peak. In the simulation, assume bipolar parameters as in Fig. 2.32 and MOS parameters as in Table 2.3 (apart from the values of $\beta_F$ and $\mu_p C_{ox}$ given above).

**5.21** Find the minimum output voltage for the circuit in Fig. 5.31.

**5.22** Design a CMOS output stage based on the circuit of Fig. 5.31 to deliver $\pm 1$ V before clipping at $V_o$ with $R_L = 1\ \mathrm{k}\Omega$ and $V_{DD} = V_{SS} = 2.5$ V. Use 10 μA bias current in $M_3$ and 100 μA idling current in $M_1$ and $M_2$. Set $(W/L)_3 = 50/1$ and $(W/L)_6 = 25/1$. Specify the $W/L$ for $M_1$-$M_6$ that minimizes the total chip area. Use the transistor parameters in Table 2.3 except assume that $L_{\mathrm{eff}} = L_{\mathrm{drwn}}$ for simplicity. The minimum channel

**Figure 5.43** BiCMOS Class AB output stage.

length is 1 μm. Assume the body of each $n$-channel transistor is connected to $-V_{SS}$, and the body of each $p$-channel transistor is connected to $V_{DD}$. Use SPICE to verify your design by plotting the $V_o$ vs. $V_i$ characteristic.

**5.23** For the circuit in Fig. 5.34, assume that the input voltage $V_i$ is high enough that $M_1$ operates in the active region but $M_2$ is cut off. Using the same assumptions as in the derivation of (5.116), show that $V_o$ is related to $V_i$ by the following expression

$$V_o = V_i + \frac{V_{ov}}{A} - V_{OSP} + \frac{1}{k'\frac{W}{L}A^2 R_L}$$

$$- \frac{1}{k'\frac{W}{L}A^2} \sqrt{\frac{1}{R_L^2} + 2k'\frac{W}{L}\frac{A^2}{R_L}\left(V_i + \frac{V_{ov}}{A} - V_{OSP}\right)}$$

**5.24** Using a circuit that is the complement of the one in Fig. 5.35, draw the schematic for the bottom error amplifier and output transistor $M_2$, which are shown in block diagram form in Fig. 5.32. In the error amplifier, label the transistors as $M_{21}$-$M_{27}$, where $M_{21}$ is the complement of $M_{11}$, $M_{22}$ is the complement of $M_{12}$, etc. Also, label the current sources complementary to $I_{BIAS}$ and $I_{TAIL}$ as $I_{BIASP}$ and $I_{TAILP}$, respectively.

**5.25** Using the schematics from Fig. 5.35 and Problem 5.24, design the output stage shown in Fig. 5.32 to satisfy the following requirements.

(a) $V_{DD} = V_{SS} = 2.5$ V.

(b) The standby power dissipation should be no more than 70 mW.

(c) $R_L = 100$ Ω.

(d) The maximum allowed gain error with zero offsets and all transistors operating in the active region is 1 percent.

(e) In Fig. 5.35, $(W/L)_{17} = (W/L)_1/100$ and $(W/L)_{13} = (W/L)_{14} = (W/L)_1/10$. Similarly, in Problem 5.24, $(W/L)_{27} = (W/L)_2/100$ and $(W/L)_{23} = (W/L)_{24} = (W/L)_2/10$.

(f) To control the quiescent current, the maximum allowed error-amplifier gain is 5.

(g) Your solution is allowed to use four ideal current sources, two in each error amplifier. To allow these ideal current sources to be replaced by real transistors in a design step not required in this problem, the voltage across each ideal current source in Fig. 5.35 must be at least 0.5 V when $V_o \geq 0$. Similarly, the voltage across each ideal current source in the complementary circuit from Problem 5.24 must be at least 0.5 V when $V_o \leq 0$.

(h) To guarantee that $M_{16}$ and $M_{26}$ do not cut off under these conditions, assume $I_{TAIL} = 5I_{BIAS}$ in Fig. 5.35 and $I_{TAILP} = 5I_{BIASP}$ in Problem 5.24.

(i) For both $n$- and $p$-channel transistors, assume that $\lambda = 0$, $L_d = X_d = 0$, and ignore the body effect. Use $L_{drwn} = 1$ μm for all transistors, and use Table 2.3 for other transistor parameters.

(j) The distortion of the output stage should be minimized under the above conditions.

Verify your design using SPICE.

# REFERENCES

1. E. M. Cherry and D. E. Hooper. *Amplifying Devices and Low-Pass Amplifier Design.* Wiley, New York, 1968, Ch. 9.

2. E. Fong and R. Zeman. "Analysis of Harmonic Distortion in Single-Channel MOS Integrated Circuits," *IEEE Journal of Solid-State Circuits*, Vol. SC-17, pp. 83–86, February 1982.

3. Y. P. Tsividis and D. L. Fraser, Jr. "Harmonic Distortion in Single-Channel MOS Integrated Circuits," *IEEE Journal of Solid-State Circuits*, Vol. SC-16, pp. 694–702, December 1981.

4. E. M. Cherry and D. E. Hooper. Op. cit., Ch. 16.

5. J. Millman and C. C. Halkias. *Integrated Electronics.* McGraw-Hill, New York, 1972, Ch. 18.

6. A. B. Grebene. *Analog Integrated Circuit Design.* Van Nostrand Reinhold, New York, 1972, Ch. 5–6.

7. T. M. Frederiksen and J. E. Solomon. "A High-Performance 3-Watt Monolithic Class-B Power Amplifier," *IEEE Journal of Solid-State Circuits*, Vol. SC-3, pp. 152–160, June 1968.

8. P. R. Gray. "A 15-W Monolithic Power Operational Amplifier," *IEEE Journal of Solid-State Circuits*, Vol. SC-7, pp. 474–480, December 1972.

9. R. G. Meyer and W. D. Mack. " A Wideband Class AB Monolithic Power Amplifier," *IEEE Journal of Solid-State Circuits*, Vol. 24, pp. 7–12, February 1989.

10. E. L. Long and T. M. Frederiksen. "High-Gain 15-W Monolithic Power Amplifier with Internal Fault Protection," *IEEE Journal of Solid-State Circuits*, Vol. SC-6, pp. 35–44, February 1971.

11. K. Tsugaru, Y. Sugimoto, M. Noda, T. Ito, and Y. Suwa. "A Single-Power-Supply 10-b Video BiCMOS Sample-and-Hold IC," *IEEE Journal of Solid-State Circuits*, Vol. 25, pp. 653–659, June 1990.

12. K. E. Brehmer and J. B. Wieser. "Large-Swing CMOS Power Amplifier," *IEEE Journal of Solid-State Circuits*, Vol. SC-18, pp. 624–629, December 1983.

13. B. K. Ahuja, P. R. Gray, W. M. Baxter, and G. T. Uehara. "A Programmable CMOS Dual Channel Interface Processor for Telecommunications Applications," *IEEE Journal of Solid-State Circuits*, Vol. SC-19, pp. 892–899, December 1984.

14. H. Khorramabadi. "A CMOS Line Driver with 80 dB Linearity for ISDN Applications," *IEEE Journal of Solid-State Circuits*, Vol. 27, pp. 539–544, April 1992.

15. J. A. Fisher. "A High-Performance CMOS Power Amplifier," *IEEE Journal of Solid-State Circuits*, Vol. SC-20, pp. 1200–1205, December 1985.

16. K. Nagaraj. "Large-Swing CMOS Buffer Amplifier," *IEEE Journal of Solid-State Circuits*, Vol. 24, pp. 181–183, February 1989.

17. H. Khorramabadi, J. Anidjar, and T. R. Peterson. "A Highly Efficient CMOS Line Driver with 80-dB Linearity for ISDN U-Interface Applications," *IEEE Journal of Solid-State Circuits*, Vol. 27, pp. 1723–1729, December 1992.

# Operational Amplifiers with Single-Ended Outputs

In the previous three chapters, the most important circuit building blocks utilized in analog integrated circuits (ICs) have been studied. Most analog ICs consist primarily of these basic circuits connected in such a way as to perform the desired function. Although the variety of standard and special-purpose custom ICs is almost limitless, a few standard circuits stand out as perhaps having the widest application in systems of various kinds. These include operational amplifiers, voltage regulators, and analog-to-digital (A/D) and digital-to-analog (D/A) converters. In this chapter, we will consider monolithic operational amplifiers (op amps) with single-ended outputs, both as an example of the utilization of the previously described circuit building blocks and as an introduction to the design and application of this important class of analog circuit. Op amps with fully differential outputs are considered in Chapter 12, and voltage-regulator circuits are considered in Chapter 8. The design of A/D and D/A converters is not covered, but it involves application of the circuit techniques described throughout the book.

An ideal op amp with a single-ended output has a differential input, infinite voltage gain, infinite input resistance, and zero output resistance. A conceptual schematic diagram is shown in Fig. 6.1. While actual op amps do not have these ideal characteristics, their performance is usually sufficiently good that the circuit behavior closely approximates that of an ideal op amp in most applications.

In op-amp design, bipolar transistors offer many advantages over their CMOS counterparts, such as higher transconductance for a given current, higher gain ($g_m r_o$), higher speed, lower input-referred offset voltage and lower input-referred noise voltage. (The topic of noise is considered in Chapter 11.) As a result, op amps made from bipolar transistors offer the best performance in many cases, including for example dc-coupled, low-offset, low-drift applications. For these reasons, bipolar op amps became commercially significant first and still usually offer superior analog performance. However, CMOS technologies have become dominant in building the digital portions of signal-processing systems because CMOS digital circuits are smaller and dissipate less power than their bipolar counterparts. Since these systems often operate on signals that originate in analog form, analog circuits such as op amps are required to interface to the digital CMOS circuits. To reduce system cost and increase portability, analog and digital circuits are now often integrated together, providing a strong economic incentive to use CMOS op amps.

In this chapter, we first explore several applications of op amps to illustrate their versatility in analog circuit and system design. CMOS op amps are considered next. Then a general-purpose bipolar monolithic op amp, the 741, is analyzed, and the ways in which the performance of the circuit deviates from ideality are described. Design considerations for improving the various aspects of monolithic op-amp low-frequency performance are described. The high-frequency and transient response of op amps are covered in Chapters 7 and 9.

**Figure 6.1** Ideal operational amplifier.

## 6.1 Applications of Operational Amplifiers

### 6.1.1 Basic Feedback Concepts

Virtually all op-amp applications rely on the principles of *feedback*. The topic of feedback amplifiers is covered in detail in Chapter 8; we now consider a few basic concepts necessary for an understanding of op-amp circuits. A generalized feedback amplifier is shown in Fig. 6.2. The block labeled $a$ is called the forward or basic amplifier, and the block labeled $f$ is called the feedback network. The gain of the basic amplifier when the feedback network is not present is called the *open-loop gain, a,* of the amplifier. The function of the feedback network is to sense the output signal $S_o$ and develop a feedback signal $S_{fb}$, which is equal to $fS_o$, where $f$ is usually less than unity. This feedback signal is subtracted from the input signal $S_i$, and the difference $S_\epsilon$ is applied to the basic amplifier. The gain of the system when the feedback network is present is called the *closed-loop gain*. For the basic amplifier we have

$$S_o = aS_\epsilon = a(S_i - S_{fb}) = a(S_i - fS_o) \tag{6.1}$$

and thus

$$\frac{S_o}{S_i} = \frac{a}{1 + af} = \frac{1}{f}\left(\frac{af}{1 + af}\right) = \frac{1}{f}\left(\frac{T}{1 + T}\right) \tag{6.2}$$

where $T = af$ is called the *loop gain*. When $T$ becomes large compared to unity, the closed-loop gain becomes

$$\lim_{T \to \infty} \frac{S_o}{S_i} = \frac{1}{f} \tag{6.3}$$

Since the feedback network is composed of passive components, the value of $f$ can be set to an arbitrary degree of accuracy and will establish the gain at a value of $1/f$ if $T \gg 1$, independent of any variations in the open-loop gain $a$. This independence of closed-loop performance from the parameters of the active amplifier is the primary factor motivating the wide use of op amps as active elements in analog circuits.

For the circuit shown in Fig. 6.2, the feedback signal tends to *reduce* the magnitude of $S_\epsilon$ below that of the open-loop case (for which $f = 0$) when $a$ and $f$ have the same sign. This case is called *negative* feedback and is the case of practical interest in this chapter.

**Figure 6.2** A conceptual feedback amplifier.

   With this brief introduction to feedback concepts, we proceed to a consideration of several examples of useful op-amp configurations. Because these example circuits are simple, direct analysis with Kirchoff's laws is easier than attempting to consider them as feedback amplifiers. In Chapter 8, more complicated feedback configurations are considered in which the use of feedback concepts as an analytical tool is more useful than in these examples.

### 6.1.2 Inverting Amplifier

The inverting amplifier connection is shown in Fig. 6.3a.[1,2,3] We assume that the op-amp input resistance is infinite, and that the output resistance is zero as shown in Fig. 6.1. From KCL at node $X$,

$$\frac{V_s - V_i}{R_1} + \frac{V_o - V_i}{R_2} = 0 \tag{6.4}$$

Since $R_2$ is connected between the amplifier output and the inverting input, the feedback is negative. Therefore, $V_i$ would be driven to zero with infinite open-loop gain. On the

**Figure 6.3** (a) Inverting amplifier configuration. (b) Noninverting amplifier configuration. (c) Voltage-follower configuration.

other hand, with finite open-loop gain $a$,

$$V_i = \frac{-V_o}{a} \tag{6.5}$$

Substituting (6.5) into (6.4) and rearranging gives

$$\frac{V_o}{V_s} = -\frac{R_2}{R_1}\left[\frac{1}{1 + \frac{1}{a}\left(1 + \frac{R_2}{R_1}\right)}\right] \tag{6.6}$$

If the gain of the op amp is large enough that

$$a\left(\frac{R_1}{R_1 + R_2}\right) \gg 1 \tag{6.7}$$

then the closed-loop gain is

$$\frac{V_o}{V_s} \simeq -\frac{R_2}{R_1} \tag{6.8}$$

When the inequality in (6.7) holds, (6.8) shows that the closed-loop gain depends primarily on the external passive components $R_1$ and $R_2$. Since these components can be selected with arbitrary accuracy, a high degree of precision can be obtained in closed-loop performance independent of variations in the active device (op-amp) parameters. For example, if the op-amp gain were to change from $5 \times 10^4$ to $10^5$, this 100 percent increase in gain would have almost no observable effect on closed-loop performance provided that (6.7) is valid.

■ **EXAMPLE**

Calculate the gain of the circuit Fig. 6.3a, for $a = 10^4$ and $a = 10^5$, and $R_1 = 1 \text{ k}\Omega$, $R_2 = 10 \text{ k}\Omega$.

From (6.6) with $a = 10^4$,

$$A = \frac{V_o}{V_s} = -10\left(\frac{1}{1 + \frac{11}{10^4}}\right) = -9.9890$$

From (6.6) with $a = 10^5$,

$$A = \frac{V_o}{V_s} = -10\left(\frac{1}{1 + \frac{11}{10^5}}\right) = -9.99890$$

The large gain of op amps allows the approximate analysis of circuits like that of Fig. 6.3a to be performed by the use of *summing-point constraints*.[1] If the op amp is connected in a negative-feedback circuit, and if the gain of the op amp is very large, then for a finite value of output voltage the input voltage must approach zero since

$$V_i = -\frac{V_o}{a} \tag{6.10}$$

Thus one can analyze such circuits approximately by assuming a priori that the op-amp input voltage is driven to zero. An implicit assumption in doing so is that the feedback is negative, and that the circuit has a *stable* operating point at which (6.10) is valid.

The assumption that $V_i = 0$ is called a *summing-point constraint*. A second constraint is that no current can flow into the op-amp input terminals, since no voltage exists across the input resistance of the op amp if $V_i = 0$. This summing-point approach allows an intuitive understanding of the operation of the inverting amplifier configuration of Fig. 6.3a. Since the inverting input terminal is forced to ground potential, the resistor $R_1$ serves to convert the voltage $V_s$ to an input current of value $V_s/R_1$. This current cannot flow in the input terminal of an ideal op amp; therefore, it flows through $R_2$, producing a voltage drop of $V_s R_2/R_1$. Because the op-amp input terminal operates at ground potential, the input resistance of the overall circuit as seen by $V_s$ is equal to $R_1$. Since the inverting input of the amplifier is forced to ground potential by the negative feedback, it is sometimes called a *virtual* ground.

### 6.1.3 Noninverting Amplifier

The noninverting amplifier is shown in Fig. 6.3b.[1,2,3] Using Fig. 6.1, assume that no current flows into the inverting op-amp input terminal. If the open-loop gain is $a$, $V_i = V_o/a$ and

$$V_x = V_o\left(\frac{R_1}{R_1 + R_2}\right) = V_s - \frac{V_o}{a} \tag{6.11}$$

Rearranging (6.11) gives

$$\frac{V_o}{V_s} = \left(1 + \frac{R_2}{R_1}\right)\frac{\dfrac{aR_1}{R_1 + R_2}}{1 + \dfrac{aR_1}{R_1 + R_2}} \approx \left(1 + \frac{R_2}{R_1}\right) \tag{6.12}$$

The approximation in (6.12) is valid to the extent that $aR_1/(R_1 + R_2) \gg 1$.

In contrast to the inverting case, this circuit displays a very high input resistance as seen by $V_s$ because of the type of feedback used. (See Chapter 8.) Also unlike the inverting case, the noninverting connection causes the common-mode input voltage of the op amp to be equal to $V_s$. An important variation of this connection is the voltage follower, in which $R_1 \to \infty$ and $R_2 = 0$. This circuit is shown in Fig. 6.3c, and its gain is close to unity if $a \gg 1$.

### 6.1.4 Differential Amplifier

The differential amplifier is used to amplify the *difference* between two voltages. The circuit is shown in Fig. 6.4.[1,2] For this circuit, $I_{i1} = 0$ and thus resistors $R_1$ and $R_2$ form a voltage divider. Voltage $V_x$ is then given by

$$V_x = V_1\left(\frac{R_2}{R_1 + R_2}\right) \tag{6.13}$$

The current $I_1$ is

$$I_1 = \left(\frac{V_2 - V_y}{R_1}\right) = I_2 \tag{6.14}$$

The output voltage is given by

$$V_o = V_y - I_2 R_2 \tag{6.15}$$

**Figure 6.4** Differential amplifier configuration.

If the open-loop gain is infinite, the summing-point constraint that $V_i = 0$ is valid and forces $V_y = V_x$. Substituting $V_y = V_x$, (6.13), and (6.14) into (6.15) and rearranging gives

$$V_o = \frac{R_2}{R_1}(V_1 - V_2) \qquad (6.16)$$

The circuit thus amplifies the *difference* voltage $(V_1 - V_2)$.

Differential amplifiers are often required to detect and amplify small differences between two sizable voltages. For example, a typical application is the measurement of the difference voltage between the two arms of a Wheatstone bridge. As in the case of the noninverting amplifier, the op amp of Fig. 6.4 experiences a common-mode input that is almost equal to the common-mode voltage $(V_1 + V_2)/2$ applied to the input terminals when $R_2 \gg R_1$.

## 6.1.5 Nonlinear Analog Operations

By including nonlinear elements in the feedback network, op amps can be used to perform nonlinear operations on one or more analog signals. The logarithmic amplifier, shown in Fig. 6.5, is an example of such an application. Log amplifiers find wide application in instrumentation systems where signals of very large dynamic range must be sensed and recorded. The operation of this circuit can again be understood by application of the summing-point constraints. Because the input voltage of the op amp must be zero, the

**Figure 6.5** Logarithmic amplifier configuration.

resistor $R$ serves to convert the input voltage $V_s$ into a current. This same current must then flow into the collector of the transistor. Thus the circuit forces the collector current of the transistor to be proportional to the input voltage. Furthermore, the transistor operates in the forward-active region because $V_{CB} \approx 0$. Since the base-emitter voltage of a bipolar transistor in the forward-active region is logarithmically related to the collector current, and since the output voltage is just the emitter-base voltage of the transistor, a logarithmic transfer characteristic is produced. In terms of equations,

$$I_1 = \frac{V_s}{R} = I_c = I_S\left[\exp\left(\frac{V_{be}}{V_T}\right) - 1\right] \approx I_S \exp\left(\frac{V_{be}}{V_T}\right) \tag{6.17}$$

and

$$V_o = -V_{be} \tag{6.18}$$

Thus

$$V_o = -V_T \ln\left(\frac{V_s}{I_S R}\right) \tag{6.19}$$

The log amplifier is only one example of a wide variety of op-amp applications in which a nonlinear feedback element is used to develop a nonlinear transfer characteristic. For example, two log amplifiers can be used to develop the logarithm of two different signals. These voltages can be summed, and then the exponential function of the result can be developed using an inverting amplifier connection with $R_1$ replaced with a diode. The result is an analog multiplier. Other nonlinear operations such as limiting, rectification, peak detection, squaring, square rooting, raising to a power, and division can be performed in conceptually similar ways.

### 6.1.6 Integrator, Differentiator

The integrator and differentiator circuits, shown in Fig. 6.6, are examples of using op amps with reactive elements in the feedback network to realize a desired frequency response or time-domain response.[1,2] In the case of the integrator, the resistor $R$ is used to develop a current $I_1$ that is proportional to the input voltage. This current flows into the capacitor $C$, whose voltage is proportional to the integral of the current $I_1$ with respect to time. Since the output voltage is equal to the negative of the capacitor voltage, the output is proportional to the integral of the input voltage with respect to time. In terms of equations,

$$I_1 = \frac{V_s}{R} = I_2 \tag{6.20}$$

(a)                                    (b)

**Figure 6.6**  (a) Integrator configuration. (b) Differentiator configuration.

and

$$V_o = -\frac{1}{C} \int_0^t I_2 d\tau + V_o(0) \tag{6.21}$$

Combining (6.20) and (6.21) yields

$$V_o(t) = -\frac{1}{RC} \int_0^t V_s(\tau) d\tau + V_o(0) \tag{6.22}$$

The performance limitations of real op amps limit the range of $V_o$ and the rate of change of $V_o$ for which this relationship is maintained.

In the case of the differentiator, the capacitor $C$ is connected between $V_s$ and the inverting op-amp input. The current through the capacitor is proportional to the time derivative of the voltage across it, which is equal to the input voltage. This current flows through the feedback resistor $R$, producing a voltage at the output proportional to the capacitor current, which is proportional to the time rate of change of the input voltage. In terms of equations,

$$I_1 = C\frac{dV_s}{dt} = I_2 \tag{6.23}$$

$$V_o = -RI_2 = -RC\frac{dV_s}{dt} \tag{6.24}$$

### 6.1.7 Internal Amplifiers

The performance objectives for op amps to be used within a monolithic analog subsystem are often quite different from those of general-purpose op amps that use external feedback elements. In a monolithic analog subsystem, only a few of the amplifiers must drive a signal off-chip where the capacitive and resistive loads are significant and variable. These amplifiers will be termed *output buffers,* and the amplifiers whose outputs do not go off chip will be termed *internal amplifiers.* Perhaps the most important difference is that the load an internal amplifier has to drive is well defined and is often purely capacitive with a value of a few picofarads. In contrast, stand-alone general-purpose amplifiers usually must be designed to achieve a certain level of performance that is independent of changes in capacitive loads up to several hundred picofarads and resistive loads down to 2 k$\Omega$ or less.

#### 6.1.7.1 Switched Capacitor Amplifier

In MOS technologies, capacitors instead of resistors are often used as passive elements in feedback amplifiers in part because capacitors are often the best available passive components. Also, capacitors can store charge proportional to analog signals of interest, and MOS transistors can act as switches to connect to the capacitors without offset and with little leakage, allowing the discrete-time signal processing of·analog quantities. The topic of MOS switched-capacitor amplifiers is one important application of internal amplifiers. Here, we introduce the application to help explain the construction of MOS op amps.

Figure 6.7 shows the schematic of an inverting amplifier with capacitive feedback in contrast to the resistive feedback shown in Fig. 6.3a. If the op amp is ideal, the gain from a change in the input $\Delta V_s$ to a change in the output $\Delta V_o$ is still given by the ratio of the impedance of the feedback element $C_2$ to the impedance of the input element $C_1$, or

$$\frac{\Delta V_o}{\Delta V_s} = -\frac{\frac{1}{\omega C_2}}{\frac{1}{\omega C_1}} = -\frac{C_1}{C_2} \tag{6.25}$$

**Figure 6.7** Inverting amplifier configuration with capacitive feedback without dc bias for the inverting op-amp input.

Unlike the case when resistors are used as passive elements, however, this circuit does not provide dc bias for the inverting op-amp input because the impedances of both capacitors are infinite at dc. To overcome this problem, switches controlled by a two-phase nonoverlapping clock are used to control the operation of the above circuit. The resulting circuit is known as a *switched-capacitor amplifier.*

Figure 6.8a shows the schematic of a switched-capacitor amplifier. Each switch in the schematic is controlled by one of two clock phases $\phi_1$ and $\phi_2$, and the timing diagram is shown in Fig. 6.8b. We will assume that each switch is closed when its controlling clock signal is high, and open when its clock signal is low. Since $\phi_1$ and $\phi_2$ are never both high at the same time, the switches controlled by one clock phase are never closed at the same time as the switches controlled by the other clock phase. Because of this property, the clock signals in Fig. 6.8b are known as *nonoverlapping*. For example, the left side of $C_1$ is connected to the input $V_s$ through switch $S_1$ when $\phi_1$ is high and to ground through switch $S_2$ when $\phi_2$ is high, but this node is never simultaneously connected to both the input and ground.

To simplify the description of the operation of switched-capacitor circuits, they are often redrawn twice, once for each nonoverlapping clock phase. Figures 6.8c and 6.8d show the connections when $\phi_1$ is high (*during $\phi_1$*) and when $\phi_2$ is high (*during $\phi_2$*), respectively. Switches that are closed are assumed to be short circuits, and switches that are open are assumed to be open circuits.

To find the output for a given input, an analysis based on charge conservation is used. After switch $S_3$ opens, the charge on the plates of the capacitors that connect to the op-amp input node is conserved until this switch closes again. This property stems partly from the fact that the passive elements connected to the op-amp input node are capacitors, which conduct zero dc current. Also, if the op amp is constructed with an MOS differential input pair, the op-amp input is connected to the gate of one transistor in the differential pair, and the gate conducts zero dc current. Finally, if we assume that switch $S_3$ conducts zero current when it is open, the charge stored cannot leak away while $S_3$ is open.

Since both sides of $C_2$ are grounded in Fig. 6.8c, the charge stored on the plates of the capacitors that connect to the the the op-amp input node during $\phi_1$ is

$$Q_1 = (0 - V_s)C_1 + (0)C_2 = (0 - V_s)C_1 \tag{6.26}$$

Because the input voltage is sampled or stored onto capacitor $C_1$ during $\phi_1$, this phase is known as the *input sample* phase. If the op amp is ideal, the voltage $V_i$ from the inverting op-amp input to ground is driven to zero by negative feedback during $\phi_2$. Therefore, the charge stored during $\phi_2$ is

$$Q_2 = (0)C_1 + (0 - V_o)C_2 = (0 - V_o)C_2 \tag{6.27}$$

Because the sampled charge appears on $C_1$ during $\phi_1$ and on $C_2$ during $\phi_2$, $\phi_2$ is known as the *charge-transfer* phase. By charge conservation, $Q_2 = Q_1$; therefore,

$$\frac{V_o}{V_s} = \frac{C_1}{C_2} \tag{6.28}$$

**Figure 6.8** (*a*) Schematic of a switched-capacitor amplifier with ideal switches. (*b*) Timing diagram of clock signals. (*c*) Connections during $\phi_1$. (*d*) Connections during $\phi_2$.

In (6.28), $V_s$ represents the input voltage at the end of $\phi_1$, and $V_o$ represents the output voltage at the end of $\phi_2$. The shape of the output voltage waveform is not predicted by (6.28) and depends on the rates at which the capacitors are charged and discharged. In practice, these rates depend on the bandwidth of the op amp and the resistances of the closed switches. The result in (6.28) is valid as long as the op amp is ideal, the input $V_s$ is dc, and the intervals over which $\phi_1$ and $\phi_2$ are high are long enough to completely charge and discharge the associated capacitors. The ratio of $V_o/V_s$ in (6.28) is positive because if $V_s > 0$ during $\phi_1$, the voltage applied between the left side of $C_1$ and ground decreases from a positive value to zero during $\phi_2$. Therefore, this negative change in the applied voltage during $\phi_2$ is multiplied by a negative closed-loop amplifier gain, giving a positive ratio in (6.28).

MOS technologies are well suited to building switched-capacitor circuits for two key reasons. First, the dc current that flows into the input terminals of MOS op amps is zero as long as the inputs are connected only to the gates of MOS transistors. In contrast, bipolar op amps have nonzero dc input currents that stem from finite $\beta_F$ in bipolar transistors. Second, the switches in Fig. 6.8 can be implemented without offset by using MOS transistors, as shown in Fig. 6.9a. The arrows indicating the source terminals of $M_1 - M_5$ are arbitrarily chosen in the sense that the source and drain terminals are interchangeable. (Since the source is the source of electrons in $n$-channel transistors, the source-to-ground voltage is lower than the drain-to-ground voltage.) Assume that the clock voltages alternate between $-V_{SS}$ and $V_{DD}$ as shown in Fig. 6.9b. Also assume that all node voltages are no lower than $-V_{SS}$ and no higher than $V_{DD}$. Finally, assume that the transistor threshold voltages are positive. Under these conditions, each transistor turns off when its gate is low. Furthermore, each transistor turns on when its gate is high as long as its source operates at least a threshold below $V_{DD}$. If $V_s$ is a dc signal, all drain currents approach zero as the capacitors become charged. As the drain currents approach zero, the MOS transistors that are on operate in the triode region, where the drain-source voltage is zero when the

(a)

(b)

**Figure 6.9** (a) Schematic of a switched-capacitor amplifier with $n$-channel MOS transistors used as switches. (b) Clock waveforms with labeled voltages.

drain current is zero. Therefore, the input voltage $V_s$ is sampled onto $C_1$ with zero offset inserted by the MOS transistors operating as switches. This property of MOS transistors is important in the implementation of switched-capacitor circuits. In contrast, bipolar transistors operating as switches do not give zero collector-emitter voltage with zero collector current.

The switched-capacitor amplifier shown in Fig. 6.9a is important in practice mainly because the gain of this circuit has little dependence on the various parasitic capacitances that are present on all the nodes in the circuit. These undesired capacitances stem in part from the drain-body and source-body junction capacitances of each transistor. Also, the op-amp input capacitance contributes to the parasitic capacitance on the op-amp input node. Furthermore, as described in Section 2.10.2, the bottom plates of capacitors $C_1$ and $C_2$ exhibit at least some capacitance to the underlying layer, which is the substrate or a well diffusion. Since the gain of the circuit is determined by charge conservation at the op-amp input node, the presence of parasitic capacitance from any node except the op-amp input to any node with a constant voltage to ground makes no difference to the accuracy of the circuit. (Such parasitics do reduce the maximum clock rate, however.) On the other hand, parasitic capacitance on the op-amp input node does affect the accuracy of the circuit gain, but the error is inversely proportional to the op-amp gain, as we will now show.

Let $C_P$ represent the total parasitic capacitance from the op-amp input to all nodes with constant voltage to ground. If the op-amp gain is $a$, the voltage from the inverting op-amp input to ground during $\phi_2$ is given by (6.10). Therefore, with finite op-amp gain, $C_1$ and $C_P$ are not completely discharged during $\phi_2$. Under these conditions, the charge stored on the op-amp input node during $\phi_2$ becomes

$$Q_2 = \left(-\frac{V_o}{a}\right)C_1 + \left(-\frac{V_o}{a}\right)C_P + \left(-\frac{V_o}{a} - V_o\right)C_2 \tag{6.29}$$

When the op-amp gain becomes infinite, (6.29) collapses to (6.27), as expected. Setting $Q_2$ in (6.29) equal to $Q_1$ in (6.26) by charge conservation gives

$$\frac{V_o}{V_s} = \frac{C_1}{C_2}\left[\frac{1}{1 + \frac{1}{a}\left(\frac{C_1 + C_2 + C_P}{C_2}\right)}\right] \tag{6.30}$$

This closed-loop gain can be written as

$$\frac{V_o}{V_s} = \frac{C_1}{C_2}(1 - \epsilon) \tag{6.31}$$

where $\epsilon$ is a gain error given by

$$\epsilon = \frac{1}{1 + a\left(\frac{C_2}{C_1 + C_2 + C_P}\right)} \tag{6.32}$$

As $a \to \infty$, $\epsilon \to 0$, and the gain of the switched-capacitor amplifier approaches $C_1/C_2$ as predicted in (6.28). As a result, the circuit gain is said to be *parasitic insensitive* to an extent that depends on the op-amp gain.

One important parameter of the switched-capacitor amplifier shown in Fig. 6.9a is the minimum clock period. This period is divided into two main parts, one for each clock phase. The duration of $\phi_2$ must be long enough for the op-amp output to reach and stay within a given level of accuracy. This time is defined as the op-amp settling time and depends on the switch resistances, the circuit capacitances, and the op-amp properties. The settling time is usually determined by SPICE simulations. Such simulations should be run for both clock phases because the op-amp output voltage during $\phi_1$ is not well controlled in practice. If the op amp is ideal, this output voltage is zero. With nonzero offset voltage, however, the output voltage will be driven to a nonzero value during $\phi_1$ that depends on both the offset voltage and the op-amp gain. If the op-amp gain is large, the offset can easily be large enough to force the output voltage to clip near one of the supplies. The output voltage at the end of $\phi_1$ can be thought of as an initial condition for the circuit during $\phi_2$. If the initial condition and the desired final output at the end of $\phi_2$ happen to have far different values, the time required for the output to reach a given level of accuracy during $\phi_2$ can be increased. Furthermore, nonzero offset can increase the time required for the op-amp output voltage to reach a constant level during $\phi_1$. Although the circuit output voltage defined in (6.30) only appears during $\phi_2$, failure to reach a constant output voltage during $\phi_1$ causes the initial condition defined above to vary, depending on the value of $V_o$ at the end of the preceding $\phi_2$. As a result of this memory effect, the circuit can behave as a filter (which is possibly nonlinear), weighting together the results of more than one previous input sample to determine any given output. The key point is that an increase in the minimum duration of either phase requires an increase in the minimum clock period. This effect should be included in simulation by intentionally simulating with nonzero offset voltages.

One way to reduce the effect of nonzero offset voltage on the minimum clock period is to include a reset switch at the op-amp output. If the op amp has a single-ended output as shown in Fig. 6.9a, such a switch can be connected between the op-amp output and a bias point between the two supplies. On the other hand, if the op amp has differential outputs as described in Chapter 12, such a reset switch can be connected between the two op-amp outputs. In either case, the reset switch would be turned on during $\phi_1$ and off during $\phi_2$. The main value of such a reset switch is that it can reduce both the maximum output voltage produced by a nonzero offset voltage during $\phi_1$ and the time required to reach this value, in turn reducing the effect of nonzero offset on the minimum durations of both phases.

The accuracy of the switched-capacitor amplifier shown in Fig. 6.9a is limited by several other factors that we will now consider briefly. First, even with an ideal op amp, the gain depends on the ratio of capacitors $C_1/C_2$, which is not controlled perfectly in practice because of random-mismatch effects. Second, op-amp offset limits the minimum signal that can be distinguished from the offset in the switched-capacitor amplifier. As shown in Section 3.5.6, the input-referred offset of CMOS differential pairs is usually worse than for bipolar differential pairs. This property extends to op amps and stems partly from the reduced transconductance-to-current ratio of MOS transistors compared to their bipolar counterparts and partly from the threshold mismatch term, which appears only in the MOS case. Third, the charge-conservation equation and accuracy of the switched-capacitor amplifier are affected by the charge stored under the gates of some of the MOS transistors acting as switches in Fig. 6.9a. For example, some of the charge stored under the gate of transistor $M_3$ in Fig. 6.9a is injected onto the op-amp input node after $M_3$ is turned off. Techniques to overcome these limitations are often used in practice but are not considered here.

### 6.1.7.2 Switched-Capacitor Integrator
Another application of an internal op amp, a switched-capacitor integrator, is illustrated in its simplest form in Fig. 6.10a. This circuit is widely utilized as the basic element of monolithic switched-capacitor filters for two main reasons. First, the frequency response

Figure 6.10 (a) Schematic of a switched-capacitor integrator. (b) Timing diagram. (c) Continuous-time equivalent circuit for input frequencies much less than the clock frequency.

of the integrator is insensitive to the various parasitic capacitances that are present on all nodes in the circuit. Second, using switched-capacitor integrators as the basic elements, the synthesis of desired filter frequency responses is relatively straightforward. In this section, we will analyze the frequency response of the switched-capacitor integrator.

The integrator consists of an op amp, a sampling capacitor $C_S$, an integrating capacitor $C_I$, and four MOS transistor switches. The load capacitance shown represents the sampling capacitor of the following integrator, plus any parasitic capacitances that may be present. Typical values for the sampling, integrating, and load capacitances are labeled in Fig. 6.10a.

Figure 6.10b shows the timing diagram of two nonoverlapping clock signals, $\phi_1$ and $\phi_2$, that control the operation of the circuit as well as typical input and output waveforms.

During the interval when clock phase $\phi_1$ is high, transistors $M_1$ and $M_3$ operate in the triode region and serve to charge the sampling capacitor to a voltage that is equal to the input voltage. Subsequently, clock signal $\phi_1$ falls. Then clock signal $\phi_2$ rises, causing transistors $M_2$ and $M_4$ to turn on and the sampling capacitor to be connected between the inverting op-amp input, which is sometimes called the *summing node,* and ground. If the op amp is ideal, the resulting change in the summing-node voltage causes the op-amp output to move so that the summing-node voltage is driven back to ground. After the transient has gone to completion, the voltage across $C_S$ is driven to zero.

To find the relationship between the input and output, a charge-conservation analysis is used. After transistor $M_1$ opens in Fig. 6.10$a$, the charge on the plates of the capacitors connected to node *Top* and the inverting op-amp input is conserved until $M_1$ closes again. Define points $[n]$ and $[n + 1/2]$ as the time indexes at which $\phi_1$ and $\phi_2$ first fall in Fig. 6.10$b$, respectively. Point $[n + 1]$ is defined as the next time index at which $\phi_1$ falls. The points $[n]$ and $[n + 1]$ are separated by one clock period $T$. If the switches and the op amp are ideal, the charge stored at time index $[n]$ is

$$Q[n] = (0 - V_s[n])C_S + (0 - V_o[n])C_I \qquad (6.33)$$

Under the same conditions, the charge stored at time index $[n + 1/2]$ is

$$Q[n + 1/2] = (0)C_S + (0 - V_o[n + 1/2])C_I \qquad (6.34)$$

From charge conservation, $Q[n + 1/2] = Q[n]$. Also, the charge stored on $C_I$ is constant during $\phi_1$ under these conditions; therefore, $V_o[n + 1] = V_o[n + 1/2]$. Combining these relations gives

$$V_o[n + 1] = V_o[n] + \left(\frac{C_S}{C_I}\right)V_s[n] \qquad (6.35)$$

Thus, one complete clock cycle results in a change in the integrator output voltage that is proportional to the value of the input voltage and to the capacitor ratio.

Equation 6.35 can be used to find the frequency response of the integrator by using the fact that the operation of delaying a signal by one clock period $T$ in the time domain corresponds to multiplication by the factor $e^{-j\omega T}$ in the frequency domain. Thus

$$V_o(j\omega) = V_o(j\omega)e^{-j\omega T} + \left(\frac{C_S}{C_I}\right)V_s(j\omega)e^{-j\omega T} \qquad (6.36)$$

Therefore, the integrator frequency response is

$$\frac{V_o}{V_s}(j\omega) = -\frac{C_S}{C_I}\left(\frac{1}{1 - e^{j\omega T}}\right) = \frac{C_S}{C_I}\left(\frac{2j}{e^{j\omega T/2} - e^{-j\omega T/2}}\right)\left(\frac{e^{-j\omega T/2}}{2j}\right) \qquad (6.37)$$

Using the identity

$$\sin x = \frac{1}{2j}(e^{jx} - e^{-jx}) \qquad (6.38)$$

in (6.37) with $x = \omega T/2$ we find

$$\frac{V_o}{V_s}(j\omega) = \frac{C_S}{C_I}\left(\frac{\omega T/2}{\sin \omega T/2}\right)\left(\frac{e^{-j\omega T/2}}{2j\omega T/2}\right) = \frac{1}{\underbrace{\frac{j\omega}{\omega_o}}}\left(\frac{\omega T/2}{\sin \omega T/2}e^{-j\omega T/2}\right) \qquad (6.39)$$

where

$$\omega_o = \frac{C_S}{TC_I} = \frac{fC_S}{C_I} = \frac{1}{T} \qquad (6.40)$$

where $\tau$ is the time constant of the integrator. Here $f$ is the clock frequency, equal to $1/T$. For input frequencies that are much less than the clock frequency, the quantity $\omega T$ is much less than unity, and the right-most term in parentheses in (6.39) reduces to unity. The remaining term is simply the frequency response of an analog integrator, as desired. In practical designs, the excess phase and magnitude error contributed by the term in parentheses in (6.39) must often be taken into account. From a conceptual standpoint, however, the circuit can be thought of as providing an analog integration of the signal. Note that the time constant of the integrator is the same as would occur if the sampling capacitor and switches were replaced by a continuous-value resistor of value $1/(fC_S)$. This equivalence is illustrated in Fig. 6.10c.

A key advantage of a switched-capacitor integrator compared to its continuous-time counterpart is that the time constant of the switched-capacitor integrator can be much better controlled in practice. The time constant of a continuous-time integrator depends on the product of a resistance and a capacitance as in (6.22). In monolithic technologies, resistance and capacitance values do not track each other. Therefore, the time constant of a continuous-time integrator is not well controlled over variations in process, supply, and temperature in general. However, the time constant of a switched-capacitor integrator is determined by the *ratio* of two capacitor values and the clock frequency, as in (6.40). If the two capacitors have the same properties, the ratio is well controlled even when the absolute values are poorly controlled. Since the clock frequency can be precisely determined by a crystal-controlled clock generator, the time constant of a switched-capacitor integrator can be well controlled in monolithic technologies.

A key requirement for the op amps in Figs. 6.9a and 6.10a is that dc currents at the input terminals must be extremely small to minimize the loss of charge over the time when the above analyses assumed that charge was conserved. Therefore, switched-capacitor amplifiers and integrators are ideally suited to the use of op amps with MOS transistors in the input stage.

## 6.2 Deviations from Ideality in Real Operational Amplifiers

Real op amps deviate from ideal behavior in significant ways. The main effects of these deviations are to limit the frequency range of the signals that can be accurately amplified, to place a lower limit on the magnitude of dc signals that can be detected, and to place an upper limit on the magnitudes of the impedance of the passive elements that can be used in the feedback network with the amplifier. This section summarizes the most important deviations from ideality and their effects in applications.

### 6.2.1 Input Bias Current

An input stage for a bipolar transistor op amp is shown in Fig. 6.11. Here $Q_1$ and $Q_2$ are the input transistors of the amplifier. The base currents of $Q_1$ and $Q_2$ flow into the amplifier input terminals, and the input bias current is defined as the average of the two input currents:

$$I_{BIAS} = \frac{I_{B1} + I_{B2}}{2} \tag{6.41}$$

Nonzero bias current violates the assumption made in summing-point analysis that the current into the input terminals is zero. Typical magnitudes for the bias current are 10 to 100 nA for bipolar input devices and less than 0.001 pA for MOS input devices. In dc

**Figure 6.11** Typical op-amp input stage.

inverting and noninverting amplifiers, this bias current can cause undesired voltage drops in the resistors forming the feedback network, with the result that a residual dc voltage appears at the output when the amplifier is ideal in all other ways and the external input voltage is zero. In integrator circuits, the input bias current is indistinguishable from the current being integrated and causes the output voltage to change at a constant rate even when $V_s$ is zero. To the extent that the currents are equal in the two input leads, however, their effects can be canceled in some applications by including a balancing resistor in series with one of the input leads so that the same resistance is seen looking away from each op-amp input. For example, the differential amplifier of Fig. 6.4 produces zero output with $V_1 = V_2 = 0$ if identical currents flow in both op-amp input leads. In practice, however, the two input currents are not exactly equal because of random mismatches, causing nonzero output in Fig. 6.4 when $V_1 = V_2 = 0$.

## 6.2.2 Input Offset Current

For the emitter-coupled pair shown in Fig. 6.11, the two input bias currents will be equal only if the two transistors have equal betas. Geometrically identical devices on the same IC die typically display beta mismatches that are described by a normal distribution with a standard deviation of a few percent of the mean value. Since this mismatch in the two currents varies randomly from circuit to circuit, it cannot be compensated by a fixed resistor. This aspect of op-amp performance is characterized by the input offset current, defined as

$$I_{OS} = I_{B1} - I_{B2} \tag{6.42}$$

Consider the differential amplifier in Fig. 6.4. Repeating the analysis in Section 6.1.4 for that circuit with nonzero $I_{OS}$ and $V_1 = V_2 = 0$ gives a dc output voltage of

$$V_O = (I_{B2} - I_{B1})R_2 = -I_{OS}R_2 \tag{6.43}$$

If $I_{OS} = 0$, then $V_O = 0$ here. This equation shows that the error in the dc output voltage is proportional to both the input offset current and the feedback resistance under these conditions. The key point is that the size of the feedback resistance is limited by the maximum offset current that can arise and by the allowed error in the dc output voltage in practice. See Problem 6.6.

### 6.2.3 Input Offset Voltage

As described in Chapter 3, mismatches result in nonzero input offset voltage in amplifiers. The input offset voltage is the differential input voltage that must be applied to drive the output to zero. For untrimmed monolithic op amps, this offset is typically 0.1 to 2 mV for bipolar input devices and 1 to 20 mV for MOS input devices. This offset can be nulled with an external potentiometer in the case of stand-alone op amps; however, the variation of offset with temperature (called *drift*) does not necessarily go to zero when the input offset is nulled. In dc amplifier applications, the offset and drift place a lower limit on the magnitude of the dc voltage that can be accurately amplified. In some sampled-data applications such as switched-capacitor filters, the input offset voltage of the op amp is sampled and stored on the capacitors every clock cycle. Thus the input offset is effectively canceled and is not a critical parameter. This same principle is used in chopper-stabilized op amps.

### 6.2.4 Common-Mode Input Range

The common-mode input range is the range of dc common-mode input voltages for which all transistors in the first stage of an op amp operate in the forward-active region. Over this range, the op amp behaves normally with its offset voltage and input bias current within specifications. Including one or both power-supply voltages in the common-mode input range is sometimes important.

### 6.2.5 Common-Mode Rejection Ratio (CMRR)

If an op amp has a differential input and a single-ended output, its small-signal output voltage can be described in terms of its differential and common-mode input voltages ($v_{id}$ and $v_{ic}$) by the following equation

$$v_o = A_{dm}v_{id} + A_{cm}v_{ic} \qquad (6.44)$$

where $A_{dm}$ is the differential-mode gain and $A_{cm}$ is the common-mode gain. As defined in (3.187), the common-mode rejection ratio of the op amp is

$$\text{CMRR} = \left| \frac{A_{dm}}{A_{cm}} \right| \qquad (6.45)$$

From an applications standpoint, the CMRR can be regarded as the change in input offset voltage that results from a unit change in common-mode input voltage. For example, assume that we apply zero common-mode input voltage to the amplifier and then apply just enough differential voltage to the input to drive the output voltage to zero. The dc voltage we have applied is just the input offset voltage $V_{OS}$. If we keep the applied differential voltage constant and increase the common-mode input voltage by an amount $\Delta V_{ic}$, the output voltage will change, by an amount

$$v_o = \Delta V_o = A_{cm}\Delta V_{ic} = A_{cm}v_{ic} \qquad (6.46)$$

To drive the output voltage back to zero, we will have to change the differential input voltage by an amount

$$v_{id} = \Delta V_{id} = \frac{\Delta V_o}{A_{dm}} = \frac{A_{cm}\Delta V_{ic}}{A_{dm}} \qquad (6.47)$$

Thus we can regard the effect of finite CMRR as causing a change in the input offset voltage whenever the common-mode input voltage is changed. Using (6.45) and (6.47),

we obtain

$$\text{CMRR} = \left|\frac{A_{dm}}{A_{cm}}\right| = \left(\frac{\Delta V_{id}}{\Delta V_{ic}}\right)^{-1}_{V_o=0} = \left(\frac{\Delta V_{OS}}{\Delta V_{ic}}\right)^{-1} \cong \left(\frac{\partial V_{OS}}{\partial V_{ic}}\right)^{-1}_{V_o=0} \tag{6.48}$$

In circuits such as the differential amplifier of Fig. 6.11, an offset voltage is produced that is a function of the common-mode signal input, producing a voltage at the output that is indistinguishable from the desired signal. For a common-mode rejection ratio of $10^4$ (or 80 dB), (6.48) shows that a 10-V common-mode signal produces a 1-mV change in the input offset voltage.

### 6.2.6 Power-Supply Rejection Ratio (PSRR)

In (6.44), we assumed that the power-supply voltages are constant so that the op-amp output voltage depends only on the differential and common-mode input voltages provided to the op amp. In practice, however, the power-supply voltages are not exactly constant, and variations in the power-supply voltages contribute to the op-amp output. Figure 6.12 shows a block diagram of an op amp with varying power-supply voltages. The small-signal variation on the positive and negative power supplies is $v_{dd}$ and $v_{ss}$, respectively. If $v_{ic} = 0$ is assumed for simplicity, the resulting small-signal op-amp output voltage is

$$v_o = A_{dm}v_{id} + A^+ v_{dd} + A^- v_{ss} \tag{6.49}$$

where $A^+$ and $A^-$ are the small-signal gains from the positive and negative power-supplies to the output, respectively. Since op amps should be sensitive to changes in their differential-mode input voltage but insensitive to changes in their supply voltages, this equation is rewritten below in a form that simplifies comparison of these gains:

$$v_o = A_{dm}\left(v_{id} + \frac{A^+}{A_{dm}}v_{dd} + \frac{A^-}{A_{dm}}v_{ss}\right)$$

$$= A_{dm}\left(v_{id} + \frac{v_{dd}}{\text{PSRR}^+} + \frac{v_{ss}}{\text{PSRR}^-}\right) \tag{6.50}$$

where

$$\text{PSRR}^+ = \frac{A_{dm}}{A^+} \quad \text{and} \quad \text{PSRR}^- = \frac{A_{dm}}{A^-} \tag{6.51}$$

**Figure 6.12** Block diagram of an op amp with varying power-supply voltages.

**Figure 6.13** Block diagram of an op amp with supply variations modeled in the input differential loop and with $v_{ic} = 0$.

Figure 6.13 shows one way to interpret (6.50), where the diagram in Fig. 6.12 is redrawn using an op amp with constant power supplies. To set the output in Fig. 6.13 equal to that in Fig. 6.12, the power-supply variations from Fig. 6.12 are included as equivalent differential inputs in Fig. 6.13. Equation 6.50 and Fig. 6.13 show that the power-supply rejection ratios should be maximized to minimize the undesired contributions to the op-amp output voltage. In practice, the power-supply rejection ratios are functions of frequency and often decrease for increasing frequency.

Power-supply rejection ratio has become an increasingly important parameter in MOS amplifier design as the level of integration increases. With small-scale integration, few transistors could be integrated on one integrated circuit. Therefore, analog and digital functions were isolated from each other on separate chips, avoiding some coupling from the digital circuits to the analog supplies. Also, such separation provides an opportunity to filter interference generated by the digital circuits at the printed-circuit-board level with external capacitors connected in parallel with the supplies. With large-scale integration, however, many transistors can be integrated on one integrated circuit. Integrating analog and digital functions on the same chip reduces cost but increases the coupling from the digital circuits to the analog supplies. In principle, monolithic filter capacitors can be used to reduce the resulting supply variations; however, the required areas of such capacitors are large in practice. For example, if the oxide thickness is 100 Å, the capacitance per unit area is 3.45 fF/$\mu m^2$. For a capacitor of 0.01 $\mu$F (a commonly used value to filter supplies on printed-circuit boards), the required area is 1.7 $mm^2$. Since many integrated circuits occupy areas less than 100 $mm^2$, this single capacitor would account for a significant fraction of the cost of many integrated circuits.

To reduce the cost, instead of concentrating only on reducing supply variations through filtering, another option is to build circuits with low sensitivities to power-supply variations. The use of fully differential circuit techniques has emerged as an important tool in this effort. Fully differential circuits represent all signals of interest as differences between two corresponding quantities such as voltages or currents. If two identical signal paths are used to determine corresponding quantities, and if the coupling from supply variations to one quantity is the same as to the other quantity, the difference can be independent of the supply variations and the coupling in principle. In practice, mismatches cause differences in the two signal paths, and the coupling may not be identical, causing imperfect cancellation. Also, if the power-supply noise is large enough, nonlinearity may result and limit the extent of the cancellation. Although the op amps considered in this chapter have differential inputs, they are not fully differential because their outputs are single-ended. Fully differential op amps are considered in Chapter 12.

### 6.2.7  Input Resistance

In bipolar transistor input stages, the input resistance is typically in the 100 k$\Omega$ to 1 M$\Omega$ range. Usually, however, the voltage gain is large enough that this input resistance has little effect on circuit performance in closed-loop feedback configurations.

Op amps whose inputs are connected to the gates of MOS transistors have essentially infinite input resistance in principle. In practice, however, MOS-transistor gates connected through package pins to the outside world must be protected against damage by static electricity. This protection is typically achieved by connecting back-biased clamping diodes from $V_{DD}$ and $V_{SS}$ to the gate, and thus the effective input leakage currents are determined by junction leakage and are of the order of pico'amps. However, protection is required only at the inputs and outputs of integrated circuits. In internal applications, where op-amp inputs are not connected to the external pins of an integrated circuit, protection is not required and op amps with MOS transistor gates as inputs do realize ultra-high input resistance.

### 6.2.8  Output Resistance

General-purpose bipolar op amps usually use a buffer as an output stage, which typically produces an output resistance on the order of 40 $\Omega$ to 100 $\Omega$. On the other hand, in MOS technologies, internal op amps usually do not have to drive resistive loads. Therefore, internal MOS op amps usually do not use a buffer output stage, and the resulting output resistance can be much larger than in the bipolar case. In both cases, however, the output resistance does not strongly affect the closed-loop performance except as it affects stability under large capacitive loading, and in the case of power op amps that must drive a small load resistance.

### 6.2.9  Frequency Response

Because of the capacitances associated with devices in the op amp, the voltage gain decreases at high frequencies. This fall-off must usually be controlled by the addition of extra capacitance, called *compensation capacitance,* to ensure that the circuit does not oscillate when connected in a feedback loop. (See Chapter 9.) This aspect of op-amp behavior is characterized by the unity-gain bandwidth, which is the frequency at which the magnitude of the open-loop voltage gain is equal to unity. For general-purpose amplifiers, this frequency is typically in the 1 to 100 MHz range. This topic is considered in detail in Chapters 7 and 9.

A second aspect of op-amp high-frequency behavior is a limitation of the rate at which the output voltage can change under large-signal conditions. This limitation stems from the limited current available within the circuit to charge the compensation capacitor. This maximum rate, called the slew rate, is described more extensively in Chapter 9.

### 6.2.10  Operational-Amplifier Equivalent Circuit

The effect of some of these deviations from ideality on the low-frequency performance of an op amp in a particular application can be calculated using the equivalent circuit shown in Fig. 6.14. (This model does not include the effects of finite PSRR or CMRR.) Here, the two current sources labeled $I_{BIAS}$ represent the *average* value of dc current flowing into the input terminals. The polarity of these current sources shown in Fig. 6.14 applies for an *npn* transistor input stage. The current source labeled $I_{OS}$ represents the *difference* between the currents flowing into the amplifier terminals. For example, if a particular circuit displayed

**Figure 6.14** Equivalent circuit for the operational amplifier including input offset voltage and current, input and output resistance, and voltage gain.

a current of 1.5 μA flowing into the noninverting input terminal and a current of 1 μA flowing into the inverting input terminal, then the value of $I_{BIAS}$ in Fig. 6.14 would be 1.25 μA, and the value of $I_{OS}$ would be 0.5 μA.

## 6.3 Basic Two-Stage MOS Operational Amplifiers

Figure 6.15 shows a schematic of a basic two-stage CMOS op amp.[4,5,6] A differential input stage drives an active load followed by a second gain stage. An output stage is usually not used but may be added for driving heavy loads off-chip. This circuit configuration provides good common-mode range, output swing, voltage gain, and CMRR in a simple circuit that

**Figure 6.15** Basic two-stage CMOS operational amplifier.

**Figure 6.16** More-detailed schematic diagram of a typical two-stage CMOS operational amplifier.

can be compensated with a single capacitor. The circuit is redrawn in Fig. 6.16, where the ideal current sources are replaced with transistor current mirrors. In this section, we will analyze the various performance parameters of this CMOS op-amp circuit.

### 6.3.1 Input Resistance, Output Resistance, and Open-Circuit Voltage Gain

The first stage in Fig. 6.16 consists of a $p$-channel differential pair $M_1$-$M_2$ with an $n$-channel current mirror load $M_3$-$M_4$ and a $p$-channel tail current source $M_5$. The second stage consists of an $n$-channel common-source amplifier $M_6$ with a $p$-channel current-source load $M_7$. Because the op-amp inputs are connected to the gates of MOS transistors, the input resistance is essentially infinite when the op amp is used in internal applications, which do not require the protection diodes described in Section 6.2.7. For the same reason, the input resistance of the second stage of the op amp is also essentially infinite.

The output resistance is the resistance looking back into the second stage with the op-amp inputs connected to small-signal ground:

$$R_o = r_{o6} \| r_{o7} \qquad (6.52)$$

Although this output resistance is almost always much larger than in general-purpose bipolar op amps, low output resistance is usually not required when driving purely capacitive loads.

Since the input resistance of the second stage is essentially infinite, the voltage gain of the amplifier in Fig. 6.16 can be found by considering the two stages separately. The first stage is precisely the same configuration as that considered in Section 4.3.5. The small-signal voltage gain is

$$A_{v1} = \frac{v_{o1}}{v_i} = G_{m1} R_{o1} \qquad (6.53)$$

where $G_{m1}$ and $R_{o1}$ are the transconductance and output resistance of the first stage, respectively. From (4.143) and (4.149),

$$A_{v1} = g_{m1}(r_{o2}\|r_{o4}) \tag{6.54}$$

Similarly, the second-stage voltage gain is

$$A_{v2} = -g_{m6}R_o \tag{6.55}$$

where $R_o$ is given in (6.52). As a result, the overall gain of the amplifier is

$$A_v = A_{v1}A_{v2} = -g_{m1}(r_{o2}\|r_{o4})g_{m6}(r_{o6}\|r_{o7}) \tag{6.56}$$

This equation shows that the overall gain is related to the quantity $(g_m r_o)^2$. Recall from (3.27) that

$$g_m r_o = \frac{2V_A}{V_{ov}} \tag{6.57}$$

Therefore, the overall voltage gain is a strong function of the Early voltage (which is proportional to the effective channel length) and the overdrive (which is set by the bias conditions).

■ **EXAMPLE**

Calculate the gain of the op amp in Fig. 6.16 assuming that it uses the 0.8-μm process technology described in Table 2.3. Also, assume that $L_{eff} = 0.8$ μm and $|V_{ov}| = |V_{GS} - V_t| = 0.2$ V for all devices.

Let $I_{D2}$, $I_{D4}$, $I_{D6}$, and $I_{D7}$ represent the bias currents flowing into the drains of $M_2$, $M_4$, $M_6$, and $M_7$, respectively. Since $I_{D4} = -I_{D2}$ and $I_{D7} = -I_{D6}$, (6.56) shows that

$$A_v = -g_{m1}\left(\frac{\dfrac{|V_{A2}|}{|I_{D2}|}\dfrac{V_{A4}}{|I_{D2}|}}{\dfrac{|V_{A2}|}{|I_{D2}|} + \dfrac{V_{A4}}{|I_{D2}|}}\right)g_{m6}\left(\frac{\dfrac{V_{A6}}{I_{D6}}\dfrac{|V_{A7}|}{I_{D6}}}{\dfrac{V_{A6}}{I_{D6}} + \dfrac{|V_{A7}|}{I_{D6}}}\right) \tag{6.58}$$

$$= -\frac{g_{m1}}{|I_{D2}|}\frac{g_{m6}}{I_{D6}}\left(\frac{|V_{A2}|V_{A4}}{|V_{A2}| + V_{A4}}\right)\left(\frac{V_{A6}|V_{A7}|}{V_{A6} + |V_{A7}|}\right)$$

where the absolute-value function has been used so that each quantity in (6.58) is positive. From (1.181),

$$A_v = -\frac{2}{|V_{ov1}|}\frac{2}{V_{ov6}}\left(\frac{|V_{A2}|V_{A4}}{|V_{A2}| + V_{A4}}\right)\left(\frac{V_{A6}|V_{A7}|}{V_{A6} + |V_{A7}|}\right) \tag{6.59}$$

because $I_{D1} = I_{D2}$ with zero differential input. From (1.163),

$$V_A = L_{eff}\left(\frac{dX_d}{dV_{DS}}\right)^{-1} \tag{6.60}$$

Substituting (6.60) into (6.59) with the given data and $dX_d/dV_{DS}$ from Table 2.3 gives

$$A_v = -\frac{2}{0.2}\frac{2}{0.2}\left(\frac{\dfrac{0.8}{0.04} \times \dfrac{0.8}{0.08}}{\dfrac{0.8}{0.04} + \dfrac{0.8}{0.08}}\right)^2 \approx -4400$$

■

The overall gain can be increased by either increasing the channel lengths of the devices to increase the Early voltages or by reducing the bias current to reduce the overdrives.

## 6.3.2 Output Swing

The output swing is defined to be the range of output voltages $V_o = V_O + v_o$ for which all transistors operate in the active region so that the gain calculated in (6.56) is approximately constant. From inspection of Fig. 6.16, $M_6$ operates in the triode region if the output voltage is less than $V_{ov6} - V_{SS}$. Similarly, $M_7$ operates in the triode region if the output voltage is more than $V_{DD} - |V_{ov7}|$. Therefore, the output swing is

$$V_{ov6} - V_{SS} \leq V_o \leq V_{DD} - |V_{ov7}| \tag{6.61}$$

This inequality shows that the op amp can provide high gain while its output voltage swings within one overdrive of each supply. Beyond these limits, one of the output transistors enters the triode region, where the overall gain of the amplifier would be greatly diminished. As a result, the output swing can be increased by reducing the overdrives of the output transistors.

## 6.3.3 Input Offset Voltage

In Sections 3.5.6 and 6.2.3, the input offset voltage of a differential amplifier was defined as the differential input voltage for which the differential output voltage is zero. Because the op amp in Fig. 6.16 has a single-ended output, this definition must be modified here. Referring to the voltage between the output node and ground as the *output voltage,* the most straightforward modification is to define the input offset voltage of the op amp as the differential input voltage for which the op-amp output voltage is zero. This definition is reasonable if $V_{DD} = V_{SS}$ because setting the output voltage to zero maximizes the allowed variation in the output voltage before one transistor operates in the triode region provided that $V_{ov6} = |V_{ov7}|$. If $V_{DD} \neq V_{SS}$, however, the output voltage should be set midway between the supply voltages to maximize the output swing. Therefore, we will define the input offset voltage of op amps with differential inputs and single-ended outputs as the differential input voltage for which the dc output voltage is midway between the supplies.

The offset voltage of an op amp is composed of two components: the systematic offset and the random offset. The former results from the design of the circuit and is present even when all the matched devices in the circuit are identical. The latter results from mismatches in supposedly identical pairs of devices.

**Systematic Offset Voltage.** In bipolar technologies, the gain of each stage in an op amp can be quite high (on the order of 500) because the $g_m r_o$ product is usually greater than 1000. As a result, the input-referred offset voltage of a bipolar op amp usually depends mainly on the design of the first stage. In MOS technologies, however, the $g_m r_o$ product is usually between about 20 and 100, reducing the gain per stage and sometimes causing the offset of the second stage to play an important role in determining the op-amp offset voltage.

To study the systematic offset, Fig. 6.17 shows the op amp of Fig. 6.16 split into two separate stages. If the inputs of the first stage are grounded, and if the matching is perfect, then the dc drain-source voltage of $M_4$ must be equal to the dc drain-source voltage of $M_3$. This result stems from the observation that if $V_{DS3} = V_{DS4}$, then $V_{DS1} = V_{DS2}$ and $I_{D1} = I_{D2} = I_{D5}/2$. Therefore, with $V_{DS3} = V_{DS4}$, $I_{D3} = I_{D4} = -I_{D5}/2$. As a result, $V_{DS3}$ must be equal to $V_{DS4}$ because this operating point is the only point for which the

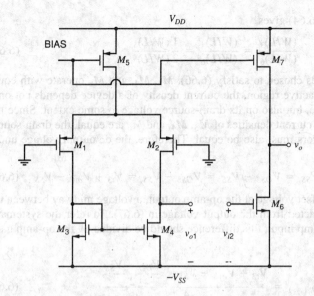

**Figure 6.17** Two-stage amplifier with first and second stages disconnected to show the effect of interstage coupling on input-referred offset voltage.

current flowing out of the drain of $M_2$ is equal to the current flowing into the drain of $M_4$. For example, increasing the drain-source voltage of $M_4$ would increase the current flowing into the drain of $M_4$ but decrease the current flowing out of the drain of $M_2$ because of the effects of channel-length modulation. Therefore, the dc drain-source voltages of $M_3$ and $M_4$ must be equal under these conditions.

On the other hand, the value of the gate-source voltage of $M_6$ required to set the amplifier output voltage midway between the supplies may differ from the dc output voltage of the first stage. If the first stage gain is 50, for example, each 50-mV difference in these voltages results in 1 mV of input-referred systematic offset. Ignoring channel-length modulation in $M_5$ and $M_7$, the current in these transistors is independent of their drain-source voltages if they operate in the active region. To set the output voltage midway between the supplies, the gate-source voltage of $M_6$ should be chosen so that the drain current of $M_6$ is equal to the drain current of $M_7$ while both transistors operate in the active region. When the input of the second stage is connected to the output of the first stage, $V_{GS6} = V_{DS4}$. With perfect matching and zero input voltages, $V_{DS4} = V_{DS3} = V_{GS3}$ and $V_{t3} = V_{t4} = V_{t6}$. Therefore,

$$V_{ov3} = V_{ov4} = V_{ov6} \tag{6.62}$$

is required. Substituting (1.166) into (6.62) gives

$$\frac{I_{D3}}{(W/L)_3} = \frac{I_{D4}}{(W/L)_4} = \frac{I_{D6}}{(W/L)_6} \tag{6.63}$$

In other words, requiring that the transistors have equal overdrives is equivalent to requiring that they have equal drain-current-to-$W/L$ ratios (or *current densities*). Since $I_{D3} = I_{D4} = |I_{D5}|/2$ and $I_{D6} = |I_{D7}|$,

$$\frac{|I_{D5}|}{2(W/L)_3} = \frac{|I_{D5}|}{2(W/L)_4} = \frac{|I_{D7}|}{(W/L)_6} \tag{6.64}$$

Since $M_5$ and $M_7$ have equal gate-source voltages,

$$\frac{I_{D5}}{I_{D7}} = \frac{(W/L)_5}{(W/L)_7} \tag{6.65}$$

Substituting (6.65) into (6.64) gives

$$\frac{(W/L)_3}{(W/L)_6} = \frac{(W/L)_4}{(W/L)_6} = \frac{1}{2}\frac{(W/L)_5}{(W/L)_7} \qquad (6.66)$$

With the aspect ratios chosen to satisfy (6.66), $M_3$, $M_4$, and $M_6$ operate with equal current densities. In the active region, the current density of a device depends not only on its gate-source voltage, but also on its drain-source voltage to some extent. Since the gate-source voltages and current densities of $M_3$, $M_4$, and $M_6$ are equal, the drain-source voltages of these transistors must also be equal. Therefore, the dc output voltage under these conditions is

$$V_O = V_{DS6} - V_{SS} = V_{DS3} - V_{SS} = V_{GS3} - V_{SS} = V_{t3} + V_{ov3} - V_{SS} \qquad (6.67)$$

To find the systematic offset voltage at the op-amp output, a voltage midway between the supplies should be subtracted from the output voltage in (6.67). To refer the systematic offset voltage to the op-amp input, this difference should be divided by the op-amp gain. The result is

$$V_{OS(sys)} = \frac{V_{t3} + V_{ov3} - V_{SS} - \dfrac{V_{DD} - V_{SS}}{2}}{A_v} \qquad (6.68)$$

where $A_v$ is the op-amp gain given in (6.56). In most cases, the dc output voltage will not be midway between the supplies because $V_{GS3} = V_{t3} + V_{ov3} \neq (V_{DD} + V_{SS})/2$. Therefore, the systematic offset is usually nonzero. Although the systematic offset voltage is nonzero in general, the choice of aspect ratios as given in (6.66) can result in an operating point that is insensitive to process variations, as explained next.

Equation 2.35 shows that the effective channel length of a MOS transistor differs from its drawn length by offset terms caused by the side diffusion of the source and drain ($L_d$) and the depletion region width around the drain ($X_d$). Similarly, the effective width of a MOS transistor differs from the drawn width by an offset term $dW$ caused by the bird's-beak effect in the oxide described in Section 2.9.1. To keep the ratio in (6.66) constant in the presence of process-induced variations in $L_d$, $X_d$, and $dW$, the drawn channel lengths and widths of the ratioed transistors can each be chosen to be identical. In this case, the ratio in (6.66) can be set equal to any rational number $J/K$ by connecting $J$ identical devices called *n-channel units* in parallel to form $M_3$ and $M_4$ while $K$ *n*-channel units in parallel form $M_6$. Then if $M_5$ is constructed of $2J$ identical devices called *p-channel units*, $M_7$ should be constructed from $K$ *p*-channel units. In practice for matched devices, the channel lengths are almost never ratioed directly because the use of small channel lengths for high-speed operation would result in a large sensitivity to process variations. On the other hand, the channel widths of matched devices are sometimes ratioed directly when the width is large enough to make the resulting sensitivity to process variations insignificant.

A key point of this analysis is that the use of identical channel lengths for $M_3$, $M_4$, and $M_6$ conflicts with a combination of other requirements. First, for stability reasons described in Chapter 9, $M_6$ should have a large transconductance and thus a short channel length. Second, for low noise and random input offset voltage, $M_3$ and $M_4$ should have a small transconductance and therefore a long channel length. Noise is considered in Chapter 11, and random input offset voltage is considered next.

**Random Input Offset Voltage.**   As described in Section 3.5.6, source-coupled pairs generally display a higher random offset than their bipolar counterparts. Ignoring the contribution of the second stage in the op amp to the input-referred random offset, a straightforward analysis for the offset voltage of the circuit of Fig. 6.16, which is analogous to the analysis leading to (3.248), gives

$$V_{OS} \simeq \Delta V_{t(1-2)} + \Delta V_{t(3-4)} \left( \frac{g_{m3}}{g_{m1}} \right)$$

$$+ \frac{V_{ov(1-2)}}{2} \left[ \frac{\Delta \left( \frac{W}{L} \right)_{(3-4)}}{\left( \frac{W}{L} \right)_{(3-4)}} - \frac{\Delta \left( \frac{W}{L} \right)_{(1-2)}}{\left( \frac{W}{L} \right)_{(1-2)}} \right] \qquad (6.69)$$

The first term represents the threshold mismatch of the input transistors. The second is the threshold mismatch of the current-mirror-load devices and is minimized by choosing the $W/L$ ratio of the load devices so that their transconductance is small compared to that of the input transistors. For this reason, selecting a longer channel length for $M_3$ and $M_4$ than for $M_1$ and $M_2$ reduces the random input offset voltage. The third term represents the effects of $W/L$ mismatches in the input transistors and loads and is minimized by operating the input transistors at low values of overdrive, typically on the order of 50 to 200 mV.

### 6.3.4 Common-Mode Rejection Ratio

For the op amp in Fig. 6.16, (6.45) gives

$$\text{CMRR} = \left| \frac{A_{dm}}{A_{cm}} \right| = \left| \frac{\dfrac{v_o}{v_{o1}} \dfrac{v_{o1}}{v_{id}}}{\dfrac{v_o}{v_{o1}} \dfrac{v_{o1}}{v_{ic}}} \right| = \text{CMRR}_1 \qquad (6.70)$$

where $\text{CMRR}_1$ is the common-mode rejection ratio of the first stage. The second stage does not contribute to the common-mode rejection ratio of the op amp because the second stage has a single-ended input and a single-ended output. In (4.182) and (4.183), the common-mode rejection ratio of a stage with a differential pair and a current-mirror load was calculated assuming perfect matching. Applying (4.183) here gives

$$\text{CMRR} \simeq (2g_{m(dp)}r_{\text{tail}})g_{m(mir)}(r_{o(dp)} \| r_{o(mir)}) \qquad (6.71)$$

where $g_{m(dp)}$ and $r_{o(dp)}$ are the transconductance and output resistance of $M_1$ and $M_2$, $g_{m(mir)}$ and $r_{o(mir)}$ are the transconductance and output resistance of $M_3$ and $M_4$, and $r_{\text{tail}}$ is the output resistance of $M_5$. By a process similar to the derivation of (6.59), this equation can be simplified to give

$$\text{CMRR} \simeq \left| \frac{2}{V_{ov(dp)}} \frac{2}{V_{ov(mir)}} \left( \frac{V_{A(dp)} V_{A(mir)}}{|V_{A(dp)}| + |V_{A(mir)}|} \right) \right| \qquad (6.72)$$

where $V_{ov(dp)}$ and $V_{A(dp)}$ are the overdrive and Early voltage of the differential pair, and $V_{ov(mir)}$ and $V_{A(mir)}$ are the overdrive and Early voltage of the mirror. Equation 6.72 shows that the common-mode rejection ratio of the op amp can be increased by reducing the overdrive voltages.

Another way to increase the common-mode rejection ratio is to replace the simple current mirror $M_5$ and $M_8$ with one of the high-output-resistance current mirrors considered in Chapter 4. Unfortunately, such a replacement would also worsen the common-mode input range.

### 6.3.5 Common-Mode Input Range

The common-mode input range is the range of dc common-mode input voltages for which all transistors in the first stage of the op amp operate in the active region. To operate in the active region, the gate-drain voltages of $n$-channel transistors must be less than their thresholds so that their channels do not exist at their drains. Similarly, $p$-channel transistors operate in the active region only if their gate-drain voltages are more than their thresholds, again so that their channels do not exist at their drains. With a pure common-mode input $V_{IC}$ applied to the inputs of the op amp in Fig. 6.16,

$$V_{DS4} = V_{DS3} = V_{GS3} = V_{t3} + V_{ov3} \tag{6.73}$$

The gate-drain voltage of $M_1$ and $M_2$ is

$$V_{GD1} = V_{GD2} = V_{IC} - V_{t3} - V_{ov3} + V_{SS} \tag{6.74}$$

When $V_{IC}$ is reduced to the point at which $V_{GD1} = V_{GD2} = V_{t1} = V_{t2}$, $M_1$ and $M_2$ operate at the edge between the the triode and active regions. This point defines the lower end of the common-mode range, which is

$$V_{IC} > V_{t1} + V_{t3} + V_{ov3} - V_{SS} \tag{6.75}$$

If $V_{IC}$ is too high, however, $M_5$ operates in the triode region. The drain-source voltage of $M_5$ is

$$V_{DS5} = V_{IC} - V_{GS1} - V_{DD} = V_{IC} - V_{t1} - V_{ov1} - V_{DD} \tag{6.76}$$

From the standpoint of drain-source voltages, $n$-channel transistors operate in the active region only if their drain-source voltage is more than their overdrive. On the other hand, $p$-channel transistors operate in the active region only if their drain-source voltage is less than their overdrive. Therefore, the upper end of the common-mode input range is

$$V_{IC} < V_{t1} + V_{ov1} + V_{ov5} + V_{DD} \tag{6.77}$$

Since $M_1$ and $M_5$ are $p$-channel transistors, their overdrives are negative; that is, their gate-source voltages must be less than their thresholds for the channel to exist at the source. Furthermore, if $M_1$ is an enhancement-mode device, its threshold is negative because it is $p$-type. Under this assumption, the common-mode range limits in (6.75) and (6.77) can be rewritten as

$$V_{t3} - |V_{t1}| + V_{ov3} - V_{SS} < V_{IC} < V_{DD} - |V_{t1}| - |V_{ov1}| - |V_{ov5}| \tag{6.78}$$

This inequality shows that the magnitudes of the overdrive terms should be minimized to maximize the common-mode range. Also, the body effect on the input transistors can be used to increase the range. If the bodies of $M_1$ and $M_2$ are connected to $V_{DD}$ as implied in Fig. 6.16, the source-body voltage of these transistors is low when $V_{IC}$ is high. Therefore, the upper limit in (6.78) can be found approximately by using the zero-bias value of $V_{t1}$. On the other hand, when $V_{IC}$ decreases, the source-body voltage of $M_1$ and $M_2$ becomes more negative, widening the depletion region around the source and making the threshold voltage of these transistors more negative. Therefore, the body effect can be used to include the negative supply in the common-mode range.

■  **EXAMPLE**

For the two-stage CMOS op amp in Fig. 6.16, choose the device sizes to give a dc voltage gain greater than 5000 and a peak output swing of at least 1 V. Use the 0.4 μm CMOS model parameters in Table 2.4. Use bias currents of $|I_{D1}| = |I_{D2}| = 100~\mu A$, and $I_{D6} = 400~\mu A$. Assume $V_{DD} = V_{SS} = 1.65~V \pm 0.15~V$. Assume perfect matching and that all transistors operate in the active (or saturation) region with dc voltages $V_{IC} = 0$ (where $V_{IC}$ is the common-mode input voltage), $V_I = 0$ and $V_O \approx 0$. Ignore the body effect.

To simplify the design, a drawn channel length $L = 1~\mu m$ will be used for all transistors. This selection avoids short-channel effects that degrade output resistance and cause transistor operation to deviate from the square-law equations.

Since the peak output swing should be 1 V and the magnitude of each supply is at least 1.5 V, (6.61) shows that

$$V_{ov6} = |V_{ov7}| \leq 0.5~V$$

To maximize the transition frequency $f_T$ of each device subject to this constraint, we will choose $V_{ov6} = |V_{ov7}| = 0.5~V$. Using (1.157) with $|I_{D7}| = I_{D6} = 400~\mu A$ gives

$$\left(\frac{W}{L}\right)_7 = \frac{2|I_{D7}|}{k'_p(V_{ov7})^2} = \frac{2(400)}{64.7(-0.5)^2} \approx 50$$

and

$$\left(\frac{W}{L}\right)_6 = \frac{2I_{D6}}{k'_n(V_{ov6})^2} = \frac{2(400)}{194(0.5)^2} \approx 16$$

Since $V_{ov5} = V_{ov7}$ by KVL and $I_{D1} + I_{D2} = I_{D7}/2$,

$$\left(\frac{W}{L}\right)_5 = \frac{1}{2}\left(\frac{W}{L}\right)_7 \approx 25$$

From (6.66),

$$\left(\frac{W}{L}\right)_3 = \left(\frac{W}{L}\right)_4 = \frac{1}{2}\frac{(W/L)_5}{(W/L)_7}(W/L)_6 \approx \frac{1}{2}\left(\frac{25}{50}\right)16 = 4$$

Since the common-mode input range should include $V_{IC} = 0$, the allowed overdrives on $M_1$ and $M_2$ are limited by (6.77), and rearranging this equation with $V_{IC} = 0$ and $V_{DD} = 1.5~V$ gives

$$V_{ov1} > V_{IC} - V_{t1} - V_{ov5} - V_{DD} = 0 - (-0.8~V) - (-0.5~V) - 1.5~V = -0.2~V$$

Therefore,

$$\left(\frac{W}{L}\right)_1 = \left(\frac{W}{L}\right)_2 > \frac{2|I_{D1}|}{k'_p(V_{ov1})^2} = \frac{2(100)}{64.7(-0.2)^2} \approx 77$$

From (6.59) and (6.60) with $L_{eff} \approx L_{drwn} - 2L_d$, and using data from Table 2.4,

$$A_v = -\frac{2}{|V_{ov1}|}\frac{2}{V_{ov6}}\left(\frac{|V_{A2}|V_{A4}}{|V_{A2}| + V_{A4}}\right)\left(\frac{V_{A6}|V_{A7}|}{V_{A6} + |V_{A7}|}\right)$$

$$= -\frac{2}{0.2}\frac{2}{0.5}\left(\frac{\dfrac{0.82}{0.04} \times \dfrac{0.82}{0.02}}{\dfrac{0.82}{0.04} + \dfrac{0.82}{0.02}}\right)^2 \approx -7500$$

This calculation assumes that $dX_d/dV_{DS}$ and $L_{eff}$ are constant for each type of transistor, allowing us to use constant Early voltages. In practice, however, $dX_d/dV_{DS}$ and $L_{eff}$

both depend on the operating point, and accurate values of the Early voltages are rarely available to circuit designers when channel lengths are less than about 1.5 μm. As a result, circuit simulations are an important part of the design process. SPICE simulation of the op amp under the conditions described above gives a gain of about 6200, which shows that ■ the hand calculations are accurate within about 20 percent.

### 6.3.6 Power-Supply Rejection Ratio (PSRR)

To calculate the PSRR from the $V_{dd}$ supply for the op amp in Fig. 6.16, we will divide the small-signal gain $A^+ = v_o/v_{dd}$ into the gain from the input. For this calculation, assume that the $V_{ss}$ supply voltage is constant and that both op-amp inputs in Fig. 6.16 are connected to small-signal grounds. The current in $M_8$ is equal to $I_{BIAS}$. If this current is constant, the gate-source voltage of $M_8$ must be constant because $M_8$ is diode connected. Therefore, $v_{gs8} = v_{gs5} = v_{gs7} = 0$, and the $g_m$ generators in $M_5$ and $M_7$ are inactive. As a result, if $r_{o5} = r_{tail} \to \infty$ and $r_{o7} \to \infty$, $v_o/v_{dd} = 0$. To find the gain with finite $r_{tail}$ and $r_{o7}$, consider the small-signal diagrams shown in Fig. 6.18, where the $g_m$ generators for $M_5$ and $M_7$ are omitted because they are inactive. In Fig. 6.18a, the output is defined as $v_{oa}$, and the $v_{dd}$ supply variation is set equal to zero at the point where $r_{tail}$ is connected. In Fig. 6.18b, the output is defined as $v_{ob}$, and the $v_{dd}$ supply variation is set equal to zero at the point where $r_{o7}$ is connected. We will find $v_{oa}$ and $v_{ob}$ separately and use superposition to find the total gain $v_o/v_{dd} = (v_{oa} + v_{ob})/v_{dd}$.

In Fig. 6.18a, the first stage experiences no variation, and $v_{gs6} = 0$. Therefore, $g_{m6}$ is inactive, and the output stage appears as a simple voltage divider to the supply variation. Since the dc drain current in $M_6$ is equal and opposite to that in $M_7$,

$$\frac{v_{oa}}{v_{dd}} = \frac{r_{o6}}{r_{o6} + r_{o7}} = \frac{\dfrac{V_{A6}}{I_{D6}}}{\dfrac{V_{A6}}{I_{D6}} + \dfrac{|V_{A7}|}{I_{D6}}} = \frac{V_{A6}}{V_{A6} + |V_{A7}|} \tag{6.79}$$

**Figure 6.18** Small-signal diagrams of the two-stage op amp used to calculate the coupling from $v_{dd}$ to the output (a) through the second stage and (b) through the first stage.

In Fig. 6.18$b$,

$$\frac{v_{ob}}{v_{dd}} = \frac{v_{gs6}}{v_{dd}} \frac{v_{ob}}{v_{gs6}} \qquad (6.80)$$

where the first term on the right side represents the gain of the first stage, and the second term represents the gain of the second stage. The $v_{dd}$ input to the first stage in Fig. 6.18$b$ is applied between the top of $r_{tail}$ and ground while the gates of $M_1$ and $M_2$ are grounded. This situation is equivalent to grounding the top of $r_{tail}$ and applying a voltage of $-v_{dd}$ between the gates of $M_1$ and $M_2$ and ground. In other words, the $v_{dd}$ input in Fig. 6.18$b$ appears as a common-mode input $v_{ic} = -v_{dd}$ to the first stage. Therefore, the gain of the first stage can be expressed as

$$\frac{v_{gs6}}{v_{dd}} = -\frac{v_{gs6}}{v_{ic}} = -G_m[cm]R_{o1} \qquad (6.81)$$

where $G_m[cm]$ is the common-mode transconductance of the first stage and $R_{o1}$ is the output resistance of the first stage. Substituting (4.149), (4.166), (4.173), and (4.179) into (6.81) gives

$$\frac{v_{gs6}}{v_{dd}} \simeq \frac{g_{m(dp)}(r_{o(dp)}\|r_{o(mir)})}{1 + 2g_{m(dp)}r_{tail}} \left( \frac{1}{1 + g_{m(mir)}r_{o(dp)}} + \frac{1}{1 + g_{m(mir)}r_{o(mir)}} \right) \qquad (6.82)$$

If $2g_{m(dp)}r_{tail} \gg 1$, $g_{m(mir)}r_{o(dp)} \gg 1$, and $g_{m(mir)}r_{o(mir)} \gg 1$,

$$\frac{v_{gs6}}{v_{dd}} \simeq \frac{r_{o(dp)}\|r_{o(mir)}}{2r_{tail}g_{m(mir)}(r_{o(dp)}\|r_{o(mir)})} = \frac{1}{2g_{m(mir)}r_{tail}} \qquad (6.83)$$

Substituting (6.83), (6.55), and (6.52) into (6.80) gives

$$\frac{v_{ob}}{v_{dd}} \simeq -\frac{g_{m6}(r_{o6}\|r_{o7})}{2g_{m(mir)}r_{tail}} \qquad (6.84)$$

If $V_{ov3} = V_{ov6}$ as in (6.62) to control the systematic offset, $g_{m6}/g_{m(mir)} = I_{D6}/I_{D3}$. Since the dc drain current in $M_6$ is equal and opposite to that in $M_7$,

$$\frac{v_{ob}}{v_{dd}} \simeq -\frac{I_{D6}}{2I_{D3}} \left( \frac{\dfrac{V_{A6}}{I_{D6}}\dfrac{|V_{A7}|}{I_{D6}}}{\dfrac{V_{A6}}{I_{D6}} + \dfrac{|V_{A7}|}{I_{D6}}} \right) \frac{|I_{D5}|}{|V_{A5}|} = -\frac{|I_{D5}|}{2I_{D3}} \left( \frac{V_{A6}}{V_{A6} + |V_{A7}|} \right) \frac{|V_{A7}|}{|V_{A5}|} \qquad (6.85)$$

$$= -\frac{V_{A6}}{V_{A6} + V_{A7}}$$

because $V_{A5} = V_{A7}$ and $|I_{D5}| = 2I_{D3}$. Combining (6.79) and (6.85) gives

$$A^+ = \frac{v_o}{v_{dd}} = \frac{v_{oa} + v_{ob}}{v_{dd}} \simeq 0 \qquad (6.86)$$

Therefore, from (6.51), $\mathrm{PSRR}^+ \to \infty$ for low frequencies with perfect matching because the coupling from $v_{dd}$ to the output through the first stage cancels that through the second stage. In practice, mismatch can increase the common-mode transconductance of the first stage as shown at the end of Section 4.3.5.3, disrupting this cancellation and decreasing the low-frequency $\mathrm{PSRR}^+$.

To calculate the PSRR from the $V_{ss}$ supply for the op amp in Fig. 6.16, we will calculate the small-signal gain $A^- = v_o/v_{ss}$ and then normalize to the gain from the input.

For this calculation, assume that the $V_{dd}$ supply voltage is constant and that both op-amp inputs in Fig. 6.16 are connected to small-signal grounds. Under these conditions, $M_1$ and $M_2$ act as common-gate amplifiers, attempting to keep the bias current in $M_3$ and $M_4$ constant. If the drain current of $M_3$ is constant, the gate-source voltage of $M_3$ must be constant because $M_3$ is diode connected. Therefore, $v_{gs3} = 0$. Since $v_{ds3} = v_{gs3}$, and since $v_{ds4} = v_{ds3}$ under these conditions, $v_{ds4} = v_{gs6} = 0$. Therefore, $g_{m6}$ is inactive, and the output stage appears as a simple voltage divider to the supply variation. Since the drain current in $M_6$ is equal and opposite to that in $M_7$,

$$A^- = \frac{v_o}{v_{ss}} = \frac{r_{o7}}{r_{o6} + r_{o7}} = \frac{\dfrac{|V_{A7}|}{I_{D6}}}{\dfrac{V_{A6}}{I_{D6}} + \dfrac{|V_{A7}|}{I_{D6}}} = \frac{|V_{A7}|}{V_{A6} + |V_{A7}|} \tag{6.87}$$

Substituting (6.59) and (6.87) into (6.51) gives

$$\text{PSRR}^- = \frac{A_{dm}}{A^-} = \frac{\dfrac{v_o}{v_{id}}}{\dfrac{v_o}{v_{ss}}} = -\frac{2}{|V_{ov1}|}\frac{2}{V_{ov6}}\left(\frac{|V_{A2}|V_{A4}}{|V_{A2}| + V_{A4}}\right)V_{A6} \tag{6.88}$$

This equation gives the low-frequency supply rejection from the negative supply. This rejection worsens as frequency increases. The topic of frequency response is covered in detail in Chapters 7 and 9, but the essence of this behavior can be understood without a complete frequency-response analysis. As the applied frequency increases, the impedance of the compensation capacitor $C_C$ in Fig. 6.16 decreases, effectively shorting the gate of $M_6$ to its drain for high-frequency ac signals. If the gate-source voltage on $M_6$ is constant, the variation on the negative supply is fed directly to the output at high frequencies. Therefore, $A^- \simeq 1$ at frequencies high enough to short circuit $C_C$, assuming that $C_C \gg C_L$, where $C_L$ is the load capacitance of the op amp connected between the op-amp output and ground. The same phenomenon causes the gains $A_{dm}$ and $A^+$ to decrease as frequency increases, so that the PSRR$^+$ remains relatively constant with increasing frequency. Since $A^-$ increases to unity as $A_{dm}$ decreases, however, PSRR$^-$ decreases and reaches unity at the frequency where $|A_{dm}| = 1$.

**Power-Supply Rejection and Supply Capacitance.** Another important contribution to nonzero gain between the power supplies and the op-amp output is termed supply capacitance.[7,8] This phenomenon manifests itself as a capacitive coupling between one or both of the power supplies and the op-amp input leads when the op amp is connected with capacitive feedback $C_I$ as shown in Fig. 6.19. For simplicity, assume that the op-amp open-loop gain is infinite. If the supply-coupling capacitance is $C_{\text{sup}}$, the gain from $C_{\text{sup}}$ to the op-amp output is $-C_{\text{sup}}/C_I$. Figure 6.19 shows two possible sources of supply capacitance, which are the gate-drain and gate-source capacitance of $M_1$. Four important ways in which supply capacitance can occur are described below.

1. If the drain current of $M_3$ is constant, a variation on $V_{ss}$ causes the voltage from the drain of $M_1$ to ground to vary to hold the gate-source voltage of $M_3$ constant. This variation couples to the summing node through the gate-drain capacitance of $M_1$; that is, the supply capacitance $C_{\text{sup}} = C_{gd1}$. This problem is usually overcome by the use of cascode transistors in series with the drains of the input transistors.

2. A variation on $V_{dd}$ or $V_{ss}$ causes the current flowing in the tail current source to vary. To understand the effect of this bias-current variation, consider Fig. 6.20a, which shows a

**Figure 6.19** Supply capacitance in a two-stage MOS amplifier with capacitive feedback.

$p$-channel source follower whose biasing current source $I_{\text{tail}} = I_{\text{TAIL}} + i_{\text{tail}}$ is not constant. The source follower models the behavior of $M_1$ in Fig. 6.19 from the standpoint of variation in $I_{\text{tail}}$ for two reasons. First, the voltage from the gate of $M_1$ to ground is held to small-signal ground by negative feedback. Second, MOS transistors that operate in the active region are controlled mainly by their gate-source voltages. For simplicity, ignore the body effect because it is not needed to demonstrate the problem here. The small-signal diagram of the source follower is shown in Fig. 6.20$b$. From KCL at the source,

$$i_{\text{tail}} = g_m v_s + \frac{v_s}{r_o} \tag{6.89}$$

Rearranging this equation gives

$$v_s = \frac{i_{\text{tail}} r_o}{1 + g_m r_o} \approx \frac{i_{\text{tail}}}{g_m} \tag{6.90}$$

Therefore, nonzero $i_{\text{tail}}$ arising from supply variations causes nonzero $v_s$ in the source follower. Similarly, in Fig. 6.19, the voltage from the source of $M_1$ to ground varies

**Figure 6.20** (a) Source follower and (b) small-signal diagram to calculate the dependence of $v_s$ on $i_{\text{tail}}$.

with $I_{\text{tail}}$, and this variation couples to the summing node through the gate-source capacitance of $M_1$; that is, the supply capacitance $C_{\text{sup}} = C_{gs1}$. A supply-independent bias reference is usually used to overcome this problem.

3. If the substrate terminal of the input transistors is connected to a supply or a supply-related voltage, then the substrate bias changes as the supply voltage changes. In turn, substrate bias variation changes the threshold through the body effect, which changes the gate-source voltage. Again, this mechanism can be studied with the help of a source follower, as shown in Fig. 6.21a. Here $I_{\text{TAIL}}$ is assumed to be constant, but $V_{dd} = V_{DD} + v_{dd}$ is assumed to vary. The small-signal diagram is shown in Fig. 6.21b. From KCL at the source,

$$g_{mb}v_{dd} = g_m v_s + g_{mb}v_s + \frac{v_s}{r_o} \tag{6.91}$$

Rearranging this equation gives

$$v_s = \frac{g_{mb}r_o}{1 + (g_m + g_{mb})r_o}v_{dd} \simeq \frac{g_{mb}}{g_m + g_{mb}}v_{dd} \tag{6.92}$$

Therefore, nonzero $v_{dd}$ in the source follower in Fig. 6.21 causes nonzero $v_s$. Similarly, in Fig. 6.19, the voltage from the source of $M_1$ to ground varies with $V_{dd}$, and this variation couples to the summing node through the gate-source capacitance of $M_1$; that is, the supply capacitance $C_{\text{sup}} = C_{gs1}$.

A solution to this problem is to place the input transistors in a well and connect the well to the sources of the input transistors to eliminate the body effect. This solution has two potential disadvantages. First, it disallows the use of the body effect on the input devices to increase the common-mode input range of the op amp, as described in Section 6.3.5. Second, this solution dictates the polarity of the input transistors in a given process. For example, in a $p$-well process, the input devices must be $n$-channel devices to place them in a $p$ well. This requirement might conflict with the polarity of the input transistors that would be chosen for other reasons. For example, $p$-channel input transistors would be used to minimize the input-referred flicker noise. (See Chapter 11.)

4. Interconnect crossovers in the op-amp and system layout can produce undesired capacitive coupling between the supplies and the summing node. In this case, the supply capacitance is a parasitic or undesired capacitance. This problem is usually overcome

Figure 6.21  (a) Source follower and (b) small-signal diagram to calculate the dependence of $v_s$ on $v_{dd}$ through the body effect.

with careful layout. In particular, one important layout technique is to shield the op-amp inputs with metal lines connected to ground.

The result of supply capacitance can be quite poor power-supply rejection in switched-capacitor filters and other sampled-data analog circuits that use capacitive feedback. In addition to the solutions to this problem mentioned above, another solution is to use fully differential op amps, which have two outputs. The output voltage of interest is the voltage difference between these outputs. Fully differential op amps, which are considered in Chapter 12, overcome the supply capacitance problem to the extent that the coupling from a given supply to one output is the same as to the other output.

### 6.3.7 Effect of Overdrive Voltages

The overdrive of a MOS transistor can be reduced by reducing the ratio of its drain current to its $W/L$. Reducing the overdrive voltages in the op amp in Fig. 6.16 improves the op-amp performance by increasing the voltage gain as shown by (6.59), increasing the swing as shown by (6.61), reducing the input offset voltage as shown by (6.69), increasing the CMRR as shown by (6.72), increasing the common-mode range as shown by (6.78), and increasing the power-supply rejection ratio as shown by (6.88). These observations are valid provided that the transistors in the op amp operate in strong inversion. Also, increasing the channel lengths increases the corresponding Early voltages as shown by (1.163), and thereby increases the op-amp gain, common-mode rejection ratio, and power-supply rejection ratio as shown by (6.59), (6.72), and (6.88). Unfortunately, the transition frequency of MOS transistors is proportional to the overdrive and inversely proportional to the square of the channel length from (1.209). Therefore, reducing overdrives and increasing the channel lengths degrades the frequency response of the transistors and in turn the amplifier. Thus we find a fundamental trade-off between the frequency response and the other measures of performance in CMOS op-amp design.

### 6.3.8 Layout Considerations

A basic objective in op-amp design is to minimize the mismatch between the two signal paths in the input differential pair so that common-mode input signals are rejected to the greatest possible extent. Mismatch affects the performance of the differential pair not only at dc, where it causes nonzero offset voltage, but also at high frequencies where it reduces the common-mode and power-supply rejection ratios.

Figure 6.22a shows a possible layout of a differential pair. Five nodes are labeled: two gates, two drains, and one source. Connections to each region are omitted for simplicity. The sources of the two transistors are connected to each other by merging the two sources together into one diffusion region. Although such a layout saves area and minimizes undesired capacitance connected to the sources, this layout is not optimum from the standpoint of matching in part because it is sensitive to alignment shifts between masks that define various layers in an integrated circuit. The key problem is that the layout in Fig. 6.22a uses only *mirror* symmetry in the sense that each transistor is a mirror image of the other. For example, suppose that two additional grounded segments of metal are added to the layout to produce the layout shown in Fig. 6.22b. In exactly these locations, the parasitic capacitance $C_{P1}$ from $D_1$ to ground is equal to the parasitic capacitance $C_{P2}$ from $D_2$ to ground. However, if the mask that defines the metal shifts to the right compared to the mask that defines the diffusion, $C_{P1}$ increases but $C_{P2}$ decreases, creating mismatch. In

Figure 6.22  Differential-pair layouts with mirror symmetry.

practice, balancing the parasitics in a way that is insensitive to alignment shifts is most important in amplifiers that have both differential inputs and differential outputs. Such amplifiers are considered in Chapter 12.

Figure 6.23 shows layouts that overcome these problems. In Fig. 6.23a-b, the transistors are drawn using translational symmetry; that is, each transistor is a copy of the other without rotation. Another option is shown in Fig. 6.23c, where each transistor has been split into two pieces. To maintain the same width/length ratio as in the previous drawings, the width of each transistor in Fig. 6.23c has been reduced by a factor of two. This structure has both translational and mirror symmetry. Structures with translational symmetry are insensitive to alignment shifts.

One limitation of these layouts is that they are sensitive to process gradients perpendicular to the line of symmetry. For example, in Fig. 6.23c, suppose the oxide thickness increases from left to right. Then the gate stripes connected to $G_1$ have thinner oxide than those connected to $G_2$, causing the transistors to have unequal thresholds and unequal transconductance parameters. The effects of process-related gradients across the die can be partially alleviated by use of common-centroid geometries. Figure 6.24 shows a common-centroid layout of the differential pair. Each side of the differential pair is split into two components that are cross connected in the layout. In a geometric sense, the centroid of both composite devices lies at center of the structure. Because any gradient can be decomposed into horizontal and vertical components, this layout overcomes the effect of linear process gradients in any direction.

Figure 6.24 also shows two layers of metal used to cross connect the devices. One layer of metal is drawn with solid lines. The other is drawn with dashed lines. The two

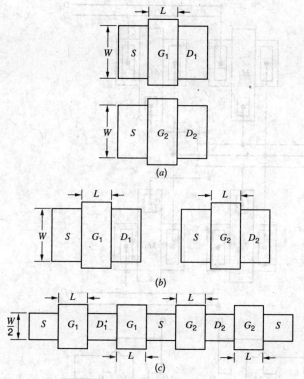

**Figure 6.23** Differential-pair layouts with translational symmetry.

layers connect at intersections only where dots are drawn. The interconnect drawn here is shift insensitive and balanced in the sense that any signal line that crosses a node on one side of the differential pair also crosses the corresponding node on the other side. This balance helps to keep undesired signals in common-mode form so they can be rejected by the differential pair. Finally, the only line that crosses the metal connected to the two input gates is the metal line to the sources of the differential pair. This characteristic is important because such crossings create a small parasitic capacitance between the two layers that cross, and can allow undesired signals to couple to the op-amp inputs. Since op amps are designed to have high gain, op-amp inputs are the most sensitive nodes in analog integrated circuits. Therefore, if any signal line is allowed to cross one gate, it should also cross the other to balance the parasitic capacitances. Since the parasitics may not be perfectly matched in practice, however, avoiding crossings is better than balancing them. In Fig. 6.24, the gates are allowed to cross the source of the differential pair because the transistors themselves already provide a large capacitance between each gate and the source in the form of the gate-source capacitance of each transistor.

A disadvantage of common-centroid layouts is also apparent in Fig. 6.24. That is, the need to cross-connect the devices increases the separation between matched devices and may worsen matching in cases where linear process gradients are not the main limitation. Therefore, the value of a common-centroid layout must be determined on a case-by-case basis.

**Figure 6.24** Common-centroid structure for the MOS differential pair.

## 6.4 Two-Stage MOS Operational Amplifiers with Cascodes

The basic two-stage op amp described above is widely used with many variations that optimize certain aspects of the performance. In this section, we consider an important variation on the basic circuit to increase the voltage gain.

The voltage gain that is available from the basic circuit shown in Fig. 6.16 may be inadequate in a given application to achieve the required accuracy in the closed-loop gain. For example, suppose the basic op amp uses transistors with $g_m r_o = 20$ and is connected in the voltage-follower configuration shown in Fig. 6.3c. The op-amp gain is given in (6.56) and is less than $(g_m r_o)^2$ in practice. For simplicity, assume that the op-amp gain is about $(g_m r_o)^2$, or 400 in this case. The closed-loop gain is given by (6.12) and is approximately unity because $R_2 = 0$ in the follower configuration. The error in this approximation is one part in the op-amp gain or at least 0.25 percent. In precision applications, this error may be too large to meet the given specifications, requiring an increase in the op-amp gain.

One approach to increasing the op-amp gain is to add another common-source gain stage to the op amp so that the overall gain is approximately $(g_m r_o)^3$ instead of $(g_m r_o)^2$. An important problem with this approach, however, stems from the fact that op amps are intended to be used in negative-feedback configurations. In practice, op-amp frequency response is not constant. If the op amp introduces an additional phase shift of 180° at some frequency, the negative feedback that was intended becomes positive feedback at that frequency, and the op amp may be unstable. The topics of frequency response and stability are covered in detail in Chapters 7 and 9, respectively. The key point here is that if an op amp is unstable in a given feedback configuration, it does not act as an amplifier but as a latch or oscillator. To avoid this problem, op amps are usually designed with no more than two gain stages because each stage contains a node for which the impedance to ground is high and as a result contributes a significant pole to the op-amp transfer function. Since the phase shift from one pole approaches −90° asymptotically, an op amp with no more than two poles cannot provide the 180° phase shift that is required to convert negative feedback into positive feedback.

To increase the voltage gain without adding another common-source gain stage, common-gate transistors can be added. Together with a common-source transistor, a common-gate transistor forms a cascode that increases the output resistance and gain of the stage while contributing a less significant pole to the amplifier transfer function than would be contributed by another common-source stage. Figure 6.25 illustrates the use of cascodes to increase the voltage gain of a two-stage amplifier. Here, a series connection of two transistors, one in the common-source connection and one in the common-gate connection, replace each common-source transistor in the first stage. Therefore, $M_1$ and $M_{1A}$ in Fig. 6.25 replace $M_1$ in Fig. 6.16. Similarly, $M_2$ and $M_{2A}$ in Fig. 6.25 replace $M_2$ in Fig. 6.16. Transistor $M_9$ and current source $I_C$ have also been added to bias the gates of $M_{1A}$ and $M_{2A}$. In practice, the $W/L$ of $M_9$ is chosen so that $M_1$ and $M_2$ are operated barely in the active region. The effect of these replacements is to increase the unloaded output impedance of the differential pair by a factor that is approximately equal to $g_m r_o$ of the cascode device.

If the current mirror $M_3 - M_4$ were not also cascoded, however, the output resistance of the first stage including the current-mirror load would be limited by the mirror. To overcome this limitation, a cascode current mirror shown in Fig. 4.9 is used instead. As a result,

**Figure 6.25** Two-stage amplifier with cascoded first stage.

the stage gain and output resistance including the load are increased by approximately a factor $g_m r_o$. In this circuit, $M_{10}$ and $M_{11}$ are included to level shift the output of the first stage down by $V_{GS10}$ so that the second stage input is driven by a signal whose dc level is $V_{GS3}$ above $-V_{SS}$. If the aspect ratios are chosen to satisfy (6.66), and if each common-gate transistor is identical to its common-source counterpart, the systematic offset voltage with this level shift is given by (6.68), where the op-amp gain here is on the order of $(g_m r_o)^3$ instead of $(g_m r_o)^2$ in Fig. 6.16. One disadvantage of this circuit is a substantial reduction in the common-mode input range. (See Problem 6.16.) To overcome this problem, cascoding could be added instead to the second stage. In that case, however, the output swing of the op amp would be degraded by the cascodes.

## 6.5  MOS Telescopic-Cascode Operational Amplifiers

As mentioned in the previous section, cascode configurations may be used to increase the voltage gain of CMOS transistor amplifier stages. In many applications, the stage gain can be increased enough so that a single common-source–common-gate stage can provide enough voltage gain to meet the accuracy requirements. The first stage of Fig. 6.25 is sometimes used by itself as an op amp and provides a gain comparable to the gain of the two-stage op-amp in Fig. 6.16. This structure has been called a *telescopic-cascode* op amp[9] because the cascodes are connected between the power supplies in series with the transistors in the differential pair, resulting in a structure in which the transistors in each branch are connected along a straight line like the lenses of a refracting telescope. The main potential advantage of telescopic cascode op amps is that they can be designed so that the signal variations are entirely handled by the fastest-polarity transistors in a given process. Such designs use fully differential configurations and are considered in Chapter 12.

In addition to the poor common-mode input range calculated in Problem 6.16, another disadvantage of the telescopic-cascode configuration is that the output swing is small. For example, ignore $M_6$, $M_7$, $M_{10}$, $M_{11}$, and $C_C$ in Fig. 6.25 and define the dc op-amp output voltage as the voltage $V_{O1}$ from the drains of $M_{2A}$ and $M_{4A}$ to ground. For simplicity, assume that all transistors are enhancement mode with identical overdrive magnitudes. To calculate the output swing, first consider the cascode current mirror by itself. If $V_{SS} = 0$, the minimum output voltage for which $M_4$ and $M_{4A}$ operate in the active region would be given by (4.59). With nonzero $V_{SS}$, this condition becomes

$$V_{O1(min)} = -V_{SS} + V_{tn} + 2V_{ov} \tag{6.93}$$

The presence of a threshold term in this equation is an important limitation because it causes a substantial reduction in the allowed output swing. Fortunately, this limitation can be overcome by using one of the high-swing cascode current mirrors shown in Figs. 4.11 and 4.12, which would eliminate the threshold term from (6.93) and give

$$V_{O1(min)} = -V_{SS} + 2V_{ov} \tag{6.94}$$

With this change, we can see that to achieve a gain comparable to $(g_m r_o)^2$ in one stage, the swing is limited at best to two overdrives away from the supply. In contrast, the basic two-stage op amp in Fig. 6.16 gives about the same gain but allows the output to swing within one overdrive of each supply, as shown by (6.61).

To find the maximum output voltage swing of the telescopic-cascode op amp, consider the cascoded differential pair shown in Fig. 6.25. Assume that the common-mode input from the gates of $M_1$ and $M_2$ to ground is $V_{IC}$. The voltage from the source of $M_1$ and $M_2$ to ground is

$$V_S = V_{IC} + |V_{tp}| + |V_{ov}| \tag{6.95}$$

To operate $M_5$ in the active region, its source-drain voltage should be at least $|V_{ov}|$. Therefore,

$$V_{DD} - V_S \geq |V_{ov}| \tag{6.96}$$

Substituting (6.95) into (6.96) and rearranging gives

$$V_{IC} \leq V_{DD} - |V_{tp}| - 2|V_{ov}| \tag{6.97}$$

If we assume that $M_9$ and $I_C$ are chosen to operate $M_1$ and $M_2$ at the edge of the active region, the maximum output voltage for which $M_2$ and $M_{2A}$ operate in the active region is

$$V_{O1(max)} = V_S - 2|V_{ov}| \tag{6.98}$$

Substituting (6.95) into (6.98) gives

$$V_{O1(max)} = V_{IC} + |V_{tp}| - |V_{ov}| \tag{6.99}$$

This equation shows another limitation of the telescopic-cascode op amp from the standpoint of output swing; that is, the maximum output voltage depends on the common-mode input. However, this limitation as well as the limitation on the common-mode input range calculated in Problem 6.16 can be overcome in switched-capacitor circuits. Such circuits allow the op-amp common-mode input voltage to be set to a level that is independent of all other common-mode voltages on the same integrated circuit. This property holds because the only coupling of signals to the op-amp inputs is through capacitors, which conduct zero dc current even with a nonzero dc voltage drop. Assuming that the op-amp inputs are biased to the maximum common-mode input voltage for which $M_5$ operates in the active region, the maximum output voltage can be found by substituting the maximum $V_{IC}$ from (6.97) into (6.99), which gives

$$V_{O1(max)} = V_{DD} - 3|V_{ov}| \tag{6.100}$$

This equation shows that the maximum output voltage of a telescopic op amp that consists of the first stage of Fig. 6.25 with optimum common-mode input biasing is three overdrives less than the positive supply. This result stems from the observation that three transistors ($M_5$, $M_2$, and $M_{2A}$) are connected between $V_{DD}$ and the output. In contrast, (6.94) shows that the minimum output swing is limited by two overdrives.

To determine the minimum required supply voltage difference, we will subtract (6.94) from (6.100), which gives

$$V_{O1(max)} - V_{O1(min)} = V_{DD} - (-V_{SS}) - 5|V_{ov}| \tag{6.101}$$

assuming that the magnitudes of all the overdrives are all equal. Rearranging this equation gives

$$V_{DD} - (-V_{SS}) = V_{O1(max)} - V_{O1(min)} + 5|V_{ov}| \tag{6.102}$$

This equation shows that the minimum difference between the supply voltages in a telescopic cascode op amp must be at least equal to the peak-to-peak output signal swing plus five overdrive voltages to operate all transistors in the active region. For example, with a peak-to-peak output swing of 1 V and $|V_{ov}| = 100$ mV for each transistor, the minimum difference between the supply voltages is 1.5 V.

In practice, this calculation has two main limitations. First, if transistors are deliberately biased at the edge of the active region, a small change in the process, supply, or temperature may cause one or more transistors to operate in the triode region, reducing the output resistance and gain of the op amp. To avoid this problem, transistors in practical op amps are usually biased so that the magnitude of the drain-source voltage of each transistor is more than the corresponding overdrive by a margin of typically at least one hundred millivolts. The margin allowed for each transistor directly adds to the minimum required supply voltage difference. Second, this calculation determines the supply requirements only for transistors between the output node and each supply, and other branches may require a larger supply difference than given in (6.102). For example, consider the path from one supply to the other through $M_5$, $M_1$, $M_{1A}$, $M_{3A}$, and $M_3$ in Fig. 6.25. Ignore the body effect for simplicity. Since $M_{3A}$ and $M_3$ are diode connected, the drain-source voltage of each is $V_t + V_{ov}$. Furthermore, if the $W/L$ of $M_{3A}$ is reduced by a factor of four to build the high-swing cascode current mirror shown in Fig. 4.11, the voltage drop from the drain of $M_{3A}$ to the source of $M_3$ is $2V_t + 3V_{ov}$. If the other three transistors in this path are biased so that $|V_{DS}| = |V_{ov}|$, the required supply difference for all the transistors in this path to operate in the active region is $2V_t + 6|V_{ov}|$. This requirement exceeds the requirement given in (6.102) if $2V_t + |V_{ov}|$ is more than the peak-to-peak output swing. However, this result does not pose a fundamental limitation to the minimum required power-supply voltage because low-threshold devices are sometimes available.

The minimum supply voltage difference in (6.102) includes five overdrive terms. In contrast, the corresponding equation for the op amp in Fig. 6.16 would include only two overdrive terms, one for $M_6$ and the other for $M_7$. The presence of the three extra overdrive terms increases the minimum required supply difference or reduces the allowed overdrives for a given supply difference. The extra three overdrive terms in (6.102) stem from the two cascode devices and the tail current source. The overdrives from the cascodes should be viewed as the cost of using cascodes; however, the overdrive of the tail current source can be eliminated from the minimum required supply difference using the circuit described in the next section.

## 6.6 MOS Folded-Cascode Operational Amplifiers

Figure 6.26 shows two cascode circuits where $V_{DD} = 0$ for simplicity. In Fig. 6.26a, both $M_1$ and $M_{1A}$ are p-channel devices. In Fig. 6.26b, $M_1$ is still a p-channel device but $M_{1A}$

**Figure 6.26** (a) Standard cascode configuration. (b) Folded-cascode configuration.

is now an $n$-channel device. In both cases, however, $M_1$ is connected in a common-source configuration, and $M_{1A}$ is connected in a common-gate configuration. Small-signal variations in the drain current of $M_1$ are conducted primarily through $M_{1A}$ in both cases because $I_{BIAS}$ is a constant current source. Therefore, both circuits are examples of cascodes. The cascode in Fig. 6.26b is said to be *folded* in the sense that it reverses the direction of the signal flow back toward ground. This reversal has two main advantages when used with a differential pair. First, it increases the output swing. Second, it increases the common-mode input range.

Figure 6.27 shows a simplified schematic of a circuit that applies the folded-cascode structure to both sides of a differential pair. As in Fig. 6.26b, $M_1$ and $M_{1A}$ form one cascode structure in Fig. 6.27. Also, $M_2$ and $M_{2A}$ form another. The current mirror converts the differential signal into a single-ended output by sending variations in the drain current of $M_{1A}$ to the output. The resulting op amp is called a *folded-cascode op amp*.[5,10] A complete schematic is shown in Fig. 6.28. Bias is realized by making the currents in current sources $M_{11}$ and $M_{12}$ larger than $|I_{D5}|/2$. Thus

$$I_{D1A} = I_{D2A} = I_{D11} - \frac{|I_{D5}|}{2} = I_{D12} - \frac{|I_{D5}|}{2} = I_{BIAS} - \frac{I_{TAIL}}{2} \qquad (6.103)$$

Compared to the other op-amp configurations we have considered, the folded-cascode configuration improves the common-mode input range. The upper end of the range is the same as in the basic two-stage op amp and the telescopic cascode op amp. On the other hand, the lower end of the range can be reduced significantly compared to both other configurations if $V_{BIAS2}$ is adjusted so that $M_{11}$ and $M_{12}$ operate at the edge of the active region. Under this condition, the bias voltage from the drain of $M_1$ to $-V_{SS}$ is $V_{ov11}$, which can be much less than in the other configurations. See (6.75), (6.77), and Problem 6.18.

To calculate the output swing, first consider the $p$-type cascode current mirror by itself. Since $M_3$ and $M_{3A}$ are diode connected, the voltage from $V_{DD}$ to the gate of $M_{4A}$ is

**Figure 6.27** Simplified schematic of a folded-cascode op amp.

**Figure 6.28** More detailed schematic of a folded-cascode op amp.

$2|V_{tp}| + 2|V_{ov}|$. Therefore, the source-drain voltage of $M_4$ is $|V_{tp}| + |V_{ov}|$, and the maximum output for which both $M_4$ and $M_{4A}$ operate in the active region is

$$V_{OUT(max)} = V_{DD} - |V_{tp}| - 2|V_{ov}|  \qquad (6.104)$$

This equation is analogous to (6.93) where an $n$-type cascode current mirror limits the minimum output swing of the telescopic op amp. The threshold term in this equation can be eliminated by using a $p$-type version of one of the high-swing cascode current mirrors shown in Figs. 4.11 and 4.12. The result is

$$V_{OUT(max)} = V_{DD} - 2|V_{ov}|  \qquad (6.105)$$

To find the minimum output voltage, assume that $V_{BIAS2}$ is adjusted so that $M_{12}$ operates at the edge of the active region. Then the drain-source voltage of $M_{12}$ is $V_{ov}$ and the minimum output voltage for which both $M_{2A}$ and $M_{12}$ operate in the active region is

$$V_{OUT(min)} = -V_{SS} + 2V_{ov}  \qquad (6.106)$$

Therefore, a folded-cascode op amp can provide nearly constant voltage gain while its output swings within two overdrives of each supply. In contrast, the output of a telescopic-cascode op amp can swing within two overdrives of one supply and three overdrives of the other while providing nearly constant gain.

   The small-signal voltage gain of this circuit at low frequencies is

$$A_v = G_m R_o  \qquad (6.107)$$

where $G_m$ is the transconductance and $R_o$ is the output resistance. When all the transistors operate in the active region, the range of typical gain magnitudes is from several hundred to several thousand. Because of the action of the current mirror $M_3 - M_4$, variation in the drain current of $M_1$ and $M_2$ contribute constructively to the transconductance. Therefore,

$$G_m = g_{m1} = g_{m2} \qquad (6.108)$$

To find $R_o$, both inputs are connected to ac ground. Although the input voltages do not move in this case, the sources of $M_1 - M_2$ do not operate at ac ground. However, connecting this node to small-signal ground as shown in Fig. 6.29a causes little change in $R_o$ because of the action of the current mirror $M_3 - M_4$, as explained next.

Let $i_{d1}$ and $i_{d2}$ represent the small-signal drain currents of $M_1$ and $M_2$ respectively. Also, let $\Delta i_{d1}$ and $\Delta i_{d2}$ represent the corresponding changes in $i_{d1}$ and $i_{d2}$ caused by connecting the sources of $M_1 - M_2$ to a small-signal ground as shown in Fig. 6.29a. If $r_o \rightarrow \infty$, $\Delta i_{d1} = \Delta i_{d2}$ because this connection introduces equal changes in the gate-source voltages of $M_1$ and $M_2$. Then $\Delta i_{d1}$ flows in the source of $M_{1A}$, where it is mirrored to the output with a gain of unity if $r_o \rightarrow \infty$ in $M_3 - M_4$. Therefore, KCL at the output shows that $\Delta i_{d1}$ and $\Delta i_{d2}$ cancel, causing no change to the output current $i_x$ or the output resistance $R_o$. As a result, $R_o$ can be found, assuming that the sources of $M_1 - M_2$ operate at ac ground. In practice, $r_o$ in all the transistors is finite, and $R_o$ is altered slightly by connecting this point to ac ground for two reasons. First, $\Delta i_{d1}$ and $\Delta i_{d2}$ are not exactly equal with finite $r_o$ because $v_{ds1}$ and $v_{ds2}$ are not exactly equal. Differences between $v_{ds1}$ and $v_{ds2}$ stem from finite $r_o$ in $M_{1A}$ and $M_{2A}$ because $M_3$ and $M_{3A}$ are diode connected but their counterparts $M_4$ and $M_{4A}$ are not diode connected. Second, the small-signal current gain of the current mirror is not exactly unity with finite $r_o$ because $v_{ds3}$ and $v_{ds4}$ are not exactly equal. However, the change in the output resistance introduced by these considerations is usually negligible. (These effects are related to the explanation of how a

**Figure 6.29** (a) Test voltage source applied to the output to calculate the output resistance. (b) Simplified circuit.

current-mirror load increases the common-mode rejection ratio of a differential pair presented in Section 4.3.5.3.)

With the sources of $M_1 - M_2$ connected to ac ground, the drain current of $M_1$ is constant. Furthermore, the Thévenin equivalent resistances presented to the gates of $M_4$ and $M_{4A}$ are small because $M_3$ and $M_{3A}$ are diode connected. So little error is introduced by assuming that the gates of $M_4$ and $M_{4A}$ are connected to small-signal ground. Therefore, the calculation of $R_o$ can be carried out using the circuit of Fig. 6.29b. By inspection,

$$R_o = (R_{out}|M2A) \| (R_{out}|M4A) \qquad (6.109)$$

The output resistance of transistor current sources with nonzero source resistance was considered in Chapter 4. The result is the same as for a common-source amplifier with source degeneration. The incremental resistance in the source of $M_{2A}$ is the $r_o$ of $M_2$ in parallel with the $r_o$ of $M_{12}$ while the incremental resistance in the source of $M_{4A}$ is the $r_o$ of $M_4$. From (3.107),

$$R_{out}|M2A = (r_{o2}\|r_{o12}) + r_{o2A}[1 + (g_{m2A} + g_{mb2A})(r_{o2}\|r_{o12})]$$
$$\simeq [g_{m2A}(r_{o2} \| r_{o12})]r_{o2A} \qquad (6.110)$$

and

$$R_{out}|M4A = r_{o4} + r_{o4A}[1 + (g_{m4A} + g_{mb4A})(r_{o4})]$$
$$\simeq (g_{m4A}r_{o4})r_{o4A} \qquad (6.111)$$

An important advantage of this circuit is that the load capacitance $C_L$ performs the compensation function (see Chapter 9). Thus no additional capacitance (such as $C_C$ in previous circuits) need be added to keep the amplifier from oscillating when connected in a feedback loop. Furthermore, in the basic two-stage op amp, $C_C$ feeds the variation from one power supply forward to the op-amp output at high frequencies, as described in Section 6.3.6. This feedforward does not occur in one-stage op amps such as the folded cascode and telescopic cascode structures, improving their high-frequency power-supply rejection ratios from the $V_{ss}$ supply.

## 6.7 MOS Active-Cascode Operational Amplifiers

One way to increase the gain of the folded-cascode op amp without cascading additional stages is to add another layer of cascodes. See Problem 6.21. Although this approach gives a gain on the order of $(g_m r_o)^3$, it reduces the output swing by at least another overdrive in each direction. This reduction becomes increasingly important as the difference between the power-supply voltages is reduced in scaled technologies. To increase the op-amp gain without reducing the output swing, the active-cascode technique described in Chapter 3 can be used.[11]

Fig. 6.30a shows the schematic of a folded-cascode op amp with active cascodes. The gates of each of the four cascode transistors $M_{1A}$, $M_{2A}$, $M_{3A}$, and $M_{4A}$ are no longer connected to a constant bias source but instead to the output of an amplifier. These auxiliary amplifiers are themselves connected in negative feedback loops to increase the resistance looking into the drain of each cascode transistor. As shown by (3.133), the active-cascode configuration increases the output resistance by increasing the effective transconductance of the cascode transistor by $(a + 1)$, where $a$ is the voltage gain of the auxiliary amplifier. Let the gains of the auxiliary amplifiers driving $M_{3A}$ and $M_{4A}$ be $A_1$. Applying (3.133) to

**Figure 6.30** (a) Folded-cascode op amp with active-cascode gain-enhancement auxiliary amplifiers.

(6.111) to find the output resistance looking into the drain of $M_{4A}$ gives

$$
\begin{aligned}
R_{\text{out}}|_{M4A} &= r_{o4} + r_{o4A}\{1 + [g_{m4A}(A_1 + 1) + g_{mb4A}](r_{o4})\} \\
&\simeq (A_1 + 1)(g_{m4A}r_{o4})r_{o4A}
\end{aligned}
\tag{6.112}
$$

Let the gains of the auxiliary amplifiers driving $M_{1A}$ and $M_{2A}$ be $A_2$. Applying (3.133) to (6.110) to find the output resistance looking into the drain of $M_{2A}$ gives

$$
\begin{aligned}
R_{\text{out}}|_{M2A} &= (r_{o2}\|r_{o12}) + r_{o2A}\{1 + [g_{m2A}(A_2 + 1) + g_{mb2A}](r_{o2}\|r_{o12})\} \\
&\simeq (A_2 + 1)[g_{m2A}(r_{o2}\| r_{o12})]r_{o2A}
\end{aligned}
\tag{6.113}
$$

To find the overall op-amp gain, (6.112) and (6.113) can be substituted into (6.109) and the result in (6.107). This analysis shows that the gain enhancement in the folded-cascode op amp does not rely on the use of auxiliary amplifiers driving the gates of $M_{1A}$ and $M_{3A}$. However, these auxiliary amplifiers are included in Fig. 6.30a because they reduce the systematic offset of the folded-cascode op amp. Also, using identical auxiliary amplifiers to drive the gates of both $M_{1A}$ and $M_{2A}$ balances the two signal paths until the differential signal is converted into single-ended form by the current mirror.

In Fig. 6.30a, the auxiliary amplifiers with gain $A_1$ drive the gates of $M_{3A}$ and $M_{4A}$ so that the voltages from the drains of $M_3$ and $M_4$ to ground are approximately equal to $V_{\text{BIAS2}}$. For simplicity, assume that the overdrive voltages for all $p$- and $n$-channel transistors operating in the active region are $V_{ovp}$ and $V_{ovn}$, respectively. Also assume that all $n$-channel transistors have positive thresholds and all $p$-channel transistors have negative thresholds. To maximize the positive output swing of the folded-cascode amplifier, the voltage drop from $V_{DD}$ to $V_{\text{BIAS2}}$ is chosen to be about $|V_{ovp}|$. Therefore, the $A_1$ amplifiers

**Figure 6.30** (b) Auxiliary amplifier with gain $A_1$. (c) Auxiliary amplifier with gain $A_2$. (d) Bias circuit.

must operate with a high common-mode input voltage. If these amplifiers use a $p$-channel differential input pair, the maximum common-mode input voltage would be no more than $V_{DD} - |V_{tp}| - 2|V_{ovp}|$. To overcome this limitation, the $A_1$ amplifiers use an $n$-channel differential pair $M_{21}$ and $M_{22}$ as shown in Fig. 6.30b. In operation, the dc voltage from $V_{DD}$ to the output of the $A_1$ amplifiers is about $|V_{tp}| + 2|V_{ovp}|$ so that the source-drain voltages of $M_3$ and $M_4$ are $|V_{ovp}|$. Therefore, the gate-drain voltage of $M_{22}$ is approximately $|V_{tp}| + |V_{ovp}|$, and $M_{22}$ operates in the active region only if its threshold (with the body effect) is greater than this value.

A similar argument can be made to explain the use of $p$-channel differential pairs in the auxiliary amplifiers with gain $A_2$. The schematic is shown in Fig. 6.30c, and the common-mode inputs are close to $V_{SS}$ in this case.

Figure 6.30d shows a circuit that produces the bias voltages needed in Fig. 6.30a-c. The voltage from $V_{DD}$ to $V_{\text{BIAS1}}$ is $|V_{tp}| + |V_{ovp}|$, and the voltage from $V_{\text{BIAS4}}$ to $V_{SS}$ is $V_{tn} + V_{ovn}$. Transistor $M_{105}$ forces $M_{106}$ to operate in the triode region, and the voltage from $V_{DD}$ to $V_{\text{BIAS2}}$ is at least $|V_{ovp}|$ if

$$\left(\frac{W}{L}\right)_{106} \leq \frac{1}{3}\left(\frac{W}{L}\right)_{105} \tag{6.114}$$

ignoring body effect as in (4.73). Similarly, the voltage from $V_{BIAS3}$ to $V_{SS}$ is at least $V_{ovn}$ if

$$\left(\frac{W}{L}\right)_{114} \leq \frac{1}{3}\left(\frac{W}{L}\right)_{113} \tag{6.115}$$

One potential problem with the structure shown in Fig. 6.30a is instability in the feedback loops around the auxiliary amplifiers. To avoid instability, a compensation capacitor can be placed from each auxiliary-amplifier output to a small-signal ground. Since the $A_1$ amplifiers are used to improve the performance of a $p$-channel current mirror, where signals are referenced to $V_{DD}$, compensation capacitors for the $A_1$ amplifiers $C_{C1}$ are connected to $V_{DD}$. Similarly, compensation capacitors for the $A_2$ amplifiers $C_{C2}$ are connected to $V_{SS}$. The need for such capacitors stems from the observation that the capacitance looking into the gates of $M_{1A}$, $M_{2A}$, $M_{3A}$, and $M_{4A}$ can be quite small because the gate-source capacitances of these transistors are *bootstrapped*. This expression means that the source of each of these transistors follows its gate when the corresponding drain current is constant. If the gate-source voltages are exactly constant, zero ac current flows into the gate-source capacitances, and the capacitances looking into the gates of the cascode transistors are independent of their gate-source capacitances. In practice, the gate-source voltages are not exactly constant because of variations in the drain currents caused by variations in the differential input voltage of the folded-cascode op amp, but the bootstrapping effect is significant. As a result, the load capacitances of the auxiliary amplifiers are dominated by parasitics that may vary considerably over variations in processing unless a capacitor is added at the output of each auxiliary amplifier. The issue of stability in feedback amplifiers is considered in detail in Chapter 9.

## 6.8 Bipolar Operational Amplifiers

The basic topology used for most bipolar-transistor op amps is shown in simplified form in Fig. 6.31. As in the case of the basic two-stage MOS op amp, it consists of an input stage with a differential pair and a current-mirror load followed by a second stage with a common-emitter amplifier and an active load. Most MOS technologies are complementary

**Figure 6.31** Basic two-stage bipolar operational amplifier.

in the sense that the performance of the $p$-channel transistors is almost as good as the $n$-channel transistors in the same technology. However, as mentioned in Section 2.5.2, most bipolar transistor technologies produce $pnp$ transistors that are far inferior to the $npn$ transistors in the same process because the lightly doped $n$-type epitaxial material is used to form the base of the $pnp$ transistors. As a result, the collector-base depletion region extends mostly into the base, and the base must be made wide enough to accommodate this depletion region. Since (1.211) shows that the transition frequency of a bipolar transistor is inversely proportional to the square of its base width, the $f_T$ of $pnp$ transistors is usually much lower than for $npn$ transistors in the same process. Although the performance of the $pnp$ transistors can be improved by increasing the complexity of the integrated-circuit processing, such changes increase cost. To minimize cost, a key challenge in bipolar op-amp design is often to produce high-performance op amps with fast $npn$ transistors but slow $pnp$ transistors. One example of such circuit design is the 741 op amp, where the $pnp$ devices are used in a way that reduces their impact on the frequency response of the op amp.

In this section, we analyze the 741 op amp. It is a widely used stand-alone op amp, and its popularity stems from the fact that it is internally compensated (see Chapter 9) and is a relatively simple circuit that can be made to fit on a die less than 1 mm (40 mils) on a side. It has large voltage gain and good common-mode and differential-mode input voltage ranges.

The 741 circuit is shown in Fig. 6.32$a$.[3] The analysis is carried out in three parts. First the operation of the circuit is described qualitatively, and then a dc analysis is carried out to determine the quiescent currents and voltages in the circuit. Finally, a small-signal analysis is carried out to determine the voltage gain, input resistance, and output resistance.

**Qualitative Description of Circuit Operation.** A simplified conceptual circuit diagram is shown in Fig. 6.32$b$. The input transistors $Q_1$ and $Q_2$ are emitter followers that maintain high input resistance and low input current. They drive the emitters of the common-base differential pair of $pnp$ devices $Q_3$ and $Q_4$. The transistors $Q_5$ and $Q_6$ form an active load for $Q_3$ and $Q_4$. These six transistors taken together actually perform three separate functions that must be carried out in monolithic op-amp realizations.

1. They provide a differential input that is relatively insensitive to common-mode voltages, has high input resistance, and provides some voltage gain. The realization of some voltage gain in the input stage is desirable since the noise and offset voltage associated with the second and later stages are divided by this gain when referred to the input.

2. Level shifting. The $pnp$ transistors produced by standard IC technology have poor frequency response, as described in Section 2.5.2. Thus the most desirable approach to an op-amp realization would be to use only $npn$ transistors. Somewhere in the amplifier, however, the dc level of the signal path must be shifted in the negative direction to maximize the range of possible op-amp output voltages. In general-purpose amplifiers like the 741, this shift is usually accomplished by inserting lateral $pnp$ transistors in the signal path. In the 741, the emitters of the $pnp$ devices $Q_3$ and $Q_4$ operate near the input voltages while the collectors rest at a potential very near the negative supply.

3. Differential to single-ended conversion. The op amps considered in this chapter have differential inputs and single-ended outputs, so within the circuit a conversion must be made to single-ended operation. The simplest approach would be to simply take *one* of the outputs of an emitter-coupled pair and feed that into a single-ended circuit. However, this approach tends to result in high sensitivity to common-mode input voltages, as described in Chapter 4. To reduce the sensitivity to common-mode inputs, an active-load circuit is used, as realized by transistors $Q_5$ and $Q_6$.

**Figure 6.32** (a) 741 operational-amplifier circuit.

**Figure 6.32** (b) Simplified, conceptual schematic diagram of the 741 amplifier.

Transistor $Q_{16}$ is an emitter follower that reduces the loading effect of $Q_{17}$ on the output of the actively loaded first stage. Transistor $Q_{17}$ is a common-emitter amplifier that also has an active load formed by $Q_{13B}$. This amplifier stage provides large voltage gain. Transistor $Q_{23}$ is another emitter follower that prevents the output stage from loading the output of the gain stage. Transistors $Q_{14}$ and $Q_{20}$ form the Class AB output stage.

Transistor $Q_{13}$ is a multicollector lateral *pnp* The geometry of the device is shown in Fig. 6.33. Note that the collector ring has been split into two parts, one that faces three-

$$I_{S1} = 0.75\, I_S$$
$$I_{S2} = 0.25\, I_S$$

Where $I_S$ = saturation current of structure with both collectors connected together

**Figure 6.33** Electrical equivalent for multicollector lateral *pnp*.

fourths of the emitter periphery and collects the holes injected from that periphery, and a second that faces one-fourth of the emitter periphery and collects holes injected from that face. Thus the structure is analogous to two *pnp* transistors whose base-emitter junctions are connected in parallel and one of which has an $I_S$ that is one-fourth that of a standard *pnp* transistor and the other an $I_S$ that is three-fourths that of a standard *pnp* with fully enclosed emitter. This equivalence is depicted in Fig. 6.33.

### 6.8.1 The dc Analysis of the 741 Operational Amplifier

The first step in evaluating the performance of the circuit is to determine the quiescent operating current and voltage of each of the transistors in the circuit. This dc analysis presents a special problem in op-amp circuits because of the very high gain involved. If we were to begin the dc analysis with the assumption that the two input terminals are grounded and then try to predict the output voltage, we would find that a small variation in the beta or output resistance of the devices in the circuit would cause large changes in the output voltage we predict. In fact, the calculation would usually show that the output stage would not operate in the active region but would be saturated in one direction or the other. This problem exists in practice; for a voltage gain of $10^5$, only 0.1 mV of input offset voltage is required to drive the output into saturation with $\pm 10$-V power supplies when the input voltage is zero. Thus the dc analysis must start with an assumption that the circuit is enclosed in a feedback loop that forces the *output* to some specified voltage, which is usually zero. We can then work backward and determine the operating points within the circuit.

A second assumption that simplifies the analysis is to assume that for the dc analysis, the output resistance of the transistors does not greatly affect the dc currents flowing in the circuit. This assumption results in 10 to 20 percent error in the calculated currents. Of course, the output resistance must be included in the small-signal analysis since it strongly affects the gain for the active-load amplifiers.

We first calculate the currents in the biasing current sources $Q_{10}$ and $Q_{13AB}$ in Fig. 6.32a. This subcircuit is shown in Fig. 6.34. Neglecting base currents and assuming that all transistors are in the forward-active region, we can calculate the reference

**Figure 6.34** Bias circuitry for the 741.

current as

$$I_{REF} = \frac{V_{CC} + V_{EE} - 2V_{BE(on)}}{39 \text{ k}\Omega} = 0.73 \text{ mA}$$

where we have assumed that $V_{BE(on)} = 0.7$ V.

The combination of $Q_{11}$ and $Q_{10}$ forms a Widlar current source, as described in Chapter 4. The output current $I_1$ must be found by trial-and-error solution of the relation

$$V_T \ln \frac{I_{REF}}{I_1} = (5 \text{ k}\Omega)I_1$$

The result is

$$I_1 = 19 \text{ } \mu\text{A}$$

The currents $I_2$ and $I_3$ are three-fourths and one-fourth of the reference current, respectively,

$$I_2 = 0.55 \text{ mA} \qquad I_3 = 0.18 \text{ mA}$$

The circuit can now be simplified to the form shown in Fig. 6.35. We first determine the bias currents in the input stage. For this analysis, we will neglect the effects of the dc base currents flowing in the *npn* transistors since these transistors typically have betas of several hundred. Since the betas of the lateral *pnp* transistors are typically much lower than for the *npn* transistors, however, we will consider the effects

**Figure 6.35** Simplified schematic of the 741 with idealized biasing current sources.

of the *pnp* base currents. Since $Q_8$ and $Q_9$ are identical, and since the effect of finite Early voltage is ignored, $I_{C8} = I_{C9}$. Therefore, from KCL at the collector of $Q_8$,

$$I_A = -I_{C9}\left(1 + \frac{2}{\beta_{pnp}}\right) \tag{6.116}$$

If we neglect the base current of $Q_1$ and $Q_2$, then KCL at the collectors of $Q_1$ and $Q_2$ together with (6.116) gives

$$I_{C1} + I_{C2} = I_A = I_{E3} + I_{E4} = -I_{C9}\left(1 + \frac{2}{\beta_{pnp}}\right) \tag{6.117}$$

From KCL at the collector of $Q_9$,

$$19\,\mu A = -I_{C9} + \frac{I_{E3}}{1 + \beta_{pnp}} + \frac{I_{E4}}{1 + \beta_{pnp}} = -I_{C9}\left[1 + \left(\frac{1 + \dfrac{2}{\beta_{pnp}}}{1 + \beta_{pnp}}\right)\right] \tag{6.118}$$

where (6.117) has been used. Substitution of (6.118) in (6.116) gives

$$I_A = 19\,\mu A\left[\frac{1 + \dfrac{2}{\beta_{pnp}}}{1 + \left(\dfrac{1 + \dfrac{2}{\beta_{pnp}}}{1 + \beta_{pnp}}\right)}\right] \simeq 19\,\mu A\left(1 + \frac{1}{\beta_{pnp}}\right) \tag{6.119}$$

Substitution of (6.119) into (6.117) with $I_{E3} + I_{E4} = (I_{C3} + I_{C4})(1 + 1/\beta_{pnp})$ gives

$$I_{C3} + I_{C4} = -\left[\frac{19\,\mu A}{1 + \dfrac{2}{\beta_{pnp}(\beta_{pnp} + 2)}}\right] \simeq -19\,\mu A \tag{6.120}$$

Equation 6.120 shows that the input stage of the 741 op amp is biased so that the sum of $I_{C3}$ and $I_{C4}$ is insensitive to $\beta_{pnp}$ and about equal to $I_{C10}$ in magnitude. This result can also be predicted by observing that the input stage of the 741 uses a structure similar to a Wilson current mirror. In Fig. 4.14, transistors $Q_1$ and $Q_3$ sense and feedback the current in $Q_2$, which is the output current of the Wilson current mirror. In Fig. 6.35, transistors $Q_8$ and $Q_9$ sense and feed back the sum of the currents in $Q_3$ and $Q_4$. As a result, if $I_{C3} + I_{C4}$ in the 741 op amp is viewed as the output of a Wilson current mirror whose input is $I_{C10} = 19\,\mu A$, (6.120) agrees with (4.100).

If the differential op-amp input voltage is zero, the base-emitter voltages of $Q_1$ and $Q_2$ are equal and the current $I_A$ splits into two equal parts. As a result, $Q_1 - Q_6$ each have collector current magnitudes of about 9.5 $\mu A$ if the *pnp* beta is reasonably large. On the other hand, if the differential input voltage is nonzero, the base-emitter voltages and collector currents of $Q_1$ and $Q_2$ are unequal. However, from KCL at the collector of $Q_8$, $I_{C1} + I_{C2}$ is still given by (6.119).

Because the feedback in the input stage of the 741 op amp acts to stabilize the sum of $I_{C3}$ and $I_{C4}$, it is an example of a *common-mode negative-feedback loop*. The 19 $\mu A$ current source pulls down on the bases of $Q_3$ and $Q_4$, increasing dc currents in $Q_3$, $Q_4$, $Q_1$, $Q_2$, $Q_8$, and $Q_9$ until $|I_{C9}| \simeq 19\,\mu A$ and equilibrium is established. This feedback action affects the common-mode (bias) quantities only and is not felt by differential signals in the circuit, since the bases of $Q_3$ and $Q_4$ and the collectors of $Q_1$ and $Q_2$ are differential-mode ac grounds. Common-mode feedback is studied in Chapter 12.

The magnitudes of the collector currents of transistors $Q_5$ and $Q_6$ are equal to those of transistors $Q_3$ and $Q_4$ if base currents are neglected. We must now calculate the dc collector current in transistor $Q_7$. The emitter current of $Q_7$ consists of the base current of $Q_5$ and $Q_6$, which we will neglect, and the current flowing in the 50-kΩ resistor. The voltage across this resistor is the sum of the base-emitter drop of $Q_5$ or $Q_6$ and the drop across the 1-kΩ resistors in series with the emitters of $Q_5$ and $Q_6$. The base-emitter drop, assuming an $I_S$ of $10^{-14}$ A and a collector current of 9.5 μA, is 537 mV. The voltage drop across the 1-kΩ resistors is 9.5 mV, so that the current in the 50-kΩ resistor is 547 mV/50 kΩ or 11 μA. Thus the collector current of $Q_7$ is equal to 11 μA.

We next consider transistor $Q_{16}$ in Fig. 6.35. The voltage from the base of $Q_{17}$ to $-V_{EE}$ is equal to the base-emitter voltage of $Q_{17}$ plus the drop across the 100-Ω resistor. If the output voltage of the amplifier is to be zero as we have assumed, the collector current of $Q_{17}$ must be equal to the current supplied by current source $Q_{13B}$, which is 550 μA. Then the voltage at the base of $Q_{17}$ with respect to $-V_{EE}$ is

$$V_{B17} = (550 \text{ μA})(100) + V_T \ln \frac{550 \times 10^{-6}}{10^{-14}} = (55 + 642) \text{ mV} = 697 \text{ mV} \quad (6.121)$$

Assuming a beta of 250, the base current of $Q_{17}$ is

$$I_{B17} = \frac{550 \text{ μA}}{250} = 2.2 \text{ μA} \quad (6.122)$$

Thus the collector current of $Q_{16}$ is the sum of the current in the 50-kΩ resistor in its emitter and the base current of $Q_{17}$, or

$$I_{C16} = \frac{697 \text{ mV}}{50 \text{ kΩ}} + 2.2 \text{ μA} = 16 \text{ μA} \quad (6.123)$$

We now consider the output stage shown in Fig. 6.36, assuming for the time being that base currents are negligible. If this is true, all of the 180-μA from the current source flows through transistor $Q_{23}$. We must now determine the dc bias currents in $Q_{14}$, $Q_{18}$, $Q_{19}$, and $Q_{20}$. We assume that the circuit is connected with feedback in such a way that the output is driven to zero volts, and the output current is zero. Thus $I_{C14}$ and $I_{C20}$ are equal in magnitude. To find $I_{C18}$ and $I_{C19}$, we will use an iterative approach. First, neglect the base current of transistor $Q_{18}$. Then the collector current of $Q_{19}$ will be *approximately* 0.6 V/40 kΩ or 15 μA. Under this assumption, the collector current of $Q_{18}$ would be approximately $(180 - 15)$ μA or 165 μA. Second, recalculating the collector current of $Q_{19}$ taking the base current in $Q_{18}$ into account gives

$$I_{C19} = \frac{165 \text{ μA}}{\beta_F} + \frac{V_T \ln \dfrac{165 \text{ μA}}{10^{-14}A}}{40 \text{ kΩ}} = 16 \text{ μA} \quad (6.124)$$

Then $I_{C18} = (180 - 16)$ μA or 164 μA. Further iterations could be used to improve the accuracy; however, since the second iteration produced little change from the first, this result is satisfactory.

Now that we know the currents in $Q_{18}$ and $Q_{19}$, we can estimate the output transistor bias current using (5.83), repeated below for convenience:

$$I_{C14} = -I_{C20} = \sqrt{I_{C19}I_{C18}} \sqrt{\frac{I_{S14}I_{S20}}{I_{S18}I_{S19}}} \quad (6.125)$$

Figure 6.36 Schematic of output stage of the 741. $V_{OUT}$ is zero for the bias current calculation.

Here we have neglected the voltage drops across the small resistors in series with the emitters of $Q_{14}$ and $Q_{20}$. The actual quiescent current that flows in the output transistors depends on their $I_S$ values, which depend on their physical geometry. Both of these transistors must carry large currents while maintaining good beta when a small value of load resistance is attached to the output, so they are made with larger geometry than the other transistors in the circuit. The specific geometry used varies with manufacturer but the $I_S$ of these devices is typically about three times as large as a small geometry device. Thus

$$I_{C14} = -I_{C20} = \sqrt{(16\ \mu A)(164\ \mu A)} \times 3 = 154\ \mu A \qquad (6.126)$$

Referring to the schematic diagram of Fig. 6.32a, we can see that the circuit contains several devices that are active only during overload conditions. Transistors $Q_{15}$, $Q_{21}$, $Q_{22}$, $Q_{24}$, and $Q_{23B}$ are normally off. Transistor $Q_{15}$ turns on only when the voltage drop across $R_6$ exceeds about 550 mV. When $Q_{15}$ turns on, it limits the emitter current of $Q_{14}$ to $V_{BE15(on)}/R_6$. Further increases in the output current are conducted through $Q_{15}$, which provides a current gain of about unity from its collector to its emitter. Since the maximum current that can be provided to the collector of $Q_{15}$ is limited by $I_{C13A} = 180\ \mu A$, the maximum output current flows almost entirely in the emitter of $Q_{14}$ and is approximately 0.55 V / 27 Ω ≈ 20 mA. Thus $Q_{15}$ performs short-circuit protection, preventing damage to the amplifier due to excess current flow and power dissipation should the output be shorted, for example, to the negative power supply.

Transistors $Q_{21}$, $Q_{22}$, and $Q_{24}$ perform a similar function for the case of the output sinking current, such as when the output is shorted to the positive power supply. As in the previous case, $Q_{21}$ turns on only when the voltage drop across $R_7$ exceeds about 550 mV. In this case, however, the collector of $Q_{21}$ is not simply connected to the base of $Q_{20}$ because $Q_{23A}$ does not operate as a current source. Instead $Q_{23A}$ operates as an emitter follower that sinks an increasing emitter current as its base voltage is decreased. To limit the maximum current that can flow in $Q_{20}$ to a level that will not destroy this device, the current in $Q_{23A}$ must also be limited under these conditions. Therefore, when current flows in $Q_{21}$, it is mirrored through $Q_{24}$ to $Q_{22}$, where it pulls down on the base of $Q_{16}$. Because the gain is noninverting from the base to the emitter of $Q_{16}$ but inverting from the base to the collector of $Q_{17}$, pulling the base of $Q_{16}$ down increases the base voltage on $Q_{23A}$. This feedback loop sets the maximum current in $Q_{20}$ to $V_{EB21(on)}/R_7$ or 25 mA.

Finally, an extra emitter on the substrate *pnp* transistor $Q_{23}$ is included to prevent $Q_{16}$ from burning out if $Q_{17}$ were allowed to saturate. The extra emitter can be thought of as a separate transistor $Q_{23B}$. Assume that the inverting input terminal is overdriven so as to make it more positive than the noninverting terminal by enough voltage to turn off $Q_1$. Without $Q_{23B}$, the current into the base of $Q_{16}$ would be 19 μA. This current would be amplified by the beta of $Q_{16}$, which can be as high as 1000, giving an emitter current of up to 19 mA. This current would flow into the base of $Q_{17}$ (which would saturate) and finally to $-V_{EE}$ through the 100-Ω resistor in the emitter of $Q_{17}$. As a result, the power dissipation in $Q_{16}$ would be (19 mA) (30 V), or about 600 mW. The extra emitter on $Q_{23}$ prevents $Q_{17}$ from saturating by diverting the base drive away from $Q_{16}$ when $V_{CB}$ of $Q_{17}$ reaches zero volts. Since $Q_{17}$ cannot saturate, its base current remains small under all conditions, limiting the power dissipation in $Q_{16}$ to approximately (16 μA)(30V), or about 0.5 mW.

### 6.8.2 Small-Signal Analysis of the 741 Operational Amplifier

Our next objective is to determine the small-signal properties of the amplifier. We will break the circuit up into its three stages—the input stage, gain stage, and output stage—and determine the input resistance, output resistance, and transconductance of each stage. Consider first the ac schematic of the input stage as shown in Fig. 6.37. Here we have assumed a pure differential-mode input to the circuit; we will consider common-mode inputs later. As a result, the collectors of $Q_1$ and $Q_2$ as well as the bases of $Q_3$ and $Q_4$ operate at ac ground. We first calculate the transconductance of the stage by shorting the output to ground and calculating the output current that results when a differential input is

**Figure 6.37** Input stage ac schematic and small-signal, two-port equivalent circuit.

applied. With the output of the first stage connected to a small-signal ground, the active-load circuit $Q_5 - Q_7$ produces a current $i_{c6}$ that is approximately equal in magnitude and opposite in sign to the collector current $i_{c3}$ of $Q_3$. Thus $i_{out}$ is equal to $-(i_{c4} - i_{c3})$, and to calculate the transconductance $G_m$ we need only consider the circuit shown in Fig. 6.38a. Since the resistance presented to the collector of $Q_3$ is relatively small compared to $r_o$ of $Q_3$, we need not consider the output resistances of the devices in this calculation. The small-signal equivalent half-circuit for Fig. 6.38a is shown in Fig. 6.38b. For the half-circuit

$$\frac{v_{id}}{2} = v_1 - v_3 \tag{6.127}$$

and KCL at the emitters gives

$$v_1 g_{m1}\left(1 + \frac{1}{\beta_{01}}\right) = -v_3 g_{m3}\left(1 + \frac{1}{\beta_{03}}\right) \tag{6.128}$$

where $\beta_{01}$ is the $\beta_0$ of $Q_1$ and $\beta_{03}$ is the $\beta_0$ of $Q_3$. Combining these equations gives

$$\frac{v_{id}}{2} = -v_3\left[\frac{g_{m3}\left(1 + \frac{1}{\beta_{03}}\right)}{g_{m1}\left(1 + \frac{1}{\beta_{01}}\right)} + 1\right] \tag{6.129}$$

(a)

(b)

Figure 6.38 (a) ac schematic and (b) small-signal equivalent half-circuit for calculation of the transconductance of the input stage.

Assuming $|I_{C1}| = |I_{C3}|$, then $g_{m1} = g_{m3}$. We also assume that $\beta_{01}, \beta_{03} \gg 1$. Thus

$$v_3 = -\frac{v_{id}}{4} \tag{6.130}$$

and

$$i_{c3} = \frac{-g_{m3}v_{id}}{4} \tag{6.131}$$

From the symmetry of the circuit,

$$i_{c4} = +\frac{g_{m3}v_{id}}{4} \tag{6.132}$$

and, referring to Fig. 6.37,

$$i_{out} = -i_{c4} + i_{c3} = -\frac{g_{m3}v_{id}}{2} \tag{6.133}$$

Thus the overall transconductance of the input stage is

$$G_{m1} = -\frac{i_{out}}{v_{id}} = \frac{g_{m1}}{2} = \frac{9.5\mu A}{2V_T} = \frac{1}{5.4\ k\Omega} \tag{6.134}$$

This calculation also yields the differential input resistance of the stage. From Fig. 6.38b, the resistance $R_{eq}$ seen looking into the emitter of $Q_3$ is given by

$$R_{eq} = \frac{1}{g_{m3}\left(1 + \frac{1}{\beta_{03}}\right)}$$

This resistance appears in the emitter of $Q_1$, so that using (3.90) we find that

$$\frac{\left(\frac{v_{id}}{2}\right)}{i_i} = r_{\pi1} + (\beta_{01} + 1)R_{eq} = r_{\pi1} + \frac{(\beta_{01} + 1)}{g_{m3}\left(1 + \frac{1}{\beta_{03}}\right)} \tag{6.135}$$

Assuming again that $\beta_{01} \gg 1$, $\beta_{03} \gg 1$, and $g_{m1} = g_{m3}$,

$$\frac{v_{id}}{2} = \left(r_{\pi1} + \frac{\beta_{01}}{g_{m3}}\right)i_i = (r_{\pi1} + r_{\pi1})i_i \tag{6.136}$$

Solving for $R_{id}$ yields

$$\frac{v_{id}}{i_i} = R_{id} = 4r_{\pi1} = 2.7\ M\Omega \tag{6.137}$$

where $\beta_0 = 250$ is assumed.

The differential-mode input resistance of the amplifier is thus four times the input resistance of one of the input transistors. In this calculation, we have neglected the fact that when $v_{id}$ changes, the output voltage of the first stage changes and produces feedback to the input through the output resistance of $Q_4$. This effect produces a difference between the input resistances seen at the two input terminals.

We now calculate the output resistance $R_{o1}$ of the input stage. To find $R_{o1}$, both inputs are connected to ac ground. Although the input voltages do not move in this case,

Figure 6.39  (a) Test voltage source $v_x$ applied to the output of the input stage for calculation of the output resistance. (b) Simplified circuit.

the collectors of $Q_1 - Q_2$ as well as the bases of $Q_3 - Q_4$ do not operate at ac ground. However, connecting these nodes to small-signal grounds as shown in Fig. 6.39a causes little change in $R_{o1}$ because of the action of the current mirror $Q_5 - Q_7$, as explained next.

Let $i_{cn}$ represent the small-signal collector current of $Q_n$, where $n$ is an integer and $1 \leq n \leq 7$. Also, let $\Delta i_{cn}$ represent the change in $i_{cn}$ caused by connecting the collectors of $Q_1 - Q_2$ and the bases of $Q_3 - Q_4$ to a small-signal ground as shown in Fig. 6.39a. If $r_o \to \infty$ in $Q_1 - Q_4$, $\Delta i_{c3} = \Delta i_{c4}$ because these connections introduce equal changes in the base-emitter voltages of $Q_3$ and $Q_4$. Ignoring base currents, $\Delta i_{c3}$ flows in the collector of $Q_5$, where it is mirrored to the stage output with a gain of unity if $r_o \to \infty$ in $Q_5 - Q_6$. Therefore, KCL at the stage output shows that $\Delta i_{c4}$ and $\Delta i_{c6}$ cancel, causing no change to the output current $i_x$ or the output resistance $R_{o1}$. As a result, $R_{o1}$ can be found assuming that the collectors of $Q_1 - Q_2$ and the bases of $Q_3 - Q_4$ operate at ac ground. In practice, $\beta_0$ and $r_o$ in $Q_1 - Q_7$ are finite, and $R_{o1}$ is altered slightly by connecting these points to ac ground for two reasons. First, $\Delta i_{c3}$ and $\Delta i_{c4}$ are not exactly equal with finite $r_o$ because $v_{ce3}$ and $v_{ce4}$ are unequal. Second, the small-signal current gain of the current mirror is not exactly unity with finite $r_o$ because $v_{ce5}$ and $v_{ce6}$ are unequal. Also, finite $\beta_0$ introduces a current-mirror gain error because not all of $\Delta i_{c3}$ flows in $Q_5$, where it can be mirrored to the output. However, the change in the output resistance introduced by these considerations is usually negligible. (These effects are related to the explanation of how a current-mirror load increases the common-mode rejection ratio of a differential pair presented in Section 4.3.5.3.)

With the collectors of $Q_1 - Q_2$ and the bases of $Q_3 - Q_4$ connected to ac ground, the collector current of $Q_3$ is constant. Furthermore, the Thévenin equivalent resistance presented to the base of $Q_6$ is small compared to $r_\pi$ of $Q_6$, so little error is introduced by assuming that the base of $Q_6$ is connected to a small-signal ground. Therefore, the calculation of $R_{o1}$ can be carried out using the circuit of Fig. 6.39b. By inspection,

$$R_{o1} = (R_{out}|_{Q4} \parallel R_{out}|_{Q6}) \tag{6.138}$$

The incremental resistance in the emitter of $Q_6$ is equal to 1 kΩ, while the incremental resistance in the emitter of $Q_4$ is the $r_e$ of $Q_2$. The output resistance of transistor current sources with a resistance in the emitter was considered in Chapter 4. The result is the same as for a common-emitter amplifier with emitter degeneration. Equation 3.98 can be used to give

$$R_{o1} = \left\{ r_{o4} \times \left[ 1 + \frac{g_{m4}\left(\frac{1}{g_{m2}}\right)}{1 + \frac{g_{m4}/g_{m2}}{\beta_{04}}} \right] \right\} \middle\| \left\{ r_{o6} \times \left[ 1 + \frac{(g_{m6})(1\ \text{k}\Omega)}{1 + \frac{(g_{m6})(1\ \text{k}\Omega)}{\beta_{06}}} \right] \right\} \tag{6.139}$$

Assuming $\beta_{04} \gg 1$ and $\beta_{06} \gg g_{m6}(1\ \text{k}\Omega)$, we obtain

$$R_{o1} = 2r_{o4} \parallel 1.36 r_{o6} \tag{6.140}$$

For $\eta_{npn} = 2 \times 10^{-4}$, $I_c = 9.5\ \mu\text{A}$, $\eta_{pnp} = 5 \times 10^{-4}$ we find

$$R_{o1} = 6.8\ \text{M}\Omega \tag{6.141}$$

Thus the equivalent circuit for the input stage is as shown in Fig. 6.40.

We now turn to the second stage, shown in Fig. 6.41a. Again we must calculate the input resistance, transconductance, and output resistance of the stage. We begin by calculating the input resistance. We first calculate the Thévenin equivalent resistance seen looking into the base of transistor $Q_{17}$, designated $R_{eq1}$ in Fig. 6.41a. Utilizing the results from Chapter 3 for the input resistance of a common-emitter amplifier with a resistance in the emitter,

$$R_{eq1} = r_{\pi 17} + (\beta_{017} + 1)100\ \Omega \tag{6.142}$$

Here we have neglected the effects of the output resistance of $Q_{17}$. The positive feedback contributed by $r_{o17}$ actually decreases $R_{eq1}$ slightly.

The circuit can now be reduced to the form shown in Fig. 6.41b. The input resistance of the stage is

$$R_{i2} = r_{\pi 16} + (\beta_{016} + 1)(R_{eq1} \parallel 50\ \text{k}\Omega) \tag{6.143}$$

**Figure 6.40** Two-port equivalent circuit for the input stage.

**Figure 6.41** (a) Small-signal equivalent circuit for second stage. (b) Circuit for calculation of input resistance. (c) Two-port equivalent circuit for second stage.

Combining (6.142) and (6.143) gives

$$R_{i2} = r_{\pi16} + (\beta_0 + 1)\{[r_{\pi17} + (\beta_0 + 1)(100\Omega)] \parallel [50 \text{ k}\Omega]\} \qquad (6.144)$$

We assume that the transistors have a $\beta_0$ of 250. Transistor $Q_{16}$ operates at a current of 16 μA whereas $Q_{17}$ operates at 550 μA. Evaluating (6.144), we find

$$R_{i2} = 406 \text{ k}\Omega + 251 \times (37 \text{ k}\Omega \parallel 50 \text{ k}\Omega)$$
$$= 5.7 \text{ M}\Omega \qquad (6.145)$$

We next calculate the transconductance of the stage. If we assume that the voltage gain of the emitter follower $Q_{16}$ is nearly unity, the transconductance $G_{m2}$ of the stage is just that of transistor $Q_{17}$ with the 100-$\Omega$ resistor in the emitter:

$$G_{m2} - \frac{g_{m17}}{1 + g_{m17}R_E} = \frac{1}{147 \ \Omega} \qquad (6.146)$$

The output resistance of the stage $R_{o2}$ is the output resistance of $Q_{13B}$ in parallel with that seen looking into the collector of $Q_{17}$. Again utilizing (3.98), we find

$$R_{o2} = r_{o13B} \parallel \left[ r_{o17} \left( 1 + \frac{g_{m17}R_E}{1 + \dfrac{g_{m17}R_E}{\beta_0}} \right) \right] \qquad (6.147)$$

Assuming $\beta_0 \gg g_{m17}R_E$ yields

$$R_{o2} = [r_{o13B}] \parallel \{r_{o17}[1 + (g_{m17})(100\Omega)]\} \qquad (6.148)$$

Assuming that

$$\eta_{pnp} = 5 \times 10^{-4} \qquad (6.149)$$

$$\eta_{npn} = 2 \times 10^{-4} \qquad (6.150)$$

(6.148) can be evaluated to give

$$R_{o2} = 83 \text{ k}\Omega \qquad (6.151)$$

Thus we have developed $R_{i2}$, $R_{o2}$, and $G_{m2}$ for the second stage. A two-port equivalent circuit is shown in Fig. 6.41c.

We now turn to the output stage. A schematic diagram is shown in Fig. 6.42. The output either sources or sinks current, depending on the output voltage and load. As a result, the input resistance and output resistance of the output stage is heavily dependent on the particular value of output voltage and current. As will become evident, the input resistance of the output stage is much larger than the output resistance of the preceding stage, and as a result the actual value of the input resistance of the output stage does not strongly influence the voltage gain of the circuit. Thus we simply assume, for example, the output current is 2 mA and that this current is flowing *out* of the output terminal. We further assume that the load resistance is 2 kΩ. Since the output current is flowing *out* of the output stage, transistor $Q_{14}$ operates in the active region and transistor $Q_{20}$ conducts

**Figure 6.42** (*a*) Simplified output-stage circuit of the 741. (*b*) Small-signal circuit when sourcing current. (*c*) Circuit for calculation of $R_{out}$.

only a small amount of current. The small-signal equivalent circuit for this case is shown in Fig. 6.42b. The voltage gain is approximately unity since the circuit consists of two emitter followers in series.

We now calculate the input resistance $R_{i3}$ of the output stage. We first calculate the resistance seen looking into the base of transistor $Q_{14}$, which is designated $R_{eq2}$ in Fig. 6.42b. Using the results from Chapter 3 on emitter followers, we find

$$R_{eq2} = r_{\pi14} + (\beta_{014} + 1)(2 \text{ k}\Omega) \tag{6.152}$$

We next calculate the Thévenin equivalent resistance seen at the emitter of $Q_{23}$, looking toward diodes $Q_{18}$ and $Q_{19}$. This resistance is designated $R_{eq3}$ in Fig. 6.42b, and is seen by inspection to be

$$R_{eq3} = r_{d18} + r_{d19} + r_{o13A} \parallel R_{eq2} \tag{6.153}$$

Finally, the input resistance of the stage is that of emitter follower $Q_{23}$ with a resistance $R_{eq3}$ in its emitter, or

$$R_{i3} = r_{\pi23} + (\beta_{023} + 1)R_{eq3} \tag{6.154}$$

Transistor $Q_{23}$ and the two diodes operate a current of 180 $\mu$A, while $Q_{14}$ operates at 2 mA. Assuming an $npn$ $\beta_0$ of 250 and a $pnp$ $\beta_0$ of 50, (6.154) can be evaluated to yield

$$R_{i3} = r_{\pi23} + 51R_{eq3} \tag{6.155}$$

and thus

$$R_{i3} = 9.1 \text{ M}\Omega \tag{6.156}$$

This input resistance is much larger than the output resistance of the preceding stage, and as a result the gain of the amplifier is not strongly affected by variations in load resistance attached to the output of the amplifier.

We now calculate the output resistance of the output stage. We must include the output resistance of the preceding stage in this calculation; the small-signal equivalent circuit for performing the calculation is shown in Fig. 6.42c.

The resistance seen looking to the left from the base of $Q_{14}$ is

$$R_{eq4} = r_{o13A} \parallel \left[ r_{d19} + r_{d18} + \frac{R_{o2} + r_{\pi23}}{\beta_{023} + 1} \right]$$

$$= 2.06 \text{ k}\Omega \tag{6.157}$$

The resistance seen looking into the output terminal is then

$$R_{out} = \frac{R_{eq4} + r_{\pi14}}{\beta_{014} + 1} = 21 \text{ }\Omega \tag{6.158}$$

To this resistance we must add the series current-limiting resistance $R_6$, which is 27 $\Omega$. The actual value of $R_{out}$ is thus 48 $\Omega$. The output resistance will change with operating point and is heavily dependent on the current flowing in the output transistor.

**Small-Signal Performance of the Complete Circuit.** The small-signal equivalent circuit for the complete amplifier is shown in Fig. 6.43. The voltage gain is

$$A_v = (G_{m1})(R_{o1} \parallel R_{i2})(G_{m2})(R_{o2} \parallel R_{i3})$$

$$= 574 \times 564 = 324,000 \tag{6.159}$$

**Figure 6.43** Small-signal equivalent circuit for the complete 741.

Note that both stages contribute about the same gain. The second stage loads the first, reducing its gain by about half. This loading gives the gain of the circuit a beta dependence that will cause the gain to vary with temperature and process variations. However, the output stage does not significantly load the output of the second stage and the voltage gain is almost independent of the load resistance attached to the output. The input and output resistances of the complete amplifier are

$$R_{id} = 2.7 \text{ M}\Omega \tag{6.160}$$

$$R_o = 48 \ \Omega \tag{6.161}$$

**Inclusion of Second-Order Effects in the Analysis; Computer Analysis.** The objective of the first-order approximate analysis procedure just carried out for the 741 was to develop an insight into the factors that are most important in affecting circuit performance. However, the simplifying assumptions made in the analysis limit the accuracy of the results related to dc operating points and voltage gain. The principal violations of the assumptions made are as follows:

1. The output resistance of the transistors was neglected in the dc analysis. Actually, the collector current of a typical lateral *pnp* transistor increases about 30 percent when $V_{CE}$ increases from zero to 15 V, assuming that the base-emitter voltage is held constant and that $V_A$ is about 50 V. For the *npn* devices, the figure is 12 percent, assuming a $V_A$ of 130 V. As a result, the bias currents in the circuit increase by from 10 to 30 percent over those calculated, reducing the calculated small-signal resistance levels.

2. The variation of transistor beta with current has been neglected. As described in Chapter 1, the transistor current gain falls at low collector current levels due to recombination in the emitter-base depletion region. As a result, the input stage devices $Q_1$ to $Q_7$ and device $Q_{16}$ have substantially lower small-signal current gain than was assumed in the analysis. The principal effect of this fall-off is to reduce the voltage gain of the amplifier and increase the input bias current.

When a detailed quantitative prediction is required regarding the performance of such circuits, a SPICE computer analysis is generally less time consuming than attempting a hand analysis, taking into account the second-order effects. Such an analysis applied to the 741 yields the bias levels shown in Fig. 6.44.

### 6.8.3 Input Offset Voltage, Input Offset Current, and Common-Mode Rejection Ratio of the 741

Two important aspects of the performance of op amps are the input offset voltage and current. These deviations from ideality limit the ability of the circuit to amplify small dc

| Transistor | $I_C$ (μA) | Transistor | $I_C$ (μA) |
|---|---|---|---|
| $Q_1$ | 12.32 | $Q_{13B}$ | −682.9 |
| $Q_2$ | 12.38 | $Q_{14}$ | 172.7 |
| $Q_3$ | −12.30 | $Q_{15}$ | Off |
| $Q_4$ | −12.36 | $Q_{16}$ | 16.87 |
| $Q_5$ | 12.10 | $Q_{17}$ | 687.3 |
| $Q_6$ | 12.11 | $Q_{18}$ | 204.0 |
| $Q_7$ | 11.34 | $Q_{19}$ | 16.38 |
| $Q_8$ | −23.53 | $Q_{20}$ | −173.4 |
| $Q_9$ | −30.56 | $Q_{21}$ | Off |
| $Q_{10}$ | 31.05 | $Q_{22}$ | Off |
| $Q_{11}$ | 732.2 | $Q_{23A}$ | −219.7 |
| $Q_{12}$ | −700.6 | $Q_{23B}$ | Off |
| $Q_{13A}$ | −221.6 | $Q_{24}$ | Off |

**Figure 6.44** Computer-predicted dc bias levels of the 741 operational amplifier obtained from SPICE.

signals accurately, since the offsets are indistinguishable from the signal. The calculation of these quantities is somewhat tedious.[12] In this section, we describe the factors influencing the offset voltage and current of the 741 circuit qualitatively.

The input offset voltage of differential amplifiers can be shown to be primarily dependent on the offset voltage of the first stage, provided that the voltage gain of the first stage is reasonably high.[1] The input stage of the 741 is somewhat complex, consisting of three pairs of transistors, $Q_1 - Q_2$, $Q_3 - Q_4$, and $Q_5 - Q_6$. The stage provides level shifting and differential-to-single-ended conversion as well as differential amplification. As a result, mismatches in each of the three device pairs, as well as mismatches in the resistor pair $R_1 - R_2$, contribute to the input offset voltage of the circuit. A typical offset voltage of about 2.6 mV would be expected for the 741 assuming typical transistor mismatch and resistor mismatch data.[12]

The input offset current of the circuit results primarily from mismatches in the beta of the two input transistors $Q_1$ and $Q_2$. A typical input offset current of about 4 nA would be expected for the circuit.[12] This value is highly dependent on the actual matching of transistor beta achieved in the circuit for the low current level at which the input stage operates. As described in Section 6.2.5, the common-mode rejection ratio can be regarded as the change in input offset voltage that results from a unit change in common-mode input voltage. This change in input offset voltage stems from two separate effects. First, when the common-mode input voltage changes, current-source transistors $Q_9$ and $Q_{10}$ experience a change in collector-emitter voltage. Because of the finite output resistance of these devices, their collector current changes, which results in a change in the bias current in the input stage. If resistors $R_1$ and $R_2$ were not present, this change in the bias current would not change the input offset voltage, but the presence of these resistors results in a change in the ratio of the collector currents of $Q_5$ and $Q_6$ if a mismatch exists between $Q_5$ and $Q_6$, or if a mismatch exists between $R_1$ and $R_2$. This change in the ratio of the collector currents of $Q_5$ and $Q_6$ results in a change in the ratio of the currents flowing in $Q_1 - Q_2$ and in $Q_3 - Q_4$, and a change in the input offset voltage.

The second source of input offset voltage change is caused by changes in the collector-emitter voltages of $Q_1, Q_2, Q_3$, and $Q_4$ when the input common-mode voltage is changed. As a result, if a base-width mismatch exists in these devices, the ratio of the saturation currents of $Q_1$ and $Q_2$ and the ratio of the saturation currents of $Q_3$ and $Q_4$ will vary also. These ratio variations result in changes in the input offset voltage.

**Comparison of Calculated Performance Parameters and Experimentally Observed Values.** The calculated and observed values of typical performance parameters of the 741 are shown in the following table.

|  | Calculated | Observed (typical) |
|---|---|---|
| Open-loop gain | 324,000 | 200,000 |
| Input resistance | 2.7 MΩ | 2.0 MΩ |
| Input bias current | 38 nA | 80 nA |
| Input offset current | 3.8 nA[12] | 10 nA |
| Input offset voltage | 2.6 mV[12] | 2 mV |
| Output resistance | 48 Ω | 75 Ω |

The differences between the calculated and observed parameters result from differences between typical device parameters obtained in production and those assumed in the analysis, and from the approximations made in the hand analysis. We now turn from the analysis problem to that of improving the performance parameters of the 741 by circuit modifications.

## 6.9 Design Considerations for Bipolar Monolithic Operational Amplifiers

Operational-amplifier design involves trade-offs between the various dc, small-signal, and transient performance parameters as well as the die size and resultant cost. In the 741, the principal design objective was to obtain an internally compensated circuit with moderate dc and ac performance while maintaining a small inexpensive die. However, by the use of more complex circuitry, the dc, small-signal, and transient performance of the circuit can be greatly improved. Frequently, steps taken to improve the transient behavior degrade dc parameters such as input offset voltage and input bias current. In this section we explore design approaches to the improvement of the input parameters: input offset voltage, input bias current, and input offset current of the 741. Since the frequency response and compensation of op amps are described extensively in Chapter 9, we defer the description of optimization of transient behavior and slew rate until then.

**Applications of Precision Operational Amplifiers.** The input characteristics of op amps, including the input offset voltage and drift, input bias current and drift, and input offset current and drift, determine the lower limit of the magnitude of dc signals that can be accurately amplified. These performance parameters are most important in instrumentation applications where very small dc potential differences must often be measured. A typical example is the thermocouple amplifier shown in Fig. 6.45. A thermocouple is a junction of two dissimilar metals that produces a potential difference that varies with temperature. When used as temperature sensors, two junctions are used in series with one held at a reference temperature. The potential difference produced by the series combination of the junctions is then proportional to the temperature difference between them. These devices have a usable sensing temperature range that extends to several thousand degrees, and

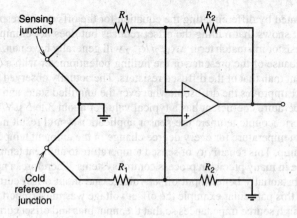

Sensing
junction

Cold
reference
junction

**Figure 6.45** Differential temperature-sensing amplifier using thermocouples.

**Figure 6.46** Equivalent circuit of the thermocouple amplifier including $I_{OS}$ and $V_{OS}$.

they are useful in furnace controllers and other such systems. For iron-constantan thermocouples, the output voltage is about 50 $\mu$V/°C.

The offset voltage and current of the op amp used will limit the resolution of this temperature-measuring system. The equivalent circuit with these imperfections included is shown in Fig. 6.46. By use of the summing-point constraints the output can be calculated to be

$$V_{out} = -\frac{R_2}{R_1}(\Delta V_i + V_{OS} + I_{OS}R_1) \qquad (6.162)$$

where $\Delta V_i = (V_1 - V_2)$ and we have assumed for simplicity that $R_2 \gg R_1$. The output contains an error term that depends on the input characteristics of the amplifier. In this case, the input offset current and voltage, and not input bias current, are the critical quantities. For example, if we use a 741 in this circuit with an iron-constantan thermocouple, the input offset voltage of 2.6 mV alone will give an error in the measured temperature of

$$T_\epsilon = \frac{2.6 \text{ mV}}{50 \, \mu\text{V/°C}} = 52°C \qquad (6.163)$$

In such a critical application, an external potentiometer would be used to null the offset voltage of the 741 to zero to eliminate this large error. This nulling is accomplished by connecting an external potentiometer between $R_1$ and $R_2$ in the 741 circuit. However, the limiting factor would then become the drift of the input offset voltage with temperature.

This drift can be calculated by differentiating the equation for the offset with respect to temperature.[12] The result shows that nulling the offset reduces but does not eliminate the drift. In particular, the resistor mismatch term $\Delta R_{1-2}/R_{1-2}$ will generally have nonzero temperature dependence because of the presence of the nulling potentiometer with a different temperature coefficient than that of the diffused resistors. The actually observed behavior is that nulling the 741 improves the drift somewhat over the unnulled state, and the residual offset voltage temperature coefficient has a typical value of about 3 to 5 $\mu$V/°C. This level of drift in the thermocouple temperature-sensor application would result in an error of 0.1°C in the sensed temperature for every degree change in the ambient temperature experienced by the op amp. This sensitivity of sensed temperature to ambient temperature would be unacceptable in many precision process control systems. Therefore, a need exists for op amps with substantially better input offset voltage and input offset current drift than the 741. While in this particular example the offset voltage was most important, many applications involve high source impedances so that the input bias and offset current are also important.

### 6.9.1  Design of Low-Drift Operational Amplifiers

The offset voltage of multistage differential amplifiers depends primarily on the offset of the first stage, provided that the stage has sufficiently high voltage gain. Thus the design of low-offset amplifiers is primarily a problem of designing an input stage in which as few component pairs as possible contribute to the stage offset voltage. In the 741, the input stage is relatively complicated since it provides gain, level shifting, and differential-to-single-ended conversion. A more optimum circuit from the standpoint of drift and offset is one that contains fewer devices to contribute to the offset voltage.[13] The simplest differential stage is the resistively loaded emitter-coupled pair shown in Fig. 6.47. From (3.216), the offset of this stage is

$$V_{OS} = V_T \left( -\frac{\Delta I_S}{I_S} - \frac{\Delta R_C}{R_C} \right) \tag{6.164}$$

The drift of this offset with temperature is given by

$$\frac{dV_{OS}}{dT} = \frac{V_{OS}}{T} \tag{6.165}$$

**Figure 6.47** Resistively loaded emitter-coupled pair.

Assume that the standard deviation of resistor matching is 1 percent and that of $I_S$ matching is 5 percent. Using (3.220), the standard deviation of the offset of the resistively loaded emitter-coupled pair alone is about 1.3 mV and the unnulled drift at room temperature is 4.4 $\mu$V/°C. These results are about half of the corresponding values for the 741 op amp. Therefore, this circuit is advantageous for use as the input stage of low-drift op amps.

One approach to the incorporation of this stage in the op amp is to simply use an emitter-coupled pair followed by a 741 or equivalent. An example of such an approach is the 725 op amp.[12,13] The gain of the input stage is chosen to be large enough that the second-stage does not contribute significantly to the offset and drift, yet the collector resistors must be kept small enough that the frequency response of the overall circuit is not excessively degraded by the response of the first stage.

If the collector resistors $R_C$ in Fig. 6.47 could be adjusted to null the offset in the emitter-coupled pair input stage, then nulling of the offset would in principle simultaneously null the offset drift. However, the external potentiometer used to adjust the collector resistor ratio generally displays different temperature dependence than the diffused resistors so that a new drift component is introduced because the $R_C$ mismatch factor becomes temperature dependent. In practice, temperature drifts of offset on the order of 1 to 2 $\mu$V/°C are achievable with external potentiometer nulling.

**Offset Trimming Techniques.** An alternate approach to the realization of very low drift is the nulling of the offset voltage using on-chip resistances that are inserted or removed from the circuit under the control of an on-chip programmable read-only memory.[14] A schematic diagram of such a circuit is shown in Fig. 6.48. The collector resistors consist of a large

**Figure 6.48** Input-stage circuit for on-chip discrete trimming using fusible or shortable links. Resistance $R'$ is much smaller than $R_C$.

portion ($R_C$) in series with a smaller portion that is divided up into binary-weighted seg-ments ($R'$, $2R'$, and $4R'$). The single-pole switches shown connected across the resistors are fusible links of aluminum that can be opened by a current pulse. The offset can be nulled when the devices are tested in wafer form, and the nulling does not introduce ad-ditional drift components because the collector resistances are all monolithic components of the same type. Since the resistors are binary weighted, the number of discrete steps into which the adjustment range is divided is proportional to $2^n$ where $n$ is the number of fusible links in one collector. This technique is a powerful and low-cost method for improving the input characteristics of precision monolithic op amps. With this technique, input offset voltages of less than 50 μV can be realized.

**Layout Considerations.** A basic objective in the design of precision circuits is the min-imization of the input offset voltage, which requires the minimization of the mismatch between the collector resistors and the input devices. One factor that limits the attainable matching is the photolithographic resolution. Therefore, an important parameter is the size of the resistor or transistor being defined in relation to the resolution. If the width of a re-sistor or the emitter area of a bipolar transistor is increased, then the effect of a constant amount of edge-location uncertainty decreases proportionately, improving matching.

The second factor limiting the matching is process-related gradients across the die. The effects of this factor can be partially alleviated by use of appropriate geometries that cause the device mismatch to be insensitive to certain types of process gradients. Such geometries are termed common centroid, and Fig. 6.49 shows a common-centroid layout for a bipolar differential pair. Here the transistors making up the pair are formed from cross-connected segments of a quad of transistors. In a geometric sense, the centroid of both composite devices lies at center of the structure. An example of the use of such a geometry is in the first stage of the 725 op amp,[12,13] where the input devices in Fig. 6.47 are split into a quad and cross-connected to provide the common-centroid geometry. The 725 op amp achieves a typical input offset voltage of 500 μV, which is about a factor of four lower than for the 741 op amp.

## 6.9.2 Design of Low-Input-Current Operational Amplifiers

In instrumentation applications in which the signal source has a low internal impedance, the input offset voltage and its associated drift usually place a lower limit on the dc voltage than can be resolved. When the source impedance is high, however, the input bias current and input offset current of the op amp flowing in the source resistance or the gain-setting resistors can be important in limiting the ability of the circuit to resolve small dc signals. Furthermore, many applications involve the direct sensing of currents; a good example is the photodiode amplifier shown in Fig. 6.50. Such photodetectors are used in a variety of applications where the level of ambient light must be sensed. Typical photodiode output currents vary from the picoampere level to the microampere level over the light flux range of interest, so that the input current of the op amp in Fig. 6.50 will limit the lower level of light flux that can be resolved. A need thus exists in this application as well as others for op amps with input currents much lower than that of the 741.

In the 741, the input bias current is the average base current of the input devices. To reduce this value, we might consider several alternatives, including reduction of the bias current in the input stage, insertion of a current source to cancel the input current, an increase in the beta of the input devices, or the use of MOS input transistors. Unfortu-nately, reducing the bias current of the stage degrades the frequency response of the cir-cuit, as will be described in Chapter 7. Furthermore, the current gain of integrated-circuit

**Figure 6.49** Common-centroid geometry for the emitter-coupled pair.

*npn* transistors tends to fall rapidly at current levels below 1 $\mu$A unless special steps are added to the fabrication process. The techniques that have gained wide acceptance are the use of a canceling current source (bias-current cancellation), an increase in the beta of the input devices (superbeta transistors), and the use of MOSFETs as the input transistors. We will describe each of these approaches.

**Bias-Current Cancellation.** Since the input bias current of the 741 op amp is equal to the average collector current of the input transistors divided by the average beta of the input transistors, a second current equal to the input current is derivable from the collector

**Figure 6.50** Integrating photodiode amplifier.

**Figure 6.51** Conceptual schematic of input-current cancellation scheme. The $I_{BIAS}$ current sources are equal in value to the base current of the input devices.

current of the input transistors by performing a division by beta. This current then can be fed back into the input terminal via a current mirror, completely canceling the input bias current in principle. A conceptual schematic of such an input stage is shown in Fig. 6.51. This technique indeed does result in a large reduction in the input bias current, the amount of the reduction being limited by the matching of the betas of the *npn* transistors in the circuit. Unfortunately, however, it does not improve the input offset current.

A practical input-current-cancellation circuit is shown in Fig. 6.52. In this circuit, transistor $Q_9$, together with diodes $Q_{10}$ and $Q_{11}$, serve to bias the emitters of $Q_6$ and $Q_8$ at a potential three diode drops more positive than the emitters of $Q_1$ and $Q_2$. Diodes $Q_7$ and

**Figure 6.52** Typical bias-current–cancellation circuit.

$Q_5$ are forward biased since they carry the base currents of $Q_3$ and $Q_4$, and so the bases of $Q_3$ and $Q_4$ are two diode drops above the emitters of $Q_1$ and $Q_2$. The emitters of $Q_3$ and $Q_4$ are then one diode drop above the emitters of $Q_1$ and $Q_2$, and these input transistors operate at approximately zero collector-base bias. Assuming the beta of the *npn* devices is large, the collector current of $Q_3$ and $Q_4$ is approximately equal to that of input transistors $Q_1$ and $Q_2$. If the *npn* betas are all the same, then the base currents of $Q_3$ and $Q_4$ are the same as the base currents of $Q_1$ and $Q_2$. The *pnp* current mirrors, $Q_5$, $Q_6$, $Q_7$ and $Q_8$, then take this base current and supply a nearly identical current back into the base of $Q_1$ and $Q_2$. With perfect matching, the extent of the cancellation depends on the magnitudes of the *pnp* and *npn* betas.

In practice, the *npn* betas are high but the *pnp* betas are rather low in this circuit because the *pnp* devices themselves operate at very low current level. Also, the betas of the *npn* transistors do not match precisely. As a result, a mismatch of from 5 to 20 percent typically exists between the base current of $Q_1$ and the collector current of $Q_6$. The resulting residual input current is typically one-fifth to one-twentieth of the original uncompensated input current.

The input offset current, on the other hand, is made worse by the presence of the cancellation circuitry. The input offset current is the sum of the original mismatch in the base currents $Q_1$ and $Q_2$, plus the mismatch in the collector currents of $Q_6$ and $Q_8$. The latter depends on the beta matching of the pairs $Q_3 - Q_4$, $Q_5 - Q_6$, and $Q_7 - Q_8$, and on the $I_S$ matching of $Q_5 - Q_6$, and $Q_7 - Q_8$. The offset current will be worsened by a factor of two to four compared with the uncompensated case. The input noise current is also increased, as described in Chapter 11. An example of a typical bias current compensated amplifier is the OP-07,[14] which also incorporates offset trimming as described in Section 6.9.1 and shown in Fig. 6.48. The resulting circuit has a typical input offset voltage of 50 $\mu$V, a typical input bias current of 4 nA, and a typical offset current of 4 nA.

**Superbeta Transistors.** A second approach to decreasing the input bias current is to increase the current gain of the input-stage transistors.[15] A practical method of achieving this result is the use of superbeta transistors as described in Section 2.7.2. From a circuit standpoint, application of these devices requires the design of an input stage in which the input devices are never subjected to a collector-emitter voltage of more than 1 or 2 V. This restriction can be satisfied using a cascode configuration as shown in Fig. 6.53. The diodes $D_1$ and $D_2$, together with current source $I_1$, bias the bases of $Q_3$ and $Q_4$ at a potential two diode drops above the emitters of $Q_1$ and $Q_2$. This results in zero collector-base voltage in $Q_1$ and $Q_2$. The 108 is a typical super-beta op amp[15] and has an input bias current of 3 nA and an offset current of 0.5 nA.

**Operational Amplifiers with MOS Input Transistors.** A third practical alternative for achieving low input bias current is the use of MOS transistors as the input devices. As described in Section 6.2, MOS transistors have intrinsic gate currents on the order of femtoamps, giving ultra-low input bias currents in internal applications, where protection diodes are not required.

One way to use MOS transistors at the op-amp inputs is simply to replace the bipolar differential pair with an MOS differential pair. Since MOS transistors give a low transconductance-to-current ratio, however, this direct substitution reduces the transconductance for a fixed tail bias current as shown by (1.181) and (1.182). As a result, source-coupled pairs of MOS transistors inherently display higher input-referred random offset voltage than bipolar pairs for the same level of geometric mismatch or process gradient

Figure 6.53 Super-$\beta$ input stage using cascode configuration.

as described in Section 3.5.6.7. To avoid the reduction in the transconductance, an alternative is to drive a bipolar differential pair with MOS source followers. In this case, the transconductance is determined by the bipolar transistors and the input-referred bias and offset currents are zero, but the MOS transistors contribute significantly to the input-referred random offset voltage. See Problem 6.31. Therefore, the use of MOS devices at the inputs of an op amp overcomes the problems associated with nonzero input currents at the expense of worsening the offset voltage.

## PROBLEMS

**6.1** For the circuit of Fig. 6.54, determine the output current as a function of the input voltage. Assume that the transistor operates in the active region.

when the input voltage is zero. Assume a nonzero input bias current, but zero input offset current and input offset voltage.

Figure 6.54 Circuit for Problem 6.1.

Figure 6.55 Circuit for Problem 6.2.

**6.2** Determine the output voltage as a function of the input voltage for the circuit of Fig. 6.55. Assume the op amp is ideal.

**6.3** In the circuit of Fig. 6.56, determine the correct value of $R_x$ so that the output voltage is zero

**6.4** The differential instrumentation amplifier shown in Fig. 6.57 must have a voltage gain of $10^3$ with an accuracy of 0.1 percent. What is the minimum required open-loop gain of the op amp? Assume the op amp open-loop gain has a tolerance

**Figure 6.56** Circuit for Problem 6.3.

**Figure 6.57** Circuit for Problem 6.4.

of +100 percent, −50 percent. Neglect the effects of $R_{in}$ and $R_{out}$ in the op amp.

**6.5** Once the offset voltage of the differential amplifier in Problem 6.4 is adjusted to zero, the input-referred offset voltage must remain less than 1 mV in magnitude for common-mode input voltages between ±10 V. What is the minimum CMRR allowable for the amplifier to meet this requirement?

**6.6** Consider the differential amplifier shown in Fig. 6.4. Choose values of $R_1$ and $R_2$ for which the gain is equal to −10 and the magnitude of the dc output voltage is less than or equal to −10 mV with $V_1 = V_2 = 0$. Assume that the op amp is ideal except that $|I_{OS}| = 100$ nA.

**6.7** Suppose an op amp with PSRR$^+$ = 10 is connected in the voltage-follower configuration shown in Fig. 6.3c. The input $V_s$ is set to zero, but a low-frequency ac signal with peak magnitude $v_{sup} = 20$ mV is is superimposed on the positive power supply. Calculate the peak magnitude of the output voltage.

**6.8** In the switched-capacitor amplifier of Fig. 6.9a, assume that the source of $M_4$ is connected to $V_s$ instead of to ground. Calculate the output voltage that appears during $\phi_2$ for a given $V_s$. Assume the op amp is ideal except that it has a finite gain $a$ and a nonzero input capacitance $C_P$. Assume ideal

MOS switches with zero on-resistance and infinite off-resistance.

**6.9(a)** Calculate and sketch the output voltage waveform of the switched-capacitor integrator of Fig. 6.10a from $t = 0$ to $t = 20$ μs assuming a fixed $V_s = 1$ V and a clock rate of 1 MHz. Assume an ideal MOS op amp with infinite gain and zero output rise time. Assume ideal MOS switches with zero on-resistance and infinite off-resistance.

**(b)** Compare the result for (a) with the output waveform of the continuous-time equivalent circuit of Fig. 6.10c.

**(c)** Investigate the effect on the output voltage waveform in (a) of a finite voltage gain of 1000 in the MOS op amp.

**6.10** Calculate the low-frequency PSRR from the $V_{dd}$ and $V_{ss}$ power supplies for the common-source amplifier shown in Fig. 6.58. Assume the transistor is biased in the active region.

**Figure 6.58** Circuit for Problem 6.10.

**6.11** Draw a two-stage op amp similar to the op amp in Fig. 6.16 except reverse the polarity of every transistor. For example, the resulting op amp should have an n-channel input pair. Calculate the following parameters: (a) low-frequency voltage gain, (b) output swing, (c) systematic input offset voltage assuming (6.66) is satisfied, (d) common-mode rejection ratio, (e) common-mode input range, and (f) low-frequency power-supply rejection ratio from both supplies.

**6.12(a)** Equation 6.69 gives the random input offset voltage of the op amp in Fig. 6.16. Explain the polarity of each term in (6.69) by assuming that the matching is perfect except for the term under consideration. Keep in mind that the overdrive is negative for p-channel transistors. Therefore, (6.69) predicts that the offset stemming from $W_3 > W_4$ is negative.

**(b)** Repeat (a) for an op amp that uses an *n*-channel differential pair and a *p*-channel current-mirror load. Equation 6.69 still applies in this case.

**6.13(a)** Calculate the random input offset voltage for the op amp in Fig. 6.16. Assume the matching is perfect except that $V_{t3} - V_{t4} = 10\text{mV}$. Also assume that all transistors have equal $W/L$ and operate in the active region. Ignore short-channel effects and use the data in Table 2.4.

**(b)** Repeat (a) for an op amp that uses an *n*-channel differential pair and a *p*-channel current-mirror load.

**(c)** Which of these two configurations gives lower input offset voltage? Explain.

**6.14** List and explain at least three reasons to select a two-stage op amp with an *n*-channel input pair instead of with a *p*-channel input pair for a given application.

**6.15** Calculate bias currents and the low-frequency small-signal voltage gain for the CMOS op amp of Fig. 6.59. Use the parameters given in Table 2.4, and assume that $X_d = 0.1\ \mu\text{m}$ and $dX_d/dV_{DS} = 0.04\ \mu\text{m/V}$ for all the transistors at the operating point. Calculate the input common-mode range assuming that the wells of $M_1$ and $M_2$

are connected to their common-source point. Calculate the low-frequency gain from each supply to the output. Check these calculations with SPICE simulations.

**6.16** Calculate the common-mode input range of the op amp in Fig. 6.25. Assume that all the transistors are enhancement-mode devices with $|V_t| = 1$ V, and ignore the body effect. Also assume that the biasing is arranged so that $|V_{ov}| = 0.2$ V for each transistor except $M_9$. Finally, assume that $M_1$ and $M_2$ are biased at the edge of the active region by $M_9$ and $I_C$.

**6.17** Draw a telescopic-cascode op amp similar to the first stage in Fig. 6.25 except use an *n*-channel input pair and a high-swing *p*-type cascode current-mirror load. Calculate the maximum output swing in terms of the common-mode input voltage. Determine the optimum common-mode input voltage for maximizing the output swing, and calculate the swing with this common-mode input voltage under the same assumptions given in Problem 6.16.

**6.18** Calculate the common-mode input range of the folded-cascode op amp in Fig. 6.28. Assume that all the transistors are enhancement-mode devices with $|V_t| = 1$ V, and ignore the body effect.

$V_{DD} = 1.5$ V

$-V_{DD} = -1.5$ V

**Figure 6.59** Circuit for Problem 6.15.

Also assume that the biasing is arranged so that $|V_{ov}| = 0.2$ V for each transistor. Finally, assume that $M_{11}$ and $M_{12}$ are biased at the edge of the active region.

**6.19** Find the low-frequency voltage gain from variation on each power supply to the op-amp output in Fig. 6.28. Assume that the bias voltages $V_{BIAS1}$, $V_{BIAS2}$, and $V_{BIAS3}$ are produced by the circuit shown in Fig. 6.60, where $M_{106}$ is the only transistor that operates in the triode region. Assume that the $W/L$ ratios are chosen so that all transistors in the op amp operate in the active region. Compare your calculations to SPICE simulations. Use models and supply voltages of your choice provided that the above conditions are satisfied.

**6.20** Design a CMOS op amp based on the folded-cascode architecture of Fig. 6.28 using supply voltages of $\pm 1.5$ V. Use the bias circuit of Fig. 4.42 (with $M_3$ and $M_4$ cascoded) to generate the bias current $I_{BIAS}$. Then design an extension to this bias circuit that produces the bias voltages $V_{BIAS1}$, $V_{BIAS2}$, and $V_{BIAS3}$ based on $I_{BIAS}$. The output current-drive capability is to be $\pm 100$ μA, the output voltage-swing capability 1.5 Volts peak-peak, and the input common-mode range should extend from 0.5 V to the negative supply. Matching requirements dictate a minimum effective channel length of 1 μm. To make the gain insensitive to small shifts in the operating point, design the

circuit so that the magnitude of the drain-source voltage for each transistor operating in the active region exceeds the magnitude of its overdrive by at least 100 mV. Specify all device geometries and bias currents. The process is the $n$-well process with parameters given in Table 2.4. Assume $X_d = 0$ and $\gamma = 0.25 V^{1/2}$ for both $n$- and $p$-channel transistors, but ignore the body effect in the hand calculations. Use SPICE to verify and refine your design as well as to determine the gain.

**6.21** Draw the schematic of a folded-cascode op amp similar to the op amp in Fig. 6.28 except with two layers of both $n$- and $p$-type cascodes. Choose a current mirror that maximizes the output swing. Assume that all transistors have equal overdrive magnitudes except where changes are needed to maximize the output swing. Use the models in Table 2.4 and ignore the body effect. Specify the $W/L$ ratios in multiples of $(W/L)_1$.

**6.22** For the folded-active-cascode op amp in Fig. 6.30, choose the device sizes to give a peak-peak output swing of at least 2.5 V. Use the 0.4 μm CMOS model parameters in Table 2.4 except let $\gamma = 0.25$ $V^{1/2}$ and $X_d = 0$ for all transistors and $V_{t0} = 0.7$ V and $-0.7$ V for $n$-channel and $p$-channel transistors, respectively. Assume the drawn channel length is $L = 1$ μm is used for all transistors to simplify the design. With $I_{BIAS} = 25$ μA, the bias currents should be

**Figure 6.60** Bias circuit for Problem 6.19.

$|I_{D5}| = I_{D11} = I_{D12} = I_{D25} = |I_{D35}| = 200 \ \mu A$. Assume $V_{DD} = V_{SS} = 1.65$ V and that the matching is perfect. When the dc input voltage $V_I = 0$, assume that all transistors except $M_{106}$ and $M_{114}$ operate in the active region with equal overdrive magnitudes. To make the gain insensitive to small shifts in the operating point, design the circuit so that the magnitude of the drain-source voltage for each transistor operating in the active region exceeds the magnitude of its overdrive by at least 100 mV. Ignore the body effect in the hand calculations. Use SPICE to verify your design, to choose the widths of $M_{106}$ and $M_{114}$, and to determine the gain. Also, use SPICE to determine the gain if $V_{t0} = 0.6$ V for $n$-channel transistors and $V_{t0} = -0.8$ V for $p$-channel transistors, as given in Table 2.4. Explain the resulting change in the op-amp gain.

**6.23** Suppose that the peak-peak output swing requirement in Problem 6.22 is reduced while the other conditions are held constant. This change allows the overdrive magnitude to be increased. Which transistor in the bias circuit of Fig. 6.30$d$ enters the triode region first if the overdrive magnitudes are increased uniformly? Explain. Exclude $M_{106}$ and $M_{114}$ from consideration because they are deliberately operated in the triode region. How can the bias circuit be redesigned to increase the allowed overdrive magnitude while operating all transistors except $M_{106}$ and $M_{114}$ in the active region? What are the disadvantages of the modified bias circuit?

**6.24(a)** Figure 6.61$a$ shows a folded version of the op amp in Fig. 6.15. A differential interstage level-shifting network composed of voltage sources $V$ has been inserted between the first and second stages. Assume that current source $I_1$ is implemented using an $n$-channel transistor with overdrive of $V_{ovn}$, which is equal to the overdrives of the other $n$-channel transistors shown in Fig. 6.61$a$. Assume that current sources $I_2$ and $I_3$ are each implemented using one $p$-channel transistor with an overdrive of $V_{ovp}$. In the resulting op amp, only $n$-channel transistors conduct time-varying currents. Find the input common-mode range and the maximum output swing of the op-amp in terms of $V_{DD}$, $-V_{SS}$, the level-shift voltage $V$, the threshold voltages of individual transistors, and the overdrives $V_{ovn}$ and $V_{ovp}$.

**(b)** Figure 6.61$b$ shows a realization of an active floating level shift (active battery). Design this level-shift circuit to give a battery voltage of 1.5 V with a small-signal resistance less than 1 k$\Omega$ at $I = 100 \ \mu A$ dc. Ignore the body effect. Use $I_B = 100 \ \mu A$ and $V_{DD} = V_{SS} = 1.65$ V. Use SPICE to plot the large-signal $I - V$ characteristic for $V = 0$ to 1.65 V. Use $\mu_n C_{ox} = 194 \ \mu A/V^2$, $\lambda = 0$, and $V_t = 0.6$ V. For SPICE simulations, connect the lower end of the battery to the negative supply.

**6.25** In the input stage of the 741, calculate the collector current change in $Q_1$ and $Q_2$ when the power-supply voltage is reduced from $\pm15$ V to $\pm10$ V. Neglect the effects of finite output resistance in the transistors. Check with a SPICE

(a)    (b)

**Figure 6.61** Circuits for Problem 6.24.

**Figure 6.62** Circuits for Problem 6.26.

simulation and then add finite output resistance in the transistors and compare the results.

**6.26** Shown in Fig. 6.62 are two alternate schemes for biasing the 741 input stage. In each case determine the required values of $I_{REF}$ to give an input transistor collector current of 10 µA. Neglect *npn* base currents. Assume that the *pnp* beta is 50 and $V_A \to \infty$ for all devices. Assume that devices of the same type are identical. Check your results with SPICE and also use SPICE to compare the small-signal transconductance of the stages for a differential input voltage drive. (Use a dc bias voltage of 1.6 V relative to $-V_{EE}$ on the output.) Discuss any differences.

**6.27** Shown in Fig. 6.63 is an alternate output-stage biasing scheme using a $V_{BE}$ multiplier. Determine the bias current as a function of the resistor ratio $R_2/R_1$. Determine the resistor ratio required to give a bias current of 50 µA. Does $I_{BIAS}$ remain constant over temperature? Assume that the output transistors $Q_3$ and $Q_4$ have a saturation current that is five times that of the small-geometry devices. Neglect the portion of the 200 µA flowing through $R_2$ and $R_1$, and neglect base currents. Assume $I_S = 10^{-15}$ A. Use SPICE to calculate bias currents in the circuit using your calculated resistor ratio and $R_1 = 100\,k\Omega$. Plot the variation in $I_{BIAS}$ from $-55°C$ to $+125°C$.

**6.28** Determine the gain of the 741 if the bias current level in the input stage is doubled.

**6.29** How is the gain of the 741 affected if the 100-$\Omega$ resistor in the emitter of $Q_{17}$ is removed? Find the new value of voltage gain.

**Figure 6.63** Circuit for Problem 6.27.

**6.30** Determine the common-mode input voltage range of the 741. By connecting the 741 in a unity-gain feedback configuration such as in Fig. 6.3c, use SPICE to investigate the effect of the common-mode input voltage limits by plotting out the overall dc transfer characteristic of the voltage follower and relating the features of the plot to the 741 parameters.

**Figure 6.64**  Circuit for Problem 6.31.

**6.31** Calculate the input referred random off-set voltage of a bipolar differential pair with resistive loads driven by source followers, as shown in Fig. 6.64. Assume nonzero mismatch occurs in the following parameters: the thresholds of the MOS transistors, the $W/L$ of the MOS transistors, the bias currents, the saturation currents of the bipolar transistors, and the load resistors. Ignore the body effect.

# REFERENCES

1. G. E. Tobey, J. G. Graeme, and L. P. Huelsman. *Operational Amplifiers*. McGraw-Hill, New York, 1971.

2. J. V. Wait, L. P. Huelsman, and G. A. Korn. *Introduction to Operational Amplifier Theory and Applications*. McGraw-Hill, New York, 1975.

3. D. Fullagar. "A New High-Performance Monolithic Op Amp," *Fairchild Semiconductor Applications Brief*, May 1968.

4. D. A. Hodges, P. R. Gray, and R. W. Brodersen. "Potential of MOS Technologies for Analog Integrated Circuits," *IEEE Journal of Solid-State Circuits*, Vol. SC-13, pp. 285–294, June 1978.

5. P. R. Gray and R. G. Meyer. "MOS Operational Amplifier Design-A Tutorial Overview," *IEEE Journal of Solid-State Circuits*, Vol. SC-17, pp. 969–982, December 1982.

6. Y. P. Tsividis. "Design Considerations in Single-Channel MOS Analog Integrated Circuits—A Tutorial," *IEEE Journal of Solid-State Circuits*, Vol. SC-13, pp. 383–391, June 1978.

7. W. C. Black, Jr., D. J. Allstot, and R. A. Reed. "A High Performance Low Power CMOS Channel Filter," *IEEE Journal of Solid-State Circuits*, Vol. SC-15, pp. 929–938, December 1980.

8. H. Ohara, P. R. Gray, W. M. Baxter, C. F. Rahim, and J. L. McCreary. "A Precision Low-Power PCM Channel Filter with On-Chip Power Supply Regulation," *IEEE Journal of Solid-State Circuits*, Vol. SC-15, pp. 1005–1013, December 1980.

9. G. Nicollini, P. Confalonieri, and D. Senderowicz, "A Fully Differential Sample-and-Hold Circuit for High-Speed Applications," *IEEE Journal of Solid-State Circuits*, Vol. 24, pp. 1461-1465, October 1989.

10. T. C. Choi, R. T. Kaneshiro, R. W. Brodersen, P. R. Gray, W. B. Jett, and M. Wilcox. "High-Frequency CMOS Switched-Capacitor Filters for Communications Application," *IEEE Journal of Solid-State Circuits*, Vol. SC-18, pp. 652–664, December 1983.

11. K. Bult and G. J. G. M. Geelen. "A Fast-Settling CMOS Op Amp for SC Circuits with 90-dB DC Gain," *IEEE Journal of Solid-State Circuits*, Vol. 25, pp. 1379–1384, December 1990.

12. P. R. Gray and R. G. Meyer. *Analysis and Design of Analog Integrated Circuits*, Third Edition, Wiley, New York, 1993.

13. G. Erdi. "A Low-Drift, Low-Noise Monolithic Operational Amplifier for Low-Level Signal Processing," *Fairchild Semiconductor Applications Brief*, July 1969.

14. G. Erdi. "A Precision Trim Technique for Monolithic Analog Circuits," *IEEE Journal of Solid-State Circuits*, Vol. SC-10, pp. 412–416, December 1975.

15. R. J. Widlar. "Design Techniques for Monolithic Operational Amplifiers," *IEEE Journal of Solid-State Circuits*, Vol. SC-4, pp. 184–191, August 1969.

# Frequency Response of Integrated Circuits

## 7.1 Introduction

The analysis of integrated-circuit behavior in previous chapters was concerned with low-frequency performance, and the effects of parasitic capacitance in transistors were not considered. However, as the frequency of the signal being processed by a circuit increases, the capacitive elements in the circuit eventually become important.

In this chapter, the small-signal behavior of integrated circuits at high frequencies is considered. The frequency response of single-stage amplifiers is treated first, followed by an analysis of multistage amplifiers. Finally, the frequency response of the 741 operational amplifier is considered, and those parts of the circuit that limit its frequency response are identified.

## 7.2 Single-Stage Amplifiers

The basic topology of the small-signal equivalent circuits of bipolar and MOS single-stage amplifiers are similar. Therefore in the following sections, the frequency-response analysis for each type of single-stage circuit is initially carried out using a general small-signal model that applies to both types of transistors, and the general results are then applied to each type of transistor. The general small-signal transistor model is shown in Fig. 7.1. Table 7.1 lists the parameters of this small-signal model and the corresponding parameters that transform it into a bipolar or MOS model. For example, $C_{in}$ in the general model becomes $C_\pi$ in the bipolar model and $C_{gs}$ in the MOS model. However, some device-specific small-signal elements are not included in the general model. For example, the $g_{mb}$ generator and capacitors $C_{sb}$ and $C_{gb}$ in the MOS models are not incorporated in the general model. The effect of such device-specific elements will be handled separately in the bipolar and MOS sections.

The common-emitter and common-source stages are analyzed in the sections below on differential amplifiers.

### 7.2.1 Single-Stage Voltage Amplifiers and the Miller Effect

Single-transistor voltage-amplifier stages are widely used in integrated circuits. Figures 7.2a and 7.2b show the ac schematics for common-emitter and common-source amplifiers with resistive loads, respectively. Resistance $R_S$ is the source resistance, and $R_L$ is the load resistance. A simple linear model that can be applied to both of these circuits is shown in Fig. 7.2c. The elements in the dashed box form the general small-signal transistor model from Fig. 7.1 without $r_o$. We will assume that the output resistance of the transistor $r_o$ is much larger than $R_L$. Since these resistors are connected in parallel in the small-signal

Figure 7.1  A general small-signal transistor model.

circuit, $r_o$ can be neglected. An approximate analysis of this circuit can be made using the *Miller-effect* approximation. This analysis is done by considering the input impedance seen looking across the plane AA in Fig. 7.2c. To find this impedance, we calculate the current $i_1$ produced by the voltage $v_1$.

$$i_1 = (v_1 - v_o)sC_f \tag{7.1}$$

KCL at the output node gives

$$g_m v_1 + \frac{v_o}{R_L} + (v_o - v_1)sC_f = 0 \tag{7.2}$$

From (7.2), the voltage gain $A_v$ from $v_1$ to $v_o$ can be expressed as

$$A_v(s) = \frac{v_o}{v_1} = -g_m R_L \left( \frac{1 - s\frac{g_m}{C_f}}{1 + sR_L C_f} \right) \tag{7.3}$$

Using $v_o = A_v(s)v_1$ from (7.3) in (7.1) gives

$$i_1 = [1 - A_v(s)]sC_f v_1 \tag{7.4}$$

Equation 7.4 indicates that the admittance seen looking across the plane AA has a value $[1 - A_v(s)]sC_f$. This modification to the admittance $sC_f$ stems from the voltage gain across $C_f$ and is referred to as the Miller effect. Unfortunately, this admittance is complicated, due to the frequency dependence of $A_v(s)$. Replacing the voltage gain $A_v(s)$ in (7.4) with its low-frequency value $A_{v0} = A_v(0)$, (7.4) indicates that a capacitance of value

$$C_M = (1 - A_{v0})C_f \tag{7.5}$$

**Table 7.1**  Small-Signal Model Elements

| General Model | Bipolar Model | MOS Model |
|:---:|:---:|:---:|
| $r_x$ | $r_b$ | 0 |
| $r_{in}$ | $r_\pi$ | $\infty$ |
| $C_{in}$ | $C_\pi$ | $C_{gs}$ |
| $C_f$ | $C_\mu$ | $C_{gd}$ |
| $r_o$ | $r_o$ | $r_o$ |

(c)

**Figure 7.2**  (a) An ac schematic of a common-emitter amplifier. (b) An ac schematic of a common-source amplifier. (c) A general model for both amplifiers.

is seen looking across plane AA. The use of the low-frequency voltage gain here is called the *Miller approximation,* and $C_M$ is called the *Miller capacitance.* From (7.3), $A_{v0} = A_v(0) = -g_m R_L$; therefore, (7.5) can be written as

$$C_M = (1 + g_m R_L)C_f \qquad (7.6)$$

The Miller capacitance is often much larger than $C_f$ because usually $g_m R_L \gg 1$.

We can now form a new equivalent circuit that is useful for calculating the *forward transmission* and input impedance of the circuit. This is shown in Fig. 7.3 using the Miller-effect approximation. Note that this equivalent circuit is *not* useful for calculating high-frequency reverse transmission or output impedance. From this circuit, we can see that at high frequencies the input impedance will eventually approach $r_x$.

The physical origin of the Miller capacitance is found in the voltage gain of the circuit. At low frequencies, a small input voltage $v_1$ produces a large output voltage $v_o = A_{v0}v_1 = -g_m R_L v_1$ of *opposite polarity.* Thus the voltage across $C_f$ in Fig. 7.2c is $(1 + g_m R_L)v_1$ and a correspondingly large current $i_1$ flows in this capacitor. The voltage across $C_M$

**Figure 7.3**  Equivalent circuit for Fig. 7.2c using the Miller approximation.

in Fig. 7.3 is only $v_1$, but $C_M$ is larger than $C_f$ by the factor $(1 + g_m R_L)$; therefore, $C_M$ conducts the same current as $C_f$.

In Fig. 7.3, the Miller capacitance adds directly to $C_{in}$ and thus reduces the bandwidth of the amplifier, which can be seen by calculating the gain of the amplifier as follows:

$$v_1 = \frac{\dfrac{r_{in}}{1 + s r_{in} C_t}}{\dfrac{r_{in}}{1 + s r_{in} C_t} + R_S + r_x} v_i \tag{7.7}$$

$$v_o = -g_m R_L v_1 \tag{7.8}$$

where

$$C_t = C_M + C_{in} \tag{7.9}$$

Substitution of (7.7) in (7.8) gives the gain

$$A(s) = \frac{v_o}{v_i} = -g_m R_L \frac{r_{in}}{R_S + r_x + r_{in}} \frac{1}{1 + s C_t \dfrac{(R_S + r_x) r_{in}}{R_S + r_x + r_{in}}} \tag{7.10a}$$

$$= K \frac{1}{1 - \dfrac{s}{p_1}} \tag{7.10b}$$

where $K$ is the low-frequency voltage gain and $p_1$ is the pole of the circuit. Comparing (7.10a) and (7.10b) shows that

$$K = -g_m R_L \frac{r_{in}}{R_S + r_x + r_{in}} \tag{7.11a}$$

$$p_1 = -\frac{R_S + r_x + r_{in}}{(R_S + r_x) r_{in}} \cdot \frac{1}{C_t} = -\frac{1}{[(R_S + r_x)\|r_{in}] C_t}$$

$$= -\frac{1}{[(R_S + r_x)\|r_{in}] \cdot [C_{in} + C_f(1 + g_m R_L)]} \tag{7.11b}$$

This analysis indicates that the circuit has a single pole, and setting $s = j\omega$ in (7.10b) shows that the voltage gain is 3 dB below its low-frequency value at a frequency

$$\omega_{-3dB} = |p_1| = \frac{R_S + r_x + r_{in}}{(R_S + r_x) r_{in}} \cdot \frac{1}{C_t} = \frac{1}{[(R_S + r_x)\|r_{in}] \cdot [C_{in} + C_f(1 + g_m R_L)]} \tag{7.12}$$

As $C_t$, $R_L$, or $R_S$ increase, the $-3$-dB frequency of the amplifier is reduced.

The exact gain expression for this circuit can be found by analyzing the equivalent circuit shown in Fig. 7.4. The poles from an exact analysis can be compared to the pole found using the Miller effect. In Fig. 7.4, a Norton equivalent is used at the input where

$$R = (R_S + r_x)\|r_{in} \tag{7.13}$$

$$i_i = \frac{v_i}{R_S + r_x} \tag{7.14}$$

KCL at node $X$ gives

$$i_i = \frac{v_1}{R} + v_1 s C_{in} + (v_1 - v_o) s C_f \tag{7.15}$$

**Figure 7.4** Figure 7.2c redrawn using a Norton equivalent circuit at the input.

KCL at node $Y$ gives

$$g_m v_1 + \frac{v_o}{R_L} + (v_o - v_1)sC_f = 0 \qquad (7.16a)$$

Equation 7.16a can be written as

$$v_1(g_m - sC_f) = -v_o\left(\frac{1}{R_L} + sC_f\right) \qquad (7.16b)$$

and thus

$$v_1 = -v_o \frac{\frac{1}{R_L} + sC_f}{g_m - sC_f} \qquad (7.17)$$

Substitution of (7.17) in (7.15) gives

$$i_i = -\left(\frac{1}{R} + sC_{in} + sC_f\right)\frac{\frac{1}{R_L} + sC_f}{g_m - sC_f}v_o - sC_f v_o$$

and the transfer function can be calculated as

$$\frac{v_o}{i_i} = -\frac{RR_L(g_m - sC_f)}{1 + s(C_f R_L + C_f R + C_{in}R + g_m R_L RC_f) + s^2 R_L RC_f C_{in}} \qquad (7.18)$$

Substitution of $i_i$ from (7.14) in (7.18) gives

$$\frac{v_o}{v_i} = -\frac{g_m R_L R}{R_S + r_x}\frac{1 - s\frac{C_f}{g_m}}{1 + s(C_f R_L + C_f R + C_{in}R + g_m R_L RC_f) + s^2 R_L RC_f C_{in}} \qquad (7.19)$$

Substitution of $R$ from (7.13) into (7.19) gives, for the low-frequency gain,

$$\left.\frac{v_o}{v_i}\right|_{\omega=0} = -g_m R_L \frac{r_{in}}{R_S + r_x + r_{in}} \qquad (7.20)$$

as obtained in (7.10).

Equation 7.19 shows that the transfer function $v_o/v_i$ has a positive real zero with magnitude $g_m/C_f$. This zero stems from the transmission of the signal directly through $C_f$ to the output. The effect of this zero is small except at very high frequencies, and it will be neglected here. However, this positive real zero can be important in the stability analysis of some operational amplifiers, and it will be considered in detail in Chapter 9. The denominator of (7.19) shows that the transfer function has two poles, which are usually real and widely separated in practice. If the poles are at $p_1$ and $p_2$, we can write the denominator of (7.19) as

$$D(s) = \left(1 - \frac{s}{p_1}\right)\left(1 - \frac{s}{p_2}\right) \qquad (7.21)$$

and thus

$$D(s) = 1 - s\left(\frac{1}{p_1} + \frac{1}{p_2}\right) + \frac{s^2}{p_1 p_2} \tag{7.22}$$

We now assume that the poles are real and widely separated, and we let the lower frequency pole be $p_1$ (the dominant pole) and the higher frequency pole be $p_2$ (the nondominant pole). Then $|p_2| \gg |p_1|$ and (7.22) becomes

$$D(s) \approx 1 - \frac{s}{p_1} + \frac{s^2}{p_1 p_2} \tag{7.23}$$

If the coefficient of $s$ in (7.23) is compared with that in (7.19), we can identify

$$p_1 = -\frac{1}{C_{in}R + C_f(R + g_m R_L R + R_L)} \tag{7.24}$$

$$= -\frac{1}{R\left[C_{in} + C_f\left(1 + g_m R_L + \dfrac{R_L}{R}\right)\right]}$$

If the value of $R$ from (7.13) is substituted in (7.24), then the dominant pole is

$$p_1 = -\frac{R_S + r_x + r_{in}}{(R_S + r_x)r_{in}} \cdot \frac{1}{\left[C_{in} + C_f\left(1 + g_m R_L + \dfrac{R_L}{R}\right)\right]} \tag{7.25}$$

$$= -\frac{1}{[(R_S + r_x)\|r_{in}] \cdot \left[C_{in} + C_f\left(1 + g_m R_L + \dfrac{R_L}{R}\right)\right]}$$

This value of $p_1$ is almost identical to that given in (7.11b) by the Miller approximation. The only difference between these equations is in the last term in the denominator of (7.25), $R_L/R$, and this term is usually small compared to the $(1 + g_m R_L)$ term. This result shows that the Miller-effect calculation is nearly equivalent to calculating the dominant pole of the amplifier and neglecting higher frequency poles. The Miller approximation gives a good estimate of $\omega_{-3dB}$ in many circuits.

Let us now calculate the nondominant pole by equating the coefficient of $s^2$ in (7.23) with that in (7.19), giving

$$p_2 = \frac{1}{p_1} \frac{1}{R_L R C_f C_{in}} \tag{7.26}$$

Substitution of $p_1$ from (7.24) in (7.26) gives

$$p_2 = -\left(\frac{1}{R_L C_f} + \frac{1}{R C_{in}} + \frac{1}{R_L C_{in}} + \frac{g_m}{C_{in}}\right) \tag{7.27}$$

The results in this section were derived using a general small-signal model. The general model parameters and the corresponding parameters for a bipolar and MOS transistor are listed in Table 7.1. By substituting values from Table 7.1, the general results of this section will be extended to the bipolar common-emitter and MOS common-source amplifiers, which appear in the half-circuits for differential amplifiers in the following sections.

### 7.2.1.1 The Bipolar Differential Amplifier: Differential-Mode Gain

A basic building block of analog bipolar integrated circuits is the differential stage shown in Fig. 7.5. For small-signal differential inputs at $v_i$, the node $E$ is a virtual ground, and we

Figure 7.5  Bipolar differential amplifier circuit.

can form the differential-mode (DM) ac half-circuit of Fig. 7.6a. The gain of this common-emitter circuit is equal to the DM gain of the full circuit. The circuit analysis that follows applies to this DM half-circuit as well as any single-stage common-emitter amplifier of the form shown in Fig. 7.6a. The small-signal equivalent circuit of Fig. 7.6a is shown in Fig. 7.6b and, for compactness, the factor of 1/2 has been omitted from the input and

Figure 7.6  (a) Differential-mode ac half-circuit for Fig. 7.5. (b) Small-signal equivalent circuit for (a).

output voltages. This change does not alter the analysis in any way. Also, for simplicity, the collector-substrate capacitance of the transistor has been omitted. Since this capacitance would be connected in parallel with $R_L$, its effect could be included in the following analysis by replacing $R_L$ with $Z_L$, where $Z_L$ equals $R_L$ in parallel with $C_{cs}$.

The small-signal circuit in Fig. 7.2c becomes the circuit in Fig. 7.6b when the bipolar model parameters in the second column of Table 7.1 are substituted for the general model parameters in Fig. 7.2c. Therefore, the analysis results from the previous section can be used here. Substituting the values in the second column of Table 7.1 into (7.19), the voltage gain is given by

$$\frac{v_o}{v_i} = -\frac{\dfrac{g_m R_L R}{R_S + r_b}\left(1 - s\dfrac{C_\mu}{g_m}\right)}{1 + s(C_\mu R_L + C_\mu R + C_\pi R + g_m R_L R C_\mu) + s^2 R_L R C_\mu C_\pi} \tag{7.28}$$

where $R = (R_S + r_b)\|r_\pi$. Using (7.25), the dominant pole is given by

$$p_1 = -\frac{1}{[(R_S + r_b)\|r_\pi]\left[C_\pi + C_\mu\left(1 + g_m R_L + \dfrac{R_L}{R}\right)\right]} \tag{7.29}$$

Calculation of $p_1$ using (7.11b), which is based on the Miller-effect approximation, gives

$$p_1 = -\frac{1}{[(R_S + r_b)\|r_\pi][C_\pi + C_\mu(1 + g_m R_L)]} = -\frac{1}{[(R_S + r_b)\|r_\pi](C_\pi + C_M)} \tag{7.30}$$

where

$$C_M = C_\mu(1 + g_m R_L) \tag{7.31}$$

is the Miller capacitance. Equation 7.30 gives virtually the same $p_1$ as (7.29) if $R_L/R \ll (1 + g_m R_L)$, which is usually true. This result shows that the Miller approximation is useful for finding the dominant pole. From (7.27), the nondominant pole is given by

$$p_2 = -\left(\frac{1}{R_L C_\mu} + \frac{1}{R C_\pi} + \frac{1}{R_L C_\pi} + \frac{g_m}{C_\pi}\right) \tag{7.32}$$

The last term of (7.32) is $g_m/C_\pi > g_m/(C_\pi + C_\mu) = \omega_T$ and thus $|p_2| > \omega_T$. (Recall that $\omega_T$ is the transition frequency for the transistor, as defined in Chapter 1.) Consequently, $|p_2|$ is a very high frequency; therefore, $|p_1|$ is almost always much less than $|p_2|$, as assumed. In the $s$ plane, the poles of the amplifier are thus widely separated, as shown in Fig. 7.7.

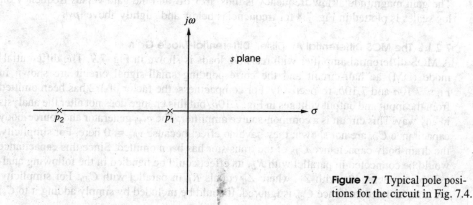

**Figure 7.7** Typical pole positions for the circuit in Fig. 7.4.

■    **EXAMPLE**

Using the Miller approximation, calculate the $-3$-dB frequency of a common-emitter transistor stage using the following parameters:

$$R_S = 1 \text{ k}\Omega \quad r_b = 200 \ \Omega \quad I_C = 1 \text{ mA} \quad \beta_0 = 100$$

$$f_T = 400 \text{ MHz (at } I_C = 1 \text{ mA)} \quad C_\mu = 0.5 \text{ pF} \quad R_L = 5 \text{ k}\Omega$$

The transistor small-signal parameters are

$$r_\pi = \frac{\beta_0}{g_m} = 100 \times 26 \ \Omega = 2.6 \text{ k}\Omega$$

$$\tau_T = \frac{1}{2\pi f_T} = 398 \text{ ps}$$

Using (1.129) gives

$$C_\pi + C_\mu = g_m \tau_T = \left(\frac{1 \text{ mA}}{26 \text{ mV}}\right) 398 \text{ ps} = 15.3 \text{ pF}$$

Thus

$$C_\pi = 14.8 \text{ pF}$$

Substitution of data in (7.31) gives for the Miller capacitance

$$C_M = (1 + g_m R_L) C_\mu = \left(1 + \frac{1 \text{ mA}}{26 \text{ mV}}(5 \text{ k}\Omega)\right)(0.5 \text{ pF}) = 96.7 \text{ pF}$$

This term is much greater than $C_\pi$ and dominates the frequency response. Substitution of values in (7.30) gives

$$f_{-3\text{dB}} = \frac{|p_1|}{2\pi} = \frac{1}{2\pi} \frac{1000 + 200 + 2600}{(1000 + 200)2600} \frac{10^{12}}{14.8 + 96.7} = 1.74 \text{ MHz}$$

For comparison, using (7.29) gives $|p_1| = 10.7$ Mrad/s and $f_{-3\text{dB}} = 1.70$ MHz, which is in close agreement with the value using the Miller effect. The low-frequency gain can be calculated from (7.28) as

$$\left.\frac{v_o}{v_i}\right|_{\omega=0} = -g_m R_L \frac{r_\pi}{R_S + r_b + r_\pi} = -\frac{5000}{26} \frac{2.6}{5 + 0.2 + 2.6} = -64.1$$

The gain magnitude at low frequency is thus 36.1 dB and the gain versus frequency on log scales is plotted in Fig. 7.8 for frequencies below and slightly above $|p_1|$.

### 7.2.1.2 The MOS Differential Amplifier: Differential-Mode Gain

A MOS differential amplifier with resistive loads is shown in Fig. 7.9. The differential-mode (DM) ac half-circuit and the corresponding small-signal circuit are shown in Figs. 7.10a and 7.10b, respectively. For compactness, the factor of 1/2 has been omitted from the input and output voltages in Fig. 7.10b, but this change does not alter the analysis in any way. This circuit is a common-source amplifier. The $g_{mb}$ generator and source-body capacitance $C_{sb}$ are not shown; they have no effect because $v_{bs} = 0$ here. For simplicity, the drain-body capacitance $C_{db}$ of the transistor has been omitted. Since this capacitance would be connected in parallel with $R_L$, its effect could be handled in the following analysis by replacing $R_L$ with $Z_L$, where $Z_L$ equals $R_L$ in parallel with $C_{db}$. For simplicity, the gate-body capacitance $C_{gb}$ is ignored. It could be included by simply adding it to $C_{gs}$.

**Figure 7.8** Gain magnitude versus frequency for the circuit in Fig. 7.3 using typical bipolar transistor data.

since $C_{gb}$ appears in parallel with $C_{gs}$ in the common-source amplifier. However, usually $C_{gs} \gg C_{gb}$, so $C_{gs} + C_{gb} \approx C_{gs}$. The analysis of this ac circuit applies to this DM half-circuit as well as any single-stage common-source amplifier of the form shown in Fig. 7.10a. The small-signal circuit in Fig. 7.10b is the same as the circuit in Fig. 7.2c if we rename the model parameters as listed in Table 7.1. Therefore, we can use the results of the analysis of Fig. 7.2c. Substituting the values from the third column in Table 7.1 in (7.19), the exact transfer function is given by

$$\frac{v_o}{v_i} = -\frac{g_m R_L \left(1 - s\dfrac{C_{gd}}{g_m}\right)}{1 + s(C_{gd}R_L + C_{gd}R_S + C_{gs}R_S + g_m R_L R_S C_{gd}) + s^2 R_L R_S C_{gd} C_{gs}} \qquad (7.33)$$

**Figure 7.9** MOS differential amplifier circuit.

**Figure 7.10** (a) Differential-mode ac half-circuit for Fig. 7.9. (b) Small-signal equivalent circuit for (a).

Using (7.25), the dominant pole is given by

$$p_1 = -\frac{1}{R_S\left[C_{gs} + C_{gd}(1 + g_m R_L + \dfrac{R_L}{R_S})\right]} \tag{7.34}$$

Calculation of $p_1$ using (7.11b), which is based on the Miller-effect approximation, gives

$$p_1 \approx -\frac{1}{R_S[C_{gs} + C_{gd}(1 + g_m R_L)]} = -\frac{1}{R_S(C_{gs} + C_M)} \tag{7.35}$$

where

$$C_M = C_{gd}(1 + g_m R_L) \tag{7.36}$$

is the Miller capacitance. Equation 7.35 gives nearly the same value for $p_1$ as (7.34) if $R_L/R_S \ll (1 + g_m R_L)$, which shows that the Miller approximation is useful for finding the dominant pole. From (7.27), the nondominant pole is given by

$$p_2 = -\left(\frac{1}{R_L C_{gd}} + \frac{1}{R_S C_{gs}} + \frac{1}{R_L C_{gs}} + \frac{g_m}{C_{gs}}\right) \tag{7.37}$$

The last term of (7.37) is $g_m/C_{gs} > g_m/(C_{gs} + C_{gd} + C_{gb}) = \omega_T$ and thus $|p_2| > \omega_T$. (Recall that $\omega_T$ is the transition frequency for the transistor, as defined in Chapter 1.) Consequently, $|p_2|$ is a very high frequency; therefore, $|p_1|$ is almost always much less than $|p_2|$. In the $s$ plane, the poles of the amplifier are thus widely separated, as shown in Fig. 7.7.

■ **EXAMPLE**

Using the Miller approximation, calculate the $-3$-dB frequency of a common-source transistor stage using the following parameters:

$$R_S = 1 \text{ k}\Omega \quad I_D = 1 \text{ mA} \quad k'\frac{W}{L} = 100 \frac{\text{mA}}{\text{V}^2}$$

$$f_T = 400 \text{ MHz (at } I_D = 1 \text{ mA)} \quad C_{gd} = 0.5 \text{ pF} \quad C_{gb} = 0 \quad R_L = 5 \text{ k}\Omega$$

The small-signal transconductance is

$$g_m = \sqrt{2\left(100\frac{\text{mA}}{\text{V}^2}\right)(1 \text{ mA})} = 14.1 \frac{\text{mA}}{\text{V}}$$

Using (1.207) from Chapter 1 and $C_{gb} = 0$ gives

$$C_{gs} + C_{gd} = \frac{g_m}{\omega_T} = \frac{14.1 \text{ mA/V}}{2\pi(400 \text{ MHz})} = 5.6 \text{ pF}$$

Thus

$$C_{gs} = 5.6 \text{ pF} - C_{gd} = 5.1 \text{ pF}$$

Substitution of data in (7.36) gives for the Miller capacitance

$$C_M = (1 + g_m R_L)C_{gd} = \left[1 + \left(14.1\frac{\text{mA}}{\text{V}}\right)(5 \text{ k}\Omega)\right](0.5 \text{ pF}) = 35.7 \text{ pF}$$

This capacitance is much greater than $C_{gs}$ and dominates the frequency response. Substitution of values in (7.35) gives

$$f_{-3\text{dB}} = \frac{|p_1|}{2\pi} = \frac{1}{2\pi} \frac{1}{(1000 \text{ }\Omega)(5.1 \text{ pF} + 35.7 \text{ pF})} = 3.9 \text{ MHz}$$

For comparison, using (7.34) gives $|p_1| = 23.1$ Mrad/s and $f_{-3\text{dB}} = 3.7$ MHz, which is close to the result using the Miller effect. The low-frequency gain can be calculated from (7.33) as

$$\left.\frac{v_o}{v_i}\right|_{\omega=0} = -g_m R_L = -\left(14.1\frac{\text{mA}}{\text{V}}\right)(5000 \text{ }\Omega) = -70.5$$

■

## 7.2.2 Frequency Response of the Common-Mode Gain for a Differential Amplifier

In Chapter 3, the importance of the common-mode (CM) gain of a differential amplifier was described. It was shown that low values of CM gain are desirable so that the circuit can reject undesired signals that are applied equally to both inputs. Because undesired CM signals may have high-frequency components, the frequency response of the CM gain is important. The CM frequency response of the differential circuits in Figures 7.5 and 7.9 can be calculated from the CM half-circuits shown in Figs. 7.11a and 7.11b. In Fig. 7.11, $R_T$ and $C_T$ are the equivalent output resistance and capacitance of the tail current source. Since impedances common to the two devices are doubled in the CM half-circuit, $R_T$ and $C_T$ become $2R_T$ and $C_T/2$, respectively. A general small-signal equivalent circuit for Fig. 7.11a-b is shown in Fig. 7.11c. The parallel combination of $2R_T$ and $C_T/2$ will be referred to as $Z_T$.

**Figure 7.11** (*a*) Common-mode ac half-circuit for Fig. 7.5. (*b*) Common-mode ac half-circuit for Fig. 7.9. (*c*) A general model for both half-circuits.

The complete analysis of Fig. 7.11*c* is quite complex. However, the important aspects of the frequency response can be calculated by making some approximations. Consider the time constant $R_T C_T$. The resistance $R_T$ is the output resistance of the current source and is usually greater than or equal to the $r_o$ of a transistor. Let us assume that this resistance is on the order of 1 M$\Omega$. The capacitor $C_T$ includes $C_{cs}$ of the bipolar current-source transistor or $C_{db}$ of the current-source transistor plus $C_{sb}$ of the input transistors in the MOS circuit. Typically, $C_T$ is 1 pF or less. Using $R_T = 1$ M$\Omega$ and $C_T = 1$ pF, the time constant $R_T C_T$ is 1 $\mu$s, and the break frequency corresponding to this time constant is $1/(2\pi R_T C_T) = 166$ kHz. Below this frequency the impedance $Z_T$ is dominated by $R_T$, and above this frequency $C_T$ dominates. Thus as the frequency of operation is increased, the impedance $Z_T$ will exhibit frequency variation before the rest of the circuit. We now calculate the frequency response assuming that $C_T$ is the only significant capacitance. Since the impedance $Z_T$ is high, almost all of $v_{ic}$ appears across $Z_T$ if $R_S$ is small. Therefore, we can approximate the CM gain as

$$A_{cm} = \frac{v_{oc}}{v_{ic}} \approx -\frac{R_L}{Z_T} \tag{7.38}$$

where

$$Z_T = \frac{2R_T}{1 + sC_T R_T} \tag{7.39}$$

Substitution of (7.39) in (7.38) gives

$$A_{cm}(s) = \frac{v_{oc}}{v_{ic}}(s) \approx -\frac{R_L}{2R_T}(1 + sC_TR_T) \qquad (7.40)$$

Equation 7.40 shows that the CM gain expression contains a zero, which causes the CM gain to rise at 6 dB/octave above a frequency $\omega = 1/R_TC_T$. This behavior is undesirable because the CM gain should ideally be as small as possible. The increase in CM gain cannot continue indefinitely, however, because the other capacitors in the circuit of Fig. 7.11c eventually become important. The other capacitors cause the CM gain to fall at very high frequencies, and this behavior is shown in the plot of CM gain versus frequency in Fig. 7.12a.

The differential-mode (DM) gain $A_{dm}$ of the circuit of Fig. 7.5 or 7.9 is plotted versus frequency in Fig. 7.12b using (7.10). As described earlier, $|A_{dm}|$ begins to fall off at a frequency given by $f = 1/2\pi RC_t$, where $R = (R_S + r_x)\|r_{in}$ and $C_t = C_{in} + C_M$. As pointed out in Chapter 3, an important differential amplifier parameter is the common-mode rejection ratio (CMRR) defined as

$$\text{CMRR} = \frac{|A_{dm}|}{|A_{cm}|} \qquad (7.41)$$

The CMRR is plotted as a function of frequency in Fig. 7.12c by simply taking the magnitude of the ratio of the DM and CM gains. This quantity begins to decrease at frequency

**Figure 7.12** Variation with frequency of the gain parameters for the differential amplifier in Fig. 7.5 or 7.9. (a) Common-mode gain. (b) Differential-mode gain. (c) Common-mode rejection ratio.

$f = 1/2\pi R_T C_T$ when $|A_{cm}|$ begins to increase. The rate of decrease of CMRR further increases when $|A_{dm}|$ begins to fall with increasing frequency. Thus differential amplifiers are far less able to reject CM signals as the frequency of those signals increases.

## 7.2.3 Frequency Response of Voltage Buffers

Single-stage voltage buffers are often used in integrated circuits. The ac circuits for bipolar and MOS voltage buffers are shown in Figs. 7.13a and 7.13b, respectively. A small-signal model that can be used to model both of these circuits is shown in Fig. 7.13c. Resistance $R_S$ is the source resistance, and $R_L$ is the load resistance. We will assume that the output resistance of the transistor $r_o$ is much larger than $R_L$. Since these resistors are in parallel in the small-signal circuit, $r_o$ can be neglected. The series input resistance in the transistor model and the source resistance are in series and can be lumped together as $R'_S = R_S + r_x$. For simplicity, the effect of capacitor $C_f$ in Fig. 7.1 is initially neglected, a reasonable approximation if $R'_S$ is small. The effect of $C_f$ is to form a low-pass circuit with $R'_S$ and to cause the gain to decrease at very high frequencies. From Fig. 7.13c,

$$v_i = i_i R'_S + v_1 + v_o \tag{7.42}$$

$$i_i = \frac{v_1}{z_{in}} \tag{7.43}$$

$$z_{in} = \frac{r_{in}}{1 + sC_{in}r_{in}} \tag{7.44}$$

(a)

(b)

(c)

**Figure 7.13** (a) An ac schematic of an emitter-follower amplifier. (b) An ac schematic of a source-follower amplifier. (c) A general model for both amplifiers.

$$i_i + g_m v_1 = \frac{v_o}{R_L} \tag{7.45}$$

Using (7.43) and (7.44) in (7.45) gives

$$\frac{v_1}{r_{in}}(1 + sC_{in}r_{in}) + g_m v_1 = \frac{v_o}{R_L}$$

and thus

$$v_1 = \frac{v_o}{R_L} \frac{1}{g_m + \dfrac{1}{r_{in}}(1 + sC_{in}r_{in})} \tag{7.46}$$

Using (7.46) and (7.43) in (7.42) gives

$$v_i = \left(\frac{R_S'}{z_{in}} + 1\right)\frac{v_o}{R_L} \frac{1}{g_m + \dfrac{1}{r_{in}}(1 + sC_{in}r_{in})} + v_o$$

Collecting terms in this equation, we find

$$\frac{v_o}{v_i} = \frac{g_m R_L + \dfrac{R_L}{r_{in}}}{1 + g_m R_L + \dfrac{R_S' + R_L}{r_{in}}} \left[\frac{1 - \dfrac{s}{z_1}}{1 - \dfrac{s}{p_1}}\right] \tag{7.47}$$

where

$$z_1 = -\frac{g_m + \dfrac{1}{r_{in}}}{C_{in}} \tag{7.48}$$

$$p_1 = -\frac{1}{R_1 C_{in}} \tag{7.49}$$

with

$$R_1 = r_{in}\|\frac{R_S' + R_L}{1 + g_m R_L} \tag{7.50}$$

Equation 7.47 shows that, as expected, the low-frequency voltage gain is about unity if $g_m R_L \gg 1$ and $g_m R_L \gg (R_S' + R_L)/r_{in}$. The high-frequency gain is controlled by the presence of a pole at $p_1$ and a zero at $z_1$.

### 7.2.3.1 Frequency Response of the Emitter Follower

The small-signal circuit for the emitter follower in Fig. 7.13a is shown in Fig. 7.14. We initially ignore $C_\mu$, as in the general analysis in Section 7.2.3. The transfer function for the emitter follower can be found by substituting the appropriate values in Table 7.1 into (7.47) through (7.50). If $g_m R_L \gg 1$ and $g_m R_L \gg (R_S' + R_L)/r_\pi$, where $R_S' = R_S + r_b$, the low-frequency gain is about unity. The zero and pole are given by

$$z_1 = -\frac{g_m + \dfrac{1}{r_\pi}}{C_\pi} \approx -\frac{g_m}{C_\pi} \approx -\omega_T \tag{7.51}$$

$$p_1 = -\frac{1}{C_\pi R_1} \tag{7.52}$$

**Figure 7.14** Small-signal model for the emitter follower in Fig. 7.13a.

where

$$R_1 = r_\pi \| \frac{R_S' + R_L}{1 + g_m R_L} \tag{7.53}$$

Typically, the zero has a magnitude that is slightly larger than the pole, and both are approximately equal to $\omega_T$ of the device. In particular, if $g_m R_L \gg 1$ and $R_S' \ll R_L$ in (7.53), then $R_1 \approx 1/g_m$ and (7.52) gives $p_1 \approx -g_m/C_\pi \approx -\omega_T$. However, if $R_S$ is large, then $R_S'$ in (7.53) becomes large compared to $R_L$, and the pole magnitude will be significantly less than $\omega_T$.

■ **EXAMPLE**

Calculate the transfer function for an emitter follower with $C_\pi = 10$ pF, $C_\mu = 0$, $R_L = 2$ kΩ, $R_S = 50$ Ω, $r_b = 150$ Ω, $\beta = 100$, and $I_C = 1$ mA.

From the data, $g_m = 38$ mA/V, $r_\pi = 2.6$ kΩ, and $R_S' = R_S + r_b = 200$ Ω. Since $C_\mu = 0$, $\omega_T$ of the device is

$$\omega_T = \frac{g_m}{C_\pi} = \frac{1 \text{ mA}}{26 \text{ mV}} \frac{1}{10 \text{ pF}} = 3.85 \times 10^9 \text{ rad/s} \tag{7.54}$$

and thus $f_T = 612$ MHz. From (7.51) and (7.54), the zero of the transfer function is

$$z_1 \approx -\omega_T = -3.85 \times 10^9 \text{ rad/s}$$

From (7.53)

$$R_1 = 2.6 \text{ k}\Omega \| \left( \frac{200 + 2000}{1 + \dfrac{2000}{26}} \Omega \right) \approx 28 \ \Omega$$

Using (7.52), the pole is

$$p_1 = -\frac{10^{12}}{10} \frac{1}{28} \text{ rad/s} = -3.57 \times 10^9 \text{ rad/s}$$

The pole and zero are thus quite closely spaced, as shown in the s-plane plot of Fig. 7.15a. The low-frequency gain of the circuit from (7.47) is

$$\frac{v_o}{v_i} = \frac{g_m R_L + \dfrac{R_L}{r_\pi}}{1 + g_m R_L + \dfrac{R_S' + R_L}{r_\pi}} = \frac{\dfrac{2000}{26} + \dfrac{2000}{2600}}{1 + \dfrac{2000}{26} + \dfrac{2200}{2600}} = 0.986$$

**Figure 7.15** (*a*) Pole-zero plot for a voltage buffer. (*b*) Voltage gain versus frequency for the voltage buffer.

The parameters derived above are used in (7.47) to plot the circuit gain versus frequency in Fig. 7.15$b$. The gain is flat with frequency until near $f_T = 612$ MHz where a decrease of 0.4 dB occurs. The analysis predicts that the gain is then flat as frequency is increased further.

By inspecting Fig. 7.14 we can see that the high-frequency gain is asymptotic to $R_L/(R_L + R_S')$ since $C_\pi$ becomes a short circuit. This forces $v_1 = 0$ and thus the controlled current $g_m v_1$ is also zero. If a value of $C_\mu = 1$ pF is included in the equivalent circuit, the more realistic dashed frequency response of Fig. 7.15$b$ is obtained. Since the collector is grounded, $C_\mu$ is connected from $B'$ to ground and thus high-frequency signals are attenuated by voltage division between $R_S'$ and $C_\mu$. As a result, the circuit has a $-3$-dB frequency of 725 MHz due to the low-pass action of $R_S'$ and $C_\mu$. However, the bandwidth of the emitter follower is still quite large, and bandwidths of the order of the $f_T$ of the device can be obtained in practice.

The preceding considerations have shown that large bandwidths are available from the emitter-follower circuit. One of the primary uses of an emitter follower is as a voltage buffer circuit due to its high input impedance and low output impedance. The behavior of these terminal impedances as a function of frequency is thus significant, especially when driving large loads, and will now be examined.

In Chapter 3, the terminal impedances of the emitter follower were calculated using a circuit similar to that of Fig. 7.14$b$ except that $C_\pi$ was not included. The results obtained there can be used here if $r_\pi$ is replaced by $z_\pi$, which is a parallel combination of $r_\pi$ and $C_\pi$. In the low-frequency calculation, $\beta_0$ was used as a symbol for $g_m r_\pi$ and thus is now replaced by $g_m z_\pi$. Using these substitutions in (3.73) and (3.76), including $r_b$ and letting $r_o \to \infty$, we obtain for the emitter follower

$$z_i = r_b + z_\pi + (g_m z_\pi + 1)R_L \tag{7.55}$$

$$z_o = \frac{z_\pi + R_S + r_b}{1 + g_m z_\pi} \tag{7.56}$$

where

$$z_\pi = \frac{r_\pi}{1 + sC_\pi r_\pi} \tag{7.57}$$

Consider first the input impedance. Substituting (7.57) in (7.55) gives

$$z_i = r_b + \frac{r_\pi}{1 + sC_\pi r_\pi} + \left(\frac{g_m r_\pi}{1 + sC_\pi r_\pi} + 1\right)R_L \tag{7.58}$$

$$= r_b + \frac{(1 + g_m R_L)r_\pi}{1 + sC_\pi r_\pi} + R_L$$

$$= r_b + \frac{(1 + g_m R_L)r_\pi}{1 + s\dfrac{C_\pi}{1 + g_m R_L}(1 + g_m R_L)r_\pi} + R_L$$

$$= r_b + \frac{R}{1 + sCR} + R_L \tag{7.59}$$

where

$$R = (1 + g_m R_L)r_\pi \tag{7.59a}$$

and

$$C = \frac{C_\pi}{1 + g_m R_L} \tag{7.59b}$$

Thus $z_i$ can be represented as a parallel R-C circuit in series with $r_b$ and $R_L$ as shown in Fig. 7.16. The effective input capacitance is $C_\pi/(1 + g_m R_L)$ and is much less than $C_\pi$ for typical values of $g_m R_L$. The collector-base capacitance $C_\mu$ may dominate the input capacitance and can be added to this circuit from $B'$ to ground. Thus, at high frequencies, the input impedance of the emitter follower becomes capacitive and its magnitude decreases.

Figure 7.16 Equivalent circuit for the input impedance of an emitter follower with $C_\mu = 0$.

The emitter-follower high-frequency output impedance can be calculated by substituting (7.57) in (7.56). Before proceeding, we will examine (7.57) to determine the high and low frequency limits on $|z_o|$. At low frequencies, $z_\pi = r_\pi$ and

$$z_o|_{\omega=0} \approx \frac{1}{g_m} + \frac{R_S + r_b}{\beta_0} \tag{7.60}$$

At high frequencies, $z_\pi \to 0$ because $C_\pi$ becomes a short circuit and thus

$$z_o|_{\omega=\infty} = R_S + r_b \tag{7.61}$$

Thus $z_o$ is resistive at very low and very high frequencies and its behavior in between depends on parameter values. At very low collector currents, $1/g_m$ is large. If $1/g_m > (R_S + r_b)$, a comparison of (7.60) and (7.61) shows that $|z_o|$ decreases as frequency increases and the output impedance appears capacitive. However, at collector currents of more than several hundred micro amperes, we usually find that $1/g_m < (R_S + r_b)$. Then $|z_o|$ increases with frequency, which represents inductive behavior that can have a major influence on the circuit behavior, particularly when driving capacitive loads. If $1/g_m = (R_S + r_b)$ then the output impedance is resistive and independent of frequency over a wide bandwidth. To maintain this condition over variations in process, supply, and temperature, practical design goals are $R_S \approx 1/g_m$ and $r_b \ll R_S$.

Assuming that the collector bias current is such that $z_o$ is inductive, we can postulate an equivalent circuit for $z_o$ as shown in Fig. 7.17. At low frequencies the inductor is a short circuit and

$$z_o|_{\omega=0} = R_1 \| R_2 \tag{7.62}$$

At high frequencies the inductor is an open circuit and

$$z_o|_{\omega=\infty} = R_2 \tag{7.63}$$

If we assume that $z_o|_{\omega=0} \ll z_o|_{\omega=\infty}$ then $R_1 \ll R_2$, and we can simplify (7.62) to

$$z_o|_{\omega=0} \approx R_1 \tag{7.64}$$

The impedance of the circuit of Fig. 7.17 can be expressed as

$$z_o = \frac{(R_1 + sL)R_2}{R_1 + R_2 + sL} \approx \frac{(R_1 + sL)R_2}{R_2 + sL} \tag{7.65}$$

assuming that $R_1 \ll R_2$.

The complete emitter-follower output impedance can be calculated by substituting (7.57) in (7.56) with $R_S' = r_b + R_S$, which gives

$$z_o = \frac{\dfrac{r_\pi}{1 + sC_\pi r_\pi} + R_S'}{1 + \dfrac{g_m r_\pi}{1 + sC_\pi r_\pi}} = \frac{r_\pi + R_S' + sC_\pi r_\pi R_S'}{\beta_0 + 1 + sC_\pi r_\pi}$$

$$\approx \frac{\left(\dfrac{1}{g_m} + \dfrac{R_S'}{\beta_0} + sC_\pi r_\pi \dfrac{R_S'}{\beta_0}\right)R_S'}{R_S' + sC_\pi r_\pi \dfrac{R_S'}{\beta_0}} \tag{7.66}$$

where $\beta_0 \gg 1$ is assumed.

Comparing (7.66) with (7.65) shows that, under the assumptions made in this analysis, the emitter-follower output impedance can be represented by the circuit of Fig. 7.17 with

**Figure 7.17**  Equivalent circuit for the output impedance of an emitter follower at moderate current levels.

$$R_1 = \frac{1}{g_m} + \frac{R'_S}{\beta_0} \tag{7.67}$$

$$R_2 = R'_S \tag{7.68}$$

$$L = C_\pi r_\pi \frac{R'_S}{\beta_0} \tag{7.69}$$

The effect of $C_\mu$ was neglected in this calculation, which is a reasonable approximation for low to moderate values of $R'_S$.

The preceding calculations have shown that the input and output impedances of the emitter follower are frequency dependent. One consequence of this dependence is that the variation of the terminal impedances with frequency may limit the useful bandwidth of the circuit.

■ **EXAMPLE**

Calculate the elements in the equivalent circuits for input and output impedance of the emitter follower in the previous example. In Fig. 7.16 the input capacitance can be calculated from (7.59)

$$\frac{C_\pi}{1 + g_m R_L} = \frac{10}{1 + \dfrac{2000}{26}}\ \text{pF} = 0.13\ \text{pF}$$

The resistance in shunt with this capacitance is

$$(1 + g_m R_L) r_\pi = \left(1 + \frac{2000}{26}\right)(2.6\ \text{k}\Omega) = 202\ \text{k}\Omega$$

In addition, $r_b = 150\ \Omega$ and $R_L = 2\ \text{k}\Omega$. The elements in the output equivalent circuit of Fig. 7.17 can be calculated from (7.67), (7.68), and (7.69) as

$$R_1 = \left(26 + \frac{200}{100}\right)\Omega = 28\ \Omega$$

$$R_2 = 200\ \Omega$$

$$L = 10^{-11} \times 2600 \times \frac{200}{100}\ \text{H} = 52\ \text{nH}$$

■   Note that the assumption $R_1 \ll R_2$ is valid in this case.

**Figure 7.18** Small-signal model for the source follower in Fig. 7.13b.

### 7.2.3.2 Frequency Response of the Source Follower

The small-signal circuit for the source follower in Fig. 7.13b is shown in Fig. 7.18. Here, $C_{gd}$, $C_{gb}$, and $C_{sb}$ are ignored initially. One key difference between Figures 7.18 and 7.13c is the $g_{mb}$ generator. Since the current through the $g_{mb}$ generator is controlled by the voltage across it, this generator can be replaced with a resistor of value $1/g_{mb}$ from $v_o$ to ground, which is in parallel with $R_L$. Therefore, the total effective load resistance is $R'_L = R_L\|(1/g_{mb})$. The transfer function for the source follower can be found by substituting the appropriate values from Table 7.1 into (7.47), (7.48), and (7.49). If $g_m R'_L \gg 1$, the low-frequency gain is about unity. The zero and pole are given by

$$z_1 = -\frac{g_m}{C_{gs}} \approx -\omega_T \tag{7.70}$$

$$p_1 = -\frac{1}{C_{gs} R_1} \tag{7.71}$$

where

$$R_1 = \frac{R_S + R'_L}{1 + g_m R'_L} \tag{7.72}$$

Typically, the zero has a magnitude that is slightly larger than the pole. If $g_m R'_L \gg 1$ and $R_S \ll R'_L$ in (7.72), then $R_1 \approx 1/g_m$ and (7.71) gives $p_1 \approx -g_m/C_{gs} \approx -\omega_T$. However, if $R_S$ in (7.72) becomes large compared to $R_L$ or if $g_m R'_L$ is not much larger than one, the pole magnitude will be significantly less than $\omega_T$.

■ **EXAMPLE**

Calculate the transfer function for a source follower with $C_{gs} = 7.33$ pF, $k'W/L = 100$ mA/V$^2$, $R_L = 2$ kΩ, $R_S = 190$ Ω, and $I_D = 4$ mA. Ignore body effect, and let $C_{gd} = 0$, $C_{gb} = 0$, and $C_{sb} = 0$.

From the data, $g_m = \sqrt{2(100)4}$ mA/V $= 28.2$ mA/V. Ignoring body effect, we have $R'_L = R_L\|(1/g_{mb}) = R_L$. Since $C_{gd} = 0$, $\omega_T$ of the device is

$$\omega_T = \frac{g_m}{C_{gs}} = \frac{28.2 \dfrac{\text{mA}}{\text{V}}}{7.33 \text{ pF}} = 3.85 \times 10^9 \text{ rad/s} \tag{7.73}$$

and thus $f_T = 612$ MHz. From (7.70) and (7.73), the zero of the transfer function is

$$z_1 = -\frac{g_m}{C_{gs}} = -3.85 \times 10^9 \text{ rad/s}$$

From (7.72)

$$R_1 = \frac{190 + 2000}{1 + 0.0282 \times 2000} \, \Omega = 38.2 \, \Omega$$

The pole from (7.71) is

$$p_1 = -\frac{10^{12}}{7.33} \frac{1}{38.2} \text{ rad/s} = -3.57 \times 10^9 \text{ rad/s}$$

The pole and zero are thus quite closely spaced, as shown in Fig. 7.15a.
The low-frequency gain of the circuit from (7.67) is

$$\frac{v_o}{v_i} = \frac{g_m R_L'}{1 + g_m R_L'} = \frac{28.2 \times 10^{-3} \times 2000}{1 + 28.2 \times 10^{-3} \times 2000} = 0.983$$

The parameters derived above can be used in (7.47) to plot the circuit gain versus frequency, and this plot is similar to the magnitude plot shown in Fig. 7.15b for $C_{gd} = 0$. The gain is flat with frequency until near $f_T = 612$ MHz, where a decrease of about 0.4 dB occurs. The analysis predicts that the gain is then flat as frequency is increased further because the input signal is simply fed forward to $R_L'$ via $C_{gs}$ at very high frequencies. In practice, capacitors $C_{gd}$, $C_{gb}$, and $C_{sb}$ that were assumed to be zero in this example cause the gain to roll off at high frequencies, as will be demonstrated in the next example.

When capacitors $C_{gd}$, $C_{gb}$, and $C_{sb}$ that were ignored above are included in the analysis, the voltage-gain expression becomes more complicated than (7.47). An exact analysis, with all the capacitors included, follows the same steps as the analysis of Fig. 7.13c and yields

$$\frac{v_o}{v_i} = \frac{g_m R_L'}{1 + g_m R_L'} \frac{1 + s\dfrac{C_{gs}}{g_m}}{1 + as + bs^2} \tag{7.74a}$$

with

$$a = \frac{R_L'(C_{gs} + C_{sb}) + R_S(C_{gs} + C_{gd}') + R_S g_m R_L' C_{gd}'}{1 + g_m R_L'}$$

$$\approx \frac{R_L'(C_{gs} + C_{sb}) + R_S C_{gs} + R_S g_m R_L' C_{gd}'}{1 + g_m R_L'} \tag{7.74b}$$

$$b = \frac{R_S R_L'[C_{sb}(C_{gs} + C_{gd}') + C_{gs} C_{gd}']}{1 + g_m R_L'} \approx \frac{R_S R_L'[C_{sb}C_{gs} + C_{gs}C_{gd}']}{1 + g_m R_L'} \tag{7.74c}$$

where $C_{gd}' = C_{gd} + C_{gb}$. The approximations for $a$ and $b$ use $C_{gs} + C_{gd}' \approx C_{gs}$ since $C_{gs} \gg C_{gd}'$. This exact transfer function has a zero at $-g_m/C_{gs}$, in agreement with (7.70), and two poles. If $C_{gd}'$ and $C_{sb}$ are set to zero, (7.74) has one pole as given by (7.71). Making approximations in (7.74) that lead to simple, useful expressions for the poles is difficult since a dominant real pole does not always exist. In fact, the poles can be complex.

■ **EXAMPLE**

Calculate the transfer function for a source follower with $C_{gs} = 7.33$ pF, $C_{gd} = 0.1$ pF, $C_{gb} = 0.05$ pF, $C_{sb} = 0.5$ pF, $k'W/L = 100$ mA/V$^2$, $R_L = 2$ kΩ, $R_S = 190$ Ω, and $I_D = 4$ mA. Ignore body effect.

These data are the same as in the last example, except we now have non-zero $C_{gd}$, $C_{gb}$, and $C_{sb}$. From the data, $g_m = 28.2$ mA/V and $C_{gd}' = C_{gd} + C_{gb} = 0.15$ pF. Also, ignoring body effect, we have $R'_L = R_L \| (1/g_{mb}) = R_L$. The low frequency gain of the circuit, as calculated in the previous example, is 0.983. From (7.74a), the zero is

$$z = -\frac{g_m}{C_{gs}} = -\frac{28.2 \, \dfrac{\text{mA}}{\text{V}}}{7.33 \, \text{pF}} = -3.85 \times 10^9 \, \text{rad/s}$$

From (7.74b) and (7.74c), the coefficients of the denominator of the transfer function are

$$a \approx \frac{2k\,(7.33p + 0.5p) + 190\,(7.33p) + 190\,(0.0282)(2k)(0.15p)}{1 + (0.0282)(2k)} \, s = 0.324 \, \text{ns}$$

$$b \approx \frac{190(2k)[(0.5p)(7.33p) + (7.33p)(0.15p)]}{1 + (0.0282)(2k)} \, s^2 = 0.0315 \, (\text{ns})^2$$

Using the quadratic formula to solve for the poles, we find that the poles are

$$p_{1,2} = -5.1 \times 10^9 \pm j2.3 \times 10^9 \, \text{rad/s}$$

The poles and zero are fairly close together, as shown in Fig. 7.19a. The gain magnitude and phase are plotted in Fig. 7.19. The −3-dB bandwidth is 1.6 GHz. Because the two poles and zero are fairly close together, the gain versus frequency approximates a one-pole roll-off.

High-frequency input signals are attenuated by capacitors $C_{gd}$ and $C_{gb}$ that connect between the gate and ground, causing the gain to roll off and approach zero as $\omega \to \infty$. However, the bandwidth of the source follower is still quite large, and bandwidths of the order of the $f_T$ of the device can be obtained in practice.

If the source follower drives a load capacitance in parallel with the load resistance, its value can be added to $C_{sb}$ in (7.74). Such a load capacitance is present whenever the source-follower transistor is fabricated in a well and its source is connected to its well to avoid body effect. The well-body capacitance can be large and may significantly affect the 3-dB bandwidth of the circuit.

In Section 7.2.3.1, calculations were carried out for the input and output impedances of the emitter follower. Since the equivalent circuit for the MOSFET is similar to that for the bipolar transistor (apart from the $g_{mb}$ generator), similar results can be found for the source follower by substituting the appropriate values from Table 7.1 in the formulas for

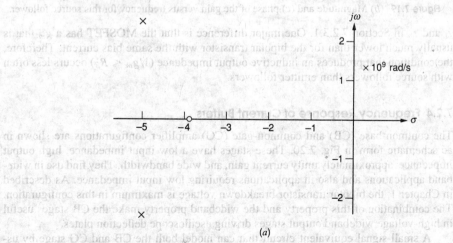

(a)

**Figure 7.19** (a) Pole-zero plot for the source-follower example using (7.74).

**Figure 7.19** (*b*) Magnitude and (*c*) phase of the gain versus frequency for this source follower.

$z_i$ and $z_o$ in Section 7.2.3.1. One major difference is that the MOSFET has a $g_m$ that is usually much lower than for the bipolar transistor with the same bias current. Therefore, the condition that produces an inductive output impedance ($1/g_m < R_S$) occurs less often with source followers than emitter followers.

### 7.2.4 Frequency Response of Current Buffers

The common-base (CB) and common-gate (CG) amplifier configurations are shown in ac schematic form in Fig. 7.20. These stages have a low input impedance, high output impedance, approximately unity current gain, and wide bandwidth. They find use in wide-band applications and also in applications requiring low input impedance. As described in Chapter 1, the bipolar transistor breakdown voltage is maximum in this configuration. The combination of this property and the wideband property make the CB stages useful in high-voltage wideband output stages driving oscilloscope deflection plates.

A small-signal equivalent circuit that can model both the CB and CG stage by using a general small-signal model is shown in Fig. 7.20c. The input voltage source and

Figure 7.20 (a) An ac schematic of a common-base amplifier. (b) An ac schematic of a common-gate amplifier. (c) A general model for both amplifiers.

source resistance are represented by a Norton equivalent. Resistance $R_S$ is neglected in the following analysis since the input impedance of the amplifier is quite low. Another good approximation if $r_x$ is small is that $C_f$ simply shunts $R_L$, as shown in Fig. 7.20c. In this analysis, $r_o$ will be neglected and the output signal $i_o$ will be taken as the output of the $g_m$ controlled source. The approximate output voltage $v_o$ is obtained by assuming $i_o$ flows in the parallel combination of $R_L$ and $C_f$.

The analysis of the circuit of Fig. 7.20c proceeds by applying KCL at node $W$. Neglecting $R_S$,

$$i_i + \frac{v_1}{z_{in}} + g_m v_1 = 0 \tag{7.75}$$

where

$$z_{in} = \frac{r_{in}}{1 + sC_{in}r_{in}} \tag{7.76}$$

From (7.75) and (7.76)

$$i_i = -v_1 \left( g_m + \frac{1}{r_{in}} + sC_{in} \right) \tag{7.77}$$

Now

$$i_o = -g_m v_1 \tag{7.78}$$

Substituting (7.77) into (7.78) gives

$$\frac{i_o}{i_i} = \frac{g_m r_{in}}{g_m r_{in} + 1}\, \frac{1}{1 + s\dfrac{r_{in}}{g_m r_{in} + 1} C_{in}} \tag{7.79}$$

### 7.2.4.1 Common-Base Amplifier Frequency Response

The small-signal circuit for the common-base (CB) amplifier of Fig. 7.20a is shown in Fig. 7.21. Substituting the values in Table 7.1 into (7.79) gives for the current gain

$$\frac{i_o}{i_i} = \frac{g_m r_\pi}{g_m r_\pi + 1}\, \frac{1}{1 + s\dfrac{r_\pi}{g_m r_\pi + 1} C_\pi} \tag{7.80}$$

Using $\beta_0 = g_m r_\pi$ and assuming $\beta_0 \gg 1$, (7.80) simplifies to

$$\frac{i_o}{i_i} \approx \frac{\beta_0}{\beta_0 + 1}\, \frac{1}{1 + s\dfrac{C_\pi}{g_m}} = \alpha_0\, \frac{1}{1 + s\dfrac{C_\pi}{g_m}} \tag{7.81}$$

where $\alpha_0 = \beta_0/(\beta_0 + 1)$. This analysis shows that the CB stage current gain has a low-frequency value $\alpha_0 \approx 1$ and a pole at $p_1 = -g_m/C_\pi \approx -\omega_T$. The CB stage is thus a wideband unity-current gain amplifier with low input impedance and high output impedance. It can be seen from the polarities in Fig. 7.20a that the phase shift between $v_i$ and $v_o$ in the CB stage is zero at low frequencies. This result can be compared with the case of the common-emitter stage of Fig. 7.2a, which has $180°$ phase shift between $v_i$ and $v_o$ at low frequencies.

If the desired output is the current flowing through $R_L$, then $C_\mu$ and $R_L$ form a current divider from $i_o$ to this desired current (under the assumption that $C_\mu$ is in parallel with $R_L$ because $r_b$ is very small). When included in the analysis, this current divider introduces an additional pole $p_2 = -1/R_L C_\mu$ in the transfer function.

Comparing Fig. 7.20a with Fig. 7.13a shows that the input impedance of the common-base stage is the same as the output impedance of the emitter follower with $R_S = 0$. Thus the common-base stage input impedance is low at low frequencies and becomes inductive at high frequencies for collector bias currents of several hundred microamperes or more. As shown in Chapter 3, the output resistance of the common-base stage at low frequencies with large $R_S$ is approximately $\beta_0 r_o$, which is extremely large.

**Figure 7.21** Small-signal model for the common-base circuit in Fig. 7.20a.

At high frequencies the output impedance is capacitive and is dominated by $C_\mu$ (and $C_{cs}$ for $npn$ transistors).

Unlike the common-emitter stage where $C_\mu$ is Miller multiplied, the common-base stage does not contain a feedback capacitance from collector to emitter to cause the Miller effect. As a consequence, the effect of large values of $R_L$ on the frequency response of the common-base stage is much less than in the common-emitter stage.

### 7.2.4.2 Common-Gate Amplifier Frequency Response

The small-signal circuit for the common-gate (CG) amplifier of Fig. 7.20b is shown in Fig. 7.22. One element in this circuit that does not appear in the general model in Fig. 7.20c is the $g_{mb}$ generator. Since $v_{bs} = v_{gs}$ and the $g_m$ and $g_{mb}$ generators are in parallel here, these controlled sources can be combined. Also, capacitors $C_{gb}$, $C_{db}$, and $C_{sb}$ are not included in the general model. Here, $C_{gb}$ is shorted and can be ignored. Capacitance $C_{db}$ is in parallel with $R_L$ and therefore can be ignored if the output variable of interest is the current $i_o$. Capacitance $C_{sb}$ appears in parallel with $C_{gs}$ in the small-signal circuit since the body and gate both connect to small-signal ground. Using the combined transconductance and input capacitance and values from Table 7.1 in (7.79) gives

$$\frac{i_o}{i_i} = \frac{1}{1 + s\dfrac{C_{gs} + C_{sb}}{g_m + g_{mb}}} \qquad (7.82)$$

From this equation, the current gain of the common-gate stage has a low-frequency value of unity and a pole at $p_1 = -(g_m + g_{mb})/(C_{gs} + C_{sb})$. If $C_{gs} \gg C_{sb}$, then $|p_1| \approx (g_m + g_{mb})/C_{gs} > g_m/C_{gs} \approx \omega_T$. The CG stage is thus a wideband unity-current-gain amplifier with low input impedance and high output impedance. It can be seen from the polarities in Fig. 7.20b that there is zero phase shift between $v_i$ and $v_o$ in the CG stage at low frequencies. This phase shift can be compared with the case of the common-source stage of Fig. 7.2b, which has 180° phase shift between $v_i$ and $v_o$ at low frequencies.

If the desired output is the current flowing through $R_L$, then $C_{db}$, $C_{gd}$, and $R_L$ form a current divider from $i_o$ to this desired current. When included in the analysis, this current divider introduces an additional pole $p_2 = -1/R_L(C_{db} + C_{gd})$ in the transfer function.

Unlike the common-source stage where $C_{gd}$ is Miller multiplied, the common-gate stage does not contain a feedback capacitance from drain to source to cause the Miller effect. As a consequence, the effect of large values of $R_L$ on the frequency response of the common-gate stage is much less than in the common-source stage.

**Figure 7.22** Small-signal model for the common-gate circuit in Fig. 7.20b.

## 7.3 Multistage Amplifier Frequency Response

The above analysis of the frequency behavior of single-stage circuits indicates the complexity that can arise even with simple circuits. The complete analysis of the frequency response of multistage circuits with many capacitive elements rapidly becomes very difficult and the answers become so complicated that little use can be made of the results. For this reason approximate methods of analysis have been developed to aid in the circuit design phase, and computer simulation is used to verify the final design. One such method of analysis is the *zero-value time constant* analysis that will now be described. First some ideas regarding dominant poles are developed.

### 7.3.1 Dominant-Pole Approximation

For any electronic circuit we can derive a transfer function $A(s)$ by small-signal analysis to give

$$A(s) = \frac{N(s)}{D(s)} = \frac{a_0 + a_1 s + a_2 s^2 + \cdots + a_m s^m}{1 + b_1 s + b_2 s^2 + \cdots + b_n s^n} \tag{7.83}$$

where $a_0, a_1, \ldots a_m$, and $b_1, b_2, \ldots b_n$ are constants. Very often the transfer function contains poles only (or the zeros are unimportant). In this case we can factor the denominator of (7.83) to give

$$A(s) = \frac{K}{\left(1 - \dfrac{s}{p_1}\right)\left(1 - \dfrac{s}{p_2}\right)\cdots\left(1 - \dfrac{s}{p_n}\right)} \tag{7.84}$$

where $K$ is a constant and $p_1, p_2, \ldots p_n$ are the poles of the transfer function.
It is apparent from (7.84) that

$$b_1 = \sum_{i=1}^{n}\left(-\frac{1}{p_i}\right) \tag{7.85}$$

An important practical case occurs when one pole is dominant. That is, when

$$|p_1| \ll |p_2|, |p_3|, \ldots \qquad \text{so that} \qquad \left|\frac{1}{p_1}\right| \gg \left|\sum_{i=2}^{n}\left(-\frac{1}{p_i}\right)\right|$$

This situation is shown in the $s$ plane in Fig. 7.23 and in this case it follows from (7.85) that

$$b_1 \simeq \left|\frac{1}{p_1}\right| \tag{7.86}$$

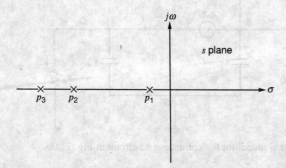

**Figure 7.23** Pole diagram for a circuit with a dominant pole.

If we return now to (7.84) and calculate the gain magnitude in the frequency domain, we obtain

$$|A(j\omega)| = \frac{K}{\sqrt{\left[1 + \left(\dfrac{\omega}{p_1}\right)^2\right]\left[1 + \left(\dfrac{\omega}{p_2}\right)^2\right]\cdots\left[1 + \left(\dfrac{\omega}{p_n}\right)^2\right]}} \tag{7.87}$$

If a dominant pole exists, then (7.87) can be approximated by

$$|A(j\omega)| \simeq \frac{K}{\sqrt{1 + \left(\dfrac{\omega}{p_1}\right)^2}} \tag{7.88}$$

This approximation will be quite accurate at least until $\omega \simeq |p_1|$, and thus (7.88) will accurately predict the $-3$-dB frequency and we can write

$$\omega_{-3\text{dB}} \simeq |p_1| \tag{7.89}$$

Use of (7.86) in (7.89) gives

$$\omega_{-3\text{dB}} \simeq \frac{1}{b_1} \tag{7.90}$$

for a dominant-pole situation.

## 7.3.2 Zero-Value Time Constant Analysis

This is an approximate method of analysis that allows an estimate to be made of the dominant pole (and thus the $-3$-dB frequency) of complex circuits. Considerable saving in computational effort is achieved because a full analysis of the circuit is not required. The method will be developed by considering a practical example.

Consider the equivalent circuit shown in Fig. 7.24. This is a single-stage bipolar transistor amplifier with resistive source and load impedances. The feedback capacitance is split into two parts ($C_x$ and $C_\mu$) as shown. This is a slightly better approximation to the actual situation than the single collector-base capacitor we have been using, but is rarely used in hand calculations because of the analysis complexity. For purposes of analysis, the

**Figure 7.24** Small-signal equivalent circuit of a common-emitter stage with internal feedback capacitors $C_\mu$ and $C_x$.

capacitor voltages $v_1$, $v_2$, and $v_3$ are chosen as variables. The external input $v_i$ is removed and the circuit excited with three independent current sources $i_1$, $i_2$, and $i_3$ across the capacitors, as shown in Fig. 7.24. We can show that with this choice of variables the circuit equations are of the form

$$i_1 = (g_{11} + sC_\pi)v_1 + g_{12}v_2 + g_{13}v_3 \qquad (7.91)$$

$$i_2 = g_{21}v_1 + (g_{22} + sC_\mu)v_2 + g_{23}v_3 \qquad (7.92)$$

$$i_3 = g_{31}v_1 + g_{32}v_2 + (g_{33} + sC_x)v_3 \qquad (7.93)$$

where the $g$ terms are conductances. Note that the terms involving $s$ contributed by the capacitors are associated only with their respective capacitor voltage variables and only appear on the diagonal of the system determinant.

The poles of the circuit transfer function are the zeros of the determinant $\Delta$ of the circuit equations, which can be written in the form

$$\Delta(s) = K_3 s^3 + K_2 s^2 + K_1 s + K_0 \qquad (7.94)$$

where the coefficients $K$ are composed of terms from the above equations. For example, $K_3$ is the sum of the coefficients of all terms involving $s^3$ in the expansion of the determinant. Equation 7.94 can be expressed as

$$\Delta(s) = K_0(1 + b_1 s + b_2 s^2 + b_3 s^3) \qquad (7.95)$$

where this form corresponds to (7.83). Note that this is a third-order determinant because there are three capacitors in the circuit. The term $K_0$ in (7.94) is the value of $\Delta(s)$ if all capacitors are zero ($C_x = C_\mu = C_\pi = 0$). This can be seen from (7.91), (7.92), and (7.93). Thus

$$K_0 = \Delta|_{C_\pi = C_\mu = C_x = 0}$$

and it is useful to define

$$K_0 \triangleq \Delta_0 \qquad (7.96)$$

Consider now the term $K_1 s$ in (7.94). This is the sum of all the terms involving $s$ that are obtained when the system determinant is evaluated. However, from (7.91) to (7.93) it is apparent that $s$ only occurs when associated with a capacitance. Thus the term $K_1 s$ can be written as

$$K_1 s = h_1 s C_\pi + h_2 s C_\mu + h_3 s C_x \qquad (7.97)$$

where the $h$ terms are constants. The term $h_1$ can be evaluated by expanding the determinant of (7.91) to (7.93) about the first row:

$$\Delta(s) = (g_{11} + sC_\pi)\Delta_{11} + g_{12}\Delta_{12} + g_{13}\Delta_{13} \qquad (7.98)$$

where $\Delta_{11}$, $\Delta_{12}$, and $\Delta_{13}$ are cofactors of the determinant. Inspection of (7.91), (7.92), and (7.93) shows that $C_\pi$ occurs only in the first term of (7.98). Thus the coefficient of $C_\pi s$ in (7.98) is found by evaluating $\Delta_{11}$ with $C_\mu = C_x = 0$, which will eliminate the other capacitive terms in $\Delta_{11}$. But this coefficient of $C_\pi s$ is just $h_1$ in (7.97), and so

$$h_1 = \Delta_{11}|_{C_\mu = C_x = 0} \qquad (7.99)$$

Now consider expansion of the determinant about the second row. This must give the same value for the determinant, and thus

$$\Delta(s) = g_{21}\Delta_{21} + (g_{22} + sC_\mu)\Delta_{22} + g_{23}\Delta_{23} \qquad (7.100)$$

In this case $C_\mu$ occurs only in the second term of (7.100). Thus the coefficient of $C_\mu s$ in this equation is found by evaluating $\Delta_{22}$ with $C_\pi = C_x = 0$, which will eliminate the other capacitive terms. This coefficient of $C_\mu s$ is just $h_2$ in (7.97), and thus

$$h_2 = \Delta_{22}|_{C_\pi = C_x = 0} \tag{7.101}$$

Similarly by expanding about the third row it follows that

$$h_3 = \Delta_{33}|_{C_\pi = C_\mu = 0} \tag{7.102}$$

Combining (7.97) with (7.99), (7.101), and (7.102) gives

$$K_1 = (\Delta_{11}|_{C_\mu = C_x = 0} \times C_\pi) + (\Delta_{22}|_{C_\pi = C_x = 0} \times C_\mu) + (\Delta_{33}|_{C_\mu = C_\pi = 0} \times C_x) \tag{7.103}$$

and

$$b_1 = \frac{K_1}{K_0} = \frac{\Delta_{11}|_{C_\mu = C_x = 0}}{\Delta_0} \times C_\pi + \frac{\Delta_{22}|_{C_\pi = C_x = 0}}{\Delta_0} \times C_\mu$$
$$+ \frac{\Delta_{33}|_{C_\mu = C_\pi = 0}}{\Delta_0} \times C_x \tag{7.104}$$

where the boundary conditions on the determinants are the same as in (7.103). Now consider putting $i_2 = i_3 = 0$ in Fig. 7.24. Solving (7.91) to (7.93) for $v_1$ gives

$$v_1 = \frac{\Delta_{11} i_1}{\Delta(s)}$$

and thus

$$\frac{v_1}{i_1} = \frac{\Delta_{11}}{\Delta(s)} \tag{7.105}$$

Equation 7.105 is an expression for the driving-point impedance at the $C_\pi$ node pair. Thus

$$\frac{\Delta_{11}|_{C_\mu = C_x = 0}}{\Delta_0}$$

is the driving-point *resistance* at the $C_\pi$ node pair with *all* capacitors equal to zero because

$$\frac{\Delta_{11}|_{C_\mu = C_x = 0}}{\Delta_0} = \frac{\Delta_{11}}{\Delta}\bigg|_{C_\mu = C_x = C_\pi = 0} \tag{7.106}$$

We now define

$$R_{\pi 0} = \frac{\Delta_{11}}{\Delta_0}\bigg|_{C_\mu = C_x = 0} \tag{7.107}$$

Similarly,

$$\frac{\Delta_{22}|_{C_\pi = C_x = 0}}{\Delta_0}$$

is the driving-point *resistance* at the $C_\mu$ node pair with all capacitors put equal to zero and is represented by $R_{\mu 0}$. Thus we can write from (7.104)

$$b_1 = R_{\pi 0} C_\pi + R_{\mu 0} C_\mu + R_{x 0} C_x \tag{7.108}$$

The time constants in (7.108) are called *zero-value time constants* because all capacitors are set equal to zero to perform the calculation. Although derived in terms of a specific example, this result is true in any circuit for which the various assumptions made in this analysis are valid. In its most general form, (7.108) becomes

$$b_1 = \Sigma T_0 \tag{7.109}$$

where $\Sigma T_0$ is the sum of the zero-value time constants.

We showed previously that if there are no dominant zeros in the circuit transfer function, and if there is a dominant pole $p_1$, then

$$\omega_{-3dB} \approx |p_1| \tag{7.110}$$

Using (7.90), (7.109), and (7.110) we can write

$$\omega_{-3dB} \approx |p_1| \approx \frac{1}{b_1} = \frac{1}{\Sigma T_0} \tag{7.111}$$

For example, consider the circuit of Fig. 7.24. By inspection,

$$R_{\pi 0} = r_\pi \| (R_S + r_b) \tag{7.112}$$

In order to calculate $R_{\mu 0}$ it is necessary to write some simple circuit equations. We apply a test current $i$ at the $C_\mu$ terminals as shown in Fig. 7.25 and calculate the resulting $v$.

$$v_1 = R_{\pi 0} i \tag{7.113}$$
$$v_o = -(i + g_m v_1) R_L \tag{7.114}$$

Substituting (7.113) in (7.114) gives

$$v_o = -(i + g_m R_{\pi 0} i) R_L \tag{7.115}$$

Now

$$R_{\mu 0} = \frac{v}{i}$$

and

$$R_{\mu 0} = \frac{v_1 - v_o}{i} \tag{7.116}$$

Substitution of (7.113) and (7.115) in (7.116) gives

$$R_{\mu 0} = R_{\pi 0} + R_L + g_m R_L R_{\pi 0} \tag{7.117}$$

$R_{x0}$ can be calculated in a similar fashion, and it is apparent that $R_{x0} \simeq R_{\mu 0}$ if $r_b \ll r_\pi$. This justifies the common practice of lumping $C_x$ in with $C_\mu$ if $r_b$ is small. Assuming that this is done, (7.111) gives, for the $-3$-dB frequency,

$$\omega_{-3dB} = \frac{1}{R_{\pi 0} C_\pi + R_{\mu 0} C_\mu} \tag{7.118}$$

**Figure 7.25** Equivalent circuit for the calculation of $R_{\mu 0}$ for Fig. 7.24.

Using (7.117) in (7.118) gives

$$\omega_{-3dB} = \cfrac{1}{R_{\pi 0}\left\{C_\pi + C_\mu\left[(1 + g_m R_L) + \cfrac{R_L}{R_{\pi 0}}\right]\right\}} \tag{7.119}$$

Equation 7.119 is identical with the result obtained in (7.29) by exact analysis. [Recall that $(R_S + r_b)\|r_\pi$ in (7.29) is the same as $R_{\pi 0}$ in (7.119).] However, the zero-value time-constant analysis gives the result with *much less* effort. It does *not* give any information on the nondominant pole.

As a further illustration of the uses and limitations of the zero-value time-constant approach, consider the emitter-follower circuit of Fig. 7.13a, where only the capacitance $C_\pi$ has been included. The value of $R_{\pi 0}$ can be calculated by inserting a current source $i$ as shown in Fig. 7.26 and calculating the resulting voltage $v_1$:

$$i = \frac{v_1}{r_\pi} + \frac{v_1 + v_o}{R_S + r_b} \tag{7.120}$$

$$\frac{v_1}{r_\pi} - i + g_m v_1 = \frac{v_o}{R_L} \tag{7.121}$$

Substituting (7.121) in (7.120) gives

$$i = \frac{v_1}{r_\pi} + \frac{v_1}{R_S + r_b} + \frac{R_L}{R_S + r_b}\left(\frac{v_1}{r_\pi} + g_m v_1 - i\right)$$

and this equation can be expressed as

$$i = \frac{v_1}{r_\pi} + v_1 \frac{1 + g_m R_L}{R_S + r_b + R_L}$$

Finally, $R_{\pi 0}$ can be calculated as

$$R_{\pi 0} = \frac{v_1}{i} = r_\pi \left\| \frac{R_S + r_b + R_L}{1 + g_m R_L} \right. \tag{7.122}$$

Thus the dominant pole of the emitter follower is at

$$|p| = \frac{1}{R_{\pi 0} C_\pi} \tag{7.123}$$

This is in agreement with the result obtained in (7.52) by exact analysis and requires less effort. However, the zero-value time-constant approach tells us nothing of the zero that

**Figure 7.26** Equivalent circuit for the calculation of $R_{\pi 0}$ for the emitter follower.

exact analysis showed. Because of the dominant zero, the dominant-pole magnitude is *not* the −3-dB frequency in this case. This shows that care must be exercised in interpreting the results of zero-value time-constant analysis. However, it *is* a useful technique, and with experience the designer can recognize circuits that are likely to contain dominant zeros. *Such circuits usually have a capacitive path directly coupling input and output as $C_\pi$ does in the emitter follower.*

### 7.3.3 Cascade Voltage-Amplifier Frequency Response

The real advantages of the zero-value time-constant approach appear when circuits containing more than one device are analyzed. For example, consider the two-stage common-source amplifier shown in Fig. 7.27. This circuit could be a drawing of a single-ended amplifier or the differential half-circuit of a fully differential amplifier. Exact analysis of this circuit to find the −3-dB frequency is extremely arduous, but the zero-value time-constant analysis is quite straightforward, as shown below. To show typical numerical calculations, specific parameter values are assumed. In the example below, as in others in this chapter, parasitic capacitance associated with resistors is neglected. This approximation is often reasonable for monolithic resistors of several thousand ohms or less, but should be checked in each case.

The zero-value time-constant analysis for Fig. 7.27 is carried out in the following example. Analysis of a two-stage common-emitter amplifier would follow similar steps.

■ **EXAMPLE**

Calculate the −3-dB frequency of the circuit of Fig. 7.27 assuming the following parameter values:

$$R_S = 10 \text{ k}\Omega \qquad R_{L1} = 10 \text{ k}\Omega \qquad R_{L2} = 5 \text{ k}\Omega$$
$$C_{gs1} = 5 \text{ pF} \qquad C_{gs2} = 10 \text{ pF} \qquad C_{gd1} = C_{gd2} = 1 \text{ pF}$$
$$C_{db1} = C_{db2} = 2 \text{ pF} \qquad g_{m1} = 3 \text{ mA/V} \qquad g_{m2} = 6 \text{ mA/V}$$

Ignore $C_{gb}$ (which is in parallel with $C_{gs}$ and is much smaller than $C_{gs}$).

The small-signal equivalent circuit of Fig. 7.27 is shown in Fig. 7.28a. The zero-value time constants for this circuit are determined by calculating the resistance seen by each capacitor across its own terminals. However, significant effort can be saved by recognizing that some capacitors in the circuit are in similar configurations and the same formula can be applied to them. For example, consider $C_{gd1}$ and $C_{gd2}$. The resistance seen by either $C_{gd}$ capacitor can be found by calculating the resistance $R_{gd0}$ in the circuit in Fig. 7.28b. This circuit is the same as the circuit in Fig. 7.25 if we let $R_A = R_{\pi 0}$ and $R_B = R_L$.

**Figure 7.27** Two-stage, common-source cascade amplifier.

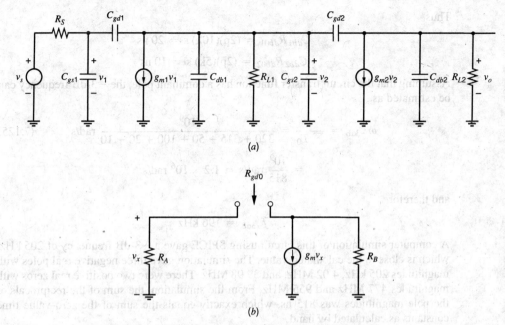

(a)

(b)

**Figure 7.28**  Small-signal equivalent circuit of Fig. 7.27.

Therefore, the resistance $R_{gd0}$ in Fig. 7.28b is given by substituting $R_A$ for $R_{\pi0}$ and $R_B$ for $R_L$ in (7.117):

$$R_{gd0} = R_A + R_B + g_m R_B R_A \qquad (7.124)$$

This equation can be used to find the zero-value time constants for both gate-drain capacitors:

$$C_{gd1} R_{gd01} = C_{gd1} \left( R_S + R_{L1} + g_{m1} R_{L1} R_S \right)$$
$$= (1p)[10k + 10k + (3 \times 10^{-3})(10k)(10k)] \text{ s} = 320 \text{ ns}$$
$$C_{gd2} R_{gd02} = C_{gd2} \left( R_{L1} + R_{L2} + g_{m2} R_{L2} R_{L1} \right)$$
$$= (1p)[10k + 5k + (6 \times 10^{-3})(10k)(5k)] \text{ s} = 315 \text{ ns}$$

The value of $R_{gs0}$ for each device can be found by inspection

$$R_{gs01} = R_S$$
$$R_{gs02} = R_{L1}$$

The corresponding time constants are

$$C_{gs1} R_{gs01} = C_{gs1} R_S = (5p)(10k) \text{ s} = 50 \text{ ns}$$
$$C_{gs2} R_{gs02} = C_{gs2} R_{L1} = (10p)(10k) \text{ s} = 100 \text{ ns}$$

Also, the value for $R_{db0}$ for each device can also be found without computation

$$R_{db01} = R_{L1}$$
$$R_{db02} = R_{L2}$$

Thus

$$C_{db1} R_{db01} = (2p)(10k) \text{ s} = 20 \text{ ns}$$

$$C_{db2} R_{db02} = (2p)(5k) \text{ s} = 10 \text{ ns}$$

Assuming that the circuit transfer function has a dominant pole, the $-3$-dB frequency can be estimated as

$$\omega_{-3dB} = \frac{1}{\sum T_0} = \frac{10^9}{320 + 315 + 50 + 100 + 20 + 10} \text{ rad/s} \qquad (7.125)$$

$$= \frac{10^9}{815} \text{ rad/s} = 1.2 \times 10^6 \text{ rad/s}$$

and therefore

$$f_{-3dB} = 196 \text{ kHz}$$

A computer simulation of this circuit using SPICE gave a $-3$-dB frequency of 205 kHz, which is close to the calculated value. The simulation gave three negative real poles with magnitudes 205 kHz, 4.02 MHz, and 39.98 MHz. There were two positive real zeros with magnitudes 477 MHz and 955 MHz. From the simulation, the sum of the reciprocals of the pole magnitudes was 815 ns, which exactly equals the sum of the zero-value time constants as calculated by hand.

An exact analysis of Fig. 7.28a would first apply KCL at three nodes and produce a transfer function with a third-order denominator, in which some coefficients would consist of a sum of many products of small-signal model parameters. Many simplifying approximations would be needed to give useful design equations. As the circuit complexity increases, the number of equations increases and the order of the denominator increases, eventually making exact analysis by hand impractical and making time-constant analysis quite attractive.

The foregoing analytical result was obtained with relatively small effort and the calculation has focused on the contributions to the $-3$-dB frequency from the various capacitors in the circuit. In this example, as is usually the case in a cascade of this kind, the time constants associated with the gate-drain capacitances are the major contributors to the $-3$-dB frequency of the circuit. *One of the major benefits of the zero-value time-constant analysis is the information it gives on the circuit elements that most affect the $-3$-dB frequency of the circuit.*

In the preceding calculation, we assumed that the circuit of Fig. 7.28 had a dominant pole. The significance of this assumption will now be examined in more detail. For purposes of illustration, assume that capacitors $C_{gd1}$, $C_{gd2}$, $C_{db1}$, and $C_{db2}$ in Fig. 7.28 are zero and that $R_S = R_{L1} = R_{L2}$ and $C_{gs1} = C_{gs2}$. Then the circuit has two identical stages, and each will contribute a pole with the same magnitude; that is, a dominant-pole situation does not exist because the circuit has two identical poles. However, inclusion of nonzero $C_{gd1}$ and $C_{gd2}$ tends to cause these poles to split apart and produces a dominant-pole situation. (See Chapter 9.) For this reason, most practical circuits of this kind do have a dominant pole, and the zero-value time-constant analysis gives a good estimate of $\omega_{-3dB}$. Even if the circuit has two identical poles, however, the zero-value time-constant analysis is still useful. Equations 7.85 and 7.109 are valid in general, and thus

$$\Sigma T_0 = \sum_{i=1}^{n} \left( -\frac{1}{p_i} \right) \qquad (7.126)$$

is always true. That is, the sum of the zero-value time constants equals the sum of the negative reciprocals of all the poles whether or not a dominant pole exists. Consider a circuit with two identical negative real poles with magnitudes $\omega_x$. Then the gain magnitude of the circuit is

$$|G(j\omega)| = \frac{G_0}{1 + \left(\dfrac{\omega}{\omega_x}\right)^2} \tag{7.127}$$

The $-3$-dB frequency of this circuit is the frequency where $|G(j\omega)| = G_0/\sqrt{2}$, which can be shown to be

$$\omega_{-3\text{dB}} = \omega_x\sqrt{\sqrt{2} - 1} = 0.64\omega_x \tag{7.128}$$

The zero-value time-constant approach predicts

$$\Sigma T_0 = \frac{2}{\omega_x}$$

and thus

$$\omega_{-3\text{dB}} = \frac{1}{\Sigma T_0} = 0.5\omega_x \tag{7.129}$$

Even in this extreme case, the prediction is only 22 percent in error and gives a pessimistic estimate.

### 7.3.4 Cascode Frequency Response

The cascode connection is a multiple-device configuration that is useful in high-frequency applications. An ac schematic of a bipolar version, shown in Fig. 7.29a, consists of a common-emitter stage driving a common-base stage. An MOS version, shown in Fig. 7.29b, consists of a common-source stage driving a common-gate stage. In both circuits, transistor $T_2$ operates as a current buffer. Therefore, the voltage gain of the cascode circuit is approximately

$$\frac{v_o}{v_i} \sim -g_{m1} R_l \tag{7.130}$$

assuming that the output resistance of the cascode circuit is large compared to $R_L$. This result is the same as the voltage gain for a common-emitter or common-source stage without the current buffer $T_2$. The cascode derives its advantage at high frequencies from the fact that the load for transistor $T_1$ is the low input impedance of the current buffer. This impedance at low frequencies was shown in Sections 3.3.3 and 3.3.4 to be

$$R_{i2} \approx \frac{1}{g_{m2}} \tag{7.131}$$

if $r_{o2} \to \infty$, ignoring body effect in the MOS transistor and assuming $r_b/(\beta_0 + 1) \ll 1/g_{m2}$ and $\beta_0 \gg 1$ for the bipolar transistor. If transistors $T_1$ and $T_2$ have equal bias currents and device dimensions, then $g_{m1} = g_{m2}$. Since the load resistance seen by $T_1$ is about $1/g_{m2}$, the magnitude of the voltage gain from $v_i$ to $v_x$ is about unity. Thus the influence of the Miller effect on $T_1$ is minimal, even for fairly large values of $R_L$. Since the current-buffer stage $T_2$ has a wide bandwidth (see Section 7.2.4), the cascode circuit

(a)

(b)

**Figure 7.29**  Cascode circuit connections (a) bipolar and (b) MOS.

overall has good high-frequency performance when compared to a single common-emitter or common-source stage, especially for large $R_L$. (See problems 7.29 and 7.30.)

If the assumption that $r_{o2} \to \infty$ is removed, the magnitude of the voltage gain from $v_i$ to $v_x$ can be larger than one. For example, $R_L$ might be the output resistance of a cascoded current source in an amplifier stage. In this case, $R_L$ is large compared to $r_{o2}$, and the input resistance of the current buffer $T_2$ is given by

$$R_{i2} \approx \frac{1}{g_{m2}} + \frac{1}{g_{m2}} \frac{R_L}{r_{o2}} \qquad (7.132)$$

from Section 3.3.5.1 [ignoring body effect in the MOS transistor and assuming $r_b/(\beta_0 + 1) \ll 1/g_{m2}$ and $\beta_0 \gg 1$ for the bipolar transistor]. Since this resistance is significantly bigger than $1/g_{m2}$ when $R_L \gg r_{o2}$, the magnitude of the gain from $v_i$ to $v_x$ can be significantly larger than one. However, this gain is still much smaller in magnitude than the gain from $v_i$ to $v_o$; therefore, the Miller effect on $T_1$ is smaller with the cascode transistor $T_2$ than without it. To further reduce the Miller effect when $R_L$ is large, the input resistance of the current buffer in (7.132) can be reduced by replacing the cascode transistor with the active cascode shown in Chapter 3.

A useful characteristic of the cascode is the small amount of reverse transmission that occurs in the circuit. The current-buffer stage provides good isolation that is required in high-frequency tuned-amplifier applications. Another useful characteristic of the cascode is its high output resistance. This characteristic is used to advantage in current-source design, as described in Chapter 4, and in operational amplifier design, as described in Chapter 6.

As an example of the calculation of the $-3$-dB frequency of a cascode amplifier, consider the circuit of Fig. 7.30. The input differential pair is biased using a resistor $R_3$. If

**Figure 7.30** Cascode differential amplifier.

common-mode rejection is an important consideration, $R_3$ can be replaced with an active current source. The resistive divider composed of $R_1$ and $R_2$ sets the bias voltage at the bases of $Q_3$ and $Q_4$, and this voltage is chosen to give adequate collector-emitter bias voltage for each device.

For purposes of analysis, the circuit is assumed driven with source resistance $R_S$ from each base to ground. If the base of $Q_2$ is grounded, the frequency response of the circuit is not greatly affected if $R_S$ is small. The circuit of Fig. 7.30 can be analyzed using the ac differential half-circuit of Fig. 7.31a. Note that in forming the differential half-circuit, the common-base point of $Q_3$ and $Q_4$ is assumed to be a virtual ground for differential signals. The frequency response $(v_o/v_s)(j\omega)$ of the circuit of Fig. 7.31a will be the same as that of Fig. 7.30 if $R_3$ in Fig. 7.30 is large enough to give a reasonable value of common-mode rejection. The small-signal equivalent circuit of Fig. 7.31a is shown in Fig. 7.31b.

■ **EXAMPLE**

Calculate the low-frequency, small-signal gain and $-3$-dB frequency of the circuit of Fig. 7.30 using the following data: $R_S = 1$ k$\Omega$, $R_E = 75$ $\Omega$, $R_3 = 4$ k$\Omega$, $R_L = 1$ k$\Omega$, $R_1 = 4$ k$\Omega$, $R_2 = 10$ k$\Omega$, and $V_{CC} = V_{EE} = 10$ V. Device data are $\beta = 200$, $V_{BE(on)} = 0.7$ V, $\tau_F = 0.25$ ns, $r_b = 200$ $\Omega$, $r_c$(active region) $= 150$ $\Omega$, $C_{je0} = 1.3$ pF, $C_{\mu0} = 0.6$ pF, $\psi_{0c} = 0.6$ V, $C_{cs0} = 2$ pF, $\psi_{0s} = 0.58$ V, and $n_s = 0.5$.

The dc bias conditions are first calculated neglecting transistor base currents. The voltage at the base of $Q_3$ and $Q_4$ is

$$V_{B3} = V_{CC} - \frac{R_1}{R_1 + R_2}(V_{CC} + V_{EE}) = 10 - \frac{4}{14} \times 20 = 4.3 \text{ V}$$

The voltage at the collectors of $Q_1$ and $Q_2$ is

$$V_{C1} = V_{B3} - V_{BE3(on)} = 3.6 \text{ V}$$

**Figure 7.31** (*a*) The ac differential half-circuit of Fig. 7.30. (*b*) Small-signal equivalent of the circuit in (*a*).

Assuming that the bases of $Q_1$ and $Q_2$ are grounded, we can calculate the collector currents of $Q_1$ and $Q_2$ as

$$I_{C1} = \frac{V_{EE} - V_{BE(on)}}{2R_3 + R_E} = \frac{10 - 0.7}{8.075} \text{mA} = 1.15 \text{ mA}$$

Therefore, we have

$$I_{C1} = I_{C2} = I_{C3} = I_{C4} = 1.15 \text{ mA}$$

The dc analysis is completed by noting that the voltage at the collectors of $Q_3$ and $Q_4$ is

$$V_{C3} = V_{CC} - I_{C3}R_L = 10 \text{ V} - 1.15 \text{ V} = 8.85 \text{ V}$$

The low-frequency gain can be calculated from the ac differential half-circuit of Fig. 7.31*a*, using the results derived in Chapter 3 for a stage with emitter resistance. If we neglect base resistance, the small-signal transconductance of $Q_1$ including $R_E$ is given by (3.93) as

$$G_{m1} \approx \frac{g_{m1}}{1 + g_{m1}R_E} = 10.24 \text{ mA/V}$$

The small-signal input resistance of $Q_1$ including $R_E$ is given by (3.90) as

$$R_{i1} \approx r_{\pi 1} + (\beta + 1)R_E = 19.5 \text{ k}\Omega$$

As shown in Chapter 3, the common-base stage has a current gain of approximately unity, and thus the small-signal collector current of $Q_1$ appears in the collector of $Q_3$. By inspection, the voltage gain of the circuit of Fig. 7.31*a* is

$$\frac{v_o}{v_s} = -\frac{R_{i1}}{R_{i1} + R_S}G_{m1}R_L = -\frac{19.5}{19.5 + 1} \times 10.24 \times 1 = -9.74$$

To calculate the $-3$-dB frequency of the circuit, the parameters in the small-signal equivalent circuit of Fig. 7.31*b* must be determined. The resistive parameters are $g_{m1} = g_{m3} = qI_{C1}/kT = 44.2 \text{ mA/V}$, $r_{\pi 1} = r_{\pi 3} = \beta/g_{m1} = 4525 \Omega$, $r_{c1} = r_{c3} = 150 \Omega$, $r_{b1} =$

$r_{b3} = 200 \ \Omega$, and $R_S + r_b = 1.2 \ k\Omega$. Because of the low resistances in the circuit, transistor output resistances are neglected.

The capacitive elements in Fig. 7.31b are calculated as described in Chapter 1. First consider base-emitter, depletion-layer capacitance $C_{je}$. As described in Chapter 1, the value of $C_{je}$ in the forward-active region is difficult to estimate, and a reasonable approximation is to double $C_{je0}$. This gives $C_{je} = 2.6 \ pF$. From (1.104) the base-charging capacitance for $Q_1$ is

$$C_{b1} = \tau_F g_{m1} = 0.25 \times 10^{-9} \times 44.2 \times 10^{-3} \ F = 11.1 \ pF$$

Use of (1.118) gives

$$C_{\pi 1} = C_{b1} + C_{je1} = 13.7 \ pF$$

Since the collector currents of $Q_1$ and $Q_3$ are equal, $C_{\pi 3} = C_{\pi 1} = 13.7 \ pF$.

The collector-base capacitance $C_{\mu 1}$ of $Q_1$ can be calculated using (1.117a) and noting that the collector-base bias voltage of $Q_1$ is $V_{CB1} = 3.6 \ V$. Thus

$$C_{\mu 1} = \frac{C_{\mu 0}}{\sqrt{1 + \dfrac{V_{CB}}{\psi_{0c}}}} = \frac{0.6}{\sqrt{1 + \dfrac{3.6}{0.6}}} \ pF = 0.23 \ pF$$

The collector-substrate capacitance of $Q_1$ can also be calculated using (1.117a) with a collector-substrate voltage of $V_{CS} = V_{C1} + V_{EE} = 13.6 \ V$. (The substrate is assumed connected to the negative supply voltage.) Thus we have

$$C_{cs1} = \frac{C_{cs0}}{\sqrt{1 + \dfrac{V_{CS}}{\psi_{0s}}}} = \frac{2}{\sqrt{1 + \dfrac{13.6}{0.58}}} \ pF = 0.40 \ pF$$

Similar calculations show that the parameters of $Q_3$ are $C_{\mu 3} = 0.20 \ pF$ and $C_{cs3} = 0.35 \ pF$.

The $-3$-dB frequency of the circuit can now be estimated by calculating the zero-value time constants for the circuit. First consider $C_{\pi 1}$. The resistance seen across its terminals is given by (7.122), which was derived for the emitter follower. The presence of resistance in series with the collector of $Q_1$ makes no difference to the calculation because of the infinite impedance of the current generator $g_{m1}v_1$. Thus from (7.122)

$$R_{\pi 01} = r_{\pi 1} \| \frac{R_S + r_{b1} + R_E}{1 + g_{m1}R_E} = \left(4525 \| \frac{1000 + 200 + 75}{1 + 44.2 \times 0.075}\right) \ \Omega = (4525\|295) \ \Omega = 277 \ \Omega$$

Note that the effect of $R_E$ is to reduce $R_{\pi 01}$, which increases the bandwidth of the circuit by reducing the zero-value time constant associated with $C_{\pi 1}$. This time constant has a value

$$C_{\pi 1}R_{\pi 01} = 13.7 \times 0.277 \ ns = 3.79 \ ns$$

The collector-substrate capacitance of $Q_1$ sees a resistance equal to $r_{c1}$ plus the common-base stage input resistance, which is

$$R_{i3} = \frac{1}{g_{m3}} + \frac{r_{b3}}{\beta + 1} = 23.6 \ \Omega$$

and thus $C_{cs1}$ sees a resistance

$$R_{cs01} = R_{i3} + r_{c1} = 174 \ \Omega$$

**Figure 7.32** (a) Circuit for the calculation of $R_{\mu01}$ for $Q_1$. (b) Equivalent circuit for the circuit in (a).

The zero-value time constant is

$$C_{cs1}R_{cs\,01} = 0.4 \times 0.174 \text{ ns} = 0.07 \text{ ns}$$

The zero-value time constant associated with $C_{\mu1}$ of $Q_1$ can be determined by calculating the resistance $R_{\mu01}$ seen across the terminals of $C_{\mu1}$ using the equivalent circuit of Fig. 7.32a. To simplify the analysis, the circuit in Fig. 7.32a is transformed into the circuit of Fig. 7.32b, where the transistor with emitter degeneration is represented by parameters $R_{i1}$ and $G_{m1}$, which were defined previously. The circuit of Fig. 7.32b is in the form of a common-emitter stage as shown in Fig. 7.25, and the formula derived for that case can be used now. Thus from (7.117)

$$R_{\mu01} = R_1 + R_{L1} + G_{m1}R_{L1}R_1 \tag{7.133}$$

where

$$R_1 = R_{i1}\|(R_S + r_b) = (19.5\|1.2)\text{k}\Omega = 1.13 \text{ k}\Omega$$

The load resistance $R_{L1}$ is just $r_{c1}$ plus the input resistance of $Q_3$. Using the previously calculated values, we obtain

$$R_{L1} = 174 \ \Omega$$

Substituting into (7.133) gives

$$R_{\mu01} = [1.13 + 0.17 + (10.24 \times 1.13 \times 0.17)] \text{ k}\Omega = 3.27 \text{ k}\Omega$$

The zero-value time constant associated with $C_{\mu 1}$ is thus

$$C_{\mu 1} R_{\mu 01} = 0.23 \times 3.27 \text{ ns} = 0.75 \text{ ns}$$

Because the input impedance of the common-base stage is small, the contribution of $C_{\mu 1}$ to the sum of the zero value time constants is much smaller than that due to $C_{\pi 1}$.

The time constant associated with $C_{\pi 3}$ of $Q_3$ can be calculated by recognizing that (7.122) derived for the emitter follower also applies here. The effective source resistance $R_S$ is zero as the base is grounded, and the effective emitter resistance $R_L$ is infinite because the collector of $Q_1$ is connected to the emitter of $Q_3$. Thus (7.122) gives

$$R_{\pi 03} = r_{\pi 3} \| \frac{1}{g_{m3}} = 22.6 \ \Omega$$

The zero-value time constant associated with $C_{\pi 3}$ is thus

$$C_{\pi 3} R_{\pi 03} = 13.7 \times 0.0023 \text{ ns} = 0.32 \text{ ns}$$

The time constant associated with collector-base capacitance $C_{\mu 3}$ of $Q_3$ can be calculated using (7.133) with $G_{m1}$ equal to zero since the effective value of $R_E$ is infinite in this case. In (7.133) the effective value of $R_1$ is just $r_b$ and thus

$$R_{\mu 03} = r_b + R_{L3}$$

where

$$R_{L3} = r_{c3} + R_L$$

and $R_{L3}$ is the load resistance seen by $Q_3$. Thus

$$R_{\mu 03} = [200 + 150 + 1000] \ \Omega = 1.35 \text{ k}\Omega$$

and the time constant is

$$C_{\mu 3} R_{\mu 03} = 0.2 \times 1.35 \text{ ns} = 0.27 \text{ ns}$$

Finally, the collector-substrate capacitance of $Q_3$ sees a resistance

$$R_{cs 03} = r_{c3} + R_L = 1.15 \text{ k}\Omega$$

and

$$C_{cs3} R_{csU3} = 0.35 \times 1.15 \text{ ns} = 0.4 \text{ ns}$$

The sum of the zero-value time constants is thus

$$\Sigma T_0 = (3.79 + 0.07 + 0.75 + 0.32 + 0.27 + 0.4) \text{ ns} = 5.60 \text{ ns}$$

The $-3$-dB frequency is estimated as

$$f_{-3dB} = \frac{1}{2\pi \Sigma T_0} = 28.4 \text{ MHz}$$

Computer simulation of this circuit using SPICE gave a $-3$-dB frequency of 34.7 MHz. The computer simulation showed six poles, of which the first two were negative real poles with magnitudes 35.8 MHz and 253 MHz. The zero-value time constant analysis has thus given a reasonable estimate of the $-3$-dB frequency and has also shown that the major limitation on the circuit frequency response comes from $C_{\pi 1}$ of $Q_1$. The circuit can thus be broadbanded even further by increasing resistance $R_E$ in the emitter of $Q_1$, since the calculation of $R_{\pi 01}$ showed that increasing $R_E$ will reduce the value of $R_{\pi 01}$. Note that this change will reduce the gain of the circuit.

Further useful information regarding the circuit frequency response can be obtained from the previous calculations by recognizing that $Q_3$ in Fig. 7.31 effectively isolates $C_{\mu 3}$ and $C_{cs3}$ from the rest of the circuit. In fact, if $r_{b3}$ is zero then these two capacitors are connected in parallel across the output and will contribute a separate pole to the transfer function. The magnitude of this pole can be estimated by summing zero-value time constants for $C_{\mu 3}$ and $C_{cs3}$ alone to give $\Sigma T_0 = 0.67$ ns. This time constant corresponds to a pole with magnitude $1/(2\pi\Sigma T_0) = 237$ MHz, which is very close to the second pole calculated by the computer. The dominant pole would then be estimated by summing the rest of the time constants to give $\Sigma T_0 = 4.93$ ns, which corresponds to a pole with magnitude 32.3 MHz and is also close to the computer-calculated value. This technique can be used any time a high degree of isolation exists between various portions of a circuit. To estimate the dominant pole of a given section, the zero-value time constants may be summed for that section.

In this example, the bandwidth of the differential-mode gain was estimated by computing the zero-value time constants for the differential half-circuit. The bandwidth of the common-mode gain could be estimated by computing the zero-value time constants for the common-mode half-circuit.

### 7.3.5 Frequency Response of a Current Mirror Loading a Differential Pair

A CMOS differential pair with current-mirror load is shown in Fig. 7.33a. The current mirror here introduces a pole and a zero that are not widely separated. To show this result, consider the simplified small-signal circuit in Fig. 7.33b for finding the transconductance $G_m = i_o/v_{id}$ with $v_o = 0$. The circuit has been simplified by letting $r_o \to \infty$ for all transistors and ignoring all capacitors except $C_x$. Here $C_x$ models the total capacitance from node $X$ to ground, which consists of $C_{gs3}$, $C_{gs4}$, and other smaller capacitances. With a purely differential input, node $Y$ is an ac ground. The zero-value time constant associated with $C_x$ is $T_0 = C_x/g_{m3}$; therefore,

$$p = -\frac{g_{m3}}{C_x} \tag{7.134}$$

An exact analysis of this circuit yields a transfer function with a pole given by (7.134) and a zero at $z = -2g_{m3}/C_x$. (See problem 7.48.) The magnitudes of the pole and zero are separated by one octave. The magnitude and phase responses for $G_m(s)$ are plotted in Fig. 7.34. The phase shift from this pole-zero pair is between 0 and $-19.4$ degrees.

The frequency-response plot can be explained as follows. The drain currents in the differential pair are $i_{d1} = g_{m1}v_{id}/2$ and $i_{d2} = -g_{m1}v_{id}/2$. At low frequencies, $M_3$ and $M_4$ mirror $i_{d1}$, giving for the output current

$$i_o = -i_{d2} - i_{d4} = -i_{d2} + i_{d1} = g_{m1}v_{id} \tag{7.135}$$

At high frequencies ($\omega \to \infty$), $C_x$ becomes a short, so $v_{gs4} \to 0$ and $i_{d4} \to 0$. Therefore,

$$i_o = -i_{d2} - i_{d4} = -i_{d2} - 0 = \frac{g_{m1}v_{id}}{2} \tag{7.136}$$

These equations show that the transconductance falls from $g_{m1}$ at low frequencies to $g_{m1}/2$ at high frequencies. This result stems from the observation that the current mirror does not contribute to the output current when $C_x$ becomes a short. The change in the transconductance occurs between frequencies $|p|$ and $|z|$. This analysis shows that the pole and zero are both important in this circuit. Since $C_x \approx C_{gs3} + C_{gs4} = 2C_{gs3}$, (7.134) gives $|p| \approx g_{m3}/2C_{gs3} \approx \omega_{T(M_3)}/2$. Therefore, the pole-zero pair has an effect only at very high

**Figure 7.33** (a) Differential pair with current-mirror load and (b) a simplified small-signal model.

frequencies, and the effect of this pair is much less than that of either an isolated pole or zero.

Analysis of a bipolar version of the circuit in Fig. 7.33a gives a similar result.

### 7.3.6 Short-Circuit Time Constants

Zero-value time-constant analysis (which is sometimes called open-circuit time-constant analysis) can be used to estimate the smallest-magnitude pole of an amplifier. This estimated pole magnitude is approximately equal to the $-3$-dB frequency of the gain of a dc-coupled amplifier with a low-pass transfer function. Another type of time-constant analysis is called *short-circuit time-constant* analysis. Short-circuit time constants can be used to estimate the location of the largest-magnitude pole. While short-circuit time-constant analysis is often used to estimate the lower $-3$-dB frequency in ac-coupled amplifiers,[1,2] we will use these time constants to estimate the magnitude of the nondominant pole in dc-coupled amplifiers that have only two widely spaced, real poles.

**Figure 7.34** (a) Magnitude and (b) phase versus frequency of the transconductance $G_m = i_o/v_{id}$ for the circuit in Fig. 7.33.

The short-circuit time-constant formulas will be derived for the small-signal circuit in Fig. 7.24. Equations 7.91 to 7.93 describe this circuit, and (7.94) is the determinant $\Delta(s)$ of these equations. This determinant can be written as

$$\Delta(s) = K_3\left(s^3 + \frac{K_2}{K_3}s^2 + \frac{K_1}{K_3}s + \frac{K_0}{K_3}\right)$$
$$= K_3(s - p_1)(s - p_2)(s - p_3) \tag{7.137}$$

since the zeros of $\Delta(s)$ are the poles of the transfer function. Expanding the right-most expression and equating the coefficients of $s^2$ gives

$$\frac{K_2}{K_3} = -\sum_{i=1}^{3} p_i \tag{7.138}$$

Now a formula for calculating $K_2/K_3$ will be derived. Evaluating the determinant of the circuit equations in (7.91) to (7.93), the term $K_3$ that multiplies $s^3$ in (7.94) is given by

$$K_3 = C_\pi C_\mu C_x \tag{7.139}$$

and the $K_2$ term is

$$K_2 = g_{11} C_\mu C_x + g_{22} C_\pi C_x + g_{33} C_\pi C_\mu \tag{7.140}$$

From (7.139) and (7.140), the ratio $K_2/K_3$ is

$$\frac{K_2}{K_3} = \frac{g_{11}}{C_\pi} + \frac{g_{22}}{C_\mu} + \frac{g_{33}}{C_x} = \frac{1}{r_{11} C_\pi} + \frac{1}{r_{22} C_\mu} + \frac{1}{r_{33} C_x} \tag{7.141}$$

where $r_{ii} = 1/g_{ii}$. Now, let us examine each term in the right-most expression. The first term is $1/(r_{11} C_\pi)$. Using (7.91), $r_{11} = 1/g_{11}$ can be found as

$$r_{11} = \frac{1}{g_{11}} = \frac{v_1}{i_1} \bigg|_{v_2 = v_3 = 0, \, C_\pi = 0} \tag{7.142}$$

That is, $r_{11}$ is the resistance in parallel with $C_\pi$, computed with $C_\pi$ removed from the circuit and with the other capacitors $C_\mu$ and $C_x$ shorted. (Note that shorting $C_\mu$ makes $v_2 = 0$; shorting $C_x$ makes $v_3 = 0$.) Therefore, the product $r_{11} C_\pi$ is called the *short-circuit time constant* for capacitor $C_\pi$. Similarly, from (7.92)

$$r_{22} = \frac{1}{g_{22}} = \frac{v_2}{i_2} \bigg|_{v_1 = v_3 = 0, \, C_\mu = 0} \tag{7.143}$$

This $r_{22}$ is the resistance in parallel with $C_\mu$, computed with $C_\mu$ removed from the circuit and with the other capacitors $C_\pi$ and $C_x$ shorted. Finally, from (7.93)

$$r_{33} = \frac{1}{g_{33}} = \frac{v_3}{i_3} \bigg|_{v_1 = v_2 = 0, \, C_x = 0} \tag{7.144}$$

So $r_{33}$ is the resistance in parallel with $C_x$, computed with $C_x$ removed from the circuit and with the other capacitors $C_\pi$ and $C_\mu$ shorted. Using (7.142) to (7.144), (7.141) can be rewritten as

$$\frac{K_2}{K_3} = \sum_{i=1}^{3} \frac{1}{\tau_{si}} \tag{7.145}$$

where $\tau_{si}$ is the short-circuit time constant associated with the $i^{\text{th}}$ capacitor in the circuit. The short-circuit time constant for the $i^{\text{th}}$ capacitor is found by multiplying its capacitance by the driving-point resistance in parallel with the $i^{\text{th}}$ capacitor, computed with all other capacitors *shorted*.

Combining (7.138) and (7.145) gives

$$\sum_{i=1}^{3} p_i = -\sum_{i=1}^{3} \frac{1}{\tau_{si}} \tag{7.146}$$

This key equation relates the sum of the poles and the sum of the reciprocals of the short-circuit time constants. This relationship holds true for any small-signal circuit that consists of resistors, capacitors, and controlled sources, assuming that the circuit has no loops of capacitors.[1]

If a circuit has $n$ poles and pole $p_n$ has a magnitude that is much larger than the magnitude of every other pole, then a general version of (7.146) can be written as

$$p_n \approx \sum_{i=1}^{n} p_i = -\sum \frac{1}{\tau_{si}} \tag{7.147}$$

For a circuit that has only two widely spaced, real poles, (7.147) simplifies to

$$p_2 \approx -\sum \frac{1}{\tau_{si}} \tag{7.148}$$

This simple relationship allows the magnitude of the nondominant pole to be readily estimated from the short-circuit time constants.

▪ **EXAMPLE**

Estimate the nondominant pole magnitude for the circuit in Fig. 7.35 with

$$R_S = 10 \text{ k}\Omega \quad R_L = 10 \text{ k}\Omega$$

$$C_{gs} = 1 \text{ pF} \quad C_f = 20 \text{ pF} \quad g_m = 3 \text{ mA/V}$$

This circuit has two poles because it has two independent capacitors. First, we will calculate the short-circuit time constant $\tau_{s1}$ for $C_f$. With $C_{gs}$ shorted and the independent source set to zero, we have $v_1 = 0$, so the current through the dependent source is also zero. Therefore, the resistance seen by $C_f$ is just $R_L$, and the corresponding time constant is

$$\tau_{s1} = C_f R_L = (20 \text{ pF})(10 \text{ k}\Omega) = 200 \text{ ns}$$

To find the short-circuit time constant for $C_{gs}$, we short $C_f$ and find the resistance seen by $C_{gs}$. With $C_f$ shorted, the dependent source is controlled by the voltage across it; therefore, it acts as a resistance of $1/g_m$. This resistance is in parallel with $R_L$ and $R_S$, so the short-circuit time constant for $C_{gs}$ is

$$\tau_{s2} = C_{gs}[R_S\|1/g_m\|R_L] = (1 \text{ pF})[10 \text{ k}\Omega\|333 \text{ }\Omega\|10 \text{ k}\Omega] = 0.312 \text{ ns} \tag{7.149}$$

From (7.148),

$$p_2 \approx -\sum \frac{1}{\tau_{si}} = -\left(\frac{1}{200 \text{ ns}} + \frac{1}{0.312 \text{ ns}}\right) = -3.21 \text{ Grad/s} \tag{7.150}$$

if the poles are real and widely spaced. An exact analysis of this circuit gives $p_2 = -3.20$ Grad/s, which is very close to the estimate above, and $p_1 = -156$ krad/s.

Using zero-value time constants, the dominant-pole magnitude can be estimated. From (7.124), the zero-value time constant for $C_f$ is

$$C_f R_{f0} = C_f (R_S + R_L + g_m R_L R_S) \tag{7.151}$$

$$= (20\text{p})[10\text{k} + 10\text{k} + (3 \times 10^{-3})(10\text{k})(10\text{k})] \text{ s} = 6.4 \text{ }\mu\text{s}$$

**Figure 7.35** Example circuit for calculating short-circuit time constants.

The zero-value time constant for $C_{gs}$ is simply

$$C_{gs}R_S = (1 \text{ pF})(10 \text{ k}\Omega) = 10 \text{ ns}$$

Therefore, (7.111) gives

$$p_1 \approx -\frac{1}{6.4 \text{ } \mu s + 10 \text{ ns}} = -156 \text{ krad/s}$$

Exact analysis of this circuit gives $p_1 = -156$ krad/s, which is the same as the estimate above. This example demonstrates that for circuits with two widely spaced, real poles, time constant analyses can give accurate estimates of the magnitudes of the dominant and nondominant poles.

In this case of widely spaced poles, note that $p_1$ and $p_2$ can be accurately estimated using only one time constant for each pole. Since $C_f$ is large compared to $C_{gs}$ and the resistance $C_f$ sees when computing its zero-value time constant is large compared to the resistance seen by $C_{gs}$, a reasonable conclusion is that $C_{gs}$ has negligible effect near the frequency $|p_1|$. Therefore, the most important zero-value time constant in (7.111) for estimating $p_1$ is the time constant for $C_f$ (computed with $C_{gs}$ replaced with an open circuit). Using only that time constant from (7.151), we estimate

$$p_1 \approx -\frac{1}{6.4 \text{ } \mu s} = -156 \text{ krad/s}$$

which is a very accurate estimate of $p_1$.

If the real poles are widely separated and the dominant pole was set by $C_f$, a reasonable assumption is that $C_f$ is a short circuit near the frequency $|p_2|$. Therefore, the important short-circuit time constant in (7.150) is the time constant for $C_{gs}$, computed with $C_f$ shorted. Using only that time constant from (7.149) in (7.148) gives

$$p_2 \approx -\frac{1}{0.312 \text{ ns}} = -3.21 \text{ Grad/s}$$

which is an accurate estimate of $p_2$.

This last set of calculations shows that if two real poles are widely spaced and if one capacitor is primarily responsible for $p_1$ and another capacitor is responsible for $p_2$, we need only compute one zero-value time constant to estimate $p_1$ and one short-circuit time constant to estimate $p_2$.

## 7.4 Analysis of the Frequency Response of the 741 Op Amp

Up to this point the analysis of the frequency response of integrated circuits has been limited to fairly simple configurations. The reason for this is apparent in previous sections, where the large amount of calculation required to estimate the dominant pole of some simple circuits was illustrated. A complete frequency analysis by hand of a large integrated circuit is thus out of the question. However, a circuit designer often needs insight into the frequency response of large circuits such as the 741 op amp, and, by making some sensible approximations, the methods of analysis described previously can be used to provide such information. We will now illustrate this by analyzing the frequency response of the 741.

### 7.4.1 High-Frequency Equivalent Circuit of the 741

A schematic of the 741 is shown in Fig. 6.32a. Its frequency response is dominated by the 30-pF integrated capacitor $C_c$, which is a compensation capacitor designed to prevent the

**Figure 7.36** An ac schematic of the high-frequency gain path of the 741.

circuit from oscillating when connected in a feedback loop. The choice of $C_c$ and its function are described in Chapter 9.

Since the 741 contains over 20 interconnected transistors, a complete analysis is not attempted even using zero-value time-constant techniques. In order to obtain an estimate of the frequency response of this circuit, the circuit designer must be able to recognize those parts of the circuit that have little or no influence on the frequency response and to discard these from the analysis. As a general rule, elements involved in the bias circuit can often be eliminated, and those portions of the circuit that are differential can be replaced by a half-circuit. This approach leads to the ac schematic of Fig. 7.36, which is adequate for an approximate calculation of the high-frequency behavior of the 741. All bias elements have been eliminated except where they contribute parasitic elements to the gain path, and these are represented by $R_{p1}$, $C_{p1}$, $R_{p2}$, and $C_{p2}$. In the output stage, either $Q_{14}$ or $Q_{20}$ will be conducting, depending on whether the output voltage is positive or negative, and the frequency response of the circuit will be slightly different in these two cases. Transistor $Q_{14}$ is assumed conducting in the schematic of Fig. 7.36.

The major approximation in Fig. 7.36 is neglect of the frequency limitations of the input-stage active load that has been eliminated from the gain path. However, the output resistance and capacitance of $Q_6$ are included as part of $R_{p1}$ and $C_{p1}$. More detailed calculation and computer simulation show that these are reasonable approximations.

As mentioned above, the frequency response of the 741 is dominated by $C_c$, and the $-3$-dB frequency can be estimated by considering the effect of this capacitance alone. However, as described in Chapter 9, the presence of poles other than the dominant one has a crucial effect on the behavior of the circuit when feedback is applied. The magnitude of the nondominant poles is thus of considerable interest, and methods of estimating their magnitudes are described. First we calculate the $-3$-dB frequency of the circuit.

### 7.4.2 Calculation of the −3-dB Frequency of the 741

The $-3$-dB frequency of the circuit of Fig. 7.36 can be estimated by calculating the zero-value resistance $R_{c0}$ seen by $C_c$. This can be calculated from the ac circuit of Fig. 7.37a, where the input resistance of $Q_{23}$ is assumed very high and is neglected. The calculation of $R_{c0}$ can be greatly simplified by representing the circuit of Fig. 7.37a as shown in Fig. 7.37b. Quantities $R_{ic}$, $R_{oc}$, and $G_{mc}$ are the input resistance, output resistance, and

**Figure 7.37** (*a*) Circuit for the calculation of the zero-value time constant for $C_c$. (*b*) Equivalent circuit for the circuit in (*a*).

transconductance, respectively, of the circuit of Fig. 7.37*a*. These quantities were calculated in Chapter 6 using nominal device data but a more accurate calculation allowing for $\beta$ variation with bias current yields the following values:

$$R_{ic} = R_{o4}\|R_{p1}\|R_{i16} = 1.95 \text{ M}\Omega$$

$$R_{oc} = R_{o17}\|R_{p2} = 86.3 \text{ k}\Omega$$

$$G_{mc} = 6.39 \text{ mA/V}$$

Note that $R_{p1}$ is the effective output resistance of $Q_6$ and $R_{p2}$ is the effective output resistance of $Q_{13B}$ in the schematic of Fig. 6.32*a*.

Since the circuit of Fig. 7.37*b* is topologically the same as that of Fig. 7.24, (7.117) can now be used to estimate $R_{c0}$.

$$R_{c0} = R_{ic} + R_{oc} + G_{mc}R_{ic}R_{oc} \tag{7.152}$$
$$= [1.95 + 0.086 + (6.39 \times 10^{-3} \times 86.3 \times 10^{3} \times 1.95)] \text{ M}\Omega$$
$$= 1.08 \times 10^{9} \ \Omega$$

This extremely large resistance when combined with $C_c = 30$ pF gives a time constant

$$C_c R_{c0} = 30 \times 10^{-12} \times 1.08 \times 10^{9} \text{ s} = 32.4 \times 10^{-3} \text{ s}$$

This totally dominates the sum of the zero-value time constants and gives a $-3$-dB frequency of

$$f_{-3dB} = \frac{1}{2\pi C_c R_{c0}} = 4.9 \text{ Hz}$$

A computer simulation of the complete 741 gave $f_{-3dB} = 5.0$ Hz.

An alternative means of calculating the effect of the frequency compensation is using the Miller effect as described in Section 7.2.1. The compensation capacitor is connected from the base of $Q_{16}$ to the collector of $Q_{17}$ and the voltage gain between these two points can be calculated from the equivalent circuit of Fig. 7.37*b*:

$$A_v = -G_{mc}R_{oc} \tag{7.153}$$

From (7.5) the Miller capacitance seen at the base of $Q_{16}$ is

$$C_M = (1 - A_v)C_c \tag{7.154}$$

and substitution of (7.153) in (7.154) gives

$$\begin{aligned}
C_M &= (1 + G_{mc}R_{oc})C_c \tag{7.155}\\
&= [1 + (6.39 \times 10^{-3} \times 86.3 \times 10^3)] \times 30 \text{ pF}\\
&= 16{,}540 \text{ pF}
\end{aligned}$$

This extremely large effective capacitance at the base of $Q_{16}$ swamps all other capacitances and, when combined with resistance $R_{ic} = 1.95$ MΩ from the base of $Q_{16}$ to ground, gives a $-3$-dB frequency for the circuit of

$$\begin{aligned}
f_{-3dB} &= \frac{1}{2\pi C_M R_{ic}}\\
&= \frac{1}{2\pi \times 16{,}540 \times 10^{-12} \times 1.95 \times 10^6} \text{ Hz}\\
&= 4.9 \text{ Hz}
\end{aligned}$$

This is the same value as predicted by the zero-value time-constant approach.

Note that an additional capacitor is introduced into the circuit along with $C_c$. This is the capacitance described in Chapter 2 from the underside of $C_c$ to the substrate. In this case, capacitor $C_c$ is connected so that the parasitic capacitance exists from the base of $Q_{16}$ to ground and is thus swamped by the Miller effect due to $C_c$. The parasitic capacitance has a relatively large value (about 14 pF) because of the large area of the 30-pF capacitor. This capacitor consumes an area 16 mil square in a chip that is 56 mil square, and thus occupies an area about 13 times that of a typical transistor in the circuit. (1000 mil = 1 inch = 25.4 mm.)

It is interesting to note that if the compensation capacitor is removed and the zero-value time constants of the circuit are calculated, then the $-3$-dB frequency of the circuit is found to be 18.9 kHz. This is dominated by the capacitance $C_{p1}$, which is about 3.4 pF and is composed largely of collector-substrate capacitance from $Q_6$ and $Q_{22}$. The resistance seen by $C_{p1}$ is $R_{ic} = 1.95$ MΩ as calculated above, giving a time constant of 6.6 μs.

### 7.4.3 Nondominant Poles of the 741

The foregoing calculations have shown that the 30-pF compensation capacitor produces a dominant pole in the 741 with a magnitude of 4.9 Hz. From the complexity of the circuit it is evident that there will be a large number of poles with larger magnitudes that we now consider.

Transistors $Q_{16}$ and $Q_{17}$ form the gain stage around which the compensation capacitor is connected. After $C_c$ is connected, the transfer function of this pair contains a pole with a magnitude of 4.9 Hz plus higher frequency poles. As shown in Chapter 9, these higher frequency poles are much less significant after $C_c$ is connected, but they still contribute phase shift at the unity-gain frequency of the amplifier (which is about 1.25 MHz). The exact calculation of these higher frequency poles is quite difficult, however.

Other sources of higher frequency poles are the active load, which has been omitted from Fig. 7.36, and also the lateral $pnp$ emitter follower $Q_{23}$. Computer simulation shows that both of these parts of the circuit contribute phase shift at the unity-gain frequency of 1.25 MHz. As in the previous case, hand calculation of the frequency response of these portions of the circuit is difficult and requires consideration of all parasitic elements.

**Figure 7.38** Small-signal equivalent circuit of $Q_4$ in Fig. 7.36.

There is, however, one portion of the circuit of Fig. 7.36 that contributes a nondominant pole that can be calculated. This is the lateral *pnp* common-base stage $Q_4$. This stage is driven by the *npn* emitter follower $Q_2$, which may be assumed to have a frequency response that is much broader than that of $Q_4$ because the $f_T$ of an *npn* device is much higher than that of a lateral *pnp*. Neglecting frequency effects in $Q_2$, we may assume that $Q_4$ is fed by $v_i$ in series with $1/g_{m2}$, which is the resistance seen looking into the emitter of $Q_2$ if $R_S$ is small. In addition, the collector of $Q_4$ may be assumed to be feeding an ac short circuit, since the large Miller capacitance produced by $C_c$ results in a very low impedance at the collector of $Q_4$. The small-signal equivalent circuit of $Q_4$ can thus be drawn as in Fig. 7.38, and this is effectively isolated from the rest of the circuit. As a result, this stage contributes a separate pole whose magnitude can now be estimated using zero-value time-constant techniques. Note that $r_{b4}$ and $C_{\mu4}$ are neglected.

We first calculate the small-signal parameters of the circuit of Fig. 7.38. The bias levels were calculated in Chapter 6 as $I_{C2} = -I_{C4} = 12$ μA and thus $g_{m2} = g_{m4} = 0.46$ mA/V. A typical value of $C_{je}$ for a lateral *pnp* in forward bias is 0.6 pF. Assuming $\tau_F = 25$ ns for the lateral *pnp*, we can calculate the base charging capacitance for $Q_4$ using (1.104) in Chapter 1:

$$C_{b4} = \tau_{F4}g_{m4} = 20 \times 10^{-9} \times \frac{12 \times 10^{-6}}{26 \times 10^{-3}} \text{ F} = 11.6 \text{ pF}$$

Using (1.118) gives

$$C_{\pi4} = C_{b4} + C_{je4} = 12.2 \text{ pF}$$

Even at this low bias current, the $C_\pi$ of the lateral *pnp* is still dominated by $C_b$ because the transit time $\tau_F$ is so large.

The magnitude of the pole contributed by $Q_4$ can now be calculated by determining the resistance $R_{\pi04}$ seen by $C_{\pi4}$. This is simply $1/g_{m2}$ in parallel with the input resistance of $Q_4$, which is approximately $1/g_{m4}$. Thus

$$R_{\pi04} = \frac{1}{2}\frac{1}{g_{m2}} = 1087 \text{ }\Omega$$

and, consequently,

$$C_{\pi4}R_{\pi04} = 12.2 \times 10^{-12} \times 1087 \text{ s} = 0.0126 \text{ }\mu\text{s}$$

The magnitude of the pole contributed by $Q_4$ is thus

$$\frac{1}{2\pi C_{\pi4}R_{\pi04}} = 12.6 \text{ MHz}$$

A negative real pole at $-15$ MHz appears in the poles and zeros of the 741 as calculated by computer and described in Chapter 9. This is the pole contributed by $Q_4$, and the slight difference in magnitude from the value calculated above is due to the more accurate modeling in the computer. Note that a pole with magnitude 12.6 MHz contributes $6°$ of phase shift at the unity-gain frequency of 1.25 MHz and this is a significant amount. However, nondominant poles contributed by $Q_{16}$, $Q_{17}$, $Q_{23}$, and the active load also produce significant phase shift at the unity-gain frequency, and an accurate estimate of the total circuit phase shift can only be made by computer simulation or direct measurement. However, the calculations of this section allow the designer to isolate those parts of the circuit contributing excess phase shift and to make design changes where necessary to improve this aspect of circuit performance.

## 7.5 Relation Between Frequency Response and Time Response

In this chapter the effect of increasing signal frequency on circuit performance has been illustrated by considering the circuit response to a sinusoidal input signal. In practice, however, an amplifier may be required to amplify nonsinusoidal signals such as pulse trains or square waves. In addition, such signals are often used in testing circuit frequency response. The response of a circuit to such input signals is thus of some interest and will now be calculated.

Initially we consider a circuit whose small-signal transfer function can be approximated by a single-pole expression

$$\frac{v_o}{v_i}(s) = \frac{K}{1 - \dfrac{s}{p_1}} \qquad (7.156)$$

where $K$ is the low-frequency gain and $p_1$ is the pole of the transfer function. As described earlier, the $-3$-dB frequency of this circuit for sinusoidal signals is $\omega_{-3\text{dB}} = -p_1$. Now consider a small input voltage step of amplitude $v_a$ applied to the circuit. If we assume that the circuit responds linearly, we can use (7.156) to calculate the circuit response using $v_i(s) = v_a/s$. Thus

$$v_o(s) = \frac{Kv_a}{s} \frac{1}{1 - \dfrac{s}{p_1}} = Kv_a \left( \frac{1}{s} - \frac{1}{s - p_1} \right)$$

an    the circuit response to a step input is

$$v_o(t) = Kv_a(1 - e^{p_1 t}) \qquad (7.157)$$

The output voltage thus approaches $Kv_a$ and the time constant of the exponential in (7.157) is $-1/p_1$. Equation 7.157 is sketched in Fig. 7.39a together with $v_i$. The rise time of the output is usually specified by the time taken to go from 10 percent to 90 percent of the final value. From (7.157) we have

$$0.1Kv_a = Kv_a(1 - e^{p_1 t_1}) \qquad (7.158)$$
$$0.9Kv_a = Kv_a(1 - e^{p_1 t_2}) \qquad (7.159)$$

From (7.158) and (7.159) we obtain, for the 10 percent to 90 percent rise time,

$$t_r = t_2 - t_1 = -\frac{1}{p_1} \ln 9 = \frac{2.2}{\omega_{-3\text{dB}}} = \frac{0.35}{f_{-3\text{dB}}} \qquad (7.160)$$

This equation shows that the pulse rise time is directly related to the $-3$-dB frequency of the circuit. For example, if $f_{-3\text{dB}} = 10$ MHz, then (7.160) predicts $t_r = 35$ ns. If a square wave is applied to a circuit with a single-pole transfer function, the response is as shown in Fig. 7.39b. The edges of the square wave are rounded as described above for a single pulse.

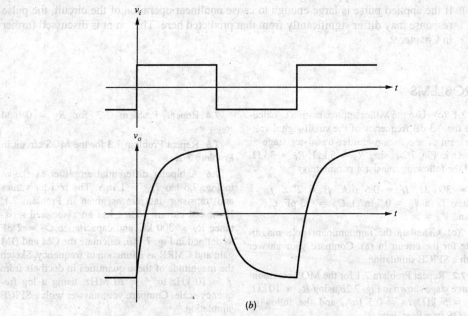

**Figure 7.39** (a) Step response of a linear circuit with gain $K$ and a single-pole transfer function. (b) Response of a linear circuit with a single-pole when a square-wave input is applied.

The calculations in this section have shown the relation between frequency response and time response for small signals applied to a circuit with a single-pole transfer function. For circuits with multiple-pole transfer functions, the same general trends apply, but the pulse response may differ greatly from that shown in Fig. 7.39. In particular, if the circuit transfer function contains complex poles leading to a frequency response with a high-frequency peak (see Chapter 9), then the pulse response will exhibit overshoot[3] and

**Figure 7.40** Typical step response of a linear circuit whose transfer function contains complex poles.

damped sinusoidal oscillation as shown in Fig. 7.40. Such a response is usually undesirable in pulse amplifiers.

Finally, it should be pointed out that all the foregoing results were derived on the assumption that the applied signals were small in the sense that the amplifier acted linearly. If the applied pulse is large enough to cause nonlinear operation of the circuit, the pulse response may differ significantly from that predicted here. This point is discussed further in Chapter 9.

## PROBLEMS

**7.1 (a)** Use the Miller approximation to calculate the $-3$-dB frequency of the small-signal voltage gain of a common-emitter transistor stage as shown in Fig. 7.2a using $R_S = 5 \text{ k}\Omega$, $R_L = 3 \text{ k}\Omega$, and the following transistor parameters:

$r_b = 300 \ \Omega$, $I_C = 0.5 \text{ mA}$, $\beta = 200$, $f_T = 500 \text{ MHz}$ (at $I_C = 0.5 \text{ mA}$), $C_\mu = 0.3 \text{ pF}$, $C_{cs} = 0$, and $V_A = \infty$.

**(b)** Calculate the nondominant pole magnitude for the circuit in (a). Compare your answer with a SPICE simulation.

**7.2** Repeat Problem 7.1 for the MOS common-source stage shown in Fig. 7.2b using $R_S = 10 \text{ k}\Omega$, $R_L = 5 \text{ k}\Omega$, $I_D = 0.5 \text{ mA}$, and the following NMOS transistor data:

*NMOS:* $W = 100 \ \mu\text{m}$, $L_{drwn} = 2 \ \mu\text{m}$, $L_d = 0.2 \ \mu\text{m}$, $X_d = 0$, $\lambda = 0$, $k'_n = 60 \ \mu\text{A/V}^2$, $\gamma = 0$, $C_{sb} = C_{db} = 0$, $C_{ox} = 0.7 \text{ fF/}(\mu\text{m}^2)$, and $C_{gd} = 14 \text{ fF}$.

**7.3** Calculate an expression for the output impedance of the circuit in Problem 7.1 as seen by $R_L$ and form an equivalent circuit. Plot the magnitude of this impedance on log scales from $f = 1 \text{ kHz}$ to $f = 100 \text{ MHz}$.

**7.4** Repeat Problem 7.3 for $R_S = 0$ and $R_S = \infty$.

**7.5** Repeat Problem 7.3 for the MOS circuit in Problem 7.2.

**7.6** A bipolar differential amplifier as shown in Fig. 7.5 has $I_{EE} = 1 \text{ mA}$. The resistor values and transistor data are as given in Problem 7.1. If the tail current source has an associated resistance $R_T = 300 \text{ k}\Omega$ and capacitance $C_T = 2 \text{ pF}$ as defined in Fig. 7.11a, calculate the CM and DM gain and CMRR as a function of frequency. Sketch the magnitude of these quantities in decibels from $f = 10 \text{ kHz}$ to $f = 20 \text{ MHz}$, using a log frequency scale. Compare your answer with a SPICE simulation.

**7.7** A MOS differential amplifier is shown in Fig. 7.9. For this circuit, carry out the calculations in Problem 7.6. Use $I_{SS} = 1 \text{ mA}$, the values of $R_T = 300 \text{ k}\Omega$ and $C_T = 2 \text{ pF}$ as defined in Fig. 7.11b, and the transistor data in Problem 7.2.

**7.8** A lateral $pnp$ emitter follower has $R_S = 250 \ \Omega$, $r_b = 200 \ \Omega$, $\beta = 50$, $I_C = -300 \ \mu\text{A}$, $f_T = 4 \text{ MHz}$, $R_E = 4 \text{ k}\Omega$, $C_\mu = 0$, and $r_o = \infty$. Calculate the small-signal voltage gain as a function of frequency. Sketch the magnitude of the voltage gain in decibels from $f = 10$ kHz to $f = 20$ MHz, using a log frequency scale.

**7.9** Calculate the values of the elements in the small-signal equivalent circuits for the input and output impedances of the emitter follower of Problem 7.8. Sketch the magnitudes of these impedances as a function of frequency from $f = 10$ kHz to $f = 20$ MHz, using log scales. Use SPICE to determine the small-signal step response of the circuit for a resistive load of 1 k$\Omega$ and then a capacitive load of 400 pF. Use a 1-mV input pulse amplitude with zero rise time. Comment on the shape of the time-domain responses. (Bias the circuit with an ideal 300-$\mu$A current source connected to the emitter for the capacitive load test.)

**7.10** For the source follower in Fig. 7.13b, find the low-frequency gain and plot the magnitude and phase of its voltage gain versus frequency from $f = 10$ kHz to $f = 20$ GHz, using log scales. Compare your plot with a SPICE simulation. Use the transistor data given in Problem 7.2 with a resistive load of 1 k$\Omega$ and then a capacitive load of 400 pF. In both cases, take $I_D = 0.5$ mA. Use a 1-mV input pulse amplitude with zero rise time. Comment on the shape of the time-domain responses. (Bias the circuit with an ideal 0.5 mA current source connected to the source for the capacitive load test.)

**7.11 (a)** Find expressions for $R_1$, $R_2$, and $L$ in the output impedance model for a MOS source follower assuming $R_S \gg 1/g_m$, $\gamma \neq 0$, and $v_{sb} = v_o$.

**(b)** Plot the magnitude of the output impedance versus frequency from $f = 10$ kHz to $f = 10$ GHz, using log scales, when $R_S = 1$ M$\Omega$, $g_m = 0.3$ mA/V, and $\gamma = 0$.

**7.12** A common-base stage has the following parameters: $I_C = 0.5$ mA, $C_\pi = 10$ pF, $C_\mu = 0.3$ pF, $r_b = 200$ $\Omega$, $\beta = 100$, $r_o = \infty$, $R_L = 0$, and $R_S = \infty$.

**(a)** Calculate an expression for the small-signal current gain of the stage as a function of frequency and thus determine the frequency where the current gain is 3 dB below its low-frequency value.

**(b)** Calculate the values of the elements in the small-signal equivalent circuits for the input and output impedances of the stage and sketch the magnitudes of these impedances from $f = 100$ kHz to $f = 100$ MHz using log scales.

**7.13** Repeat Problem 7.12 for a NMOS common-gate stage using $R_L = 0$ and $R_S = \infty$. Use $I_D = 0.5$ mA and the MOS transistor data in Problem 7.2. Plot the impedance magnitudes from $f = 100$ kHz to $f = 100$ GHz.

**7.14** The ac schematic of a common-emitter stage is shown in Fig. 7.2a. Calculate the low-frequency small-signal voltage gain $v_o/v_i$ and use the zero-value time-constant method to estimate the $-3$-dB frequency for $R_S = 10$ k$\Omega$ and $R_L = 5$ k$\Omega$.

Data: $\beta = 200$, $f_T = 600$ MHz (at $I_C = 1$ mA), $C_\mu = 0.2$ pF, $C_{je} = 2$ pF, $C_{cs} = 1$ pF, $r_b = 0$, $r_o = \infty$, and $I_C = 1$ mA.

**7.15** Repeat Problem 7.14 if an emitter degeneration resistor of value 300 $\Omega$ is included in the circuit.

**7.16** Repeat Problem 7.14 if a resistor of value 30 k$\Omega$ is connected between collector and base of the transistor.

**7.17** Repeat the calculations in Problem 7.14 for the common-source stage in Fig. 7.2b. Take $V_{DB} = 7.5$ V and $I_D = 0.5$ mA. Use the same transistor data and resistor values as in Problem 7.2 with the following exceptions:

1.  $C_{ox}$ and $C_{gd}$ are not given, but $f_T = 3$ GHz.

2.  $C_{db}$ is not equal to 0. Calculate the zero-bias drain-bulk capacitance as $C_{db0} = A_D(C_{j0}) + P_D(C_{jsw0})$, where $A_D = (5 \ \mu m)W$, and use $P_D = W$. Let $C_{j0} = 0.4$ fF/($\mu m^2$) and $C_{jsw0} = 0.4$ fF/$\mu$m. Then use (1.202) with $\psi_0 = 0.6$ V to calculate $C_{db}$.

**7.18** Repeat Problem 7.14 using a NMOS transistor in place of the bipolar transistor. Use $I_D = 0.5$ mA and the transistor data in Problem 7.2.

**7.19** Repeat Problem 7.18 if a 900 $\Omega$ source-degeneration resistor is included in the circuit.

**7.20** Repeat Problem 7.18 if a resistor of value 50 k$\Omega$ is connected between drain and gate of the transistor.

**7.21** A Darlington stage and a common-collector–common-emitter cascade are shown schematically in Fig. 7.41, where $R_S = 100$ k$\Omega$ and $R_L = 3$ k$\Omega$.

**(a)** Calculate the low-frequency small-signal voltage gain $v_o/v_i$ for each circuit.

**(b)** Use the zero-value time-constant method to calculate the $-3$-dB frequency of the gain of each circuit.

Data: $\beta = 100$, $f_T = 500$ MHz at $I_C = 1$ mA, $C_\mu = 0.4$ pF, $C_{je} = 2$ pF, $C_{cs} = 1$ pF, $r_b = 0$, $r_o = \infty$, $I_{C1} = 10$ $\mu$A, and $I_{C2} = 1$ mA. (Values of $C_\mu$, $C_{cs}$, and $C_{je}$ are at the bias point.)

**7.22** Repeat Problem 7.21 if a bleed resistor of 15 k$\Omega$ is added from the emitter of $Q_1$ to ground, which increases the collector bias current in $Q_1$ to 50 $\mu$A.

**7.23** Repeat Problem 7.21 if the input signal is a current source of value $i_i$ applied at the base of $Q_1$. (That is, $i_i$ replaces the voltage source $v_i$ and resistance $R_S$.) The transfer function is then a transresistance $v_o/i_i$.

**7.24** Replace the bipolar transistors in Fig. 7.41 with NMOS transistors. Repeat the calculations in Problem 7.21, using $R_S = 100$ kΩ, $R_L = 3$ kΩ, and the NMOS transistor model data in Problem 7.2, but use $C_{db} = 200$ fF and $C_{sb} = 180$ fF here. Take $I_{D1} = 50$ μA and $I_{D2} = 1$ mA.

(a)

(b)

**Figure 7.41** The ac schematics of (a) Darlington stage and (b) common-collector–common-emitter stage.

**7.25** An amplifier stage is shown in Fig. 7.42 where bias current $I_B$ is adjusted so that $V_O = 0$ V dc. Take $V_{SUPPLY} = 10$ V.

**(a)** Calculate the low-frequency, small-signal transresistance $v_o/i_i$ and use the zero-value time-constant method to estimate the $-3$-dB frequency.

Data: *npn*: $\beta = 100$, $f_T = 500$ MHz at $I_C = 1$ mA, $C_{\mu0} = 0.7$ pF, $C_{je} = 3$ pF (at the bias point), $C_{cs0} = 2$ pF, $r_b = 0$, and $V_A = 120$ V. Assume $n = 0.5$ and $\psi_0 = 0.55$ V for all junctions.

*pnp*: $\beta = 50$, $f_T = 4$ MHz at $I_C = -0.5$ mA, $C_{\mu0} = 1.0$ pF, $C_{je} = 3$ pF (at the bias point), $C_{bs0} = 2$ pF, $r_b = 0$, and $|V_A| = 50$ V. Assume $n = 0.5$ and $\psi_0 = 0.55$ V for all junctions.

**(b)** Repeat (a) if a 20-pF capacitor is connected from collector to base of $Q_1$.

**Figure 7.42** Amplifier stage.

**7.26** Repeat Problem 7.25 with the following changes:

1. Replace $Q_1$ with a *p*-channel MOS transistor, $M_1$. Replace $Q_2$ and $Q_3$ with *n*-channel MOS transistors, $M_2$ and $M_3$.
2. Add a resistor of value $1/g_{m1}$ from the gate to the source of $M_1$.
3. Take $V_{SUPPLY} = 2.5$ V.
4. Use the formula for $C_{db0}$ given in Problem 7.17.
5. For all transistors: $L_{drwn} = 2$ μm, $L_d = 0.2$ μm, $X_d = 1$ μm, and $\gamma = 0$. $W_1 = 200$ μm and $W_2 = W_3 = 100$ μm. Use (1.201) and (1.202) with $\psi_0 = 0.6$ V for the junction capacitances. Use the equations in Problem 7.17 for $C_{db0}$.

*NMOS* data: $V_{tn} = 1$ V, $k'_n = 60$ μA/V$^2$, $\lambda_n = 1/(100$ V), $C_{ox} = 0.7$ fF/(μm$^2$), $C_{j0} = 0.4$ fF/(μm$^2$), and $C_{jsw0} = 0.4$ fF/μm.

*PMOS* data: $V_{tp} = -1$ V, $k'_p = 20$ μA/V$^2$, $|\lambda_p| = 1/(50$ V), $C_{ox} = 0.7$ fF/(μm$^2$), $C_{j0} = 0.2$ fF/(μm$^2$), and $C_{jsw0} = 0.2$ fF/μm.

**7.27** A differential circuit employing active loads is shown in Fig. 7.43. Bias voltage $V_B$ is adjusted so that the collectors of $Q_1$ and $Q_2$ are at $+5$ V dc. Biasing resistors are $R_{B1} = 10$ kΩ and $R_{B2} = 20$ kΩ. Calculate the low-frequency, small-signal voltage gain $v_o/v_i$, and use the zero-value time-constant method in the DM half-circuit to estimate the $-3$-dB frequency of the DM gain. Use the device data in Problem 7.25.

**Figure 7.43** Differential circuit with active loads.

**7.28** Repeat Problem 7.27, replacing the bipolar transistors with MOS transistors. Assume that the values of $R_{B1}$ and $R_{B2}$ set $I_{D5} = 1$ mA. Use $W_1 = W_2 = W_5 = W_6 = 100 \ \mu\text{m}$, $W_3 = W_4 = 50 \ \mu\text{m}$, and $L_{\text{drwn}} = 2 \ \mu\text{m}$. See Problem 7.26 for all other MOS transistor data.

**7.29** The ac schematics of a common-source stage and a common-source–common-gate (cascode) stage are shown in Fig. 7.44 with $R_S = 10 \ \text{k}\Omega$ and $R_L = 20 \ \text{k}\Omega$. Using the transistor and operating-point data in Problem 7.2:

(a) Calculate the low-frequency, small-signal voltage gain $v_o/v_i$ for each circuit.

(b) Use the zero-value time-constant method to calculate and compare the $-3$-dB frequencies of the gain of the two circuits.

(c) Estimate the 10 to 90 percent rise time for each circuit for a small step input and sketch the output voltage waveform over 0 to 300 ns for a 1-mV step input.

**7.30** Replace the NMOS transistors in Fig. 7.44 with $npn$ transistors. The resulting ac schematics are of a common-emitter stage and a common-emitter–common-base (cascode) stage. Repeat the calculations in Problem 7.29 using $R_S = 5 \ \text{k}\Omega$, $R_L = 3 \ \text{k}\Omega$, and the following data.

**Figure 7.44** An ac schematic of (a) common-source stage and (b) cascode stage.

**Figure 7.45** Amplifier stage.

Data: $I_C = 1$ mA, $\beta = 100$, $r_b = 0$, $C_{cs} = 1$ pF, $C_\mu = 0.4$ pF, $f_T = 500$ MHz (at $I_C = 1$ mA), and $r_o = \infty$.

**7.31** An amplifier stage is shown in Fig. 7.45.

**(a)** Calculate the low-frequency, small-signal voltage gain $v_o/v_i$.

**(b)** Apply the zero-value time-constant method to the DM half-circuit to calculate the $-3$-dB frequency of the gain.

Data: $C_{cs0} = 2$ pF, $C_{\mu 0} = 0.5$ pF, $C_{je} = 4$ pF (at the bias point), $f_T = 500$ MHz (at $I_C = 2$ mA), $\beta = 200$, $r_b = 0$, and $r_o = \infty$. Assume $n = 0.5$ and $\psi_0 = 0.55$ V for all junctions.

**(c)** Use SPICE to find the small-signal gain and bandwidth of the amplifier and also the magnitude and phase of the transfer function at 100 MHz.

**(d)** Investigate the influence of base resistance by repeating (c) with $r_b = 200\ \Omega$ and comparing the results.

**7.32** Repeat Problem 7.31 with $n$-channel MOS transistors replacing all bipolar transistors. Assume $W = 100\ \mu$m, $L_{drwn} = 2\ \mu$m, $L_d = 0.2\ \mu$m, $X_d = 0$, $\lambda = 0$, $k'_n = 60\ \mu$A/V$^2$, $\gamma = 0$, $V_t = 1$ V, $C_{ox} = 0.7$ fF/$\mu$m$^2$, $C_{ol} = 0.15$ fF/$\mu$m, $C_{j0} = 0.4$ fF/$\mu$m$^2$, and $C_{jsw0} = 0.4$ fF/$\mu$m. Use (1.201) and (1.202) with $\psi_0 = 0.6$ V for the junctions. Use the information in Problem 7.17 to calculate $C_{db0} = C_{sb0}$. Skip part (d) in Problem 7.31.

**7.33** The ac schematic of a wideband MOS current amplifier is shown in Fig. 7.46. The $W/L$ of $M_2$ is four times that of $M_1$ and corresponding bias currents are $I_{D1} = 1$ mA and $I_{D2} = 4$ mA. Calculate the low-frequency, small-signal current gain $i_o/i_i$ and use the zero-value time-constant method to estimate the $-3$-dB frequency. Calculate the 10 to

90 percent rise time for a small step input.

Data at the operating point:
$M_1$: $C_{gd} = 0.05$ pF, $C_{gs} = 0.2$ pF, $C_{sb} = C_{db} = 0.09$ pF, $V_{ov} = 0.3$ V, and $r_o = \infty$.
$M_2$: $C_{gd} = 0.2$ pF, $C_{gs} = 0.8$ pF, $C_{sb} = C_{db} = 0.36$ pF, $V_{ov} = 0.3$ V, and $r_o = \infty$.

**Figure 7.46** An ac schematic of a MOS current amplifier.

**7.34** Replace the MOS transistors in the amplifier in Fig. 7.46 with bipolar $npn$ transistors. The emitter area of $Q_2$ is four times that of $Q_1$ and corresponding bias currents are $I_{C1} = 1$ mA and $I_{C2} = 4$ mA. Repeat the calculations in Problem 7.33 using the following data.

Data at the operating point:
$Q_1 : \beta = 200$, $\tau_F = 0.2$ ns, $C_\mu = 0.2$ pF, $C_{je} = 1$ pF, $C_{cs} = 1$ pF, $r_b = 0$, and $r_o = \infty$.
$Q_2 : \beta = 200$, $\tau_F = 0.2$ ns, $C_\mu = 0.8$ pF, $C_{je} = 4$ pF, $C_{cs} = 4$ pF, $r_b = 0$, and $r_o = \infty$.

**7.35** A two-stage amplifier is shown in Fig. 7.47. Calculate the low-frequency, small-signal gain and use the zero-value time-constant method to estimate the $-3$-dB frequency. Calculate the 10 to 90 percent rise time for a small step input. Use SPICE to determine the $-3$-dB frequency and also

**Figure 7.47** Two-stage amplifier.

the frequency where the phase shift in the transfer function is $-135°$ beyond the low-frequency value.

Data: $\beta = 200$, $f_T = 600$ MHz at $I_C = 1$ mA, $C_\mu = 0.2$ pF, $C_{je} = 2$ pF, $C_{cs} = 1$ pF, $r_b = 0$, $V_{BE(\text{on})} = 0.6$ V, and $r_o = \infty$. (Values of $C_\mu$, $C_{cs}$, and $C_{je}$ are at the bias point.)

**7.36** A two-stage bipolar amplifier is shown in Fig. 7.48. Calculate the low-frequency, small-signal voltage gain $v_o/v_i$ and use the zero-value time-constant method to estimate the $-3$-dB frequency. Use a DM half-circuit for the differential pair. Use SPICE to estimate the first and second most dominant poles of the circuit.

**Figure 7.48** Two-stage amplifier with *pnp* second stage.

**Figure 7.49** Wideband MOS amplifier stage.

Data: *npn*: $\beta = 200$, $f_T = 400$ MHz (at $I_C = 1$ mA), $C_\mu = 0.3$ pF, $C_{je} = 3$ pF, $C_{cs} = 1.5$ pF, $r_b = 0$, $V_{BE(on)} = 0.6$ V, and $r_o = \infty$.
*pnp*: $\beta = 100$, $f_T = 6$ MHz (at $I_C = -0.5$ mA), $C_\mu = 0.3$ pF, $C_{je} = 3$ pF, $C_{bs} = 1.5$ pF, $r_b = 0$, $V_{BE(on)} = -0.6$ V, and $r_o = \infty$. (All values of $C_\mu$, $C_{cs}$, $C_{bs}$, and $C_{je}$ are at the bias point.)

**7.37 (a)** A wideband MOS amplifier stage is shown in Fig. 7.49. Calculate the small-signal, low-frequency gain and use the zero-value time-constant method to estimate the −3-dB band-width. Use $\mu_n C_{ox} = 60$ μA/V², $t_{ox} = 20$ nm, $C_{ol} = 0.3$ fF/(μm of gate width), $\psi_o = 0.6$ V, $V_t = 0.7$ V, $\gamma = 0.4$ V$^{1/2}$, $\lambda = 0$, and $V_O = 2.5$ V dc. For $C_{db}$ and $C_{sb}$, use $C_{db0} = C_{sb0} = $

0.8 fF/(μm of gate width). Assume that the sub-strate is grounded. Compare your calculation with a SPICE simulation, and also use SPICE to estimate the second most dominant pole. Use SPICE to plot the small-signal bandwidth as the dc input voltage is varied from 0 to 5 V.

**(b)** Calculate the small-signal gain and −3-dB bandwidth including short-channel ef-fects with $\mathscr{E}_c = 1.5 \times 10^6$ V/m. Assume the same bias currents as in (a) and model MOSFET short-channel effects with a resistor in series with the source. Connect the device capacitances to the lower end of the added source resistor.

**7.38** A CMOS amplifier stage is shown in Fig. 7.50. Select $W/L$ for $M_1$ and $M_5$ to give

**Figure 7.50** CMOS amplifier stage.

$V_i = V_O = 2.5$ V dc and $|I_D| = 100$ μA bias in all devices. The minimum value of $L$ and $W$ is 2 μm. Calculate the small-signal, low-frequency gain and the $-3$-dB frequency of the stage. Verify with SPICE. Use device data from Problem 7.37(a) with $|\lambda| = 0.03$ V$^{-1}$, $\mu_p C_{ox} = 30$ μA/V$^2$, and $V_{tp} = -0.7$ V.

**7.39** For the BiCMOS circuit of Fig. 3.78, use the zero-value time-constant method to estimate the first and second most dominant poles of the circuit. Assume an input voltage drive. Use bipolar transistor data from Fig. 2.32 and MOSFET parameters $C_{gd} = 90$ fF, $C_{sb} = C_{db} = 200$ fF, and $C_{gs} = 200$ fF at the bias point. Further assume $\mu_n C_{ox} = 40$ μA/V$^2$, $V_t = 0.8$ V, $\lambda = 0$, and $\gamma = 0$. Use SPICE to check your result.

**7.40** Use the zero-value time-constant method to estimate the small-signal dominant pole for the current gain of the MOS cascode current mirror of Fig. 4.9. Assume an input ac current source in parallel with $I_{IN}$ and a zero load impedance with $V_{out} = V_{GS3} + V_{GS4}$. The bias current $I_{IN} = 100$ μA. Compare your answer with the $f_T$ value of the devices. Device parameters are $\mu_n C_{ox} = 60$ μA/V$^2$, $\gamma = 0$, $\lambda = 0$, $V_t = 0.7$ V, $W = 10$ μm, $L_{eff} = 1$ μm, $C_{gs} = 20$ fF, $C_{gd} = 3$ fF, $C_{sb} = C_{db} = 10$ fF at the bias point. Compare your answer with a SPICE simulation of the bandwidth of the circuit and use SPICE to find the bandwidth for $I_{IN} = 50$ μA and $I_{IN} = 200$ μA.

**7.41** Repeat Problem 7.40 including short-channel effects with $\mathscr{E}_c = 1.5 \times 10^6$ V/m.

**7.42** Use the short-circuit time-constant method to estimate the nondominant pole that originates at the drain nodes of $M_1$ and $M_2$ in the CMOS folded cascode of Fig. 6.28. Assume the gates of $M_{1A}$, $M_{2A}$, $M_5$, $M_{11}$, and $M_{12}$ are biased from low-impedance points and that a voltage drive is applied at $v_i$. All device sizes and parameters are as given in Problem 7.40 except for $M_{11}$ and $M_{12}$, which have twice the width of the other transistors. All bias currents are 100 μA except for $M_5$, $M_{11}$, and $M_{12}$, which have $|I_D| = 200$ μA. Assume $V_{GD}$ of $M_{11}$ and $M_{12}$ is zero volts. Use $C_L = 1$ pF and $\mu_p C_{ox} = 30$ μA/V$^2$. How much phase shift is contributed to the amplifier transfer function by this nondominant pole at the amplifier unity-gain frequency? Check your calculations with SPICE simulations.

**7.43** A MOS cascode stage is shown in Fig. 7.44b. Replace the load resistor with a load capacitor $C_L = 2$ pF. Assume the total capacitance that connects to the drain of $M_1$ can be modeled by a

capacitor $C_p = 0.2$ pF from that drain to ac ground. Ignore all other capacitors. Therefore, the gain for this circuit has only two poles. For both transistors, take $I_D = 100$ μA, $W = 20$ μm, $L_{eff} = 0.5$ μm, $k' = 180$ μA/V$^2$, and $\lambda = 0.04$ V$^{-1}$.

(a) Use zero-value time constants to estimate the dominant pole.

(b) Use short-circuit time constants to estimate the nondominant pole.

(c) Compare your answers with a SPICE simulation.

**7.44 (a)** For the common-emitter amplifier in Problem 7.1, use zero-value time constants to estimate the dominant pole and short-circuit time constants to estimate the nondominant pole.

(b) Compare your estimates with a SPICE simulation.

**7.45 (a)** Use zero-value time constants to estimate the dominant pole and short-circuit time constants to estimate the nondominant pole for the common-source amplifier in Problem 7.2.

(b) Compare your answers with a SPICE simulation.

**7.46 (a)** An integrator is shown in Fig. 7.51. Use zero-value time constants to estimate the dominant pole and short-circuit time constants to estimate the nondominant pole for this circuit. Use $R = 20$ kΩ, $C = 50$ pF, $C_{in} = 0.2$ pF, $a_v = 1000$, and $R_o = 5$ kΩ.

(b) Compare your answers with a SPICE simulation.

**7.47** Add a 0.5 pF load capacitor from the output to ground to the integrator in Fig. 7.51. When this capacitor is added, the circuit has a loop of three capacitors. Direct application of the short-circuit time-constant method here gives zero for each short-circuit time-constant. (Verify this.)

The problem here is that three short-circuit time constants are being calculated for the three capacitors, and the sum of the reciprocal of these time constants equals the sum of three poles, as shown in (7.146). However, this circuit has only two poles because only two of the capacitor voltages are independent.

An alternative approach to estimating the nondominant pole is to calculate the zero-value time constants and determine if one zero-value time constant is much larger than the others. If so, the capacitor associated with the largest zero-value time constant is shorted, and one time constant for the remaining capacitors, which are in parallel, is the short-circuit time constant. Carry out these steps,

**Figure 7.51** An integrator stage.

and compare the estimated nondominant pole with a SPICE simulation.

**7.48** Find an expression for $G_m(s) = i_o(s)/v_{id}(s)$ for the circuit in Fig. 7.33 and verify the equations for the pole and zero given in Section 7.3.5.

**7.49** Calculate the pole and zero associated with the current-mirror load in Fig. 7.33 if $I_{D3} = -100\,\mu\text{A}$, $|V_{ov3}| = 0.2$ V, and $C_x = 0.1$ pF

# REFERENCES

1. P. E. Gray and C. L. Searle. *Electronic Principles: Physics, Models, and Circuits.* Wiley, New York, 1969.

2. A. S. Sedra and K. C. Smith. *Microelectronic Circuits.* Oxford University Press, New York, 1998.

3. K. Ogata. *Modern Control Engineering.* Second Edition, Prentice-Hall, Englewood Cliffs, N.J., 1990.

4. R. D. Thorton, et al. *Multistage Transistor Circuits.* Wiley, New York, 1965.

# Feedback

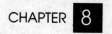

Negative feedback is widely used in amplifier design because it produces several important benefits. One of the most significant is that negative feedback stabilizes the gain of the amplifier against parameter changes in the active devices due to supply voltage variation, temperature changes, or device aging. A second benefit is that negative feedback allows the designer to modify the input and output impedances of the circuit in any desired fashion. Another significant benefit of negative feedback is the reduction in signal waveform distortion that it produces, and for this reason almost all high-quality audio amplifiers employ negative feedback around the power output stage. Finally, negative feedback can produce an increase in the bandwidth of circuits and is widely used in broadband amplifiers.

However, the benefits of negative feedback listed above are accompanied by two disadvantages. First, the gain of the circuit is reduced in almost direct proportion to the other benefits achieved. Thus, it is often necessary to make up the decrease in gain by adding extra amplifier stages with a consequent increase in hardware cost. The second potential problem associated with the use of feedback is the tendency for oscillation to occur in the circuit, and careful attention by the designer is often required to overcome this problem.

In this chapter, the various benefits of negative feedback are considered, together with a systematic classification of feedback configurations. Two different methods for analyzing feedback circuits are presented. The problem of feedback-induced oscillation and its solution are considered in Chapter 9.

## 8.1 Ideal Feedback Equation

Consider the idealized feedback configuration of Fig. 8.1. In this figure $S_i$ and $S_o$ are input and output signals that may be voltages or currents. The feedback network (which is usually linear and passive) has a transfer function $f$ and feeds back a signal $S_{fb}$ to the input. At the input, signal $S_{fb}$ is subtracted from input signal $S_i$ at the input differencing node. Error signal $S_\epsilon$ is the difference between $S_i$ and $S_{fb}$, and $S_\epsilon$ is fed to the basic amplifier with transfer function $a$. Note that another common convention is to assume that $S_i$ and $S_{fb}$ are added together in an input *summing* node, and this leads to some sign changes in the analysis. It should be pointed out that negative-feedback amplifiers in practice have an input differencing node and thus the convention assumed here is more convenient for amplifier analysis.

From Fig. 8.1

$$S_o = aS_\epsilon \qquad (8.1)$$

Figure 8.1  Ideal feedback configuration.

assuming that the feedback network does not load the basic amplifier. Also

$$S_{fb} = fS_o \qquad (8.2)$$

$$S_\epsilon = S_i - S_{fb} \qquad (8.3)$$

Substituting (8.2) in (8.3) gives

$$S_\epsilon = S_i - fS_o \qquad (8.4)$$

Substituting (8.4) in (8.1) gives

$$S_o = aS_i - afS_o$$

and thus

$$\frac{S_o}{S_i} = A = \frac{a}{1 + af} \qquad (8.5)$$

Equation 8.5 is the fundamental equation for negative feedback circuits where $A$ is the overall gain with feedback applied. ($A$ is often called the *closed-loop gain*.)

It is useful to define a quantity $T$ called the *loop gain* such that

$$T = af \qquad (8.6)$$

and

$$\frac{S_o}{S_i} = A = \frac{a}{1 + T} \qquad (8.7)$$

$T$ is the total gain around the feedback loop. If $T \gg 1$, then, from (8.5), gain $A$ is given by

$$A \simeq \frac{1}{f} \qquad (8.8)$$

That is, for large values of loop gain $T$, the overall amplifier gain is determined by the feedback transfer function $f$. Since the feedback network is usually formed from stable, passive elements, the value of $f$ is well defined and so is the overall amplifier gain.

The feedback loop operates by forcing $S_{fb}$ to be nearly equal to $S_i$. This is achieved by amplifying the difference $S_\epsilon = S_i - S_{fb}$, and the feedback loop then effectively minimizes error signal $S_\epsilon$. This can be seen by substituting (8.5) in (8.4) to obtain

$$S_\epsilon = S_i - f \frac{aS_i}{1 + af}$$

and this leads to

$$\frac{S_\epsilon}{S_i} = \frac{1}{1 + af} = \frac{1}{1 + T} \qquad (8.9)$$

As $T$ becomes much greater than 1, $S_\epsilon$ becomes much less than $S_i$. In addition, substituting (8.5) in (8.2) gives

$$S_{fb} = fS_i \frac{a}{1 + af}$$

and thus

$$\frac{S_{fb}}{S_i} = \frac{T}{1 + T} \tag{8.10}$$

If $T \gg 1$, then $S_{fb}$ is approximately equal to $S_i$. That is, feedback signal $S_{fb}$ is a replica of the input signal. Since $S_{fb}$ and $S_o$ are directly related by (8.2), it follows that if $|f| < 1$, then $S_o$ is an amplified replica of $S_i$. This is the aim of a feedback amplifier.

## 8.2 Gain Sensitivity

In most practical situations, gain $a$ of the basic amplifier is not well defined. It is dependent on temperature, active-device operating conditions, and transistor parameters. As mentioned previously, the negative-feedback loop reduces variations in overall amplifier gain due to variations in $a$. This effect may be examined by differentiating (8.5) to obtain

$$\frac{dA}{da} = \frac{(1 + af) - af}{(1 + af)^2}$$

and this reduces to

$$\frac{dA}{da} = \frac{1}{(1 + af)^2} \tag{8.11}$$

If $a$ changes by $\delta a$, then $A$ changes by $\delta A$ where

$$\delta A = \frac{\delta a}{(1 + af)^2}$$

The fractional change in $A$ is

$$\frac{\delta A}{A} = \frac{1 + af}{a} \frac{\delta a}{(1 + af)^2}$$

This can be expressed as

$$\frac{\delta A}{A} = \frac{\dfrac{\delta a}{a}}{1 + af} = \frac{\dfrac{\delta a}{a}}{1 + T} \tag{8.12}$$

Equation 8.12 shows that the fractional change in $A$ is reduced by $(1 + T)$ compared to the fractional change in $a$. For example, if $T = 100$ and $a$ changes by 10 percent due to temperature change, then the overall gain $A$ changes by only 0.1 percent using (8.12).

## 8.3 Effect of Negative Feedback on Distortion

The foregoing results show that even if the basic-amplifier gain $a$ changes, the negative feedback keeps overall gain $A$ approximately constant. This suggests that feedback should be effective in reducing distortion because distortion is caused by changes in the slope of

**Figure 8.2** Basic-amplifier transfer characteristic.

the basic-amplifier transfer characteristic. The feedback should tend to reduce the effect of these slope changes since $A$ is relatively independent of $a$. This is explained next.

Suppose the basic amplifier has a transfer characteristic with a nonlinearity as shown in Fig. 8.2. It is assumed that two regions exist, each with constant but different slopes $a_1$ and $a_2$. When feedback is applied, the overall gain will still be given by (8.5) but the appropriate value of $a$ must be used, depending on which region of Fig. 8.2 is being traversed. Thus the *overall* transfer characteristic with feedback applied will also have two regions of different slope, as shown in Fig. 8.3. However, slopes $A_1$ and $A_2$ are almost equal because of the effect of the negative feedback. This can be seen by substituting in (8.5) to give

$$A_1 = \frac{a_1}{1 + a_1 f} \simeq \frac{1}{f} \tag{8.13}$$

$$A_2 = \frac{a_2}{1 + a_2 f} \simeq \frac{1}{f} \tag{8.14}$$

Thus the transfer characteristic of the feedback amplifier of Fig. 8.3 shows much less nonlinearity than the original basic-amplifier characteristics of Fig. 8.2.

Note that the horizontal scale in Fig. 8.3 has been *compressed* as compared to Fig. 8.2 in order to allow easy comparison of the two graphs. This scale change is necessary because

**Figure 8.3** Feedback-amplifier transfer characteristic corresponding to the basic-amplifier characteristic of Fig. 8.2.

the negative feedback *reduces the gain*. The reduction in gain by the factor $(1 + T)$, which accompanies the use of negative feedback, presents few serious problems, since the gain can easily be made up by placing a preamplifier in front of the feedback amplifier. Since the preamplifier handles much smaller signals than does the output amplifier, distortion is usually not a problem in that amplifier.

One further point that should be made about Figs. 8.2 and 8.3 is that both show hard saturation of the output amplifier (i.e., the output becomes independent of the input) at an output signal level of $S_{o2}$. Since the incremental slope $a_3 = 0$ in that region, negative feedback cannot improve the situation as $A_3 = 0$ also, using (8.5).

## 8.4 Feedback Configurations

The treatment in the previous sections was based on the idealized configuration shown in Fig. 8.1. Practical feedback amplifiers are composed of circuits that have current or voltage signals as inputs and produce output currents or voltages. In order to pursue feedback amplifier design at a practical level, it is necessary to specify the details of the feedback sampling process and the circuits used to realize this operation. There are four basic feedback amplifier connections. These are specified according to whether the output signal $S_o$ is a current or a voltage and whether the feedback signal $S_{fb}$ is a current or a voltage. It is apparent that four combinations exist and these are now considered.

### 8.4.1 Series-Shunt Feedback

Suppose it is required to design a feedback amplifier that stabilizes a voltage transfer function. That is, a given input voltage should produce a well-defined proportional output voltage. This will require sampling the output voltage and feeding back a proportional voltage for comparison with the incoming voltage. This situation is shown schematically in Fig. 8.4. The basic amplifier has gain $a$, and the feedback network is a two-port with transfer function $f$ that *shunts* the output of the basic amplifier to sample $v_o$. *Ideally*, the impedance $z_{22f} = \infty$, and the feedback network does not load the basic amplifier. The feedback voltage $v_{fb}$ is connected in *series* with the input to allow comparison with $v_i$ and, ideally, $z_{11f} = 0$. The signal $v_\epsilon$ is the *difference* between $v_i$ and $v_{fb}$ and is fed to the basic amplifier. The basic amplifier and feedback circuits are assumed *unilateral* in that the basic amplifier transmits only from $v_\epsilon$ to $v_o$ and the feedback network transmits only from $v_o$ to $v_{fb}$. This point will be taken up later.

This feedback is called *series-shunt* feedback because the feedback network is connected in *series* with the input and *shunts* the output.

**Figure 8.4** Series-shunt feedback configuration.

**Figure 8.5** Series-shunt configuration fed from a finite source impedance.

From Fig. 8.4

$$v_o = av_\epsilon \tag{8.15}$$

$$v_{fb} = fv_o \tag{8.16}$$

$$v_\epsilon = v_i - v_{fb} \tag{8.17}$$

From (8.15), (8.16), and (8.17),

$$\frac{v_o}{v_i} = \frac{a}{1 + af} \tag{8.18}$$

Thus the ideal feedback equation applies. Equation 8.18 indicates that the transfer function that is stabilized is $v_o/v_i$, as desired. If the circuit is fed from a high source impedance as shown in Fig. 8.5, the ratio $v_o/v_i$ is still stabilized [and given by (8.18)], *but* now $v_i$ is given by

$$v_i = \frac{Z_i}{Z_i + z_s} v_s \tag{8.19}$$

where $Z_i$ is the input impedance seen by $v_i$. If $z_s \approx Z_i$, then $v_i$ depends on $Z_i$, which is *not* usually well defined since it often depends on active-device parameters. Thus the overall gain $v_o/v_s$ will not be stabilized. Consequently, the full benefits of gain stabilization are achieved for a series-shunt feedback amplifier when the source impedance is low compared to the input impedance of the closed-loop amplifier. The ideal driving source is a voltage source.

Consider now the effect of series-shunt feedback on the terminal impedances of the amplifier. Assume the basic amplifier has input and output impedances $z_i$ and $z_o$ as shown in Fig. 8.6. Again assume the feedback network is ideal and feeds back a voltage $fv_o$ as shown. Both networks are unilateral. The applied voltage $v_i$ produces input current $i_i$ and output voltage $v_o$. From Fig. 8.6

$$v_o = av_\epsilon \tag{8.20}$$

$$v_i = v_\epsilon + fv_o \tag{8.21}$$

**Figure 8.6** Series-shunt configuration with finite impedances in the basic amplifier.

Substituting (8.20) in (8.21) gives

$$v_i = v_\epsilon + afv_\epsilon = v_\epsilon(1 + af) \tag{8.22}$$

Also

$$i_i = \frac{v_\epsilon}{z_i} \tag{8.23}$$

Substituting (8.22) in (8.23) gives

$$i_i = \frac{v_i}{z_i} \frac{1}{1 + af} \tag{8.24}$$

Thus, from (8.24), input impedance $Z_i$ with feedback applied is

$$Z_i = \frac{v_i}{i_i} = (1 + T)z_i \tag{8.25}$$

Series feedback at the input *always* raises the input impedance by $(1 + T)$.

The effect of series-shunt feedback on the output impedance can be calculated using the circuit of Fig. 8.7. The input voltage is removed (the input is shorted) and a voltage $v$ applied at the output. From Fig. 8.7

$$v_\epsilon + fv = 0 \tag{8.26}$$

$$i = \frac{v - av_\epsilon}{z_o} \tag{8.27}$$

Substituting (8.26) in (8.27) gives

$$i = \frac{v + afv}{z_o} \tag{8.28}$$

From (8.28) output impedance $Z_o$ with feedback applied is

$$Z_o = \frac{v}{i} = \frac{z_o}{1 + T} \tag{8.29}$$

Shunt feedback at the output *always* lowers the output impedance by $(1 + T)$. This makes the output a better voltage source so that series-shunt feedback produces a *good voltage amplifier*. It stabilizes $v_o/v_i$, raises $Z_i$, and lowers $Z_o$.

The original series-shunt feedback amplifier of Fig. 8.6 can now be represented as shown in Fig. 8.8a using (8.18), (8.25), and (8.29). As the forward gain $a$ approaches infinity, the equivalent circuit approaches that of Fig. 8.8b, which is an ideal voltage amplifier.

**Figure 8.7** Circuit for the calculation of the output impedance of the series-shunt feedback configuration.

**Figure 8.8** (*a*) Equivalent circuit of a series-shunt feedback amplifier. (*b*) Equivalent circuit of a series-shunt feedback amplifier for $a \rightarrow \infty$.

## 8.4.2 Shunt-Shunt Feedback

This configuration is shown in Fig. 8.9. The feedback network again shunts the output of the basic amplifier and samples $v_o$ and, ideally, $z_{22f} = \infty$ as before. However, the feedback network now *shunts* the input of the main amplifier as well and feeds back a proportional current $fv_o$. Ideally, $z_{11f} = \infty$ so that the feedback network does not produce any shunt loading on the amplifier input. Since the feedback signal is a current, it is more convenient to deal with an error *current* $i_\epsilon$ at the input. The input signal in this case is ideally a current $i_i$ and this is assumed. From Fig. 8.9

$$a = \frac{v_o}{i_\epsilon} \tag{8.30}$$

where $a$ is a *transresistance*,

$$f = \frac{i_{fb}}{v_o} \tag{8.31}$$

where $f$ is a *transconductance*, and

$$v_o = ai_\epsilon \tag{8.32}$$

$$i_\epsilon = i_i - i_{fb} \tag{8.33}$$

Substitution of $i_{fb}$ from (8.31) in (8.33) gives

$$i_\epsilon = i_i - fv_o \tag{8.34}$$

**Figure 8.9** Shunt-shunt feedback configuration.

Substitution of (8.32) in (8.34) gives

$$\frac{v_o}{a} = i_i - f v_o$$

Rearranging terms we find

$$\frac{v_o}{i_i} = \frac{a}{1 + af} = A \tag{8.35}$$

Again the ideal feedback equation applies. Note that although $a$ and $f$ have dimensions of resistance and conductance, the loop gain $T = af$ is *dimensionless*. This is always true.

In this configuration, if the source impedance $z_s$ is finite, a division of input current $i_i$ occurs between $z_s$ and the amplifier input, and the ratio $v_o/i_i$ will not be as well defined as (8.35) suggests. The full benefits of negative feedback for a shunt-shunt feedback amplifier are thus obtained for $z_s \gg Z_i$, which approaches a current-source drive.

The input impedance of the circuit of Fig. 8.9 can be calculated using (8.32) and (8.35) to give

$$i_\epsilon = \frac{i_i}{1 + af} \tag{8.36}$$

The input impedance $Z_i$ with feedback is

$$Z_i = \frac{v_i}{i_i} \tag{8.37}$$

Substituting (8.36) in (8.37) gives

$$Z_i = \frac{v_i}{i_\epsilon} \frac{1}{1 + af} = \frac{z_i}{1 + T} \tag{8.38}$$

Thus shunt feedback at the input *reduces* the amplifier input impedance by $(1 + T)$. This is always true.

It is easily shown that the output impedance in this case is

$$Z_o = \frac{z_o}{1 + T} \tag{8.39}$$

as before, for shunt feedback at the output.

Shunt-shunt feedback has made this amplifier a good *transresistance* amplifier. The transfer function $v_o/i_i$ has been stabilized and both $Z_i$ and $Z_o$ are lowered.

The original shunt-shunt feedback amplifier of Fig. 8.9 can now be represented as shown in Fig. 8.10a using (8.35), (8.38), and (8.39). As forward gain $a$ approaches infinity, the equivalent circuit approaches that of Fig. 8.10b, which is an ideal transresistance amplifier.

### 8.4.3 Shunt-Series Feedback

The shunt-series configuration is shown in Fig. 8.11. The feedback network samples $i_o$ and feeds back a proportional current $i_{fb} = f i_o$. Since the desired output signal is a current $i_o$, it is more convenient to represent the output of the basic amplifier with a Norton equivalent. In this case both $a$ and $f$ are dimensionless current ratios, and the ideal input source is a

**Figure 8.10** (*a*) Equivalent circuit of a shunt-shunt feedback amplifier. (*b*) Equivalent circuit of a shunt-shunt feedback amplifier for $a \to \infty$.

**Figure 8.11** Shunt-series feedback configuration.

current source $i_i$. It can be shown that

$$\frac{i_o}{i_i} = \frac{a}{1 + af} \tag{8.40}$$

$$Z_i = \frac{z_i}{1 + T} \tag{8.41}$$

$$Z_o = z_o(1 + T) \tag{8.42}$$

This amplifier is a good *current* amplifier and has stable current gain $i_o/i_i$, low $Z_i$, and high $Z_o$.

### 8.4.4 Series-Series Feedback

The series-series configuration is shown in Fig. 8.12. The feedback network samples $i_o$ and feeds back a proportional voltage $v_{fb}$ in *series* with the input. The forward gain $a$ is a transconductance and $f$ is a transresistance, and the ideal driving source is a voltage

**Figure 8.12** Series-series feedback configuration.

source $v_i$. It can be shown that

$$\frac{i_o}{v_i} = \frac{a}{1 + af} \tag{8.43}$$

$$Z_i = z_i(1 + T) \tag{8.44}$$

$$Z_o = z_o(1 + T) \tag{8.45}$$

This amplifier is a good transconductance amplifier and has a stabilized gain $i_o/v_i$, as well as high $Z_i$ and $Z_o$.

## 8.5 Practical Configurations and the Effect of Loading

In practical feedback amplifiers, the feedback network causes loading at the input and output of the basic amplifier, and the division into basic amplifier and feedback network is not as obvious as the above treatment implies. In such cases, the circuit can always be analyzed by writing circuit equations for the whole amplifier and solving for the transfer function and terminal impedances. However, this procedure becomes very tedious and difficult in most practical cases, and the equations so complex that one loses sight of the important aspects of circuit performance. Thus it is profitable to identify a basic amplifier and feedback network in such cases and then to use the ideal feedback equations derived above. In general it will be necessary to include the loading effect of the feedback network on the basic amplifier, and methods of including this loading in the calculations are now considered. The *method* will be developed through the use of two-port representations of the circuits involved, although this method of representation is not necessary for practical calculations, as we will see.

### 8.5.1 Shunt-Shunt Feedback

Consider the shunt-shunt feedback amplifier of Fig. 8.9. The effect of nonideal networks may be included as shown in Fig. 8.13a, where finite input and output admittances are assumed in both forward and feedback paths, as well as reverse transmission in each. Finite source and load admittances $y_S$ and $y_L$ are assumed. The most convenient two-port

Basic amplifier

Feedback network

(a)

New basic amplifier

New feedback network

(b)

**Figure 8.13** (a) Shunt-shunt feedback configuration using the $y$-parameter representation. (b) Circuit of (a) redrawn with generators $y_{21a}v_i$ and $y_{12a}v_o$ omitted.

representation in this case is the short-circuit admittance parameters or $y$ parameters,[1] as used in Fig. 8.13a. The reason for this is that the basic amplifier and the feedback network are connected in parallel at input and output, and thus have identical *voltages* at their terminals. The $y$ parameters specify the response of a network by expressing the terminal currents in terms of the terminal voltages, and this results in very simple calculations when two networks have identical terminal voltages. This will be evident in the circuit calculations to follow. The $y$-parameter representation is illustrated in Fig. 8.14.

From Fig. 8.13a, at the input

$$i_s = (y_S + y_{11a} + y_{11f})v_i + (y_{12a} + y_{12f})v_o \tag{8.46}$$

Summation of currents at the output gives

$$0 = (y_{21a} + y_{21f})v_i + (y_L + y_{22a} + y_{22f})v_o \tag{8.47}$$

It is useful to define

$$y_i = y_S + y_{11a} + y_{11f} \tag{8.48}$$

$$y_o = y_L + y_{22a} + y_{22f} \tag{8.49}$$

$$i_1 = y_{11} v_1 + y_{12} v_2$$
$$i_2 = y_{21} v_1 + y_{22} v_2$$

$$y_{11} = \frac{i_1}{v_1}\bigg|_{v_2 = 0} \qquad\qquad y_{12} = \frac{i_1}{v_2}\bigg|_{v_1 = 0}$$

$$y_{21} = \frac{i_2}{v_1}\bigg|_{v_2 = 0} \qquad\qquad y_{22} = \frac{i_2}{v_2}\bigg|_{v_1 = 0}$$

**Figure 8.14** The $y$-parameter representation of a two-port.

Solving (8.46) and (8.47) by using (8.48) and (8.49) gives

$$\frac{v_o}{i_s} = \frac{-(y_{21a} + y_{21f})}{y_i y_o - (y_{21a} + y_{21f})(y_{12a} + y_{12f})} \tag{8.50}$$

The equation can be put in the form of the ideal feedback equation of (8.35) by dividing by $y_i y_o$ to give

$$\frac{v_o}{i_s} = \frac{\dfrac{-(y_{21a} + y_{21f})}{y_i y_o}}{1 + \dfrac{-(y_{21a} + y_{21f})}{y_i y_o}(y_{12a} + y_{12f})} \tag{8.51}$$

Comparing (8.51) with (8.35) gives

$$a = -\frac{y_{21a} + y_{21f}}{y_i y_o} \tag{8.52}$$

$$f = y_{12a} + y_{12f} \tag{8.53}$$

At this point, a number of approximations can be made that greatly simplify the calculations. First, we assume that the signal transmitted by the basic amplifier is much greater than the signal fed forward by the feedback network. Since the former has gain (usually large) while the latter has loss, this is almost invariably a valid assumption. This means that

$$|y_{21a}| \gg |y_{21f}| \tag{8.54}$$

Second, we assume that the signal fed back by the feedback network is much greater than the signal fed back through the basic amplifier. Since most active devices have very small reverse transmission, the basic amplifier has a similar characteristic, and this assumption is almost invariably quite accurate. This assumption means that

$$|y_{12a}| \ll |y_{12f}| \tag{8.55}$$

Using (8.54) and (8.55) in (8.51) gives

$$\frac{v_o}{i_s} = A \simeq \frac{\dfrac{-y_{21a}}{y_i y_o}}{1 + \left(\dfrac{-y_{21a}}{y_i y_o}\right)y_{12f}} \tag{8.56}$$

Comparing (8.56) with (8.35) gives

$$a = -\frac{y_{21a}}{y_i y_o} \tag{8.57}$$

$$f = y_{12f} \tag{8.58}$$

A circuit representation of (8.57) and (8.58) can be found as follows. Equations 8.54 and 8.55 mean that in Fig. 8.13a the feedback generator of the basic amplifier and the forward-transmission generator of the feedback network may be neglected. If this is done the circuit may be redrawn as in Fig. 8.13b, where the terminal admittances $y_{11f}$ and $y_{22f}$ of the feedback network have been absorbed into the basic amplifier, together with source and load impedances $y_S$ and $y_L$. The new basic amplifier thus *includes the loading effect* of the original feedback network, and the new feedback network is an ideal one as used in Fig. 8.9. If the transfer function of the basic amplifier of Fig. 8.13b is calculated (by first removing the feedback network), the result given in (8.57) is obtained. Similarly, the transfer function of the feedback network of Fig. 8.13b is given by (8.58). Thus Fig. 8.13b is a *circuit representation* of (8.57) and (8.58).

Since Fig. 8.13b has a direct correspondence with Fig. 8.9, all the results derived in Section 8.4.2 for Fig. 8.9 can now be used. The loading effect of the feedback network on the basic amplifier is now included by simply shunting input and output with $y_{11f}$ and $y_{22f}$, respectively. As shown in Fig. 8.14, these terminal admittances of the feedback network are calculated with the other port of the network short-circuited. In practice, loading term $y_{11f}$ is simply obtained by shorting the output node of the amplifier and calculating the feedback circuit input admittance. Similarly, term $y_{22f}$ is calculated by shorting the input node in the amplifier and calculating the feedback circuit output admittance. The feedback transfer function $f$ given by (8.58) is the short-circuit reverse transfer admittance of the feedback network and is defined in Fig. 8.14. This is readily calculated in practice and is often obtained by inspection. Note that the use of $y$ parameters in further calculations is *not* necessary. Once the circuit of Fig. 8.13b is established, any convenient network analysis method may be used to calculate gain $a$ of the basic amplifier. We have simply used the two-port representation as a general means of illustrating how loading effects may be included in the calculations.

For example, consider the common shunt-shunt feedback circuit using an op amp as shown in Fig. 8.15a. The equivalent circuit is shown in Fig. 8.15b and is redrawn in 8.15c to allow for loading of the feedback network on the basic amplifier. The $y$ parameters of the feedback network can be found from Fig. 8.15d.

$$y_{11f} = \left.\frac{i_1}{v_1}\right|_{v_2=0} = \frac{1}{R_F} \tag{8.59}$$

$$y_{22f} = \left.\frac{i_2}{v_2}\right|_{v_1=0} = \frac{1}{R_F} \tag{8.60}$$

$$y_{12f} = \left.\frac{i_1}{v_2}\right|_{v_1=0} = -\frac{1}{R_F} = f \tag{8.61}$$

Using (8.54), we neglect $y_{21f}$.

The basic-amplifier gain $a$ can be calculated from Fig. 8.15c by putting $i_{fb} = 0$ to give

$$v_1 = \frac{z_i R_F}{z_i + R_F} i_i \tag{8.62}$$

$$v_o = -\frac{R}{R + z_o} a_v v_1 \tag{8.63}$$

(a)

(b)

(c)

(d)

**Figure 8.15** (a) Shunt-shunt feedback circuit using an op amp as the gain element. (b) Equivalent circuit of (a). (c) Division of the circuit in (b) into forward and feedback paths. (d) Circuit for the calculation of the $y$ parameters of the feedback network of the circuit in (b).

where

$$R = R_F \| R_L \tag{8.64}$$

Substituting (8.62) in (8.63) gives

$$\frac{v_o}{i_i} = a = -\frac{R}{R + z_o} a_v \frac{z_i R_F}{z_i + R_F} \tag{8.65}$$

Using the formulas derived in Section 8.4.2 we can now calculate all parameters of the feedback circuit. The input and output impedances of the basic amplifier now *include* the effect of feedback loading, and it is *these impedances* that are divided by $(1 + T)$ as described in Section 8.4.2. Thus the input impedance of the basic amplifier of Fig. 8.15c is

$$z_{ia} = R_F \| z_i = \frac{R_F z_i}{R_F + z_i} \tag{8.66}$$

When feedback is applied, the input impedance is

$$Z_i = \frac{z_{ia}}{1 + T} \tag{8.67}$$

Similarly for the output impedance of the basic amplifier

$$z_{oa} = z_o \| R_F \| R_L \tag{8.68}$$

When feedback is applied, this becomes

$$Z_o = \frac{z_o \| R_F \| R_L}{1 + T} \tag{8.69}$$

Note that these calculations can be made using the circuit of Fig. 8.15c *without* further need of two-port $y$ parameters.

Since the loop gain $T$ is of considerable interest, this is now calculated using (8.61) and (8.65):

$$T = af = \frac{R_F R_L}{R_F R_L + z_o R_F + z_o R_L} a_v \frac{z_i}{z_i + R_F} \tag{8.70}$$

■  **EXAMPLE**

Assuming that the circuit of Fig. 8.15a is realized using a 741 op amp with $R_F = 1\ \text{M}\Omega$ and $R_L = 10\ \text{k}\Omega$, calculate the terminal impedances, loop gain, and overall gain of the feedback amplifier at low frequencies. Typical 741 data are $z_i = 2\ \text{M}\Omega$, $z_o = 75\ \Omega$, and $a_v = 200,000$.

From (8.66) the low-frequency input impedance of the basic amplifier including loading is

$$z_{ia} = \frac{10^6 \times 2 \times 10^6}{10^6 + 2 \times 10^6} \Omega = 666.7\ \text{k}\Omega \tag{8.71}$$

From (8.68), the low-frequency output impedance of the basic amplifier is

$$z_{oa} = 75\ \Omega \| 1\ \text{M}\Omega \| 10\ \text{k}\Omega \simeq 75\ \Omega \tag{8.72}$$

The low-frequency loop gain can be calculated from (8.70) as

$$T = \frac{10^6 \times 10^4}{10^6 \times 10^4 + 75 \times 10^6 + 75 \times 10^4} \times 200,000 \times \frac{2 \times 10^6}{2 \times 10^6 + 10^6}$$

$$= 133,333 \tag{8.73}$$

The loop gain in this case is quite large. Note that a finite source resistance at the input could reduce this significantly.

The input impedance with feedback applied is found by substituting (8.71) and (8.73) in (8.67) to give

$$Z_i = \frac{666.7 \times 10^3}{133,333} \, \Omega = 5 \, \Omega$$

The output impedance with feedback applied is found by substituting (8.72) and (8.73) in (8.69) to give

$$Z_o = \frac{75}{133,333} \, \Omega = 0.000563 \, \Omega$$

In practice, second-order effects in the circuit may result in a larger value of $Z_o$.

The overall transfer function with feedback can be found approximately from (8.8) as

$$\frac{v_o}{i_i} = A \simeq \frac{1}{f} \tag{8.74}$$

Using (8.61) in (8.74) gives

$$\frac{v_o}{i_i} = A \simeq -R_F$$

Substituting for $R_F$ we obtain

$$\frac{v_o}{i_i} = A \simeq -1 \, \text{M}\Omega \tag{8.75}$$

A more exact value of $A$ can be calculated from (8.5). Since the loop gain is very large in this case, it is useful to transform (8.5) as follows:

$$A = \frac{1}{f} \cdot \frac{1}{1 + \dfrac{1}{af}} \tag{8.76}$$

$$= \frac{1}{f} \cdot \frac{1}{1 + \dfrac{1}{T}} \tag{8.77}$$

Since $T$ is so high in this example, $A$ differs very little from $1/f$. Substituting $T = 133,333$ and $1/f = -1 \, \text{M}\Omega$ in (8.77), we obtain

$$A = -999,992 \, \Omega \tag{8.78}$$

For most practical purposes, (8.75) is sufficiently accurate.

## 8.5.2 Series-Series Feedback

Consider the series-series feedback connection of Fig. 8.12. The effect of nonideal networks can be calculated using the representation of Fig. 8.16$a$. In this case the most convenient two-port representation is the use of the open-circuit impedance parameters or $z$ parameters because the basic amplifier and the feedback network are now connected in series at input and output and thus have identical *currents* at their terminals. As shown in Fig. 8.17, the $z$ parameters specify the network by expressing terminal voltages in terms of terminal currents, and this results in simple calculations when the two networks have

(a)

(b)

**Figure 8.16** (a) Series-series feedback configuration using the z-parameter representation. (b) Circuit of (a) redrawn with generators $z_{21f}i_i$ and $z_{12a}i_o$ omitted.

$$v_1 = z_{11}i_1 + z_{12}i_2$$

$$v_2 = z_{21}i_1 + z_{22}i_2$$

$$z_{11} = \frac{v_1}{i_1}\bigg|_{i_2 = 0} \qquad z_{12} = \frac{v_1}{i_2}\bigg|_{i_1 = 0}$$

$$z_{21} = \frac{v_2}{i_1}\bigg|_{i_2 = 0} \qquad z_{22} = \frac{v_2}{i_2}\bigg|_{i_1 = 0}$$

**Figure 8.17** The $z$-parameter representation of a two-port.

common terminal currents. The calculation in this case proceeds as the exact dual of that in Section 8.5.1. From Fig. 8.16, summation of voltages at the input gives

$$v_s = (z_S + z_{11a} + z_{11f})i_i + (z_{12a} + z_{12f})i_o \tag{8.79}$$

Summing voltages at the output we obtain

$$0 = (z_{21a} + z_{21f})i_i + (z_L + z_{22a} + z_{22f})i_o \tag{8.80}$$

It is useful to define

$$z_i = z_S + z_{11a} + z_{11f} \tag{8.81}$$

$$z_o = z_L + z_{22a} + z_{22f} \tag{8.82}$$

Again neglecting reverse transmission through the basic amplifier, we assume that

$$|z_{12a}| \ll |z_{12f}| \tag{8.83}$$

Also neglecting feed-forward through the feedback network, we can write

$$|z_{21a}| \gg |z_{21f}| \tag{8.84}$$

With these assumptions it follows that

$$\frac{i_o}{v_s} = A \simeq \frac{\dfrac{-z_{21a}}{z_i z_o}}{1 + \left(\dfrac{-z_{21a}}{z_i z_o}\right)z_{12f}} = \frac{a}{1 + af} \tag{8.85}$$

where

$$a = -\frac{z_{21a}}{z_i z_o} \tag{8.86}$$

$$f = z_{12f} \tag{8.87}$$

A circuit representation of $a$ in (8.86) and $f$ in (8.87) can be found by removing generators $z_{21f}i_i$ and $z_{12a}i_o$ from Fig. 8.16a in accord with (8.83) and (8.84). This gives the approximate representation of Fig. 8.16b, where the new basic amplifier includes the loading effect of the original feedback network. The new feedback network is an ideal one as used in Fig. 8.12. The transfer function of the basic amplifier of Fig. 8.16b is the same as in (8.86), and the transfer function of the feedback network of Fig. 8.16b is given by (8.87). Thus Fig. 8.16b is a circuit representation of (8.86) and (8.87).

Since Fig. 8.16*b* has a direct correspondence with Fig. 8.12, all the results of Section 8.4.4 can now be used. The loading effect of the feedback network on the basic amplifier is included by connecting the feedback-network terminal impedances $z_{11f}$ and $z_{22f}$ in series at input and output of the basic amplifier. Terms $z_{11f}$ and $z_{22f}$ are defined in Fig. 8.17 and are obtained by calculating the terminal impedances of the feedback network with the other port *open circuited*. Feedback function $f$ given by (8.87) is the *reverse transfer impedance* of the feedback network.

Consider, for example, the series-series feedback triple of Fig. 8.18*a*, which is useful as a wideband feedback amplifier. $R_{E2}$ is usually a small resistor that samples the output current $i_o$, and the resulting voltage across $R_{E2}$ is sampled by the divider $R_F$ and $R_{E1}$ to produce a feedback voltage across $R_{E1}$. Usually $R_F \gg R_{E1}$ and $R_{E2}$.

The two-port theory derived earlier cannot be applied directly in this case because the basic amplifier cannot be represented by a two-port. However, the techniques developed previously using two-port theory can be used with minor modification by first noting that the feedback network can be represented by a two-port as shown in 8.18*b*. One problem with this circuit is that the feedback generator $z_{12f}i_{e3}$ is in the emitter of $Q_1$ and not in the input lead where it can be compared directly with $v_s$. This problem can be overcome by considering the small-signal equivalent of the input portion of this circuit as shown in Fig. 8.19. For this circuit

$$v_s = i_i z_S + v_{be} + i_{e1} z_{11f} + z_{12f} i_{e3} \tag{8.88}$$

Using

$$i_{e3} = \frac{i_o}{\alpha_3} \tag{8.89}$$

in (8.88) gives

$$v_s - z_{12f} \frac{i_o}{\alpha_3} = i_i z_S + v_{be} + i_{e1} z_{11f} \tag{8.90}$$

where the quantities in these equations are *small-signal* quantities. Equation 8.90 shows that the feedback voltage generator $z_{12f}(i_o/\alpha_3)$ can be *moved back* in series with the input lead; if this was done, exactly the same equation would result. (See Fig. 8.18*c*.) Note that the common-base current gain $\alpha_3$ of $Q_3$ appears in this feedback expression because the output current is sampled by $R_{E2}$ in the *emitter* of $Q_3$ in order to feed back a correcting signal to the input. This problem is common to most circuits employing series feedback at the output, and the $\alpha_3$ of $Q_3$ is *outside* the feedback loop. There are many applications where this is not a problem, since $\alpha \simeq 1$. However, if high gain precision is required, variations in $\alpha_3$ can cause difficulties.

The $z$ parameters of the feedback network can be determined from Fig. 8.20 as

$$z_{12f} = \left.\frac{v_1}{i_2}\right|_{i_1=0} = \frac{R_{E1}R_{E2}}{R_{E1} + R_{E2} + R_F} \tag{8.91}$$

$$z_{22f} = \left.\frac{v_2}{i_2}\right|_{i_1=0} = R_{E2}\|(R_{E1} + R_F) \tag{8.92}$$

$$z_{11f} = \left.\frac{v_1}{i_1}\right|_{i_2=0} = R_{E1}\|(R_F + R_{E2}) \tag{8.93}$$

Using (8.84), we neglect $z_{21f}$.

From the foregoing results we can redraw the circuit of Fig. 8.18*b* as shown in Fig. 8.18*c*. As in previous calculations, the signal fed forward via the feedback network (in this case $z_{21f}i_{e1}$) is neglected. The feedback voltage generator is placed in series with the

(a)

(b)

(c)

**Figure 8.18** (a) Series-series feedback triple. (b) Circuit of (a) redrawn using a two-port $z$-parameter representation of the feedback network. (c) Approximate representation of the circuit in (b).

**Figure 8.19** Small-signal equivalent circuit of the input stage of the circuit in Fig. 8.18b.

input lead and an ideal differencing node then exists at the input. The effect of feedback loading on the basic amplifier is represented by the impedances in the emitters of $Q_1$ and $Q_3$. Note that this case does differ somewhat from the example of Fig. 8.16b in that the impedances $z_{11f}$ and $z_{22f}$ of the feedback network appear in *series* with the input and output leads in Fig. 8.16b, whereas in Fig. 8.18c these impedances appear in the emitters of $Q_1$ and $Q_3$. This is due to the fact that the basic amplifier of the circuit of Fig. 8.18a cannot be represented by two-port z parameters but makes no difference to the method of analysis. Since the feedback voltage generator in Fig. 8.18c is directly in series with the input and is proportional to $i_o$, a direct correspondence with Fig. 8.16b can be established and the results of Section 8.4.4 can be applied. There is no further need of the z parameters, and by inspection we can write

$$\frac{i_o}{v_s} = A \simeq \frac{a}{1 + af}$$ (8.94)

where

$$f = \frac{z_{12f}}{\alpha_3} = \frac{1}{\alpha_3} \frac{R_{E1} R_{E2}}{R_{E1} + R_{E2} + R_F}$$ (8.95)

and $a$ is the transconductance of the circuit of Fig. 8.18c with the feedback generator $[(z_{12f}/\alpha_3)i_o]$ removed.

The *input impedance* seen by $v_s$ with feedback applied is $(1 + af) \times$ (input impedance of the basic amplifier of Fig. 8.18c *including* feedback loading).

The *output impedance* with feedback applied is $(1 + af)$ times the output impedance of the basic amplifier *including* feedback loading.

If the loop gain $T = af$ is large, then the gain with feedback applied is

$$A = \frac{i_o}{v_s} \simeq \frac{1}{f} = \alpha_3 \frac{R_{E1} + R_{E2} + R_F}{R_{E1} R_{E2}}$$ (8.96)

**Figure 8.20** Circuit for the calculation of the z parameters of the feedback network of the circuit in Fig 8.18a.

■ **EXAMPLE**

A commercial integrated circuit[2] based on the series-series triple is the MC 1553 shown in Fig. 8.21*a*. Calculate the terminal impedances, loop gain, and overall gain of this amplifier at low frequencies.

The MC 1553 is a wideband amplifier with a bandwidth of 50 MHz at a voltage gain of 50. The circuit gain is realized by the series-series triple composed of $Q_1$, $Q_2$, and $Q_3$. The output voltage is developed across the load resistor $R_C$ and is then fed to the output via emitter follower $Q_4$, which ensures a low output impedance. The rest of the circuit is largely for bias purposes except capacitors $C_P$, $C_F$, and $C_B$. Capacitors $C_P$ and $C_F$ are

$R_{E1} = 100\ \Omega,\ R_{E2} = 100\ \Omega,\ R_F = 640\ \Omega,\ R_A = 9\ \text{k}\Omega,$
$R_B = 5\ \text{k}\Omega,\ R_C = 600\ \Omega,\ R_D = 12\ \text{k}\Omega,\ R_G = 3\ \text{k}\Omega,$
$R_K = 6\ \text{k}\Omega$

(*a*)

(*b*)

**Figure 8.21** (*a*) Circuit of the MC 1553 wideband integrated circuit. (*b*) Basic amplifier of the series-series triple in (*a*).

$$I_{C1} = 0.6 \text{ mA} \qquad\qquad I_{C2} = 1 \text{ mA} \qquad\qquad I_{C3} = 4 \text{ mA}$$

$$r_{\pi 1} = 4.33 \text{ k}\Omega \qquad\qquad r_{\pi 2} = 2.6 \text{ k}\Omega \qquad\qquad r_{\pi 3} = 650 \ \Omega$$

$$g_{m1} = \frac{1}{43.3} \ \mho \qquad\qquad g_{m2} = \frac{1}{26} \ \mho \qquad\qquad g_{m3} = \frac{4}{26} \ \mho$$

(c)

**Figure 8.21** (c) Small-signal equivalent circuit of the basic amplifier in (b).

small capacitors of several picofarads and are included on the chip. They ensure stability of the feedback loop, and their function will be described in Chapter 9. Capacitor $C_B$ is external to the chip and is a large bypass capacitor used to decouple the bias circuitry at the signal frequencies of interest.

**Bias Calculation.** The analysis of the circuit begins with the bias conditions. The bias current levels are set by the reference current $I_{RK}$ in the resistor $R_K$, and assuming $V_{BE(\text{on})} = 0.6$ V and $V_{CC} = 6$ V, we obtain

$$I_{RK} = \frac{V_{CC} - 2V_{BE(\text{on})}}{R_K} \tag{8.97}$$

Substituting data in (8.97) gives

$$I_{RK} = \frac{6 - 1.2}{6000}\text{A} = 0.80 \text{ mA}$$

The current in the output emitter follower $Q_4$ is determined by the currents in $Q_6$ and $Q_8$. Transistor $Q_8$ has an area three times that of $Q_7$ and $Q_6$ and thus

$$I_{C8} = 3 \times 0.8 \text{ mA} = 2.4 \text{ mA}$$

$$I_{C6} = 0.8 \text{ mA}$$

where $\beta_F$ is assumed large in these bias calculations. If the base current of $Q_1$ is small, all of $I_{C6}$ and $I_{C8}$ flow through $Q_4$ and

$$I_{C4} \simeq I_{C6} + I_{C8} \tag{8.98}$$

Thus

$$I_{C4} \simeq 3.2 \text{ mA}$$

Transistor $Q_8$ supplies most of the bias current to $Q_4$, and this device functions as a Class A emitter-follower output stage of the type described in Section 5.2. The function of $Q_6$ is to allow formation of a negative-feedback bias loop for stabilization of the dc operating point, and resistor $R_G$ is chosen to cause sufficient dc voltage drop to allow connection of $R_D$ back to the base of $Q_1$. Transistors $Q_1, Q_2, Q_3$, and $Q_4$ are then connected in a negative-feedback bias loop and the dc conditions can be ascertained approximately as follows.

If we assume that $Q_2$ is on, the voltage at the collector of $Q_1$ is about 0.6 V and the voltage across $R_A$ is 5.4 V. Thus the current through $R_A$ is

$$I_{RA} = \frac{5.4}{R_A}$$

$$= \frac{5.4}{9000} = 0.6 \text{ mA} \qquad (8.99)$$

If $\beta_F$ is assumed high, it follows that

$$I_{C1} \simeq I_{RA} = 0.6 \text{ mA} \qquad (8.100)$$

Since the voltage across $R_{E1}$ is small, the voltage at the base of $Q_1$ is approximately 0.6 V, and if the base current of $Q_1$ is small, this is also the voltage at the collector of $Q_6$ since any voltage across $R_D$ will be small. The dc output voltage can be written

$$V_O = V_{C6} + I_{C6}R_G \qquad (8.101)$$

Substitution of data gives

$$V_O = (0.6 + 0.8 \times 3) \text{ V} = 3 \text{ V}$$

The voltage at the base of $Q_4$ (collector of $Q_3$) is $V_{BE}$ above $V_O$ and is thus 3.6 V. The collector current of $Q_3$ is

$$I_{C3} \simeq \frac{V_{CC} - V_{C3}}{R_C} \qquad (8.102)$$

Substitution of parameter values gives

$$I_{C3} \simeq \frac{6 - 3.6}{600} \text{ A} = 4 \text{ mA}$$

The voltage at the base of $Q_3$ (collector of $Q_2$) is

$$V_{B3} \simeq -I_{E3}R_{E2} + V_{BE(on)} \qquad (8.103)$$

Thus

$$V_{B3} = V_{C2} \simeq (4 \times 0.1 + 0.6) \text{ V} = 1 \text{ V}$$

$I_{C2}$ may be calculated from

$$I_{C2} \simeq \frac{V_{CC} - V_{C2}}{R_B} \qquad (8.104)$$

and substitution of parameter values gives

$$I_{C2} \simeq \frac{6 - 1}{5000} \text{ A} = 1 \text{ mA}$$

**The ac Calculation.**  The ac analysis can now proceed using the methods previously developed in this chapter. For purposes of ac analysis, the feedback triple composed of $Q_1$, $Q_2$, and $Q_3$ in Fig. 8.21a is identical to the circuit in Fig. 8.18a, and the results derived previously for the latter circuit are directly applicable to the triple in Fig. 8.21a. To obtain the voltage gain of the circuit of Fig. 8.21a, we simply multiply the transconductance of the triple by the load resistor $R_C$, since the gain of the emitter follower $Q_4$ is almost exactly unity. Note that resistor $R_D$ is assumed grounded for ac signals by the large capacitor $C_B$, and thus has no influence on the ac circuit operation, except for a shunting effect at the input that will be discussed later. From (8.95) the feedback factor $f$ of the series-series triple of Fig. 8.21a is

$$f = \frac{1}{0.99} \frac{100 \times 100}{100 + 100 + 640} \, \Omega = 12.0 \, \Omega \tag{8.105}$$

where $\beta_0 = 100$ has been assumed.

If the loop gain is large, the transconductance of the triple of Fig. 8.21a can be calculated from (8.96) as

$$\frac{i_{o3}}{v_s} \simeq \frac{1}{f} = \frac{1}{12} \, \text{A/V} \tag{8.106}$$

where $i_{o3}$ is the small-signal collector current in $Q_3$ in Fig. 8.21a. If the input impedance of the emitter follower $Q_4$ is large, the load resistance seen by $Q_3$ is $R_C = 600 \, \Omega$ and the voltage gain of the circuit is

$$\frac{v_o}{v_s} = -\frac{i_{o3}}{v_s} \times R_C \tag{8.107}$$

Substituting (8.106) in (8.107) gives

$$\frac{v_o}{v_s} = -50.0 \tag{8.108}$$

Consider now the loop gain of the circuit of Fig. 8.21a. This can be calculated by using the basic-amplifier representation of Fig. 8.18c to calculate the forward gain $a$. Fig. 8.18c is redrawn in Fig. 8.21b using data from this example, assuming that $z_S = 0$ and omitting the feedback generator. The small-signal, low-frequency equivalent circuit is shown in Fig. 8.21c assuming $\beta_0 = 100$, and it is a straightforward calculation to show that the gain of the basic amplifier is

$$a = \frac{i_3}{v_s} = 20.3 \, \text{A/V} \tag{8.109}$$

Combination of (8.105) and (8.109) gives

$$T = af = 12 \times 20.3 = 243.6 \tag{8.110}$$

The transconductance of the triple can now be calculated more accurately from (8.94) as

$$\frac{i_{o3}}{v_s} = \frac{a}{1 + T} = \frac{20.3}{244.6} \, \text{A/V} = 0.083 \, \text{A/V} \tag{8.111}$$

Substitution of (8.111) in (8.107) gives for the overall voltage gain

$$\frac{v_o}{v_s} = -\frac{i_{o3}}{v_s} R_C = -0.083 \times 600 = -49.8 \tag{8.112}$$

This is close to the approximate value given by (8.108).

The input resistance of the basic amplifier is readily determined from Fig. 8.21c to be

$$r_{ia} = 13.2 \, \text{k}\Omega \tag{8.113}$$

The input resistance when feedback is applied is

$$R_i = r_{ia}(1 + T) \tag{8.114}$$

Substituting (8.113) and (8.110) in (8.114) gives

$$R_i = 13.2 \times 244.6 \, \text{k}\Omega = 3.23 \, \text{M}\Omega \tag{8.115}$$

As expected, series feedback at the input results in a high input resistance. In this example, however, the bias resistor $R_D$ directly shunts the input for ac signals and is *outside* the feedback loop. Since $R_D = 12\ \text{k}\Omega$ and is much less than $R_i$, the resistor $R_D$ determines the input resistance for this circuit.

Finally, the output resistance of the circuit is of some interest. The output resistance of the triple can be calculated from Fig. 8.21c by including output resistance $r_o$ in the model for $Q_3$. The resistance obtained is then multiplied by $(1 + T)$ and the resulting value is much greater than the collector load resistor of $Q_3$, which is $R_C = 600\ \Omega$. The output resistance of the full circuit is thus essentially the output resistance of emitter follower $Q_4$ fed from a 600-$\Omega$ source resistance, and this is

$$R_o = \frac{1}{g_{m4}} + \frac{R_C}{\beta_4} = \left(\frac{26}{3.2} + \frac{600}{100}\right)\Omega = 14\ \Omega \tag{8.116}$$

### 8.5.3 Series-Shunt Feedback

Series-shunt feedback is shown schematically in Fig. 8.4. The basic amplifier and the feedback network have the same input current and the same output voltage. A two-port representation that uses input current and output voltage as the independent variables is the hybrid $h$-parameter representation shown in Fig. 8.22. The $h$ parameters can be used to represent nonideal circuits in a series-shunt feedback as shown in Fig. 8.23a. Summation of voltages at the input of this figure gives

$$v_s = (z_S + h_{11a} + h_{11f})i_i + (h_{12a} + h_{12f})v_o \tag{8.117}$$

Summing currents at the output yields

$$0 = (h_{21a} + h_{21f})i_i + (y_L + h_{22a} + h_{22f})v_o \tag{8.118}$$

We now define

$$z_i = z_S + h_{11a} + h_{11f} \tag{8.119}$$
$$y_o = y_L + h_{22a} + h_{22f} \tag{8.120}$$

and make the same assumptions as in previous examples:

$$|h_{12a}| \ll |h_{12f}| \tag{8.121}$$
$$|h_{21a}| \gg |h_{21f}| \tag{8.122}$$

$$v_1 = h_{11}i_1 + h_{12}v_2$$
$$i_2 = h_{21}i_1 + h_{22}v_2$$

$$h_{11} = \left.\frac{v_1}{i_1}\right|_{v_2 = 0} \qquad h_{12} = \left.\frac{v_1}{v_2}\right|_{i_1 = 0}$$

$$h_{21} = \left.\frac{i_2}{i_1}\right|_{v_2 = 0} \qquad h_{22} = \left.\frac{i_2}{v_2}\right|_{i_1 = 0}$$

**Figure 8.22** The $h$-parameter representation of a two-port.

**Figure 8.23** (a) Series-shunt feedback configuration using the $h$-parameter representation. (b) Circuit of (a) redrawn with generators $h_{21f}i_i$ and $h_{12a}v_o$ omitted.

It can then be shown that

$$\frac{v_o}{v_s} = A \simeq \frac{-\dfrac{h_{21a}}{z_i y_o}}{1 + \left(-\dfrac{h_{21a}}{z_i y_o}\right)h_{12f}} = \frac{a}{1 + af} \tag{8.123}$$

Feedback network

**Figure 8.24** Series-shunt feedback circuit using an op amp as the gain element.

where

$$a = -\frac{h_{21a}}{z_i y_o} \tag{8.124}$$

$$f = h_{12f} \tag{8.125}$$

A circuit representation of $a$ in (8.124) and $f$ in (8.125) can be found by removing the generators $h_{12a}v_o$ and $h_{21f}i_i$ from Fig. 8.23a as suggested by the approximations of (8.121) and (8.122). This gives the approximate representation of Fig. 8.23b, where the new basic amplifier includes the loading effect of the original feedback network. As in previous examples, the circuit of Fig. 8.23b is a circuit representation of (8.123), (8.124), and (8.125) and has the form of an ideal feedback loop. Thus all the equations of Section 8.4.1 can be applied to the circuit.

For example, consider the common series-shunt op amp circuit of Fig. 8.24, which fits exactly the model described above. We first determine the $h$ parameters of the feedback network from Fig. 8.25:

$$h_{22f} = \left.\frac{i_2}{v_2}\right|_{i_1=0} = \frac{1}{R_F + R_E} \tag{8.126}$$

$$h_{12f} = \left.\frac{v_1}{v_2}\right|_{i_1=0} = \frac{R_E}{R_E + R_F} \tag{8.127}$$

$$h_{11f} = \left.\frac{v_1}{i_1}\right|_{v_2=0} = R_E \| R_F \tag{8.128}$$

**Figure 8.25** Circuit for the determination of the $h$ parameters of the feedback network in Fig. 8.24.

**Figure 8.26** Equivalent circuit for Fig. 8.24.

Using (8.122), we neglect $h_{21f}$. The complete feedback amplifier including loading effects is shown in Fig. 8.26 and has a direct correspondence with Fig. 8.23b. (The only difference is that the op amp output is represented by a Thévenin rather than a Norton equivalent.)

The gain $a$ of the basic amplifier can be calculated from Fig. 8.26 by initially disregarding the feedback generator to give

$$a = \frac{z_i}{z_i + R} a_v \frac{z_{LX}}{z_{LX} + z_o} \tag{8.129}$$

where

$$R = R_E \| R_F \tag{8.130}$$

$$z_{LX} = z_L \| (R_E + R_F) \tag{8.131}$$

Also

$$f = \frac{R_E}{R_E + R_F} \tag{8.132}$$

Thus the overall gain of the feedback circuit is

$$A = \frac{v_o}{v_s} = \frac{a}{1 + af} \tag{8.133}$$

and $A$ can be evaluated using (8.129) and (8.132).

■ **EXAMPLE**

Assume that the circuit of Fig. 8.24 is realized, using a differential amplifier with low-frequency parameters $z_i = 100\ \text{k}\Omega$, $z_o = 10\ \text{k}\Omega$, and $a_v = 3000$. Calculate the input impedance of the feedback amplifier at low frequencies if $R_E = 5\ \text{k}\Omega$, $R_F = 20\ \text{k}\Omega$, and $z_L = 10\ \text{k}\Omega$. Note that $z_o$ in this case is not small as is usually the case for an op amp, and this situation can arise in some applications.

This problem is best approached by first calculating the input impedance of the basic amplifier and then multiplying by $(1 + T)$ as indicated by (8.25) to calculate the input impedance of the feedback amplifier. By inspection from Fig. 8.26 the input impedance of the basic amplifier is

$$z_{ia} = z_i + R_E \| R_F = (100 + 5 \| 20)\ \text{k}\Omega = 104\ \text{k}\Omega$$

The parallel combination of $z_L$ and $(R_F + R_E)$ in Fig. 8.27 is

$$z_{LX} = \frac{10 \times 25}{35} = 7.14\ \text{k}\Omega$$

**Figure 8.27** Series-shunt feedback circuit.

Substitution in (8.129) gives, for the gain of the basic amplifier of Fig. 8.26,

$$a = \frac{100}{100 + 4} \times 3000 \times \frac{7.14}{7.14 + 10} = 1202$$

From (8.127) the feedback factor $f$ for this circuit is

$$f = \frac{5}{5 + 20} = 0.2$$

and thus the loop gain is

$$T = af = 1202 \times 0.2 = 240$$

The input impedance of the feedback amplifier is thus

$$Z_i = z_{ia}(1 + T) = 104 \times 241 \text{ k}\Omega = 25 \text{ M}\Omega$$

In this example the loading effect produced by $(R_F + R_E)$ on the output has a significant effect on the gain $a$ of the basic amplifier and thus on the input impedance of the feedback amplifier.

As another example of a series-shunt feedback circuit, consider the series-series triple of Fig. 8.18$a$ but assume that the output signal is taken as the voltage at the emitter of $Q_3$, as shown in Fig. 8.27. This is an example of how the same circuit can realize two different feedback functions if the output is taken from different nodes. As in the case of Fig. 8.18$a$, the basic amplifier of Fig. 8.27 cannot be represented as a two-port. However, the feedback network *can* be represented as a two-port and the appropriate parameters are the $h$ parameters as shown in Fig. 8.28. The $h$ parameters for this feedback network are given by (8.126), (8.127), and (8.128) and $h_{21f}$ is neglected. The analysis of Fig. 8.28 then proceeds in the usual manner.

### 8.5.4 Shunt-Series Feedback

Shunt-series feedback is shown schematically in Fig. 8.11. In this case the basic amplifier and the feedback network have common input voltages and output currents, and hybrid $g$ parameters as defined in Fig. 8.29 are best suited for use in this case. The feedback circuit is shown in Fig. 8.30$a$, and, at the input, we find that

$$i_s = (y_S + g_{11a} + g_{11f})v_i + (g_{12a} + g_{12f})i_o \qquad (8.134)$$

**Figure 8.28** Circuit equivalent to that of Fig. 8.27 using a two-port representation of the feedback network.

$$i_1 = g_{11}v_1 + g_{12}i_2$$
$$v_2 = g_{21}v_1 + g_{22}i_2$$

$$g_{11} = \left.\frac{i_1}{v_1}\right|_{i_2 = 0} \qquad g_{12} = \left.\frac{i_1}{i_2}\right|_{v_1 = 0}$$

$$g_{21} = \left.\frac{v_2}{v_1}\right|_{i_2 = 0} \qquad g_{22} = \left.\frac{v_2}{i_2}\right|_{v_1 = 0}$$

**Figure 8.29** The g-parameter representation of a two-port.

At the output

$$0 = (g_{21a} + g_{21f})v_i + (z_L + g_{22a} + g_{22f})i_o \qquad (8.135)$$

Defining

$$y_i = y_S + g_{11a} + g_{11f} \qquad (8.136)$$
$$z_o = z_L + g_{22a} + g_{22f} \qquad (8.137)$$

and making the assumptions

$$|g_{12a}| \ll |g_{12f}| \qquad (8.138)$$
$$|g_{21a}| \gg |g_{21f}| \qquad (8.139)$$

we find

$$\frac{i_o}{i_s} = A \simeq \frac{-\dfrac{g_{21a}}{y_i z_o}}{1 + \left(-\dfrac{g_{21a}}{y_i z_o}\right)g_{12f}} = \frac{a}{1 + af} \qquad (8.140)$$

where

$$a = -\frac{g_{21a}}{y_i z_o} \qquad (8.141)$$

**Figure 8.30** (a) Shunt-series feedback configuration using the g-parameter representation. (b) Circuit of (a) redrawn with generators $g_{21f}v_i$ and $g_{12a}i_o$ omitted.

$$f = g_{12f} \qquad (8.142)$$

Following the procedure for the previous examples, we can find a circuit representation for this case by eliminating the generators $g_{21f}v_i$ and $g_{12a}i_o$ to obtain the approximate representation of Fig. 8.30b. Since this has the form of an ideal feedback circuit, all the results of Section 8.4.3 may now be used.

**Figure 8.31** Current feedback pair.

**Figure 8.32** Circuit for the calculation of the $g$ parameters of the feedback network in Fig. 8.31.

A common shunt-series feedback amplifier is the current-feedback pair of Fig. 8.31. Since the basic amplifier of Fig. 8.31 cannot be represented by a two-port, the representation of Fig. 8.30b cannot be used directly. However, as in previous examples, the feedback network *can* be represented by a two-port, and the $g$ parameters can be calculated using Fig. 8.32 to give

$$g_{11f} = \left.\frac{i_1}{v_1}\right|_{i_2=0} = \frac{1}{R_F + R_E} \qquad (8.143)$$

$$g_{12f} = \left.\frac{i_1}{i_2}\right|_{v_1=0} = -\frac{R_E}{R_E + R_F} \qquad (8.144)$$

$$g_{22f} = \left.\frac{v_2}{i_2}\right|_{v_1=0} = R_E\|R_F \qquad (8.145)$$

Using (8.139), we neglect $g_{21f}$. Assuming that $g_{21f}v_i$ is negligible, we can redraw the circuit of Fig. 8.31 as shown in Fig. 8.33. This circuit has an ideal input differencing

**Figure 8.33** Circuit equivalent to that of Fig. 8.31 using a two-port representation of the feedback network.

node, and the feedback function can be identified as

$$f = -\frac{R_E}{R_E + R_F}\frac{1}{\alpha_2}$$ 

(8.146)

The gain $a$ of the basic amplifier is determined by calculating the current gain of the circuit of Fig. 8.33 with the feedback generator removed. The overall current gain with feedback applied can then be calculated from (8.40).

### 8.5.5 Summary

The results derived above regarding practical feedback circuits and the effect of feedback loading can be summarized as follows.

First, input and output variables must be identified and the feedback identified as shunt or series at input and output.

The feedback function $f$ is found by the following procedure. If the feedback is *shunt* at the *input*, short the input feedback node to ground and calculate the feedback *current*. If the feedback is *series* at the *input*, *open circuit* the input feedback node and calculate the feedback *voltage*. In both these cases, if the feedback is *shunt* at the *output*, drive the feedback network with a voltage source. If the feedback is *series* at the *output*, drive with a current source.

The effect of feedback loading on the basic amplifier is found as follows. If the feedback is *shunt* at the *input*, *short* the input feedback node to ground to find the feedback loading on the *output*. If the feedback is *series* at the input, *open* circuit the input feedback node to calculate *output* feedback loading. Similarly, if the feedback is *shunt* or *series* at the *output*, then *short* or *open* the output feedback node to calculate feedback loading on the input.

These results along with other information are summarized in Table 8.1.

## 8.6 Single-Stage Feedback

The considerations of feedback circuits in this chapter have been mainly directed toward the general case of circuits with multiple stages in the basic amplifier. However, in dealing with some of these circuits (such as the series-series triple of Fig. 8.18a), equivalent circuits were derived in which one or more stages contained an emitter resistor. (See Fig. 8.18c.) Such a stage represents *in itself* a feedback circuit as will be shown. Thus the circuit of Fig. 8.18c contains feedback loops within a feedback loop, and this has a direct effect on the amplifier performance. For example, the emitter of $Q_3$ in Fig. 8.18c has a linearizing effect on $Q_3$, and so does the overall feedback when the loop is closed. It is thus important to calculate the effects of both *local* and *overall* feedback loops. The term *local* feedback is often used instead of *single-stage* feedback. Local feedback is often used in isolated stages as well as being found inside overall feedback loops. In this section, the low-frequency characteristics of two basic single-stage feedback circuits will be analyzed.

### 8.6.1 Local Series-Series Feedback

A local series-series feedback stage in bipolar technology (emitter degeneration) is shown in Fig. 8.34a. The characteristics of this circuit were considered previously in Section 3.3.8,

**Table 8.1**

| Feedback Configuration | Two-Port Parameter Representation | Output Variable | Input Variable | Transfer Function Stabilized | $Z_i$ | $Z_o$ | To Calculate Feedback Loading | | To Calculate Feedback Function $f$ |
|---|---|---|---|---|---|---|---|---|---|
| | | | | | | | At Input | At Output | |
| Shunt-shunt | $y$ | $v_o$ | $i_s$ | $\dfrac{v_o}{i_s}$ Transresistance | Low | Low | Short circuit output feedback node | Short circuit input feedback node | Drive the feedback network with a voltage at its output and calculate the current flowing into a short at its input |
| Shunt-series | $g$ | $i_o$ | $i_s$ | $\dfrac{i_o}{i_s}$ Current gain | Low | High | Open circuit output feedback node | Short circuit input feedback node | Drive the feedback network with a current and calculate the current flowing into a short |
| Series-shunt | $h$ | $v_o$ | $v_s$ | $\dfrac{v_o}{v_s}$ Voltage gain | High | Low | Short circuit output feedback node | Open circuit input feedback node | Drive the feedback network with a voltage and calculate the voltage produced into an open circuit |
| Series-series | $z$ | $i_o$ | $v_s$ | $\dfrac{i_o}{v_s}$ Transconductance | High | High | Open circuit output feedback node | Open circuit input feedback node | Drive the feedback network with a current and calculate the voltage produced into an open circuit |

**Figure 8.34** (a) Single-stage series-series feedback circuit. (b) Low-frequency equivalent circuit of (a). (c) Circuit equivalent to (b) using a Thévenin equivalent across the plane AA.

and it will be considered again here from the feedback viewpoint. Similar results are found for MOS transistors with source degeneration.

The circuit of Fig. 8.34a can be recognized as a degenerate series-series feedback configuration as described in Sections 8.4.4 and 8.5.2. Instead of attempting to use the generalized forms of those sections, we can perform a more straightforward calculation in this simple case by working directly from the low-frequency, small-signal equivalent circuit shown in Fig. 8.34b. For simplicity, source impedance is assumed zero but can be lumped in with $r_b$ if desired. If a Thévenin equivalent across the plane $AA$ is calculated, Fig. 8.34b can be redrawn as in Fig. 8.34c. The existence of an input differencing node is apparent, and quantity $i_o R_E$ is identified as the feedback voltage $v_{fb}$. Writing equations for Fig. 8.34c we find

$$v_1 = \frac{r_\pi}{r_\pi + r_b + R_E}(v_s - v_{fb}) \qquad (8.147)$$

$$i_o = g_m v_1 \tag{8.148}$$

$$v_{fb} = i_o R_E \tag{8.149}$$

These equations are of the form of the ideal feedback equations where $v_1$ is the error voltage, $i_o$ is the output signal, and $v_{fb}$ is the feedback signal. From (8.147) and (8.148) we know that

$$i_o = \frac{g_m r_\pi}{r_\pi + r_b + R_E}(v_s - v_{fb}) \tag{8.150}$$

and thus we can identify

$$a = \frac{g_m r_\pi}{r_\pi + r_b + R_E} = \frac{g_m}{1 + \dfrac{r_b + R_E}{r_\pi}} \tag{8.151}$$

From (8.149)

$$f = R_E \tag{8.152}$$

Thus for the complete circuit

$$\frac{i_o}{v_s} = A = \frac{a}{1 + af} = \frac{1}{R_E} \frac{1}{1 + \dfrac{1}{R_E}\left(\dfrac{1}{g_m} + \dfrac{r_b + R_E}{\beta_0}\right)} \tag{8.153}$$

and $A \simeq 1/R_E$ for large loop gain.

The loop gain is given by $T = af$ and thus

$$T = \frac{g_m R_E}{1 + \dfrac{r_b + R_E}{r_\pi}} \tag{8.154}$$

If $(r_b + R_E) \ll r_\pi$ we find

$$T \simeq g_m R_E \tag{8.155}$$

The input resistance of the circuit is given by

Input resistance $= (1 + T) \times$ (input resistance with $v_{fb} = 0$)

$$= (1 + T)(r_b + r_\pi + R_E) \tag{8.156}$$

Using (8.154) in (8.156) gives

Input resistance $= r_b + R_E + r_\pi(1 + g_m R_E) \tag{8.157}$

$$= r_b + r_\pi + (\beta_0 + 1)R_E \tag{8.158}$$

We can also show that if the output resistance $r_o$ of the transistor is included, the output resistance of the circuit is given by

$$\text{Output resistance} \simeq r_o\left(1 + \frac{g_m R_E}{1 + \dfrac{r_b + R_E}{r_\pi}}\right) \tag{8.159}$$

Both input and output resistance are increased by the application of emitter feedback, as expected.

■ **EXAMPLE**

Calculate the low-frequency parameters of the series-series feedback stage represented by $Q_3$ in Fig. 8.21$b$. The relevant parameters are as follows:

$$R_E = 88\ \Omega \qquad r_\pi = 650\ \Omega \qquad g_m = \frac{4}{26}\ \text{A/V} \qquad \beta_0 = 100 \qquad r_b = 0$$

The loading produced by $Q_3$ at the collector of $Q_2$ is given by the input resistance expression of (8.158) and is

$$R_{i3} = (650 + 101 \times 88)\ \Omega\ = 9.54\ \text{k}\Omega \tag{8.160}$$

The output resistance seen at the collector of $Q_3$ can be calculated from (8.159) using $r_b = 5\ \text{k}\Omega$ to allow for the finite source resistance in Fig. 8.21$b$. If we assume that $r_o = 25\ \text{k}\Omega$ at $I_C = 4\ \text{mA}$ for $Q_3$, then from (8.159) we find that

$$R_{o3} = 25\left(1 + \frac{\frac{4}{26} 88}{1 + \frac{5088}{650}}\right)\ \text{k}\Omega\ = 63\ \text{k}\Omega \tag{8.161}$$

In the example of Fig. 8.21$b$, the above output resistance would be multiplied by the loop gain of the series-series triple.

Finally, when ac voltage $v_4$ at the collector of $Q_2$ in Fig. 8.21$c$ is determined, output current $i_3$ in $Q_3$ can be calculated using (8.153):

$$\frac{i_3}{v_4} = \frac{1}{88}\frac{1}{1 + \frac{1}{88}\left(\frac{26}{4} + \frac{88}{100}\right)}\ \text{A/V} = \frac{1}{95.4}\ \text{A/V} \tag{8.162}$$

Note that since the voltage $v_4$ exists at the base of $Q_3$, the effective source resistance in the above calculation is zero.

### 8.6.2 Local Series-Shunt Feedback

Another example of a local feedback stage is the common-drain stage shown in Fig. 8.35$a$. This circuit is a series-shunt feedback configuration. The small-signal model is shown in Fig. 8.35$b$. The current through the $g_{mb}$ controlled source is controlled by the voltage across it; therefore, it can be replaced by a resistor of value $1/g_{mb}$. Using this transformation, the small-signal model in Fig. 8.35$b$ is redrawn in Fig. 8.35$c$, where

$$R'_L = R_L \| r_o \| \frac{1}{g_{mb}} \tag{8.163}$$

The feedback network is taken to be $R'_L$. Using Fig. 8.35$d$, the $h$ two-port parameters for the feedback network are

$$h_{11f} = \left.\frac{v_1}{i_1}\right|_{v_2 = 0} = 0 \tag{8.164}$$

$$h_{22f} = \left.\frac{i_2}{v_2}\right|_{i_1 = 0} = \frac{1}{R'_L} \tag{8.165}$$

(a)

(b)

(c)

(d)

Feedback network

(e)

**Figure 8.35**  (a) A source follower driving a resistive load. (b) A small-signal model for the circuit in (a). (c) A simplified small-signal model. (d) Circuit for finding the two-port parameters for the feedback network. (e) The circuit in (c) with the feedback network replaced by a two-port model.

and the feedback factor is

$$f = h_{12f} = \frac{v_1}{v_2}\bigg|_{i_1 = 0} = 1 \tag{8.166}$$

Here we neglect the forward transmission through the feedback network, $h_{21f}$, as was done in Section 8.5.3.

Figure 8.35$b$ is redrawn in Fig. 8.35$e$ with the feedback network replaced by a two-port model. The gain of the basic amplifier $a$ is found by setting the feedback to zero in Fig. 8.35$e$

$$a = \frac{v_o}{v_s}\bigg|_{v_{fb} = 0} = g_m R_L' \tag{8.167}$$

Using (8.166) and (8.167), the closed-loop gain is

$$A = \frac{a}{1 + af} = \frac{g_m R_L'}{1 + g_m R_L'} \tag{8.168}$$

This closed-loop gain is always less than one and approaches unity as $g_m R_L' \to \infty$.

From Fig. 8.35$e$, the output resistance without feedback is $R_L'$, and the closed-loop output resistance is

$$R_o = \frac{R_L'}{1 + af} = \frac{R_L'}{1 + g_m R_L'} = \frac{1}{\dfrac{1}{R_L'} + g_m} = \frac{1}{\dfrac{1}{R_L} + \dfrac{1}{r_o} + g_{mb} + g_m} \tag{8.169}$$

where (8.163) is used in the right-most expression. The output resistance is reduced because of the feedback. The input resistance is infinite because the resistance from the gate to the source in the model in Fig. 8.35 is infinite.

## 8.7 The Voltage Regulator as a Feedback Circuit

As an example of a practical feedback circuit, the operation of a voltage regulator will be examined. This section is introduced for the dual purpose of illustrating the use of feedback in practice and for describing the elements of voltage regulator design.

Voltage regulators are widely used components that accept a poorly specified (possibly fluctuating) dc input voltage and produce from it a constant, well-specified output voltage that can then be used as a supply voltage for other circuits.[3] In this way, fluctuations in the supply voltage are essentially eliminated, and this usually results in improved performance for circuits powered from such a supply.

A common type of voltage regulator is the *series* regulator shown schematically in Fig. 8.36. The name *series* comes from the fact that the output voltage is controlled by a power transistor in series with the output. This is the last stage of a high-gain voltage amplifier, as shown in Fig. 8.36.

Many of the techniques discussed in previous chapters are utilized in the design of circuits of this kind. A stable reference voltage $V_R$ can be generated using a Zener diode or a bandgap reference, as described in Chapter 4. This is then fed to the noninverting input of the high-gain amplifier, where it is compared with a sample of the output taken by resistors $R_1$ and $R_2$. This is recognizable as a series-shunt feedback arrangement, and using (8.132) we find that for large loop gain

$$V_O = V_R \frac{R_1 + R_2}{R_2} \tag{8.170}$$

The output voltage can be varied by changing ratio $R_1/R_2$.

**Figure 8.36** Schematic of a series voltage regulator.

The characteristics required in the amplifier of Fig. 8.36 are those of a good op amp, as described in Chapter 6. In particular, low drift and offset are essential so that the output voltage $V_O$ is as stable as possible. Note that the series-shunt feedback circuit will present a high input impedance to the reference generator, which is desirable to minimize loading effects. In addition, a very low output impedance will be produced at $V_O$, which is exactly the requirement for a good voltage source. If the effects of feedback loading are neglected (usually a good assumption in such circuits), the low-frequency output resistance of the regulator is given by (8.29) as

$$R_o = \frac{r_{oa}}{1+T} \qquad (8.171)$$

where

$$T = a\frac{R_2}{R_1 + R_2} \qquad (8.172)$$

$r_{oa}$ = output resistance of the amplifier without feedback

$a$ = magnitude of the forward gain of the regulator amplifier

If the output voltage of the regulator is varied by changing ratio $R_1/R_2$, then (8.171) and (8.172) indicate that $T$ and thus $R_o$ also change. Assuming that $V_R$ is constant and $T \gg 1$, we can describe this behavior by substituting (8.170) and (8.172) in (8.171) to give

$$R_o = \frac{r_{oa}}{aV_R}V_O \qquad (8.173)$$

which shows $R_o$ to be a function of $V_O$ if $a$, $V_R$, and $r_{oa}$ are fixed. If the output current drawn from the regulator changes by $\Delta I_O$, then $V_O$ changes by $\Delta V_O$, where

$$\Delta V_O = R_o\Delta I_O \qquad (8.174)$$

Substitution of (8.173) in (8.174) gives

$$\frac{\Delta V_O}{V_O} = \frac{r_{oa}}{aV_R}\Delta I_O \tag{8.175}$$

This equation allows calculation of the *load regulation* of the regulator. This is a widely used specification, which gives the percentage change in $V_O$ for a specified change in $I_O$ and should be as small as possible.

Another common regulator specification is the *line regulation*, which is the percentage change in output voltage for a specified change in input voltage. Since $V_O$ is directly proportional to $V_R$, the line regulation is determined by the change in reference voltage $V_R$ with changes in input voltage and depends on the particular reference circuit used.

As an example of a practical regulator, consider the circuit diagram of the 723 monolithic voltage regulator shown in Fig. 8.37. The correspondence to Fig. 8.36 can be recognized, with the portion of Fig. 8.37 to the right of the dashed line being the voltage amplifier with feedback. The divider resistors $R_1$ and $R_2$ in Fig. 8.36 are labeled $R_A$ and $R_B$ in Fig. 8.37 and are external to the chip. The output power transistor $Q_{15}$ is on the chip and is Darlington connected with $Q_{14}$ for high gain. Differential pair $Q_{11}$ and $Q_{12}$, together with active load $Q_8$, contribute most of the gain of the amplifier. Resistor $R_C$ couples the reference voltage to the amplifier and $C_2$ is an external capacitor, which is needed to prevent oscillation in the high-gain feedback loop. Its function is discussed in Chapter 9.

- **EXAMPLE**

Calculate the bias conditions and load regulation of the 723. Assume the total supply voltage is 15 V.

The bias calculation begins at the left-hand side of Fig. 8.37. Current source $I_1$ models a transistor current source that uses a junction field-effect transistor (JFET)[4] that behaves like an *n*-channel MOS transistor with a negative threshold voltage. Diodes $D_1$ and $D_2$ are Zener diodes.[4] When operating in reverse breakdown, the voltage across a Zener diode is nearly constant as described in Chapter 2.

The Zener diode $D_1$ produces a voltage drop of about 6.2 V, which sets up a reference current in $Q_2$:

$$\begin{aligned} I_{C2} &= -\frac{6.2 - |V_{BE2}|}{R_1 + R_2} \\ &= -\frac{6.2 - 0.6}{16{,}000}\text{ A} \\ &= -348\ \mu\text{A} \end{aligned} \tag{8.176}$$

Note that $I_{C2}$ is almost independent of supply voltage because it is dependent only on the Zener diode voltage.

The voltage across $R_1$ and $Q_2$ establishes the currents in current sources $Q_3$, $Q_7$, and $Q_8$.

$$I_{C7} = I_{C8} = -174\ \mu\text{A} \tag{8.177}$$
$$I_{C3} = -10.5\ \mu\text{A} \tag{8.178}$$

Current source $Q_3$ establishes the operating current in the voltage reference circuit composed of transistors $Q_4$, $Q_5$, $Q_6$, resistors $R_6$, $R_7$, $R_8$, and Zener diode $D_2$. This circuit can be recognized as a variation of the Wilson current source described in Chapter 4, and

**Figure 8.37** Circuit diagram of the 723 monolithic voltage regulator.

$$R_C = \frac{R_A R_B}{R_A + R_B} \quad \text{(external)}$$

$$C_2 = 100 \text{ pF (external)}$$

the negative feedback loop forces the current in $Q_6$ to equal $I_{C3}$ so that

$$I_{C6} = 10.5 \ \mu A \qquad (8.179)$$

where the base current of $Q_4$ has been neglected.

The output reference voltage $V_R$ is composed of the sum of the Zener diode voltage $D_2$ plus the base-emitter voltage of $Q_6$, giving a reference voltage of about 6.8 V. The current in the Zener is established by $V_{BE6}$ and $R_8$ giving

$$I_{D2} = \frac{V_{BE6}}{R_8} = \frac{600}{5} \ \mu A = 120 \ \mu A \qquad (8.180)$$

The Darlington pair $Q_4$, $Q_5$ helps give a large loop gain that results in a very low output impedance at the voltage reference node. Resistor $R_6$ limits the current and protects $Q_5$ in case of an accidental grounding of the voltage reference node. Resistor $R_7$ and capacitor $C_1$ form the high-frequency compensation required to prevent oscillation in the feedback loop. Note that the feedback is shunt at the output node. Any changes in reference-node voltage (due to loading for example) are detected at the base of $Q_6$, amplified, and fed to the base of $Q_4$ and thus back to the output where the original change is opposed.

The biasing of the amplifier is achieved via current sources $Q_7$ and $Q_8$. The current in $Q_7$ also appears in $Q_{10}$ (neglecting the base current of $Q_9$). Transistor $Q_{13}$ has an area twice that of $Q_{10}$ and one half the emitter resistance. Thus

$$I_{C13} = 2I_{C10} = 2I_{C7} = 348 \ \mu A \qquad (8.181)$$

Transistor $Q_9$ provides current gain to minimize the effect of base current in $Q_{10}$ and $Q_{13}$. This beta-helper current mirror was described in Chapter 4.

The bias current in each half of the differential pair $Q_{11}$, $Q_{12}$ is thus

$$I_{C11} = I_{C12} = \frac{1}{2}I_{C13} = 174 \ \mu A \qquad (8.182)$$

Since $Q_8$ and $R_5$ are identical to $Q_7$ and $R_4$, the current in $Q_8$ is given by

$$I_{C8} = -174 \ \mu A \qquad (8.183)$$

Transistor $Q_8$ functions as an active load for $Q_{12}$, and, since the collector currents in these two devices are nominally equal, the input offset voltage for the differential pair is nominally zero.

The current in output power transistor $Q_{15}$ depends on the load resistance but can go as high as 150 mA before a current-limit circuit (not shown) prevents further increase. Resistor $R_{12}$ provides bleed current so that $Q_{14}$ always has at least 0.04 mA of bias current, even when the current in $Q_{15}$ is low and/or its current gain is large.

In order to calculate the load regulation of the 723, (8.175) indicates that it is necessary to calculate the open-loop gain and output resistance of the regulator amplifier. For this purpose, a differential ac equivalent circuit of this amplifier is shown in Fig. 8.38. Load resistance $R_{L12}$ is the output resistance presented by $Q_8$, which is

$$R_{L12} \simeq r_{o8}(1 + g_{m8}R_5) \qquad (8.184)$$

Assuming that the magnitude of the Early voltage of $Q_8$ is 100 V and $I_{C8} = -174 \ \mu A$, we can calculate the value of $R_{L12}$ as

$$R_{L12} = \frac{100}{0.174}\left(1 + \frac{0.174}{26}1000\right) \ k\Omega = 4.42 \ M\Omega \qquad (8.185)$$

**Figure 8.38** An ac equivalent circuit of the regulator amplifier of the 723 voltage regulator.

Since $g_{m11} = g_{m12}$, the impedance in the emitter of $Q_{12}$ halves the transconductance and gives an effective output resistance of

$$R_{o12} = \left(1 + g_{m12}\frac{1}{g_{m11}}\right)r_{o12} \qquad (8.186)$$

where $r_{o12}$ is the output resistance of $Q_{12}$ alone and is 575 kΩ if the Early voltage is 100 V.

Thus

$$R_{o12} = 1.15 \text{ M}\Omega \qquad (8.187)$$

The external load resistance $R_L$ determines the load current and thus the bias currents in $Q_{14}$ and $Q_{15}$. However, $R_L$ is not included in the small-signal calculation of output resistance because this quantity is the resistance seen by $R_L$ looking back into the circuit. Thus, for purposes of calculating the ac output resistance, $R_L$ may be assumed infinite and the output Darlington pair then produces no loading at the collector of $Q_{12}$. The voltage gain of the circuit may then be calculated as

$$a = \left|\frac{v_o}{v_i}\right| = \left|\frac{v_1}{v_i}\right| = \frac{g_{m12}}{2}(R_{o12}\|R_{L12})$$

$$= \frac{0.174}{26}\frac{1}{2}(1.15\|4.42) \times 10^6$$

$$= 3054 \qquad (8.188)$$

The output resistance $r_{oa}$ of the circuit of Fig. 8.38 is the output resistance of a Darlington emitter follower. If $R_{12}$ is assumed large compared with $r_{\pi15}$ then

$$r_{oa} = \frac{1}{g_{m15}} + \frac{1}{\beta_{0(15)}}\left(\frac{1}{g_{m14}} + \frac{R_S}{\beta_{0(14)}}\right) \qquad (8.189)$$

where

$$R_S = R_{o12}\|R_{L12} = 913 \text{ k}\Omega \qquad (8.190)$$

If we assume collector bias currents of 20 mA in $Q_{15}$ and 0.5 mA in $Q_{14}$ together with $\beta_{0(15)} = \beta_{0(14)} = 100$, then substitution in (8.189) gives

$$r_{oa} = \left[1.3 + \frac{1}{100}\left(52 + \frac{913,000}{100}\right)\right]\Omega$$

$$= (1.3 + 92)\,\Omega$$

$$= 93\,\Omega \qquad (8.191)$$

Substituting for $r_{oa}$ and $a$ in (8.175) and using $V_R = 6.8$ V, we obtain, for the load regulation,

$$\frac{\Delta V_O}{V_O} = \frac{93}{3054 \times 6.8} \Delta I_O$$
$$= 4.5 \times 10^{-3} \Delta I_O \qquad (8.192)$$

where $\Delta I_O$ is in Amps.
   If $\Delta I_O$ is 50 mA, then (8.192) gives

$$\frac{\Delta V_O}{V_O} = 2 \times 10^{-4} = 0.02 \text{ percent} \qquad (8.193)$$

This answer is close to the value of 0.03 percent given on the specification sheet. Note the extremely small percentage change in output voltage for a 50-mA change in load current.

## 8.8 Feedback Circuit Analysis Using Return Ratio

The feedback analysis presented so far has used two-ports to manipulate a feedback circuit into unilateral forward amplifier and feedback networks. Since real feedback circuits have bilateral feedback networks and possibly bilateral amplifiers, some work is required to find the amplifier $a$'and feedback $f$ networks. The correct input and output variables and the type of feedback must be identified, and the correct two-port representation ($y$, $z$, $h$, or $g$) must be used. After this work, the correspondence between the original circuit and modified two-ports is small, which can make these techniques difficult to use.

Alternatively, a feedback circuit can be analyzed in a way that does not use two-ports. This alternative analysis, which is often easier than two-port analysis, is called return-ratio analysis.[5,6,7] Here, the closed-loop properties of a feedback circuit are described in terms of the *return ratio* for a dependent source in the small-signal model of an active device. The return ratio for a dependent source in a feedback loop is found by the following procedure:

1. Set all independent sources to zero.
2. Disconnect the dependent source from the rest of the circuit, which introduces a break in the feedback loop.
3. On the side of the break that is not connected to the dependent source, connect an independent test source $s_t$ of the same sign and type as the dependent source.
4. Find the return signal $s_r$ generated by the dependent source.

Then the return ratio ($\mathcal{R}$) for the dependent source is $\mathcal{R} = -s_r/s_t$, where the variable $s$ represents either a current or a voltage.

Figure 8.39a shows a negative feedback amplifier that includes a dependent voltage source. Figure 8.39b shows how the circuit is modified to find the return ratio. The dependent source is disconnected from the rest of the circuit by breaking the connections at the two X's marked in Fig. 8.39a. A test signal $v_t$ is connected on the side of the break that is not connected to the controlled source. The return signal $v_r$ is measured at the open circuit across the controlled source to find the return ratio $\mathcal{R} = -v_r/v_t$.

**Figure 8.39** (*a*) A feedback circuit that gives an inverting voltage gain. The "×" marks indicate where the loop will be broken. (*b*) The circuit in (*a*) modified to find the return ratio for the dependent voltage source.

■ **EXAMPLE**

Find the return ratio for the circuit in Fig. 8.39*b*.

The return ratio can be found with little computation because the resistors form a voltage divider

$$v_x = \frac{R_S \| r_i}{R_S \| r_i + R_F + r_o} v_t \qquad (8.194)$$

The return voltage $v_r$ is

$$v_r = -a_v v_x \qquad (8.195)$$

Combining these equations gives

$$\mathcal{R} = -\frac{v_r}{v_t} = \frac{R_S \| r_i}{R_S \| r_i + R_F + r_o} a_v \qquad (8.196)$$

■

Figure 8.40*a* is a single-stage feedback circuit. Its small-signal model shown in Fig. 8.40*b* includes a dependent current source. Figure 8.40*c* illustrates how the return ratio is found in this case. Here, the dependent source is disconnected from the rest of the circuit, and a test current source $i_t$ is connected on the side of the break that is not connected to the dependent source. A short circuit is applied across the dependent current source to provide a path for the return current $i_r$ to flow. The return ratio is computed as $\mathcal{R} = -i_r/i_t$.

$V_{DD}$

$R_C = 10 \text{ k}\Omega$

$R_F = 20 \text{ k}\Omega$

$V_o$

$Q_1$

$i_{in}$

(a)

$R_F$

$i_{in}$   $v_{be}$   $r_\pi$   $g_m v_{be}$   $r_o$   $R_C$   $v_o$

(b)

$R_F = 20 \text{ k}\Omega$

$i_\pi$

$v_{be}$   $r_\pi = 5 \text{ k}\Omega$   $g_m v_{be}$   $i_t$   $r_o = 1 \text{ M}\Omega$   $R_C = 10 \text{ k}\Omega$   $v_o$

$g_m = 40 \dfrac{\text{mA}}{\text{V}}$

(c)

**Figure 8.40** (a) A transresistance feedback circuit. (b) The small-signal model for the circuit in (a). The "×" marks indicate where the loop will be broken. (c) The circuit in (b) modified to find the return ratio for the dependent current source.

## 8.8.1 Closed-Loop Gain Using Return Ratio

A formula for the closed-loop gain of a feedback amplifier in terms of the return ratio will now be derived. Consider a feedback amplifier as shown in Fig. 8.41. The feedback amplifier consists of linear elements: passive components, controlled sources, and transistor small-signal models. A controlled source with value $k$ that is part of the small-signal model of an active device is shown explicitly. The output of the controlled source is $s_{oc}$, and the

**Figure 8.41** Linear feedback amplifier used to derive the closed-loop gain formula.

controlling signal is $s_{ic}$. The equation that describes the controlled source is

$$s_{oc} = k s_{ic} \qquad (8.197)$$

(For example, the output of the controlled source in Fig. 8.40b is $s_{oc} = g_m v_{be}$; the controlling signal is $s_{ic} = v_{be}$, and the value of the controlled source is $k = g_m$.) Each signal $s$ in the figure is labeled as if it is a voltage, but each signal could be either a current or a voltage. Because the feedback amplifier is linear, signals $s_{ic}$ and $s_{out}$ can be expressed as linear functions of the outputs of the two sources, $s_{oc}$ and $s_{in}$,

$$s_{ic} = B_1 s_{in} - H s_{oc} \qquad (8.198)$$
$$s_{out} = d s_{in} + B_2 s_{oc} \qquad (8.199)$$

The terms $B_1$, $B_2$, and $H$ in (8.198) and (8.199) are defined by

$$B_1 = \left. \frac{s_{ic}}{s_{in}} \right|_{s_{oc}=0} = \left. \frac{s_{ic}}{s_{in}} \right|_{k=0} \qquad (8.200a)$$

$$B_2 = \left. \frac{s_{out}}{s_{oc}} \right|_{s_{in}=0} \qquad (8.200b)$$

$$H = -\left. \frac{s_{ic}}{s_{oc}} \right|_{s_{in}=0} \qquad (8.200c)$$

So $B_1$ is the transfer function from the input to the controlling signal evaluated with $k = 0$, $B_2$ is the transfer function from the dependent source to the output evaluated with the input source set to zero, and $H$ is the transfer function from the output of the dependent source to the controlling signal evaluated with the input source set to zero, times $-1$.

Also, the direct feedthrough $d$ is given by

$$d = \left. \frac{s_{out}}{s_{in}} \right|_{s_{oc}=0} = \left. \frac{s_{out}}{s_{in}} \right|_{k=0} \qquad (8.200d)$$

which is the transfer function from the input to the output evaluated with $k = 0$. The calculation of $d$ usually involves signal transfer through passive components that provide a signal path directly from the input to output, a path that goes around rather than through the controlled source $k$.

Equations (8.197), (8.198), and (8.199) can be solved for the closed-loop gain. Substituting (8.197) in (8.198) and rearranging gives

$$s_{ic} = \frac{B_1}{1 + kH} s_{in} \qquad (8.201)$$

Substituting (8.197) in (8.199), then substituting (8.201) in the resulting equation and rearranging terms gives the closed-loop gain $A$

$$A = \frac{s_{\text{out}}}{s_{\text{in}}} = \frac{B_1 k B_2}{1 + kH} + d \tag{8.202}$$

The term $kH$ in the denominator is equal to the return ratio, as will be shown next. The return ratio is found by setting $s_{\text{in}} = 0$, disconnecting the dependent source from the circuit, and connecting a test source $s_t$ where the dependent source was connected. After these changes, $s_{oc} = s_t$ and (8.198) becomes

$$s_{ic} = -Hs_t \tag{8.203}$$

Then the output of the dependent source is the return signal $s_r = k s_{ic} = -kHs_t$. Therefore

$$\mathcal{R} = -\frac{s_r}{s_t} = kH \tag{8.204}$$

So the closed-loop gain in (8.202) can be rewritten as

$$A = \frac{s_{\text{out}}}{s_{\text{in}}} = \frac{B_1 k B_2}{1 + \mathcal{R}} + d \tag{8.205a}$$

or

$$A = \frac{s_{\text{out}}}{s_{\text{in}}} = \frac{g}{1 + \mathcal{R}} + d \tag{8.205b}$$

where

$$g = B_1 k B_2 \tag{8.206}$$

Here $g$ is the gain from $s_{\text{in}}$ to $s_{\text{out}}$ if $H = 0$ and $d = 0$, and $d$ is the direct signal feedthrough, which is the value of $A$ when the controlled source is set to zero ($k = 0$).

The closed-loop gain formula in (8.205a) requires calculations of four terms: $B_1$, $B_2$, $d$, and $\mathcal{R}$. That equation can be manipulated into a more convenient form with only three terms. Combining terms in (8.205b) using a common denominator $1 + \mathcal{R}$ gives

$$A = \frac{g + d(1 + \mathcal{R})}{1 + \mathcal{R}} = \frac{g + d\mathcal{R}}{1 + \mathcal{R}} + \frac{d}{1 + \mathcal{R}} = \frac{\left(\dfrac{g}{\mathcal{R}} + d\right)\mathcal{R}}{1 + \mathcal{R}} + \frac{d}{1 + \mathcal{R}} \tag{8.207}$$

Defining

$$A_\infty = \frac{g}{\mathcal{R}} + d \tag{8.208}$$

allows (8.207) to be rewritten as

$$A = A_\infty \frac{\mathcal{R}}{1 + \mathcal{R}} + \frac{d}{1 + \mathcal{R}} \tag{8.209}$$

This is a useful expression for the closed-loop gain. Here, if $\mathcal{R} \to \infty$, then $A = A_\infty$ because $\mathcal{R}/(1 + \mathcal{R}) \to 1$ and $d/(1 + \mathcal{R}) \to 0$. So $A_\infty$ is the closed-loop gain when the feedback circuit is ideal (that is, when $\mathcal{R} \to \infty$).

A block-diagram representation of (8.209) is shown in Fig. 8.42. The gain around the feedback loop is $\mathcal{R}$, and the effective forward gain in the loop is $\mathcal{R}A_\infty$. A key difference between the two-port and return-ratio analyses can be seen by comparing Figs. 8.1 and 8.42.

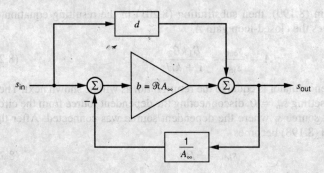

**Figure 8.42** A block diagram for the closed-loop gain formula in (8.209).

In the two-port analysis, all forward signal transfer through the amplifier and the feedback network is lumped into $a$. In the return-ratio analysis, there are two forward signal paths: one path ($d$) for the feedforward through the feedback network and another path ($\mathcal{R}A_\infty$) for the effective forward gain.

Typically, $A_\infty$ is determined by a passive feedback network and is equal to $1/f$ from two-port analysis. The value of $A_\infty$ can be found readily since $A_\infty = A$ when $k \to \infty$. Letting $k \to \infty$ causes $\mathcal{R} = kH \to \infty$. (Here we assumed $k > 0$. If $k < 0$ in a negative feedback circuit, then $\mathcal{R} \to \infty$ when $k \to -\infty$.) When $k \to \infty$, the controlling signal $s_{ic}$ for the dependent source must be zero if the output of the dependent source is finite. The controlled source output will be finite if the feedback is negative. These facts can be used to find $A_\infty$ with little computation in many circuits, as is demonstrated in the next example.

▪ **EXAMPLE**

Compute the closed-loop gain for the circuit of Fig. 8.40 using (8.209). Use the component values given in the figure.

To use (8.209), $A_\infty$, $\mathcal{R}$, and $d$ are needed. Here, the only controlled source is the $g_m$ source, so $k = g_m$. Also, $s_{in} = i_{in}$, $s_{out} = v_o$, and $s_{ic} = v_{be}$. To find $A_\infty$, let $g_m \to \infty$, which forces the controlling voltage $v_{be}$ to equal zero, assuming that the output current from the $g_m$ generator is finite. With $v_{be} = 0$, no current flows through $r_\pi$, and therefore the input current $i_{in}$ flows through $R_F$ to produce $v_o$. Thus

$$A_\infty = \left. \frac{v_o}{i_{in}} \right|_{g_m = \infty} = -R_F = -20 \text{ k}\Omega. \tag{8.210}$$

Next, $d$ is found by setting $k = g_m = 0$ and computing the transfer function from input to output

$$d = \left. \frac{v_o}{i_{in}} \right|_{g_m = 0} = (r_o \| R_C) \cdot \frac{r_\pi}{r_\pi + R_F + r_o \| R_C}$$

$$= (1 \text{ M}\Omega \| 10 \text{ k}\Omega) \cdot \frac{5 \text{ k}\Omega}{5 \text{ k}\Omega + 10 \text{ k}\Omega + 1 \text{ M}\Omega \| 100 \text{ k}\Omega} \tag{8.211}$$

$$= 1.4 \text{ k}\Omega$$

Finally, the return ratio for the $g_m$ generator can be calculated using Fig. 8.40c. Applying a current-divider formula gives the current $i_\pi$ through $r_\pi$ as

$$i_\pi = -\frac{r_o \| R_C}{r_o \| R_C + R_F + r_\pi} i_t \tag{8.212}$$

The return current is

$$i_r = g_m v_{be} = g_m r_\pi i_\pi \qquad (8.213)$$

Combining these equations gives

$$\mathcal{R} \doteq -\frac{i_r}{i_t} = g_m r_\pi \cdot \frac{r_o \| R_C}{r_o \| R_C + R_F + r_\pi} \qquad (8.214)$$

$$= (40 \text{ mA/V}) \cdot 5 \text{ k}\Omega \cdot \frac{1 \text{ M}\Omega \| 10 \text{ k}\Omega}{1 \text{ M}\Omega \| 10 \text{ k}\Omega + 20 \text{ k}\Omega + 5 \text{ k}\Omega} = 56.7 \qquad (8.215)$$

Then, using (8.209),

$$A = A_\infty \frac{\mathcal{R}}{1 + \mathcal{R}} + \frac{d}{1 + \mathcal{R}} = -20 \text{ k}\Omega \frac{56.7}{1 + 56.7} + \frac{1.4 \text{ k}\Omega}{1 + 56.7} = -19.6 \text{ k}\Omega \qquad (8.216)$$

In (8.209), the second term that includes $d$ can be neglected whenever $|d| \ll |A_\infty \mathcal{R}|$. This condition usually holds at low frequencies because $d$ is the forward signal transfer through a passive network, while $|A_\infty \mathcal{R}|$ is large because it includes the gain through the active device(s). For example, ignoring the $d/(1 + \mathcal{R})$ term in (8.216) gives $A \approx -19.7 \text{ k}\Omega$, which is close to the exact value. As the frequency increases, however, the gain provided by the transistors falls. As a result, $d$ may become significant at high frequencies.

The effective forward gain $A_\infty \mathcal{R}$ can be computed after $A_\infty$ and $\mathcal{R}$ have been found. Alternatively, this effective forward gain can be found directly from the feedback circuit.[8] Call this forward gain $b$, so

$$b = A_\infty \cdot \mathcal{R} \qquad (8.217)$$

Then the closed-loop gain in (8.209) can be written as

$$A = \frac{b}{1 + \mathcal{R}} + \frac{d}{1 + \mathcal{R}} \qquad (8.218)$$

Using (8.206), (8.208), and $\mathcal{R} = kH$, $b$ can be expressed as

$$b = A_\infty \cdot \mathcal{R} = \left( \frac{g}{\mathcal{R}} + d \right) \cdot \mathcal{R} = (B_1 k B_2 + d\mathcal{R})$$
$$= (B_1 k B_2 + dkH) = \left[ B_1 + \frac{dH}{B_2} \right] k B_2 \qquad (8.219)$$

This final expression breaks $b$ into parts that can be found by analyzing the feedback circuit. In (8.200b), $B_2$ is defined as the transfer function from the output of the controlled source $s_{oc}$ to $s_{out}$ evaluated with $s_{in} = 0$. The term in brackets in (8.219) is equal to the transfer function from $s_{in}$ to $s_{ic}$ when $s_{out} = 0$, as will be shown next.

If $s_{out} = 0$, then (8.199) simplifies to

$$B_2 s_{oc} = -d s_{in} \qquad (8.220)$$

Substituting (8.220) into (8.198) gives

$$s_{ic} = B_1 s_{in} + \frac{dH}{B_2} s_{in} \qquad (8.221)$$

Therefore

$$\left. \frac{s_{ic}}{s_{in}} \right|_{s_{out}=0} = B_1 + \frac{dH}{B_2} \qquad (8.222)$$

(a)

**Figure 8.43** Circuits for finding the effective forward gain $b$. ($a$) The circuit for the input side. ($b$) The circuit for the output side.

(b)

which is the expression in brackets in (8.219). Substituting (8.222) and (8.200b) into (8.219) gives

$$b = \left.\frac{s_{ic}}{s_{in}}\right|_{s_{out}=0} \cdot k \cdot \left.\frac{s_{out}}{s_{oc}}\right|_{s_{in}=0} \tag{8.223}$$

The effective forward gain $b$ can be found using this formula.

■ **EXAMPLE**

Compute the effective forward gain $b = A_\infty \mathcal{R}$ for the circuit in Fig. 8.40.

As in the previous example, $k = g_m$, $s_{in} = i_{in}$, $s_{out} = v_o$, $s_{ic} = v_{be}$, and $s_{oc} = i_{oc} = g_m v_{be}$. To compute the first term in (8.223), the output $v_o$ must be set to zero by shorting the output to ground. The resulting circuit is shown in Fig. 8.43a. The calculation gives

$$\left.\frac{s_{ic}}{s_{in}}\right|_{s_{out}=0} = \left.\frac{v_{be}}{i_{in}}\right|_{v_o=0} = r_\pi \| R_F = 5\text{ k}\Omega \| 20\text{ k}\Omega = 4.0\text{ k}\Omega \tag{8.224}$$

The last term in (8.223) is found by setting the input $i_{in}$ to zero. This input current can be set to zero by replacing the source $i_{in}$ with an open circuit, as shown in Fig. 8.43b. Treating the $g_m$ generator as an independent source with value $i_{oc}$ for this calculation, the result is

$$\left.\frac{s_{out}}{s_{oc}}\right|_{s_{in}=0} = \left.\frac{v_o}{i_{oc}}\right|_{i_{in}=0} = -[r_o\|R_c\|(R_F + r_\pi)]$$
$$= -[1\text{ M}\Omega\|10\text{ k}\Omega\|(20\text{ k}\Omega + 5\text{ k}\Omega)] = -7.09\text{ k}\Omega \tag{8.225}$$

Substituting (8.224) and (8.225) into (8.223) gives

$$b = 4.0\text{ k}\Omega(g_m)(-7.09\text{ k}\Omega) = 4.0\text{ k}\Omega(40\text{ mA/V})(-7.09\text{ k}\Omega) = -1134\text{ k}\Omega$$

For comparison, we can find $b$ using (8.217) and the values of $A_\infty$ and $\mathscr{R}$ computed in the previous example:

$$b = A_\infty \mathscr{R} = -20 \text{ k}\Omega \ (56.7) = -1134 \text{ k}\Omega$$

■ Both calculations give the same value for the effective forward gain $b$.

### 8.8.2 Closed-Loop Impedance Formula Using Return Ratio

Feedback affects the input and output impedance of a circuit. In this section, a useful expression for the impedance at any port in a feedback circuit in terms of return ratio[9] is derived. Consider the feedback circuit shown in Fig. 8.44. This feedback amplifier consists of linear elements: passive components, controlled sources, and transistor small-signal models. A controlled source $k$ that is part of the small-signal model of an active device is shown explicitly. The derivation is carried out for the impedance $Z_{port}$ looking into an arbitrary port that is labeled as *port X* in Fig. 8.44a. The port impedance can be found by driving the port by an independent current source as shown in Fig. 8.44b and computing $Z_{port} = v_x/i_x$. Since the circuit in Fig. 8.44b is linear, the signals $s_{ic}$ and $v_x$ are linear functions of the signals $i_x$ and $s_y$ applied to the ports labeled X and Y. Therefore, we can write

$$v_x = a_1 i_x + a_2 s_y \tag{8.226}$$

$$s_{ic} = a_3 i_x + a_4 s_y \tag{8.227}$$

From (8.226), the impedance looking into the port when $k = 0$ is

$$Z_{port}(k = 0) = \left.\frac{v_x}{i_x}\right|_{k=0} = \left.\frac{v_x}{i_x}\right|_{s_y=0} = a_1 \tag{8.228}$$

Next we compute two return ratios for the controlled source $k$ under different conditions. Both are used in the final formula for the closed-loop impedance. The first return ratio is

**Figure 8.44** (a) The linear feedback circuit used to derive Blackman's impedance formula with respect to port X. (b) The circuit with port X driven by an independent current source.

found with the port open. With port X open, $i_x = 0$. The return ratio is found by disconnecting the controlled source from the circuit and connecting a test source $s_t$ where the dependent source was connected. With these changes to the circuit, $s_y = s_t$ and (8.227) becomes

$$s_{ic} = a_4 s_t \tag{8.229}$$

The output of the controlled source is the return signal

$$s_r = k s_{ic} \tag{8.230}$$

From the last two equations, we find

$$\mathcal{R}(\text{port open}) = -\frac{s_r}{s_t} = -k a_4 \tag{8.231}$$

The other return ratio is found with the port shorted. With port X shorted, the voltage $v_x$ is zero. To find the return ratio, we disconnect the controlled source and connect test source $s_t$ where the dependent source was connected. With these changes, (8.226) gives

$$i_x = -\frac{a_2}{a_1} s_t \tag{8.232}$$

Substituting (8.232) into (8.227), using $s_y = s_t$, and rearranging terms gives

$$s_{ic} = \left( a_4 - \frac{a_2 a_3}{a_1} \right) s_t \tag{8.233}$$

The return signal is

$$s_r = k s_{ic} \tag{8.234}$$

Combining these last two equations gives the return ratio with the port shorted

$$\mathcal{R}(\text{port shorted}) = -\frac{s_r}{s_t} = -k \left( a_4 - \frac{a_2 a_3}{a_1} \right) \tag{8.235}$$

Shortly, we will see that (8.228), (8.231), and (8.235) can be combined to give a useful formula for the port impedance.

To complete the derivation, we find the impedance looking into the port in Fig. 8.44b using

$$Z_{\text{port}} = \frac{v_x}{i_x} \tag{8.236}$$

Using (8.226), (8.227), and $s_y = k s_{ic}$, we get (after some manipulation)

$$Z_{\text{port}} = \frac{v_x}{i_x} = a_1 \left( \frac{1 - k \left( a_4 - \dfrac{a_2 a_3}{a_1} \right)}{1 - k a_4} \right) \tag{8.237}$$

Substituting (8.228), (8.231), and (8.235) into (8.237) yields

$$Z_{\text{port}} = Z_{\text{port}}(k = 0) \left[ \frac{1 + \mathcal{R}(\text{port shorted})}{1 + \mathcal{R}(\text{port open})} \right] \tag{8.238}$$

This expression is called *Blackman's impedance formula*.[9] The two return ratios, with the port open and shorted, are computed with respect to the same controlled source $k$.

Equation 8.238 can be used to compute the impedance at any port, including the input and output ports. A key advantage of this formula is that it applies to any feedback circuit, regardless of the type of feedback. Usually, one of the two return ratios in (8.238) is zero, and in those cases Blackman's formula shows that feedback either increases or decreases the impedance by a factor $(1 + \mathcal{R})$.

■ **EXAMPLE**

Use Blackman's formula to find the output resistance for the feedback circuit in Fig. 8.40. From Blackman's formula, the output resistance is given by

$$R_{\text{out}} = R_{\text{out}}(g_m = 0)\left[\frac{1 + \mathcal{R}(\text{output port shorted})}{1 + \mathcal{R}(\text{output port open})}\right] \tag{8.239}$$

Shorting the output port in Fig. 8.40c causes $v_{be} = 0$ so $i_r = g_m v_{be} = 0$; therefore, $\mathcal{R}(\text{output port shorted}) = 0$. The $\mathcal{R}(\text{output port open})$ is the same return ratio that was computed in (8.215), so $\mathcal{R}(\text{output port open}) = 56.7$. The only remaining value to be computed is the resistance at the output port when $g_m = 0$:

$$R_{\text{out}}(g_m = 0) = r_o\|R_C\|(R_F + r_\pi) = 1\ \text{M}\Omega\|10\ \text{k}\Omega\|(20\ \text{k}\Omega + 5\ \text{k}\Omega)$$
$$= 7.1\ \text{k}\Omega \tag{8.240}$$

Substituting into (8.239) yields

$$R_{\text{out}} = 7.1\ \text{k}\Omega\left[\frac{1+0}{1+56.7}\right] = 120\ \Omega \tag{8.241}$$

The negative feedback reduces the output resistance, which is desirable because the output is a voltage, and a low output resistance is desired in series with a voltage source.

■ **EXAMPLE**

Find the output resistance for the MOS *super-source follower* shown in Fig. 8.45a. Ignore body effect here to simplify the analysis.

The super-source follower uses feedback to reduce the output impedance. Ideal current sources $I_1$ and $I_2$ bias the transistors and are shown rather than transistor current sources to simplify the circuit. With current source $I_1$ forcing the current in $M_1$ to be constant, $M_2$ provides the output current when driving a load. There is feedback from $v_{\text{out}}$ to $v_{gs2}$ through $M_1$. The small-signal model for this circuit is shown in Fig. 8.45b. In this circuit, either $g_{m1}$ or $g_{m2}$ could be chosen as $k$. Here, we will use $k = g_{m2}$. In all the following calculations, the input source $v_{\text{in}}$ is set to zero. First, the output resistance when $g_{m2} = 0$ is

$$R_{\text{out}}(g_{m2} = 0) = r_{o2} \tag{8.242}$$

This result may seem surprising at first, since the output is connected to the source of $M_1$, which is usually a low-impedance point. However, an ideal current source, which is a small-signal open circuit, is connected to the drain of $M_1$. Therefore the current in the $g_{m1}$ generator flows only in $r_{o1}$, so $M_1$ has no effect on the output resistance when $g_{m2} = 0$. The return ratio for the $g_{m2}$ source with the output port open is found to be

$$\mathcal{R}(\text{output open}) = g_{m2}r_{o2}(1 + g_{m1}r_{o1}) \tag{8.243}$$

The return ratio with the output port shorted is

$$\mathcal{R}(\text{output shorted}) = 0 \tag{8.244}$$

**Figure 8.45** (a) The super-source-follower circuit. (b) The circuit with each transistor replaced by its small-signal model.

because shorting the output port forces $v_{out} = 0$ and $v_1 = -v_{out} = 0$. Hence no current flows in $M_1$, so $v_2 = 0$ and therefore the return ratio is zero. Substituting the last three equations into (8.238) gives the closed-loop output resistance

$$R_{out} = r_{o2}\left[\frac{1+0}{1+g_{m2}r_{o2}(1+g_{m1}r_{o1})}\right] \tag{8.245}$$

Assuming $g_m r_o \gg 1$, then

$$R_{out} \approx \frac{r_{o2}}{g_{m2}r_{o2}g_{m1}r_{o1}} = \frac{1}{g_{m2}g_{m1}r_{o1}} \tag{8.246}$$

which is much lower than the output resistance of a conventional source follower, which is about $1/g_m$. This result agrees with (3.137), which was derived without the use of feedback principles. Although $g_{mb1}$ appears in (3.137), it does not appear in (8.246) because the body effect is ignored here.

The next example demonstrates an unusual case where neither return ratio vanishes in Blackman's impedance formula.

■ **EXAMPLE**

In the Wilson current source in Fig. 8.46a, assume that the three bipolar transistors are identical with $\beta_0 \gg 1$ and are biased in the forward-active region. Find the output resistance.

Blackman's impedance formula can be used here because there is a feedback loop formed by the current mirror $Q_1$-$Q_3$ with $Q_2$. With all transistors forward active and $\beta_F \gg 1$,

**Figure 8.46** (a) The Wilson current mirror. (b) The circuit with each transistor replaced by its small-signal model. (c) The small-signal model modified for calculation of $\mathcal{R}$ for $g_{m1}$.

$I_{C1} = I_{C2} = I_{C3} = I_{REF}$. (The output is connected to other circuitry that is not shown, so $I_{C2}$ is nonzero.) The small-signal model is shown in Fig. 8.46b, where diode-connected $Q_1$ is modeled by a resistor of value $1/g_{m1}$. Resistor $r_{\pi3}$, which is in parallel with $1/g_{m1}$, is ignored (since $r_{\pi3} = \beta_0/g_{m3} = \beta_0/g_{m1} \gg 1/g_{m1}$). Also $r_{o3}$ is ignored, assuming that it is much larger than the resistance looking into the base of $Q_2$. Selecting $k = g_{m3}$ and calculating the first term in (8.238) gives

$$R_{out}(g_{m3} = 0) = r_{o2} + \frac{1}{g_{m1}} \approx r_{o2} \tag{8.247}$$

since setting $g_{m3} = 0$ forces the current through $r_{\pi2}$ to be zero. Therefore, the voltage across $r_{\pi2}$ is zero, which causes the current through the $g_{m2}$ source to be zero.

The return ratios in Blackman's formula can be found using the circuit shown in Fig. 8.46c. First, let us find $\mathcal{R}$(output port open). When the output port is open, the current in the $g_{m2}$ generator can only flow through the parallel resistor $r_{o2}$, so the currents through $r_{\pi2}$ and $1/g_{m1}$ are equal and are supplied by the test source $i_t$. Therefore,

$$v_x = -i_t \frac{1}{g_{m1}} \tag{8.248}$$

Also

$$i_r = g_{m3}v_x \tag{8.249}$$

Combining these two equations gives

$$\mathcal{R}(\text{output open}) = -\frac{i_r}{i_t} = \frac{g_{m3}}{g_{m1}} = 1 \tag{8.250}$$

where $g_{m1} = g_{m3}$ because $I_{C1} = I_{C3}$.

When the output port is shorted, the current through the $g_{m2}$ generator is not restricted to flow only through $r_{o2}$. First, notice that with the output port shorted, $r_{o2}$ is in parallel with $1/g_{m1}$, so $r_{o2}$ can be ignored. With this simplification, the current through the resistance $1/g_{m1}$ is from the test and $g_{m2}$ sources, so

$$v_x = \frac{1}{g_{m1}}(-i_t + g_{m2}v_y) \tag{8.251}$$

Now

$$v_y = -i_t r_{\pi2} \tag{8.252}$$

Combining these two equations gives

$$v_x = \frac{1}{g_{m1}}(-i_t - i_t g_{m2} r_{\pi2}) = -\frac{i_t}{g_{m1}}(1 + \beta_0) \tag{8.253}$$

where the relation $\beta_0 = g_{m2}r_{\pi2}$ has been used. The return current is

$$i_r = g_{m3}v_x \tag{8.254}$$

Therefore

$$\mathcal{R}(\text{output shorted}) = -\frac{i_r}{i_t} = \frac{g_{m3}}{g_{m1}}(1 + \beta_0) = 1 + \beta_0 \tag{8.255}$$

Substituting in Blackman's formula gives

$$R_{\text{out}}(\text{closed loop}) = r_{o2} \cdot \frac{1 + (\beta_0 + 1)}{1 + 1} = \frac{r_{o2}(\beta_0 + 2)}{2} \approx \frac{\beta_0 r_{o2}}{2} \tag{8.256}$$

This approximate result agrees with (4.91), which was derived without the use of Blackman's formula.

## 8.8.3 Summary—Return-Ratio Analysis

Return-ratio analysis is an alternative approach to feedback circuit analysis that does not use two-ports. The loop transmission is measured by the return ratio $\mathcal{R}$. The return ratio is a different measure of loop transmission than $af$ from two-port analysis. (The return ratio $\mathcal{R}$ is referred to as *loop gain* in some textbooks. That name is not associated with $\mathcal{R}$ here to avoid confusion with $T = af$, which is called loop gain in this chapter.) For negative feedback circuits, $\mathcal{R} > 0$. In an ideal feedback circuit, $\mathcal{R} \to \infty$ and the closed-loop gain is $A_\infty$, which typically depends only on passive components. The actual gain of a feedback circuit is close to $A_\infty$ if $\mathcal{R} \gg 1$. Blackman's impedance formula (8.238) gives the closed-loop impedance in terms of two return ratios.

Return-ratio analysis is often simpler than two-port analysis of feedback circuits. For example, return-ratio analysis uses equations that are independent of the type of feedback, and simple manipulations of the circuit allow computation of the various terms in the equations. In contrast, two-port analysis uses different two-port representations for each of the four feedback configurations (series-series, series-shunt, shunt-series, and shunt-shunt). Therefore, the type of feedback must be correctly identified before undertaking two-port analysis. The resulting two-ports for the amplifier and feedback networks must be manipulated to find the open-loop forward gain $a$ and the open-loop input and output impedances. With two-port analysis, the open-loop impedance is either multiplied or divided by $(1 + T)$ to give the closed-loop impedance, depending upon the type of feedback. In contrast, Blackman's formula gives an equation for finding the closed-loop impedance, and this one equation applies to any port in any feedback circuit.

## 8.9 Modeling Input and Output Ports in Feedback Circuits

Throughout this chapter, the source and load impedances have been included when analyzing a feedback circuit. For instance, the inverting voltage-gain circuit in Fig. 8.47a, with source resistance $R_S$ and load resistance $R_L$, can be analyzed using the two-port or return-ratio methods described in this chapter. The resulting model is shown in Fig. 8.47b. The source and load resistances do not appear explicitly in the model, but the gain $A$, input resistance $R_i$, and output resistance $R_o$ are functions of the source and load resistances. Therefore, use of this model requires that both the source and load resistances are known. However, both the source and load are not always known or fixed in value. For example, a feedback amplifier might have to drive a range of load resistances. In that case, it would be desirable to have a simple model of the amplifier with the following properties: the elements in the model do not depend on the load, and the effect of a load on the gain can be easily calculated.

If only one of the resistances $R_S$ and $R_L$ is known, a useful model can be generated. First, consider Fig. 8.47a when the source resistance is unknown but the load is known. Then, the model in Fig. 8.47c can be used. Here, the key differences from the model in Fig. 8.47b are that $R_i'$ and $A'$ are used rather than $R_i$ and $A$, $R_S$ is shown explicitly, and the controlling voltage for $A'$ is the voltage $v_i$ across $R_i'$ rather than the source voltage $v_s$. (The single-prime mark here denotes that the quantity is computed with $R_S$ unknown.) The input resistance $R_i'$ and gain $A'$ are computed with the load connected and with an ideal input driving network. Here, the Thévenin driving network is ideal if the source resistance $R_S$ is zero. (If the input is a Norton equivalent consisting of a current source and parallel source resistance, $R_i'$ and $A'$ are found with $R_S \to \infty$.) The resulting $A'$ and $R_i'$ are not functions of $R_S$. The source resistance $R_S$ in Fig. 8.47c forms a voltage divider with $R_i'$; therefore, the overall voltage gain can be found by

$$\frac{v_o}{v_s} = \frac{v_o}{v_i} \cdot \frac{v_i}{v_s} = A' \frac{R_i'}{R_i' + R_S} \tag{8.257}$$

Next, consider Fig. 8.47a when the load is unknown but the source resistance is known. Fig. 8.47d shows the appropriate model. Here, the key differences from the model in Fig. 8.47b are that $R_o''$ and $A''$ are used rather than $R_o$ and $A$, and $R_L$ is shown explicitly. (The double-prime mark denotes that the quantity is computed with $R_L$ unknown.) The output resistance $R_o''$ and gain $A''$ for this Thévenin model are computed assuming an ideal load, which is an open circuit here ($R_L \to \infty$). The load resistance $R_L$ in Fig. 8.47d forms a voltage divider with $R_o''$, so the loaded voltage gain is

$$\frac{v_o}{v_s} = A'' \frac{R_L}{R_o'' + R_L} \tag{8.258}$$

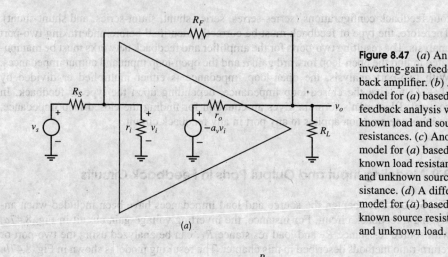

**Figure 8.47** (*a*) An inverting-gain feedback amplifier. (*b*) A model for (*a*) based on feedback analysis with known load and source resistances. (*c*) Another model for (*a*) based on known load resistance and unknown source resistance. (*d*) A different model for (*a*) based on known source resistance and unknown load.

■ **EXAMPLE**

Model Fig. 8.47*a* with the circuit in Fig. 8.47*d*, assuming the load resistance is unknown.

The model in Fig. 8.47*d* can be used when $R_L$ is unknown. Using return-ratio analysis, the calculations of $R_o''$ and $A''$ are as follows. With $R_L \to \infty$, the circuit in Fig. 8.47*a* is identical to Fig. 8.39*a*, and therefore the return ratio is given by (8.196):

$$\mathcal{R}'' = \mathcal{R}(R_L \to \infty) = \frac{R_S \| r_i}{R_S \| r_i + R_F + r_o} a_v \qquad (8.259)$$

The output resistance with $R_L \to \infty$, $R_o''$, can be found using Blackman's formula. First, the output resistance with the controlled source set to zero is

$$R_o''(a_v = 0) = r_o \| (R_F + r_i \| R_S) \tag{8.260}$$

The return ratio with the output port open is given in (8.259). The return ratio with the output port shorted is zero because shorting the output eliminates the feedback. Therefore, for the closed-loop output resistance, (8.238) gives

$$R_o'' = r_o \| (R_F + r_i \| R_S) \frac{1 + 0}{1 + \dfrac{R_S \| r_i}{R_S \| r_i + R_F + r_o} a_v} \tag{8.261}$$

Calculation of $A''$ requires that $A_\infty''$ and $d''$ be found with $R_L \to \infty$.

$$A_\infty'' = \left. \frac{v_o}{v_s} \right|_{a_v = \infty \,\&\, R_L = \infty} = -\frac{R_F}{R_S} \tag{8.262}$$

and

$$d'' = \left. \frac{v_o}{v_s} \right|_{a_v = 0 \,\&\, R_L = \infty} = \frac{(R_F + r_o) \| r_i}{R_S + (R_F + r_o) \| r_i} \cdot \frac{r_o}{R_F + r_o} \tag{8.263}$$

Using the results for $A_\infty''$, $\mathcal{R}''$, and $d''$, we can compute

$$A'' = A_\infty'' \frac{\mathcal{R}''}{1 + \mathcal{R}''} + \frac{d''}{1 + \mathcal{R}''} \tag{8.264}$$

[Typically, the $d''/(1 + \mathcal{R}'')$ term is small and can be ignored.] The voltage gain when a resistive load is connected can be found using (8.258). The only element of the model that was not computed is the input resistance $R_i$. It is a function of $R_L$, so it can only be computed once $R_L$ is known.

The output-port model in Fig. 8.47d could be drawn as a Thévenin or Norton equivalent. With the Thévenin equivalent shown (a controlled voltage source in series with an output resistance), $R_o''$ and $A''$ are computed with $R_L \to \infty$. When the output port is modeled by a Norton equivalent with a controlled current source and parallel output resistance, their values are found with $R_L = 0$.

# PROBLEMS

Note: In these problems, *loop transmission* is used generically to refer to loop gain $T = af$ or return ratio $\mathcal{R}$.

**8.1(a)** In a feedback amplifier, forward gain $a$ = 100,000 and feedback factor $f = 10^{-3}$. Calculate overall gain $A$ and the percentage change in $A$ if $a$ changes by 10 percent.

**(b)** Repeat (a) if $f = 0.1$.

**8.2** For the characteristic of Fig. 8.2 the following data apply:

$$S_{o2} = 15 \text{ V} \quad S_{o1} = 7 \text{ V} \quad a_1 = 50,000$$
$$a_2 = 20,000$$

**(a)** Calculate and sketch the overall transfer characteristic of Fig 8.3 for the above amplifier when placed in a feedback loop with $f = 10^{-4}$.

**(b)** Repeat (a) with $f = 0.1$.

**8.3(a)** For the conditions in Problem 8.2(b), sketch the output voltage waveform $S_o$ and the error voltage waveform $S_\epsilon$ if a sinusoidal input voltage $S_i$ with amplitude 1.5 V is applied.

**(b)** Repeat (a) with an input amplitude of 2 V.

**8.4** Verify (8.40), (8.41), and (8.42) for a shunt-series feedback amplifier.

**8.5** Verify (8.43), (8.44), and (8.45) for a series-series feedback amplifier.

**Figure 8.48** An ac schematic of a shunt-shunt feedback amplifier.

**8.6** For the shunt-shunt feedback amplifier of Fig. 8.15a, take $R_F = 100$ k$\Omega$ and $R_L = 15$ k$\Omega$. For the op amp, assume that $R_i = 500$ k$\Omega$, $R_o = 200$ $\Omega$, and $a_v = 75,000$. Calculate input resistance, output resistance, loop transmission, and closed-loop gain:

**(a)** Using the formulas from two-port analysis (Section 8.5).

**(b)** Using the formulas from return-ratio analysis (Section 8.8).

**8.7** The ac schematic of a shunt-shunt feedback amplifier is shown in Fig. 8.48. All transistors have $I_D = 1$ mA, $W/L = 100$, $k' = 60$ $\mu$A/V$^2$, and $\lambda = 1/(50$ V$)$.

**(a)** Calculate the overall gain $v_o/i_i$, the loop transmission, the input impedance, and the output impedance at low frequencies. Use the formulas from two-port analysis (Section 8.5).

**(b)** If the circuit is fed from a source resistance of 1 k$\Omega$ in parallel with $i_i$, what is the new output resistance of the circuit?

**8.8(a)** Repeat Problem 8.7(a) with all NMOS transistors in Fig. 8.48 replaced by bipolar $npn$ transistors. All collector currents are 1 mA and $\beta = 200$, $V_A = 50$ V, and $r_b = 0$.

**(b)** If the circuit is fed from a source resistance of 1 k$\Omega$ in parallel with $i_i$, what is the new output resistance of the circuit?

**8.9** Repeat Problem 8.7 using the formulas from return-ratio analysis (Section 8.8).

**8.10** Repeat Problem 8.8 using the formulas from return-ratio analysis (Section 8.8).

**8.11** The half-circuit of a balanced monolithic series-series triple is shown in Fig. 8.18a. Calculate the input impedance, output impedance, loop gain, and overall gain of the half-circuit at low frequencies using the following data:

$$R_{E1} = R_{E2} = 290\ \Omega \quad R_F = 1.9\ \text{k}\Omega$$
$$R_{L1} = 10.6\ \text{k}\Omega \quad R_{L2} = 6\ \text{k}\Omega$$

For the transistors, $I_{C1} = 0.5$ mA, $I_{C2} = 0.77$ mA, $I_{C3} = 0.73$ mA, $\beta = 120$, $r_b = 0$, and $V_A = 40$ V.

**8.12** Repeat Problem 8.11 if the output signal is taken as the voltage at the emitter of $Q_3$.

**8.13** A feedback amplifier is shown in Fig. 8.49. Device data are as follows: $\beta_{npn} = 200$, $\beta_{pnp} = 100$, $|V_{BE(on)}| = 0.7$ V, $r_b = 0$, and $|V_A| = \infty$. If the dc input voltage is zero, calculate the overall gain $v_o/v_i$, the loop gain, and the input and output impedance at low frequencies. Compare your answers with a SPICE simulation. Also use SPICE to plot the complete large-signal transfer characteristic and find the second and third harmonic distortion in $v_o$ for a sinusoidal input voltage with peak-peak amplitude of 0.5 V at $v_i$.

**Figure 8.49** Feedback amplifier circuit.

**Figure 8.50** Balanced series-shunt feedback amplifier.

**8.14** Replace $npn$ transistors $Q_1$-$Q_2$ in Fig. 8.49 with NMOS transistors $M_1$-$M_2$, and replace the $pnp$ transistor $Q_3$ with PMOS transistor $M_3$. Also, replace the 1.25 kΩ resistor in the drain of $M_1$ with a 4.35 kΩ resistor. Repeat the calculations and simulations in Problem 8.13. For all transistors, use $W/L = 100$, $\gamma = 0$, and $|\lambda| = 0$. Also, $V_{tn} = -V_{tp} = 1$ V, $k_n' = 60$ μA/V$^2$, and $k_p' = 20$ μA/V$^2$.

**8.15** A balanced monolithic series-shunt feedback amplifier is shown in Fig. 8.50.

(a) If the common-mode input voltage is zero, calculate the bias current in each device. Assume that $\beta_F$ is large.

(b) Calculate the voltage gain, input impedance, output impedance, and loop gain of the circuit at low frequencies using the following data:

$$\beta = 100 \quad r_b = 50 \ \Omega \quad V_A = \infty \quad V_{BE(on)} = 0.7 \text{ V}$$

(c) Compare your answers with a SPICE simulation (omit the loop gain) and also use SPICE to plot the complete large-signal transfer characteristic. If the resistors have a temperature coefficient of +1000 ppm/°C, use SPICE to determine the temperature coefficient of the circuit gain over the range −55°C to +125°C.

**8.16** How does the loop gain $T = af$ of the circuit of Fig. 8.50 change as the following circuit elements change? Discuss qualitatively.

(a) 50 Ω emitter resistor of the input stage

(b) 500 Ω feedback resistor

(c) 200 Ω load resistor on the output

**8.17** The ac schematic of a shunt-series feedback amplifier is shown in Fig. 8.31. Element values are $R_F = 1$ kΩ, $R_E = 100$ Ω, $R_{L1} = 4$ kΩ, $R_S = 1/y_S = 1$ kΩ, and $z_L = 0$. Device data: $\beta = 200$, $r_b = 0$, $I_{C1} = I_{C2} = 1$ mA, $V_A = 100$ V.

(a) Calculate the overall gain $i_o/i_i$, the loop transmission, and the input and output impedances at low frequencies.

(b) If the value of $R_{L1}$ changes by +10 percent, what is the approximate change in overall transmission and input impedance?

**8.18(a)** Repeat Problem 8.17(a) with $R_F = 5$ kΩ, $R_E = 200$ Ω, $R_{L1} = 10$ kΩ, and $y_s = 0$.

(b) If the collector current of $Q_1$ increases by 20 percent, what will be the approximate change in overall gain and output resistance?

**8.19** Calculate the transconductance, input impedance, output impedance, and loop transmission at low frequencies of the local series-feedback stage of Fig. 8.34 with parameters $R_E = 200$ Ω, $\beta = 150$, $I_C = 1$ mA, $r_b = 200$ Ω, and $V_A = 80$ V.

**Figure 8.51** Circuit diagram of the 733 wideband monolithic amplifier.

**8.20** A commercial wideband monolithic feedback amplifier (the 733) is shown in Fig. 8.51. This consists of a local series-feedback stage feeding a two-stage shunt-shunt feedback amplifier. The current output of the input stage acts as a current drive to the shunt-shunt output stage.

**(a)** Assuming all device areas are equal, calculate the collector bias current in each device.

**(b)** Calculate input impedance, output impedance, and overall gain $v_o/v_i$ for this circuit at low frequencies with $R_L = 2$ k$\Omega$. Also calculate the loop gain of the output stage.

*Data:* $\beta = 100$, $r_b = 0$, $r_o = \infty$.

**(c)** Compare your answers with a SPICE simulation of the bias currents, input and output impedances, and the voltage gain.

**8.21** If the 723 voltage regulator is used to realize an output voltage $V_o = 10$ V with a 1-k$\Omega$ load, calculate the output resistance and the loop gain of the regulator. If a 500-$\Omega$ load is connected to the regulator in place of the 1-k$\Omega$ load, calculate the new value of $V_o$. Use SPICE to determine the line regulation and load regulation of the circuit. Use $I_1 = 1$ mA, $\beta = 100$, $V_A = 100$ V, $I_s = 10^{-15}$ A, and $r_b = 0$.

**8.22** Assume the BiCMOS amplifier of Fig. 3.78 is fed from a current source. Calculate the low-frequency small-signal transresistance $v_o/i_i$, the loop gain, and the input and output impedances of the circuit. Use data as in Problem 3.17. Compare your answers with a SPICE simulation and also use SPICE to plot the complete large-signal transfer characteristic of the circuit.

**8.23** A variable-gain CMOS amplifier is shown in Fig. 8.52. Note that $M_4$ represents shunt feedback around $M_6$. Assuming that the bias value of $V_i$ is adjusted so that $V_{GD6} = 0$ V dc, calculate bias currents in all devices and the small-signal voltage gain and output resistance for $V_c$ equal to 3 V and then 4 V. Compare your answer with a SPICE simulation and use SPICE to plot out the complete large-signal transfer characteristic of the circuit. Use $\mu_n C_{ox} = 60$ $\mu$A/V$^2$, $\mu_p C_{ox} = 30$ $\mu$A/V$^2$, $V_{tn} = 0.8$ V, $V_{tp} = -0.8$ V, $\lambda_n = \lambda_p = 0$, and $\gamma_n = 0.5$ V$^{1/2}$.

**8.24** A CMOS feedback amplifier is shown in Fig. 8.53. If the dc input voltage is zero, calculate the overall gain $v_o/v_i$ and the output resistance. Compare your answer with a SPICE

**Figure 8.52**  Variable-gain CMOS amplifier for Problem 8.23.

**Figure 8.53**  CMOS feedback amplifier for Problem 8.24.

simulation.  Use  $\mu_n C_{ox} = 60 \times 10^{-6}$  A/V², $\mu_p C_{ox} = 30 \times 10^{-6}$ A/V², $V_{tn} = 0.8$ V, $V_{tp} = -0.8$ V, $\lambda_n = |\lambda_p| = 0.03$ V⁻¹, and $\gamma_n = \gamma_p = 0$.

**8.25**  An active-cascode gain stage is shown in Fig. 8.54. Assume the amplifier $A_1$ has a voltage gain $a = 1 \times 10^3$ and infinite input impedance. For the transistors, $k_n' = 140 \ \mu$A/V², $V_{ov} = 0.3$ V, $\gamma = 0$, and $\lambda_n = 0.03$ V⁻¹. Assume all transistors are active. Calculate the output resistance using Blackman's impedance formula. Then calculate the voltage gain $v_o/v_i$.

**8.26**  Use Blackman's impedance formula to find the output resistance of the active-cascode current source in Fig. 8.55. Express the result in

terms of $g_{m1}$, $g_{m2}$, $r_{o1}$, $r_{o2}$, and $a$, which is the voltage gain of the op amp. Assume all transistors are active with $(W/L)_1 = (W/L)_2 = (W/L)_3$ and $\gamma = 0$. (The drain of $M_2$ connects to other circuitry that is not shown.) Also, assume that the op amp has infinite input impedance and zero output impedance.

**(a)**  Carry out the calculations with respect to controlled source $g_{m2}$.

**(b)**  Repeat the calculations with respect to the voltage-controlled voltage source $a$ in the amplifier.

**(c)**  Compare the results of (a) and (b).

**Figure 8.54** An active-cascode gain stage.

**Figure 8.55** An active-cascode current source.

**8.27** Use return-ratio analysis and Blackman's impedance formula to find the closed-loop gain, return ratio, input resistance, and output resistance for the inverting gain amplifier in Fig. 8.56. For the op amp, assume that $R_i = 1$ MΩ, $R_o = 10$ kΩ, and $a_v = 200$.

**8.28** An ac schematic of a local shunt-shunt feedback circuit is shown in Fig. 8.57. Take $R_F = 100$ kΩ and $R_L = 15$ kΩ. For the MOS transistor, $I_D = 0.5$ mA, $W/L = 100$, $k' = 180$ μA/V², and

**Figure 8.56** An inverting feedback amplifier.

**Figure 8.57** A local shunt-shunt feedback amplifier.

$r_o = \infty$. Calculate input resistance, output resistance, loop transmission, and closed-loop gain:

**(a)** Using the formulas from two-port analysis (Section 8.5).

**(b)** Using the formulas from return-ratio analysis (Section 8.8).

**8.29** Replace the MOS transistor in Fig. 8.57 by a *npn* transistor. Take $R_F = 2$ k$\Omega$, $R_L = 2$ k$\Omega$, $\beta = 200$, $I_C = 1$ mA, $r_b = 0$, and $V_A = 100$ V.

**(a)** Repeat Problem 8.28(a).

**(b)** Repeat Problem 8.28(b).

**8.30** A voltage-follower feedback circuit is shown in Fig. 8.58. For the MOS transistor, $I_D = 0.5$ mA, $k' = 180$ $\mu$A/V$^2$, $r_o = \infty$, $W/L = 100$, $|\phi_f| = 0.3$ V, and $\gamma = 0.3$ V$^{1/2}$. For the op amp, assume that $R_i = 1$ M$\Omega$, $R_o = 10$ k$\Omega$, and $a_v = 1,000$. Calculate input resistance, output resistance, loop transmission, and closed-loop gain:

**(a)** Using the formulas from two-port analysis (Section 8.5).

**(b)** Using the formulas from return-ratio analysis (Section 8.8).

**8.31** Replace the MOS transistor in Fig. 8.58 with a *npn* transistor. For the transistor, $I_C = 0.5$ mA and $r_o = \infty$.

**(a)** Repeat the calculations in Problem 8.30(a).

**(b)** Repeat the calculations in Problem 8.30(b).

**8.32** For the noninverting amplifier shown in Fig. 8.59, $R_1 = 1$ k$\Omega$, and $R_2 = 5$ k$\Omega$. For the op amp, take $R_i = 1$ M$\Omega$, $R_o = 100$ $\Omega$, and $a_v = 1 \times 10^4$. Calculate input resistance, output resistance, loop transmission, and closed-loop gain:

**(a)** Using the formulas from two-port analysis (Section 8.5).

**(b)** Using the formulas from return-ratio analysis (Section 8.8).

**8.33** Calculation of return ratio begins by breaking a feedback loop at a controlled source. However, breaking a feedback loop at a controlled source is often impossible in a SPICE simulation because the controlled source (e.g., the $g_m$ source in a transistor's small-signal model) is embedded in a small-signal model. Therefore, it cannot be accessed or disconnected in simulation. A technique that can be used to simulate the return ratio with SPICE is illustrated in Fig. 8.60 for the circuit in Fig. 8.59. First, the independent source $V_i$ is set to zero. Next, ac

**Figure 8.58** A voltage follower.

**Figure 8.59** A noninverting feedback amplifier.

(a)

**Figure 8.60** The feedback circuit in Fig. 8.59 modified to calculate (a) $\mathcal{R}_i'$ and (b) $\mathcal{R}_v'$.

(b)

test signals $v_t$ and $i_t$ are injected into the loop at a convenient point (e.g., at the "×" in Fig. 8.59), creating two modified versions of the circuit as shown in Fig. 8.60a and 8.60b. Using Fig. 8.60a, calculate $\mathcal{R}_i' = -i_m/i_d$. Using Fig. 8.60b, calculate $\mathcal{R}_v' = -v_m/v_d$. The amplitudes of test signals $i_t$ and $v_t$ do not affect $\mathcal{R}_i'$ or $\mathcal{R}_v'$. Also, these ac test signals do not affect the dc operating point of the feedback circuit. The return ratio $\mathcal{R}$ for the controlled source is related to $\mathcal{R}_i'$ and $\mathcal{R}_v'$ by[10]

$$\frac{1}{1+\mathcal{R}} = \frac{1}{1+\mathcal{R}_i'} + \frac{1}{1+\mathcal{R}_v'}$$

(a) Compute $\mathcal{R}_i'$ and $\mathcal{R}_v'$ for the circuit in Fig. 8.60. Use element values from Problem 8.32. Then combine these values using the equation above to find $\mathcal{R}$.

(b) Compute $\mathcal{R}$ directly by breaking the loop at the $a_v$ controlled source. Compare the results in (a) and (b).

(c) Carry out a SPICE simulation to find $\mathcal{R}_i'$ and $\mathcal{R}_v'$. Then combine these values using the equation above to find $\mathcal{R}$. Compare with your results from (a).

**8.34 (a)** Calculate the loop gain $T = af$ for the series-shunt feedback circuit in Fig. 8.59 using $h$-parameter two-ports. Take $R_1 = 200$ kΩ, and $R_2 = 100$ kΩ. For the op amp, assume $R_i = 50$ kΩ, $R_o = 1$ MΩ, and $a_v = 1 \times 10^3$.

(b) If the input source location and type in Fig. 8.59 are changed as shown in Fig. 8.61, the feedback is now shunt-shunt. Calculate the loop

**Figure 8.61** The feedback circuit in Fig. 8.59 with a different input-signal source.

gain $T = af$ for this shunt-shunt feedback circuit using y-parameter two-ports. Use the element values in (a).

(c) Calculate the return ratio $\mathcal{R}$ for the circuit in Fig. 8.61, again using the element values in (a).

This return ratio is the same as the return ratio for the circuit in Fig. 8.59. Why?

(d) Compare the results in (a), (b), and (c).

# REFERENCES

1. C. A. Desoer and E. S. Kuh, *Basic Circuit Theory,* McGraw-Hill, New-York, 1969.

2. J. E. Solomon and G. R. Wilson, "A Highly Desensitized, Wideband Monolithic Amplifier," *IEEE J. Solid State Circuits,* Vol. SC-1, pp. 19–28, September 1966.

3. A. B. Grebene, *Analog Integrated Circuit Design,* Van Nostrand Reinhold, New York, 1972, Chapter 6.

4. R. S. Muller and T. I. Kamins, *Device Electronics for Integrated Circuits,* Wiley, New York, 1977.

5. H. W. Bode, *Network Analysis and Feedback Amplifier Design,* Van Nostrand, New York, 1945.

6. E. S. Kuh and R. A. Rohrer, *Theory of Linear Active Networks,* Holden-Day, San Francisco, 1967.

7. S. Rosenstark, *Feedback Amplifier Principles,* MacMillan, New York, 1986.

8. B. Nikolic and S. Marjanovic, "A General Method of Feedback Amplifier Analysis," *IEEE Int'l Symp. on Circuits and Systems,* pp. 415–418, Monterey, CA, 1998.

9. R. B. Blackman, "Effect of Feedback on Impedance," *Bell Sys. Tech. J.,* Vol. 23, pp. 269–277, October 1943.

10. R. D. Middlebrook, "Measurement of Loop Gain in Feedback Systems," *Int. J. Electronics,* Vol. 38, no. 4, pp. 485–512, 1975.

# Frequency Response and Stability of Feedback Amplifiers

## 9.1 Introduction

In Chapter 8, we considered the effects of negative feedback on circuit parameters such as gain and terminal impedance. We saw that application of negative feedback resulted in a number of performance improvements, such as reduced sensitivity of gain to active-device parameter changes and reduction of distortion due to circuit nonlinearities.

In this chapter, we see the effect of negative feedback on the frequency response of a circuit. The possibility of *oscillation* in feedback circuits is illustrated, and methods of overcoming these problems by *compensation* of the circuit are described. Finally, the effect of compensation on the large-signal high-frequency performance of feedback amplifiers is investigated.

Much of the analysis in this chapter is based on the ideal block diagram in Fig. 9.1. This block diagram includes the forward gain $a$ and feedback factor $f$, which are the parameters used in two-port analysis of feedback circuits in Chapter 8. The equations and results in this chapter could be expressed in terms of the parameters used in the return-ratio analysis in Chapter 8 by an appropriate change of variables, as shown in Appendix A9.1.

The equations and relationships in this chapter are general and can be applied to any feedback circuit. However, for simplicity we will often assume the feedback factor $f$ is a positive, unitless constant. One circuit that has such an $f$ is the series-shunt feedback circuit shown in Fig 8.24. In this circuit, the feedback network is a resistive voltage divider, so $f$ is a constant with $0 \le f \le 1$. The forward gain $a$ is a voltage gain that is positive at low frequencies. This circuit gives a noninverting closed-loop voltage gain.

## 9.2 Relation Between Gain and Bandwidth in Feedback Amplifiers

Chapter 8 showed that the performance improvements produced by negative feedback were obtained at the expense of a reduction in gain by a factor $(1 + T)$, where $T$ is the loop gain. The performance specifications that were improved were also changed by the factor $(1 + T)$.

In addition to the foregoing effects, negative feedback also tends to *broadband* the amplifier. Consider first a feedback circuit as shown in Fig. 9.1 with a simple basic amplifier whose gain function contains a single pole

$$a(s) = \frac{a_0}{1 - \dfrac{s}{p_1}} \tag{9.1}$$

**Figure 9.1** Feedback circuit configuration.

where $a_0$ is the low-frequency gain of the basic amplifier and $p_1$ is the basic-amplifier pole in radians per second. Assume that the feedback path is purely resistive and thus the feedback function $f$ is a positive constant. Since Fig. 9.1 is an ideal feedback arrangement, the *overall* gain is

$$A(s) = \frac{v_o}{v_i} = \frac{a(s)}{1 + a(s)f} \tag{9.2}$$

where the loop gain is $T(s) = a(s)f$. Substitution of (9.1) in (9.2) gives

$$A(s) = \frac{\dfrac{a_0}{1 - \dfrac{s}{p_1}}}{1 + \dfrac{a_0 f}{1 - \dfrac{s}{p_1}}} = \frac{a_0}{1 - \dfrac{s}{p_1} + a_0 f} = \frac{a_0}{1 + a_0 f} \cdot \frac{1}{1 - \dfrac{s}{p_1}\dfrac{1}{1 + a_0 f}} \tag{9.3}$$

From (9.3) the low-frequency gain $A_0$ is

$$A_0 = \frac{a_0}{1 + T_0} \tag{9.4}$$

where

$$T_0 = a_0 f = \text{low-frequency loop gain} \tag{9.5}$$

The $-3$-dB bandwidth of the feedback circuit (i.e., the new pole magnitude) is $(1 + a_0 f) \cdot |p_1|$ from (9.3). Thus the feedback has reduced the low-frequency gain by a factor $(1 + T_0)$, which is consistent with the results of Chapter 8, but it is now apparent that the $-3$-dB frequency of the circuit has been *increased* by the same quantity $(1 + T_0)$. Note that the gain-handwidth product is constant. These results are illustrated in the Bode plots of Fig. 9.2, where the magnitudes of $a(j\omega)$ and $A(j\omega)$ are plotted versus frequency on log

**Figure 9.2** Gain magnitude versus frequency for the basic amplifier and the feedback amplifier.

**Figure 9.3** Locus of the pole of the circuit of Fig. 9.1 as loop gain $T_0$ varies.

scales. It is apparent that the gain curves for any value of $T_0$ are contained in an envelope bounded by the curve of $|a(j\omega)|$.

Because the use of negative feedback allows the designer to trade gain for bandwidth, negative feedback is widely used as a method for designing broadband amplifiers. The gain reduction that occurs is made up by using additional gain stages, which in general are also feedback amplifiers.

Let us now examine the effect of the feedback on the pole of the overall transfer function $A(s)$. It is apparent from (9.3) that as the low-frequency loop gain $T_0$ is increased, the magnitude of the pole of $A(s)$ increases. This is illustrated in Fig. 9.3, which shows the *locus* of the pole of $A(s)$ in the $s$ plane as $T_0$ varies. The pole starts at $p_1$ for $T_0 = 0$ and moves out along the negative real axis as $T_0$ is made positive. Figure 9.3 is a simple *root-locus* diagram and will be discussed further in Section 9.5.

## 9.3 Instability and the Nyquist Criterion[1]

In the above simple example the basic amplifier was assumed to have a single-pole transfer function, and this situation is closely approximated in practice by internally compensated general-purpose op amps. However, many amplifiers have multipole transfer functions that cause deviations from the above results. The process of compensation overcomes these problems, as will be seen later.

Consider an amplifier with a three-pole transfer function

$$T(s) \qquad a(s) = \frac{a_0}{\left(1 - \dfrac{s}{p_1}\right)\left(1 - \dfrac{s}{p_2}\right)\left(1 - \dfrac{s}{p_3}\right)} \qquad (9.6)$$

where $|p_1|$, $|p_2|$, and $|p_3|$ are the pole magnitudes in rad/s. The poles are shown in the $s$ plane in Fig. 9.4 and gain magnitude $|a(j\omega)|$ and phase ph $a(j\omega)$ are plotted versus frequency in

**Figure 9.4** Poles of an amplifier in the $s$ plane.

**Figure 9.5** Gain and phase versus frequency for a circuit with a three-pole transfer function.

Fig. 9.5 assuming about a factor of 10 separation between the poles. Only asymptotes are shown for the magnitude plot. At frequencies above the first pole magnitude $|p_1|$, the plot of $|a(j\omega)|$ falls at 6 dB/octave and ph $a(j\omega)$ approaches $-90°$. Above $|p_2|$ these become 12 dB/octave and $-180°$, and above $|p_3|$ they become 18 dB/octave and $-270°$. The frequency where ph $a(j\omega) = -180°$ has special significance and is marked $\omega_{180}$, and the value of $|a(j\omega)|$ at this frequency is $a_{180}$. If the three poles are fairly widely separated (by a factor of 10 or more), the phase shifts at frequencies $|p_1|$, $|p_2|$, and $|p_3|$ are approximately $-45°$, $-135°$, and $-225°$, respectively. This will now be assumed for simplicity. In addition, the gain magnitude will be assumed to follow the asymptotic curve and the effect of these assumptions in practical cases will be considered later.

Now consider this amplifier connected in a feedback loop as in Fig. 9.1 with $f$ a positive constant. Since $f$ is constant, the loop gain $T(j\omega) = a(j\omega)f$ will have the same variation with frequency as $a(j\omega)$. A plot of $af(j\omega) = T(j\omega)$ in magnitude and phase on a polar plot (with $\omega$ as a parameter) can thus be drawn using the data of Fig. 9.5 and the magnitude of $f$. Such a plot for this example is shown in Fig. 9.6 (not to scale) and is called a *Nyquist diagram*. The variable on the curve is frequency and varies from $\omega = -\infty$ to $\omega = \infty$. For $\omega = 0$, $|T(j\omega)| = T_0$ and ph $T(j\omega) = 0$, and the curve meets the real axis with an intercept $T_0$. As $\omega$ increases, as Fig. 9.5 shows, $|a(j\omega)|$ decreases and ph $a(j\omega)$ becomes negative and thus the plot is in the fourth quadrant. As $\omega \to \infty$, ph $a(j\omega) \to -270°$ and $|a(j\omega)| \to 0$. Consequently, the plot is asymptotic to the origin and is tangent to the imaginary axis. At the frequency $\omega_{180}$ the phase is $-180°$ and the curve crosses the negative real axis. If $|a(j\omega_{180})f| > 1$ at this point, the Nyquist diagram will encircle the point $(-1, 0)$ as shown, and this has particular significance, as will now become apparent. For

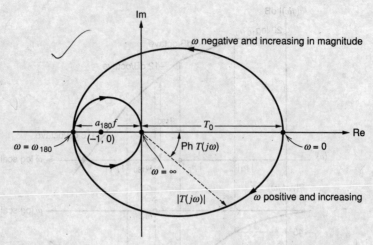

**Figure 9.6** Nyquist diagram [polar plot of $T(j\omega)$ in magnitude and phase] corresponding to the characteristic of Fig. 9.5 (not to scale).

the purposes of this treatment, the *Nyquist criterion* for stability of the amplifier can be stated as follows:

"Consider a feedback amplifier with a stable $T(s)$ (i.e., all poles of $T(s)$ are in the left half-plane). If the Nyquist plot of $T(j\omega)$ encircles the point $(-1, 0)$, the feedback amplifier is unstable."

This criterion simply amounts to a mathematical test for poles of transfer function $A(s)$ in the right half-plane. If the Nyquist plot encircles the point $(-1, 0)$, the amplifier has poles in the right half-plane and the circuit will *oscillate*. In fact the number of encirclements of the point $(-1, 0)$ gives the number of right half-plane poles and in this example there are two. The significance of poles in the right half-plane can be seen by assuming that a circuit has a pair of complex poles at $(\sigma_1 \pm j\omega_1)$ where $\sigma_1$ is positive. The transient response of the circuit then contains a term $K_1 \exp \sigma_1 t \sin \omega_1 t$, which represents a *growing* sinusoid if $\sigma_1$ is positive. ($K_1$ is a constant representing initial conditions.) This term is then present even if no further input is applied, and a circuit behaving in this way is said to be *unstable* or *oscillatory*.

The significance of the point $(-1, 0)$ can be appreciated if the Nyquist diagram is assumed to pass through this point. Then at the frequency $\omega_{180}$, $T(j\omega) = a(j\omega)f = -1$ and $A(j\omega) = \infty$ using (9.2) in the frequency domain. The feedback amplifier is thus calculated to have a forward gain of infinity, and this indicates the onset of instability and oscillation. This situation corresponds to poles of $A(s)$ on the $j\omega$ axis in the $s$ plane. If $T_0$ is then increased by increasing $a_0$ or $f$, the Nyquist diagram expands *linearly* and then encircles $(-1, 0)$. This corresponds to poles of $A(s)$ in the right half-plane, as shown in Fig. 9.7.

From the above criterion for stability, a *simpler* test can be derived that is useful in most common cases.

"If $|T(j\omega)| > 1$ at the frequency where ph $T(j\omega) = -180°$, then the amplifier is unstable." The validity of this criterion for the example considered here is apparent from inspection of Fig. 9.6 and application of the Nyquist criterion.

In order to examine the effect of feedback on the stability of an amplifier, consider the three-pole amplifier with gain function given by (9.6) to be placed in a negative-feedback loop with $f$ constant. The gain (in decibels) and phase of the amplifier are shown again in

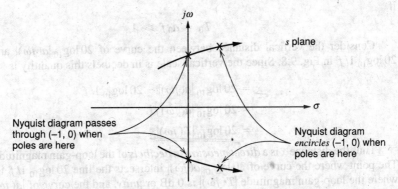

Nyquist diagram passes through (−1, 0) when poles are here

Nyquist diagram *encircles* (−1, 0) when poles are here

**Figure 9.7** Pole positions corresponding to different Nyquist diagrams.

Fig. 9.8, and also plotted is the quantity $20 \log_{10} 1/f$. The value of $20 \log_{10} 1/f$ is approximately equal to the low-frequency gain in decibels with feedback applied since

$$A_0 = \frac{a_0}{1 + a_0 f} \tag{9.7}$$

and thus

$$\frac{1}{f} \approx A_0 \tag{9.8}$$

**Figure 9.8** Amplifier gain and phase versus frequency showing the phase margin.

if

$$T_0 = a_0 f \gg 1$$

Consider the vertical distance between the curve of $20 \log_{10} |a(j\omega)|$ and the line $20 \log_{10} 1/f$ in Fig. 9.8. Since the vertical scale is in decibels this quantity is

$$x = 20 \log_{10} |a(j\omega)| - 20 \log_{10} 1/f \tag{9.9}$$

$$= 20 \log_{10} |a(j\omega)f|$$

$$= 20 \log_{10} |T(j\omega)| \tag{9.10}$$

Thus the distance $x$ is a *direct measure in decibels* of the loop-gain magnitude, $|T(j\omega)|$. The point where the curve of $20 \log_{10} |a(j\omega)|$ intersects the line $20 \log_{10} 1/f$ is the point where the loop-gain magnitude $|T(j\omega)|$ is 0 dB or *unity*, and the curve of $|a(j\omega)|$ in decibels in Fig. 9.8 can thus be considered a curve of $|T(j\omega)|$ in decibels *if the dotted line at* $20 \log_{10} 1/f$ is taken as the new zero axis.

The simple example of Section 9.1 showed that the gain curve versus frequency with feedback applied ($20 \log_{10} |A(j\omega)|$) follows the $20 \log_{10} A_0$ line until it intersects the gain curve $20 \log_{10} |a(j\omega)|$. At higher frequencies the curve $20 \log_{10} |A(j\omega)|$ simply follows the curve of $20 \log_{10} |a(j\omega)|$ for the basic amplifier. The reason for this is now apparent in that at the higher frequencies the loop gain $|T(j\omega)| \to 0$ and the feedback then has *no influence* on the gain of the amplifier.

Figure 9.8 shows that the loop-gain magnitude $|T(j\omega)|$ is unity at frequency $\omega_0$. At this frequency the phase of $T(j\omega)$ has not reached $-180°$ for the case shown, and using the modified Nyquist criterion stated above we conclude that *this feedback loop is stable*. Obviously $|T(j\omega)| < 1$ at the frequency where ph $T(j\omega) = -180°$. If the polar Nyquist diagram is sketched for this example, it does *not* encircle the point $(-1, 0)$.

As $|T(j\omega)|$ is made closer to unity at the frequency where ph $T(j\omega) = -180°$, the amplifier has a *smaller margin* of stability, and this can be specified in two ways. The most common is the *phase margin*, which is defined as follows:

Phase margin $= 180° + $ (ph $T(j\omega)$ at frequency where $|T(j\omega)| = 1$). The phase margin is indicated in Fig. 9.8 and must be greater than 0° for stability.

Another measure of stability is the *gain margin*. This is defined to be $1/|T(j\omega)|$ in decibels at the frequency where ph $T(j\omega) = -180°$, and this must be greater than 0 dB for stability.

The significance of the phase-margin magnitude is now explored. For the feedback amplifier considered in Section 9.1, where the basic amplifier has a single-pole response, the phase margin is obviously 90° if the low-frequency loop gain is reasonably large. This is illustrated in Fig. 9.9 and results in a very stable amplifier. A typical lower allowable limit for the phase margin in practice is 45°, with a value of 60° being more common.

Consider a feedback amplifier with a phase margin of 45° and a feedback function $f$ that is real (and thus constant). Then

$$\text{ph } T(j\omega_0) = -135° \tag{9.11}$$

where $\omega_0$ is the frequency defined by

$$|T(j\omega_0)| = 1 \tag{9.12}$$

Now $|T(j\omega_0)| = |a(j\omega_0)f| = 1$ implies that

$$|a(j\omega_0)| = \frac{1}{f} \tag{9.13}$$

assuming that $f$ is positive real.

**Figure 9.9** Gain and phase versus frequency for a single-pole basic amplifier showing the phase margin for a low-frequency loop gain $T_0$.

The overall gain is

$$A(j\omega) = \frac{a(j\omega)}{1 + T(j\omega)} \qquad (9.14)$$

Substitution of (9.11) and (9.12) in (9.14) gives

$$A(j\omega_0) = \frac{a(j\omega_0)}{1 + e^{-j135°}} = \frac{a(j\omega_0)}{1 - 0.7 - 0.7j} = \frac{a(j\omega_0)}{0.3 - 0.7j}$$

and thus

$$|A(j\omega_0)| = \frac{|a(j\omega_0)|}{0.76} = \frac{1.3}{f} \qquad (9.15)$$

using (9.13).

The frequency $\omega_0$, where $|T(j\omega_0)| = 1$, is the nominal $-3$-dB point for a single-pole basic amplifier, but in this case there is 2.4 dB (1.3 ×) of *peaking* above the low-frequency gain of $1/f$.

Consider a phase margin of 60°. At the frequency $\omega_0$ in this case

$$\text{ph } T(j\omega_0) = -120° \qquad (9.16)$$

and

$$|T(j\omega_0)| = 1 \qquad (9.17)$$

Following a similar analysis we obtain

$$|A(j\omega_0)| = \frac{1}{f}$$

In this case there is no peaking at $\omega = \omega_0$, but there has also been no gain reduction at this frequency.

Finally, the case where the phase margin is 90° can be similarly calculated. In this case

$$\text{ph } T(j\omega_0) = -90° \tag{9.18}$$

and

$$|T(j\omega_0)| = 1 \tag{9.19}$$

A similar analysis gives

$$|A(j\omega_0)| = \frac{0.7}{f} \tag{9.20}$$

As expected in this case, the gain at frequency $\omega_0$ is 3 dB below the midband value.

These results are illustrated in Fig. 9.10, where the normalized overall gain versus frequency is shown for various phase margins. The plots are drawn assuming the response is dominated by the first two poles of the transfer function, except for the case of the 90° phase margin, which has one pole only. As the phase margin diminishes, the gain peak becomes larger until the gain approaches infinity and oscillation occurs for phase margin = 0°. The gain peak usually occurs close to the frequency where $|T(j\omega)| = 1$, but for a phase margin of 60° there is 0.2 dB of peaking just below this frequency. Note that after the peak, the gain curves approach an asymptote of $-12$ dB/octave for phase margins other than 90°. This is because the open-loop gain falls at $-12$ dB/octave due to the presence of two poles in the transfer function.

The simple tests for stability of a feedback amplifier (i.e., positive phase and gain margins) can only be applied when the phase and gain margins are uniquely defined. The phase margin is uniquely defined if there is only one frequency at which the magnitude of the loop gain equals one. Similarly, the gain margin is uniquely defined if there is only one frequency at which the phase of the loop gain equals $-180°$. In most feedback circuits, these margins are uniquely defined. However, if either of these margins is not uniquely

**Figure 9.10** Normalized overall gain for feedback amplifiers versus normalized frequency for various phase margins. Frequency is normalized to the frequency where the loop gain is unity.

defined, then stability should be checked using a Nyquist diagram and the Nyquist criterion.

The loop gain $T = af$ can be examined to determine the stability of a feedback circuit, as explained in this section. Alternatively these measures of stability can be applied to the return ratio $\mathcal{R}$, as explained in Appendix A9.1. Techniques for simulating $\mathcal{R}$[2–5] and $T = af$[4] using SPICE have been developed, based on methods for measuring loop transmission.[6,7] These techniques measure the loop transmission at the closed-loop dc operating point. An advantage of SPICE simulation of the loop transmission is that parasitics that might have an important effect are included. For example, parasitic capacitance at the op-amp input introduces frequency dependence in the feedback network in Fig. 8.24, which may degrade the phase margin.

## 9.4 Compensation

### 9.4.1 Theory of Compensation

Consider again the amplifier whose gain and phase is shown in Fig. 9.8. For the feedback circuit in which this was assumed to be connected, the forward gain was $A_0$, as shown in Fig. 9.8, and the phase margin was positive. Thus the circuit was stable. It is apparent, however, that if the amount of feedback is increased by making $f$ larger (and thus $A_0$ smaller), oscillation will eventually occur. This is shown in Fig. 9.11, where $f_1$ is chosen to give a zero phase margin and the corresponding overall gain is $A_1 \simeq 1/f_1$. If the feedback

**Figure 9.11** Gain and phase versus frequency for a three-pole basic amplifier. Feedback factor $f_1$ gives a zero phase margin and factor $f_2$ gives a negative phase margin.

is increased to $f_2$ (and $A_2 \simeq 1/f_2$ is the overall gain), the phase margin is negative and the circuit will oscillate. Thus if this amplifier is to be used in a feedback loop with loop gain larger than $a_0 f_1$, efforts must be made to increase the phase margin. This process is known as *compensation*. Note that without compensation, the forward gain of the feedback amplifier cannot be made less than $A_1 \simeq 1/f_1$ because of the oscillation problem.

The simplest and most common method of compensation is to reduce the bandwidth of the amplifier (often called *narrowbanding*). That is, a dominant pole is deliberately introduced into the amplifier to force the phase shift to be less than $-180°$ when the loop gain is unity. This involves a direct sacrifice of the frequency capability of the amplifier.

If $f$ is constant, the most difficult case to compensate is $f = 1$, which is a unity-gain feedback configuration. In this case the loop-gain curve is identical to the gain curve of the basic amplifier. Consider this situation and assume that the basic amplifier has the same characteristic as in Fig. 9.11. To compensate the amplifier, we introduce a new dominant pole with magnitude $|p_D|$, as shown in Fig. 9.12, and assume that this does not affect the original amplifier poles with magnitudes $|p_1|$, $|p_2|$, and $|p_3|$. This is often not the case but is assumed here for purposes of illustration.

The introduction of the dominant pole with magnitude $|p_D|$ into the amplifier gain function causes the gain magnitude to decrease at 6 dB/octave until frequency $|p_1|$ is reached, and over this region the amplifier phase shift asymptotes to $-90°$. If frequency $|p_D|$ is chosen so that the gain $|a(j\omega)|$ is unity at frequency $|p_1|$ as shown, then the loop gain is also unity at frequency $|p_1|$ for the assumed case of unity feedback with $f = 1$. The phase margin in this case is then $45°$, which means that the amplifier is stable. The original amplifier would have been *unstable* in such a feedback connection.

**Figure 9.12** Gain and phase versus frequency for a three-pole basic amplifier. Compensation for unity-gain feedback operation ($f = 1$) is achieved by introduction of a negative real pole with magnitude $|p_D|$.

The price that has been paid for achieving stability in this case is that with the feedback removed, the basic amplifier has a unity-gain bandwidth of only $|p_1|$, which is much less than before. Also, with feedback applied, the loop gain now begins to decrease at a frequency $|p_D|$, and all the benefits of feedback diminish as the loop gain decreases. For example, in Chapter 8 it was shown that shunt feedback at the input or output of an amplifier *reduces* the basic terminal impedance by $[1 + T(j\omega)]$. Since $T(j\omega)$ is frequency dependent, the terminal impedance of a shunt-feedback amplifier will begin to *rise* when $|T(j\omega)|$ begins to decrease. Thus the high-frequency terminal impedance will appear *inductive*, as in the case of $z_0$ for an emitter follower, which was calculated in Chapter 7. (See Problem 9.8.)

■ **EXAMPLE**

Calculate the dominant-pole magnitude required to give unity-gain compensation of the 702 op amp with a phase margin of 45°. The low-frequency gain is $a_0 = 3600$ and the circuit has poles at $-(p_1/2\pi) = 1$ MHz, $-(p_2/2\pi) = 4$ MHz, and $-(p_3/2\pi) = 40$ MHz.

In this example, the second pole $p_2$ is sufficiently close to $p_1$ to produce significant phase shift at the amplifier $-3$-dB frequency. The approach to this problem will be to use the approximate results developed above to obtain an initial estimate of the required dominant-pole magnitude and then to empirically adjust this estimate to obtain the required results.

The results of Fig. 9.12 indicate that a dominant pole with magnitude $|p_D|$ should be introduced so that gain $a_0 = 3600$ is reduced to unity at $|p_1/2\pi| = 1$ MHz with a 6-dB/octave decrease as a function of frequency. The product $|a|\omega$ is constant where the slope of the gain-magnitude plot is $-6$ dB/octave; therefore

$$\left|\frac{p_D}{2\pi}\right| = \frac{1}{a_0}\left|\frac{p_1}{2\pi}\right| = \frac{10^6}{3600}\text{Hz} = 278 \text{ Hz}$$

This would give a transfer function

$$a(j\omega) = \frac{3600}{\left(1 + \dfrac{j\omega}{|p_D|}\right)\left(1 + \dfrac{j\omega}{|p_1|}\right)\left(1 + \dfrac{j\omega}{|p_2|}\right)\left(1 + \dfrac{j\omega}{|p_3|}\right)} \tag{9.21}$$

where the pole magnitudes are in radians per second. Equation 9.21 gives a unity-gain frequency [where $|a(j\omega)| = 1$] of 780 kHz. This is slightly below the design value of 1 MHz because the actual gain curve is 3 dB below the asymptote at the break frequency $|p_1|$. At 780 kHz the phase shift obtained from (9.21) is $-139°$ instead of the desired $-135°$ and this includes a contribution of $-11°$ from pole $p_2$. Although this result is close enough for most purposes, a phase margin of precisely 45° can be achieved by empirically reducing $|p_D|$ until (9.21) gives a phase shift of $-135°$ at the unity gain frequency. This occurs for $|p_D/2\pi| = 260$ Hz, which gives a unity-gain frequency of 730 kHz.

■ Consider now the performance of the amplifier whose characteristic is shown in Fig. 9.12 (with dominant pole magnitude $|p_D|$) when used in a feedback loop with $f < 1$ (i.e., overall gain $A_0 > 1$). This case is shown in Fig. 9.13. The loop gain now falls to unity at frequency $\omega_x$ and the phase margin of the circuit is now approximately 90°. The $-3$-dB bandwidth of the feedback circuit is $\omega_x$. The circuit now has more compensation than is needed, and, in fact, bandwidth is being wasted. Thus, although it is convenient to compensate an amplifier for unity gain and then use it unchanged for other applications (as is done in many op amps), this procedure is quite wasteful of bandwidth. Fixed-gain amplifiers that are designed for applications where maximum bandwidth is required are usually

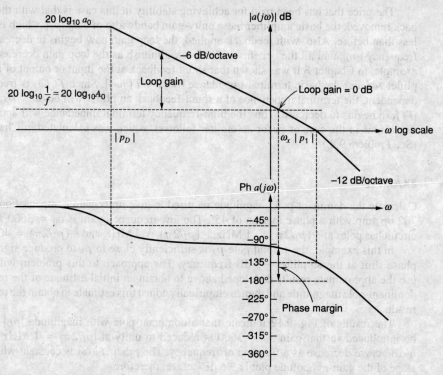

**Figure 9.13** Gain and phase versus frequency for an amplifier compensated for use in a feedback loop with $f = 1$ and a phase margin of 45°. The phase margin is shown for operation in a feedback loop with $f < 1$.

compensated for a specified phase margin (typically 45° to 60°) at the required gain value. However, op amps are general-purpose circuits that are used with differing feedback networks with $f$ values ranging from 0 to 1. Optimum bandwidth is achieved in such circuits if the compensation is tailored to the gain value required, and this approach gives much higher bandwidths for high gain values, as seen in Fig. 9.14. This figure shows compensation of the amplifier characteristic of Fig. 9.11 for operation in a feedback circuit with forward gain $A_0$. A dominant pole is added with magnitude $|p'_D|$ to give a phase margin of 45°. Frequency $|p'_D|$ is obviously $\gg |p_D|$, and the $-3$-dB bandwidth of the feedback amplifier is nominally $|p_1|$, at which frequency the loop gain is 0 dB (disregarding peaking). The $-3$-dB frequency from Fig. 9.13 would be only $\omega_x = |p_1|/A_0$ if unity-gain compensation had been used. Obviously, since $A_0$ can be large, the improvement in bandwidth is significant.

In the compensation schemes discussed above, an additional dominant pole was assumed to be added to the amplifier, and the original amplifier poles were assumed to be unaffected by this procedure. In terms of circuit bandwidth, a much more efficient way to compensate the amplifier is to add capacitance to the circuit in such a way that the original amplifier dominant pole magnitude $|p_1|$ is reduced so that it performs the compensation function. This technique requires access to the internal nodes of the amplifier, and knowledge of the nodes in the circuit where added capacitance will reduce frequency $|p_1|$.

Consider the effect of compensating for unity-gain operation the amplifier characteristic of Fig. 9.11 in this way. Again assume that higher frequency poles $p_2$ and $p_3$ are unaffected by this procedure. In fact, depending on the method of compensation, these

**Figure 9.14** Gain and phase versus frequency for an amplifier compensated for use in a feedback loop with $f < 1$ and a phase margin of $45°$. Compensation is achieved by adding a new pole $p'_D$ to the amplifier.

poles are usually moved up or down in magnitude by the compensation. This point will be taken up later.

Compensation of the amplifier by reducing $|p_1|$ is shown in Fig. 9.15. For a $45°$-phase margin in a unity-gain feedback configuration, dominant pole magnitude $|p'_1|$ must cause the gain to fall to unity at frequency $|p_2|$ (the second pole magnitude). Thus the nominal bandwidth in a unity-gain configuration is $|p_2|$, and the loop gain is unity at this frequency. This result can be contrasted with a bandwidth of $|p_1|$, as shown in Fig. 9.12 for compensation achieved by adding another pole with magnitude $|p_D|$ to the amplifier. In practical amplifiers, frequency $|p_2|$ is often 5 or 10 times frequency $|p_1|$ and substantial improvements in bandwidth are thus achieved.

The results of this section illustrate why the basic amplifier of a feedback circuit is usually designed with as few stages as possible. Each stage of gain inevitably adds more poles to the transfer function, complicating the compensation problem, particularly if a wide bandwidth is required.

### 9.4.2 Methods of Compensation

In order to compensate a circuit by the common method of narrowbanding described above, it is necessary to add capacitance to create a dominant pole with the desired magnitude. One method of achieving this is shown in Fig. 9.16, which is a schematic of the first two stages of a simple amplifier. A large capacitor $C$ is connected between the collectors of the input stage. The output stage, which is assumed relatively broadband, is not shown.

**Figure 9.15** Gain and phase versus frequency for an amplifier compensated for use in a feedback loop with $f = 1$ and a phase margin of 45°. Compensation is achieved by reducing the magnitude $|p_1|$ of the dominant pole of the original amplifier.

A differential half-circuit of Fig. 9.16 is shown in Fig. 9.17, and it should be noted that the compensation capacitor is doubled in the half-circuit. The major contributions to the dominant pole of a circuit of this type (if $R_S$ is not large) come from the input capacitance of $Q_4$ and Miller capacitance associated with $Q_4$. Thus the compensation as shown will reduce the magnitude of the dominant pole of the original amplifier so that it performs the required compensation function. Almost certainly, however, the higher frequency poles of the amplifier will also be changed by the addition of $C$. In practice, the best method

**Figure 9.16** Compensation of an amplifier by introduction of a large capacitor $C$.

**Figure 9.17** Differential half-circuit of Fig. 9.16

of approaching the compensation design is to use computer simulation to determine the original pole positions. A first estimate of $C$ is made on the assumption that the higher frequency poles do not change in magnitude and a new computer simulation is made with $C$ included to check this assumption. Another estimate of $C$ is then made on the basis of the new simulation, and this process usually converges after several iterations.

The magnitude of the dominant pole of Fig. 9.17 can be estimated using zero-value time constant analysis. However, if the value of $C$ required is very large, this capacitor will dominate and a good estimate of the dominant pole can be made by considering $C$ only and ignoring other circuit capacitance. In that case the dominant-pole magnitude is

$$|p_D| = \frac{1}{2CR} \tag{9.22}$$

where

$$R = R_{L1} \| R_{i4} \tag{9.23}$$

and

$$R_{i4} = r_{b4} + r_{\pi 4} \tag{9.24}$$

One disadvantage of the above method of compensation is that the value of $C$ required is quite large (typically $> 1000$ pF) and cannot be realized on a monolithic chip.

Many general-purpose op amps have unity-gain compensation included on the monolithic chip and require no further compensation from the user. (The sacrifice in bandwidth caused by this technique when using gain other than unity was described earlier.) In order to realize an internally compensated monolithic op amp, compensation must be achieved using capacitance less than about 50 pF. This can be achieved using *Miller multiplication* of the capacitance as shown in Fig. 9.18 for the 741 op amp. The 30-pF compensation capacitor is connected around the Darlington pair $Q_{16}$–$Q_{17}$ and produces a pole with magnitude 4.9 Hz, as shown in Chapter 7 using zero-value time constant analysis. The resulting gain and phase curves for the 741 are shown in Fig. 9.19. These curves were generated using the program SPICE and typical 741 device data. Use of these data shows that the unity-gain frequency is 1.25 MHz, the phase margin is 80°, and the low-frequency gain is 108 dB. It should be pointed out that somewhat different performance is obtained from some commercial 741 circuits because of different integrated circuit processes giving different device parameters.

As well as allowing use of a small capacitor that can be integrated on the monolithic chip, this type of compensation has another significant advantage. This is due to the phenomenon of *pole splitting*.[8] To illustrate pole splitting, the important poles and zeros of the 741 as calculated by a computer program before and after compensation are plotted (not to scale) in Fig. 9.20. Before compensation, the circuit has two important low-frequency poles with magnitudes 18.9 kHz and 328 kHz. Computer simulations show that the

**Figure 9.18** Simplified schematic of the 741 op amp showing compensation by Miller effect using a 30-pF capacitor connected around the Darlington pair $Q_{16}$-$Q_{17}$.

dominant pole with magnitude 18.9 kHz is produced largely by shunt capacitance at the base of $Q_{16}$. Computer runs made with charge storage deleted in various parts of the circuit show that the pole with magnitude 328 kHz is also contributed by transistors $Q_{16}$ and $Q_{17}$. The rest of the poles and zeros come from various parts of the circuit, including input and output stages.

**Figure 9.19** Gain and phase versus frequency for the 741 op amp.

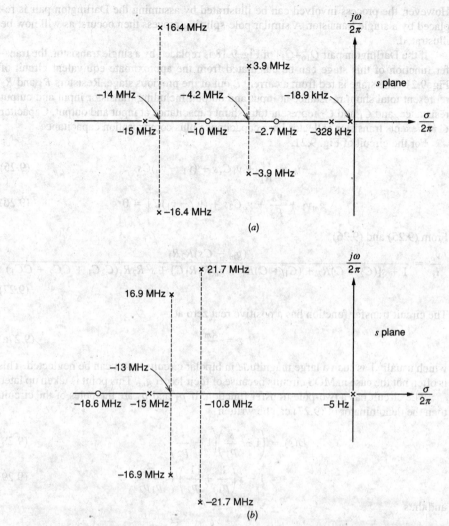

**Figure 9.20** Poles and zeros of the 741 op amp as calculated by computer. (*a*) Before compensation. (*b*) After compensation. (Not to scale.)

After compensation, there is a dramatic change in the poles and zeros of the circuit, as shown in Fig. 9.20*b*. The amplifier now has a dominant pole with magnitude 5 Hz as desired, but an additional bonus has been gained because the original second-most-dominant pole with magnitude 328 kHz has been effectively removed. The second and higher most dominant poles now form a cluster with real magnitudes 10 to 15 MHz and include complex poles. Since the amplifier gain must be made to fall to unity at a frequency below the second-most-dominant pole magnitude (for adequate phase margin), the removal of the pole with magnitude 328 kHz has greatly increased the realizable bandwidth of the circuit. If this pole did not move, the compensation capacitor would have to be adjusted to cause the gain of the 741 to fall to unity at a frequency *less than* 328 kHz.

The splitting of the two low-frequency poles of the 741 described above is a rather complex process involving other higher frequency poles and zeros in the Darlington pair.

However, the process involved can be illustrated by assuming the Darlington pair is replaced by a single transistor. A similar pole-splitting process then occurs, as will now be illustrated.

If the Darlington pair $Q_{16}$–$Q_{17}$ of Fig. 9.18 is replaced by a single transistor, the transfer function of this stage can be calculated from the approximate equivalent circuit of Fig. 9.21. The stage is fed from a current $i_s$ out of the previous stage. Resistors $R_1$ and $R_2$ represent total shunt resistance at input and output, including transistor input and output resistance, and $C_1$ and $C_2$ represent total shunt capacitance at input and output. Capacitor $C$ represents transistor collector-base capacitance plus compensation capacitance.

For the circuit of Fig. 9.21,

$$-i_s = \frac{v_1}{R_1} + v_1 C_1 s + (v_1 - v_o)Cs \tag{9.25}$$

$$g_m v_1 + \frac{v_o}{R_2} + v_o C_2 s + (v_o - v_1)Cs = 0 \tag{9.26}$$

From (9.25) and (9.26)

$$\frac{v_o}{i_s} = \frac{(g_m - Cs)R_2 R_1}{1 + s[(C_2 + C)R_2 + (C_1 + C)R_1 + g_m R_2 R_1 C] + s^2 R_2 R_1 (C_2 C_1 + C C_2 + C C_1)} \tag{9.27}$$

The circuit transfer function has a positive real zero at

$$z = \frac{g_m}{C} \tag{9.27a}$$

which usually has such a large magnitude in bipolar circuits that it can be neglected. This is often not the case in MOS circuits because of their lower $g_m$. This point is taken up later.

The circuit has a two-pole transfer function. If $p_1$ and $p_2$ are the poles of the circuit, then the denominator of (9.27) can be written

$$D(s) = \left(1 - \frac{s}{p_1}\right)\left(1 - \frac{s}{p_2}\right) \tag{9.28}$$

$$= 1 - s\left(\frac{1}{p_1} + \frac{1}{p_2}\right) + \frac{s^2}{p_1 p_2} \tag{9.29}$$

and thus

$$D(s) \simeq 1 - \frac{s}{p_1} + \frac{s^2}{p_1 p_2} \tag{9.30}$$

if the poles are real and widely separated, which is usually true. Note that $p_1$ is assumed to be the dominant pole.

**Figure 9.21** Small-signal equivalent circuit of a single transistor stage. Feedback capacitor $C$ includes compensation capacitance.

If the coefficients in (9.27) and (9.30) are equated then

$$p_1 = -\frac{1}{(C_2 + C)R_2 + (C_1 + C)R_1 + g_m R_2 R_1 C} \qquad (9.31)$$

and this can be approximated by

$$p_1 \simeq -\frac{1}{g_m R_2 R_1 C} \qquad (9.32)$$

since the Miller effect due to $C$ will be dominant if $C$ is large and $g_m R_1, g_m R_2 \gg 1$. Equation 9.31 is the same result for the dominant pole as is obtained using zero-value time constant analysis.

The nondominant pole $p_2$ can now be estimated by equating coefficients of $s^2$ in (9.27) and (9.30) and using (9.32).

$$p_2 \simeq -\frac{g_m C}{C_2 C_1 + C(C_2 + C_1)} \qquad (9.33)$$

Equation 9.32 indicates that the dominant-pole magnitude $|p_1|$ *decreases* as $C$ *increases*, whereas (9.33) shows that $|p_2|$ *increases* as $C$ *increases*. Thus, increasing $C$ causes the poles to *split apart*. As $C$ becomes very much greater than $C_1$ and $C_2$, the value of $|p_2|$ approaches $g_m/(C_1 + C_2)$, which is usually a relatively high frequency (tens or hundreds of MHz for typical parameter values). In the limit as $C \to \infty$, $p_2 \to -g_m/(C_2 + C_1)$. Since Fig. 9.21 has only two poles, this nondominant pole could be estimated using short-circuit time constants, as described in Chapter 7. Assuming $C$ is large and determines the dominant pole [as shown in (9.32)], then $p_2$ can be estimated from the time constants for the other capacitors when $C$ is shorted. With $C$ shorted, $C_1$ and $C_2$ are connected in parallel and can be treated as a single capacitor. Also, the voltage that controls the $g_m$ generator ($v_1$ in Fig. 9.21) appears across the generator. Therefore, the generator acts like a resistance of value $1/g_m$, which is in parallel with $R_2$. Assuming $1/g_m \ll R_2$, the short-circuit time constant for $C_1 + C_2$ is $\tau = (1/g_m)(C_1 + C_2)$; therefore, $|p_2| \approx 1/\tau = g_m/(C_1 + C_2)$.

It is interesting to note that the poles of the circuit of Fig. 9.21 for $C = 0$ are

$$p_1 = -\frac{1}{R_1 C_1} \qquad (9.34a)$$

$$p_2 = -\frac{1}{R_2 C_2} \qquad (9.34b)$$

Thus as $C$ increases from zero, the locus of the poles of the circuit of Fig. 9.21 is as shown in Fig. 9.22.

**Figure 9.22** Locus of the poles of the circuit of Fig. 9.21 as $C$ is increased from zero, for the case $-1/R_1 C_1 > -1/R_2 C_2$.

Another explanation of pole splitting is as follows. The circuit in Fig. 9.21 has two poles. The compensation capacitor across the second stage provides feedback and causes the second stage to act like an integrator. The two poles split apart as $C$ increases. One pole moves to a low frequency (toward dc), and the other moves to a high frequency (toward $-\infty$) to approximate an ideal integrator, which has only one pole at dc.

The previous calculations have shown how compensation of an amplifier by addition of a large Miller capacitance to a single transistor stage causes the nondominant pole to move to a much higher frequency. A similar process occurs in the 741 op amp and is the reason for the elimination of the pole with magnitude 328 kHz after compensation, as shown in Fig. 9.20. It is interesting to consider the performance attainable if the 741 is compensated by simply adding shunt capacitance to ground at the base of $Q_{16}$ in Fig. 9.18. In order to achieve the same phase margin of 80° using the same device parameters, it was found by computer simulation that a compensation capacitance of 0.3 μF was required. This gave a dominant pole with magnitude 0.27 Hz and a unity-gain frequency of only 63 kHz. The second most dominant pole had a magnitude 294 kHz. Thus very little movement of the second most dominant pole had occurred, and the change that did occur was a *decrease* in the pole magnitude. As a consequence, the realizable bandwidth of the circuit when compensated in this way is only 1/20 of that obtained with Miller effect compensation. The other disadvantage is that a capacitance of 0.3μF cannot be included on the monolithic chip.

The effect of different methods of compensation described above can be seen in the circuit of Fig. 9.21. If $C_1$ is made large in that circuit to produce a dominant pole, then the pole can be calculated from (9.31) as $p_1 \simeq -1/R_1C_1$. The nondominant pole can be estimated by equating coefficients of $s^2$ in (9.27) and (9.30) and using this value of $p_1$. This gives $p_2 \simeq -1/R_2(C_2 + C)$. This value of $p_2$ is approximately the same as that given by (9.34b), which is for $C = 0$ and is *before* pole splitting occurs. Thus, creation of a dominant pole in the circuit of Fig. 9.21 by making $C_1$ large will result in a second pole magnitude $|p_2|$ that is much smaller than that obtained if the dominant pole is created by increasing $C$. The same general trend is true in the more complex situation that exists in the 741 op amp.

The results derived in this section are useful in further illuminating the considerations of Section 7.3.3. In that section, it was stated that in a common-source cascade, the existence of drain-gate capacitance tends to cause pole splitting and to produce a dominant-pole situation. If the equivalent circuit of Fig. 9.21 is taken as a representative section of a cascade of common-source stages ($C_2$ is the input capacitance of the following stage) and capacitor $C$ is taken as $C_{gd}$, the calculations of this section show that the presence of $C_{gd}$ does, in fact, tend to produce a dominant-pole situation because of the pole splitting that occurs. Thus, the zero-value time constant approach gives a good estimate of $\omega_{-3dB}$ in such circuits.

The theory of compensation that was developed in this chapter was illustrated with some bipolar-transistor circuit examples. The theory applies in general to any active circuit, but the unique device parameters of MOSFETs cause some of the approximations that were made in the preceding analyses to become invalid. The special aspects of MOS amplifier compensation are now considered.

### 9.4.3 Two-Stage MOS Amplifier Compensation

The basic two-stage CMOS op amp topology shown in Fig. 6.16 is essentially identical to its bipolar counterpart. As a consequence, the equivalent circuit of Fig. 9.21 can be used to represent the second stage with its compensation capacitance. The poles of the

**Figure 9.23** Typical gain and phase of the CMOS op amp of Fig. 6.16.

circuit are again given by (9.32) and (9.33) and the zero by (9.27a). In the case of the MOS transistor, however, the value of $g_m$ is typically an order of magnitude lower than for a bipolar transistor, and the break frequency caused by the right half-plane zero in (9.27) may actually fall below the nominal unity-gain frequency of the amplifier. The effect of this is shown in Fig. 9.23. At the frequency $|z|$ the gain characteristic of the amplifier flattens out because of the contribution to the gain of +6 dB/octave from the zero. In the same region the phase is made 90° more *negative* by the positive real zero. As a consequence, the amplifier will have negative phase margin and be unstable when the influence of the next most dominant pole is felt. In effect, the zero halts the gain roll-off intended to stabilize the amplifier and simultaneously pushes the phase in the negative direction. Note also from (9.33) that the low $g_m$ of the MOSFET will tend to reduce the value of $|p_2|$ relative to a bipolar amplifier.

Another way to view this problem is to note from Fig. 9.21 that at high frequencies, feedforward through $C$ tends to overwhelm the normal gain path via $g_m$ of the second stage if $g_m$ is small. The feedforward path does not have the 180° phase shift of the normal gain stage, and thus the gain path loses an inverting stage. Any feedback applied around the overall amplifier will then be positive instead of negative feedback, resulting in oscillation. At very high frequencies, $C$ acts like a short circuit diode-connecting the second stage, which then simply presents a resistive load of $1/g_m$ to the first stage, again showing the loss of 180° of phase shift.

The right half-plane (RHP) zero is caused by the interaction of current from the $g_m$ generator and the frequency-dependent current that flows forward from the input node to the output node through $C$. The current through $C$ in Fig. 9.21 is

$$i_c = sC(v_o - v_1) \tag{9.35}$$

This current can be broken into two parts: a feedback current $i_{fb} = sCv_o$ that flows from the output back toward the input and a feedforward current $i_{ff} = sCv_1$ that flows forward from the input toward the output. This feedforward current is related to $v_1$. The current $g_m v_1$ from the controlled source flows out of the output node and is also related to $v_1$. Subtracting these two currents gives the total current at the output node that is related to $v_1$:

$$i_{v_1} = (g_m - sC)v_1 \tag{9.36}$$

A zero exists in the transfer function where this current equals zero, at $z = g_m/C$.

   Three techniques have been used to eliminate the effect of the RHP zero. One approach is to put a source follower in series with the compensation capacitor,[9] as shown in Fig. 9.24a. The source follower blocks feedforward current through $C$ from reaching the output node and therefore eliminates the zero. This will be shown by analyzing Fig. 9.21 with $C$ replaced by the model in Fig. 9.24b. Here the source follower is modeled as an ideal voltage buffer. Equation 9.25 still holds because the same elements are connected to the input node and the voltage across $C$ remains $v_o - v_1$. However, summing currents at the output node gives a different equation than (9.26) because no current flows through $C$ to the output node due to the buffer. The new equation is

$$g_m v_1 + \frac{v_o}{R_2} + sC_2 v_o = 0 \tag{9.37}$$

Combining this equation with (9.25) gives

$$\frac{v_o}{i_s} = \frac{g_m R_1 R_2}{1 + s[R_1(C_1 + C) + R_2 C_2 + g_m R_2 R_1 C] + s^2 R_1 R_2 C_2(C_1 + C)} \tag{9.38}$$

The zero has been eliminated. Assuming $g_m R_1, g_m R_2 \gg 1$ and $C$ is large, the same steps that led from (9.27) to (9.32) and (9.33) give

$$p_1 \approx -\frac{1}{g_m R_2 R_1 C} \tag{9.39a}$$

$$p_2 \approx -\frac{g_m C}{(C_1 + C)C_2} \approx -\frac{g_m}{C_2} \tag{9.39b}$$

(a)                                    (b)

**Figure 9.24**  (a) Compensation capacitor $C$ in Fig. 9.21 is replaced by $C$ in series with a source follower. (b) A simple model for the capacitor and source follower.

The dominant pole $p_1$ is unchanged, and $p_2$ is about the same as before if $C_2 \gg C_1$. This approach eliminates the zero, but the follower requires extra devices and bias current. Also, the source follower has a nonzero dc voltage between its input and output. This voltage will affect the output voltage swing since the source-follower transistor must remain in the active region to maintain the desired feedback through $C$.

A second approach to eliminate the RHP zero is to block the feedforward current through $C$ using a common-gate transistor, [10] as illustrated in Fig. 9.25a. This figure shows a two-stage op amp, with the addition of two current sources of value $I_2$ and transistor $M_{11}$. The compensation capacitor is connected from the op-amp output to the source of $M_{11}$. Here, common-gate $M_{11}$ allows capacitor current to flow from the output back toward the input of the second stage. However, the impedance looking into the drain of $M_{11}$ is very large. Therefore, feedforward current through $C$ is very small. If the feedforward current is zero, the RHP zero is eliminated. A simplified small-signal model for the common-gate stage and compensation capacitor is shown in Fig. 9.25b. Here common-gate $M_{11}$ is modeled as an ideal current buffer. Replacing $C$ in Fig. 9.21 with the model in Fig. 9.25b yields

$$-i_s = \frac{v_1}{R_1} + v_1 C_1 s - v_o C s \tag{9.40a}$$

$$g_m v_1 + \frac{v_o}{R_2} + v_o C s + v_o C_2 s = 0 \tag{9.40b}$$

Combining these equations gives

$$\frac{v_o}{i_s} = \frac{g_m R_1 R_2}{1 + s[R_1 C_1 + R_2(C + C_2) + g_m R_1 R_2 C] + s^2 R_1 R_2 C_1 (C_2 + C)} \tag{9.41}$$

(a)

(b)

**Figure 9.25** (a) A two-stage CMOS op amp with common-gate $M_{11}$ connected to compensation capacitor $C$. (b) Simple small-signal model for $M_{11}$ and $C$.

The zero has been eliminated. Again assuming $g_m R_1, g_m R_2 \gg 1$ and $C$ is large, the poles are

$$p_1 \approx -\frac{1}{g_m R_2 R_1 C} \tag{9.42a}$$

$$p_2 \approx -\frac{g_m}{C + C_2} \cdot \frac{C}{C_1} \tag{9.42b}$$

The dominant pole is the same as before. However, the nondominant pole $p_2$ is different. This $p_2$ is at a higher frequency than in the two previous approaches because $C \gg C_1$ when $C$ and $C_2$ are comparable. (In this section, we assume that the two-stage MOS op amp in Fig. 9.21 drives a load capacitor $C_2$ that is much larger than parasitic capacitance $C_1$; therefore $C_2 \gg C_1$.) Therefore, a smaller compensation capacitor $C$ can be used here for a given load capacitance $C_2$, when compared to the previous approaches. The increase in $|p_2|$ arises because the input node is not connected to, and therefore is not loaded by, the compensation capacitor. An advantage of this scheme is that it provides better high-frequency negative-power-supply rejection than Miller compensation. (Power-supply rejection was introduced in Section 6.3.6.) With Miller compensation, $C$ is connected from the gate to drain of $M_6$, and it shorts the gate and drain at high frequencies. Assuming $V_{gs6}$ is approximately constant, high-frequency variations on the negative supply are coupled directly to the op-amp output. Connecting $C$ to common-gate $M_{11}$ eliminates this coupling path. Drawbacks of this approach are that extra devices and dc current are needed to implement the scheme in Fig. 9.25a. Also, if there is a mismatch between the $I_2$ current sources, the difference current must flow in the input stage, which disrupts the balance in the input stage and affects the input-offset voltage of the op amp.

When the first stage of the op amp uses a cascode transistor, the compensation capacitor can be connected to the source of the cascode device as shown in Fig. 9.26.[11] This connection reduces the feedforward current through $C$, when compared to connecting $C$ to node (Y), if the voltage swing at the source of the cascode device is smaller than the swing at its drain. This approach eliminates the feedforward path, and therefore the zero, if the

**Figure 9.26** A two-stage CMOS op amp with a cascoded current-mirror load in the input stage, and with the compensation capacitor $C$ connected to the cascode node.

voltage swing at the source of the cascode device is zero. An advantage of this approach is that it avoids the extra devices, bias current, and mismatch problems in Fig. 9.25a.

A third way to deal with the RHP zero is to insert a resistor in series with the compensation capacitor, as shown in Fig. 9.27a.[12,13] Rather than eliminate the feedforward current, the resistor modifies this current and allows the zero to be moved to infinity. If the zero moves to infinity, the total forward current at the output node that is related to $v_1$ must go to zero when $\omega \to \infty$. When $\omega \to \infty$, capacitor $C$ is a short circuit and therefore the feedforward current is only due to $R_Z$:

$$i_{ff}(\omega \to \infty) = -\frac{v_1}{R_Z} \tag{9.43}$$

When this current is added to the current from the $g_m$ source, the total current at the output node that is related to $v_1$ is

$$i_{v_1} = \left(g_m - \frac{1}{R_Z}\right)v_1 \tag{9.44}$$

when $\omega \to \infty$. If $R_Z = 1/g_m$, this term vanishes, and the zero is at infinity.

The complete transfer function can be found by carrying out an analysis similar to that performed for Fig. 9.21, which gives

$$\frac{v_o}{i_s} = \frac{g_m R_1 R_2 \left[1 - sC\left(\dfrac{1}{g_m} - R_Z\right)\right]}{1 + bs + cs^2 + ds^3} \tag{9.45}$$

where

$$b = R_2(C_2 + C) + R_1(C_1 + C) + R_Z C + g_m R_1 R_2 C \tag{9.46a}$$
$$c = R_1 R_2(C_1 C_2 + C C_1 + C C_2) + R_Z C(R_1 C_1 + R_2 C_2) \tag{9.46b}$$
$$d = R_1 R_2 R_Z C_1 C_2 C \tag{9.46c}$$

Figure 9.27 (a) Small-signal equivalent circuit of a compensation stage with nulling resistor. (b) Pole-zero diagram showing movement of the transmission zero for various values of $R_z$.

Again assuming $g_m R_1, g_m R_2 \gg 1$ and $C$ is large, the poles can be approximated by

$$p_1 \approx -\frac{1}{g_m R_2 R_1 C} \tag{9.47a}$$

$$p_2 \approx -\frac{g_m C}{C_1 C_2 + C(C_1 + C_2)} \approx -\frac{g_m}{C_1 + C_2} \tag{9.47b}$$

$$p_3 \approx -\frac{1}{R_Z C_1} \tag{9.47c}$$

The first two poles, $p_1$ and $p_2$, are the same as for the original circuit in Fig. 9.21. The third pole is at a very high frequency with $|p_3| \gg |p_2|$ because typically $C_1 \ll C_2$ (since $C_1$ is a small parasitic capacitor and $C_2$ is the load capacitor) and $R_Z$ will be about equal to $1/g_m$ if the zero is moved to a high frequency [from (9.44)]. This circuit has three poles because there are three independent capacitors. In contrast, Fig. 9.21 has three capacitors that form a loop, so only two of the capacitor voltages are independent. Thus there are only two poles associated with that circuit.

The zero of (9.45) is

$$z = \frac{1}{\left(\dfrac{1}{g_m} - R_Z\right)C} \tag{9.48}$$

This zero moves to infinity when $R_Z$ equals $1/g_m$. Making the resistor greater than $1/g_m$ moves the zero into the left half-plane, which can be used to provide positive phase shift at high frequencies and improve the phase margin of a feedback circuit that uses this op amp.[13] The movement of the zero for increasing $R_Z$ is shown in Fig. 9.27b.

Figure 9.28a shows a Miller-compensated op amp using a resistor $R_Z$ in series with the compensation capacitor. In practice, resistor $R_Z$ is usually implemented using a MOS transistor biased in the triode region. From (1.152), a MOS transistor operating in the triode region behaves like a linear resistor if $V_{ds} \ll 2(V_{GS} - V_t)$. The on-resistance $R_Z$ of the triode device can be made to track $1/g_m$ of common-source transistor $M_6$ if the two transistors are identical and have the same $V_{GS} - V_t$. When this MOS transistor is placed to the left of the compensation capacitor as shown in Fig. 9.28, its source voltage is set by $V_{gs6}$, which is approximately constant. Therefore, $V_{GS}$ of the triode transistor can be set by connecting its gate to a dc bias voltage, which can be generated using replica biasing.[13] (See Problem 9.23.)

Another way to shift the zero location that can be used in multistage op amps will be presented in Section 9.4.5.

In all the compensation approaches described so far, the dominant pole is set by compensation capacitor $C$ and is independent of the load capacitor $C_2$. However, the second pole is a function of $C_2$. If the op amp will be used in different applications with a range of load capacitors, the compensation capacitor should be selected to give an acceptable phase margin for the largest $C_2$. Then the phase margin will increase as the load capacitor decreases because $|p_2|$ is inversely proportional to $C_2$.

■ **EXAMPLE**

Compensate the two-stage CMOS op amp from the example in Section 6.3.5 (Fig. 6.16) to achieve a phase margin of 45° or larger when driving a load capacitance of 5 pF, assuming the op amp is connected in unity-gain feedback.

With the op amp in unity-gain feedback, $f = 1$ and the loop gain $T = af = a$ (or, equivalently, $A_\infty = 1$ and the return ratio $\mathcal{R} = a$). Therefore, the phase and gain margins can be determined from Bode plots of $|a|$ and ph($a$).

**Figure 9.28** (a) A two-stage CMOS op amp. (b) A small-signal model for the op amp.

The two-stage op amp and a simplified model for this op amp are shown in Fig. 9.28. In the model, all capacitances that connect to node ⊗ are lumped into $C_1$, and all capacitances that connect to the output node are lumped into $C_2$. If we apply an input voltage $v_i$ in Fig. 9.28b, a current $i_1 = g_{m1}v_i$ is generated. This $i_1$ drives a circuit that is the same as the circuit that $i_s$ drives in Fig. 9.21. Therefore, the equations for the two poles and one zero for the circuit in Fig. 9.21 apply here with $i_s = g_{m1}v_i$, $g_m = g_{m6}$, $R_1 = r_{o2}||r_{o4}$, and $R_2 = r_{o6}||r_{o7}$.

We will use Miller compensation with a series resistance to eliminate the zero. To achieve a 45° phase margin, the compensation capacitor $C$ should be chosen so that $|p_2|$ equals the unity-gain frequency (assuming the zero has been eliminated and $|p_3| \gg |p_2|$). Since the gain roll-off from $|p_1|$ to $|p_2|$ is −6 dB/octave, $|a(j\omega)| \cdot \omega$ is constant from $|p_1|$ to $|p_2|$. Therefore,

$$a_o \cdot |p_1| = 1 \cdot |p_2| \qquad (9.49)$$

where

$$a_o = g_{m1}(r_{o2}||r_{o4})g_{m6}(r_{o6}||r_{o7}) = g_{m1}R_1 g_{m6}R_2 \qquad (9.50)$$

is the dc gain of the op amp. Substitution of (9.47) and (9.50) into (9.49) gives

$$g_{m1}R_1 g_{m6}R_2 \cdot \frac{1}{g_{m6}R_2 R_1 C} = 1 \cdot \frac{g_{m6}}{C_1 + C_2}.$$

or

$$\frac{g_{m1}}{C} = \frac{g_{m6}}{C_1 + C_2} \tag{9.51}$$

The capacitance $C_2$ at the output is dominated by the 5-pF load capacitance, and the internal parasitic capacitance $C_1$ is much smaller than 5 pF (SPICE simulation gives $C_1 \approx$ 120 fF). Therefore $C_1 + C_2 \approx 5$ pF. From the example in Section 6.3.5, we find

$$g_{m1} = k_p'(W/L)_1|V_{ov1}| = (64.7 \ \mu\text{A/V}^2)(77)(0.2 \text{ V}) = 1 \text{ mA/V}$$

and

$$g_{m6} = k_n'(W/L)_6(V_{ov6}) = (194 \ \mu\text{A/V}^2)(16)(0.5 \text{ V}) = 1.55 \text{ mA/V}$$

Substituting these values into (9.51) and rearranging gives

$$C = \frac{g_{m1}}{g_{m6}}(C_1 + C_2) \approx \frac{1 \text{ mA/V}}{1.55 \text{ mA/V}}(5 \text{ pF}) = 3.2 \text{ pF}$$

To eliminate the zero due to feedforward through $C$, a resistor $R_Z$ of value $1/g_{m6} = 645 \ \Omega$ can be connected in series with the compensation capacitor $C$. (In practice, this resistance should be implemented with an NMOS transistor that is a copy of $M_6$ biased in the triode region, so that $R_Z = 1/g_{m6}$. See Problem 9.23.)

SPICE simulations (using models based on Table 2.4) of the op amp before and after compensation give the magnitude and phase plots shown in Fig. 9.29. Before compensation, the amplifier is unstable and has a phase margin of $-6°$. After compensation with $R_Z = 645 \ \Omega$ and $C = 3.2$ pF the phase margin improves to $41°$ with a unity-gain frequency of 35 MHz, and the gain margin is 15 dB. This phase margin is less than the desired $45°$. The simulated value of $g_{m6}$ is 1.32 mA/V and differs somewhat from the calculated $g_{m6}$, because the formulas used to calculate $g_m$ are based on square-law equations that are only approximately correct. Changing $R_Z$ to $1/g_{m6}$(SPICE) $= 758 \ \Omega$ gives a phase margin of $46°$ with a unity-gain frequency of 35 MHz, and the gain margin is 22 dB. Without $R_Z$, the phase margin is $14°$, so eliminating the right-half-plane zero significantly improves the phase margin.

Two earlier assumptions can be checked from SPICE simulations. First, $C_1 \approx$ 120 fF from SPICE and $C_2 \approx 5$ pF; therefore, the assumption that $C_1 \ll C_2$ is valid. Also, $|p_3| \gg |p_2|$ follows from $|p_3| \approx 1/(R_Z C_1) = g_{m6}/C_1$, $|p_2| \approx g_{m6}/C_2$, and $C_1 \ll C_2$. ■

### 9.4.4 Compensation of Single-Stage CMOS Op Amps

Single-stage op amps, such as the telescopic cascode or folded cascode, have only one gain stage; therefore Miller compensation is not possible. These op amps have high open-loop output resistance and are typically used in switched-capacitor circuits, where the load is purely capacitive. Therefore, the dominant pole is associated with the output node, and the load capacitor provides the compensation.

A simplified, fully differential, telescopic-cascode op amp is shown in Fig. 9.30a. The simplifications here are that ideal current sources replace biasing transistors and all capacitances have been lumped into the load capacitors $C_L$ and the parasitic capacitors $C_p$ at the cascode nodes. The differential-mode (DM) voltage gain can be found by analyzing the half-circuit shown in Fig. 9.30b. Since there are two independent capacitors, the DM gain has two poles. An exact analysis, ignoring body effect, gives a DM gain of

$$\frac{v_{od}}{v_{id}} = -\frac{g_{m1}r_{o1}(g_{m1A}r_{o1A} + 1)}{1 + s(r_{o1A}C_L + r_{o1}C_p + r_{o1}C_L + g_{m1A}r_{o1A}r_{o1}C_L) + s^2 r_{o1}r_{o1A}C_pC_L} \tag{9.52}$$

**Figure 9.29** Plots of the simulated (*a*) magnitude and (*b*) phase of the op-amp gain before and after compensation ($C = 3.2$ pF, $R_Z = 645\ \Omega$) for the op amp in Fig. 9.28.

If $g_m r_o \gg 1$, (9.52) simplifies to

$$\frac{v_{od}}{v_{id}} = \frac{g_{m1}r_{o1}g_{m1A}r_{o1A}}{1 + sg_{m1A}r_{o1A}r_{o1}C_L + s^2 r_{o1}r_{o1A}C_pC_L} \tag{9.53}$$

The gain has two poles and no zeros. Assuming widely spaced real poles, the poles can be approximated using (9.29) and (9.30):

$$p_1 \approx -\frac{1}{g_{m1A}r_{o1A}r_{o1}C_L} \approx -\frac{1}{R_oC_L} \tag{9.54a}$$

$$p_2 \approx -\frac{g_{m1A}}{C_p} \tag{9.54b}$$

where $R_o$ is the output resistance of the DM half-circuit and $R_o \approx g_{m1A}r_{o1A}r_{o1}$. Alternatively, these poles can be estimated using time-constant analysis as shown in Chapter 7. The dominant pole is set by the zero-value time constant for $C_L$, which is computed with $C_p$ open and equals $R_oC_L$. The nondominant pole can be approximated using the short-circuit time constant for $C_p$, which is computed with $C_L$ shorted. When $C_L$ is shorted, the

**Figure 9.30** (a) Simplified CMOS telescopic-cascode op amp. (b) The differential-mode half-circuit.

resistance seen by $C_p$ is the resistance looking into the source of $M_{1A}$, which is $1/g_{m1A}$ (ignoring body effect). Typically, $|p_1| \ll |p_2|$ because $R_o \gg 1/g_{m1A}$ and $C_L \gg C_p$. If the phase margin is not large enough for a given feedback application, additional capacitance can be added at the output node to increase $C_L$, which decreases $|p_1|$ without affecting $p_2$ and therefore increases the phase margin.

Capacitance $C_p$ consists of $C_{gs1A}$ plus smaller capacitances such as $C_{db1}$ and $C_{sb1A}$. Assuming $C_p \approx C_{gs1A}$, then $|p_2| \approx g_{m1A}/C_p \approx g_{m1A}/C_{gs1A} \approx \omega_T$ of $M_{1A}$. Thus, the frequency at which the magnitude of the op-amp gain equals one, which is called the unity-gain bandwidth, can be very high with this op amp.

A simplified, fully differential, folded-cascode op amp is shown in Fig. 9.31a. As above, the simplifications are that ideal current sources replace biasing transistors and all capacitances have been lumped into the load capacitors $C_L$ and the parasitic capacitors $C_p'$ at the cascode nodes. With these simplifications, the DM voltage gain can be found by analyzing the half-circuit shown in Fig. 9.31b. This circuit is identical to Fig. 9.30b except that the cascode device is p-channel rather than n-channel and $C_p'$ replaces $C_p$. Therefore, the gain is identical to (9.52) with $C_p$ replaced by $C_p'$. Hence the dominant pole has the same form as (9.54a)

$$p_1 \approx -\frac{1}{g_{m1A}r_{o1A}r_{o1}C_L} \approx -\frac{1}{R_oC_L} \qquad (9.55a)$$

(a)

(b)

**Figure 9.31** (a) Simplified CMOS folded-cascode op amp. (b) The differential-mode half-circuit.

The second pole is associated with $C_p'$ and is approximately given by

$$p_2 \approx -\frac{g_{m1A}}{C_p'} \qquad (9.55b)$$

Equations 9.55b and 9.54b look similar, but $|p_2|$ for the folded-cascode op amp will usually be smaller than $|p_2|$ for the telescopic-cascode op amp. The reason is that, while the transconductances of the cascode devices in the two circuits are often comparable, $C_p'$ will be significantly larger than $C_p$. One cause of the higher capacitance is that more devices are connected to the node associated with $C_p'$ in the folded-cascode op amp than are connected to the node associated with $C_p$ in the telescopic cascode. (Recall that the output of each ideal current source in Fig. 9.31a is the drain of a transistor.) Also, $W/L$ of the p-channel cascode transistor $M_{1A}$ in Fig. 9.31b must be larger than $W/L$ of the n-channel cascode device in Fig. 9.30b to make their transconductances comparable. The larger $W/L$ will cause $C_p'$ to be larger than $C_p$. The smaller $|p_2|$ for the folded cascode leads to a smaller unity-gain bandwidth, if the two op amps are compensated to give the same phase margin in a given feedback application.

The circuits in Figs. 9.30 and 9.31 are fully differential. These op amps can be converted to single-ended op amps by replacing a pair of matched current sources with a current mirror. In Fig. 9.30a, the two $I$ current sources would be replaced with a p-channel current mirror. In Fig. 9.31a, the two $I_2$ current sources would be replaced with an n-channel current mirror. As shown in Section 7.3.5, a current mirror introduces a closely spaced pole-zero pair, in addition to the poles $p_1$ and $p_2$ in (9.54) and (9.55).

Active cascodes can be used to increase the low-frequency gain of an op amp, as shown in Fig. 6.30$a$. There are four active cascodes in Fig. 6.30$a$; each consists of a cascode transistor ($M_{1A}$–$M_{4A}$) and an auxiliary amplifier ($A_1$ or $A_2$) in a feedback loop. When such an op amp is placed in feedback, multiple feedback loops are present. There are four local feedback loops associated with the active cascodes in the op amp and one global feedback loop that consists of the op amp and a feedback network around the op amp. All these feedback loops must be stable to avoid oscillation. The stability of each local feedback loop can be determined from its loop gain or return ratio. Since the auxiliary amplifiers in these loops are op amps, each auxiliary amplifier can be compensated using the techniques described in this chapter to ensure stability of these local loops. Then the global feedback loop can be compensated to guarantee its stability.

### 9.4.5 Nested Miller Compensation

Many feedback circuits require an op amp with a high voltage gain. While cascoding is commonly used to increase the gain in op amps with a total supply voltage of 5 V or more, cascoding becomes increasingly difficult as the power-supply voltage is reduced. (See Chapter 4.) To overcome this problem, simple gain stages without cascoding can be cascaded to achieve high gain. When three or more voltage-gain stages must be cascaded to achieve the desired gain, the op amp will have three or more poles, and frequency compensation becomes complicated. Nested Miller compensation can be used with more than two gain stages.[14,15] This compensation scheme involves repeated, nested application of Miller compensation. An example of nested Miller compensation applied to three cascaded gain stages is shown in Fig. 9.32$a$. Two noninverting gain stages are followed by an inverting gain stage. Each voltage-gain stage is assumed to have a high-output resistance and therefore is labeled as a $g_m$ block. The sign of the dc voltage gain of each stage is given by the sign of the transconductance. Two Miller compensation capacitors are used: $C_{m1}$, which is placed around the last gain stage, and $C_{m2}$, which is connected across the last two gain stages. Because the dc gain of the second stage is positive and the dc gain of the third stage is negative, both capacitors are in negative feedback loops.

A simplified circuit schematic is shown in Fig. 9.32$b$. Each noninverting gain stage is composed of a differential pair with a current-source load. The inverting gain stage consists of a common-source amplifier with a current-source load. A simplified small-signal model is shown in Fig. 9.32$c$. The main simplification here is that all capacitances associated with the gain stages are modeled by $C_0$, $C_1$, and $C_2$.

Without the compensation capacitors, this amplifier has three real poles that are not widely spaced if the $R_i C_i$ time constants are comparable. When $C_{m1}$ is added, the two poles associated with the input and output nodes of the last stage split apart along the real axis due to the Miller compensation, but the pole associated with $C_0$ does not change. When $C_{m2}$ is also added, these three poles are further modified. The pole locations can be found from an exact analysis of the small-signal circuit. The analysis can be carried out by summing currents at the outputs of the $g_m$ generators, then manipulating the resulting three equations. These steps are not conceptually difficult but are not shown here. The exact transfer function from the output of the current generator in the input stage, $i_s = g_{m0}v_{in}$, to the output voltage $v_o$ is

$$\frac{v_o}{i_s} = -\frac{N(s)}{D(s)} \tag{9.56}$$

$$= -\frac{R_0 g_{m1} R_1 g_{m2} R_2 - (g_{m1} R_1 C_{m1} + C_{m2}) R_0 R_2 s - R_0 R_1 R_2 C_{m2}(C_1 + C_{m1})s^2}{1 + a_1 s + a_2 s^2 + a_3 s^3}$$

(a)

(b)

(c)

**Figure 9.32** (a) Block diagram for a three-stage op amp with nested Miller compensation. (b) A simplified schematic for such an op amp in CMOS. (c) A small-signal model.

where

$$a_1 = K + R_0(C_{m2} + C_0) + g_{m1}R_1 g_{m2}R_2 R_0 C_{m2} \tag{9.57a}$$

$$\begin{aligned} a_2 &= R_1 R_2 (C_2 + C_{m1} + C_{m2})(C_1 + C_{m1}) - R_1 R_2 C_{m1}^2 + R_0(C_{m2} + C_0)K \\ &\quad - g_{m1}R_1 C_{m1}C_{m2}R_0 R_2 - R_0 R_2 C_{m2}^2 \end{aligned} \tag{9.57b}$$

$$\begin{aligned} a_3 &= R_0 R_1 R_2 [(C_2 C_{m2} + C_0 C_2 + C_0 C_{m2})(C_1 + C_{m1}) + C_1 C_{m1} C_{m2} \\ &\quad + C_0 C_1 C_{m1}] \end{aligned} \tag{9.57c}$$

with

$$K = R_2(C_2 + C_{m1} + C_{m2}) + R_1(C_1 + C_{m1}) + R_1 C_{m1} g_{m2} R_2 \qquad (9.57d)$$

Equation 9.56 is the transfer function from $i_s$ to $v_o$. The transfer function of the voltage gain from $v_{in}$ to $v_o$ is found by multiplying (9.56) by $g_{m0}$ (since $i_s = g_{m0} v_{in}$); therefore, the voltage gain and (9.56) have the same poles and zeros. The transfer function in (9.56) has two zeros and three poles. Let us first examine the poles. The expressions for the $a_i$ coefficients are complicated and involve many terms. Therefore assumptions are needed to simplify the equations. If $g_{m1} R_1 g_{m2} R_2 \gg 1$, which is usually true, then

$$a_1 \approx g_{m1} R_1 g_{m2} R_2 R_0 C_{m2} \qquad (9.58)$$

Assuming there is a dominant pole $p_1$, then

$$p_1 \approx -\frac{1}{a_1} = -\frac{1}{g_{m1} R_1 g_{m2} R_2 R_0 C_{m2}} \qquad (9.59)$$

Another way to arrive at this estimate of $p_1$ is to apply the Miller effect to $C_{m2}$. The effective Miller capacitor is about $C_{m2}$ times the negative of the gain across $C_{m2}$, which is $g_{m1} R_1 g_{m2} R_2$. This capacitor appears in parallel with $R_0$, giving a time constant of $(g_{m1} R_1 g_{m2} R_2) R_0 C_{m2}$.

The other poles $p_2$ and $p_3$ could be found by factoring the third-order denominator in (9.56), which can be done using a computer but is difficult by hand. However, these poles can be estimated from a quadratic equation under certain conditions. If there is a dominant pole $p_1$, then $|p_2|, |p_3| \gg |p_1|$. At high frequencies, where $|s| \gg |p_1| \approx 1/a_1$, we have $|a_1 s| \gg 1$, so the denominator in (9.56) can be approximated by dropping the constant "1" to give

$$D(s) \approx a_1 s + a_2 s^2 + a_3 s^3 = a_1 s \left( 1 + \frac{a_2}{a_1} s + \frac{a_3}{a_1} s^2 \right) \qquad (9.60)$$

This equation gives three poles. One pole is at dc, which models the effect of the dominant pole $p_1$ for frequencies well above $|p_1|$. Poles $p_2$ and $p_3$ are the other roots of (9.60). They can be found by concentrating on the quadratic term in parenthesis in (9.60), which is

$$D'(s) = \frac{D(s)}{a_1 s} \approx 1 + \frac{a_2}{a_1} s + \frac{a_3}{a_1} s^2 \approx \left( 1 - \frac{s}{p_2} \right)\left( 1 - \frac{s}{p_3} \right) \qquad (9.61)$$

Assuming that $R_0, R_1, R_2 \gg |1/(g_{m2} - g_{m1})|$ and $C_o$ is small compared to the other capacitors, (9.57b) and (9.57c) simplify to

$$a_2 \approx R_0 R_1 R_2 (g_{m2} - g_{m1}) C_{m1} C_{m2} \qquad (9.62)$$

$$a_3 \approx R_0 R_1 R_2 (C_1 C_2 C_{m2} + C_2 C_{m1} C_{m2} + C_1 C_{m1} C_{m2}) \qquad (9.63)$$

Using (9.58), (9.62), and (9.63), the coefficients in $D'(s)$ are

$$\frac{a_2}{a_1} \approx \frac{g_{m2} - g_{m1}}{g_{m1} g_{m2}} C_{m1} \qquad (9.64)$$

$$\frac{a_3}{a_1} \approx \frac{C_1 C_2 + C_{m1} C_1 + C_2 C_{m1}}{g_{m1} g_{m2}} \qquad (9.65)$$

To ensure that the high-frequency poles are in the left half-plane (LHP), $a_2/a_1$ must be positive (see Appendix A9.2). Therefore, $g_{m2}$ must be larger than $g_{m1}$. Poles $p_2$ and $p_3$ can be real or complex, and in general the quadratic formula must be used to solve for these poles. However, if these poles are real and widely spaced and if $C_{m1} \gg C_1, C_2$, then approximate expressions can be found. If $|p_2| \ll |p_3|$, then $-1/p_2$ is approximately equal to the coefficient of $s$ in $D'(s)$, so

$$p_2 \approx -\frac{a_1}{a_2} = -\frac{g_{m1}g_{m2}}{(g_{\bar{m}2} - g_{m1})C_{m1}} \tag{9.66a}$$

Also $1/(p_2 p_3)$ is equal to the coefficient of $s^2$ in $D'(s)$, so

$$p_3 \approx \frac{a_1}{a_3}\frac{1}{p_2} = -\frac{g_{m1}g_{m2}}{C_1 C_2 + C_{m1}C_1 + C_2 C_{m1}} \cdot \frac{(g_{m2} - g_{m1})C_{m1}}{g_{m1}g_{m2}} \tag{9.66b}$$

$$= -\frac{(g_{m2} - g_{m1})C_{m1}}{C_1 C_2 + C_{m1}(C_1 + C_2)} \approx -\frac{g_{m2} - g_{m1}}{C_1 + C_2}$$

The final approximation here follows if $C_{m1}$ is large. Equations 9.66a and 9.66b are accurate if $|p_2| \ll |p_3|$. Substituting (9.66a) and (9.66b) into this inequality produces an equivalent condition

$$|p_2| \approx \frac{g_{m1}g_{m2}}{(g_{m2} - g_{m1})C_{m1}} \ll \frac{(g_{m2} - g_{m1})C_{m1}}{C_1 C_2 + C_{m1}(C_1 + C_2)} \approx |p_3| \tag{9.67}$$

If this condition is not satisfied, $p_2$ and $p_3$ are either complex conjugates or real but closely spaced. $C_{m1}$ can always be chosen large enough to satisfy the inequality in (9.67). While it is possible to make the high-frequency poles real and widely separated, higher unity-gain bandwidth may be achievable when $p_2$ and $p_3$ are not real and widely separated.[16]

In the simplified equations (9.66a) and (9.66b), poles $p_2$ and $p_3$ are dependent on $C_{m1}$ but not on $C_{m2}$. In contrast, dominant pole $p_1$ is inversely proportional to $C_{m2}$ and is independent of $C_{m1}$. The poles can be positioned to approximate a two-pole op amp by making $|p_1| \ll |p_2| \ll |p_3|$ and positioning $|p_3|$ well beyond the unity-gain frequency of the op amp.

The zero locations can be found by factoring the second-order numerator $N(s)$ in (9.56). The coefficients of $s$ and $s^2$ in the numerator are negative and the constant term is positive. As a result, the zeros are real. One is positive and the other is negative, as is shown in Appendix A9.2.

The zeros will be found using some simplifying assumptions. First, the numerator of (9.56) can be rewritten as

$$N(s) = R_0 g_{m1} R_1 g_{m2} R_2 \left[ 1 - s\left(\frac{C_{m1}}{g_{m2}} + \frac{C_{m2}}{g_{m1}R_1 g_{m2}}\right) - s^2 \frac{C_{m2}(C_1 + C_{m1})}{g_{m1}g_{m2}} \right] \tag{9.68}$$

Assuming that $C_{m1} \gg C_1$ and $C_{m1} \gg C_{m2}/(g_{m1}R_1)$, then

$$N(s) \approx R_0 g_{m1} R_1 g_{m2} R_2 \left[ 1 - s\frac{C_{m1}}{g_{m2}} - s^2 \frac{C_{m2}C_{m1}}{g_{m1}g_{m2}} \right] \tag{9.69}$$

The zeros are the roots of $N(s) = 0$. Using the quadratic formula and (9.69), the zeros are

$$z_{1,2} = -\frac{g_{m1}}{2C_{m2}} \pm \sqrt{\left(\frac{g_{m1}}{2C_{m2}}\right)^2 + \frac{g_{m1}g_{m2}}{C_{m1}C_{m2}}} = -\frac{g_{m1}}{2C_{m2}}\left(1 \pm \sqrt{1 + \frac{4g_{m2}C_{m2}}{g_{m1}C_{m1}}}\right) \tag{9.70}$$

Taking the positive square root in the right-most formula in (9.70) yields a value that is larger than one. Adding this value to 1 gives a positive value for the term in parentheses; subtracting this value from 1 gives a negative quantity with a smaller magnitude than the sum. Therefore, one zero is in the LHP and has a magnitude greater than $g_{m1}/(2C_{m2})$. The other zero is in the RHP and has a smaller magnitude than the LHP zero. As a result, the effect of the RHP zero is felt at a lower frequency than the LHP zero.

The magnitude of one or both zeros can be comparable to $|p_2|$. Because the RHP zero is at a lower frequency than the LHP zero, the RHP zero can cause significant negative phase

**Figure 9.33**  (*a*) Block diagram of a two-stage op amp with Miller compensation and a feedforward transconductor. (*b*) A small-signal model.

shift for frequencies at or below $|p_2|$, which would degrade the phase margin of a feedback loop. This undesired negative phase shift would not occur if the transfer function did not have zeros. Unfortunately, the three techniques considered in Section 9.4.3 to eliminate a RHP zero have important limitations in a low-supply application. First, the zeros could be eliminated by adding a source-follower buffer between the op-amp output and the right-hand side of capacitors $C_{m1}$ and $C_{m2}$ (as in Fig. 9.24), thereby eliminating the feedforward paths through the capacitors. However, the source follower has a nonzero dc voltage between its input and output. This voltage may limit the op-amp output swing to an unacceptably low value in a low-power-supply application. Second, cascode stages could be used to eliminate the zeros, as shown in Fig. 9.26. However, the requirement that all transistors in the cascode stage operate in the active region may limit the minimum supply voltage. Finally, a series zero-canceling resistance (as in Fig. 9.27a) implemented with a transistor may require a large gate voltage that exceeds the power supply.

A different technique for eliminating a RHP zero that can be used with cascaded stages in a low-supply application is shown in Fig. 9.33a.[16,17] Two gain stages and one Miller compensation capacitor are shown. A transconductance stage, $g_{mf}$, is included. It provides a feedforward path that can be used to move the zero to infinity. The small-signal circuit is shown in Fig. 9.33b. To allow a simple explanation of this circuit, initially assume that $C_1 = C_2 = 0$. The circuit has one pole due to $C_m$ and one zero due to the feedforward current through $C_m$. If the zero moves to infinity, the total forward current must go to zero when $\omega \to \infty$. Also, if the zero moves to infinity, the output voltage will go to zero as $\omega \to \infty$ due to the pole in the transfer function. When $\omega \to \infty$, capacitor $C_m$ becomes a short circuit, so $v_2 = 0$ when $\omega \to \infty$. Therefore at infinite frequency, the current $g_{m1}v_1$ from the $g_{m1}$ source flows through $C_m$. Adding this feedforward current to the current $g_{mf}v_1$ from the $g_{mf}$ generator gives the total current at the output node that is related to $v_1$

$$i_{ff}(\omega \to \infty) = (-g_{m1} + g_{mf})v_1 \tag{9.71}$$

If $g_{mf} = g_{m1}$, this current equals zero, which means the zero is at infinity.
An exact analysis of the circuit in Fig. 9.33 gives a transfer function

$$\frac{v_o}{v_1} = \tag{9.72}$$

$$\frac{-g_{m1}R_1 g_{m2}R_2 - g_{mf}R_2 - sR_1 R_2[g_{mf}(C_1 + C_m) - g_{m1}C_m]}{1 + s[g_{m2}R_1 R_2 C_m + R_2(C_2 + C_m) + R_1(C_1 + C_m)] + s^2 R_1 R_2(C_1 C_2 + C_1 C_m + C_2 C_m)}$$

The zero can be moved to infinity by choosing $g_{mf}$ so that the coefficient of $s$ in the numerator is zero, which occurs when

$$g_{mf} = g_{m1}\frac{C_m}{C_1 + C_m} = \frac{g_{m1}}{1 + \dfrac{C_1}{C_m}} \tag{9.73}$$

This value of $g_{mf}$ depends on the ratio of an internal parasitic capacitance $C_1$, which is not well controlled, and compensation capacitor $C_m$. Using $g_{mf} = g_{m1}$ moves the zero into the LHP to about $-g_{m2}/C_1$; the magnitude of this zero is usually above the unity-gain frequency of the op amp. If the $g_{m1}$ stage has a differential input, the $-g_{mf}$ stage can be realized using a replica of the $g_{m1}$ stage with the inputs reversed to change the sign of the transconductance.

This zero-cancellation scheme can be used repeatedly in a three-stage op amp to eliminate the zeros, as shown in Fig. 9.34a. A small-signal model is shown in Fig. 9.34b. Analysis of this circuit gives a voltage gain of

$$\frac{v_o}{v_{in}} = \frac{R_2(n_0 + n_1 s + n_2 s^2)}{1 + b_1 s + b_2 s^2 + b_3 s^3} \tag{9.74}$$

where $b_1$-$b_3$ are related to $a_1$-$a_3$ in (9.57) by

$$b_1 = a_1 + g_{mf1}R_0 R_2 C_{m2} \tag{9.75a}$$
$$b_2 = a_2 + g_{mf1}R_0 R_1 R_2(C_1 + C_{m1})C_{m2} \tag{9.75b}$$
$$b_3 = a_3 \tag{9.75c}$$

and the coefficients in the numerator are

$$n_0 = -g_{m0}g_{m1}g_{m2}R_0 R_1 - g_{mf0} - g_{m0}g_{mf1}R_0 \tag{9.76a}$$

$$n_1 = g_{m0}(g_{m1} - g_{mf1})R_0 R_1 C_{m1} + (g_{m0} - g_{mf0})R_0 C_{m2}$$
$$\quad - g_{mf0}R_1(C_1 + C_{m1}) - g_{mf0}R_0 C_0 - g_{m0}g_{mf1}R_0 R_1 C_1 \tag{9.76b}$$

$$n_2 = (g_{m0} - g_{mf0})R_0 R_1(C_1 + C_{m1})C_{m2} - g_{mf0}R_0 R_1(C_1 + C_{m1})C_0 \tag{9.76c}$$

The coefficients of $s$ and $s^2$ in the numerator include both positive and negative terms. Therefore, they can be set to zero, which eliminates the zeros, by properly choosing $g_{mf0}$ and $g_{mf1}$. As in (9.73) above, these values depend on parasitic capacitances $C_0$ and $C_1$, which are not well controlled in practice. An alternative choice is to set $g_{mf0} = g_{m0}$ and $g_{mf1} = g_{m1}$. When these values are substituted into (9.76a)–(9.76c), $n_0$, $n_1$, and $n_2$ are negative. Therefore, both zeros are in the LHP (see Appendix A9.2), and the RHP zero has been eliminated.

With $g_{mf1} = g_{m1}$ and $g_{mf0} = g_{m0}$, the term added to $a_1$ in (9.75a) is small compared to the dominant term in $a_1$, which is $g_{m1}R_1 g_{m2}R_2 R_0 C_{m2}$, if $g_{m2}R_1 \gg 1$. Therefore $b_1 \approx a_1$, and the dominant pole $p_1$ is still given by (9.59). However, $b_2$ can be significantly

**Figure 9.34** (a) Block diagram of a three-stage op amp with nested Miller compensation and two feedforward transconductors. (b) Small-signal model.

different from $a_2$, and therefore $p_2$ and $p_3$ will be different from the values given by (9.66a) and (9.66b). The new values of the high frequency poles can be found by solving the quadratic equation that results when $b_1$-$b_3$ are substituted for $a_1$-$a_3$ in (9.60).

The selection of the nested Miller compensation capacitors is complicated because the values of two compensation capacitors must be chosen, and they affect the pole and zero locations. The compensation capacitors can be chosen with the aid of a computer to achieve a particular settling-time or phase-margin goal in a feedback application. Computer optimization can be carried out on the closed-loop transfer function based on the op-amp transfer function or on the loop gain or return ratio, if the small-signal model parameters are known. Alternatively, the capacitor values can be estimated using approximations and the equations presented above. Then SPICE simulations can be run on the transistor circuit starting with the initial estimates of the compensation capacitors and varying the capacitors by small amounts to determine the best values. This approach is used in the following example.

## ■  EXAMPLE

Design the 3-stage op amp in Fig. 9.34 to give a low-frequency gain of 86 dB and 45° phase margin for unity feedback ($f = 1$) when driving a 5 pF load. Compensate the op amp so that all the poles are real and widely spaced. To simplify this example, assume that the output resistance of each stage is 5 kΩ and the internal node capacitances $C_0$ and $C_1$ are each 0.05 pF. Determine the compensation capacitors and the transconductances for the op amp.

The feedforward transconductances $g_{mf0}$ and $g_{mf1}$ will be used to move the zeros to well beyond the unity-gain frequency. To simplify the design equations, let $g_{mf0} = g_{m0}$ and $g_{mf1} = g_{m1}$, based on (9.73)–(9.76) and the assumption that $C_0$ and $C_1$ are small compared to $C_{m1}$ and $C_{m2}$.

When $g_{mf0} = g_{mf1} = 0$, the coefficients $a_i$ of the denominator of the transfer function are given by (9.57). With nonzero $g_{mf0}$ and $g_{mf1}$, however, the coefficients of $s$ and $s^2$ in the denominator of the transfer function change and are given by (9.75). From (9.75c), $b_3 = a_3$. Also, as noted in the text following (9.76), the term added to $a_1$ in (9.75a) is small compared to $a_1$, so $b_1 \approx a_1$ and $p_1$ is given by (9.59). Hence, poles $p_2$ and $p_3$ are changed due to the added term that includes $g_{mf1}$ in $b_2$ in (9.75b). Assuming $C_1 \ll C_{m1}$, (9.75b) reduces to

$$b_2 \approx a_2 + g_{mf1}R_0R_1R_2C_{m1}C_{m2}$$

Substituting the approximate expression for $a_2$ in (9.62) and using $g_{mf1} = g_{m1}$, this equation becomes

$$b_2 \approx g_{m2}R_0R_1R_2C_{m1}C_{m2}$$

Following the analysis from (9.60) to (9.67), we find

$$p_2 \approx -\frac{b_1}{b_2} \approx -\frac{g_{m1}}{C_{m1}} \tag{9.77a}$$

$$p_3 \approx \frac{b_1}{b_3}\frac{1}{p_2} \approx -\frac{g_{m2}}{C_2} \tag{9.77b}$$

To satisfy $|p_2| \ll |p_3|$, let $|p_3| = 10|p_2|$. Substituting (9.77) in this equality and rearranging yields

$$C_{m1} = 10\frac{g_{m1}}{g_{m2}}C_2 \tag{9.78}$$

To ensure that $C_{m1}$ is not much larger than $C_2 = 5$ pF we need $g_{m1}/g_{m2} \ll 1$ in (9.78). Here, we chose $g_{m1}/g_{m2} = 0.2$. Substituting this value into (9.78) gives

$$C_{m1} = 10(0.2)(5 \text{ pF}) = 10 \text{ pF}$$

With widely spaced poles, placing $|p_2|$ at the unity-gain frequency gives a 45° phase margin. Since $|gain| \times frequency$ is constant for frequencies between $|p_1|$ and $|p_2|$, we can write

$$|a_0| \cdot |p_1| = 1 \cdot |p_2| \tag{9.79}$$

where

$$|a_0| = g_{m0}R_0g_{m1}R_1g_{m2}R_2 \tag{9.80}$$

is the low-frequency gain. Substitution of (9.59), (9.77a), and (9.80) into (9.79) gives

$$\frac{g_{m0}}{C_{m2}} = \frac{g_{m1}}{C_{m1}}$$

If the first two gain stages are made identical to reduce the circuit-design effort, $g_{m0} = g_{m1}$, and the last equation reduces to

$$C_{m2} = C_{m1} = 10 \text{ pF}$$

Now the transconductances can be found from the low-frequency gain requirement and (9.80),

$$|a_0| = g_{m0}R_0 g_{m1} R_1 g_{m2} R_2 = \frac{g_{m1}^3}{0.2}(5 \text{ k}\Omega)^3 = 20,000 = 86 \text{ dB}$$

since $g_{m0} = g_{m1} = 0.2g_{m2}$ has been selected. Solving gives $g_{m1} = g_{m0} = g_{mf1} = g_{mf0} = 3.2 \text{ mA/V}$ and $g_{m2} = g_{m1}/0.2 = 16 \text{ mA/V}$.

SPICE simulation of this op amp gives a dc gain of 86.3 dB and a phase margin of 52 degrees with a unity-gain frequency of 40 MHz. These values are close enough to the specifications to illustrate the usefulness of the calculations. The pole locations are $|p_1|/2\pi = 2.3 \text{ kHz}$, $|p_2|/2\pi = 59 \text{ MHz}$, and $|p_3|/2\pi = 464 \text{ MHz}$. The zero locations are complex with a magnitude much larger than the unity-gain frequency, at $z_{1,2}/2\pi = -345 \text{ MHz} \pm j1.58 \text{ GHz}$. Running simulations with slight changes to the compensation capacitors, we find that using $C_{m1} = 10.4 \text{ pF}$ and $C_{m2} = 8.3 \text{ pF}$ gives a phase margin of 47 degrees with a unity-gain frequency of 45 MHz.

## 9.5 Root-Locus Techniques[1,18]

To this point the considerations of this chapter have been mainly concerned with calculations of feedback amplifier stability and compensation using frequency-domain techniques. Such techniques are widely used because they allow the design of feedback amplifier compensation without requiring excessive design effort. The *root-locus* technique involves calculation of the actual poles and zeros of the amplifier and of their movement in the $s$ plane as the low-frequency, loop-gain magnitude $T_0$ is changed. This method thus gives more information about the amplifier performance than is given by frequency-domain techniques, but also requires more computational effort. In practice, some problems can be solved equally well using either method, whereas others yield more easily to one or the other. The circuit designer needs skill in applying both methods. The root-locus technique will be first illustrated with a simple example.

### 9.5.1 Root Locus for a Three-Pole Transfer Function

Consider an amplifier whose transfer function has three identical poles. The transfer function can be written as

$$a(s) = \frac{a_0}{\left(1 - \dfrac{s}{p_1}\right)^3} \tag{9.81}$$

where $a_0$ is the low-frequency gain and $|p_1|$ is the pole magnitude. Consider this amplifier placed in a negative-feedback loop as in Fig. 9.1, where the feedback network has a transfer function $f$, which is a constant. If we assume that the effects of feedback loading are small, the overall gain with feedback is

$$A(s) = \frac{a(s)}{1 + a(s)f} \tag{9.82}$$

Using (9.81) in (9.82) gives

$$A(s) = \frac{a_0}{1 + \dfrac{a_0 f}{\left(1 - \dfrac{s}{p_1}\right)^3}} = \frac{a_0}{\left(1 - \dfrac{s}{p_1}\right)^3 + T_0} \tag{9.83}$$

where $T_0 = a_0 f$ is the low-frequency loop gain.

The *poles* of $A(s)$ are the *roots* of the equation

$$\left(1 - \frac{s}{p_1}\right)^3 + T_0 = 0 \tag{9.84}$$

That is

$$\left(1 - \frac{s}{p_1}\right)^3 = -T_0$$

and thus

$$1 - \frac{s}{p_1} = \sqrt[3]{-T_0} = -\sqrt[3]{T_0} \quad \text{or} \quad \sqrt[3]{T_0}e^{j60°} \quad \text{or} \quad \sqrt[3]{T_0}e^{-j60°}$$

Thus the three roots of (9.84) are

$$\begin{aligned} s_1 &= p_1\left(1 + \sqrt[3]{T_0}\right) \\ s_2 &= p_1\left(1 - \sqrt[3]{T_0}e^{j60°}\right) \\ s_3 &= p_1\left(1 - \sqrt[3]{T_0}e^{-j60°}\right) \end{aligned} \tag{9.85}$$

These three roots are the poles of $A(s)$ and (9.83) can be written as

$$A(s) = \frac{a_0}{1 + T_0} \frac{1}{\left(1 - \dfrac{s}{s_1}\right)\left(1 - \dfrac{s}{s_2}\right)\left(1 - \dfrac{s}{s_3}\right)} \tag{9.86}$$

The equations in (9.85) allow calculation of the poles of $A(s)$ for any value of low-frequency loop gain $T_0$. For $T_0 = 0$, all three poles are at $p_1$ as expected. As $T_0$ increases, one pole moves out along the negative real axis while the other two leave the axis at an angle of 60° and move toward the right half-plane. The *locus of the roots* (or the *root locus*) is shown in Fig. 9.35, and each point of this root locus can be identified with the corresponding value of $T_0$. One point of significance on the root locus is the value of $T_0$ at which the two complex poles cross into the right half-plane, as this is the value of loop gain causing *oscillation*. From the equation for $s_2$ in (9.85), this is where $\mathrm{Re}(s_2) = 0$, from which we obtain

$$1 - \mathrm{Re}(\sqrt[3]{T_0}e^{j60°}) = 0$$

That is,

$$\sqrt[3]{T_0}\cos 60° = 1$$

and

$$T_0 = 8$$

**Figure 9.35** Root locus for a feedback amplifier with three identical poles in $T(s)$.

Thus, *any* amplifier with three identical poles becomes unstable for low-frequency loop gain $T_0$ greater than 8. This is quite a restrictive condition and emphasizes the need for compensation if larger values of $T_0$ are required. Note that not only does the root-locus technique give the value of $T_0$ causing instability, it also allows calculation of the amplifier poles for values of $T_0 < 8$, and thus allows calculation of both sinusoidal *and* transient response of the amplifier.

The frequency of oscillation can be found from Fig. 9.35 by calculating the distance

$$\omega_0 = |p_1| \tan 60° = 1.732 |p_1|  \tag{9.87}$$

Thus, when the poles just enter the right half-plane, their imaginary part has a magnitude $1.732 |p_1|$ and this will be the frequency of the increasing sinusoidal response. That is, if the complex poles are at $(\sigma \pm j\omega_0)$ where $\sigma$ is small and positive, the transient response of the circuit contains a term $K e^{\sigma t} \sin \omega_0 t$, which represents a *growing* sinusoid. ($K$ is set by an initial condition.)

It is useful to calculate the value of $T_0$ causing instability in this case by using the frequency-domain approach and the Nyquist criterion. From (9.81) the loop gain is

$$T(j\omega) = \frac{a_0 f}{\left(1 + \dfrac{j\omega}{|p_1|}\right)^3} = \frac{T_0}{\left(1 + j\dfrac{\omega}{|p_1|}\right)^3}  \tag{9.88}$$

The magnitude and phase of $T(j\omega)$ as a function of $\omega$ are sketched in Fig. 9.36. The frequency $\omega_{180}$ where the phase shift of $T(j\omega)$ is $-180°$ can be calculated from (9.88) as

$$180° = 3 \arctan \frac{\omega_{180}}{|p_1|}$$

and this gives

$$\omega_{180} = 1.732 |p_1|  \tag{9.89}$$

Comparing (9.87) with (9.89) shows that

$$\omega_{180} = \omega_0  \tag{9.90}$$

The loop-gain magnitude at $\omega_{180}$ can be calculated from (9.88) as

$$|T(j\omega_{180})| = \frac{T_0}{\left|1 + j\dfrac{\omega_{180}}{|p_1|}\right|^3} = \frac{T_0}{8}  \tag{9.91}$$

**Figure 9.36** Magnitude and phase of $T(j\omega)$ for a feedback amplifier with three identical poles in $T(s)$.

using (9.89). The Nyquist criterion for stability indicates it is necessary that $|T(j\omega_{180})| <$ 1. This requires that $T_0 < 8$, the same result as obtained using root-locus techniques.

### 9.5.2 Rules for Root-Locus Construction

In the above simple example, it was possible to calculate exact expressions for the amplifier poles as a function of $T_0$, and thus to plot the root loci exactly. In most practical cases this is quite difficult since the solution of third- or higher order polynomial equations is required. Consequently, rules have been developed that allow the root loci to be sketched without requiring exact calculation of the pole positions, and much of the useful information is thus obtained without extensive calculation.

In general, the basic-amplifier transfer function and the feedback function may be expressed as a ratio of polynomials in $s$.

$$a(s) = a_0 \frac{1 + a_1 s + a_2 s^2 + \cdots}{1 + b_1 s + b_2 s^2 + \cdots} \qquad (9.92)$$

This can be written as

$$a(s) = a_0 \frac{N_a(s)}{D_a(s)} \qquad (9.93)$$

Also assume that

$$f(s) = f_0 \frac{1 + c_1 s + c_2 s^2 + \cdots}{1 + d_1 s + d_2 s^2 + \cdots} \qquad (9.94)$$

This can be written as

$$f(s) = f_0 \frac{N_f(s)}{D_f(s)} \tag{9.95}$$

*Loading* produced by the feedback network on the basic amplifier is assumed to be included in (9.92). It is further assumed that the low-frequency loop gain $a_0 f_0$ can be changed without changing the poles and zeros of $a(s)$ or $f(s)$.

The overall gain when feedback is applied is

$$A(s) = \frac{a(s)}{1 + a(s)f(s)} \tag{9.96}$$

Using (9.93) and (9.95) in (9.96) gives

$$A(s) = \frac{a_0 N_a(s) D_f(s)}{D_f(s) D_a(s) + T_0 N_a(s) N_f(s)} \tag{9.97}$$

where

$$T_0 = a_0 f_0 \tag{9.98}$$

is the low-frequency loop gain.

Equation 9.97 shows that the *zeros* of $A(s)$ are the *zeros* of $a(s)$ *and* the *poles* of $f(s)$. From (9.97) it is apparent that the *poles* of $A(s)$ are the roots of

$$D_f(s) D_a(s) + T_0 N_a(s) N_f(s) = 0 \tag{9.99}$$

Consider the two extreme cases.

(a) Assume that there is no feedback and that $T_0 = 0$. Then, from (9.99), the *poles* of $A(s)$ are the *poles* of $a(s)$ and $f(s)$. However, the *poles* of $f(s)$ are also *zeros* of $A(s)$ and these cancel, leaving the *poles* of $A(s)$ composed of the *poles* of $a(s)$ as expected. The *zeros* of $A(s)$ are the *zeros* of $a(s)$ in this case.

(b) Let $T_0 \to \infty$. Then (9.99) becomes

$$N_a(s) N_f(s) = 0 \tag{9.100}$$

This equation shows that the *poles* of $A(s)$ are now the zeros of $a(s)$ and the *zeros* of $f(s)$. However, the *zeros* of $a(s)$ are also *zeros* of $A(s)$ and these cancel, leaving the *poles* of $A(s)$ composed of the *zeros* of $f(s)$. The *zeros* of $A(s)$ are the *poles* of $f(s)$ in this case.

**Rule 1.** The branches of the root locus start at the poles of $T(s) = a(s)f(s)$ where $T_0 = 0$, and terminate on the zeros of $T(s)$ where $T_0 = \infty$. If $T(s)$ has more poles than zeros, some of the branches of the root locus will terminate at infinity.

Examples of loci terminating at infinity are shown in Figs. 9.3 and 9.35. More rules for the construction of root loci can be derived by returning to (9.99) and dividing it by $D_f(s) D_a(s)$. Poles of $A(s)$ are roots of

$$1 + T_0 \frac{N_a(s)}{D_a(s)} \frac{N_f(s)}{D_f(s)} = 0$$

That is

$$T_0 \frac{N_a(s)}{D_a(s)} \frac{N_f(s)}{D_f(s)} = -1$$

The complete expression including poles and zeros is

$$T_0 \frac{\left(1 - \dfrac{s}{z_{a1}}\right)\left(1 - \dfrac{s}{z_{a2}}\right)\cdots\left(1 - \dfrac{s}{z_{f1}}\right)\left(1 - \dfrac{s}{z_{f2}}\right)\cdots}{\left(1 - \dfrac{s}{p_{a1}}\right)\left(1 - \dfrac{s}{p_{a2}}\right)\cdots\left(1 - \dfrac{s}{p_{f1}}\right)\left(1 - \dfrac{s}{p_{f2}}\right)\cdots} = -1 \tag{9.101}$$

where

> $z_{a1}, z_{a2} \cdots$ are zeros of $a(s)$
> $z_{f1}, z_{f2} \cdots$ are zeros of $f(s)$
> $p_{a1}, p_{a2} \cdots$ are poles of $a(s)$
> $p_{f1}, p_{f2} \cdots$ are poles of $f(s)$

Equation 9.101 can be written as

$$T_0 \frac{(-p_{a1})(-p_{a2})\cdots(-p_{f1})(-p_{f2})\cdots}{(-z_{a1})(-z_{a2})\cdots(-z_{f1})(-z_{f2})\cdots}$$

$$\times \frac{(s - z_{a1})(s - z_{a2})\cdots(s - z_{f1})(s - z_{f2})\cdots}{(s - p_{a1})(s - p_{a2})\cdots(s - p_{f1})(s - p_{f2})\cdots} = -1 \tag{9.102}$$

If the poles and zeros of $a(s)$ and $f(s)$ are restricted to the left half-plane [this does *not* restrict the poles of $A(s)$], then $-p_{a1}$, $-p_{a2}$, and so on are *positive* numbers and (9.102) can be written

$$T_0 \frac{|p_{a1}| \cdot |p_{a2}| \cdots |p_{f1}| \cdot |p_{f2}| \cdots}{|z_{a1}| \cdot |z_{a2}| \cdots |z_{f1}| \cdot |z_{f2}| \cdots} \times \frac{(s - z_{a1})(s - z_{a2})\cdots(s - z_{f1})(s - z_{f2})\cdots}{(s - p_{a1})(s - p_{a2})\cdots(s - p_{f1})(s - p_{f2})\cdots} = -1 \tag{9.103}$$

Values of complex variable $s$ satisfying (9.103) are *poles* of closed-loop function $A(s)$. Equation 9.103 requires the fulfillment of two conditions simultaneously, and these conditions are used to determine points on the root locus.

The *phase condition* for values of $s$ satisfying (9.103) is

$$\underline{/s - z_{a1}} + \underline{/s - z_{a2}} \cdots + \underline{/s - z_{f1}} + \underline{/s - z_{f2}} + \cdots$$
$$- (\underline{/s - p_{a1}} + \underline{/s - p_{a2}} \cdots + \underline{/s - p_{f1}} + \underline{/s - p_{f2}} \cdots) = (2n - 1)\pi \tag{9.104}$$

The magnitude condition for values of $s$ satisfying (9.103) is

$$T_0 \frac{|p_{a1}| \cdot |p_{a2}| \cdots |p_{f1}| \cdot |p_{f2}| \cdots}{|z_{a1}| \cdot |z_{a2}| \cdots |z_{f1}| \cdot |z_{f2}| \cdots} \frac{|s - z_{a1}| \cdot |s - z_{a2}| \cdots |s - z_{f1}| \cdot |s - z_{f2}| \cdots}{|s - p_{a1}| \cdot |s - p_{a2}| \cdots |s - p_{f1}| \cdot |s - p_{f2}| \cdots} = 1 \tag{9.105}$$

Consider an amplifier with poles and zeros of $T(s)$ as shown in Fig. 9.37. In order to determine if some arbitrary point $X$ is on the root locus, the phase condition of (9.104) is used. Note that the vectors of (9.104) are formed by drawing lines *from* the various poles and zeros of $T(s)$ to the point $X$ and the angles of these vectors are then substituted in (9.104) to check the phase condition. This is readily done for points $Y$ and $Z$ on the axis. At $Y$

$$\underline{/s_Y - z_1} = 0°$$
$$\underline{/s_Y - p_1} = 0°$$

and so on. All angles are zero for point $Y$ and thus the phase condition is not satisfied. This is the case for all points to the right of $p_1$.

**Figure 9.37** Poles and zeros of loop gain $T(s)$ of a feedback amplifier. Vectors are drawn to the point $X$ to determine if this point is on the root locus.

At $Z$

$$\underline{/s_Z - z_1} = 0°$$
$$\underline{/s_Z - p_1} = 180°$$
$$\underline{/s_Z - p_2} = 0°$$
$$\underline{/s_Z - p_3} = 0°$$
$$\underline{/s_Z - p_4} = 0°$$

In this case, the phase condition of (9.104) *is* satisfied, and points on the axis between $p_1$ and $p_2$ *are* on the locus. By similar application of the phase condition, the locus can be shown to exist on the real axis between $p_3$ and $z_1$ and to the left of $p_4$.

In general, if $T(s)$ has all its zeros and poles in the LHP, the locus is situated along the real axis where there is an odd number of poles and zeros of $T(s)$ to the right. In some cases, however, all the zeros of $T(s)$ are not in the LHP. For example, an op amp that uses Miller compensation can have a RHP zero in $a(s)$ and therefore in $T(s)$. If $a(s)$ has at least one RHP zero, at least one of the $-z_{ai}$ terms in (9.102) is negative, rather than positive as assumed in (9.103). If the number of RHP zeros is even, an even number of $-z_{ai}$ terms that are negative appear in the denominator of (9.102). The product of these negative terms is positive, and therefore (9.103) and (9.104) remain correct. However, if the number of RHP zeros is odd, the product of the $-z_{ai}$ terms in (9.102) is negative. As a result, a minus sign appears on the left-hand side of (9.103) that causes a $\pi$ term to be added on the left side of (9.104). This change to the phase condition is reflected in the following rule.

**Rule 2.** If $T(s)$ has all its zeros in the LHP or if $T(s)$ has an even number of RHP zeros, the locus is situated along the real axis wherever there is an odd number of poles and zeros of $T(s)$ to the right. However, if $T(s)$ has an odd number of RHP zeros, the locus is situated along the real axis wherever there is an even number of poles and zeros of $T(s)$ to the right.

Consider again the situation in Fig. 9.37. Rule 1 indicates that branches of the locus must start at $p_1$, $p_2$, $p_3$, and $p_4$. Rule 2 indicates that the locus exists between $p_3$ and $z_1$, and thus the branch beginning at $p_3$ ends at $z_1$. Rule 2 also indicates that the locus exists to the left of $p_4$, and thus the branch beginning at $p_4$ moves out to negative infinity. The branches beginning at $p_1$ and $p_2$ must also terminate at infinity, which is possible only if these branches *break away* from the real axis as shown in Fig. 9.38. This can be stated as follows.

**Rule 3.** All segments of loci that lie on the real axis between pairs of poles (or pairs of zeros) of $T(s)$ must, at some internal break point, branch out from the real axis.

The following rules can be derived.[19]

**Rule 4.** The locus is symmetrical with respect to the real axis (because complex roots occur only in conjugate pairs).

**Rule 5.** Branches of the locus that leave the real axis do so at *right angles,* as illustrated in Fig. 9.38.

**Rule 6.** If branches of the locus break away from the real axis, they do so at a point where the vector sum of reciprocals of distances to the poles of $T(s)$ equals the vector sum of reciprocals of distances to the zeros of $T(s)$.

**Rule 7.** If $T(s)$ has no RHP zeros or an even number of RHP zeros, branches of the locus that terminate at infinity do so asymptotically to straight lines with angles to the real axis of $[(2n-1)\pi]/(N_p - N_z)$ for $n = 0, 1, \ldots, N_p - N_z - 1$, where $N_p$ is the number of poles and $N_z$ is the number of zeros. However, if $T(s)$ has an odd number of RHP zeros, the asymptotes intersect the real axis at angles given by $(2n\pi)/(N_p - N_z)$.

**Rule 8.** The asymptotes of branches that terminate at infinity all intersect on the real axis at a point given by

$$\sigma_a = \frac{\sum[\text{poles of } T(s)] - \sum[\text{zeros of } T(s)]}{N_p - N_z} \tag{9.106}$$

A number of other rules have been developed for sketching root loci, but those described above are adequate for most requirements in amplifier design. The rules are used to obtain a rapid idea of the shape of the root locus in any situation, and to calculate amplifier performance in simple cases. More detailed calculation on circuits

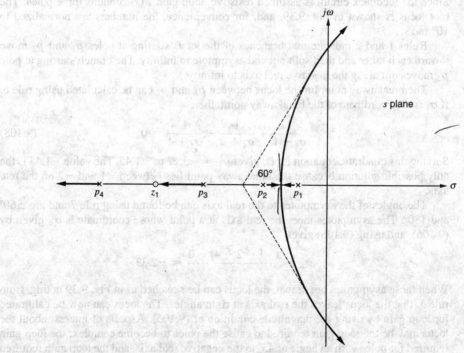

**Figure 9.38** Root-locus construction for the poles and zeros of Fig. 9.37.

exhibiting complicated pole-zero patterns generally require computer calculation of the root locus.

Note t'  .t the above rules are all based on the *phase condition* of (9.104). Once the locus has been sketched, it can then be *calibrated* with values of low-frequency loop gain $T_0$ calculated at any desired point using the *magnitude condition* of (9.105).

The procedures described above will now be illustrated with examples.

## ■ EXAMPLE

In Section 9.5.1 the root locus was calculated for an amplifier with three identical poles. This example was chosen because it was analytically tractable. Now consider a more practical case where the amplifier has three nonidentical poles and resistive feedback is applied. It is required to plot the root locus for this amplifier as feedback factor $f$ is varied (thus varying $T_0$), and it is assumed that variations in $f$ do not cause significant changes in the basic-amplifier transfer function $a(s)$.

Assume that the basic amplifier has a transfer function

$$a(s) = \frac{100}{\left(1 - \dfrac{s}{p_1}\right)\left(1 - \dfrac{s}{p_2}\right)\left(1 - \dfrac{s}{p_3}\right)} \qquad (9.107)$$

where

$$p_1 = -1 \times 10^6 \text{ rad/s}$$
$$p_2 = -2 \times 10^6 \text{ rad/s}$$
$$p_3 = -4 \times 10^6 \text{ rad/s}$$

Since the feedback circuit is assumed resistive, loop gain $T(s)$ contains three poles. The root locus is shown in Fig. 9.39, and, for convenience, the numbers are normalized to $10^6$ rad/s.

Rules 1 and 2 indicate that branches of the locus starting at poles $p_1$ and $p_2$ move toward each other and then split out and asymptote to infinity. The branch starting at pole $p_3$ moves out along the negative real axis to infinity.

The breakaway point for the locus between $p_1$ and $p_2$ can be calculated using rule 6. If $\sigma_i$ is the coordinate of the breakaway point, then

$$\frac{1}{\sigma_i + 1} + \frac{1}{\sigma_i + 2} + \frac{1}{\sigma_i + 4} = 0 \qquad (9.108)$$

Solving this quadratic equation for $\sigma_i$ gives $\sigma_i = -3.22$ or $-1.45$. The value $-1.45$ is the only possible solution because the breakaway point lies between $-1$ and $-2$ on the real axis.

The angles of the asymptotes to the real axis can be found using rule 7 and are $\pm 60°$ and $180°$. The asymptotes meet the real axis at a point whose coordinate is $\sigma_a$ given by (9.106), and using (9.106) gives

$$\sigma_a = \frac{(-1 - 2 - 4) - 0}{3} = -2.33$$

When these asymptotes are drawn, the locus can be sketched as in Fig. 9.39 noting, from rule 5, that the locus leaves the real axis at right angles. The locus can now be calibrated for loop gain by using the magnitude condition of (9.105). Aspects of interest about the locus may be the loop gain required to cause the poles to become complex, the loop gain required for poles with an angle of 45° to the negative real axis, and the loop gain required for oscillation (right half-plane poles).

**Figure 9.39** Root-locus example for poles of $T(s)$ at $-1 \times 10^6$, $-2 \times 10^6$, and $-4 \times 10^6$ rad/s.

Consider first the loop gain required to cause the poles to become complex. This is a point on the locus on the real axis at $\sigma_i = -1.45$. Substituting $s = -1.45$ in (9.105) gives

$$T_0 \frac{1 \times 2 \times 4}{0.45 \times 0.55 \times 2.55} = 1 \qquad (9.109)$$

where

$$|p_1| = 1 \qquad |p_2| = 2 \qquad |p_3| = 4$$
$$|s - p_1| = 0.45 \qquad |s - p_2| = 0.55 \qquad |s - p_3| = 2.55$$

and

$$s = -1.45 \text{ at the point being considered}$$

From (9.109), $T_0 = 0.08$. Thus a very small loop-gain magnitude causes poles $p_1$ and $p_2$ to come together and split.

The loop gain required to cause right half-plane poles can be estimated by assuming that the locus coincides with the asymptote at that point. Thus we assume the locus crosses the imaginary axis at the point

$$j2.33 \tan 60° = 4.0j$$

Then the loop gain at this point can be calculated using (9.105) to give

$$T_0 \frac{1 \times 2 \times 4}{4.1 \times 4.5 \times 5.7} = 1 \qquad (9.110)$$

where

$$|s - p_1| = 4.1 \quad |s - p_2| = 4.5 \quad |s - p_3| = 5.7$$

and

$$s = 4j \text{ at this point on the locus}$$

From (9.110), $T_0 = 13.2$. Since $a_0 = 100$ for this amplifier [from (9.107)], the overall gain of the feedback amplifier to $T_0 = 13.2$ is

$$A_0 = \frac{a_0}{1 + T_0} = 7.04$$

and

$$f = \frac{T_0}{a_0} = 0.132$$

The loop gain when the complex poles make an angle of $45°$ with the negative real axis can be calculated by making the assumption that this point has the same real-axis coordinate as the breakaway point. Then, using (9.105) with $s = (-1.45 + 1.45j)$, we obtain

$$T_0 \frac{1 \times 2 \times 4}{1.52 \times 1.55 \times 2.93} = 1$$

and thus

$$T_0 = 0.86$$

Finally, the loop gain required to move the locus out from pole $p_3$ is of interest. When the real-axis pole is at $-5$, the loop gain can be calculated using (9.105) with $s = -5$ to give

$$T_0 \frac{1 \times 2 \times 4}{1 \times 3 \times 4} = 1$$

That is,

$$T_0 = 1.5$$

When this pole is at $-6$, the loop gain is

$$T_0 \frac{1 \times 2 \times 4}{2 \times 4 \times 5} = 1$$

and thus

$$T_0 = 5$$

These values are marked on the root locus of Fig. 9.39.

In this example, it is useful to compare the prediction of instability at $T_0 = 13.2$ with the results using the Nyquist criterion. The loop gain in the frequency domain is

$$T(j\omega) = \frac{T_0}{\left(1 + \dfrac{j\omega}{10^6}\right)\left(1 + \dfrac{j\omega}{2 \times 10^6}\right)\left(1 + \dfrac{j\omega}{4 \times 10^6}\right)} \qquad (9.111)$$

A series of trial substitutions shows that $\angle T(j\omega) = -180°$ for $\omega = 3.8 \times 10^6$ rad/s. Note that this is close to the value of $4 \times 10^6$ rad/s where the root locus was assumed to cross the $j\omega$ axis. Substitution of $\omega = 3.8 \times 10^6$ in (9.111) gives, for the loop gain at that frequency,

$$|T(j\omega)| = \frac{T_0}{11.6} \qquad (9.112)$$

Thus, for stability, the Nyquist criterion requires that $T_0 < 11.6$ and this is close to the answer obtained from the root locus. If the point on the $j\omega$ axis where the root locus crossed had been determined more accurately, it would have been found to be at $3.8 \times 10^6$ rad/s, and both methods would predict instability for $T_0 > 11.6$.

It should be pointed out that the root locus for Fig. 9.39 shows the movement of the *poles* of the feedback amplifier as $T_0$ changes. The theory developed in Section 9.5.2 showed that the *zeros* of the feedback amplifier are the *zeros* of the basic amplifier and the *poles* of the feedback network. In this case there are no zeros in the feedback amplifier, but this is not always the case. It should be kept in mind that if the basic amplifier has zeros in its transfer function, these may be an important part of the overall transfer function.

The rules for drawing a root locus were presented for varying $T_0$, assuming that the poles and zeros of $a(s)$ and $f(s)$ do not change when $T_0$ changes. This assumption is often not valid in practice, since changing the circuit to change $T_0 = a_0 f$ usually affects at least some of the poles and zeros. Alternatively, these rules can be used to draw a root locus of the poles of a transfer function as the value $x$ of an element in the circuit changes if the closed-loop gain $A(s)$ can be written in the form

$$A(s) = \frac{M(s)}{G(s) + xH(s)} \tag{9.113}$$

where $M(s)$, $G(s)$, and $H(s)$ are polynomials in $s$, and $G(s)$ and $H(s)$ are not functions of $x$. The poles of $A(s)$ are the roots of $G(s) = 0$ when $x = 0$ and the roots of $H(s) = 0$ when $x \to \infty$. The roots of $G(s) = 0$ are the starting points of the root locus, and the roots of $H(s) = 0$ are the ending points of the root locus. The complete locus for all values of $x$ can be drawn by following the rules given in this section. For example, this approach could be used to plot a locus of the poles of the transfer function in (9.27) as the compensation capacitor $C$ varies. (In this case, $x = C$.)

## 9.5.3 Root Locus for Dominant-Pole Compensation

Consider an op amp that has been compensated by creation of a dominant pole at $p_1$. If we assume the second most dominant pole is at $p_2$ and neglect the effect of higher order poles, the root locus when resistive feedback is applied is as shown in Fig. 9.40. Using rules 1 and 2 indicates that the root locus exists on the axis between $p_1$ and $p_2$, and the breakaway point is readily shown to be

$$\upsilon_i = \frac{p_1 + p_2}{2} \tag{9.114}$$

using rule 6. Using rules 7 and 8 shows that the asymptotes are at 90° to the real axis and meet the axis at $\sigma_i$.

As $T_0$ is increased, the branches of the locus come together and then split out to become complex. As $T_0$ becomes large, the imaginary part of the poles becomes large, and the circuit will then have a high-frequency *peak* in its overall gain function $A(j\omega)$. This is consistent with the previous viewpoint of gain peaking that occurred with diminishing phase margin.

Assume that maximum bandwidth in this amplifier is required, but that little or no peaking is allowed. This means that with maximum loop gain applied, the poles should not go beyond the points marked $X$ and $Y$ on the locus where an angle of 45° is made between the negative real axis and a line drawn from $X$ or $Y$ to the origin. At $X$, the loop gain can be calculated using (9.105)

$$T_0 \frac{|p_1| \cdot |p_2|}{|s - p_1| \cdot |s - p_2|} = 1 \tag{9.115}$$

**Figure 9.40** Root locus for an op amp with two poles in its transfer function. The feedback is assumed resistive.

If $p_1$ is a dominant pole, we can assume that $|p_1| \ll |p_2|$ and $\sigma_i = p_2/2$. For poles at 45°, $|s - p_1| = |s - p_2| \simeq \sqrt{2}|p_2|/2$. Thus (9.115) becomes

$$T_0 = \frac{1}{|p_1| \cdot |p_2|} \left( \sqrt{2} \frac{|p_2|}{2} \right)^2$$

This gives

$$T_0 = \frac{1}{2} \frac{|p_2|}{|p_1|} \tag{9.116}$$

for the value of $T_0$ required to produce poles at $X$ and $Y$ in Fig. 9.40. The effect of narrow-banding the amplifier is now apparent. As $|p_1|$ is made smaller, it requires a larger value of $T_0$ to move the poles out to 45°. From (9.116), the dominant-pole magnitude $|p_1|$ required to ensure adequate performance with a given $T_0$ and $|p_2|$ can be calculated.

### 9.5.4 Root Locus for Feedback-Zero Compensation

The techniques of compensation described earlier in this chapter involved modification of the basic amplifier only. This is the universal method used with op amps that must be compensated for use with a wide variety of feedback networks chosen by the user. However, this method is quite wasteful of bandwidth, as was apparent in the calculations.

In this section, a different method of compensation will be described that involves modification of the feedback path and is generally limited to fixed-gain amplifiers. This method finds application in the compensation of wideband feedback amplifiers where bandwidth is of prime importance. An example is the shunt-series feedback amplifier of Fig. 8.31, which is know as a *current feedback pair*. The method is generally useful in amplifiers of this type, where the feedback is over two stages, and in circuits such as the series-series triple of Fig. 8.18a.

A shunt-series feedback amplifier including a feedback capacitor $C_F$ is shown in Fig. 9.41. The basic amplifier including feedback loading for this circuit is shown in Fig. 9.42. Capacitors $C_F$ at input and output have only a minor effect on the circuit transfer function. The feedback circuit for this case is shown in Fig. 9.43 and feedback function $f$ is given by

$$f = \frac{i_i}{i_2} = -\frac{R_E}{R_F + R_E} \frac{1 + R_F C_F s}{1 + \dfrac{R_E R_F}{R_E + R_F} C_F s} \tag{9.117}$$

**Figure 9.41** Shunt-series feedback amplifier including a feedback capacitor $C_F$.

**Figure 9.42** Basic amplifier including feedback loading for the circuit of Fig. 9.41.

**Figure 9.43** Circuit for the calculation of feedback function $f$ for the amplifier of Fig. 9.41.

Feedback function $f$ thus contains a zero with a magnitude

$$\omega_z = \frac{1}{R_F C_F} \tag{9.118}$$

and a pole with a magnitude

$$\omega_p = \frac{R_E + R_F}{R_E} \frac{1}{R_F C_F} \tag{9.119}$$

Quantity $(R_E + R_F)/R_E$ is approximately the low-frequency gain of the overall circuit with feedback applied, and, since it is usually true that $(R_E + R_F)/R_E \gg 1$, the pole magnitude given by (9.119) is usually much larger than the zero magnitude. This will be assumed

**Figure 9.44** Root locus for the circuit of Fig. 9.41 assuming the basic amplifier contributes two poles to $T(s)$ and the feedback circuit contributes one zero.

and the effects of the pole will be neglected, but if $(R_E + R_F)/R_E$ becomes comparable to unity, the pole will be important and must be included.

The basic amplifier of Fig. 9.42 has two significant poles contributed by $Q_1$ and $Q_2$. Although higher magnitude poles exist, these do not have a dominant influence and will be neglected. The effects of this assumption will be investigated later. The loop gain of the circuit of Fig. 9.41 thus contains two forward-path poles and a feedback zero, giving rise to the root locus of Fig. 9.44. For purposes of illustration, the two poles are assumed to be $p_1 = -10 \times 10^6$ rad/s and $p_2 = -20 \times 10^6$ rad/s and the zero is $z = -50 \times 10^6$ rad/s. For convenience in the calculations, the numbers will be normalized to $10^6$ rad/s.

Assume now that the loop gain of the circuit of Fig. 9.41 can be varied without changing the parameters of the basic amplifier of Fig. 9.42. Then a root locus can be plotted as the loop gain changes, and using rules 1 and 2 indicates that the root locus exists on the axis between $p_1$ and $p_2$, and to the left of $z$. The root locus must thus break away from the axis between $p_1$ and $p_2$ at $\sigma_1$ as shown, and return again at $\sigma_2$. One branch then extends to the right along the axis to end at the zero while the other branch heads toward infinity on the left. Using rule 6 gives

$$\frac{1}{\sigma_1 + 10} + \frac{1}{\sigma_1 + 20} = \frac{1}{\sigma_1 + 50} \tag{9.120}$$

Solution of (9.120) for $\sigma_1$ gives

$$\sigma_1 = -84.6 \quad \text{or} \quad -15.4$$

Obviously $\sigma_1 = -15.4$ and the other value is $\sigma_2 = -84.6$. Note that these points are equidistant from the zero, and, in fact, it can be shown that in this example the portion of the locus that is off the real axis is a *circle* centered on the zero. An aspect of the root-locus diagrams that is a useful aid in sketching the loci is apparent from Fig. 9.39 and Fig. 9.44. The locus tends to *bend toward* zeros as if attracted and tends to *bend away* from poles as if repelled.

The effectiveness of the feedback zero in compensating the amplifier is apparent from Fig. 9.44. If we assume that the amplifier has poles $p_1$ and $p_2$ and there is no feedback zero, then when feedback is applied the amplifier poles will split out and move parallel to the $j\omega$ axis. For practical values of loop gain $T_0$, this would result in "high $Q$" poles

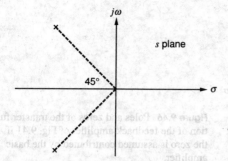

**Figure 9.45** Poles of the transfer function of the feedback amplifier of Fig. 9.41. The transfer function contains no zeros.

near the $j\omega$ axis, which would give rise to an excessively *peaked* response. In practice, oscillation can occur because higher magnitude poles do exist and these would tend to give a locus of the kind of Fig. 9.39, where the remote poles cause the locus to bend and enter the right half-plane. (Note that this behavior is consistent with the alternative approach of considering a diminished phase margin to be causing a peaked response and eventual instability.) The inclusion of the feedback zero, however, *bends* the locus away from the $j\omega$ axis and allows the designer to position the poles in any desired region.

An important point that should be stressed is that the root locus of Fig. 9.44 gives the *poles* of the feedback amplifier. The zero in that figure is a zero of loop gain $T(s)$ and thus must be included in the root locus. However, the zero is contributed by the *feedback network* and is *not* a zero of the overall feedback amplifier. As pointed out in Section 9.5.2, the *zeros* of the overall feedback amplifier are the *zeros* of basic amplifier $a(s)$ and the *poles* of feedback network $f(s)$. Thus the transfer function of the overall feedback amplifier in this case has two poles and no zeros, as shown in Fig. 9.45, and the poles are assumed placed at 45° to the axis by appropriate choice of $z$. Since the feedback zero affects the root locus but does *not* appear as a zero of the overall amplifier, it has been called a *phantom zero*.

On the other hand, if the zero $z$ were contributed by the basic amplifier, the situation would be different. For the same zero, the root locus would be identical but the transfer function of the overall feedback amplifier would then *include* the zero as shown in Fig. 9.46. This zero would then have a significant effect on the amplifier characteristics. This point is made simply to illustrate the difference between forward path and feedback-path zeros. There is no practical way to introduce a useful forward-path zero in this situation.

Before leaving this subject, we mention the effect of higher magnitude poles on the root locus of Fig. 9.44, and this is illustrated in Fig. 9.47. A remote pole $p_3$ will cause the locus to deviate from the original as shown and produce poles with a larger imaginary part than expected. The third pole, which is on the real axis, may also be significant in the final amplifier. Acceptable performance can usually be obtained by modifying the value of $z$ from that calculated above.

Finally, the results derived in this chapter explain the function of capacitors $C_P$ and $C_F$ in the circuit of the MC 1553 series-series triple of Fig. 8.21$a$, which was described in Chapter 8. Capacitor $C_P$ causes pole splitting to occur in stage $Q_2$ and produces a dominant pole in the basic amplifier, which aids in the compensation. However, as described above, a large value of $C_P$ will cause significant loss of bandwidth in the amplifier, and so a feedback zero is introduced via $C_F$, which further aids in the compensation by moving the root locus away from the $j\omega$ axis. The final design is a combination of two methods of compensation in an attempt to find an optimum solution.

**Figure 9.46** Poles and zeros of the transfer function of the feedback amplifier of Fig. 9.41 if the zero is assumed contributed by the basic amplifier.

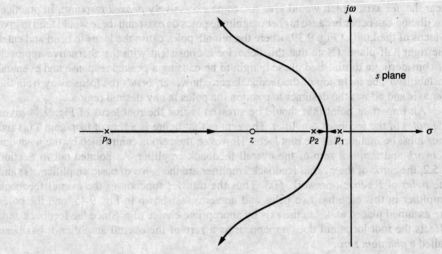

**Figure 9.47** Root locus of the circuit of Fig. 9.41 when an additional pole of the basic amplifier is included. (Not to scale.)

## 9.6 Slew Rate[8]

The previous sections of this chapter have been concerned with the small-signal behavior of feedback amplifiers at high frequencies. However, the behavior of feedback circuits with large input signals (either step inputs or sinusoidal signals) is also of interest, and the effect of frequency compensation on the large-signal, high-frequency performance of feedback amplifiers is now considered.

### 9.6.1 Origin of Slew-Rate Limitations

A common test of the high-frequency, large-signal performance of an amplifier is to apply a step input voltage from 0 to +5 V as shown in Fig. 9.48. This figure shows an op amp in a unity-gain feedback configuration and will be used for purposes of illustration in this development. Suppose initially that the circuit operates linearly when this input is applied, and further that the circuit has a single-pole transfer function given by

$$\frac{V_o}{V_i}(s) = \frac{A}{1 + s\tau} \tag{9.121}$$

**Figure 9.48** Circuit for testing slew-rate performance.

where

$$\tau = \frac{1}{2\pi f_o} \tag{9.122}$$

and $f_o$ is the $-3$-dB frequency. Since the circuit is connected as a voltage follower, the low-frequency gain $A$ will be close to unity. If we assume that this is so, the response of the circuit to this step input $[V_i(s) = 5/s]$ is given by

$$V_o(s) = \frac{1}{1 + s\tau} \frac{5}{s} \tag{9.123}$$

using (9.121). Equation 9.123 can be factored to the form

$$V_o(s) = \frac{5}{s} - \frac{5}{s + \dfrac{1}{\tau}} \tag{9.124}$$

From (9.124)

$$V_o(t) = 5(1 - e^{-t/\tau}) \tag{9.125}$$

The predicted response from (9.125) is shown in Fig. 9.49a using data for the 741 op amp with $f_o \simeq 1.3$ MHz. This shows an exponential rise of $V_o(t)$ to 5 V and the output reaches 90 percent of its final value in about 0.3 μs.

A typical output for a 741 op amp in such a test is shown in Fig. 9.49b and exhibits a completely different response. The output voltage is a slow ramp of almost constant slope and takes about 5 μs to reach 90 percent of its final value. Obviously the small-signal linear analysis is inadequate for predicting the circuit behavior under these conditions. The response shown in Fig. 9.49b is typical of op amp performance with a large input step voltage applied. The rate of change of output voltage $dV_o/dt$ in the region of constant slope is called the *slew rate* and is usually specified in V/μs.

The reason for this discrepancy between predicted and observed behavior noted above can be appreciated by examining the circuit of Fig. 9.48 and considering the responses in Fig. 9.49. At $t = 0$, the input voltage steps to $+5$ V, but the output voltage cannot respond instantaneously and is initially zero. Thus the op-amp differential input is $V_{id} = 5$ V, which drives the input stage completely out of its linear range of operation. This can be seen by considering a two-stage op amp; simplified schematics for a bipolar and CMOS op amp for use in this analysis are shown in Fig. 9.50. The Miller compensation capacitor $C$ connects around the high-gain second stage and causes this stage to act as an integrator.

**Figure 9.49** Response of the circuit of Fig. 9.48 when a 5-V step input is applied. (a) Response predicted by (9.125) for the 741 op amp. (b) Measured response for the 741.

The current from the input stage, which charges the compensation capacitor, is $I_x$. The large-signal transfer characteristic from the op-amp differential input voltage $V_{id}$ to $I_x$ is that of a differential pair, which is shown in Fig. 9.51. From Fig. 9.51, the maximum current available to charge $C$ is $2I_1$, which is the tail current in the input stage. For a bipolar differential pair, $|I_x| \approx 2I_1$ if $|V_{id}| > 3V_T$. For a MOS differential pair, $|I_x| \approx 2I_1$ if $|V_{id}| > \sqrt{2}|V_{ov1}|$. (See Chapter 3.) Thus, when $V_{id} = 5$ V as described above, the input stage *limits* and $I_x \approx 2I_1$ (assuming that $\sqrt{2}|V_{ov1}| < 5$ V for the MOS circuit). The circuit thus operates *nonlinearly,* and linear analysis fails to predict the behavior. If the input stage did act linearly, the input voltage of 5 V would produce a very large current $I_x$ to charge the compensation capacitor. The fact that this current is limited to the fairly small value of $2I_1$ is the reason for the slew rate being much less than a linear analysis would predict.

Consider a large input voltage applied to the circuits of Fig. 9.50 so that $I_x = 2I_1$. Then the second stage acts as an integrator with an input current $2I_1$, and the output voltage $V_o$ can be written as

$$V_o = \frac{1}{C} \int 2I_1 dt \qquad (9.126)$$

and thus

$$\frac{dV_o}{dt} = \frac{2I_1}{C} \qquad (9.127)$$

Equation 9.127 predicts a constant rate of change of $V_o$ during the slewing period, which is in agreement with the experimental observation. For the 741 op amp, $I_1 = 12\ \mu\text{A}$ and $C = 30$ pF giving $dV_o/dt = 0.8$ V/$\mu$s, which is close to the measured value. The above calculation of slew rate was performed on the circuits of Fig. 9.50, which have no overall feedback. Since the input stage produces a constant output current that is independent of its input during the slewing period, the presence of a feedback connection to the input does not affect the circuit operation during this time. Thus, the slew rate of the amplifier is the same whether feedback is applied or not.

(a)

(b)

**Figure 9.50** Simplified schematics of a two-stage (a) bipolar and (b) MOS op amp for slew rate calculations.

**Figure 9.51** Approximate large signal transfer characteristic for the input stages in Fig. 9.50. For the bipolar differential pair, $V_{IL} \approx 3V_T$. For the MOS differential pair, $V_{IL} \approx \sqrt{2}|V_{ov1}|$.

## 9.6.2 Methods of Improving Slew-Rate in Two-Stage Op Amps

In order to examine methods of slew-rate improvement, a more general analysis is required. This can be performed using the circuit of Fig. 9.52, which is a general representation of an op amp circuit. The input stage has a small-signal transconductance $g_{ml}$ and, with a large input voltage, can deliver a maximum current $I_{xm}$ to the next stage. The compensation is shown as the Miller effect using the capacitor $C$, since this representation describes most two-stage integrated-circuit op amps.

From Fig. 9.52 and using (9.127), we can calculate the slew rate for a large input voltage as

$$\frac{dV_o}{dt} = \frac{I_{xm}}{C} \tag{9.128}$$

Consider now *small-signal* operation. For the input stage, the small-signal transconductance is

$$\frac{\Delta I_x}{\Delta V_i} = g_{ml} \tag{9.129}$$

For the second stage (which acts as an integrator) the transfer function at high frequencies is

$$\frac{\Delta V_o}{\Delta I_x} = \frac{1}{sC}$$

and in the frequency domain

$$\frac{\Delta V_o}{\Delta I_x}(j\omega) = \frac{1}{j\omega C} \tag{9.130}$$

Combining (9.129) and (9.130) gives

$$\frac{\Delta V_o}{\Delta V_i}(j\omega) = \frac{g_{ml}}{j\omega C} \tag{9.131}$$

In our previous consideration of compensation, it was shown that the small-signal, open-loop voltage gain $(\Delta V_o/\Delta V_i)(j\omega)$ must fall to unity at or before a frequency equal to the magnitude of the second most dominant pole $(\omega_2)$. If we assume, for ease of calculation, that the circuit is compensated for unity-gain operation with $45°$ phase margin as shown in Fig. 9.15, the gain $(\Delta V_o/\Delta V_i)(j\omega)$ as given by (9.131) must fall to unity at frequency $\omega_2$. (Compensation capacitor $C$ must be chosen to ensure that this occurs.) Thus from (9.131)

$$1 = \frac{g_{ml}}{\omega_2 C}$$

and thus

$$\frac{1}{C} = \frac{\omega_2}{g_{ml}} \tag{9.132}$$

**Figure 9.52** Generalized representation of an op amp for slew-rate calculations.

Note that (9.132) was derived on the basis of a *small-signal* argument. This result can now be substituted in the *large-signal* equation (9.128) to give

$$\text{Slew rate} = \frac{dV_o}{dt} = \frac{I_{xm}}{g_{mI}}\omega_2 \qquad (9.133)$$

Equation 9.133 allows consideration of the effect of circuit parameters on slew rate, and it is apparent that, for a given $\omega_2$, the ratio $I_{xm}/g_{mI}$ must be increased if slew rate is to be increased.

### 9.6.3 Improving Slew-Rate in Bipolar Op Amps

The analysis of the previous section can be applied to a bipolar op amp that uses Miller compensation. In the case of the op amp in Fig. 9.50a, we have $I_{xm} = 2I_1$, $g_{mI} = qI_1/kT$, and substitution in (9.133) gives

$$\text{Slew rate} = 2\frac{kT}{q}\omega_2 \qquad (9.134)$$

Since both $I_{xm}$ and $g_{mI}$ are proportional to bias current $I_1$, the influence of $I_1$ cancels in the equation and slew rate is *independent* of $I_1$ for a given $\omega_2$. However, increasing $\omega_2$ will increase the slew rate, and this course is followed in most high-slew-rate circuits. The limit here is set by the frequency characteristics of the transistors in the IC process, and further improvements depend on circuit modifications as described below.

The above calculation has shown that varying the input-stage bias current of a two-stage bipolar op amp does not change the circuit slew rate. However, (9.133) indicates that for a given $I_{xm}$, slew rate can be increased by *reducing* the input-stage transconductance. One way this can be achieved is by including emitter-degeneration resistors to reduce $g_{mI}$ as shown in Fig. 9.53. The small-signal transconductance of this input stage can be shown to be

$$g_{mI} = \frac{\Delta I_x}{\Delta V_{id}} = g_{m1}\frac{1}{1 + g_{m1}R_E} \qquad (9.135)$$

where

$$g_{m1} = \frac{qI_1}{kT} \qquad (9.136)$$

**Figure 9.53** Inclusion of emitter resistors in the input stage in Fig. 9.50a to improve slew rate.

The value of $I_{xm}$ is still $2I_1$. Substituting (9.135) in (9.133) gives

$$\text{Slew rate} = \frac{2kT}{q}\omega_2\left(1 + g_{m1}R_E\right) \tag{9.137}$$

Thus the slew rate is increased by the factor $[1+(g_{m1}R_E)]$ over the value given by (9.134). The fundamental reason for this is that, for a given bias current $I_1$, reducing $g_{ml}$ reduces the compensation capacitor $C$ required, as shown by (9.132).

The practical limit to this technique is due to the fact that the emitter resistors of Fig. 9.53 have a dc voltage across them, and mismatches in the resistor values give rise to an input dc offset voltage. The use of large-area resistors can give resistors whose values match to within 0.2 percent (1 part in 500). If the maximum contribution to input offset voltage allowed from the resistors is 1 mV, then these numbers indicate that the maximum voltage drop allowed is

$$I_1R_E\big|_{\text{max}} = 500\,\text{mV} \tag{9.138}$$

Thus

$$g_{m1}R_E\big|_{\text{max}} = \frac{q}{kT}I_1R_E\big|_{\text{max}} = \frac{500}{26} = 20 \tag{9.139}$$

Using (9.139) in (9.137) shows that given these data, the maximum possible improvement in slew rate by use of emitter resistors is a factor of 21 times.

Finally, in this description of methods of slew-rate improvement, we mention the *class AB* input stage described by Hearn.[20] In this technique, the small-signal transconductance of the input stage is left essentially unchanged, but the limit $I_{xm}$ on the maximum current available for charging the compensation capacitor is greatly increased. This is done by providing alternative paths in the input stage that become operative for large inputs and deliver large charging currents to the compensation point. This has resulted in slew rates of the order of 30 V/μs in bipolar op amps, and, as in the previous cases, the limitation is an increase in input offset voltage.

### 9.6.4 Improving Slew Rate in MOS Op Amps

A two-stage Miller-compensated MOS op amp is shown in Fig. 9.50b, and its slew rate is given by (9.127). From the analysis in Section 9.6.2; (9.133) shows that the slew rate can be increased by increasing $\omega_2$. On the other hand, if $\omega_2$ is fixed, increasing the ratio $I_{xm}/g_{ml}$ improves the slew rate. Using (1.180), (9.133) can be rewritten as

$$\text{Slew rate} = \frac{I_{xm}}{g_{ml}}\omega_2 = \frac{2I_1}{\sqrt{2k'(W/L)_1 I_1}}\omega_2 = \sqrt{\frac{2I_1}{k'(W/L)_1}}\omega_2 \tag{9.140}$$

This equation shows that the slew rate increases if $(W/L)_1$ decreases with $I_1$ constant. In this case, $g_{ml} = g_{m1}$ decreases. From (9.132), a smaller compensation capacitor can then be used; therefore, the slew rate in (9.127) increases because $I_1$ is unchanged. Equation 9.140 also shows that the slew rate can be increased by increasing $I_1$. Assume that $I_1$ increases by a factor $x$ where $x > 1$. Then the ratio $I_{xm}/g_{ml}$ increases by the factor $\sqrt{x}$ because $g_{m1}$ is proportional to $\sqrt{I_1}$. From (9.132), the compensation capacitor must be increased by the factor $\sqrt{x}$ if $\omega_2$ is fixed. With these changes, the slew rate in (9.127) becomes

$$\frac{dV_o}{dt} = \frac{2xI_1}{C\sqrt{x}} = \frac{2I_1\sqrt{x}}{C} \tag{9.141}$$

Since $x > 1$, the slew rate is increased.

Alternatively, the ratio $I_{xm}/g_{mI}$ of the input stage can be increased by adding degeneration resistors $R_S$ in series with the sources of $M_1$ and $M_2$ to give

$$g_{mI} = \frac{g_{m1}}{1 + (g_{m1} + g_{mb1})R_S} \qquad (9.142)$$

For fixed $I_1$, increasing $R_S$ decreases $g_{mI}$ and increases $I_{xm}/g_{mI}$, which increases the slew rate.

These approaches increase the slew rate but have some drawbacks. First, decreasing $g_{mI}$ of the input stage while keeping its bias current constant will usually lower the dc gain of the first stage and hence reduce the dc gain of the entire op amp. Also, increasing $I_1$ or reducing $(W/L)_1$ tends to increase the input-offset voltage of the op amp, as can be seen from (3.248). Finally, if source-degeneration resistors are added, mismatch between these resistors degrades the input-offset voltage.

For single-stage MOS op amps, such as the telescopic-cascode and folded-cascode op amps, the slew rate is set by the maximum output current divided by the capacitance that loads the output. The maximum output current is equal to the tail current in these op amps.

■ **EXAMPLE**

Find the output slew rate for the cascode op amp shown in Fig. 9.54.

Assuming the op amp has a large positive differential input voltage applied, $M_2$ is cutoff and $I_{TAIL}$ flows through $M_1$. Therefore the drain current in $M_{2A}$ is zero, and the drain current in $M_3$ is $I_{d3} = -I_{TAIL}$. The current mirror $M_3$-$M_4$ forces $I_{d3} = I_{d4}$. It follows that $I_{d4A} = I_{d4} = -I_{TAIL}$. The current flowing into the load capacitor $C_L$ is

$$I_o = -I_{d2A} - I_{d4A} = -0 - (-I_{TAIL}) = I_{TAIL}$$

Therefore the positive output slew rate is

$$\frac{dV_o}{dt} = \frac{I_o}{C_L} = \frac{I_{TAIL}}{C_L} \qquad (9.143)$$

Figure 9.54 A CMOS telescopic-cascode op amp.

Application of a large negative input forces $M_1$ into cutoff so $I_{TAIL}$ must flow through $M_2$. Therefore, $I_{d4A} = I_{d4} = I_{d3} = 0$ and $I_{d2A} = I_{d2} = I_{TAIL}$. The current $I_o$ following through $C_L$ is

$$I_o = -I_{d2A} - I_{d4A} = -I_{TAIL} - 0 = -I_{TAIL}$$

▪ Hence, the negative slew rate is the opposite of the value in (9.143), $-I_{TAIL}/C_L$.

CMOS op amps are often used without an output stage when the output loading is purely capacitive, as is the case in switched-capacitor circuits. Avoiding an output stage saves power and is possible because low-output resistance is not needed to drive a capacitive load. An example of such a circuit is the switched-capacitor integrator shown in Fig. 6.10a. This circuit is redrawn in Fig. 9.55 when clock phase $\phi_2$ is high and $\phi_1$ is low, assuming that MOS transistors $M_1$-$M_4$ behave like ideal switches. The additional capacitor $C_{ip}$ here models the total parasitic capacitance at the op-amp input and includes the input capacitance of the op amp. A question that arises is: "For the feedback circuit in Fig. 9.55, what value of output load capacitance should be used to compute the slew rate for a single-stage op amp?" When the op amp is slewing, its behavior is nonlinear. Therefore the feedback is not effective and the virtual ground at the negative op-amp input is lost. With the feedback loop broken, the total capacitance seen from the output to ground is

$$C_L + C_I \| (C_S + C_{ip})  \tag{9.144}$$

This is the capacitance seen looking from the op-amp output node to ground, with the connection to the op-amp inverting input replaced with an open circuit. The effective output load capacitance in (9.144) is the same as the output load found when the feedback loop is broken to find the return ratio.

For the CMOS op amps considered so far in this section, the slew rate is proportional to a bias current in the op amp. A CMOS op amp with a Class AB input stage can give a slew rate that is not limited by a dc bias current in the op amp. An example[21,22] is shown in Fig. 9.56. The input voltage is applied between the gates of $M_1$, $M_2$ and $M_3$, $M_4$. Transistors $M_1$ and $M_4$ act simply as unity-gain source followers to transfer the input voltage to the gates of $M_6$ and $M_7$. Diode-connected transistors $M_5$ and $M_8$ act as level shifts, which, together with bias current sources $I_1$, set the quiescent Class AB current in $M_2$, $M_3$, $M_6$, and $M_7$. The currents in $M_3$ and $M_7$ are delivered to the output via cascode current mirrors $M_9$, $M_{10}$, $M_{13}$, $M_{14}$ and $M_{11}$, $M_{12}$, $M_{15}$, $M_{16}$. Bias currents can be determined by assuming that the input voltage $V_i = 0$, giving

$$V_{GS1} + |V_{GS5}| = |V_{GS6}| + V_{GS3}  \tag{9.145}$$

Assuming that (1.157) is valid we have

$$V_{tn} + \sqrt{2\frac{I_1}{k_n'}\left(\frac{L}{W}\right)_1} + |V_{tp}| + \sqrt{2\frac{I_1}{k_p'}\left(\frac{L}{W}\right)_5} = |V_{tp}| + \sqrt{2\frac{I_B}{k_P'}\left(\frac{L}{W}\right)_6} + V_{tn} + \sqrt{2\frac{I_B}{k_n'}\left(\frac{L}{W}\right)_3}$$

$$\tag{9.146}$$

Figure 9.55  An op amp with capacitive load and feedback. This is the switched-capacitor integrator of Fig. 6.10a during $\phi_2$, assuming ideal MOS switches.

**Figure 9.56** CMOS amplifier with a Class AB input stage.

where $I_B = |I_{D6}| = I_{D3} = I_{D2} = |I_{D7}|$ is the bias current and subscripts $n$ and $p$ indicate NMOS and PMOS, respectively. The two sides of the input stage are assumed symmetrical. From (9.146) we have

$$\sqrt{I_B}\left[\sqrt{\frac{2}{k_p'}\left(\frac{L}{W}\right)_6} + \sqrt{\frac{2}{k_n'}\left(\frac{L}{W}\right)_3}\right] = \sqrt{I_1}\left[\sqrt{\frac{2}{k_p'}\left(\frac{L}{W}\right)_5} + \sqrt{\frac{2}{k_n'}\left(\frac{L}{W}\right)_1}\right] \quad (9.147)$$

Equation 9.147 is the design equation for the input-stage bias current $I_B$.

Assuming that the cascode current mirrors in Fig. 9.56 have unity current gain, the bias currents in $M_9$-$M_{16}$ all equal $I_B$. To analyze this circuit, we will connect a voltage $V_i$ to the noninverting op-amp input and ground the inverting op-amp input. If a positive $V_i$ is applied, the magnitude of the currents in $M_3$ and $M_6$ increase, while the magnitude of the currents in $M_2$ and $M_7$ decrease. When mirrored to the output, these changes drive $I_o$ and $V_o$ positive. To calculate the small-signal gain, we neglect body effect. We can consider $M_6$ to act as source degeneration for $M_3$. The resistance looking into the source of $M_6$ is $1/g_{m6}$, thus

$$i_{d3} = \frac{g_{m3}}{1 + \dfrac{g_{m3}}{g_{m6}}}v_i \quad (9.148)$$

Similarly, $M_2$ acts as source degeneration for $M_7$, so

$$i_{d7} = \frac{g_{m7}}{1 + \dfrac{g_{m7}}{g_{m2}}}v_i = \frac{g_{m2}}{1 + \dfrac{g_{m2}}{g_{m7}}}v_i \quad (9.149)$$

where the right-most expression is found by rearranging. Thus, the transconductance of the amplifier is

$$G_m = \left.\frac{i_o}{v_i}\right|_{v_o=0} = \frac{i_{d3} + i_{d7}}{v_i} = \frac{2g_{m3}}{1 + \dfrac{g_{m3}}{g_{m6}}} \tag{9.150}$$

using $g_{m2} = g_{m3}$ and $g_{m6} = g_{m7}$. If $g_{m3} = g_{m6}$, then $G_m = g_{m3}$.

The output resistance of this op amp is just the output resistance of the cascodes in parallel and is

$$R_o \approx (r_{o14}g_{m14}r_{o13})\|(r_{o15}g_{m15}r_{o16}) \tag{9.151}$$

Finally, the small-signal voltage gain is

$$A_v = G_m R_o \tag{9.152}$$

The small-signal analysis above showed that a small positive $V_i$ causes a positive $I_o$. If $V_i$ continues to increase beyond the small-signal linear range of the input stage, $M_2$ and $M_7$ will be cut off, while $M_3$ and $M_6$ will be driven to larger values of $|V_{gs}|$. The currents in $M_3$ and $M_6$ can increase to quite large values, which gives a correspondingly large positive $I_o$. For large negative values of $V_i$, $M_3$ and $M_6$ turn off, $M_2$ and $M_7$ conduct large currents, and $I_o$ becomes large negative. Thus this circuit is capable of supplying large positive and negative currents to a load capacitance, and the magnitude of these output currents can be much larger than the bias current $I_B$ in the input stage. Therefore, this op amp does not display slew-rate limiting in the usual sense.

One disadvantage of this structure is that about half the transistors turn completely off during slewing. As a result, the time required to turn these transistors back on can be an important limitation to the high-frequency performance. To overcome this problem, the op amp can be designed so that the minimum drain currents are set to a nonzero value.[23]

### 9.6.5 Effect of Slew-Rate Limitations on Large-Signal Sinusoidal Performance

The slew-rate limitations described above can also affect the performance of the circuit when handling large sinusoidal signals at higher frequencies. Consider the circuit of Fig. 9.48 with a large sinusoidal signal applied as shown in Fig. 9.57a. Since the circuit is connected as a voltage follower, the output voltage $V_o$ will be forced to follow the $V_i$ waveform. The maximum value of $dV_i/dt$ occurs as the waveform crosses the axis, and if $V_i$ is given by

$$V_i = \hat{V}_i \sin \omega t \tag{9.153}$$

then

$$\frac{dV_i}{dt} = \omega \hat{V}_i \cos \omega t$$

and

$$\left.\frac{dV_i}{dt}\right|_{\max} = \omega \hat{V}_i \tag{9.154}$$

As long as the value of $dV_i/dt|_{\max}$ given by (9.154) is less than the slew-rate limit, the output voltage will closely follow the input. However, if the product $\omega \hat{V}_i$ is greater than the slew-rate limit, the output voltage will be unable to follow the input, and waveform distortion of the kind shown in Fig. 9.57b will result. If a sine wave with $\hat{V}_i$ equal to the supply voltage is applied to the amplifier, slew limiting will eventually occur as the sine-wave frequency is increased. The frequency at which this occurs is called the *full-power*

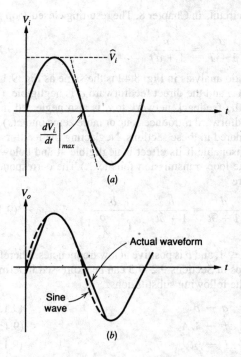

**Figure 9.57** (a) Large sinusoidal input voltage applied to the circuit of Fig. 9.48. (b) Output voltage resulting from input (a) showing slew limiting.

bandwidth of the circuit. (In practice, a value of $\hat{V}_i$ slightly less than the supply voltage is used to avoid clipping distortion of the type described in Chapter 5.)

■ **EXAMPLE**

Calculate the *full-power* bandwidth of the 741. Use $\hat{V}_i$ = supply voltage = 15 V. From (9.154) put

$$\omega \hat{V}_i = \text{slew rate}$$

This gives

$$\omega = \frac{0.8 \text{ V}/\mu s}{15 \text{ V}} = 53.3 \times 10^3 \text{ rad/s}$$

Thus

$$f = 8.5 \text{ kHz}$$

This means that a 741 op amp with a sinusoidal output of 15 V amplitude will begin to ■ show slew-limiting distortion if the frequency exceeds 8.5 kHz.

# APPENDIX

## A9.1 ANALYSIS IN TERMS OF RETURN-RATIO PARAMETERS

Much of the analysis in this chapter is based on the ideal block diagram in Fig. 9.1. This block diagram includes the forward gain $a$ and feedback $f$, which are the parameters used in two-port analysis of feedback circuits in Chapter 8. The resulting closed-loop gain expression is

$$A = \frac{a}{1 + T} = \frac{a}{1 + af} \tag{9.155}$$

The block diagram from return-ratio analysis in Fig. 8.42 is the same as Fig. 9.1 if $a$ is replaced by $b$, $f$ is replaced by $1/A_\infty$, and the direct feedforward $d$ is negligible. (The contribution of feedforward through the feedback network to $a$ is also neglected in the analysis in Sections 9.2–9.5, since feedforward introduces one or more zeros into $a(s)$, but only one- and two-pole $a(s)$ are considered in these sections. Neglecting the feedforward in $a$ or the direct feedthrough $d$ is reasonable if its effect is negligible at and below the frequency where the magnitude of the loop transmission falls to 1.) The corresponding equations from return-ratio analysis are

$$A = \frac{b}{1 + \mathcal{R}} + \frac{d}{1 + \mathcal{R}} \approx \frac{b}{1 + \mathcal{R}} = \frac{b}{1 + \dfrac{b}{A_\infty}} \tag{9.156}$$

For the circuit in Fig. 8.24, $0 \le 1/A_\infty \le 1$, and $b$ is positive at low frequencies. Therefore, the equations, graphs, and relationships in Sections 9.2–9.5 can be expressed in terms of the return-ratio variables by making the following substitutions:

$$a \to b \tag{9.157a}$$

$$f \to 1/A_\infty \tag{9.157b}$$

$$T \to \mathcal{R} \tag{9.157c}$$

$$af \to b/A_\infty \tag{9.157d}$$

The return ratio can be used to check stability of an amplifier with a single feedback loop because $A_\infty$ and $d$ are stable transfer functions associated with passive networks, and $\mathcal{R}(s)$ is stable because it is the signal transfer around a loop that consists of one gain stage or a cascade of stable gain stages. Therefore the zeros of $1 + \mathcal{R}(s)$, which are poles of the closed-loop gain $A$, determine the stability of the feedback circuit.[24] From the Nyquist stability criterion, these zeros are in the left half-plane if a polar plot of $\mathcal{R}(j\omega)$ does not encircle the point $(-1,0)$. In most cases, this stability condition is equivalent to having a positive phase margin. The phase margin is measured at the frequency where $|\mathcal{R}(j\omega)| = 1$.

Since the equations for two-port and return-ratio analyses are not identical, $T(s)$ and $\mathcal{R}(s)$ may be different for a given circuit.[25] In general, the phase margins using $T$ and $\mathcal{R}$ may differ, but both will have the same sign and therefore will agree on the stability of the feedback circuit.

## A9.2 ROOTS OF A QUADRATIC EQUATION

A second-order polynomial often appears in the denominator or numerator of a transfer function, and the zeros of this polynomial are the poles or zeros of the transfer function. In this appendix, the relationships between the zeros of a quadratic and its coefficients are explored for a few specific cases of interest. Also, the conditions under which a dominant root exists are derived.

Consider the roots of the quadratic equation

$$as^2 + bs + c = 0 \tag{9.158}$$

The two roots of this equation, $r_1$ and $r_2$, are given by the quadratic formula:

$$r_{1,2} = \frac{-b \pm \sqrt{b^2 - 4ac}}{2a} \tag{9.159}$$

where it is understood that the square root of a positive quantity is positive. Factoring $b$ out of the square root and rearranging gives

$$r_{1,2} = -\frac{b}{2a}\left(1 \pm \sqrt{1 - \frac{4ac}{b^2}}\right) \tag{9.160a}$$

$$= -\frac{b}{2a}\left(1 \pm \sqrt{D}\right) \tag{9.160b}$$

The quantity under the square root in (9.160a) has been replaced by $D$ in (9.160b), where

$$D = 1 - \frac{4ac}{b^2} \tag{9.161}$$

Now, consider the locations of the roots if coefficients $a$, $b$, and $c$ all have the same sign. In this case, both roots are in the left half-plane (LHP), as will be shown next. First, note that if all the coefficients have the same sign, then

$$\frac{b}{2a} > 0 \tag{9.162}$$

and

$$\frac{4ac}{b^2} > 0. \tag{9.163}$$

Let us divide (9.163) into two different regions. First, if

$$0 < \frac{4ac}{b^2} \leq 1 \tag{9.164}$$

then $D$ will be positive and less than one. Therefore, $\sqrt{D} < 1$, so $1 + \sqrt{D}$ and $1 - \sqrt{D}$ are both positive. As a result, the roots are both negative and real, because $-b/2a < 0$.

Now, consider the other region for (9.163), which is

$$\frac{4ac}{b^2} > 1 \tag{9.165}$$

In this case, $D < 0$; therefore $\sqrt{D}$ is imaginary. The roots are complex conjugates with a real part of $-b/2a$, which is negative. So the roots are again in the LHP. Therefore, when coefficients $a$, $b$, and $c$ all have the same sign, both roots are in the LHP.

Next, consider the locations of the roots if coefficients $a$ and $b$ have the same sign and $c$ has a different sign. In this case, one real root is in the right half-plane (RHP) and the other is in the LHP. To prove this, first note from (9.161) that $D > 1$ here because $4ac/b^2 < 0$. Therefore both roots are real and $\sqrt{D} > 1$, so

$$1 + \sqrt{D} > 0 \tag{9.166a}$$

and

$$1 - \sqrt{D} < 0 \tag{9.166b}$$

Substituting into (9.160), one root will be positive and the other negative (the sign of $-b/2a$ is negative here).

Finally, let us consider the conditions under which LHP roots are real and widely spaced. From (9.160), real LHP roots are widely spaced if

$$-\frac{b}{2a}(1 + \sqrt{D}) \ll -\frac{b}{2a}(1 - \sqrt{D}) \qquad (9.167)$$

or

$$1 + \sqrt{D} \gg 1 - \sqrt{D} \qquad (9.168)$$

Substituting the expression for $D$ in (9.161) into (9.168) and simplifying leads to an equivalent condition for widely spaced roots, which is

$$\frac{4ac}{b^2} \ll 1 \qquad (9.169)$$

Under this condition, one root is

$$r_2 = -\frac{b}{2a}(1 + \sqrt{D}) \approx -\frac{b}{2a}(1 + 1) = -\frac{b}{a} \qquad (9.170a)$$

The other root is

$$r_1 = -\frac{b}{2a}(1 - \sqrt{D})$$

$$= -\frac{b}{2a}\left(1 - \sqrt{1 - \frac{4ac}{b^2}}\right) \qquad (9.170b)$$

$$\approx -\frac{b}{2a}\left(1 - \left(1 - \frac{4ac}{2b^2}\right)\right)$$

$$= -\frac{c}{b}$$

where the approximation

$$\sqrt{1 - x} \approx 1 - \frac{x}{2} \quad \text{for} \quad |x| \ll 1 \qquad (9.171)$$

has been used. Here, $|r_1| \ll |r_2|$ because $|r_1| \approx c/b \ll b/a \approx |r_2|$ (which follows from $4ac/b^2 \ll 1$). If these roots are poles, $r_1$ corresponds to the dominant pole, and $r_2$ gives the nondominant pole. Equations 9.170a and 9.170b are in agreement with (9.30) through (9.33).

Table 9.1 summarizes the location of the roots of (9.158) for the cases considered in this appendix. When both roots are in the LHP, the roots are both real if (9.164) is satisfied. These roots are widely spaced if (9.169) is satisfied.

**Table 9.1**

| Sign of Coefficient Values in (9.158) | | | Roots |
|---|---|---|---|
| $a$ | $b$ | $c$ | |
| + | + | + | Both in LHP |
| − | − | − | Both in LHP |
| + | + | − | One in LHP, one in RHP |
| − | − | + | One in LHP, one in RHP |

# PROBLEMS

**9.1** An amplifier has a low-frequency forward gain of 200 and its transfer function has three negative real poles with magnitudes 1 MHz, 2 MHz, and 4 MHz. Calculate and sketch the Nyquist diagram for this amplifier if it is placed in a negative feedback loop with $f = 0.05$. Is the amplifier stable? Explain.

**9.2** For the amplifier in Problem 9.1, calculate and sketch plots of gain (in decibels) and phase versus frequency (log scale) with no feedback applied. Determine the value of $f$ that just causes instability and the value of $f$ giving a 60° phase margin.

**9.3** If an amplifier has a phase margin of 20°, how much does the closed-loop gain peak (above the low-frequency value) at the frequency where the loop-gain magnitude is unity?

**9.4** An amplifier has a low-frequency forward gain of 40,000 and its transfer function has three negative real poles with magnitudes 2 kHz, 200 kHz, and 4 MHz.

**(a)** If this amplifier is connected in a feedback loop with $f$ constant and with low-frequency gain $A_0 = 400$, estimate the phase margin.

**(b)** Repeat (a) if $A_0$ is 200 and then 100.

**9.5** An amplifier has a low-frequency forward gain of 5000 and its transfer function has three negative real poles with magnitudes 300 kHz, 2 MHz, and 25 MHz.

**(a)** Calculate the dominant-pole magnitude required to give unity-gain compensation of this amplifier with a 45° phase margin if the original amplifier poles remain fixed. What is the resulting bandwidth of the circuit with the feedback applied?

**(b)** Repeat (a) for compensation in a feedback loop with a forward gain of 20 dB and 45° phase margin.

**9.6** The amplifier of Problem 9.5 is to be compensated by reducing the magnitude of the most dominant pole.

**(a)** Calculate the dominant-pole magnitude required for unity-gain compensation with 45° phase margin, and the corresponding bandwidth of the circuit with the feedback applied. Assume that the remaining poles do not move.

**(b)** Repeat (a) for compensation in a feedback loop with a forward gain of 20 dB and 45° phase margin.

**9.7** Repeat Problem 9.6 for the amplifier of Problem 9.4.

**9.8** An op amp has a low-frequency voltage gain of 100,000 and a frequency response with a single negative-real pole with magnitude 5 Hz. This amplifier is to be connected in a series-shunt feedback loop with $f = 0.01$ giving a low-frequency closed-loop voltage gain $A_0 \approx 100$. If the output impedance without feedback is resistive with a value of 100 $\Omega$, show that the output impedance of the feedback circuit can be represented as shown in Fig. 9.58, and calculate the values of these elements. Sketch the magnitude of the output impedance of the feedback circuit on log scales from 1 Hz to 100 kHz.

**Figure 9.58** Circuit representation of the output impedance of a series-shunt feedback circuit.

**9.9** An op amp is fabricated using the 741 circuit but with different processing so that the transfer function before compensation has three negative real poles with magnitudes 30 kHz, 500 kHz, and 10 MHz. The circuit is compensated in the same manner as the 741, and pole-splitting causes the second most dominant pole to become negligible. Calculate the value of capacitance required to achieve a 60° phase margin in a unity-gain feedback connection and calculate the frequency where the resulting open-loop gain is 0 dB. Use low-frequency data as given in Chapter 7 for the 741 and assume that the pole with magnitude 10 MHz is unaffected by the compensation. The low-frequency gain of the 741 is 108 dB.

**9.10** Repeat Problem 9.9 if the circuit is compensated by using shunt capacitance to ground at the base of $Q_{16}$. Assume that this affects only the most dominant pole.

**9.11** An amplifier has gain $a_0 = 200$ and its transfer function has three negative real poles with magnitudes 1 MHz, 3 MHz, and 4 MHz. Calculate and sketch the root locus when feedback is applied as $f$ varies from 0 to 1. Estimate the value of $f$ causing instability.

**9.12** Calculate and sketch the root locus for the amplifier of Problem 9.4 as $f$ varies from 0 to 1.

Estimate the value of $f$ causing instability and check using the Nyquist criterion.

**9.13** For the circuit of Fig. 9.41, parameter values are $R_F = 5$ k$\Omega$, $R_E = 50$ $\Omega$, and $C_F = 1.5$ pF. The basic amplifier of the circuit is shown in Fig. 9.42 and has two negative real poles with magnitudes 3 MHz and 6 MHz. The low-frequency *current gain* of the basic amplifier is 4000. Assuming that the loop gain of the circuit of Fig. 9.41 can be varied without changing the parameters of the basic amplifier, sketch root loci for this circuit as $f$ varies from 0 to 0.01 both with and without $C_F$. Estimate the pole positions of the current-gain transfer function of the feedback amplifier of Fig. 9.41 with the values of $R_F$ and $R_E$ specified both with and without $C_F$. Sketch graphs in each case of gain magnitude versus frequency on log scales from $f = 10$ kHz to $f = 100$ MHz.

**9.14** An op amp has two negative real open-loop poles with magnitudes 100 Hz and 120 kHz and a negative real zero with magnitude 100 kHz. The low-frequency open-loop voltage gain of the op amp is 100 dB. If this amplifier is placed in a negative feedback loop, sketch the root locus as $f$ varies from 0 to 1. Calculate the poles and zeros of the feedback amplifier for $f = 10^{-3}$ and $f = 1$.

**9.15** Repeat Problem 9.14 if the circuit has negative real poles with magnitudes 100 Hz and 100 kHz and a negative real zero with magnitude 120 kHz.

**9.16** The input stages of an op amp are shown in the schematic of Fig. 9.59.

**(a)** Assuming that the frequency response is dominated by a single pole, calculate the frequency

where the magnitude of the small-signal voltage gain $|v_o(j\omega)/v_i(j\omega)|$ is unity and also the output slew rate of the amplifier.

**(b)** Sketch the response $V_o(t)$ from 0 to 20 $\mu$s for a step input at $V_i$ from $-5$ V to $+5$ V. Assume that the circuit is connected in a noninverting unity-gain feedback loop.

**(c)** Compare your results with a SPICE simulation using parameters $\beta = 100$, $V_A = 130$ V, and $I_S = 10^{-15}$ A for all devices.

**9.17** Repeat Problem 9.16 if the circuit of Fig. 9.59 is compensated by a capacitor of 0.05 $\mu$F connected from the base of $Q_5$ to ground. Assume that the voltage gain from the base of $Q_5$ to $V_o$ is $-500$.

**9.18** The slew rate of the circuit of Fig. 9.59 is to be increased by using 10 k$\Omega$ resistors in the emitters $Q_1$ and $Q_2$. If the same unity-gain frequency is to be achieved, calculate the new value of compensation capacitor required and the improvement in slew rate. Check your result with SPICE simulations.

**9.19** Repeat Problem 9.18 if PMOS transistors replace $Q_1$ and $Q_2$ (with no degeneration resistors). Assume that the PMOS transistors are biased to 300 $\mu$A each ($I_{EE} = 600$ $\mu$A), at which bias value the MOS transistors have $g_m = 300$ $\mu$A/V.

**9.20(a)** Calculate the full-power bandwidth of the circuit of Fig. 9.59.

**(b)** If this circuit is connected in a noninverting unity-gain feedback loop, sketch the output waveform $V_o$ if $V_i$ is a sinusoid of 10 V amplitude and frequency 45 kHz.

**Figure 9.59**  Input stages of an op amp.

**Figure 9.60** Circuit for Problem 9.21.

**9.21** For the CMOS operational amplifier shown in Fig. 9.60, calculate the open-loop voltage gain, unity-gain bandwidth, and slew rate. Assume the parameters of Table 2.1 with $X_d = 1$ μm. Assume that the gate of $M_9$ is connected to the positive power supply and that the $W/L$ of $M_9$ has been chosen to cancel the right half-plane zero. Compare your results with a SPICE simulation.

**9.22** Repeat Problem 9.21 except use the aspect ratios, supply voltages, and bias current given in Fig. 6.59 instead of the values in Fig. 9.60. Also, assume that $X_d = 0.1$ μm for all transistors operating in the active region, and use Table 2.4 for other parameters.

**9.23** If the circuit of Fig. 9.61 is used to generate the voltage to be applied to the gate of $M_9$ in Fig. 9.60, calculate the $W/L$ of $M_9$ required to move the right half-plane zero to infinity. Use data from Table 2.1 with $X_d = 1$ μm. Check your result with SPICE.

**9.24** Repeat Problem 9.23, but skip the SPICE simulation. Here, $M_9$ will be used in the op amp in Fig. 6.59. Let $V_{DD} = V_{SS} = 1.5$ V and $I_S = 200$ μA. Use $L = 1$ μm for all transistors, $W_8 = W_{10} = 150$ μm, and $W_{11} = W_{12} = 100$ μm. Assume that $X_d = 0.1$ μm for all transistors operating in the active region, and use Table 2.4 for other parameters.

**Figure 9.61** Circuit for Problem 9.23.

**9.25** Assuming that the zero has been moved to infinity, determine the maximum load capacitance that can be attached directly to the output of the circuit of Fig. 9.60 and still maintain a phase margin of 45°. Neglect all higher order poles except any due to the load capacitance. Use the value of $W/L$ obtained in Problem 9.23 for $M_9$ with the bias circuit of Fig. 9.61.

**9.26** Repeat Problem 9.25 except, for the op amp, use the aspect ratios, supply voltages, and bias current given in Fig. 6.59 instead of the values in Fig. 9.60. Also, for the bias circuit, use the aspect ratios, supply voltages, and bias current given in Problem 9.24. Ignore junction capacitance for all transistors. Also, assume that $X_d = 0.1$ μm for all transistors operating in the active region, and use Table 2.4 for other parameters.

**9.27** For the CMOS op amp of Fig. 9.60, assume that $M_9$ and the compensation capacitor are removed and the output is loaded with a 1 MΩ resistor. Using the data of Table 2.1, use SPICE to determine the gain and phase versus frequency of the small-signal circuit voltage gain.

The amplifier is to be connected in a negative feedback loop with the 1-MΩ resistor connected from the output to the gate of $M_1$, and a resistor $R_x$ from the $M_1$ gate to ground. An input voltage is applied from the gate of $M_2$ to ground. From your previous simulated data, determine the forward voltage gain of the feedback configuration and the corresponding values of $R_x$ giving phase margins of 80°, 60°, 45°, and 20°. For each case use SPICE to plot out the corresponding overall small-signal voltage gain versus frequency for the feedback circuit and also the step response for an output voltage step of 100 mV. Compare and comment on the results obtained. Assume $X_d = 1$ μm and that the drain and source regions are 2 μm wide.

**9.28** The CMOS circuit of Fig. 9.56 is to be used as a high-slew-rate op amp. A load capacitance of $C_L = 10$ pF is connected from $V_o$ to ground. Supply voltages are ±5 V and $I_1 = 20$ μA. Devices $M_1$–$M_4$ have $W = 20$ μm and $L = 1$ μm and devices $M_5$–$M_8$ have $W = 60$ μm and $L = 1$ μm. All other NMOS devices have $W = 60$ μm and $L = 1$ μm, and all other PMOS devices have $W = 300$ μm and $L = 1$ μm. Device data are $\mu_n C_{ox} = 60$ μA/V$^2$, $V_{tn} = 0.7$ V, $V_{tp} = -0.7$ V, $\gamma = 0$, and $|\lambda| = 0.05$ V$^{-1}$.

**(a)** Calculate the small-signal open-loop gain and unity-gain bandwidth of the circuit. Derive an expression for the large-signal transfer function $I_o/V_i$ when all four devices $M_2, M_3, M_6$, and $M_7$ are on, and also for larger $V_i$ when two of them cut off. At what value of $V_i$ does the transition occur?

**(b)** Connect the circuit in a unity-gain negative feedback loop ($V_o$ to the gate of $M_1$) and drive the circuit with a voltage step from $-1.5$ V to $+1.5$ V at the gate of $M_4$. Calculate and sketch the corresponding output waveform $V_o$ assuming linear operation, and compare all your results with a SPICE simulation. What is the peak current delivered to $C_L$ during the transient?

**9.29** Using the basic topology of Fig. 8.53, design a CMOS feedback amplifier with $R_i = \infty$, $R_o < 30$ Ω, $A_v = v_o/v_i = 10$, and small-signal bandwidth $f_{-3dB} > 2$ MHz. No peaking is allowed in the gain-versus-frequency response. Supply current must be less than 2 mA from each of ±5 V supplies. The circuit operates with $R_L = 1$ kΩ to ground and must be able to swing $V_o = \pm 1$ V before clipping occurs. Use the process data of Table 2.1 with $X_d = 0.5$ μm and $\gamma_n = 0.5$ V$^{1/2}$. Source and drain regions are 9 μm wide. Verify your hand calculations with SPICE simulations.

**9.30** Determine the compensation capacitor for the two-stage op amp in the example in Section 9.4.3 that gives a 60° phase margin.

**9.31** The Miller-compensated two-stage op amp in Fig. 9.28a can be modeled as shown in Fig. 9.28b. In the model, let $g_{m1} = 0.5$ mA/V, $R_1 = 200$ kΩ, $g_{m6} = 2$ mA/V, $R_2 = 100$ kΩ, $C_1 = 0.1$ pF, and $C_2 = 8$ pF.

**(a)** Assume the op amp is connected in negative feedback with $f = 0.5$. What is the value of $C$ that gives a 45° phase margin? Assume the right half-plane (RHP) zero has been eliminated, and assume the feedback network does not load the op amp.

**(b)** What value of $R_z$ in Fig. 9.28 eliminates the RHP zero?

**9.32** Repeat Problem 9.31(a) for the common-gate compensation scheme in Fig. 9.25a.

**9.33** The simple model for the common-gate $M_{11}$ in Fig. 9.25b has zero input impedance. Show that if the common-gate stage $M_{11}$ is modeled with nonzero input impedance, the compensation scheme in Fig. 9.25a introduces a zero at $-g_{m11}/C$ in the amplifier gain. To simplify this analysis, assume that $r_{o11} = \infty$, $\gamma = 0$, and ignore all device capacitances.

**9.34** Plot a locus of the poles of (9.27) as $C$ varies from 0 to ∞. Use $R_1 = 200$ kΩ, $g_m = 2$ mA/V, $R_2 = 100$ kΩ, $C_1 = 0.1$ pF, and $C_2 = 8$ pF.

**9.35** For the three-stage op amp with nested Miller compensation in Fig. 9.32c, determine the values of the compensation capacitors that give a

**Figure 9.62** Feedback circuit for Problem 9.40.

45° phase margin when the op amp is in a unity-gain negative feedback loop ($f = 1$). Assume that the zeros due to feedforward have been eliminated. Design for widely spaced real poles. Take $R_0 = R_1 = R_2 = 5$ k$\Omega$, $C_0 = C_1 = 0.5$ pF, and $C_2 = 6$ pF. Use $g_{m0} = g_{m1}$ and $g_{m2} = 6g_{m1}$.

**9.36** For the three-stage op amp with nested Miller compensation in Fig. 9.32c, determine the values of the compensation capacitors that give a 60° phase margin when the op amp is in a unity-gain negative feedback loop ($f = 1$). Assume that the zeros due to feedforward have been eliminated. Design for complex poles $p_2$ and $p_3$. Use $R_0 = R_1 = R_2 = 5$ k$\Omega$, $C_0 = C_1 = 0.5$ pF, and $C_2 = 6$ pF. Use $g_{m0} = g_{m1}$ and $g_{m2} = 6g_{m1}$.

**9.37** The single-stage op amp in Fig. 9.54 has a 45° phase margin when the op amp is in a unity-gain negative feedback loop ($f = 1$) with an output load capacitance $C_L = 2$ pF. What value of $C_L$ will give a 60° phase margin? (Assume that the capacitance at the op-amp output is dominated by $C_L$ and the op-amp gain $a_v(s)$ can be modeled as having two poles.)

**9.38** The single-stage op amp in Fig. 9.54 has a nondominant pole $p_2$ with $|p_2| = 200$ Mrad/s. The op amp is in a unity-gain negative feedback loop ($f = 1$).

**(a)** If $g_{m1} = 0.3$ mA/V, what value of $C_L$ gives a 45° phase margin? (Assume that the capacitance at the op amp output is dominated by $C_L$ and the op-amp gain $a(s)$ can be modeled as having two poles.)

**(b)** If $I_{TAIL} = 0.5$ mA, what is the output slew rate with this $C_L$?

**9.39** The feedback circuit in Fig. 9.55 is a switched-capacitor circuit during one clock phase. Assume the op amp is the telescopic-cascode op amp in Fig. 9.54. Take $C_L = 1.5$ pF, $C_I = 4$ pF, $C_S = 0.4$ pF, and $C_{ip} = 0.1$ pF.

**(a)** If $I_{TAIL} = 0.2$ mA, what is the output slew rate?

**(b)** Assume that $g_{m1} = 0.1$ mA/V, the loop transmission [loop gain $T(s)$ or return ratio $\mathcal{R}(s)$] can be modeled as having two poles, and the magnitude of the nondominant pole $p_2$ is $|p_2| = 200$ Mrad/s. What is the phase margin of this feedback circuit?

**9.40** Calculate the return ratio for the feedback circuit in Fig. 9.62. Assume that the amplifier voltage gain is constant with $a_v > 0$. Show that this feedback circuit is always stable if each impedance is either a resistor or a capacitor.

**9.41** Calculate the return ratio for the integrator in Fig. 9.63. Show that this feedback circuit is stable for all values of $R$ and $C$ if $a_v(s)$ has two left half-plane poles and $a_v(s = 0) > 0$.

**9.42** Calculate the return ratio for the inverting amplifier in Fig. 9.64. Here, the controlled source and $C_{in}$ form a simple op-amp model. Assume $a_v(s) = 1000/[(1 + s/100)(1 + s/10^6)]$.

**(a)** Assume the op-amp input capacitance $C_{in} = 0$. What is the frequency at which

**Figure 9.63** Circuit for Problem 9.41.

Figure 9.64  Circuit for Problem 9.42.

Figure 9.65  Circuit for Problem 9.45.

$|\mathcal{R}(j\omega)| = 1$? How does this frequency compare to the frequency at which $|a_v(j\omega)| = 1$?

(b) Find the phase margin for the cases $C_{in} = 0$, $C_{in} = 4$ pF, and $C_{in} = 20$ pF.

**9.43** A technique that allows the return ratio to be simulated using SPICE without disrupting the dc operating point is shown in Fig. 8.60 and explained in Problem 8.33.

(a) Use that technique to simulate the return ratio for the op amp from Problem 9.21 connected in a noninverting unity-gain configuration for $f = 1$ kHz, 100 kHz, 10 MHz, and 1 GHz.

(b) Use that technique to plot the magnitude and phase of the return ratio. Determine the unity-gain frequency for the return ratio and the phase

and gain margins. [Note: This calculation requires combining the complex values of $\mathcal{R}_i'(j\omega)$ and $\mathcal{R}_v'(j\omega)$ to find the complex quantity $\mathcal{R}(j\omega)$.]

**9.44** Repeat Problem 9.43 for the circuit in Fig. 9.64 with $C_{in} = 4$ pF. Inject the test sources on the left-hand side of the feedback resistor. Use $a_v(s)$ from Problem 9.42. Compare the simulation results with the calculated values from Problem 9.42.

**9.45** Repeat Problem 9.43 for the local feedback circuit in Fig. 9.65. For the transistor, $W = 50$ μm and $L_{eff} = 0.6$ μm. Use the device data in Table 2.4. Ignore the drain-body junction capacitance (assuming it is small compared to the 2-pF load capacitor).

# REFERENCES

1.  K. Ogata. *Modern Control Engineering*, 2nd Edition. Prentice-Hall, Englewood Cliffs, NJ, 1990.

2.  P. W. Tuinenga. *SPICE: A Guide to Circuit Simulation and Analysis using PSPICE*, 3rd Edition. Prentice-Hall, Englewood Cliffs, NJ, 1995.

3.  G. W. Roberts and A.S. Sedra. *SPICE*, 2nd Edition. Oxford Press, New York, 1997.

4.  P. J. Hurst. "Exact Simulation of Feedback Circuit Parameters," *IEEE Trans. on Circuits and Systems*, Vol. CAS-38, No. 11, pp. 1382–1389, November 1991.

5.  P. J. Hurst and S.H. Lewis. "Determination of Stability Using Return Ratios in Balanced Fully Differential Feedback Circuits," *IEEE Trans. on Circuits and Systems II*, pp. 805–817, December 1995.

6.  S. Rosenstark. *Feedback Amplifier Principles*, MacMillan, New York, 1986.

7.  R. D. Middlebrook. "Measurement of Loop Gain in Feedback Systems," *Int. J. Electronics*, Vol. 38, No. 4, pp. 485–512, 1975.

8. J. E. Solomon. "The Monolithic Op Amp: A Tutorial Study," *IEEE J. Solid-State Circuits*, Vol. SC-9, pp. 314–332, December 1974.

9. Y. P. Tsividis and P.R. Gray. "An Integrated NMOS Operational Amplifier with Internal Compensation," *IEEE J. Solid-State Circuits*, Vol. SC-11, pp. 748–753, December 1976.

10. B. K. Ahuja. "An Improved Frequency Compensation Technique for CMOS Operational Amplifiers," *IEEE J. Solid-State Circuits*, Vol. SC-18, pp. 629–633, December 1983.

11. D. B. Ribner and M. A. Copeland. "Design Techniques for Cascoded CMOS Op Amps with Improved PSRR and Common-Mode Input Range," *IEEE J. Solid-State Circuits*, pp. 919–925, December 1984.

12. D. Senderowicz, D. A. Hodges, and P. R. Gray. "A High-Performance NMOS Operational Amplifier," *IEEE J. Solid-State Circuits*, Vol. SC-13, pp. 760–768, December 1978.

13. W. C. Black, D. J. Allstot, and R. A. Reed. "A High Performance Low Power CMOS Channel Filter," *IEEE J. Solid-State Circuits*, Vol. SC-15, pp. 929–938, December 1980.

14. E. M. Cherry. "A New Result in Negative Feedback Theory and Its Application to Audio Power Amplifiers," *Int. J. Circuit Theory*, Vol. 6, pp. 265–288, July 1978.

15. J. H. Huijsing and D. Linebarger. "Low-Voltage Operational Amplifier with Rail-to-Rail Input and Output Ranges," *IEEE J. Solid-State Circuits*, Vol. 20, pp. 1144–1150. December 1985.

16. R. G. H. Eschauzier and J. H. Huijsing. *Frequency Compensation Techniques for Low-Power Operational Amplifiers.* Kluwer, Dordrecht, The Netherlands, 1995.

17. F. You, H. K. Embabi, and E. Sanchez-Sinencio. "A Multistage Amplifier Topology with Nested Gm-C Compensation," *IEEE J. Solid-State Circuits*, Vol. 32, pp. 2000–2011, Dec. 1997.

18. P. E. Gray and C. L. Searle. *Electronic Principles: Physics, Models, and Circuits.* Wiley, New York, 1969.

19. J. D'Azzo and C. Houpis. *Linear Control System Analysis and Design: Conventional and Modern.* McGraw-Hill, New York, 1975.

20. W. E. Hearn. "Fast Slewing Monolithic Operational Amplifier," *IEEE J. Solid-State Circuits*, Vol. SC-6, pp. 20–24, February 1971.

21. P. W. Li, M. J. Chin, P. R. Gray, and R. Castello. "A Ratio-Independent Algorithmic Analog-to-Digital Conversion Technique," *IEEE J. Solid-State Circuits*, Vol. SC-19, pp. 828–836, December 1984.

22. E. Seevinck and R. Wassenaar. "A Versatile CMOS Linear Transconductor/Square-Law Function Circuit," *IEEE J. Solid-State Circuits*, Vol. SC-22, pp. 366–377, June 1987.

23. F. N. L. O. Eynde, P. F. M. Ampe, L. Verdeyen, and W. M. C. Sansen. "A CMOS Large-Swing Low-Distortion Three-Stage Class AB Power Amplifier," *IEEE J. Solid-State Circuits*, Vol. SC-25, pp. 265–273, February 1990.

24. H. W. Bode. *Network Analysis and Feedback Amplifier Design.* Van Nostrand, New York, 1945.

25. P. J. Hurst. "A Comparison of Two Approaches to Feedback Circuit Analysis," *IEEE Trans. on Education*, Vol. 35, No. 3, pp. 253–261, August 1992.

# Nonlinear Analog Circuits

## 10.1 Introduction

Chapters 1 through 9 have dealt almost entirely with analog circuits whose primary function is linear amplification of signals. Although some of the circuits discussed (such as Class AB output stages) were actually nonlinear in their operation, the operations performed on the signal passing through the amplifier were well approximated by linear relations.

Nonlinear operations on continuous-valued analog signals are often required in instrumentation, communication, and control-system design. These operations include rectification, modulation, demodulation, frequency translation, multiplication, and division. In this chapter we analyze the most commonly used techniques for performing these operations within a monolithic integrated circuit. We first discuss the use of diodes together with active elements to perform precision rectification. We then discuss the use of the bipolar transistor to synthesize nonlinear analog circuits and analyze the Gilbert multiplier cell, which is the basis for a wide variety of such circuits. Next we consider the application of this building block as a small-signal analog multiplier, as a modulator, as a phase comparator, and as a large-signal, four-quadrant multiplier.

Following the multiplier discussion, we introduce a highly useful circuit technique for performing demodulation of FM and AM signals and, at the same time, performing bandpass filtering. This circuit, the phase-locked-loop (PLL), is particularly well-suited to monolithic construction. After exploring the basic concepts involved, the behavior of the PLL in the locked condition is analyzed. The capture transient is then considered, and an actual phase-locked-loop integrated circuit is analyzed. Finally, some methods of realizing arbitrary nonlinear transfer functions using bipolar transistors are considered.

## 10.2 Precision Rectification

Perhaps the most basic nonlinear operation performed on time-varying signals is rectification. An ideal half-wave rectifier is a circuit that passes signal currents or voltages of only one polarity while blocking signal voltages or currents of the other polarity. The transfer characteristic of an ideal half-wave rectifier is shown in Fig. 10.1. Also shown in Fig. 10.1 is the transfer characteristic of a second useful rectifier, the full-wave type. Practical rectifiers can be divided into two categories. The first class is termed *power rectifiers*, and these are used to convert ac power to dc form. These circuits almost always use silicon diodes to perform rectification, and the performance objectives are high efficiency and low cost. We will not consider this class of rectifier explicitly since most realizations of this type of high-power circuit utilize discrete components.

The second class of rectifiers has, as its objective, not the conversion of power but the extraction of information from a signal. Full-wave rectifiers of this type are used, for example, in the determination of the rms value of a signal, in certain types of demodulators, and

**Figure 10.1** Rectifier transfer characteristic and response for sinusoidal input waveform. (a) Half-wave rectifier. (b) Full wave rectifier.

in instrumentation systems that must sense signals of both positive and negative polarity. We term this class of rectifier the *precision rectifier*. The precision rectification function is often required within integrated analog subsystems, and we discuss circuit approaches to its realization in this section.

The simplest form of diode half-wave rectifier is shown in Fig. 10.2a. When the input voltage is positive, the diode is reverse biased, and the signal at the output is equal to that at the input, as shown in the equivalent circuit of Fig 10.2b. As the input voltage is driven negative from zero, the output voltage remains equal to the input voltage until the diode begins to conduct current. This occurs at a value of input voltage roughly equal to $-0.6$ V. As the magnitude of the input voltage is increased beyond this value, the diode clamps the output voltage at $-0.6$ V, as indicated in the equivalent circuit of Fig. 10.2c. The net resulting dc transfer characteristic is shown in Fig. 10.2d. If a sinusoid is applied to the input, the output is a half-wave rectified version of the input, as illustrated in Fig. 10.2e.

An important drawback of this rectifier circuit is the fact that the rectification is not precise; the forward drop in the diode causes the circuit to pass the signal when it has a value between zero and $-0.6$ V. If the signal amplitude were, for example, only 2 or 3 V, the output waveform would not be a precise replica of the rectified version of the input

**Figure 10.2** Simple diode half-wave rectifier. *(a)* Rectifier circuit. *(b)* Equivalent circuit for $V_{in} > -0.6$ V. *(c)* Equivalent circuit for $V_{in} < -0.6$ V. *(d)* dc transfer characteristic. *(e)* Response to sinusoidal input.

waveform as shown in Fig. 10.1. In many signal-processing applications this error would be too large to be acceptable.

The performance of the rectifier can be greatly enhanced by the addition of active elements. Consider the active rectifier of Fig. 10.3. The diode has been replaced by a subcircuit consisting of a diode together with an operational amplifier with a gain $a$. We first consider the *I-V* characteristic of the diode op amp combination. If we assume that the op amp is ideal, then the current into its input terminals is zero and all of the current ($I$) flows through the diode and into the output terminal of the op amp.

The forward drop in the diode is equal to the difference between the op amp input voltage $V_i$ and the op amp output voltage $V_o$, so that the diode current $I$ is

$$I = -I_S \left[ \exp\left(\frac{V_o - V_i}{V_T}\right) - 1 \right] \qquad (10.1)$$

The op amp has a gain $a$, so that

$$V_o = -aV_i \qquad (10.2)$$

Note that the output voltage of the circuit $V_{out}$ is not the output voltage of the op amp $V_o$. The output of the op amp serves only to drive the diode. The output voltage of the circuit is equal to the *input* voltage of the op amp. For the case in which the diode is forward biased, this voltage can be found by combining (10.1) and (10.2):

$$V_i = -\frac{V_T}{a+1} \ln\left(\frac{-I}{I_S} + 1\right) = V_{out} \qquad (10.3)$$

Notice that the forward voltage drop is reduced by a factor $(a + 1)$ compared with the diode alone. Since a voltage gain $a$ of many thousands is readily obtained in an op amp, the factor that determines the forward drop in the circuit will actually be the input offset voltage of the op amp itself.

When the input voltage is made positive, the op amp drives the diode into the reverse-biased state, and the behavior of the circuit is not well described by (10.3). Because of the presence of the diode, no current larger than the reverse leakage current of the diode can flow *into* the composite device. Thus, when the input voltage of Fig. 10.3 becomes positive, no current flows in the resistor and op amp input voltage $V_i$ becomes equal to $V_{in}$. This causes the output voltage of the op amp to be driven in the negative direction until the output stage saturates. Thus, for positive input voltages, input voltage $V_{in}$ is applied directly across the op amp input terminals and the amplifier saturates.

The dc transfer characteristic of the rectifier of Fig. 10.3a is shown in Fig. 10.3b. Note that the curve closely approaches that of an ideal rectifier.

**Improved Precision Half-Wave Rectifier.** The rectifier circuit of Fig. 10.3 has the property that for positive inputs the operational amplifier output saturates in the negative direction. As illustrated in Fig. 10.3c, the op-amp output voltage is required to change instantaneously from this saturated voltage $(V_s^-)$ to $+0.6$ V when the input waveform passes through zero. Because of the limited slew rate of real operational amplifiers (see Chapter 9), this cannot occur, and the output waveform will not be a precisely rectified version of the input waveform as the frequency of the input sinusoid is increased. An alternate circuit that greatly alleviates this problem is shown in Fig. 10.4. This circuit is similar to the original one except that one additional diode $D_2$ and one additional resistor are added.

For input voltages less than zero, operation of the circuit is exactly the same as the circuit of Fig. 10.3. The equivalent circuit for this condition is shown in Fig. 10.4b. Diode $D_1$ is forward biased and the op amp is in the active region. The inverting input of the op amp is clamped at ground by the feedback through $D_1$, and, since no current flows in $R_2$, the output voltage is also at ground. When the input voltage is made positive, no current can flow in the reverse direction through $D_1$ so the output voltage of the op amp $V_o$ is driven in the negative direction. This reverse biases $D_1$ and forward biases $D_2$. The resulting equivalent circuit is shown in Fig. 10.4c and is simply an inverting amplifier with a forward-biased diode in series with the output lead of the op amp. Because of the

(a)

**Figure 10.3** Active precision half-wave rectifier. (a) Rectifier circuit.

(b)

(c)

**Figure 10.3** (b) dc transfer characteristic. The output voltage for $V_{in} < 0$ is in the microvolt range if the op amp has no offset. (c) Input and output waveforms for the precision half-wave rectifier. $V_o$ is output voltage of the op amp. During the positive excursions of the input, $V_o$ takes on the value of $V_s^-$, which is the output voltage at which the op amp output stage saturates.

**Figure 10.4** Improved precision rectifier. (*a*) Rectifier circuit. (*b*) Equivalent circuit for $V_{in} < 0$. (*c*) Equivalent circuit for $V_{in} > 0$.

large gain of the op amp, this diode has no effect on its behavior as long as it is forward biased, and so the circuit behaves as an inverting amplifier giving an output voltage of

$$V_{out} = -\frac{R_2}{R_1}V_{in} \tag{10.4}$$

As shown in Fig. 10.5, the output voltage of the operational amplifier need only change in value by approximately two diode drops when the input signal changes from positive to negative. Actually, this is but one of a wide variety of active-rectifier circuits, some of which are capable of even faster operation.[1]

**Figure 10.5** Waveforms within the improved precision rectifier for a sinusoidal input.

## 10.3 Analog Multipliers Employing the Bipolar Transistor

In analog-signal processing the need often arises for a circuit that takes two analog inputs and produces an output proportional to their product. Such circuits are termed *analog multipliers*. In the following sections we examine several analog multipliers that depend on the exponential transfer function of bipolar transistors.

### 10.3.1 The Emitter-Coupled Pair as a Simple Multiplier

The emitter-coupled pair, shown in Fig. 10.6, was shown in Chapter 3 to produce output currents that are related to the differential input voltage by

$$I_{c1} = \frac{I_{EE}}{1 + \exp\left(-\dfrac{V_{id}}{V_T}\right)} \tag{10.5}$$

$$I_{c2} = \frac{I_{EE}}{1 + \exp\left(\dfrac{V_{id}}{V_T}\right)} \tag{10.6}$$

**Figure 10.6** Emitter-coupled pair.

where base current has been neglected. Equations 10.5 and 10.6 can be combined to give the *difference* between the two output currents:

$$\Delta I_c = I_{c1} - I_{c2} = I_{EE} \tanh\left(\frac{V_{id}}{2V_T}\right) \tag{10.7}$$

This relationship is plotted in Fig. 10.7 and shows that the emitter-coupled pair by itself can be used as a primitive multiplier. We first assume that the differential input voltage $V_{id}$ is much less than $V_T$. If this is true, we can utilize the approximation

$$\tanh\frac{V_{id}}{2V_T} \approx \frac{V_{id}}{2V_T} \qquad \frac{V_{id}}{2V_T} \ll 1 \tag{10.8}$$

And (10.7) becomes

$$\Delta I_c \approx I_{EE}\left(\frac{V_{id}}{2V_T}\right) \tag{10.9}$$

The current $I_{EE}$ is actually the bias current for the emitter-coupled pair. With the addition of more circuitry, we can make $I_{EE}$ proportional to a second input signal $V_{i2}$, as shown in Fig. 10.8. Thus we have

$$I_{EE} \approx K_o(V_{i2} - V_{BE(\text{on})}) \tag{10.10}$$

**Figure 10.7** The dc transfer characteristic of emitter-coupled pair.

**Figure 10.8** Two-quadrant analog multiplier.

The differential output current of the emitter-coupled pair can be calculated by substituting (10.10) in (10.9) to give

$$\Delta I_c = \frac{K_o V_{id}(V_{i2} - V_{BE(\text{on})})}{2V_T} \tag{10.11}$$

Thus we have produced a circuit that functions as a multiplier under the assumption that $V_{id}$ is small, and that $V_{i2}$ is greater than $V_{BE(\text{on})}$. The latter restriction means that the multiplier functions in only two quadrants of the $V_{id}$–$V_{i2}$ plane, and this type of circuit is termed a two-quadrant multiplier. The restriction to two quadrants of operation is a severe one for many communications applications, and most practical multipliers allow four-quadrant operation. The Gilbert multiplier cell,[2] shown in Fig. 10.9, is a modification of the emitter-coupled cell, which allows four-quadrant multiplication. It is the basis for most integrated-circuit balanced multiplier systems. The series connection of an emitter-coupled pair with two cross-coupled, emitter-coupled pairs produces a particularly useful transfer characteristic, as shown in the next section.

### 10.3.2 The dc Analysis of the Gilbert Multiplier Cell

In the following analysis, we assume that the transistors are identical, that the output resistance of the transistors and that of the biasing current source can be neglected, and the base currents can be neglected. For the Gilbert cell shown in Fig. 10.9, the collector currents of $Q_3$ and $Q_4$ are, using (10.5) and (10.6),

$$I_{c3} = \frac{I_{c1}}{1 + \exp\left(-\dfrac{V_1}{V_T}\right)} \tag{10.12}$$

$$I_{out} = I_{c3-5} - I_{c4-6}$$

**Figure 10.9** Gilbert multiplier circuit.

$$I_{c4} = \frac{I_{c1}}{1 + \exp\left(\dfrac{V_1}{V_T}\right)} \tag{10.13}$$

Similarly, the collector currents of $Q_5$ and $Q_6$ are given by

$$I_{c5} = \frac{I_{c2}}{1 + \exp\left(\dfrac{V_1}{V_T}\right)} \tag{10.14}$$

$$I_{c6} = \frac{I_{c2}}{1 + \exp\left(-\dfrac{V_1}{V_T}\right)} \tag{10.15}$$

The two currents $I_{c1}$ and $I_{c2}$ can be related to $V_2$ by again using (10.5) and (10.6):

$$I_{c1} = \frac{I_{EE}}{1 + \exp\left(-\dfrac{V_2}{V_T}\right)} \tag{10.16}$$

$$I_{c2} = \frac{I_{EE}}{1 + \exp\left(\dfrac{V_2}{V_T}\right)} \tag{10.17}$$

Combining (10.12) through (10.17), we obtain expressions for collector currents $I_{c3}$, $I_{c4}$, $I_{c5}$, and $I_{c6}$ in terms of input voltages $V_1$ and $V_2$.

$$I_{c3} = \frac{I_{EE}}{\left[1 + \exp\left(-\dfrac{V_1}{V_T}\right)\right]\left[1 + \exp\left(-\dfrac{V_2}{V_T}\right)\right]} \tag{10.18}$$

$$I_{c4} = \cfrac{I_{EE}}{\left[1 + \exp\left(-\dfrac{V_2}{V_T}\right)\right]\left[1 + \exp\left(\dfrac{V_1}{V_T}\right)\right]} \tag{10.19}$$

$$I_{c5} = \cfrac{I_{EE}}{\left[1 + \exp\left(\dfrac{V_1}{V_T}\right)\right]\left[1 + \exp\left(\dfrac{V_2}{V_T}\right)\right]} \tag{10.20}$$

$$I_{c6} = \cfrac{I_{EE}}{\left[1 + \exp\left(\dfrac{V_2}{V_T}\right)\right]\left[1 + \exp\left(-\dfrac{V_1}{V_T}\right)\right]} \tag{10.21}$$

The differential output current is then given by

$$\begin{aligned}
\Delta I &= I_{c3-5} - I_{c4-6} = I_{c3} + I_{c5} - (I_{c6} + I_{c4}) \\
&= (I_{c3} - I_{c6}) - (I_{c4} - I_{c5}) \tag{10.22} \\
&= I_{EE}\left[\tanh\left(\dfrac{V_1}{2V_T}\right)\right]\left[\tanh\left(\dfrac{V_2}{2V_T}\right)\right] \tag{10.23}
\end{aligned}$$

The dc transfer characteristic, then, is the product of the hyperbolic tangent of the two input voltages.

Practical applications of the multiplier cell can be divided into three categories according to the magnitude relative to $V_T$ of applied signals $V_1$ and $V_2$. If the magnitude of $V_1$ and $V_2$ are kept small with respect to $V_T$, the hyperbolic tangent function can be approximated as linear and the circuit behaves as a multiplier, developing the product of $V_1$ and $V_2$. However, by including nonlinearity to compensate for the hyperbolic tangent function in series with each input, the range of input voltages over which linearity is maintained can be greatly extended. This technique is used in so-called four-quadrant analog multipliers.

The second class of applications is distinguished by the application to one of the inputs of a signal that is large compared to $V_T$, causing the transistors to which that signal is applied to behave like switches rather than near-linear devices. This effectively multiplies the applied small signal by a square wave, and in this mode of operation the circuit acts as a modulator.

In the third class of applications, the signals applied to both inputs are large compared to $V_T$, and all six transistors in the circuit behave as nonsaturating switches. This mode of operation is useful for the detection of phase differences between two amplitude-limited signals, as is required in phase-locked loops, and is sometimes called the phase-detector mode.

We first consider the application of the circuit as an analog multiplier of two continuous signals.

### 10.3.3 The Gilbert Cell as an Analog Multiplier

As mentioned earlier, the hyperbolic-tangent function may be represented by the infinite series:

$$\tanh x = x - \frac{x^3}{3} \cdots \tag{10.24}$$

Assuming that $x$ is much less than one, the hyperbolic tangent can then be approximated by

$$\tanh x \approx x \tag{10.25}$$

**Figure 10.10** Gilbert multiplier with emitter degeneration applied to improve input voltage range on $V_2$ input.

Applying this relation to (10.23), we have

$$\Delta I \approx I_{EE}\left(\frac{V_1}{2V_T}\right)\left(\frac{V_2}{2V_T}\right) \quad V_1, V_2 \ll V_T \tag{10.26}$$

Thus for small-amplitude signals, the circuit performs an analog multiplication. Unfortunately, the amplitudes of the input signals are often much larger than $V_T$, but larger signals can be accommodated in this mode in a number of ways. In the event that only one of the signals is large compared to $V_T$, emitter degeneration can be utilized in the lower emitter-coupled pair, increasing the linear input range for $V_2$ as shown in Fig. 10.10. Unfortunately, this cannot be done with the cross-coupled pairs $Q_3$-$Q_6$ because the degeneration resistors destroy the required nonlinear relation between $I_c$ and $V_{be}$ in those devices.

An alternate approach is to introduce a nonlinearity that predistorts the input signals to compensate for the hyperbolic tangent transfer characteristic of the basic cell. The required nonlinearity is an inverse hyperbolic tangent characteristic, and a hypothetical example of such a system is shown in Fig. 10.11. Fortunately, this particular nonlinearity is straightforward to generate.

Referring to Fig. 10.12, we assume for the time being that the circuitry within the box develops a differential output current that is linearly related to the input voltage $V_1$. Thus

$$I_1 = I_{o1} + K_1 V_1 \tag{10.27}$$

$$I_2 = I_{o1} - K_1 V_1 \tag{10.28}$$

Here $I_{o1}$ is the dc current that flows in each output lead if $V_1$ is equal to zero, and $K_1$ is the transconductance of the voltage-to-current converter. The differential voltage developed

**Figure 10.11** Gilbert multiplier with predistortion circuits.

across the two diode-connected transistors is

$$\Delta V = V_T \ln\left(\frac{I_{o1} + K_1 V_1}{I_S}\right) - V_T \ln\left(\frac{I_{o1} - K_1 V_1}{I_S}\right)$$

$$= V_T \ln\left(\frac{I_{o1} + K_1 V_1}{I_{o1} - K_1 V_1}\right) \tag{10.29}$$

This function can be transformed using the identity

$$\tanh^{-1} x = \frac{1}{2}\ln\left(\frac{1 + x}{1 - x}\right) \tag{10.30}$$

**Figure 10.12** Inverse hyperbolic tangent circuit.

into the desired relationship.

$$\Delta V = 2V_T \tanh^{-1}\left(\frac{K_1 V_1}{I_{o1}}\right) \tag{10.31}$$

Thus if this functional block is used as the compensating nonlinearity in series with each input as shown in Fig. 10.11, the overall transfer characteristic becomes, using (10.23),

$$\Delta I = I_{EE}\left(\frac{K_1 V_1}{I_{o1}}\right)\left(\frac{K_2 V_2}{I_{o2}}\right) \tag{10.32}$$

where $I_{o2}$ and $K_2$ are the parameters of the functional block following $V_2$.

Equation 10.32 shows that the differential output current is directly proportional to the product $V_1 V_2$, and, in principle, this relationship holds for all values of $V_1$ and $V_2$ for which the two output currents of the differential voltage-to-current converters are positive. For this to be true, $I_1$ and $I_2$ must always be positive, and from (10.27) and (10.28), we have

$$-\frac{I_{o1}}{K_1} < V_1 < \frac{I_{o1}}{K_1} \tag{10.33}$$

$$-\frac{I_{o2}}{K_2} < V_2 < \frac{I_{o2}}{K_2} \tag{10.34}$$

Note that the inclusion of a compensating nonlinearity on the $V_2$ input simply makes the collector currents of $Q_1$ and $Q_2$ directly proportional to input voltage $V_2$ rather than to its hyperbolic tangent. Thus the combination of the pair $Q_1$-$Q_2$ and the compensating nonlinearity on the $V_2$ input is redundant, and the output currents of the voltage-to-current converter on the $V_2$ input can be fed directly into the emitters of the $Q_3$-$Q_4$ and $Q_5$-$Q_6$ pairs with exactly the same results. The multiplier then takes on the form shown in Fig. 10.13.

### 10.3.4  A Complete Analog Multiplier[3]

In order to be useful in a wide variety of applications, the multiplier circuit must develop an output voltage that is referenced to ground and can take on both positive and negative values. The transistors $Q_3$, $Q_4$, $Q_5$, $Q_6$, $Q_7$, and $Q_8$, shown in Fig. 10.13, are referred to as the multiplier core and produce a differential current output that then must be amplified, converted to a single-ended signal, and referenced to ground. An output amplifier is thus required, and the complete multiplier consists of two voltage-current converters, the "core" transistors, and an output current-to-voltage amplifier. While the core configuration of Fig. 10.13 is common to most four-quadrant transconductance multipliers, the rest of the circuitry can be realized in a variety of ways.

The most common configurations used for the voltage-current converters are emitter-coupled pairs with emitter degeneration as shown in Fig. 10.10. The differential-to-single-ended converter of Fig. 10.13 is often realized with an op amp circuit of the type shown in Fig. 6.4. If this circuit has a transresistance given by

$$\frac{V_{out}}{\Delta I} = K_3 \tag{10.35}$$

then substitution in (10.32) gives for the overall multiplier characteristic

$$V_{out} = I_{EE}K_3\frac{K_1 K_2}{I_{o1} I_{o2}}V_1 V_2 \tag{10.36}$$

**Figure 10.13**   Complete four-quadrant multiplier.

The output voltage is thus proportional to the product $V_1V_2$ over a wide range. The constants in (10.36) are usually chosen so that

$$V_{\text{out}} = 0.1V_1V_2 \qquad (10.37)$$

and all voltages have a $\pm 10$-V range.

### 10.3.5 The Gilbert Multiplier Cell as a Balanced Modulator and Phase Detector

The four-quadrant multiplier just described is an example of an application of the multiplier cell in which all the devices remain in the active region during normal operation. Used in this way the circuit is capable of performing precise multiplication of one continuously varying analog signal by another. In communications systems, however, the need frequently arises for the multiplication of a continuously varying signal by a square wave. This is easily accomplished with the multiplier circuit by applying a sufficiently large signal (i.e., large compared to $2V_T$) directly to the cross-coupled pair so that two of the four transistors alternately turn completely off and the other two conduct all the current. Since the transistors in the circuit do not enter saturation, this process can be accomplished at high speed. A set of typical waveforms that might result when a sinusoid is applied to the small-signal input and a square wave to the large-signal input is shown in Fig. 10.14. Note that since the devices in the multiplier are being switched on and off by the incoming square wave, the amplitude of the output waveform is independent of the amplitude of the square wave as long as it is large enough to cause the devices in the multiplier circuit to be fully on or fully off. Thus the circuit in this mode does not perform a linear multiplication of two waveforms, but actually causes the output voltage of the circuit produced by the small-signal input to be alternately multiplied by $+1$ and $-1$.

The spectrum of the output may be developed directly from the Fourier series of the two inputs. For the low-frequency modulating sinusoidal input,

$$V_m(t) = V_m \cos \omega_m t \qquad (10.38)$$

**Figure 10.14** Input and output waveforms for a phase detector with large input signals.

and for the high-frequency square wave input, which we assume has an amplitude of $\pm 1$ as discussed above,

$$V_c(t) = \sum_{n=1}^{\infty} A_n \cos n\omega_c t, \qquad A_n = \frac{\sin \dfrac{n\pi}{2}}{\dfrac{n\pi}{4}} \qquad (10.39)$$

Thus the output signal is

$$V_o(t) = K[V_c(t)V_m(t)] = K\sum_{n=1}^{\infty} A_n V_m \cos \omega_n t \cos n\omega_c t \qquad (10.40)$$

$$= K\sum_{n=1}^{\infty} \frac{A_n V_m}{2}\left[\cos(n\omega_c + \omega_m)t + \cos(n\omega_c - \omega_m)t\right] \qquad (10.41)$$

where $K$ is the magnitude of the gain of the multiplier from the small-signal input to the output.

The spectrum has components located at frequencies $\omega_m$ above and below each of the harmonics of $\omega_c$, but no component at the carrier frequency $\omega_c$ or its harmonics. The spectrum of the input signals and the resulting output signal is shown in Fig. 10.15. The lack of an output component at the carrier frequency is a very useful property of balanced modulators. The signal is usually filtered following the modulation process so that only the components near $\omega_c$ are retained.

If a dc component is added to the modulating input, the result is a signal component in the output at the carrier frequency and its harmonics. If the modulating signal is given by

$$V_m(t) = V_m(1 + M\cos \omega_m t) \qquad (10.42)$$

where the parameter $M$ is called the modulation index, then the output is given by

$$V_o(t) = K\sum_{n=1}^{\infty} A_n V_m\left[\cos(n\omega_c t) + \frac{M}{2}\cos(n\omega_c + \omega_m)t + \frac{M}{2}\cos(n\omega_c - \omega_m)t\right]$$

$$(10.43)$$

**Figure 10.15** Input and output spectra for a balanced modulator.

This dc component can be introduced intentionally to provide conventional amplitude modulation or it can be the result of offset voltages in the devices within the modulator, which results in undesired carrier feedthrough in suppressed-carrier modulators.

Note that the balanced modulator actually performs a frequency translation. Information contained in the modulating signal $V_m(t)$ was originally concentrated at the modulating frequency $\omega_m$. The modulator has translated this information so that it is now contained in spectral components located near the harmonics of the high-frequency signal $V_c(t)$, usually called the carrier. Balanced modulators are also useful for performing demodulation, which is the extraction of information from the frequency band near the carrier and re-translation of the information back down to low frequencies.

In frequency translation, signals at two different frequencies are applied to the two inputs, and the sum or the difference frequency component is taken from the output. If unmodulated signals of identical frequency $\omega_o$ are applied to the two inputs, the circuit behaves as a *phase detector* and produces an output whose dc component is proportional to the phase difference between the two inputs. For example, consider the two input waveforms in Fig. 10.16, which are applied to the Gilbert multiplier shown in the same figure. We assume first for simplicity that both inputs are large in magnitude so that all the transistors in the circuit are behaving as switches. The output waveform that results is shown in Fig. 10.16c and consists of a dc component and a component at twice the incoming frequency. The dc component of this waveform is given by

$$V_{\text{average}} = \frac{1}{2\pi} \int_0^{2\pi} V_o(t)\,d(\omega_0 t) \tag{10.44}$$

$$= \frac{-1}{\pi}(A_1 - A_2) \tag{10.45}$$

**Figure 10.16** Typical input and output waveforms for a phase detector.

where areas $A_1$ and $A_2$ are as indicated in Fig. 10.16c. Thus,

$$V_{average} = -\left[I_{EE}R_C\frac{(\pi - \phi)}{\pi} - \frac{I_{EE}R_C\phi}{\pi}\right] \tag{10.46}$$

$$= I_{EE}R_C\left(\frac{2\phi}{\pi} - 1\right) \tag{10.47}$$

This phase relationship is plotted in Fig. 10.17. This phase demodulation technique is widely used in phase-locked loops.

We assumed above that the input waveforms were large in amplitude and were square waves. If the input signal amplitude is large, the actual waveform shape is unimportant since the multiplier simply switches from one state to the other at the zero crossings of the

**Figure 10.17** Phase detector output versus phase difference.

waveform. For the case in which the amplitude of one or both of the input signals has an amplitude comparable to or smaller than $V_T$, the circuit still acts as a phase detector. However, the output voltage then depends both on the phase difference *and* on the *amplitude* of the two input waveforms. The operation of the circuit in this mode is considered further in Section 10.4.3.

## 10.4 Phase-Locked Loops (PLL)

The phase-locked loop concept was first developed in the 1930s.[4] It has since been used in communications systems of many types, particularly in satellite communications systems. Until recently, however, phase-locked systems have been too complex and costly for use in most consumer and industrial systems, where performance requirements are more modest and other approaches are more economical. The PLL is particularly amenable to monolithic construction, however, and integrated-circuit phase-locked loops can now be fabricated at very low cost.[5] Their use has become attractive for many applications such as FM demodulators, stereo demodulators, tone detectors, frequency synthesizers, and others. In this section we first explore the basic operation of the PLL, and then consider analytically the performance of the loop in the locked condition. We then discuss some applications and, finally, the design of monolithic PLLs.

### 10.4.1 Phase-Locked Loop Concepts

A block diagram of the basic phase-locked loop system is shown in Fig. 10.18. The elements of the system are a phase comparator, a loop filter, an amplifier, and a voltage-controlled oscillator. The voltage-controlled oscillator, or VCO, is simply an oscillator whose frequency is proportional to an externally applied voltage. When the loop is locked on an incoming periodic signal, the VCO frequency is exactly equal to that of the incoming signal. The phase detector produces a dc or low-frequency signal proportional to the phase difference between the incoming signal and the VCO output signal. This phase-sensitive signal is then passed through the loop filter and amplifier and is applied to the control input of the VCO. If, for example, the frequency of the incoming signal shifts slightly, the phase difference between the VCO signal and the incoming signal will begin to increase with time. This will change the control voltage on the VCO in such a way as to bring the VCO frequency back to the same value as the incoming signal. Thus the loop can maintain lock

**Figure 10.18**  Phase-locked-loop system.

when the input signal frequency changes, and the VCO input voltage is proportional to the frequency of the incoming signal. This behavior makes PLLs particularly useful for the demodulation of FM signals, where the frequency of the incoming signal varies in time and contains the desired information. The range of input signal frequencies over which the loop can maintain lock is called the *lock range*.

An important aspect of PLL performance is the capture process, by which the loop goes from the unlocked, free-running condition to that of being locked on a signal. In the unlocked condition, the VCO runs at the frequency corresponding to zero applied dc voltage at its control input. This frequency is called the center frequency, or free-running frequency. When a periodic signal is applied that has a frequency near the free-running frequency, the loop may or may not lock on it depending on a number of factors. The capture process is inherently nonlinear in nature, and we will describe the transient in only a qualitative way.

First assume that the loop is opened between the loop filter and the VCO control input, and that a signal whose frequency is near, but not equal to, the free-running frequency is applied to the input of the PLL. The phase detector is usually of the type discussed in the last section, but for this qualitative discussion we assume that the phase detector is simply an analog multiplier that multiplies the two sinusoids together. Thus the output of the multiplier-phase detector contains the sum and difference frequency components, and we assume that the sum frequency component is sufficiently high in frequency that it is filtered out by the low-pass filter. The output of the low-pass filter, then, is a sinusoid with a frequency equal to the difference between the VCO free-running frequency and the incoming signal frequency.

Now assume that the loop is suddenly closed, and the difference frequency sinusoid is now applied to the VCO input. This will cause the VCO frequency itself to become a sinusoidal function of time. Let us assume that the incoming frequency was lower than the free-running frequency. Since the VCO frequency is varying as a function of time, it will alternately move *closer* to the incoming signal frequency and *further away* from the incoming signal frequency. The output of the phase detector is a near-sinusoid whose frequency is the *difference* between the VCO frequency and the input frequency. When the VCO frequency moves away from the incoming frequency, this sinusoid moves to a higher frequency. When the VCO frequency moves closer to the incoming frequency, the sinusoid moves to a lower frequency. If we examine the effect of this on the phase detector output, we see that the *frequency* of this sinusoidal difference-frequency waveform is reduced when its incremental amplitude is negative, and increased when its amplitude is positive. This causes the phase detector output to have an asymmetrical waveform during capture, as shown in Fig. 10.19. This asymmetry in the waveform introduces a dc component in the phase detector output that shifts the average VCO frequency toward the incoming signal frequency, so that the difference frequency gradually decreases. Once the system becomes locked, of course, the difference frequency becomes zero and only a dc voltage remains at the loop-filter output.

**Figure 10.19** Typical phase detector output during capture transient.

The capture range of the loop is that range of input frequencies around the center frequency onto which the loop will become locked from an unlocked condition. The pull-in time is the time required for the loop to capture the signal. Both these parameters depend on the amount of gain in the loop itself, and the bandwidth of the loop filter. The objective of the loop filter is to filter out difference components resulting from interfering signals far away from the center frequency. It also provides a memory for the loop in case lock is momentarily lost due to a large interfering transient. Reducing the loop filter bandwidth thus improves the rejection of out-of-band signals, but, at the same time, the capture range is decreased, the pull-in time becomes longer, and the loop phase margin becomes poorer.

## 10.4.2 The Phase-Locked Loop in the Locked Condition

Under locked conditions, a linear relationship exists between the output voltage of the phase detector and the phase difference between the VCO and the incoming signal. This fact allows the loop to be analyzed using standard linear feedback concepts when in the locked condition. A block diagram representation of the system in this mode is shown in Fig. 10.20. The gain of the phase comparator is $K_D$ V/rad of phase difference, the loop-filter transfer function is $F(s)$, and any gain in the forward loop is represented by $A$. The VCO gain is $K_o$ rad/s per volt.

If a constant input voltage is applied to the VCO control input, the output frequency of the VCO remains constant. However, the phase comparator is sensitive to the difference between the *phase* of the VCO output and the *phase* of the incoming signal. The phase of the VCO output is actually equal to the time integral of the VCO output frequency, since

$$\omega_{osc}(t) = \frac{d\phi_{osc}(t)}{dt} \tag{10.48}$$

**Figure 10.20** Block diagram of the PLL system.

and thus

$$\phi_{\text{osc}}(t) = \phi_{osc}\big|_{t=0} + \int_0^t \omega_{\text{osc}}(t)dt \tag{10.49}$$

Thus an integration inherently takes place within the phase-locked loop. This integration is represented by the $1/s$ block in Fig. 10.20.

For practical reasons, the VCO is actually designed so that when the VCO input voltage (i.e., $V_o$) is zero, the VCO frequency is not zero. The relation between the VCO output frequency $\omega_{\text{osc}}$ and $V_o$ is actually

$$\omega_{\text{osc}} = \omega_o + K_O V_o$$

where $\omega_o$ is the free-running frequency that results when $V_o = 0$.

The system can be seen from Fig. 10.20 to be a classical linear feedback control system.[6] The closed-loop transfer function is given by

$$\frac{V_o}{\phi_i} = \frac{K_D F(s)A}{1 + K_D F(s)A \dfrac{K_o}{s}} \tag{10.50}$$

$$= \frac{sK_D F(s)A}{s + K_D K_O A F(s)} \tag{10.51}$$

Usually we are interested in the response of this loop to *frequency* variations at the input, so that the input variable is frequency rather than phase. Since

$$\omega_i = \frac{d\phi_i}{dt} \tag{10.52}$$

then

$$\omega_i(s) = s\phi_i(s) \tag{10.53}$$

and

$$\frac{V_o}{\omega_i} = \frac{1}{s}\frac{V_o}{\phi_i} = \frac{K_D F(s)A}{s + K_D K_O A F(s)} \tag{10.54}$$

We first consider the case in which the loop filter is removed entirely, and $F(s)$ is unity. This is called a first-order loop and we have

$$\frac{V_o}{\omega_i} = \left(\frac{K_v}{s + K_v}\right)\left(\frac{1}{K_O}\right) \tag{10.55}$$

where

$$K_v = K_O K_D A \tag{10.56}$$

Thus the loop inherently produces a first-order, low-pass transfer characteristic. Remember that we regard the input variable as the frequency $\omega_i$ of the incoming signal. The response calculated above, then, is really the response from the frequency modulation on the incoming carrier to the loop voltage output.

The constant above ($K_v$) is termed the loop bandwidth. If the loop is locked on a carrier signal, and the frequency of that carrier is made to vary sinusoidally in time with a frequency $\omega_m$, then a sinusoid of frequency $\omega_m$ will be observed at the loop output. When $\omega_m$ is increased above $K_v$, the magnitude of the sinusoid at the output falls. The loop bandwidth $K_v$, then, is the effective bandwidth for the *modulating* signal that is being demodulated

**Figure 10.21** (a) Root locus and frequency response of a first-order, phase-locked loop. (b) Response of the loop output voltage to step changes in input frequency, example first-order loop.

by the PLL. In terms of the loop parameters, $K_v$ is simply the product of the phase detector gain, VCO gain, and any other electrical gain in the loop. The root locus of this single pole as a function of loop gain $K_v$ is shown in Fig. 10.21a. The frequency response is also shown in this figure. The response of the loop to variations in input frequency is illustrated in Fig. 10.21b and by the following example.

■ **EXAMPLE**

A PLL has a $K_O$ of $2\pi$ (1 kHz/V), a $K_v$ of $500\,\text{s}^{-1}$, and a free-running frequency of 500 Hz.
(a) For a constant input signal frequency of 250 Hz and 1 kHz, find $V_o$.

$$V_o = \frac{\omega_i - \omega_o}{K_O}$$

where

$$\omega_o = \text{oscillator free-running frequency}$$

At 250 Hz

$$V_o = \frac{2\pi\,(250\;\text{Hz}) - 2\pi\,(500\;\text{Hz})}{2\pi\,(1\;\text{kHz/V})} = -0.25\text{V}$$

At 1 kHz

$$V_o = \frac{2\pi\,(1\;\text{kHz}) - 2\pi\,(500\;\text{Hz})}{2\pi\,(1\;\text{kHz/V})} = +0.5\text{V}$$

(b) Now the input signal is frequency modulated, so that

$$\omega_i(t) = (2\pi)\,500\;\text{Hz}\,[1 + 0.1\sin(2\pi \times 10^2)\,t]$$

Find the output signal $V_o(t)$. From (10.55) we have

$$\frac{V_o(j\omega)}{\omega_i(j\omega)} = \frac{1}{K_O}\left(\frac{K_v}{K_v + j\omega}\right) = \frac{1}{K_O}\left[\frac{K_v}{K_v + j(2\pi \times 10^2)}\right]$$

$$= \frac{1}{2\pi\,(1\;\text{kHz/V})}\left(\frac{500}{500 + j628}\right)$$

$$= \frac{1}{2\pi\,(1\;\text{kHz/V})}(0.39 - j0.48)$$

The *magnitude* of $\omega_i(j\omega)$ is

$$|\omega_i(j\omega)| = (0.1)\,(500\;\text{Hz})\,(2\pi) = (50)\,(2\pi)$$

Therefore

$$V_o(j\omega) = \frac{50\;\text{Hz}}{1\;\text{kHz}}(0.39 - j0.48) = \frac{50}{1000}(0.62\,\underline{/-51^\circ})$$

and

$$V_o(t) = 0.031\sin[(2\pi \times 10^2 t) - 51^\circ]$$

■

Operating the loop with no loop filter has several practical drawbacks. Since the phase detector is really a multiplier, it produces a sum frequency component at its output as well as the difference frequency component. This component at twice the carrier frequency will be fed directly to the output if there is no loop filter. Also, all the out-of-band interfering signals present at the input will appear, shifted in frequency, at the output. Thus, a loop filter is very desirable in applications where interfering signals are present.

The most common configuration for integrated circuit PLLs is the second-order loop. Here, loop filter $F(s)$ is simply a single-pole, low-pass filter, usually realized with a single resistor and capacitor. Thus

$$F(s) = \left(\frac{1}{1 + \dfrac{s}{\omega_1}}\right) \tag{10.57}$$

**Figure 10.22** Root locus and frequency response of second-order, phase-locked loop.

By substituting into (10.54), the transfer function becomes

$$\frac{V_o}{\omega_1}(s) = \frac{1}{K_O}\left(\frac{1}{1 + \dfrac{s}{K_v} + \dfrac{s^2}{\omega_1 K_v}}\right) \tag{10.58}$$

The root locus for this feedback system as $K_v$ varies is shown in Fig. 10.22, along with the corresponding frequency response. The roots of the transfer function are

$$s = -\frac{\omega_1}{2}\left(1 \pm \sqrt{1 - \frac{4K_v}{\omega_1}}\right) \tag{10.59}$$

Equation 10.58 can be expressed as

$$\frac{V_o}{\omega_i} = \frac{1}{K_O}\left(\frac{1}{\dfrac{s^2}{\omega_n^2} + \dfrac{2\zeta}{\omega_n}s + 1}\right) \tag{10.60}$$

where

$$\omega_n = \sqrt{K_v \omega_1} \tag{10.61}$$

$$\zeta = \frac{1}{2}\sqrt{\frac{\omega_1}{K_v}} \tag{10.62}$$

The basic factor setting the loop bandwidth is $K_v$ as in the first-order case. The magnitude $\omega_1$ of the additional pole is then made as low as possible without causing an unacceptable amount of peaking in the frequency response. This peaking is of concern both because it distorts the demodulated FM output and because it causes the loop to ring, or experience a poorly damped oscillatory response, when a transient disturbs the loop. A good compromise is using a maximally flat low-pass pole configuration in which the poles are placed on radials angled 45° from the negative real axis. For this response, the damping factor

$\zeta$ should be equal to $1/\sqrt{2}$. Thus

$$\frac{1}{\sqrt{2}} = \frac{1}{2}\sqrt{\frac{\omega_1}{K_v}} \tag{10.63}$$

and

$$\omega_1 = 2K_v \tag{10.64}$$

The $-3$-dB frequency of the transfer function $(V_o/\omega_i)(j\omega)$ is then

$$\omega_{-3\text{dB}} = \omega_n = \sqrt{K_v\omega_1} = \sqrt{2}K_v \tag{10.65}$$

A disadvantage of the second-order loop as discussed thus far is that the $-3$-dB bandwidth of the loop is basically dictated by loop gain $K_v$ as shown by (10.65). As we will show, the loop gain also sets the lock range, so that with the simple filter used above these two parameters are constrained to be comparable. Situations do arise in phase-locked communications in which a wide lock range is desired for tracking large signal-frequency variations, yet a narrow loop bandwidth is desired for rejecting out-of-band signals. Using a very small $\omega_1$ would accomplish this were it not for the fact that this produces underdamped loop response. By adding a zero to the loop filter, the loop filter pole can be made small while still maintaining good loop dampening.

The effect of the addition of a zero on the loop response is best seen by examining the open-loop response of the circuit. Shown in Fig. 10.23$a$ is the open-loop response of the circuit with no loop filter. Because of the integration inherent in the loop, the response has a $-20$-dB/decade slope throughout the frequency range and crosses unity gain at $K_v$. In Fig. 10.23$b$, a loop filter in which $\omega_1$ is much less than $K_v$ has been added, and, as a result, the loop phase shift is very nearly $180°$ at the crossover frequency. The result is a sharp peak in the closed-loop frequency response at the crossover frequency. By adding a zero in the loop filter at $\omega_2$, as shown in Fig. 10.23$c$, the loop phase margin can be greatly improved. Note that for this case the loop bandwidth, which is equal to the crossover frequency, is much lower than $K_v$. This ability to set loop bandwidth and $K_v$ independently is an advantage of this type of loop filter. An R-C circuit that provides the necessary pole and zero in the filter response is shown in Fig. 10.23$d$. The root locus for this loop filter and the resulting closed-loop response are also shown.

Figure 10.23   ($a$) PLL open-loop response with no loop filter.

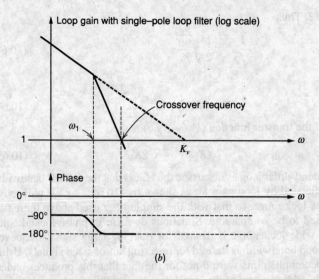

Figure 10.23  (b) PLL open-loop response with a single-pole filter and $\omega_1 \ll K_v$.

Figure 10.23  (c) PLL open-loop response with a zero added in loop filter at $s = -\omega_2$.

**Loop Lock Range.** The loop lock range is the range of input frequencies about the center frequency for which the loop maintains lock. In most cases, it is limited by the fact that the phase comparator has a limited phase comparison range; once the phase difference between the input signal and the VCO output reaches some critical value, the phase comparator ceases to behave linearly. The transfer characteristic of a typical analog phase comparator is shown in Fig. 10.17. It is clear from this figure that in order to maintain lock, the phase difference between the VCO output and the incoming signal must be kept between zero and $\pi$. If the phase difference is equal to either zero or $\pi$, then the magnitude of the dc voltage at the output of the phase comparator is

$$V_{o(\text{max})} = \pm K_D \left( \frac{\pi}{2} \right) \tag{10.66}$$

$$F(s) = \left(\frac{1 + \dfrac{s}{\omega_2}}{1 + \dfrac{s}{\omega_1}}\right)$$

$$\omega_2 = \frac{1}{CR_2}$$

$$\omega_1 = \frac{1}{C(R_1 + R_2)}$$

**Figure 10.23** (*d*) Root locus and frequency response of a second-order PLL with a zero. Frequency response shown is for large loop gain such that poles are located as shown in the root locus.

This dc voltage is amplified by the electrical gain $A$, and the result is applied to the VCO input, producing a frequency shift away from the free-running center frequency of

$$\Delta\omega_{osc} = K_D A K_O \left(\frac{\pi}{2}\right) = \left(\frac{K_v \pi}{2}\right) \tag{10.67}$$

If the input frequency is now shifted away from the free-running frequency, more voltage will have to be applied to the VCO in order for the VCO frequency to shift accordingly. However, the phase detector can produce no more dc output voltage to shift the VCO frequency further, so the loop will lose lock. The lock range $\omega_L$ is then given by

$$\omega_L = K_v \frac{\pi}{2} \tag{10.68}$$

This is the frequency range on either side of the free-running frequency for which the loop will track input frequency variations. It is a parameter that depends only on the dc gain in the loop and is independent of the properties of the loop filter. Other types[7] of phase detectors can give larger linear ranges of phase-comparator operation.

The capture range is the range of input frequencies for which the initially unlocked loop will lock on an input signal when initially in an unlocked condition and is always less than the lock range. When the input frequency is swept through a range around the center frequency, the output voltage as a function of input frequency displays a hysteresis effect,

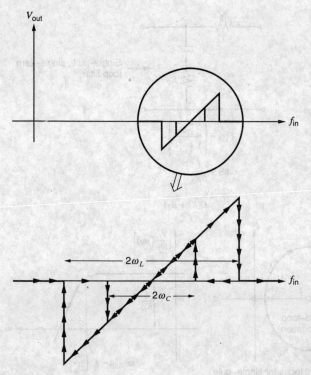

**Figure 10.24** PLL output versus frequency of input.

as shown in Fig. 10.24. As discussed earlier, the capture range is difficult to predict analytically. As a very rough rule of thumb, the approximate capture range can be estimated using the following procedure: refer to Fig. 10.18 and assume that the loop is opened at the loop-amplifier output and that a signal with a frequency not equal to the free-running VCO frequency is applied at the input of the PLL. The sinusoidal *difference* frequency component that appears at the output of the phase detector has the value

$$V_p(t) = \frac{\pi}{2} K_D \cos (\omega_i - \omega_{\text{osc}})t \qquad (10.69)$$

where $\omega_i$ is the input signal frequency and $\omega_{\text{osc}}$ is the VCO free-running frequency. This component is passed through the loop filter, and the output from the loop amplifier resulting from this component is

$$V_o(t) = \frac{\pi}{2} K_D A \left| F[j(\omega_i - \omega_{\text{osc}})] \right| \cos [(\omega_i - \omega_{\text{osc}})t + \phi] \qquad (10.70)$$

where

$$\phi = \underline{/F} [j(\omega_i - \omega_{\text{osc}})]$$

The output from the loop amplifier thus consists of a sinusoid at the difference frequency whose *amplitude* is reduced by the loop filter. In order for capture to occur, the magnitude of the voltage that must be applied to the VCO input is

$$|V_{\text{osc}}| = \frac{\omega_i - \omega_{\text{osc}}}{K_O} \qquad (10.71)$$

The capture process itself is rather complex, but the capture range can be estimated by setting the magnitudes of (10.70) and (10.71) equal. The result is that capture is likely to occur if the following inequality is satisfied:

$$\left|(\omega_i - \omega_{\text{osc}})\right| < \frac{\pi}{2} K_D K_O A \left|F[j(\omega_i - \omega_{\text{osc}})]\right| \qquad (10.72)$$

This equation implicitly gives an estimation of the capture range. For the first-order loop, where $F(s)$ is unity, it predicts that the lock range and capture range are approximately equal, and that for the second-order loop the capture range is significantly less than the lock range because $\left|F[j(\omega_i - \omega_{\text{osc}})]\right|$ is then less than unity.

### 10.4.3 Integrated-Circuit Phase-Locked Loops

The principle reason that PLLs have come to be widely used as system components is that the elements of the phase-locked loop are particularly suited to monolithic construction, and complete PLL systems can be fabricated on a single chip. We now discuss the design of the individual PLL components.

**Phase Detector.** Phase detectors for monolithic PLL applications are generally of the Gilbert multiplier configuration shown in Fig. 10.9. As illustrated in Fig. 10.16, if two signals large enough in amplitude that they cause limiting in the emitter-coupled pairs making up the circuit are applied to the two inputs, the output will contain a dc component

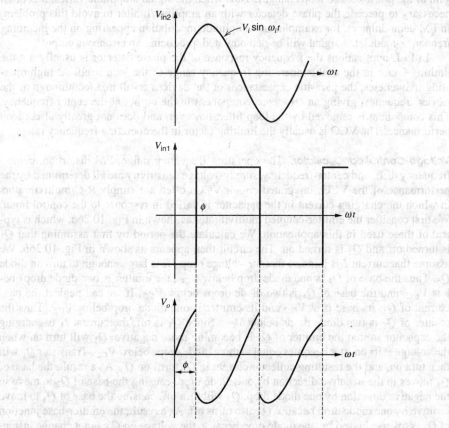

**Figure 10.25** Sinusoid multiplied by a synchronous square wave.

given by

$$V_{\text{average}} = -I_{EE}R_C\left(1 - \frac{2\phi}{\pi}\right) \qquad (10.73)$$

where $\phi$ is the phase difference between the input signals. An important aspect of the performance of this phase detector is that if the amplitude of the applied signal at $V_{\text{in2}}$ is small compared to the thermal voltage $V_T$, the circuit behaves as a balanced modulator, and the dc compartment of the output depends on the amplitude of the low-level input. The output waveform is then a sinusoid multiplied by a synchronous square wave, as shown in Fig. 10.25. In the limiting case when the small input is small compared to $V_T$, the dc component in the output becomes, referring to Fig. 10.25,

$$V_{\text{average}} = \frac{1}{\pi} g_m R_C V_i\left[\int_0^\phi (\sin \omega t)\, d(\omega t) - \int_\phi^\pi (\sin \omega t)\, d(\omega t)\right] \qquad (10.74)$$

$$= -\frac{2g_m R_C V_i \cos \phi}{\pi} \qquad (10.75)$$

where $R_C$ is the collector resistor in the Gilbert multiplier and $g_m$ is the transconductance of the transistors. The phase detector output voltage then becomes proportional to the amplitude $V_i$ of the incoming signal, and if the signal amplitude varies, then the loop gain of the phase-locked loop changes. Thus when the signal amplitude varies, it is often necessary to precede the phase detector with an amplifier/limiter to avoid this problem. In FM demodulators, for example, any amplitude modulation appearing on the incoming frequency-modulated signal will be demodulated, producing an erroneous output.

In PLL applications the frequency response of the phase detector is usually not the limiting factor in the usable operating frequency range of the loop itself. At high operating frequencies, the parasitic capacitances of the devices result in a feedthrough of the carrier frequency, giving an erroneous component in the output at the center frequency. This component is removed by the loop filter, however, and does not greatly affect loop performance. The VCO is usually the limiting factor in the operating frequency range.

*Voltage-Controlled Oscillator.* The operating frequency range, FM distortion, center-frequency drift, and center-frequency, supply-voltage sensitivity are all determined by the performance of the VCO. Integrated-circuit VCOs often are simply R-C multivibrators in which the charging current in the capacitor is varied in response to the control input. We first consider the emitter-coupled multivibrator as shown in Fig. 10.26a, which is typical of those used in this application. We calculate the period by first assuming that $Q_1$ is turned off and $Q_2$ is turned on. The circuit then appears as shown in Fig. 10.26b. We assume that current $I$ is large so that the voltage drop $IR$ is large enough to turn on diode $Q_6$. Thus the base of $Q_4$ is one diode drop below $V_{CC}$, the emitter is two diode drops below $V_{CC}$, and the base of $Q_1$ is two diode drops below $V_{CC}$. If we can neglect the base current of $Q_3$, its base is at $V_{CC}$ and its emitter is one diode drop below $V_{CC}$. Thus the emitter of $Q_2$ is two diode drops below $V_{CC}$. Since $Q_1$ is off, the current $I_1$ is charging the capacitor so that the emitter of $Q_1$ is becoming more negative. $Q_1$ will turn on when the voltage at its emitter becomes equal to three diode drops below $V_{CC}$. Transistor $Q_1$ will then turn on, and the resulting collector current in $Q_1$ turns on $Q_5$. As a result, the base of $Q_3$ moves in the negative direction by one diode drop, causing the base of $Q_2$ to move in the negative direction by one diode drop. $Q_2$ will turn off, causing the base of $Q_1$ to move positive by one diode drop because $Q_6$ also turns off. As a result, the emitter-base junction of $Q_2$ is reverse biased by one diode drop because the voltage on $C$ cannot change instan-

**Figure 10.26** (*a*) Voltage-controlled, emitter-coupled multivibrator.

**Figure 10.26** (*b*) Equivalent circuit during one half-cycle.

taneously. Current $I_1$ must now charge the capacitor voltage in the negative direction by an amount equal to two diode drops before the circuit will switch back again. Since the circuit is symmetrical, the half period is given by the time required to charge the capacitor and is

$$\frac{T}{2} = \frac{Q}{I_1} \qquad (10.76)$$

**Figure 10.26** (*c*) Waveforms within the emitter-coupled multivibrator.

where $Q = C\Delta V = 2CV_{BE(\text{on})}$ is the charge on the capacitor. The frequency of the oscillator is thus

$$f = \frac{1}{T} = \frac{I_1}{4CV_{BE(\text{on})}} \qquad (10.77)$$

The various waveforms in the circuit are shown in Fig. 10.26c. This emitter-coupled configuration is nonsaturating and contains only *npn* transistors. Furthermore, the voltage swings within the circuit are small. As a result, the circuit is capable of operating up to approximately 1 GHz for typical integrated-circuit transistors. However, the usable frequency range is limited to a value lower than this because the center frequency drift with temperature variations becomes large at the higher frequencies. This drift occurs because the switching transients themselves become a large percentage of the period of the oscillation, and the duration of the switching transients depends on circuit parasitics, circuit resistances, transistor transconductance, and transistor input resistance, which are all temperature sensitive.

Although the emitter-coupled configuration is capable of high operating speed, it displays considerable sensitivity of center frequency to temperature even at low frequencies, since the period is dependent on $V_{BE(on)}$. Utilizing (10.77) we can calculate the temperature coefficient of the period as

$$\frac{1}{\omega_{osc}} \frac{d\omega_{osc}}{dT} = -\frac{1}{V_{BE(on)}} \frac{dV_{BE(on)}}{dT} = \frac{+2 \text{ mV/°C}}{600 \text{ mV}} = +3300 \text{ ppm/°C} \quad (10.78)$$

This temperature sensitivity of center frequency can be compensated by causing current $I_1$ to be temperature sensitive in such a way that its effect is equal and opposite to the effect of the variation of $V_{BE(on)}$.

### 10.4.4 Analysis of the 560B Monolithic Phase-Locked Loop

The first practical monolithic PLLs were the 560/561/562 series circuits. These circuits contain a phase detector of the Gilbert type, an emitter-coupled, temperature-compensated VCO, and provision for use of an external $R$-$C$ circuit to perform the loop filter function. A schematic diagram of the 560B is shown in Fig. 10.27a. Transistors $Q_1$ to $Q_{14}$ form the bias reference circuit that provides a 13-V supply-independent, Zener-referenced voltage for the phase detector and the VCO. It also provides a dc reference potential for the differential inputs, through $R_3$ and $R_4$, so that the input can be ac coupled. Transistors $Q_{13}$ and $Q_{14}$ provide a reference voltage for the current sources in the VCO, and transistor $Q_{11}$ provides the bias current for the phase detector.

The VCO is composed of transistors $Q_{23}$ and $Q_{24}$ and emitter followers $Q_{27}$ and $Q_{28}$. The phase detector is composed of transistors $Q_{15}$ to $Q_{20}$ and the differential output of the phase detector is fed to the VCO through emitter followers $Q_{21}$ and $Q_{22}$, and emitter-coupled pair $Q_{35}$ to $Q_{38}$.

We will now analyze the circuit with the objective of determining the $K_D$ and $K_o$ parameters of the loop. We begin by analyzing the bias reference circuit shown separately in Fig. 10.27b. The bias circuit generates a regulated 13 V subsupply for the VCO and the phase comparator so that the bias voltages in these circuits remain constant when the supply voltage changes over the allowed 16- to 26-V range. We will assume the supply voltage is 16 V; the only current level in the circuit affected by supply voltage is that in the chain through $R_{18}$ and $Q_3$ to $Q_6$. Zener diodes $Q_3$ and $Q_5$ are reverse-biased emitter-base junctions with breakdown voltages near 6.2 V so that

$$I_1 = \frac{V_{CC} - V_{Z3} - V_{BE4} - V_{Z5} - V_{BE6}}{R_{18}} \quad (10.79)$$

$$I_1 = \frac{(V_{CC} - 6.2 - 0.6 - 6.2 - 0.6) \text{ V}}{5.3 \text{ k}\Omega} = \frac{16 - 13.6}{5.3 \text{ k}\Omega} = 0.45 \text{ mA} \quad (10.80)$$

Thus the voltage on the emitters of $Q_1$, $Q_2$, and $Q_9$ is 13.0 V. Assuming that $Q_7$ is conducting current, we can see that the voltage at the top of $Q_7$ is 6.8 V. Thus the current in $R_{17}$ is

$$I_{R17} = \frac{V_{Z7} + V_{BE8} - V_{BE13} - V_{BE14}}{R_{17}} \quad (10.81)$$

$$I_{R17} = \frac{6.2 + 0.6 - 0.6 - 0.6}{11 \text{ k}\Omega} = 0.51 \text{ mA} \quad (10.82)$$

Phase detector, loop filter, and amplifier

**Figure 10.27** (a) 560B phase-locked loop circuit schematic.

737

Figure 10.27 (*b*) Bias circuit for 560B phase-locked loop.

The current in $Q_{11}$, which is the bias current for the phase comparator, is equal to that in $Q_{10}$, which is

$$I_{C10} = I_{C11} = \frac{V_{Z7} + V_{BE8} - V_{BE10}}{R_{13} + R_{14} + R_{15}} \tag{10.83}$$

$$= \frac{6.8 \text{ V} - 0.6 \text{ V}}{8.14 \text{ k}\Omega} = 0.77 \text{ mA} \tag{10.84}$$

The bias voltage $V_{12}$, which supplies the dc reference for the input terminals, is then

$$V_{12} = V_{BE10} + (V_{BE8} + V_{Z7} - V_{BE10})\left(\frac{R_{14} + R_{13}}{R_{15} + R_{14} + R_{13}}\right) - V_{BE12} \tag{10.85}$$

and thus

$$V_{12} = 0.6 \text{ V} + (6.8 - 0.6)\left(\frac{4.84}{3.3 + 4.84}\right)\text{V} - 0.6 \text{ V} = 3.69 \text{ V} \tag{10.86}$$

The voltage applied to the bases of current-source transistors $Q_{30}$ to $Q_{34}$ is equal to two diode drops above ground. The voltage across the 1.2-k$\Omega$ resistors $R_{26}$ through $R_{25}$, $R_{20}$, $R_{19}$, and $R_{23}$ is thus one diode drop, giving a current of approximately 0.5 mA. It is

**Figure 10.28**  Phase comparator of the 560B phase-locked loop.

important to note that these currents have a large negative temperature coefficient, given by

$$\frac{dI}{dT} = \frac{d}{dT}\left[\frac{V_{BE(\text{on})}}{R}\right] = \frac{V_{BE(\text{on})}}{R}\left[\frac{1}{V_{(BE\text{on})}}\frac{dV_{BE(\text{on})}}{dT} - \frac{1}{R}\frac{dR}{dT}\right] \quad (10.87)$$

$$= \frac{V_{BE(\text{on})}}{R}\left(\frac{-2\text{ mV/}^\circ\text{C}}{600\text{ mV}} - 1500 \times 10^{-6}\right) \quad (10.88)$$

and thus

$$\frac{1}{I}\frac{dI}{dT} = -4800\text{ ppm/}^\circ\text{C} \quad (10.89)$$

This temperature sensitivity partially compensates the center frequency drift of the VCO, which results from the temperature variation in $V_{BE(\text{on})}$ within the VCO.

We now analyze the phase detector shown in Fig. 10.28. If the base currents of $Q_{21}$ and $Q_{22}$ are negligible, and a large limiting signal is applied to the input, then the voltages appearing at the bases of $Q_{21}$ and $Q_{22}$ take on one of two values:

$$V_{\text{hi}} = 13\text{ V} \quad (10.90)$$

$$V_{\text{lo}} = 13\text{ V} - (I_{C11})(6\text{ k}\Omega) = 8.38\text{ V} \quad (10.91)$$

The amplitude of the differential square wave output is thus 4.62 V. Since $I_{C11}$ has a temperature coefficient that is approximately the negative of that of a diffused resistor $(R_{13} + R_{14} + R_{15})$, and the output voltage swing is the product of this current with $R_1$ and $R_2$, the net temperature coefficient of the output amplitude is small. The purpose of the $Q_{21}$-$Q_{40}$-$R_6$-$R_8$ and $Q_{22}$-$Q_{41}$-$R_7$-$R_9$ bias strings is to level shift the signal prior to driving the VCO input. The voltages at the bases of $Q_{35}$ and $Q_{38}$ take on two values:

$$V_{hi} = (13 \text{ V} - V_{BE21} - V_{Z40})\left(\frac{R_8}{R_6 + R_8}\right) \tag{10.92}$$

$$= (13 \text{ V} - 0.6 \text{ V} - 6.2 \text{ V})\left(\frac{8.2}{8.2 + 1.25}\right) = 5.38 \text{ V} \tag{10.93}$$

$$V_{lo} = (8.38 \text{ V} - V_{BE21} - V_{Z40})\left(\frac{R_8}{R_6 + R_8}\right) = 1.37 \text{ V} \tag{10.94}$$

The peak amplitude of the phase detector differential output is thus 4.0 V. Using (10.47) we find that the dc component of the differential output is

$$V_{average} = -(4.0 \text{ V})\left(1 - \frac{2\phi}{\pi}\right) \qquad 0 < \phi < \pi \tag{10.95}$$

$$= K_D\left(\phi - \frac{\pi}{2}\right) \qquad 0 < \phi < \pi \tag{10.96}$$

Thus

$$K_D = \frac{4.0 \text{ V}}{\pi/2} = 2.55 \text{ V/rad} \tag{10.97}$$

If the signal applied to the input is small so that limiting does not occur, then the phase detector gain becomes, utilizing (10.75),

$$K_D = \frac{V_i}{\pi}(2g_{m19}R_1)\frac{R_8}{R_8 + R_6} \tag{10.98}$$

$$= \frac{V_i}{\pi}\left[(2)\left(\frac{0.38 \text{ mA}}{26 \text{ mV}}\right)(6 \text{ k}\Omega)\right]\left(\frac{8.2}{9.45}\right) \tag{10.99}$$

$$= 48.4V_i \text{ (rad)}^{-1} \tag{10.100}$$

where $V_i$ is the peak amplitude of the sinusoidal input. In terms of the rms value,

$$K_D = 68.4 \ V_i\big|_{rms} \text{ (rad)}^{-1} \tag{10.101}$$

Thus for a 1-mV rms input, for example, the value of $K_D$ is equal to 0.068 V/rad.

We now analyze the voltage-controlled oscillator shown in Fig. 10.29. We initially assume that the input differential voltage is zero, so the four emitter-coupled transistors ($Q_{35}$ to $Q_{38}$) all conduct the same current. The collector currents of $Q_{37}$ and $Q_{38}$ are thus 125 μA, and the total current flowing from the emitters of $Q_{23}$ and $Q_{24}$ is 625 μA. This emitter-coupled multivibrator circuit was analyzed earlier, and the free-running frequency is given by (10.77) as

$$f_o = \frac{I}{4CV_{BE(on)}} \tag{10.102}$$

Assuming a $V_{BE(on)}$ of 0.6 V, the VCO center frequency is thus

$$f_o = \frac{625 \times 10^{-6}}{4C \times 0.6} = \frac{0.26 \times 10^{-3}}{C} \tag{10.103}$$

The required value of $C$ to give a frequency $f_o$ is

$$C = \frac{260}{f_o}\mu\text{F} \tag{10.104}$$

**Figure 10.29** Voltage-controlled oscillator of the 560B phase-locked loop.

where $f_o$ is in Hertz and $C$ is in microfarads. An important aspect of PLL performance is the center frequency sensitivity to temperature. Again, utilizing (10.77), we obtain

$$\frac{1}{f_o}\frac{df_o}{dT} = \frac{1}{I}\frac{dI}{dT} - \frac{1}{V_{BE}}\frac{dV_{BE}}{dT} - \frac{1}{C}\frac{dC}{dT} \tag{10.105}$$

The bias circuit that produces $I_{31}$, $I_{32}$, and $I_{34}$ was analyzed previously, where it was determined that

$$\frac{1}{I}\frac{dI}{dT} = \frac{1}{V_{BE}}\frac{dV_{BE}}{dT} - \frac{1}{R}\frac{dR}{dT} \tag{10.106}$$

Consequently, for this circuit, substituting (10.106) in (10.105) gives

$$\frac{1}{f_o}\frac{df_o}{dT} = -\frac{1}{R}\frac{dR}{dT} - \frac{1}{C}\frac{dC}{dT} \tag{10.107}$$

Assuming that an external capacitor with a low temperature coefficient is used, the center frequency temperature variation is related to the temperature variation of the diffused resistors making up the circuit. This temperature coefficient is usually on the order of 1000 to 1500 ppm/°C. This rather high drift can be reduced by redesigning the bias circuit to temperature compensate the resistor variation.

Since the collector currents of $Q_{37}$ and $Q_{38}$ can vary between zero and 250 μA, the total current charging the capacitor can vary from 500 to 750 μA, and the VCO frequency can vary ±20 percent about its center frequency. Regarding $Q_{37}$ and $Q_{38}$ together as one device, we can calculate the ratio of the small-signal input voltage of the emitter-coupled pair to the total small-signal output current flowing in $Q_{37}$-$Q_{38}$.

$$\frac{i_o}{v_{\text{in}}} = \frac{1}{2}\left(\frac{g_{m37-38}}{1 + g_{m37-38}R_{24}}\right) = \frac{1}{2}\frac{\left(\dfrac{1}{104\ \Omega}\right)}{1 + \left(\dfrac{325}{104}\right)} = \frac{1}{2}\left(\frac{1}{430\ \Omega}\right) \tag{10.108}$$

Half of the output current of $Q_{37}$-$Q_{38}$ charges the capacitor at any given time, so that

$$\frac{dI}{dV_{\text{in}}} = \frac{1}{2}\frac{i_o}{v_{\text{in}}} = \frac{1}{2}\frac{1}{860\ \Omega} \tag{10.109}$$

where $V_{\text{in}}$ is the input to the pair $Q_{35}$-$Q_{38}$, and $I$ is the current that sets the frequency of the VCO. From (10.77)

$$\frac{df}{dI} = \frac{1}{4CV_{BE(\text{on})}} \tag{10.110}$$

Equations (10.109) and (10.110) can be combined to give

$$K_O = \frac{d\omega}{dV_{\text{in}}} = 2\pi\frac{df}{dI}\frac{dI}{dV_{\text{in}}} = \frac{1}{8}\frac{2\pi}{860CV_{BE(\text{on})}} \tag{10.111}$$

Substituting of (10.77) in (10.111) gives

$$K_O = \frac{2\pi f_o}{1720 I_o} \tag{10.112}$$

where $I_o = 625\ \mu\text{A}$ is the value of $I$ when $V_{\text{in}} = 0$, and $f_o$ is the corresponding value of the VCO frequency. This is called the VCO *free-running frequency*. Thus

$$K_O = \frac{2\pi f_o}{1.08}\ \text{rad/V-s} = 0.93\omega_o\ \text{rad/V-s} \tag{10.113}$$

where $f_o = \omega_o/2\pi$. The value of $K_o$ thus depends on the free-running frequency of the VCO through $C$ in (10.111).

The analysis of the 560B is now complete. By combining the calculated values for $K_O$ and $K_D$, the inherent loop bandwidth $K_v$ for large inputs is found to be

$$K_v = K_D K_O = 2.55 \times 0.93\omega_o\ \text{s}^{-1} = 2.36\omega_o\ \text{s}^{-1} \tag{10.114}$$

Note that $A = 1$ in this case, since all the gain in the loop has been absorbed into $K_D$ and $K_O$. Equations 10.114 and 10.68 show that if no other limiting factor is present, the loop will be able to track carrier signals whose frequency deviates from the center frequency by as much as 3.7 times the value of the VCO free-running frequency. Actually, the lock range will be much smaller than this because of the fact that while the phase comparator can produce a maximum output voltage of about 4 V for 90° of phase error, the voltage-to-current converter that controls the VCO has a linear range on its input of only about 250 mV. As a result, the lock range is limited by the VCO control range to about ±25% of the VCO free-running frequency. An important consequence of the large value of $K_v$, however, is the fact that when the circuit is used as a first-order loop with no additional attenuation in the loop, the bandwidth of the loop used as an FM demodulator is quite broad. This bandwidth can be narrowed to any desired value by using a second-order loop with a zero in the loop filter for stability.

In the 560B circuit, the user can modify the control range of the VCO, thereby controlling the lock range of the PLL. This is accomplished by controlling the bias current in the emitter-coupled pair $Q_{35}$-$Q_{38}$, which is the current that produces the variation in VCO frequency. This current can be either increased or decreased by the user in the

**Figure 10.30** Bipolar non-linear function circuits. (a) Square root. (b) Square law.

actual circuit with external components so that the lock range is controllable externally. The advantage of this method of limiting the lock range is that it is independently controllable from the loop bandwidth $K_v$.

The actual loop bandwidth $K_v$ can be controlled by the user of the PLL in several ways. First, external resistors can be inserted in parallel with $R_1$ and $R_2$ in Fig. 10.28 to reduce their effective value. This directly reduces $K_D$ and thus $K_v$. Second, a loop filter that contains a zero can be used. This allows placing the pole of the loop filter at a frequency far below the inherent loop bandwidth $K_v$ without excessive peaking in the loop frequency response.

## 10.5 Nonlinear Function Synthesis

The need often arises in electronic systems for circuits with arbitrary nonlinear transfer functions. For example, a common need is for square-law and square-root transfer characteristics in order to generate true rms quantities. The unique, precision exponential transfer characteristic of the bipolar transistor can be used[8,9] to generate these and many other nonlinear functions.

Consider the circuit shown in Fig. 10.30a. We have

$$V_{BE1} + V_{BE2} - V_{BE3} - V_{BE4} = 0 \qquad (10.115)$$

Neglecting base currents and assuming all devices are forward active, we find

$$V_T \ln\frac{I_B}{I_{S1}} + V_T \ln\frac{I_i}{I_{S2}} - V_T \ln\frac{I_o}{I_{S3}} - V_T \ln\frac{I_o}{I_{S4}} = 0$$

and thus

$$I_o = \sqrt{I_i}\,\sqrt{I_B}\sqrt{\frac{I_{S3}I_{S4}}{I_{S1}I_{S2}}} \qquad (10.116)$$

This circuit thus realizes a square-root transfer function with a scale factor set only by the bias current $I_B$ (which could be another input signal) and device area ratios. There is no (first-order) dependence on supply voltage or temperature. Not that the input current source $I_i$ must be capable of working into a dc bias voltage of one $V_{BE}$ set by $Q_1$. The small-signal input impedance of the circuit is very low due to the feedback provided by $Q_1$ and $Q_2$. Since all nodes in the circuit are low impedance, parasitic capacitance has little influence, and the bandwidth of the circuit can be on the order of the device $f_T$.

For the circuit in Fig. 10.30b we have

$$V_{BE1} + V_{BE5} + V_{BE2} = V_{BE3} + V_{BE4} + V_{BE6} \qquad (10.117)$$

from which

$$I_o = I_i^2 \frac{I_{B1}}{I_{B2}^2}\frac{I_{S3}I_{S4}I_{S6}}{I_{S1}I_{S5}I_{S2}} \qquad (10.118)$$

Thus this circuit realizes the square-law transfer function with very wide bandwidth and insensitivity to temperature and supply voltage. Simpler versions of this circuit can be derived if the current source $I_{B1}$ is used as a signal input. However, this requires that $I_{B1}$ be realized by an active *pnp* current source (or a PMOS current source in BiCMOS technology), which will usually restrict the circuit bandwidth.

## PROBLEMS

**10.1** Determine the dc transfer characteristics of the circuit shown in Fig. 10.31. The Zener diodes have a reverse breakdown voltage of 6.2 V and zero incremental resistance in the breakdown region. In the forward direction $V_{BE(on)} = 0.6$ V.

**Figure 10.31** Circuit for Problem 10.1.

**10.2** Determine and sketch the dc transfer characteristic of the circuit shown in Fig. 10.32. Assume that $V_{BE(on)} = 0.6$ V. Check your result using SPICE, assuming $I_S = 10^{-16}$ A for the transistor. Approximate the op amp by a voltage-controlled voltage source with a gain of 10,000.

**10.3** Determine and sketch the dc transfer characteristic of the circuit of Fig. 10.33.

**10.4** Sketch the dc transfer curve $I_{out}$ versus $V_2$ for the Gilbert multiplier of Fig. 10.9 for $V_1$ equal to $0.1V_T$, $0.5V_T$, and $V_T$.

**10.5** For the emitter-coupled pair of Fig. 10.6, determine the magnitude of the dc differential input voltage required to cause the *slope* of the transfer

**Figure 10.32** Circuit for Problem 10.2.

**Figure 10.33** Circuit for Problem 10.3.

curve to be different by 1 percent from the slope through the origin.

**10.6** Assume that a sinusoidal voltage signal is applied to the emitter-coupled pair of Fig. 10.6. Determine the maximum allowable magnitude of the sinusoid such that the magnitude of the third harmonic in the output is less than 1 percent of the fundamental. To work this problem, approximate the transfer characteristic of the pair with the first two terms of the Taylor series for the tanh function. Then assume that all the other harmonics in the output are negligible and that the output is approximately

$$I_{out}(t) = I_o(\sin \omega_o t + \delta \sin 3\omega_o t)$$

where $\delta$ = fractional third-harmonic distortion. Use SPICE to check your result. For the same sinusoidal input voltage amplitude, use SPICE to find the third harmonic distortion in the output if emitter resistors $R_E$ are added to each device such that $I_{E1}R_E = I_{E2}R_E = 100$ mV.

**10.7** Determine the worst-case input offset voltage of the voltage-current converter shown in Fig. 10.34. Assume that the op amps are ideal, that the resistors mismatch by ±0.3 percent, and that transistor $I_S$ values mismatch by ±2 percent.

Neglect base currents. Use SPICE to determine the second and third harmonic distortion in the output for a sinusoidal input drive of amplitude 20 V peak-peak. Assume $I_S = 10^{-16}$ A for the transistor and approximate the op amps by voltage-controlled voltage sources with a gain of 10,000.

**10.8** Determine the dc transfer characteristic of the circuit of Fig. 10.35. Assume that $Z = 0.1XY$ for the multiplier.

**10.9** A phase-locked loop has a center frequency of $10^5$ rad/s, a $K_O$ of $10^3$ rad/V-s, and a $K_D$ of 1 V/rad. There is no other gain in the loop. Determine the loop bandwidth in the first-order loop configuration. Determine the single-pole, loop-filter pole location to give the closed-loop poles located on 45° radials from the origin.

**10.10** For the same PLL of Problem 10.9, design a loop filter with a zero that gives a crossover frequency for the loop gain of 100 rad/s. The loop phase shift at the loop crossover frequency should be −135°.

**10.11** Estimate the capture range of the PLL of Problem 10.10, assuming that it is not artificially limited by the VCO frequency range.

**Figure 10.34** Circuit for Problem 10.7. All op amps are ideal.

**Figure 10.35** Circuit for Problem 10.8. The op amp is ideal.

**10.12** An FM demodulator using the 560B has a center frequency of 2 kHz and is implemented as a first-order loop. The input signal alternates between 1.95 kHz and 2.05 kHz at a rate of 200 Hz with instantaneous transitions between the two frequency values. Sketch the demodulated output voltage waveform.

**10.13** Design a voltage-controlled oscillator based on the circuit of Fig. 10.26a. The center frequency is to be 10 kHz, $C = 0.01$ μF, and $V_{CC} = 5$ V. For the transistors $\beta = 100$ and $I_S = 10^{-16}$ A. The frequency is to be varied by 2:1 by an input $\Delta V_{in} = 200$ mV. Specify all resistors and the dc value of $V_{in}$. Use SPICE to check your design and also to produce a plot of the transfer characteristic from $V_{in}$ to frequency.

**10.14** Using the methods of Section 10.5, design a circuit with a transfer characteristic $I_o = KI_i^{3/2}$ for $I_i \geqslant 0$. The input bias voltage must be $\geqslant V_{BE}$, and the output bias voltage is equal to $2V_{BE}$. The value of $I_o$ should be 100 μA for $I_i = 100$ μA. The supply voltage available is $V_{CC} = 5$ V and device data are $\beta = 100$ and $I_S = 10^{-17}$A. Use SPICE to verify your design and then examine the effect of finite $r_b = 200$ Ω and $r_e = 2$ Ω.

**10.15** Show that the CMOS circuit of Fig. 10.36 realizes a square-law transfer characteristic from $V_i$ to $I_o$ assuming that the MOSFETs have square-law characteristics. Specify the range of $V_i$ over which this holds. (The bias analysis of Section 9.6.4 applies.) All PMOS devices have $W/L = 60$ and all

**Figure 10.36** CMOS square-law circuit.

NMOS have $W/L = 20$. Device data are $\mu_n C_{ox} = 60$ $\mu A/V^2$, $\mu_p C_{ox} = 20$ $\mu A/V^2$, $V_{tn} = 0.7$ V, $V_{tp} = -0.7$ V, $\gamma = 0$, and $\lambda = 0$.

Use SPICE to verify your result by plotting and evaluating the dc transfer characteristic. Then apply an input sine-wave voltage drive at $V_i$ within the square-law range and examine the first and second harmonics in $I_o$ and comment.

# REFERENCES

1. G. E. Tobey, J. G. Graeme, and L. P. Huelsman. *Operational Amplifiers*. McGraw-Hill, New York, 1971.

2. B. Gilbert. "A Precise Four-Quadrant Multiplier with Subnanosecond Response," *IEEE J. Solid-State Circuits*, Vol. SC-3, pp. 365–373, December 1968.

3. B. Gilbert. "A New High-Performance Monolithic Multiplier Using Active Feedback," *IEEE J. Solid-State Circuits*, Vol. SC-9, pp. 364–373, December 1974.

4. F. M. Gardner. *Phase-Lock Techniques*. Wiley, New York, 1966.

5. A. B. Grebene and H. R. Camenzind. "Frequency Selective Integrated Circuits Using Phase-Locked Techniques," *IEEE J. Solid-State Circuits*, Vol. SC-4, pp. 216–225, August 1969.

6. *Applications of Phase-Locked Loops*, Signetics Corporation, 1974.

7. M. Soyuer and R. G. Meyer. "Frequency Limitations of a Conventional Phase-Frequency Detector," *IEEE J. Solid-State Circuits*, Vol. 25, pp. 1019–1022, August 1990.

8. B. Gilbert. "General Technique for N-Dimensional Vector Summation of Bipolar Signals," *Electronics Letters*, Vol. 12, pp. 504–505, September 16, 1976.

9. E. Seevinck. *Analysis and Synthesis of Translinear Integrated Circuits*. Elsevier, Amsterdam, 1988.

# Noise in Integrated Circuits

## 11.1 Introduction

This chapter deals with the effects of *electrical noise* in integrated circuits. The noise phenomena considered here are caused by the small current and voltage fluctuations that are generated within the devices themselves, and we specifically exclude extraneous pickup of man-made signals that can also be a problem in high-gain circuits. The existence of noise is basically due to the fact that electrical charge is not continuous but is carried in discrete amounts equal to the electron charge, and thus noise is associated with fundamental processes in the integrated-circuit devices.

The study of noise is important because it represents a lower limit to the size of electrical signal that can be amplified by a circuit without significant deterioration in signal quality. Noise also results in an upper limit to the useful gain of an amplifier, because if the gain is increased without limit, the output stage of the circuit will eventually begin to limit (that is, a transistor will leave the active region) on the amplified noise from the input stages.

In this chapter the various sources of electronic noise are considered, and the equivalent circuits of common devices including noise generators are described. Methods of circuit analysis with noise generators as inputs are illustrated, and the noise analysis of complex circuits such as op amps is performed. Methods of computer analysis of noise are examined, and, finally, some common methods of specifying circuit noise performance are described.

## 11.2 Sources of Noise

### 11.2.1 Shot Noise[1,2,3,4]

Shot noise is *always* associated with a direct-current flow and is present in diodes, MOS transistors, and bipolar transistors. The origin of shot noise can be seen by considering the diode of Fig. 11.1$a$ and the carrier concentrations in the device in the forward-bias region as shown in Fig. 11.1$b$. As explained in Chapter 1, an electric field $\mathscr{E}$ exists in the depletion region and a voltage $(\psi_0 - V)$ exists between the $p$-type and the $n$-type regions, where $\psi_0$ is the built-in potential and $V$ is the forward bias on the diode. The forward current of the diode $I$ is composed of holes from the $p$ region and electrons from the $n$ region, which have sufficient energy to overcome the potential barrier at the junction. Once the carriers have crossed the junction, they diffuse away as minority carriers.

The passage of each carrier across the junction, which can be modeled as a random event, is dependent on the carrier having sufficient energy and a velocity directed toward the junction. Thus external current $I$, which appears to be a steady current, is, in fact, composed of a large number of random independent current pulses. If the current is examined on a sensitive oscilloscope, the trace appears as in Fig. 11.2, where $I_D$ is the average current.

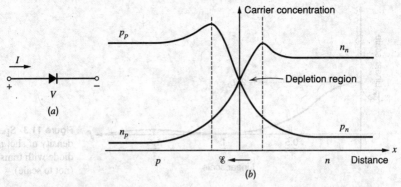

**Figure 11.1** (a) Forward-biased pn junction diode. (b) Carrier concentrations in the diode (not to scale).

The fluctuation in $I$ is termed *shot noise* and is generally specified in terms of its mean-square variation about the average value. This is written as $\overline{i^2}$, where

$$\overline{i^2} = \overline{(I - I_D)^2}$$
$$= \lim_{T \to \infty} \frac{1}{T} \int_0^T (I - I_D)^2 \, dt \qquad (11.1)$$

It can be shown that if a current $I$ is composed of a series of random independent pulses with average value $I_D$, then the resulting noise current has a mean-square value

$$\boxed{\overline{i^2} = 2qI_D \, \Delta f} \qquad (11.2)$$

where $q$ is the electronic charge ($1.6 \times 10^{-19}$ C) and $\Delta f$ is the bandwidth in hertz. This equation shows that the noise current has a mean-square value that is *directly proportional* to the bandwidth $\Delta f$ (in hertz) of the measurement. Thus a noise-current *spectral density* $\overline{i^2}/\Delta f$ (with units square amperes per hertz) can be defined that is *constant* as a function of frequency. Noise with such a spectrum is often called *white noise*. Since noise is a purely random signal, the *instantaneous value* of the waveform cannot be predicted at any time. The only information available for use in circuit calculations concerns the *mean square* value of the signal given by (11.2). Bandwidth $\Delta f$ in (11.2) is determined by the circuit in which the noise source is acting.

Equation 11.2 is valid until the frequency becomes comparable to $1/\tau$, where $\tau$ is the carrier transit time through the depletion region. For most practical electronic devices,

**Figure 11.2** Diode current $I$ as a function of time (not to scale).

Figure 11.3 Spectral density of shot noise in a diode with transit time $\tau$ (not to scale).

$\tau$ is extremely small and (11.2) is accurate well into the gigahertz region. A sketch of noise-current spectral density versus frequency for a diode is shown in Fig. 11.3 assuming that the passage of each charge carrier across the depletion region produces a square pulse of current with width $\tau$.

■ **EXAMPLE**

Calculate the shot noise in a diode current of 1 mA in a bandwidth of 1 MHz. Using (11.2) we have

$$\overline{i^2} = 2 \times 1.6 \times 10^{-19} \times 10^{-3} \times 10^6 \text{ A}^2 = 3.2 \times 10^{-16} \text{ A}^2$$

and thus

$$i = 1.8 \times 10^{-8} \text{A rms}$$

■    where $i$ represents the root-mean-square (rms) value of the noise current.

The effect of shot noise can be represented in the low-frequency, small-signal equivalent circuit of the diode by inclusion of a current generator shunting the diode, as shown in Fig. 11.4. Since this noise signal has random phase and is defined solely in terms of its mean-square value, it also has no polarity. Thus the arrow in the current source in Fig. 11.2 has no significance and is included only to identify the generator as a current source. This practice is followed in this chapter where we deal only with noise generators having random phase.

The noise-current signal produced by the shot noise mechanism has an amplitude that varies randomly with time and that can only be specified by a *probability-density* function. It can be shown that the amplitude distribution of shot noise is Gaussian and the probability-density function $p(I)$ of the diode current is plotted versus current in Fig. 11.5

Figure 11.4 Junction diode small-signal equivalent circuit with noise.

Figure 11.5 Probability density function for the diode current $I$ (not to scale).

(not to scale). The probability that the diode current lies between values $I$ and $(I + dI)$ at any time is given by $p(I)dI$. If $\sigma$ is the standard deviation of the Gaussian distribution, then the diode current amplitude lies between limits $I_D \pm \sigma$ for 68 percent of the time. By definition, variance $\sigma^2$ is the mean-square value of $(I - I_D)$ and thus, from (11.1),

$$\sigma^2 = \overline{i^2}$$

and

$$\sigma = \sqrt{2qI_D \Delta f} \tag{11.3}$$

using (11.2). Note that, theoretically, the noise amplitude can have positive or negative values approaching infinity. However, the probability falls off very quickly as amplitude increases and an effective limit to the noise amplitude is $\pm 3\sigma$. The noise signal is within these limits for 99.7 percent of the time. A brief description of the Gaussian distribution is given in Appendix A.3.1 in Chapter 3.

It is important to note that the distribution of noise in frequency as shown in Fig. 11.3 is due to the random nature of the hole and electron transitions across the *pn* junction. Consider the situation if all the carriers made transitions with uniform time separation. Since each carrier has a charge of $1.6 \times 10^{-19}$ C, a 1-mA current would then consist of current pulses every $1.6 \times 10^{-16}$ s. The Fourier analysis of such a waveform would give the spectrum of Fig. 11.6, which shows an average or dc value $I_D$ and harmonics at multiples of $1/\Delta t$, where $\Delta t$ is the period of the waveform and equals $1.6 \times 10^{-16}$ s. Thus the first harmonic is at $6 \times 10^6$ GHz, which is far beyond the useful frequency of the device. There would be *no noise produced* in the normal frequency range of operation.

Figure 11.6 Shot-noise spectrum assuming uniform emission of carriers.

### 11.2.2 Thermal Noise[1,3,5]

Thermal noise is generated by a completely different mechanism from shot noise. In conventional resistors it is due to the random thermal motion of the electrons and is unaffected by the presence or absence of direct current, since typical electron drift velocities in a conductor are much less than electron thermal velocities. Since this source of noise is due to the thermal motion of electrons, we expect that it is related to absolute temperature $T$. In fact thermal noise is *directly proportional* to $T$ (unlike shot noise, which is *independent of T*) and, as $T$ approaches zero, thermal noise also approaches zero.

In a resistor $R$, thermal noise can be shown to be represented by a series voltage generator $\overline{v^2}$ as shown in Fig. 11.7a, or by a shunt current generator $\overline{i^2}$ as in Fig. 11.7b. These representations are equivalent and

$$\overline{v^2} = 4kTR\,\Delta f \tag{11.4}$$

$$\overline{i^2} = 4kT\frac{1}{R}\Delta f \tag{11.5}$$

where $k$ is Boltzmann's constant. At room temperature $4kT = 1.66 \times 10^{-20}$ V-C. Equations 11.4 and 11.5 show that the noise spectral density is again *independent* of frequency and, for thermal noise, this is true up to $10^{13}$ Hz. Thus thermal noise is another source of white noise. Note that the Norton equivalent of (11.5) can be derived from (11.4) as

$$\overline{i^2} = \frac{\overline{v^2}}{R^2} \tag{11.6}$$

*A useful number* to remember for thermal noise is that at room temperature (300°K), the thermal noise spectral density in a 1-k$\Omega$ resistor is $\overline{v^2}/\Delta f \simeq 16 \times 10^{-18}$ V$^2$/Hz. This can be written in rms form as $v \simeq 4$ nV/$\sqrt{\text{Hz}}$ where the form nV/$\sqrt{\text{Hz}}$ is used to emphasize that the *rms noise voltage* varies as the *square root* of the bandwidth. Another useful equivalence is that the thermal noise-current generator of a 1-k$\Omega$ resistor at room temperature is the same as that of 50 $\mu$A of direct current exhibiting shot noise.

Thermal noise as described above is a fundamental physical phenomenon and is present in *any* linear passive resistor. This includes conventional resistors and the radiation resistance of antennas, loudspeakers, and microphones. In the case of loudspeakers and microphones, the source of noise is the thermal motion of the air molecules. In the case of antennas, the source of noise is the black-body radiation of the object at which the antenna is directed. In all cases, (11.4) and (11.5) give the mean-square value of the noise.

(a)                    (b)

**Figure 11.7** Alternative representations of thermal noise.

The amplitude distribution of thermal noise is again Gaussian. Since both shot and thermal noise each have a flat frequency spectrum and a Gaussian amplitude distribution, they are indistinguishable once they are introduced into a circuit. The waveform of shot and thermal noise combined with a sinewave of equal power is shown in Fig. 11.21.

### 11.2.3 Flicker Noise[6,7,8] (1/f Noise)

This is a type of noise found in all active devices, as well as in some discrete passive elements such as carbon resistors. The origins of flicker noise are varied, but it is caused mainly by traps associated with contamination and crystal defects. These traps capture and release carriers in a random fashion and the time constants associated with the process give rise to a noise signal with energy concentrated at low frequencies.

Flicker noise, which is always associated with a flow of direct current, displays a spectral density of the form

$$\overline{i^2} = K_1 \frac{I^a}{f^b} \Delta f \tag{11.7}$$

where

$\Delta f$ = small bandwidth at frequency $f$
$I$ = direct current
$K_1$ = constant for a particular device
$a$ = constant in the range 0.5 to 2
$b$ = constant of about unity

If $b = 1$ in (11.7), the noise spectral density has a $1/f$ frequency dependence (hence the alternative name $1/f$ noise), as shown in Fig. 11.8. It is apparent that flicker noise is most significant at low frequencies, although in devices exhibiting high flicker noise levels, this noise source may dominate the device noise at frequencies well into the megahertz range.

It was noted above that flicker noise only exists in association with a direct current. Thus, in the case of carbon resistors, no flicker noise is present until a direct current is passed through the resistor (however, *thermal* noise *always* exists in the resistor and is *unaffected* by any direct current as long as the temperature remains constant). Consequently, carbon resistors can be used if required as external elements in low-noise, low-frequency integrated circuits as long as they carry no direct current. If the external resistors for such circuits must carry direct current, however, metal film resistors that have no flicker noise should be used.

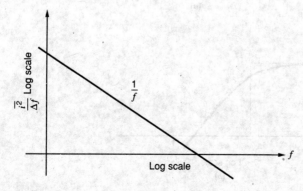

Figure 11.8 Flicker noise spectral density versus frequency.

In earlier sections of this chapter, we saw that shot and thermal noise signals have well-defined mean-square values that can be expressed in terms of current flow, resistance, and a number of well-known physical constants. By contrast, the mean-square value of a flicker noise signal as given by (11.7) contains an unknown constant $K_1$. This constant not only varies by orders of magnitude from one device type to the next, but it can also vary widely for different transistors or integrated circuits from the same process wafer. This is due to the dependence of flicker noise on contamination and crystal imperfections, which are factors that can vary randomly even on the same silicon wafer. However, experiments have shown that if a typical value of $K_1$ is determined from measurements on a number of devices from a given process, then this value can be used to predict average or typical flicker noise performance for integrated circuits from that process.[9]

The final characteristic of flicker noise that is of interest is its amplitude distribution, which is often non-Gaussian, as measurements have shown.

### 11.2.4 Burst Noise[7] (*Popcorn Noise*)

This is another type of low-frequency noise found in some integrated circuits and discrete transistors. The source of this noise is not fully understood, although it has been shown to be related to the presence of heavy-metal ion contamination. Gold-doped devices show very high levels of burst noise.

Burst noise is so named because an oscilloscope trace of this type of noise shows bursts of noise on a number (two or more) of discrete levels, as illustrated in Fig. 11.9*a*. The repetition rate of the noise pulses is usually in the audio frequency range (a few kilohertz or less) and produces a *popping* sound when played through a loudspeaker. This has led to the name *popcorn noise* for this phenomenon.

(a)

(b)

**Figure 11.9** (*a*) Typical burst noise waveform. (*b*) Burst noise spectral density versus frequency.

The spectral density of burst noise can be shown to be of the form

$$\overline{i^2} = K_2 \frac{I^c}{1 + \left(\dfrac{f}{f_c}\right)^2} \Delta f \tag{11.8}$$

where

$K_2$ = constant for a particular device
$I$ = direct current
$c$ = constant in the range 0.5 to 2
$f_c$ = particular frequency for a given noise process

This spectrum is plotted in Fig. 11.9b and illustrates the typical hump that is characteristic of burst noise. At higher frequencies the noise spectrum falls as $1/f^2$.

Burst noise processes often occur with multiple time constants, and this gives rise to multiple humps in the spectrum. Also, flicker noise is invariably present as well so that the composite low-frequency noise spectrum often appears as in Fig. 11.10. As with flicker noise, factor $K_2$ for burst noise varies considerably and must be determined experimentally. The amplitude distribution of the noise is also non-Gaussian.

### 11.2.5 Avalanche Noise[10]

This is a form of noise produced by Zener or avalanche breakdown in a *pn* junction. In avalanche breakdown, holes and electrons in the depletion region of a reverse-biased *pn* junction acquire sufficient energy to create hole-electron pairs by colliding with silicon atoms. This process is cumulative, resulting in the production of a random series of large noise spikes. The noise is always associated with a direct-current flow, and the noise produced is much greater than shot noise in the same current, as given by (11.2). This is because a single carrier can start an avalanching process that results in the production of a current burst containing many carriers moving together. The total noise is the sum of a number of random bursts of this type.

The most common situation where avalanche noise is a problem occurs when Zener diodes are used in the circuit. These devices display avalanche noise and are generally avoided in low-noise circuits. If Zener diodes are present, the noise representation of Fig. 11.11 can be used, where the noise is represented by a series voltage generator $v^2$. The dc voltage $V_z$ is the breakdown voltage of the diode, and the series resistance $R$ is typically 10 to 100 $\Omega$. The magnitude of $\overline{v^2}$ is difficult to predict as it depends on the

**Figure 11.10** Spectral density of combined multiple burst noise sources and flicker noise.

**Figure 11.11** Equivalent circuit of a Zener diode including noise.

device structure and the uniformity of the silicon crystal, but a typical measured value is $\overline{v^2}/\Delta f \approx 10^{-14}$ V$^2$/Hz at a dc Zener current of 0.5 mA. Note that this is equivalent to the thermal noise voltage in a 600-k$\Omega$ resistor and completely overwhelms thermal noise in $R$. The spectral density of the noise is approximately flat, but the amplitude distribution is generally non-Gaussian.

## 11.3  Noise Models of Integrated-Circuit Components

In the above sections, the various physical sources of noise in electronic circuits were described. In this section, these sources of noise are brought together to form the small-signal equivalent circuits including noise for diodes and for bipolar and MOS transistors.

### 11.3.1  Junction Diode

The equivalent circuit for a forward-biased junction diode was considered briefly in the consideration of shot noise. The basic equivalent circuit of Fig. 11.4 can be made complete by adding series resistance $r_s$ as shown in Fig. 11.12. Since $r_s$ is a physical resistor due to the resistivity of the silicon, it exhibits thermal noise. Experimentally it has been found that any flicker noise present can be represented by a current generator in shunt with $r_d$, and can be conveniently combined with the shot-noise generator as indicated by (11.10)

**Figure 11.12** Complete diode small-signal equivalent circuit with noise sources.

to give

$$\overline{v_s^2} = 4kTr_s\,\Delta f \tag{11.9}$$

$$\overline{i^2} = 2qI_D\,\Delta f + K\frac{I_D^a}{f}\,\Delta f \tag{11.10}$$

### 11.3.2 Bipolar Transistor[11]

In a bipolar transistor in the forward-active region, minority carriers diffuse and drift across the base region to be collected at the collector-base junction. Minority carriers entering the collector-base depletion region are accelerated by the field existing there and swept across this region to the collector. The time of arrival at the collector-base junction of the diffusing (or drifting) carriers can be modeled as a random process, and thus the transistor collector current consists of a series of random current pulses. Consequently, collector current $I_c$ shows *full shot noise* as given by (11.2), and this is represented by a shot noise current generator $\overline{i_c^2}$ from collector to emitter as shown in the equivalent circuit of Fig. 11.13.

Base current $I_B$ in a transistor is due to recombination in the base and base-emitter depletion regions and also to carrier injection from the base into the emitter. All of these are independent random processes, and thus $I_B$ also shows *full shot noise*. This is represented by shot noise current generator $\overline{i_b^2}$ in Fig. 11.13.

Transistor base resistor $r_b$ is a physical resistor and thus has thermal noise. Collector series resistor $r_c$ also shows thermal noise, but since this is in series with the high-impedance collector node, this noise is negligible and is usually not included in the model. Note that resistors $r_\pi$ and $r_o$ in the model are *fictitious* resistors that are used for modeling purposes only, and they do *not* exhibit thermal noise.

Flicker noise and burst noise in a bipolar transistor have been found experimentally to be represented by current generators across the internal base-emitter junction. These are conveniently combined with the shot noise generator in $\overline{i_b^2}$. Avalanche noise in bipolar transistors is found to be negligible if $V_{CE}$ is kept at least 5 V below the breakdown voltage $BV_{CEO}$, and this source of noise will be neglected in subsequent calculations.

The full small-signal equivalent circuit including noise for the bipolar transistor is shown in Fig. 11.13. Since they arise from separate, independent physical mechanisms, all the noise sources are *independent* of each other and have mean-square values:

$$\overline{v_b^2} = 4kTr_b\,\Delta f \tag{11.11}$$

$$\overline{i_c^2} = 2qI_C\,\Delta f \tag{11.12}$$

$$\overline{i_b^2} = \underbrace{2qI_B\,\Delta f}_{\text{Shot noise}} + \underbrace{K_1\frac{I_B^a}{f}\,\Delta f}_{\text{Flicker noise}} + \underbrace{K_2\frac{I_B^c}{1+\left(\dfrac{f}{f_c}\right)^2}\,\Delta f}_{\text{Burst noise}} \tag{11.13}$$

This equivalent circuit is valid for both *npn* and *pnp* transistors. For *pnp* devices, the magnitudes of $I_B$ and $I_C$ are used in the above equations.

The base-current noise spectrum can be plotted using (11.13), and this has been done in Fig. 11.14, where burst noise has been neglected for simplicity. The shot noise and flicker noise asymptotes meet at a frequency $f_a$, which is called the flicker noise *corner* frequency. In some transistors using careful processing, $f_a$ can be as low as 100 Hz. In other transistors, $f_a$ can be as high as 10 MHz.

**Figure 11.13** Complete bipolar transistor small-signal equivalent circuit with noise sources.

**Figure 11.14** Spectral density of the base-current noise generator in a bipolar transistor.

### 11.3.3 MOS Transistor[12]

The structure of MOS transistors was described in Chapter 1. We showed there that the resistive channel under the gate is modulated by the gate-source voltage so that the drain current is controlled by the gate-source voltage. Since the channel material is *resistive*, it exhibits *thermal noise*, which is a major source of noise in MOS transistors. This noise source can be represented by a noise-current generator $\overline{i_d^2}$ from drain to source in the small-signal equivalent circuit of Fig. 11.15.

Another source of noise in MOS transistors is flicker noise. Because MOS transistors conduct current near the surface of the silicon where surface states act as traps that capture and release current carriers, their flicker noise component can be large. Flicker noise in the MOS transistor is also found experimentally to be represented by a drain-source current generator, and the flicker and thermal noise can be lumped into one noise generator $\overline{i_d^2}$ in

**Figure 11.15** MOSFET small-signal equivalent circuit with noise sources.

Fig. 11.15 with

$$\overline{i_d^2} = \underbrace{4kT\left(\frac{2}{3}g_m\right)\Delta f}_{\text{Thermal noise}} + \underbrace{K\frac{I_D^a}{f}\Delta f}_{\text{Flicker noise}} \qquad (11.14)$$

where

$I_D$ = drain bias current
$K$ = constant for a given device
$a$ = constant between 0.5 and 2
$g_m$ = device transconductance at the operating point

This equation is valid for long-channel devices. For channel lengths less than 1 μm, thermal noise 2 to 5 times larger than given by the first term in (11.14) has been measured.[13] This increase in thermal noise may be attributed to hot electrons in short-channel devices.

Another source of noise in the MOS transistor is shot noise generated by the gate leakage current. This noise can be represented by $\overline{i_g^2}$ in Fig. 11.15, with

$$\overline{i_g^2} = 2qI_G\,\Delta f \qquad (11.15)$$

This noise current is usually very small since the dc gate current $I_G$ is typically less than $10^{-15}$ A. The noise terms in (11.14) and (11.15) are *all independent* of each other.

There is one other component of noise that is usually insignificant at low frequencies but important in very high-frequency MOS circuits, such as radio-frequency amplifiers, for example. At an arbitrary point in the channel, the gate-to-channel voltage has a random component due to fluctuations along the channel caused by thermal noise. These voltage variations generate a noisy ac gate current $i_g$ due to the capacitance between the gate and channel. The mean-squared value of this gate current for a long-channel device in the active region is

$$\overline{i_g^2} = \frac{16}{15}kT\omega^2 C_{gs}^2\,\Delta f \qquad (11.16)$$

where $C_{gs} = (2/3)C_{ox}WL$. The gate-current noise in (11.16) is correlated with the thermal-noise term in (11.14) because both noise currents stem from thermal fluctuations in the channel. The magnitude of the correlation between these currents is 0.39.[12] For channel lengths less than 1 μm, this component of gate-current noise may be larger than given by (11.16) if thermal noise associated with the channel increases due to hot electrons as noted above.[14] The total gate-current noise is the sum of the terms in (11.15) and (11.16).

## 11.3.4 Resistors

Monolithic and thin-film resistors display thermal noise as given by (11.4) and (11.5), and the circuit representation of this is shown in Fig. 11.7. As mentioned in Section 11.2.3, discrete carbon resistors also display flicker noise, and this should be considered if such resistors are used as external components to the integrated circuit.

## 11.3.5 Capacitors and Inductors

Capacitors are common elements in integrated circuits, either as unwanted parasitics or as elements introduced for a specific purpose. Inductors are sometimes realized on the silicon die in integrated high-frequency communication circuits. There are *no sources of noise* in *ideal* capacitors or inductors. In practice, real components have parasitic resistance that *does* display noise as given by the thermal noise formulas of (11.4) and (11.5). In the case of integrated-circuit capacitors, the parasitic resistance usually consists of a small value in series with the capacitor. Parasitic resistance in inductors can be modeled by either series or shunt elements.

## 11.4 Circuit Noise Calculations[15,16]

The device equivalent circuits including noise that were derived in Section 11.3 can be used for the calculation of circuit noise performance. First, however, methods of circuit calculation with noise generators as sources must be established, and attention is now given to this problem.

Consider a noise current source with mean-square value

$$\overline{i^2} = S(f)\Delta f \tag{11.17}$$

where $S(f)$ is the *noise spectral density*. The value of $S(f)$ is plotted versus frequency in Fig. 11.16*a* for an arbitrary noise generator. In a small bandwidth $\Delta f$, the mean-square value of the noise current is given by (11.17), and the rms values can be written as

$$i = \sqrt{S(f)\Delta f} \tag{11.18}$$

The noise current in bandwidth $\Delta f$ can be represented approximately[15] by a sinusoidal current generator with rms value $i$ as shown in Fig. 11.16*b*. If the noise current in bandwidth $\Delta f$ is now applied as an input signal to a circuit, its effect can be calculated by substituting the sinusoidal generator and performing circuit analysis in the usual fashion. When the circuit response to the sinusoid is calculated, the mean-square value of the output sinusoid gives the mean-square value of the output noise in bandwidth $\Delta f$. *Thus network noise calculations reduce to familiar sinusoidal circuit-analysis calculations.* The only difference occurs when multiple noise sources are applied, as is usually the case in practical circuits. Each noise source is then represented by a separate sinusoidal generator, and the output contribution of each one is separately calculated. The total output noise

(a)

$$i = \sqrt{S(f)\Delta f}$$

(b)

**Figure 11.16** Representation of noise in a bandwidth $\Delta f$ by an equivalent sinusoid with the same rms value.

in bandwidth $\Delta f$ is calculated as a *mean-square* value by *adding* the individual *mean-square* contributions from each output sinusoid. This depends, however, on the original noise sources being *independent*, as will be shown below. This requirement is usually satisfied if the equivalent noise circuits derived in previous sections are used, as all the noise sources except the induced gate noise in (11.16) arise from separate mechanisms and are thus independent.

For example, consider two resistors $R_1$ and $R_2$ connected in series as shown in Fig. 11.17. Resistors $R_1$ and $R_2$ have respective noise generators

$$\overline{v_1^2} = 4kTR_1\Delta f \tag{11.19a}$$

$$\overline{v_2^2} = 4kTR_2\Delta f \tag{11.19b}$$

In order to calculate the mean-square noise voltage $\overline{v_T^2}$ produced by the two resistors in series, let $v_T(t)$ be the instantaneous value of the total noise voltage and $v_1(t)$ and $v_2(t)$ the instantaneous values of the individual generators. Then

$$v_T(t) = v_1(t) + v_2(t) \tag{11.20}$$

and thus

$$\overline{v_T(t)^2} = \overline{[v_1(t) + v_2(t)]^2}$$
$$= \overline{v_1(t)^2} + \overline{v_2(t)^2} + \overline{2v_1(t)v_2(t)} \tag{11.21}$$

Now, since noise generators $v_1(t)$ and $v_2(t)$ arise from separate resistors, they must be *independent*. Thus the *average* value of their product $\overline{v_1(t)v_2(t)}$ will be zero and (11.21) becomes

$$\overline{v_T^2} = \overline{v_1^2} + \overline{v_2^2} \tag{11.22}$$

Thus the mean-square value of the sum of a number of independent noise generators is the sum of the individual mean-square values. Substituting (11.19a) and (11.19b) in (11.22) gives

$$\overline{v_T^2} = 4kT(R_1 + R_2)\Delta f \tag{11.23}$$

Equation 11.23 is just the value that would be predicted for thermal noise in a resistor ($R_1 + R_2$) using (11.4), and thus the results are consistent. These results are also consistent with

**Figure 11.17** Circuit for the calculation of the total noise $\overline{v_T^2}$ produced by two resistors in series.

the representation of the noise generators by *independent* sinusoids as described earlier. It is easily shown that when two or more such generators are connected in series, the mean-square value of the total voltage is equal to the sum of the individual mean-square values.

In the above calculation, two noise voltage sources were considered connected in series. It can be similarly shown that an analogous result is true for independent noise *current* sources connected in *parallel*. The mean-square value of the combination is the sum of the individual mean-square values. This result was assumed in the modeling of Section 11.3 where, for example, three independent noise-current generators (shot, flicker, and burst) were combined into a single base-emitter noise source for a bipolar transistor.

### 11.4.1 Bipolar Transistor Noise Performance

As an example of the manipulation of noise generators in circuit calculations, consider the noise performance of the simple transistor stage with the ac schematic shown in Fig. 11.18a. The small-signal equivalent circuit including noise is shown in Fig. 11.18b. (It should be pointed out that, for noise calculations, the equivalent circuit analyzed must be the actual circuit configuration used. That is, Fig. 11.18a cannot be used as a half-circuit representation of a differential pair for the purposes of noise calculation because noise sources in each half of a differential pair affect the total output noise.)

In the equivalent circuit of Fig. 11.18b, the external input signal $v_i$ has been ignored so that output signal $v_o$ is due to noise generators only. $C_\mu$ is assumed small and is neglected. Output resistance $r_o$ is also neglected. The transistor noise generators are as described previously and in addition

$$\overline{v_s^2} = 4kTR_S\Delta f \qquad (11.24)$$

$$\overline{i_l^2} = 4kT\frac{1}{R_L}\Delta f \qquad (11.25)$$

The total output noise can be calculated by considering each noise source in turn and performing the calculation *as if* each noise source were a sinusoid with rms value equal to that of the noise source being considered. Consider first the noise generator $v_s$ due to $R_S$.

**Figure 11.18** (a) Simple transistor amplifier ac schematic. (b) Small-signal equivalent circuit with noise sources.

Then

$$v_1 = \frac{Z}{Z + r_b + R_S} v_s \tag{11.26}$$

where

$$Z = r_\pi \left\| \frac{1}{j\omega C_\pi} \right. \tag{11.27}$$

The output noise voltage due to $v_s$ is

$$v_{o1} = -g_m R_L v_1 \tag{11.28}$$

Use of (11.26) in (11.28) gives

$$v_{o1} = -g_m R_L \frac{Z}{Z + r_b + R_S} v_s \tag{11.29}$$

The phase information contained in (11.29) is irrelevant because the noise signal has random phase and the only quantity of interest is the mean-square value of the output voltage produced by $v_s$. From (11.29) this is

$$\overline{v_{o1}^2} = g_m^2 R_L^2 \frac{|Z|^2}{|Z + r_b + R_S|^2} \overline{v_s^2} \tag{11.30}$$

By similiar calculations it is readily shown that the noise voltage produced at the output by $\overline{v_b^2}$ and $\overline{i_b^2}$ is

$$\overline{v_{o2}^2} = g_m^2 R_L^2 \frac{|Z|^2}{|Z + r_b + R_S|^2} \overline{v_b^2} \tag{11.31}$$

$$\overline{v_{o3}^2} = g_m^2 R_L^2 \frac{(R_S + r_b)^2 |Z|^2}{|Z + r_b + R_S|^2} \overline{i_b^2} \tag{11.32}$$

Noise at the output due to $\overline{i_l^2}$ and $\overline{i_c^2}$ is

$$\overline{v_{o4}^2} = \overline{i_l^2} R_L^2 \tag{11.33}$$

$$\overline{v_{o5}^2} = \overline{i_c^2} R_L^2 \tag{11.34}$$

Since all five noise generators are *independent*, the total output noise is

$$\overline{v_o^2} = \sum_{n=1}^{5} \overline{v_{on}^2} \tag{11.35}$$

$$= g_m^2 R_L^2 \frac{|Z|^2}{|Z + r_b + R_S|^2} \left[ \overline{v_s^2} + \overline{v_b^2} + (R_S + r_b)^2 \overline{i_b^2} \right]$$

$$+ R_L^2 (\overline{i_l^2} + \overline{i_c^2}) \tag{11.36}$$

Substituting expressions for the noise generators we obtain

$$\frac{\overline{v_o^2}}{\Delta f} = g_m^2 R_L^2 \frac{|Z|^2}{|Z + r_b + R_S|^2} [4kT(R_S + r_b) + (R_S + r_b)^2 2qI_B]$$

$$+ R_L^2 \left( 4kT \frac{1}{R_L} + 2qI_C \right) \tag{11.37}$$

where flicker noise has been assumed small and neglected. Substituting for $Z$ from (11.27) in (11.37) we find

$$\frac{\overline{v_o^2}}{\Delta f} = g_m^2 R_L^2 \frac{r_\pi^2}{(r_\pi + R_S + r_b)^2} \frac{1}{1 + \left(\frac{f}{f_1}\right)^2} [4kT(R_S + r_b) + (R_S + r_b)^2 2qI_B]$$

$$+ R_L^2 \left(4kT \frac{1}{R_L} + 2qI_C\right) \tag{11.38}$$

where

$$f_1 = \frac{1}{2\pi[r_\pi \| (R_S + r_b)]C_\pi} \tag{11.39}$$

The output noise-voltage spectral density represented by (11.38) has a frequency-dependent part and a constant part. The frequency dependence arises because the gain of the stage begins to fall above frequency $f_1$, and noise due to generators $\overline{v_s^2}$, $\overline{v_b^2}$, and $\overline{i_b^2}$, which appears amplified in the output, also begins to fall. The constant term in (11.38) is due to noise generators $\overline{i_l^2}$ and $\overline{i_c^2}$. Note that this noise contribution would also be frequency dependent if the effect of $C_\mu$ had not been neglected. The noise-voltage spectral density represented by (11.38) has the form shown in Fig. 11.19.

## ▪ EXAMPLE

In order to give an appreciation of the numbers involved, specific values will now be assigned to the parameters of (11.38), and the various terms in the equation will be evaluated. Assume that

$$I_C = 100 \ \mu A \qquad \beta = 100 \qquad r_b = 200 \ \Omega$$
$$R_S = 500 \ \Omega \qquad C_\pi = 10 \ pF$$
$$R_L = 5 \ k\Omega$$

Substituting these values in (11.38) and using $4kT = 1.66 \times 10^{-20}$ V-C gives

$$\frac{\overline{v_o^2}}{\Delta f} = \left[ 5.82 \times 10^{-18} \frac{1}{1 + \left(\frac{f}{f_1}\right)^2} (700 + 9.4) + 1.66 \times 10^{-20} (5000 + 48,080) \right] \text{V}^2/\text{Hz}$$

$$= \left[ \frac{4.13 \times 10^{-15}}{1 + \left(\frac{f}{f_1}\right)^2} + 0.88 \times 10^{-15} \right] \text{V}^2/\text{Hz} \tag{11.40}$$

Equation 11.39 gives

$$f_1 = 23.3 \text{ MHz} \tag{11.41}$$

Equation 11.40 shows the output noise-voltage spectral density is $5.0 \times 10^{-15}$ V$^2$/Hz at low frequencies, and it approaches $0.88 \times 10^{-15}$ V$^2$/Hz at high frequencies. The major contributor to the output noise in this case is the source resistance $R_S$, follow by the base resistance of the transistor. The noise spectrum given by (11.40) is plotted in Fig. 11.19.

**Figure 11.19** Noise voltage spectrum at the output of the circuit of Fig. 11.18.

## ■ EXAMPLE

Suppose the amplifier in the above example is followed by later stages that limit the bandwidth to a sharp cutoff at 1 MHz. Since the noise spectrum as shown in Fig. 11.19 does not begin to fall significantly until $f_1 = 23.3$ MHz, the noise spectrum may be assumed constant at $5.0 \times 10^{-15}$ V$^2$/Hz over the bandwidth 0 to 1 MHz. Thus the *total* noise voltage at the output of the circuit of Fig. 11.18a in a 1-MHz bandwidth is

$$\overline{v_{oT}^2} = 5.0 \times 10^{-15} \times 10^6 \text{ V}^2 = 5.0 \times 10^{-9} \text{ V}^2$$

and thus

$$v_{oT} = 71 \ \mu\text{V rms} \tag{11.42}$$

Now suppose that the amplifier of Fig. 11.18a is *not* followed by later stages that limit the bandwidth but is fed directly to a wideband detector (this could be an oscilloscope or a voltmeter). In order to find the total output noise voltage in this case, the contribution from each frequency increment $\Delta f$ must be summed at the output. This reduces to *integration* across the bandwidth of the detector of the noise-voltage spectral-density curve of Fig. 11.19. For example, if the detector had a 0 to 50-MHz bandwidth with a sharp cutoff, then the total output noise would be

$$\overline{v_{oT}^2} = \sum_{f=0}^{50 \times 10^6} S_o(f) \Delta f$$

$$= \int_0^{50 \times 10^6} S_o(f) \, df \tag{11.43}$$

where

$$S_o(f) = \frac{\overline{v_o^2}}{\Delta f} \tag{11.44}$$

is the noise spectral density defined by (11.40). In practice, the exact evaluation of such integrals is often difficult and approximate methods are often used. Note that if the integration of (11.43) is done graphically, the noise spectral density versus frequency must be plotted on *linear scales*.

■

**Figure 11.20** Representation of circuit noise performance by an equivalent input noise voltage.

Noiseless

## 11.4.2 Equivalent Input Noise and the Minimum Detectable Signal

In the previous section, the output noise produced by the circuit of Fig. 11.18 was calculated. The significance of the noise performance of a circuit is, however, the limitation it places on the smallest input signals the circuit can handle before the noise degrades the quality of the output signal. For this reason, the noise performance is usually expressed in terms of an *equivalent input noise signal*, which gives the same output noise as the circuit under consideration. In this way, the equivalent input noise can be compared directly with incoming signals and the effect of the noise on those signals is easily determined. For this purpose, the circuit of Fig. 11.18 can be represented as shown in Fig. 11.20, where $\overline{v_{iN}^2}$ is an input noise-voltage generator that produces the same output noise as all of the original noise generators. All other sources of noise in Fig. 11.20 are considered removed. Using the same equivalent circuit as in Fig. 11.18b, we obtain, for the output noise from Fig. 11.20,

$$\overline{v_o^2} = g_m^2 R_L^2 \frac{|Z|^2}{|Z + r_b + R_S|^2} \overline{v_{iN}^2} \tag{11.45}$$

If this noise expression is equated to $\overline{v_o^2}$ from (11.37), the equivalent input noise voltage for the circuit can be calculated as

$$\frac{\overline{v_{iN}^2}}{\Delta f} = 4kT(R_S + r_b) + (R_S + r_b)^2 2qI_B$$

$$+ \frac{1}{g_m^2 R_L^2} \frac{|Z + r_b + R_S|^2}{|Z|^2} R_L^2 \left(4kT \frac{1}{R_L} + 2qI_C\right) \tag{11.46}$$

Note that the noise-voltage spectral density given by (11.46) *rises* at high frequencies because of the variation of $|Z|$ with frequency. This is due to the fact that as the *gain* of the device falls with frequency, output noise generators $\overline{i_c^2}$ and $\overline{i_l^2}$ have a larger effect when referred back to the input.

■ **EXAMPLE**

Calculate the *total* input noise voltage $\overline{v_{iNT}^2}$ for the circuit of Fig. 11.18 in a bandwidth of 0 to 1 MHz.

This could be calculated using (11.46), derived above. Alternatively, since the total output noise voltage $\overline{v_{oT}^2}$ has already been calculated, this can be used to calculate $\overline{v_{iNT}^2}$ (in a 1-MHz bandwidth) by dividing by the circuit voltage gain squared. If $A_v$ is the low-frequency, small-signal voltage gain of Fig. 11.18, then

$$A_v = \frac{r_\pi}{r_b + r_\pi + R_S} g_m R_L$$

Use of the previously specified data for this circuit gives

$$A_v = \frac{26{,}000}{200 + 26{,}000 + 500} \frac{5000}{260} = 18.7$$

Since the noise spectrum is flat up to 1 MHz, the low-frequency gain can be used to calculate $\overline{v_{iNT}^2}$ as

$$\overline{v_{iNT}^2} = \frac{\overline{v_{oT}^2}}{A_v^2} = \frac{5 \times 10^{-9}}{18.7^2} V^2 = 14.3 \times 10^{-12} \ V^2$$

Thus we have

$$v_{iNT} = 3.78 \ \mu V \ \text{rms}$$

The above example shows that in a bandwidth of 0 to 1 MHz, the noise in the circuit *appears to come* from a 3.78-μV rms noise-voltage source in series with the input. This noise voltage can be used to estimate the smallest signal that the circuit can effectively amplify, sometimes called the *minimum detectable signal* (MDS). This depends strongly on the nature of the signal and the application. If no special filtering or coding techniques are used, the MDS can be taken as equal to the equivalent input noise voltage in the passband of the amplifier. Thus, in this case

$$MDS = 3.78 \ \mu V \ \text{rms}$$

If a sinewave of magnitude 3.78 μV rms were applied to this circuit, and the output in a 1-MHz bandwidth examined on an oscilloscope, the sine wave would be barely detectable in the noise, as shown in Fig. 11.21. The noise waveform in this figure is typical of that produced by shot and thermal noise.

**Figure 11.21** Output voltage waveform of the circuit of Fig. 11.18 with a 3.78-μV rms sinewave applied at the input. The circuit bandwidth is limited to 1 MHz, which gives an equivalent input noise voltage of 3.78 μV rms.

**Figure 11.22** Representation of noise in a two-port network by equivalent input voltage and current generators.

## 11.5 Equivalent Input Noise Generators[17]

In the previous section, the equivalent input noise voltage for a particular configuration was calculated. This gave rise to an expression for an equivalent input noise-voltage generator that was dependent on the source resistance $R_S$, as well as the transistor parameters. This method is now extended to a more general and more useful representation in which the noise performance of *any* two-port network is represented by *two* equivalent input noise generators. The situation is shown in Fig. 11.22, where a two-port network containing noise generators is represented by the *same* network with internal noise sources removed (the *noiseless* network) and with a noise voltage $\overline{v_i^2}$ and current generator $\overline{i_i^2}$ connected at the input. It can be shown that this representation is valid for *any* source impedance, provided that *correlation* between the two noise generators is considered. That is, the two noise generators are not independent in general because they are both dependent on the same set of original noise sources.

The inclusion of correlation in the noise representation results in a considerable increase in the complexity of the calculations, and if correlation is important, it is often easier to return to the original network with internal noise sources to perform the calculations. However, in a larger number of practical circuits, the correlation is small and may be neglected. In addition, if either equivalent input generator $\overline{v_i^2}$ or $\overline{i_i^2}$ dominates, the correlation my be neglected in any case. The use of this method of representation is then extremely useful, as will become apparent.

The need for both an equivalent input noise voltage generator and an equivalent input noise current generator to represent the noise performance of the circuit for any source resistance can be appreciated as follows. Consider the extreme case of source resistance $R_S$ equal to zero or infinity. If $R_S = 0$, $\overline{i_i^2}$ in Fig. 11.22 is shorted out, and since the original circuit will still show output noise in general, we need an equivalent input noise voltage $\overline{v_i^2}$ to represent this behavior. Similarly, if $R_S \rightarrow \infty$, $\overline{v_i^2}$ in Fig. 11.22 cannot produce output noise and $\overline{i_i^2}$ represents the noise performance of the original noisy network. For finite values of $R_S$, both $\overline{v_i^2}$ and $\overline{i_i^2}$ contribute to the equivalent input noise of the circuit.

The values of the equivalent input generators of Fig. 11.22 are readily determined. This is done by first short-circuiting the input of both circuits and equating the output noise in each case to calculate $\overline{v_i^2}$. The value of $\overline{i_i^2}$ is found by open-circuiting the input of each circuit and equating the output noise in each case. This will now be done for the bipolar transistor and the MOS transistor.

### 11.5.1 Bipolar Transistor Noise Generators

The equivalent input noise generators for a bipolar transistor can be calculated from the equivalent circuit of Fig. 11.23a. The output noise is calculated with a short-circuited

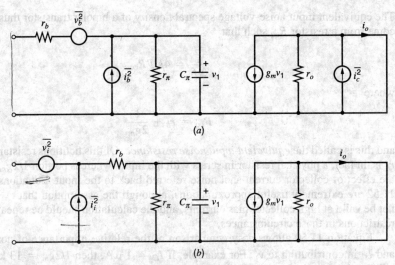

**Figure 11.23** (a) Bipolar transistor small-signal equivalent circuit with noise generators. (b) Representation of the noise performance of (a) by equivalent input generators.

load, and $C_\mu$ is neglected. This will be justified later. The circuit of Fig. 11.23a is to be equivalent to that of Fig. 11.23b in that each circuit should give the *same* output noise for *any* source impedance.

The value of $\overline{v_i^2}$ can be calculated by short-circuiting the input of each circuit and equating the output noise $i_o$. We use rms noise quantities in the calculations, but make no attempt to preserve the signs of the noise quantities as the noise generators are all independent and have random phase. The polarity of the noise generators does not affect the answer. Short-circuiting the inputs of both circuits in Fig. 11.23, assuming that $r_b$ is small ($\ll r_\pi$) and equating $i_o$, we obtain

$$g_m v_b + i_c = g_m v_i \qquad (11.47)$$

which gives

$$v_i = v_b + \frac{i_c}{g_m} \qquad (11.48)$$

Since $r_b$ is small, the effect of $\overline{i_b^2}$ is neglected in this calculation.

Using the fact that $v_b$ and $i_c$ are *independent*, we obtain, from (11.48),

$$\overline{v_i^2} = \overline{v_b^2} + \frac{\overline{i_c^2}}{g_m^2} \qquad (11.49)$$

Substituting in (11.49) for $\overline{v_b^2}$ and $\overline{i_c^2}$ from (11.11) and (11.12) gives

$$\overline{v_i^2} = 4kTr_b\Delta f + \frac{2qI_C\,\Delta f}{g_m^2}$$

and thus

$$\frac{\overline{v_i^2}}{\Delta f} = 4kT\left(r_b + \frac{1}{2g_m}\right) \qquad (11.50)$$

The equivalent input noise-voltage spectral density of a bipolar transistor thus appears to come from a resistor $R_{eq}$ such that

$$\frac{\overline{v_i^2}}{\Delta f} = 4kTR_{eq} \qquad (11.51)$$

where

$$R_{eq} = r_b + \frac{1}{2g_m} \qquad (11.52)$$

and this is called the *equivalent input noise resistance*. Of this fictitious resistance, portion $r_b$ is, in fact, a physical resistor in series with the input, whereas portion $1/2g_m$ represents the effect of collector current shot noise referred back to the input. Equations 11.50 and 11.52 are extremely useful approximations, although the assumption that $r_b \ll r_\pi$ may not be valid at high collector bias currents, and the calculation should be repeated without restrictions in those circumstances.

Equation 11.50 allows easy comparison of the relative importance of noise from $r_b$ and $I_C$ in contributing to $\overline{v_i^2}$. For example, if $I_C = 1\ \mu A$, then $1/2g_m = 13\ k\Omega$ and this will dominate typical $r_b$ values of about $100\ \Omega$. Alternately, if $I_C = 10\ mA$, then $1/2g_m = 1.3\ \Omega$ and noise from $r_b$ will totally dominate $\overline{v_i^2}$. Since $\overline{v_i^2}$ is the important noise generator for low source impedance (since $\overline{i_i^2}$ then tends to be shorted), it is apparent that good noise performance from a low source impedance requires minimization of $R_{eq}$. This is achieved by designing the transistor to have a low $r_b$ and running the device at a large collector bias current to reduce $1/2g_m$. Finally, it should be noted from (11.50) that the equivalent input noise-voltage spectral density of a bipolar transistor is independent of frequency.

In order to calculate the equivalent input noise current generator $\overline{i_i^2}$, the inputs of both circuits in Fig. 11.23 are open-circuited and output noise currents $i_o$ are equated. Using rms noise quantities, we obtain

$$\beta(j\omega)i_i = i_c + \beta(j\omega)i_b \qquad (11.53)$$

which gives

$$i_i = i_b + \frac{i_c}{\beta(j\omega)} \qquad (11.54)$$

Since $i_b$ and $i_c$ are independent generators, we obtain, from (11.54),

$$\overline{i_i^2} = \overline{i_b^2} + \frac{\overline{i_c^2}}{|\beta(j\omega)|^2} \qquad (11.55)$$

where

$$\beta(j\omega) = \frac{\beta_0}{1 + j\dfrac{\omega}{\omega_\beta}} \qquad (11.56)$$

and $\beta_0$ is the low-frequency, small-signal current gain. [See (1.122) and (1.126)].

Substituting in (11.55) for $\overline{i_b^2}$ and $\overline{i_c^2}$ from (11.13) and (11.12) gives

$$\frac{\overline{i_i^2}}{\Delta f} = 2q\left[I_B + K_1'\frac{I_B^a}{f} + \frac{I_C}{|\beta(j\omega)|^2}\right] \qquad (11.57)$$

where

$$K_1' = \frac{K_1}{2q} \qquad (11.57a)$$

and the burst noise term has been omitted for simplicity. The last term in parentheses in (11.57) is due to collector current noise referred to the input. At low frequencies this becomes $I_C/\beta_0^2$ and is negligible compared with $I_B$ for typical $\beta_0$ values. When this is true, $\overline{i_i^2}$ and $\overline{v_i^2}$ do not contain common noise sources and are *totally independent*. At high frequencies, however, the last term in (11.57) increases and can become dominant, and correlation between $\overline{v_i^2}$ and $\overline{i_i^2}$ may then be important since both contain a contribution from $\overline{i_c^2}$.

The equivalent input noise current spectral density given by (11.57) appears to come from a current $I_{eq}$ showing full shot noise, such that

$$\frac{\overline{i_i^2}}{\Delta f} = 2qI_{eq} \tag{11.58}$$

where

$$I_{eq} = I_B + K_1'\frac{I_B^a}{f} + \frac{I_C}{|\beta(j\omega)|^2} \tag{11.59}$$

and this is called the *equivalent input shot noise current*. This is a fictitious current composed of the base current of the device plus a term representing flicker noise and one representing collector-current noise transformed to the input. It is apparent from (11.59) that $I_{eq}$ is minimized by utilizing low bias currents in the transistor, and also using high-$\beta$ transistors. Since $\overline{i_i^2}$ is the dominant equivalent input noise generator in circuits where the transistor is fed from a high source impedance, low bias currents and high $\beta$ are obviously required for good noise performance under these conditions. Note that the requirement for low bias currents to minimize $\overline{i_i^2}$ conflicts with the requirement for *high* bias current to minimize $\overline{v_i^2}$.

Spectral density $\overline{i_i^2}/\Delta f$ of the equivalent input noise current generator can be plotted as a function of frequency using (11.57). This is shown in Fig. 11.24 for typical transistor parameters. In this case, the spectral density is frequency dependent at both low and high frequencies, the low-frequency rise being due to flicker noise and the high-frequency rise

**Figure 11.24** Equivalent input noise current spectral density of a bipolar transistor with $I_C = 100\ \mu\text{A}$, $\beta_0 = \beta_F = 100$, $f_T = 500$ MHz. Typical flicker noise is included.

being due to collector-current noise referred to the input. This input-referred noise rises at high frequencies because the transistor current gain begins to fall, and this is the reason for degradation in transistor noise performance observed at high frequencies.

Frequency $f_b$ in Fig. 11.24 is the point where the high-frequency noise asymptote intersects the midband asymptote. This can be calculated from (11.57) as follows:

$$\beta(jf) = \frac{\beta_0}{1 + j\dfrac{f}{f_T}\beta_0} \tag{11.60}$$

where $\beta_0$ is the low-frequency, small-signal current gain. Thus the collector current noise term in (11.57) is

$$2q\frac{I_C}{|\beta(jf)|^2} = 2q\frac{I_C}{\beta_0^2}\left(1 + \frac{f^2}{f_T^2}\beta_0^2\right) \simeq 2qI_C\frac{f^2}{f_T^2} \tag{11.61}$$

at high frequencies. Equation 11.61 shows that the equivalent input noise current spectrum rises as $f^2$ at high frequencies. Frequency $f_b$ can be calculated by equating (11.61) to the midband noise, which is $2q[I_B + (I_C/\beta_0^2)]$. For typical values of $\beta_0$, this is approximately $2qI_B$, and equating this quantity to (11.61) we obtain

$$2qI_B = 2qI_C\frac{f_b^2}{f_T^2}$$

and thus

$$f_b = f_T\sqrt{\frac{I_B}{I_C}} \tag{11.62}$$

The large-signal (or dc) current gain is defined as

$$\beta_F = \frac{I_C}{I_B} \tag{11.63}$$

and thus (11.62) becomes

$$f_b = \frac{f_T}{\sqrt{\beta_F}} \tag{11.64}$$

Using the data given in Fig. 11.24, we obtain $f_b = 50$ MHz for that example.

Once the above input noise generators have been calculated, the transistor noise performance with any source impedance is readily calculated. For example, consider the simple circuit of Fig. 11.25a with a source resistance $R_S$. The noise performance of this circuit can be represented by the *total* equivalent noise voltage $v_{iN}^2$ in series with the input of the

$(a)$    $(b)$

**Figure 11.25** Representation of circuit noise by a single equivalent input noise voltage generator. ($a$) Original circuit. ($b$) Equivalent representation.

circuit as shown in Fig. 11.25b. Neglecting noise in $R_L$ (this will be discussed later), and equating the total noise voltage at the base of the transistor in Figs. 11.25a and 11.25b, we obtain

$$v_{iN} = v_s + v_i + i_i R_S$$

If correlation between $v_i$ and $i_i$ is neglected this equation gives

$$\overline{v_{iN}^2} = \overline{v_s^2} + \overline{v_i^2} + \overline{i_i^2} R_S^2 \qquad (11.65)$$

Using (11.50) and (11.57) in (11.65) and neglecting flicker noise, we find

$$\frac{\overline{v_{iN}^2}}{\Delta f} = 4kTR_S + 4kT\left(r_b + \frac{1}{2g_m}\right) + R_S^2 2q\left[I_B + \frac{I_C}{|\beta(jf)|^2}\right] \qquad (11.66)$$

Equation 11.66 is similar to (11.46) if $r_b$ is small, as has been assumed.

■ **EXAMPLE**

Using data from the example in Section 11.4.1, calculate the total input noise voltage for the circuit of Fig. 11.25a in a bandwidth 0 to 1 MHz neglecting flicker noise and using (11.66). At low frequencies, (11.66) becomes

$$\frac{\overline{v_{iN}^2}}{\Delta f} = 4kT\left(R_S + r_b + \frac{1}{2g_m}\right) + R_S^2 2qI_B$$

$$= [1.66 \times 10^{-20}(500 + 200 + 130) + 500^2 \times 3.2 \times 10^{-19} \times 10^{-6}] \text{ V}^2/\text{Hz}$$

$$= (13.8 + 0.08) \times 10^{-18} \text{ V}^2/\text{Hz}$$

$$= 13.9 \times 10^{-18} \text{ V}^2/\text{Hz}$$

The total input noise in a 1-MHz bandwidth is

$$\overline{v_{iNT}^2} = 13.9 \times 10^{-18} \times 10^6 \text{ V}^2$$

$$= 13.9 \times 10^{-12} \text{ V}^2$$

and thus

$$v_{iNT} = 3.73 \text{ μV rms}$$

This is almost identical to the answer obtained in Section 11.4.1. However, the method described above has the advantage that once the equivalent input generators are known for any particular device, the answer can be written down almost by inspection and requires much less labor. Also, the relative contributions of the various noise generators are more easily seen. In this case, for example, the equivalent input noise current is obviously a negligible factor.

## 11.5.2 MOS Transistor Noise Generators

The equivalent input noise generators for a MOS field-effect transistor (MOSFET) can be calculated from the equivalent circuit of Fig. 11.26a. This circuit is to be made equivalent to that of Fig. 11.26b. The output noise in each case is calculated with a short-circuit load and $C_{gd}$ is neglected.

If the input of each circuit in Fig. 11.26 is short-circuited and resulting output noise currents $i_o$ are equated, we obtain

$$i_d = g_m v_i$$

Figure 11.26  (a) MOSFET small-signal equivalent circuit with noise generators. (b) Representation of (a) by two input noise generators.

and thus

$$\overline{v_i^2} = \frac{\overline{i_d^2}}{g_m^2} \tag{11.67}$$

Substituting $\overline{i_d^2}$ from (11.14) in (11.67) gives

$$\frac{\overline{v_i^2}}{\Delta f} = 4kT\frac{2}{3}\frac{1}{g_m} + K\frac{I_D^a}{g_m^2 f} \tag{11.68a}$$

The equivalent input noise resistance $R_{eq}$ of the MOS transistor is defined as

$$\frac{\overline{v_i^2}}{\Delta f} = 4kTR_{eq}$$

where

$$R_{eq} = \frac{2}{3}\frac{1}{g_m} + K'\frac{I_D^a}{g_m^2 f} \tag{11.68b}$$

and

$$K' = \frac{K}{4kT}$$

At frequencies above the flicker noise region, $R_{eq} = (2/3)(1/g_m)$. For $g_m = 1$ mA/V, this gives $R_{eq} = 667\ \Omega$, which is significantly *higher* than for a bipolar transistor at a comparable bias current (about 1 mA). The equivalent input noise-voltage spectral density for a typical MOS transistor is plotted versus frequency in Fig. 11.27. Unlike the bipolar transistor, the equivalent input noise-voltage generator for a MOS transistor contains flicker noise, and it is not uncommon for the flicker noise to extend well into the megahertz region.

In MOS field-effect transistors, the presence of electron energy states at the Si-SiO$_2$ interface tends to result in an input-referred flicker noise component that is larger than the thermal noise component for frequencies below 1 to 10 kHz for most bias conditions and device geometries. Thus, an accurate representation of the input-referred flicker noise

**Figure 11.27** Typical equivalent input noise voltage spectral density for a MOSFET.

component in MOS transistors is important for the optimization of the noise performance of MOS analog circuits.

The physical mechanisms giving rise to $1/f$ noise in MOS transistors have received extensive study.[18] The exact dependence of the magnitude of the input-referred flicker noise on transistor bias conditions and device geometry is dependent on the details of the process that is used to fabricate the device. In most cases, the magnitude of the input-referred flicker noise component is approximately independent of bias current and voltage and is inversely proportional to the active gate area of the transistor. The latter occurs because as the transistor is made larger, a larger number of surface states are present under the gate, so that an averaging effect occurs that reduces the overall noise. Its is also observed that the input-referred flicker noise is an inverse function of the gate-oxide capacitance per unit area. This is physically reasonable since the surface states can be thought of as a time-varying component of the surface-state charge $Q_{ss}$. From (1.139) this produces a time-varying component in the threshold voltage that is inversely proportional to $C_{ox}$. For a MOS transistor, then, the equivalent input-referred voltage noise can often be written as

$$\frac{\overline{v_i^2}}{\Delta f} = 4kT\frac{2}{3}\frac{1}{g_m} + \frac{K_f}{WLC_{ox}f}$$

(11.69)

A typical value for $K_f$ is $3 \times 10^{-24}$ V²-F, or $3 \times 10^{-12}$V²-pF.

The equivalent input noise-current generator $i_i^2$ for the MOSFET can be calculated by open-circuiting the input of each circuit in Fig. 11.26 and equating the output noise. This gives

$$i_i\frac{g_m}{j\omega C_{gs}} = i_g\frac{g_m}{j\omega C_{gs}} + i_d$$

and thus

$$i_i = i_g + \frac{j\omega C_{gs}}{g_m}i_d$$

(11.70)

Since $i_g$ and $i_d$ represent *independent generators*, (11.70) can be written as

$$\overline{i_i^2} = \overline{i_g^2} + \frac{\omega^2 C_{gs}^2}{g_m^2}\overline{i_d^2}$$

(11.71)

Ignoring (11.16) and substituting (11.14) and (11.15) in (11.17) gives

$$\frac{\overline{i_i^2}}{\Delta f} = 2qI_G + \frac{\omega^2 C_{gs}^2}{g_m^2}\left(4kT\frac{2}{3}g_m + K\frac{I_D^a}{f}\right) \tag{11.72}$$

In (11.72) the ac current gain of the MOS transistor can be identified as

$$A_I = \frac{g_m}{\omega C_{gs}} \tag{11.73}$$

and thus the noise generators at the output are divided by $A_I^2$ when referred back to the input. At low frequencies the input noise-current generator is determined by the gate leakage current $I_G$, which is very small ($10^{-15}$ A or less). For this reason, MOS transistors have noise performance that is *much superior* to bipolar transistors when the driving source impedance is large. Under these circumstances the input noise-current generator is dominant and is much smaller for a MOS transistor than for a bipolar transistor. It should be emphasized, however, that the input noise-*voltage* generator of a bipolar transistor in (11.50) is typically *smaller* than that of a MOS transistor in (11.68a) because the bipolar transistor has a larger $g_m$ for a given bias current. Thus for *low* source impedances, a bipolar transistor often has noise performance *superior* to that of a MOS transistor.

## 11.6 Effect of Feedback on Noise Performance

The representation of circuit noise performance with two equivalent input noise generators is extremely useful in the consideration of the effect of feedback on noise performance. This will be illustrated by considering first the effect of ideal feedback on the noise performance of an amplifier. Practical aspects of feedback and noise performance will then be considered.

### 11.6.1 Effect of Ideal Feedback on Noise Performance

In Fig. 11.28a a series-shunt feedback amplifier is shown where the feedback network is ideal in that the signal feedback to the input is a pure voltage source and the feedback network is unilateral. Noise in the basic amplifier is represented by equivalent input generators $\overline{v_{ia}^2}$ and $\overline{i_{ia}^2}$. The noise performance of the overall circuit is represented by equivalent input generators $\overline{v_i^2}$ and $\overline{i_i^2}$ as shown in Fig. 11.28b. The value of $\overline{v_i^2}$ can be found by short-circuiting the input of each circuit and equating the output signal. However, since the output of the feedback network has a zero impedance, the current generators in each circuit

(a)                                              (b)

**Figure 11.28** (a) Series-shunt feedback amplifier with noise generators. (b) Equivalent representation of (a) with two input noise generators.

are then short-circuited and the two circuits are identical only if

$$\overline{v_i^2} = \overline{v_{ia}^2} \tag{11.74}$$

If the input terminals of each circuit are open-circuited, both voltage generators have a floating terminal and thus no effect on the circuit, and for equal output it is necessary that

$$\overline{i_i^2} = \overline{i_{ia}^2} \tag{11.75}$$

Thus, for the case of *ideal feedback*, the equivalent input noise generators can be moved *unchanged outside* the feedback loop and the feedback has *no effect* on the circuit noise performance. Since the feedback reduces the circuit gain, the *output noise* is reduced by the feedback, but desired signals are reduced by the same amount and the signal-to-noise ratio will be unchanged. The above result is easily shown for all four possible feedback configurations described in Chapter 8.

## 11.6.2 Effect of Practical Feedback on Noise Performance

The idealized series-shunt feedback circuit considered in the previous section is usually realized in practice as shown in Fig. 11.29a. The feedback circuit is a resistive divider consisting of $R_E$ and $R_F$. If the noise of the basic amplifier is represented by equivalent input noise generators $\overline{i_{ia}^2}$ and $\overline{v_{ia}^2}$ and the thermal noise generators in $R_F$ and $R_E$ are included, the circuit is as shown in Fig. 11.29b. The noise performance of the circuit is to be represented by two equivalent input generators $\overline{v_i^2}$ and $\overline{i_i^2}$, as shown in Fig. 11.29c.

(a)

(b)

(c)

**Figure 11.29** (a) Series-shunt feedback circuit. (b) Series-shunt feedback circuit including noise generators. (c) Equivalent representation of (b) with two input noise generators.

In order to calculate $\overline{v_i^2}$, consider the inputs of the circuits of Fig. 11.29b and 11.29c short-circuited, and equate the output noise. It is readily shown that

$$v_i = v_{ia} + i_{ia}R + \frac{R_F}{R_F + R_E}v_e + \frac{R_E}{R_F + R_E}v_f \tag{11.76}$$

where

$$R = R_F \| R_E \tag{11.77}$$

Assuming that all noise sources in (11.76) are independent, we have

$$\overline{v_i^2} = \overline{v_{ia}^2} + \overline{i_{ia}^2}R^2 + 4kTR\Delta f \tag{11.78}$$

where the following substitutions have been made:

$$\overline{v_e^2} = 4kTR_E \Delta f \tag{11.79}$$

$$\overline{v_f^2} = 4kTR_F \Delta f \tag{11.80}$$

Equation 11.78 shows that in this practical case, the equivalent input noise voltage of the overall amplifier contains the input noise voltage of the basic amplifier plus two other terms. The second term in (11.78) is usually negligible, but the third term represents thermal noise in $R = R_E \| R_F$ and is often significant.

The equivalent input noise current $\overline{i_i^2}$ is calculated by open-circuiting both inputs and equating output noise. It is apparent that

$$\overline{i_i^2} \simeq \overline{i_{ia}^2} \tag{11.81}$$

since noise in the feedback resistors is no longer amplified, but appears only in shunt with the output. Thus the equivalent input noise current is *unaffected* by the application of feedback. The above results are true in general for series feedback at the input. For single-stage series feedback, the above equations are valid with $R_F \to \infty$ and $R = R_E$.

If the basic amplifier in Fig. 8.29 is an op amp, the calculation is slightly modified. This is due to the fact (shown in Section 11.8 and Fig. 11.39) that an op amp must be considered a three-port device for noise representation. However, if the circuit of Fig. 11.39 is used as the basic amplifier in the above calculation, expressions very similar to (11.78) and (11.81) are obtained.

Consider now the case of shunt feedback at the input, and as an example consider the shunt-shunt feedback circuit of Fig. 11.30a. This is shown in Fig. 11.30b with noise sources $v_{ia}^2$ and $i_{ia}^2$ of the basic amplifier, and noise source $i_f^2$ due to $R_F$. These noise sources are referred back to the input to give $\overline{v_i^2}$ and $\overline{i_i^2}$ as shown in Fig. 11.30c.

Open-circuiting the inputs of Fig. 11.30b and 11.30c, and equating output noise, we calculate

$$i_i = i_{ia} + \frac{v_{ia}}{R_F} + i_f \tag{11.82}$$

Assuming that all noise sources in (11.82) are independent, we find

$$\overline{i_i^2} = \overline{i_{ia}^2} + \frac{\overline{v_{ia}^2}}{R_F^2} + 4kT\frac{1}{R_F}\Delta f \tag{11.83}$$

Thus the equivalent input noise current with shunt feedback applied consists of the input noise current of the basic amplifier together with a term representing thermal noise in the feedback resistor. The second term in (11.83) is usually negligible. These results are true in general for shunt feedback at the input. A *general rule* for calculating the equivalent input noise contribution due to thermal noise in the feedback resistors is to follow the

**Figure 11.30** (*a*) Shunt-shunt feedback circuit. (*b*) Shunt-shunt feedback circuit including noise generators. (*c*) Equivalent representation of (*b*) with two input noise generators.

two-port methods described in Chapter 8 for calculating feedback-circuit loading on the basic amplifier. Once the shunt or series resistors representing feedback loading at the input have been determined, these same resistors may be used to calculate the thermal noise contribution at the input due to the feedback resistors.

If the inputs of the circuits of Fig. 11.30*b* and 11.30*c* are short-circuited, and the output noise is equated, it follows that

$$\overline{v_i^2} \simeq \overline{v_{ia}^2} \tag{11.84}$$

Equations 11.83 and 11.84 are true in general for shunt feedback at the input. They apply directly when the basic amplifier of Fig. 11.30 is an op amp, since one input terminal of the basic amplifier is grounded and the op amp becomes a two-port device.

The above results allow justification of some assumptions made earlier. For example, in the calculation of the equivalent input noise generators for a bipolar transistor in Section 11.5.1, collector-base capacitance $C_\mu$ was ignored. This capacitance represents single-stage *shunt feedback* and thus does *not* significantly affect the equivalent input noise generators of a transistor, *even if* the Miller effect is dominant. Note that there is no thermal noise contribution from the capacitor as there was from $R_F$ in Fig. 11.30. Also, the second term in (11.83) becomes $\overline{v_{ia}^2}/|Z_F|^2$ where $Z_F$ is the impedance of $C_\mu$. Since $|Z_F|$ is quite large at all frequencies of interest, this term is negligible.

■ **EXAMPLE**

As an example of calculations involving noise in feedback amplifiers, consider the wideband current-feedback pair whose ac schematic is shown in Fig. 11.31. The circuit is fed from a current source and the frequency response $|(i_o/i_i)(j\omega)|$ is flat with frequency to 100 MHz, where it falls rapidly. We calculate the minimum input signal $i_s$ required for an output signal-to-noise ratio greater than 20 dB. Data are as follows: $\beta_1 = \beta_2 = 100, f_{T1} = 300\,\text{MHz}, I_{C1} = 0.5\,\text{mA}, I_{C2} = 1\,\text{mA}, f_{T2} = 500\,\text{MHz}, r_{b1} = r_{b2} = 100\,\Omega$. Flicker noise is neglected.

**Figure 11.31**  An ac schematic of a current feedback pair.

The methods developed above allow the equivalent input noise generators for this circuit to be written down by inspection. A preliminary check shows that the noise due to the 20-kΩ interstage resistor and the base current noise of $Q_2$ are negligible. Using the rule stated in Section 11.2.2, we find that the 20-kΩ resistor contributes an equivalent noise current of 2.5 μA. The base current of $Q_2$ is 10 μA. Both of these can be neglected when compared to the 500 μA collector current of $Q_1$. Thus the input noise generators of the whole circuit are those of $Q_1$ moved outside the feedback loop, together with the noise contributed by the feedback resistors.

Using the methods of Chapter 8, we can derive the basic amplifier including feedback loading and noise sources for the circuit of Fig. 11.31 as shown in Fig. 11.32. The equivalent input noise-current generator for the overall circuit can be calculated from Fig. 11.32 or by using (11.83) with $R_F = 5.5$ kΩ. Since the circuit is assumed to be driven from a current source, the equivalent input noise voltage is not important. From (11.83)

$$\overline{i_i^2} = \overline{i_{ia}^2} + \frac{\overline{v_{ia}^2}}{(5500)^2} + 4kT\frac{1}{5500}\Delta f \qquad (11.85)$$

Using (11.57) and neglecting flicker noise, we have for $\overline{i_{ia}^2}$

$$\overline{i_{ia}^2} = 2q\left(I_B + \frac{I_C}{|\beta(jf)|^2}\right)\Delta f$$

and thus

$$\frac{\overline{i_{ia}^2}}{\Delta f} = 2q\left(5 + \frac{500}{|\beta|^2}\right)\times 10^{-6}\ \text{A}^2/\text{Hz} \qquad (11.86)$$

Substitution of (11.86) in (11.85) gives

$$\frac{\overline{i_i^2}}{\Delta f} = 2q\left(5 + \frac{500}{|\beta|^2}\right)\times 10^{-6} + \frac{\overline{v_{ia}^2}}{(5500)^2\Delta f} + 2q(9.1)\times 10^{-6} \qquad (11.87)$$

where the noise in the 5.5-kΩ resistor has been expressed in terms of the equivalent noise current of 9.1 μA.

Use of (11.50) gives

$$\frac{\overline{v_{ia}^2}}{\Delta f} = 4kT\left(r_{b1} + \frac{1}{2g_m}\right) = 4kT(126)$$

Division of this equation by $(5500)^2$ gives

$$\frac{\overline{v_{ia}^2}}{(5500)^2\,\Delta f} = 4kT\frac{1}{240,000} \qquad (11.88)$$

$$= 2q(0.2)\times 10^{-6} \qquad (11.89)$$

**Figure 11.32** Basic amplifier for the circuit of Fig. 11.31 including feedback loading and noise sources.

Thus the term involving $\overline{v_{ia}^2}$ in (11.87) is seen to be equivalent to thermal noise in a 240-k$\Omega$ resistor using (11.88), and this can be expressed as noise in 0.2 $\mu$A of equivalent noise current, as shown in (11.89). This term is negligible in this example, as is usually the case.

Combining all these terms we can express (11.87) as

$$\frac{\overline{i_i^2}}{\Delta f} = 2q\left(5 + \frac{500}{|\beta|^2} + 0.2 + 9.1\right) \times 10^{-6} \text{ A}^2/\text{Hz}$$

$$= 2q\left(14.3 + \frac{500}{|\beta|^2}\right) \times 10^{-6} \text{ A}^2/\text{Hz} \tag{11.90}$$

Equation 11.90 shows that the equivalent input noise-current spectral density rises at high frequencies (as $|\beta|$ falls) as expected for a transistor. In a single transistor without feedback, the equivalent input noise current also rises with frequency, but because the transistor gain falls with frequency, the output noise spectrum of a transistor without feedback always *falls* as frequency rises (see Section 11.4.1). However, in this case, the negative feedback holds the gain constant with frequency, and thus the *output* noise spectrum of this circuit will *rise* as frequency increases, until the amplifier band edge is reached. This is illustrated in Fig. 11.33, where the input noise-current spectrum, the amplifier frequency response squared, and the output noise-current spectrum (product of the first two) are shown. The current gain of the circuit is $A_I \simeq 11$.

The total output noise from the circuit $\overline{i_{oT}^2}$ is obtained by integrating the output noise spectral density, which is

$$\frac{\overline{i_o^2}}{\Delta f} = A_I^2 \frac{\overline{i_i^2}}{\Delta f} \tag{11.91}$$

Thus

$$\overline{i_{oT}^2} = \int_0^B A_I^2 \frac{\overline{i_i^2}}{\Delta f} df$$

$$= A_I^2 \int_0^B 2q\left(14.3 + \frac{500}{|\beta(jf)|^2}\right) \times 10^{-6} df \tag{11.92}$$

where (11.90) has been used and $A_I^2$ is assumed constant up to $B = 10^8$ Hz as specified earlier. The current gain is

$$\beta(jf) = \frac{\beta_0}{1 + j\dfrac{\beta_0 f}{f_{T1}}} \tag{11.93}$$

and

$$\frac{1}{|\beta(jf)|^2} = \frac{1}{\beta_0^2}\left(1 + \frac{\beta_0^2 f^2}{f_{T1}^2}\right) - \tag{11.94}$$

**Figure 11.33** Noise performance of the circuit of Fig. 11.32. (*a*) Equivalent input noise spectrum. (*b*) Frequency response squared. (*c*) Output noise spectrum.

Substitution of (11.94) in (11.92) gives

$$\overline{i_{oT}^2} = A_I^2 2q \times 10^{-6} \int_0^B \left[ 14.3 + \frac{500}{\beta_0^2}\left( 1 + \frac{\beta_0^2 f^2}{f_{T1}^2} \right) \right] df \tag{11.95}$$

$$= A_I^2 2q \times 10^{-6} \left[ 14.3f + \frac{500}{\beta_0^2} f + \frac{500}{f_{T1}^2}\frac{f^3}{3} \right]_0^B \tag{11.96}$$

Using $\beta_0 = 100$ and $B = 100\,\text{MHz} = f_{T1}/3$ gives

$$\overline{i_{oT}^2} = A_I^2 \times 2q \times 10^{-6}(14.3B + 18.6B) \tag{11.97}$$

$$\overline{i_{oT}^2} = A_I^2 \times 1.05 \times 10^{-15}\,\text{A}^2 \tag{11.98}$$

The equivalent input noise current is

$$\overline{i_{iT}^2} = \frac{\overline{i_{oT}^2}}{A_I^2} = 1.05 \times 10^{-15}\,\text{A}^2$$

and from this

$$i_{iT} = 32.4 \text{ nA rms} \tag{11.99}$$

Thus the equivalent input noise current is 32.4 nA rms and (11.97) shows that the frequency-dependent part of the equivalent input noise is dominant. For a 20-dB signal-to-noise ratio, input signal current $i_s$ must be greater than 0.32 $\mu$A rms.

## 11.7 Noise Performance of Other Transistor Configurations

Transistor configurations other than the common-emitter and common-source stages considered so far are often used in integrated-circuit design. For example, the 741 operational amplifier has a differential input stage with emitter followers driving common-base stages. The noise performance of these types of configuration will now be considered. To avoid repetition, the discussion will be directed toward bipolar devices only. However, all the results carry over directly to FET circuits.

### 11.7.1 Common-Base Stage Noise Performance

The common-base stage is sometimes used as a low-input-impedance current amplifier and, as mentioned above, is used as a level shift in the 741 op amp input stage. The noise performance of this circuit is thus of some interest.

A common-base stage is shown in Fig. 11.34a and the small-signal equivalent circuit is shown in Fig. 11.34b together with the equivalent input noise generators derived for a common-emitter stage. Since these noise generators represent the noise performance of the transistor in any connection, Fig. 11.34b is a valid representation of common-base noise performance. In Fig. 11.34c the noise performance of the common-base stage is represented in the standard fashion with equivalent input noise generators $\overline{v_{iB}^2}$ and $\overline{i_{iB}^2}$. These can be related to the common-emitter input generators by alternately short circuiting and open circuiting the circuits of Fig. 11.34b and 11.34c and equating output noise. It then follows that

$$\overline{i_{iB}^2} = \overline{i_i^2} \tag{11.100}$$

$$\overline{v_{iB}^2} = \overline{v_i^2} \tag{11.101}$$

Thus the equivalent input noise generators of common-emitter and common-base connections are the same and the noise performance of the two configurations is identical, even though their input impedances differ greatly.

Although the noise performances of common-emitter and common-base stages are nominally identical (for the same device parameters), there is one characteristic of the common-base stage that makes it generally *unsuitable* for use as a low-noise input stage. This is due to the fact that its current gain $\alpha \simeq 1$, and thus any noise current at the *output* of the common-base stage is referred directly back to the input *without* reduction. Thus a 10-k$\Omega$ load resistor that has an equivalent noise current of 5 $\mu$A produces this amount of equivalent noise current at the input. In many circuits this would be the dominant source of input current noise. The equivalent input noise currents of following stages are also referred back unchanged to the input of the common-base stage. This problem can be overcome in discrete common-base circuits by use of a transformer that gives current gain at the output of the common-base stage. This option is not available in integrated-circuit design unless resort is made to external components.

**Figure 11.34** (*a*) Common-base transistor configuration. (*b*) Common-base equivalent circuit with noise generators. (*c*) Common-base equivalent circuit with input noise generators.

## 11.7.2 Emitter-Follower Noise Performance

Consider the emitter follower shown in Fig. 11.35. The noise performance of this circuit can be calculated using the results of previous sections. The circuit can be viewed as a series-feedback stage and the equivalent input noise generators of the transistor can be moved unchanged back to the input of the complete circuit. Thus, if noise in $z_L$ is neglected, the emitter follower has the same equivalent input noise generators as the common-emitter and common-base stages. However, since the emitter follower has unity voltage gain, the equivalent input noise voltage of the following stage is transformed unchanged to the input, thus degrading the noise performance of the circuit. Noise due to $z_L$ must also be included, but since the follower output is taken at the emitter, which is a low impedance point, the noise due to $z_L$ is greatly attenuated compared with its effect on a series-feedback stage.

**Figure 11.35** Emitter-follower circuit.

### 11.7.3 Differential-Pair Noise Performance

The differential pair is the basic building block of linear integrated circuits and, as such, its noise performance is of considerable importance. A bipolar differential pair is shown in Fig. 11.36$a$, and the base of each device is generally independently accessible, as shown. Thus this circuit cannot in general be represented as a two-port, and its noise performance cannot be represented in the usual fashion by two input noise generators. However, the techniques developed previously can be used to derive an equivalent noise representation of the circuit that employs two noise generators at *each* input. This is illustrated in Fig. 11.36$b$, and a simpler version of this circuit, which employs only three noise generators, is shown in Fig. 11.36$c$.

The noise representation of Fig. 11.36$b$ can be derived by considering noise due to each device separately. Consider first noise in $Q_1$, which can be represented by input noise generators $\overline{v_i^2}$ and $\overline{i_i^2}$ as shown in Fig. 11.37$a$. These noise generators are those for a single transistor as given by (11.50) and (11.57). Transistor $Q_2$ is initially assumed *noiseless* and the impedance seen looking in its emitter is $z_{E2}$. Note that $z_{E2}$ will be a function of the impedance connected from the base of $Q_2$ to ground. As described in previous sections, the noise generators of Fig. 11.37$a$ can be moved unchanged to the input of the circuit (independent of $z_{E2}$) as shown in Fig. 11.37$b$. This representation can then be used to calculate the output noise produced by $Q_1$ in the differential pair for *any* impedances connected from the base of $Q_1$ and $Q_2$ to ground.

Now consider noise due to $Q_2$. In similar fashion this can be represented by noise generators $\overline{v_i^2}$ and $\overline{i_i^2}$, as shown in Fig. 11.37$c$. In this case $Q_1$ is assumed noiseless and $z_{E1}$ is the impedance seen looking in at the emitter of $Q_1$. If $Q_1$ and $Q_2$ are identical, the equivalent input noise generators of Fig. 11.37$b$ and 11.37$c$ are identical. However, since they are produced by different transistors, the noise generators of Fig. 11.37$b$ and 11.37$c$ are *independent*. The total noise performance of the differential pair including noise due to both $Q_1$ and $Q_2$ can thus be represented as shown in Fig. 11.36$b$, and this representation is valid for *any* source resistance connected to either input terminal. Noise generators $\overline{v_i^2}$ and $\overline{i_i^2}$ are basically those due to each transistor alone. If noise due to $R_L$ or following stages is significant, it should be referred back symmetrically to the appropriate input. In practice, current source $I_{EE}$ will also contain noise, and this can be included in the representation. However, if the circuit is perfectly balanced, the current-source noise represents a common-mode signal and will produce no differential output.

(a)

(b)

**Figure 11.36** (a) Differential-pair circuit. (b) Complete differential pair noise representation.

The noise representation of Fig. 11.36b can be simplified somewhat if the common-mode rejection of the circuit is high. In this case, one of the noise-voltage generators can be moved to the other side of the circuit, as shown in Fig. 11.36c. This can be justified if equal noise-voltage generators are added in series with each input and these generators are chosen such that the noise voltage at the base of $Q_2$ is canceled. This leaves two independent noise-voltage generators in series with the base of $Q_1$, and these can be represented as a single noise-voltage generator of value $\overline{2v_i^2}$. Thus for the circuit of Fig. 11.36c we can write

$$\overline{v_{dp}^2} = \overline{2v_i^2} \qquad (11.102)$$

**Figure 11.36** (c) Simplified noise representation.

**Figure 11.37** (a) ac schematic of a differential pair including noise due to $Q_1$ only. (b) ac schematic of a differential pair with noise due to $Q_1$ referred to the input. (c) ac schematic of a differential pair including noise due to $Q_2$ only.

$$\overline{i_{dp}^2} = \overline{i_i^2} \tag{11.103}$$

where $\overline{v_{dp}^2}$ and $\overline{i_{dp}^2}$ are the equivalent input noise generators of the differential pair.

The differential pair is often operated with the base of $Q_2$ grounded, and in this case the noise-current generator at the base of $Q_2$ is short circuited. The noise performance of the circuit is then represented by the two noise generators connected to the base of $Q_1$ in Fig. 11.36c. In this case the equivalent input noise-current generator of the differential pair is simply that due to one transistor alone, whereas the equivalent input noise-voltage generator has a mean-square value *twice* that of either transistor. Thus from a low source impedance, a differential pair has an equivalent input noise voltage 3 dB higher than a common-emitter stage with the same collector current as the devices in the pair.

## 11.8 Noise in Operational Amplifiers

Integrated-circuit amplifiers designed for low-noise operation generally use a simple common-emitter or common-source differential-pair input stage with resistive loads. Since the input stage has both current and voltage gain, the noise of following stages is generally not significant, and the resistive loads make only a small noise contribution. The noise analysis of such circuits is quite straightforward using the techniques described in this chapter. However, circuits of this type (the 725 op amp is an example) are inefficient in terms of optimizing important op amp parameters such as gain and bandwidth. For example, using active loads as in the 741 allows realization of very high gain in relatively few stages, and this is a significant advantage in circuit design. However, by their very nature, active loads amplify their own internal noise and cause considerable degradation of circuit noise performance. An approximate noise analysis of the 741 will now be made to illustrate these points and show the compromises involved in the design of general-purpose circuits.

A simplified schematic of the input stage of the 741 is shown in Fig. 11.38a. Transistor $Q_5$ may be considered to be diode connected as shown. Components $Q_5$, $Q_6$, $R_1$, and $R_3$ of the active load generate noise and contribute to the output noise at $i_o$. Since transistors $Q_3$ and $Q_4$ present a high impedance to the active load, the noise due to the active load can be calculated from the isolated portion of the circuit shown in Fig. 11.38b. Noise due to $Q_6$ and $R_3$ is represented by equivalent input noise generators $\overline{v_{i6}^2}$ and $\overline{i_{i6}^2}$. Since the diode $Q_5$ and resistor $R_1$ present a relatively low impedance at the base of $Q_6$, $\overline{i_{i6}^2}$ may be neglected. Using the results of Section 11.6.2 and neglecting flicker noise we have

$$\frac{\overline{v_{i6}^2}}{\Delta f} = 4kT \left( r_{b6} + \frac{1}{2g_{m6}} + R_3 \right) \tag{11.104}$$

The noise current due to diode $Q_5$ (using Section 11.2.1) is

$$\frac{\overline{i_5^2}}{\Delta f} = 2qI_{C5} \tag{11.105}$$

Since the diode small-signal impedance is $r_d = kT/qI_{C5} = 1/g_{m5}$, the diode noise can be transformed to a Thévenin equivalent voltage in series with the diode

$$\frac{\overline{v_5^2}}{\Delta f} = 2qI_{C5}\frac{1}{g_{m5}^2} = 4kT\frac{1}{2g_{m5}} \tag{11.106}$$

(b)

**Figure 11.38** (a) Simplified schematic of the 741 op amp input stage. (b) ac schematic (including noise) of the active load of the 741 op amp.

There will also be a noise voltage in the series with $Q_5$ due to its base resistance

$$\frac{\overline{v_{b5}^2}}{\Delta f} = 4kTr_{b5} \qquad (11.107)$$

Finally, the noise due to $R_1$ is

$$\frac{\overline{v_1^2}}{\Delta f} = 4kTR_1 \qquad (11.108)$$

Combining (11.106), (11.107), (11.108), and (11.104) into one noise-voltage generator $\overline{v_A^2}$ in series with the base of $Q_6$, we obtain

$$\frac{\overline{v_A^2}}{\Delta f} = 4kT\left(r_{b6} + \frac{1}{2g_{m6}} + R_3 + \frac{1}{2g_{m5}} + r_{b5} + R_1\right) \tag{11.109}$$

This noise generator can be evaluated as follows. The bias current in $Q_5$ and $Q_6$ is approximately 12 $\mu$A, giving $1/2g_{m5} = 1/2g_{m6} = 1.68$ k$\Omega$. Also $R_1 = R_3 = 1$ k$\Omega$ and a typical value of $r_b$ for small devices at low currents is 500 $\Omega$. Thus (11.109) becomes

$$\frac{\overline{v_A^2}}{\Delta f} = 4kT(5160) \tag{11.110}$$

This produces a noise output $i_{oA}$ where

$$i_{oA} \simeq \frac{1}{\dfrac{1}{g_{m6}} + R_3} v_A \simeq \frac{v_A}{3160} \tag{11.111}$$

Using (11.110) in (11.111) gives

$$\frac{\overline{i_{oA}^2}}{\Delta f} = 4kT\frac{5160}{3160^2} \tag{11.112}$$

This can be referred back to the input of the complete circuit of Fig. 11.38a in the standard manner. Consider the contribution to the equivalent input noise voltage. A voltage applied at the input of the full circuit of Fig. 11.38a gives

$$\frac{i_o}{v_s} = \frac{g_{m1}}{2}$$

and thus

$$\overline{i_o^2} = \frac{g_{m1}^2}{4}\overline{v_i^2} \tag{11.113}$$

Equating output noise current in (11.112) and (11.113), we obtain an equivalent input noise voltage due to $\overline{i_{oA}^2}$ as

$$\frac{\overline{v_{iA}^2}}{\Delta f} = 4kT\frac{5160}{3160^2}\frac{4}{g_{m1}^2} = 4kT\frac{5160}{3160^2}4 \times 2160^2 = 4kT(9640) \tag{11.114}$$

Thus the active load causes a contribution of 9.64 k$\Omega$ to the equivalent input noise resistance of the 741 op amp. The remaining important contributions can be written down by inspecting Fig. 11.38a. The equivalent input noise voltages of $Q_3$ and $Q_4$ at their own emitters were shown in Section 11.7.1 to be that of a common-emitter stage, and the results of Section 11.7.2 show that this noise can then be transformed unchanged to the input of the complete circuit because emitter followers $Q_1$ and $Q_2$ have unity voltage gain. The equivalent input noise currents of $Q_3$ and $Q_4$ at their own emitters have little influence because the source impedance seen by these devices looking into the emitters of $Q_1$ and $Q_2$ is fairly low. Thus these contributions are neglected in this approximate analysis. Finally, the results of Section 11.7.3 show that the equivalent input noise voltage squared of the differential input stage is just the sum of the values of each half of the circuit. This gives an input noise-voltage contribution due to $Q_1$–$Q_4$ of

$$\frac{\overline{v_{iB}^2}}{\Delta f} = 4kT\left(\frac{1}{2g_{m1}} + \frac{1}{2g_{m2}} + \frac{1}{2g_{m3}} + \frac{1}{2g_{m4}} + r_{b1} + r_{b2} + r_{b3} + r_{b4}\right) \tag{11.115}$$

Assuming a collector bias current of 12 μA for each device, and $r_b = 500\ \Omega$ in (11.115), we calculate

$$\frac{\overline{v_{iB}^2}}{\Delta f} = 4kT(6320) \tag{11.116}$$

Combining (11.114) and (11.116) gives, for the total input noise voltage for the 741,

$$\frac{\overline{v_i^2}}{\Delta f} = 4kT(16,000) \tag{11.117}$$

Thus the input noise voltage of the 741 is represented by an equivalent input noise resistance of 16 kΩ. This is a large value and is very close to the measured and computer-calculated result. Note that the active load is the main contributor to the noise. The magnitude of the noise voltage can be appreciated by noting that if a 741 is fed from a 1-kΩ source resistance for example, the circuit adds 16 times as much noise power as is contributed by the source resistance itself.

The calculations above concerned the equivalent input noise voltage of the 741. A similar calculation performed to determine the equivalent input noise current shows that this is dominated by the base current of the input device. The current gain of the input emitter followers is sufficient to ensure that following stage noise, including noise in the active loads, gives a negligible contribution to input current noise. Since the circuit is differential, the complete noise representation consists of the equivalent input noise voltage calculated above plus two equivalent input noise-current generators as shown in Fig. 11.39. This follows from the discussion of differential-pair noise performance in Section 11.7.3. The equivalent input noise-current generators are (neglecting flicker noise)

$$\frac{\overline{i_i^2}}{\Delta f} \simeq 2qI_B$$

where $I_B$ is the base current of $Q_1$ or $Q_2$ in Fig. 11.38a. Substitution of typical data gives

$$\frac{\overline{i_i^2}}{\Delta f} \simeq 2q(0.2 \times 10^{-6}) \tag{11.118}$$

In Chapter 6, a number of special op amp configurations were described, and the noise performance of these can now be considered. Two techniques were described for the reduction of the input bias current of an op amp, and these result in significantly different noise performance. First, the bias-current cancellation scheme of Fig. 6.52 functions by injecting input bias currents from $Q_6$ and $Q_8$ to cancel the base currents of $Q_1$ and $Q_2$. However, the collector currents of $Q_6$ and $Q_8$ contain noise that is *uncorrelated* with the base-current noise of $Q_1$ and $Q_2$ and thus the total input noise current is *increased* by this

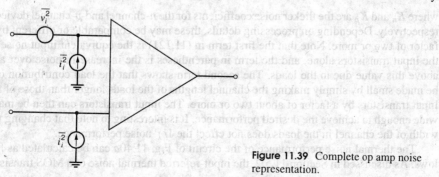

**Figure 11.39** Complete op amp noise representation.

arrangement and the noise performance is actually *degraded*. The equivalent input noise voltage is essentially unaffected and is determined by the bias currents in $Q_1$ and $Q_2$ since there is no active load on the input stage of this circuit.

The other circuit described for the reduction of the input bias current uses super-$\beta$ input devices as in Fig. 6.53. This technique results in significantly *reduced* input noise current and thus *improved* current noise performance. The equivalent input noise voltage in this circuit depends on the bias currents of the input devices.

Consider the case of the CMOS input stage shown in Fig. 11.40. If the noise in each MOS transistor is represented as shown by its equivalent input noise voltage generator, the equivalent input noise voltage of the circuit $\overline{v_{eqT}^2}$ can be calculated by equating the output current noise $\overline{i_o^2}$ for the circuits in Fig. 11.40a and Fig. 11.40b giving

$$\overline{v_{eqT}^2} = \overline{v_{eq1}^2} + \overline{v_{eq2}^2} + \left(\frac{g_{m3}}{g_{m1}}\right)^2 (\overline{v_{eq3}^2} + \overline{v_{eq4}^2}) \tag{11.119}$$

where it has been assumed that $g_{m1} = g_{m2}$ and that $g_{m3} = g_{m4}$. Thus, the input transistors contribute to the input noise directly while the contribution of the loads is reduced by the square of the ratio of their transconductance to that of the input transistors. The significance of this in the design can be further appreciated by considering the input-referred $1/f$ noise and the input-referred thermal noise separately.

The dependence of the $1/f$ portion of the device equivalent input noise-voltage spectrum on device geometry and bias conditions was considered earlier. Considerable discrepancy exists in the published data on $1/f$ noise, indicating that it arises from a mechanism that is strongly affected by details of device fabrication. The most widely accepted model for $1/f$ noise is that, for a given device, the gate-referred equivalent mean-square voltage noise is approximately independent of bias conditions in saturation and is inversely proportional to the gate capacitance of the device. The following analytical results are based on this model, but it should be emphasized that the actual dependence must be verified for each process technology and device type. Thus we let

$$\overline{v_{eq}^2} = \frac{K_f \Delta f}{C_{ox} W L f} \tag{11.120}$$

where the parameter $K_f$ is the flicker-noise coefficient. Utilizing this assumption, and using (11.119), we obtain for the equivalent input $1/f$ noise generator for the circuit of Fig. 11.40a

$$\overline{v_{1/f}^2} = \frac{2K_p}{f W_1 L_1 C_{ox}} \left(\frac{K_n \mu_n L_1^2}{K_p \mu_p L_3^2}\right) \Delta f \tag{11.121}$$

where $K_n$ and $K_p$ are the flicker noise coefficients for the n-channel and p-channel devices, respectively. Depending on processing details, these may be comparable or different by a factor of two or more. Note that the first term in (11.121) is the equivalent input noise of the input transistors alone, and the term in parentheses is the increase in noise over and above this value due to the loads. The second term shows that the load contribution can be made small by simply making the channel lengths of the loads longer than those of the input transistors by a factor of about two or more. The input transistors can then be made wide enough to achieve the desired performance. It is interesting to note that changing the width of the channel in the loads does not effect the $1/f$ noise performance.

The thermal noise performance of the circuit of Fig. 11.40a can be calculated as follows. As discussed in Section 11.5.2, the input-referred thermal noise of a MOS transistor

(a)

(b)

**Figure 11.40** (a) CMOS input stage device noise contributions. (b) Equivalent input noise representation.

is given by

$$\overline{v_{eq}^2} = 4kT\left(\frac{2}{3g_m}\right)\Delta f \tag{11.122}$$

Utilizing the same approach as for the flicker noise, we obtain for the equivalent input thermal noise of the circuit of Fig. 11.40a

$$\overline{v_{Th}^2} = 4kT\frac{4}{3\sqrt{2\mu_p C_{ox}(W/L)_1 I_D}}\left(1 + \sqrt{\frac{\mu_n(W/L)_3}{\mu_p(W/L)_1}}\right)\Delta f \tag{11.123}$$

where $I_D$ is the bias current in each device. Again, the first term represents the thermal noise from the input transistors and the term in parentheses represents the fractional increase in noise due to the loads. The term in parentheses will be small if the $W/L$ ratios are chosen so that the transconductance of the input devices is much larger than that of the loads. If this condition is satisfied, then the input noise is simply determined by the transconductance of the input transistors.

## 11.9 Noise Bandwidth

In the noise analysis performed thus far, the circuits considered were generally assumed to have simple gain-frequency characteristics with abrupt band edges as shown in Fig. 11.33b. The calculation of total circuit noise then reduced to an integration of the noise spectral density across this band. In practice, many circuits do not have such ideal gain-frequency characteristics, and the calculation of total circuit noise can be much more complex in those cases. However, if the equivalent input noise spectral density of a circuit is *constant* and independent of frequency (i.e., if the noise is white), we can simplify the calculations using the concept of *noise bandwidth* described below.

Consider an amplifier as shown in Fig. 11.41, and assume it is fed from a low source impedance so that the equivalent input noise voltage $\overline{v_i^2}$ determines the noise performance. Assume initially that the spectral density $\overline{v_i^2}/\Delta f = S_i(f) = S_{i0}$ of the input noise voltage is flat as shown in Fig. 11.42a. Further assume that the magnitude squared of the voltage gain $|A_v(jf)|^2$ of the circuit is as shown in Fig. 11.42b. The output noise-voltage spectral density $S_o(f) = \overline{v_o^2}/\Delta f$ is the product of the input noise-voltage spectral density and the square of the voltage gain and is shown in Fig. 11.42c. The *total* output noise voltage is obtained by summing the contribution from $S_o(f)$ in each frequency increment $\Delta f$ between zero and infinity to give

$$\overline{v_{oT}^2} = \sum_{f=0}^{\infty} S_o(f)\Delta f = \int_0^\infty S_o(f)df = \int_0^\infty |A_v(jf)|^2 S_{i0}df$$

$$= S_{i0}\int_0^\infty |A_v(jf)|^2 df \tag{11.124}$$

**Figure 11.41** Circuit with equivalent input noise voltage generator.

**Figure 11.42** Assumed parameters for the circuit of Fig. 11.41. (*a*) Equivalent input noise-voltage spectral density. (*b*) Circuit transfer function squared. (*c*) Output noise-voltage spectral density.

The evaluation of the integral of (11.124) is often difficult except for very simple transfer functions. However, if the problem is transformed into a *normalized* form, the integrals of common circuit functions can be evaluated and tabulated for use in noise calculations. For this purpose, consider a transfer function as shown in Fig. 11.43 with the same low-frequency value $A_{v0}$ as the original circuit but with an abrupt band edge at a frequency $f_N$. Frequency $f_N$ is chosen to give the *same* total output noise voltage as the original circuit when the same input noise voltage is applied. Thus

$$\overline{v_{oT}^2} = S_{i0}A_{v0}^2 f_N \tag{11.125}$$

If (11.124) and (11.125) are equated, we obtain

$$f_N = \frac{1}{A_{v0}^2} \int_0^\infty |A_v(jf)|^2 df \tag{11.126}$$

where $f_N$ is the *equivalent noise bandwidth* of the circuit. Although derived for the case of a voltage transfer function, this result can be used for any type of transfer function.

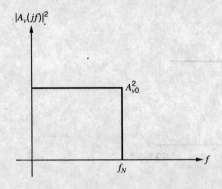

**Figure 11.43** Transfer function of a circuit giving the same output noise as a circuit with a transfer function as specified in Fig. 11.42*b*.

Note that the integration of (11.126) can be performed numerically if measured data for the circuit transfer function is available.

Once the noise bandwidth is evaluated using (11.126), the total output noise of the circuit is readily calculated using (11.125). The advantage of the form of (11.126) is that the circuit gain is *normalized* to its low-frequency value and thus the calculation of $f_N$ concerns only the frequency response of the circuit. This can be done in a general way so that whole classes of circuits are covered by one calculation. For example, consider an amplifier with a single-pole frequency response given by

$$A_v(jf) = \frac{A_{v0}}{1 + j\dfrac{f}{f_1}} \qquad (11.127)$$

where $f_1$ is the $-3$-dB frequency. The noise bandwidth of this circuit can be calculated from (11.126) as

$$f_N = \int_0^\infty \frac{df}{1 + \left(\dfrac{f}{f_1}\right)^2} = \frac{\pi}{2} f_1 = 1.57 f_1 \qquad (11.128)$$

This gives the noise bandwidth of *any* single-pole circuit and shows that it is larger than the $-3$-dB bandwidth by a factor of 1.57. Thus a circuit with the transfer function of (11.127) produces noise *as if* it had an abrupt band edge at a frequency $1.57 f_1$.

As the steepness of the transfer function fall-off with frequency becomes greater, the noise bandwidth approaches the $-3$-dB bandwidth. For example, a two-pole transfer function with complex poles at 45° to the negative real axis has a noise bandwidth only 11 percent greater than the $-3$-dB bandwidth.

■ **EXAMPLE**

As an example of noise bandwidth calculations, suppose a 741 op amp is used in a feedback configuration with a low-frequency gain of $A_{v0} = 100$ and it is desired to calculate the total output noise $v_{oT}$ from the circuit with a zero source impedance and neglecting flicker noise. If the unity-gain bandwidth of the op amp is 1.5 MHz, then the transfer function in a gain of 100 configuration will have a $-3$-dB frequency of 15 kHz with a single-pole response. From (11.128) the noise bandwidth is

$$f_N = 1.57 \times 15 \text{ kHz} = 23.5 \text{ kHz} \qquad (11.129)$$

Assuming that the circuit is fed from a zero source impedance, and using the previously calculated value of 16 k$\Omega$ as the equivalent input noise resistance, we can calculate the low-frequency input noise voltage spectral density of the 741 as

$$S_{i0} = \frac{\overline{v_i^2}}{\Delta f} = 4kT(16{,}000) = 2.66 \times 10^{-16} \, \text{V}^2/\text{Hz} \tag{11.130}$$

Using $A_{v0} = 100$ together with substitution of (11.129) and (11.130) in (11.125) gives, for the total output noise voltage,

$$\overline{v_{oT}^2} = 2.66 \times 10^{-16} \times 10^4 \times 23.5 \times 10^3 \, \text{V}^2 = 6.25 \times 10^{-8} \, \text{V}^2$$

■  and thus $v_{oT} = 250 \, \mu\text{V}$ rms.

The calculations of noise bandwidth considered above were based on the assumption of a flat input noise spectrum. This is often true in practice and the concept of noise bandwidth is useful in those cases, but there are also many examples where the input noise spectrum varies with frequency. In these cases, the total output noise voltage is given by

$$\overline{v_{oT}^2} = \int_0^\infty S_o(f) df \tag{11.131}$$

$$= \int_0^\infty |A_v(jf)|^2 S_i(f) df \tag{11.132}$$

where $A_v(jf)$ is the voltage gain of the circuit and $S_i(f)$ is the input noise-voltage spectral density. If the circuit has a voltage gain $A_{vS}$ at the frequency of the applied input signal, then the total equivalent input noise voltage becomes

$$\overline{v_{iT}^2} = \frac{1}{A_{vS}^2} \int_0^\infty |A_v(jf)|^2 S_i(f) df \tag{11.133}$$

$$= \int_0^\infty \left| \frac{A_v(jf)}{A_{vS}} \right|^2 S_i(f) df \tag{11.134}$$

Equation 11.134 shows that, in general, the total equivalent input noise voltage of a circuit is obtained by integrating the product of the input noise-voltage spectrum and the normalized voltage gain function.

One last topic that should be mentioned in this section is the problem that occurs in calculating the flicker noise in direct-coupled amplifiers. Consider an amplifier with an input noise spectral density as shown in Fig. 11.44a and a voltage gain that extends down to dc and up to $f_1 = 10$ kHz with an abrupt cutoff, as shown in Fig. 11.44b. Then, using (11.134), we can calculate the total equivalent input noise voltage as

$$\overline{v_{iT}^2} = \int_0^{f_1} S_i(f) df$$

$$= \int_0^{f_1} \left( 1 + \frac{1000}{f} \right) \times 10^{-16} df$$

$$= 10^{-16} [f + 1000 \ln f]_0^{f_1} \tag{11.135}$$

Evaluating (11.135) produces a problem since $\overline{v_{iT}^2}$ is infinite when a lower limit of zero is used on the integration. This suggests infinite power in the $1/f$ noise signal. In practice, measurements of $1/f$ noise spectra show a continued $1/f$ dependence to as low a frequency as is measured (cycles per day or less). This problem can be resolved only by noting that $1/f$ noise eventually becomes indistinguishable from thermal drift and that the lower limit of the integration must be specified by the period of observation. For example, taking a lower limit to the integration of $f_2 = 1$ cycle/day, we have $f_2 = 1.16 \times 10^{-5}$ Hz. Changing

Figure 11.44 (*a*) Input noise-voltage spectral density for a circuit. (*b*) Circuit transfer function squared.

the limit in (11.135) we find

$$\overline{v_{iT}^2} = 10^{-16}[f + 1000 \ln f]_{f_2}^{f_1}$$

$$= 10^{-16}\left[(f_1 - f_2) + 1000 \ln \frac{f_1}{f_2}\right] \quad (11.136)$$

Using $f_1 = 10$ kHz and $f_2 = 1.16 \times 10^{-5}$ Hz in (11.136) gives

$$\overline{v_{iT}^2} = 10^{-16}(10,000 + 20,600)$$

$$= 3.06 \times 10^{-12} \text{ V}^2$$

and thus

$$v_{iT} = 1.75 \ \mu\text{V rms}$$

If the lower limit of integration is changed to 1 cycle/year $= 3.2 \times 10^{-8}$ Hz, then (11.136) becomes

$$\overline{v_{iT}^2} = 10^{-16}(10,000 + 26,500)$$

$$= 3.65 \times 10^{-12} \text{ V}^2$$

and thus

$$v_{iT} = 1.9 \ \mu\text{V rms}$$

The noise voltage changes very slowly as $f_2$ is reduced further because of the ln function in (11.136).

### 11.10 Noise Figure and Noise Temperature

#### 11.10.1 Noise Figure

The most general method of specifying the noise performance of circuits is by specifying input noise generators as described above. However, a number of specialized methods of specifying noise performance have been developed that are convenient in particular situations. Two of these methods are now described.

The *noise figure* ($F$) is a commonly used method of specifying the noise performance of a circuit or a device. Its disadvantage is that it is limited to situations where the source impedance is resistive, and this precludes its use in many applications where noise performance is important. However, it is widely used as a measure of noise performance in communication systems where the source impedance is often resistive.

The definition of the noise figure of a circuit is

$$F = \frac{\text{input } S/N \text{ ratio}}{\text{output } S/N \text{ ratio}} \qquad (11.137)$$

and $F$ is usually expressed in decibels. The utility of the noise-figure concept is apparent from the definition, as it gives a direct measure of the signal-to-noise ($S/N$) ratio degradation that is caused by the circuit. For example, if the $S/N$ ratio at the input to a circuit is 50 dB, and the circuit noise figure is 5 dB, then the $S/N$ ratio at the output of the circuit is 45 dB.

Consider a circuit as shown in Fig. 11.45, where $S$ represents signal power and $N$ represents noise power. The input noise power $N_i$ is always taken as the noise in the *source resistance*. The output noise power $N_o$ is the total output noise including the circuit contribution and noise transmitted from the source resistance. From (11.137) the noise figure is

$$F = \frac{S_i}{N_i} \frac{N_o}{S_o} \qquad (11.138)$$

For an *ideal noiseless amplifier*, all output noise comes from the source resistance at the input, and thus if $G$ is the circuit power gain, then the output signal $S_o$ and the output noise $N_o$ are given by

$$S_o = GS_i \qquad (11.139)$$
$$N_o = GN_i \qquad (11.140)$$

Substituting (11.139) and (11.140) in (11.138) gives $F = 1$ or 0 dB in this case.

A useful alternative definition of $F$ may be derived from (11.138) as follows:

$$F = \frac{S_i}{N_i} \frac{N_o}{S_o} = \frac{N_o}{GN_i} \qquad (11.141)$$

Equation 11.141 can be written as

$$F = \frac{\text{total output noise}}{\text{that part of the output noise due to the source resistance}} \qquad (11.142)$$

$S_i, N_i$    Circuit    $S_o, N_o$

**Figure 11.45** Signal and noise power at the input and output of a circuit.

Note that since $F$ is specified by a *power* ratio, the value in decibels is given by $10\log_{10}$ (numerical ratio).

The calculations of the previous sections have shown that the noise parameters of most circuits vary with frequency, and thus the bandwidth must be specified when the noise figure of a circuit is calculated. The noise figure is often specified for a *small bandwidth* $\Delta f$ at a frequency $f$ where $\Delta f \ll f$. This is called the *spot noise figure* and applies to tuned amplifiers and also to broadband amplifiers that may be followed by frequency-selective circuits. For broadband amplifiers whose output is utilized over a wide bandwidth, an *average* noise figure is often specified. This requires calculation of the total output noise over the frequency band of interest using the methods described in previous sections.

In many cases, the most convenient way to calculate noise figure is to return to the original equivalent circuit of the device with its basic noise generators to perform the calculation. However, some insight into the effect of circuit parameters on noise figure can be obtained by using the equivalent input noise generator representation of Fig. 11.46. In this figure, a circuit with input impedance $z_i$ and voltage gain $G = v_o/v_x$ is fed from a source resistance $R_S$ and drives a load $R_L$. The source resistance shows thermal noise $\overline{i_s^2}$, and the noise of the circuit itself is represented by $\overline{i_i^2}$ and $\overline{v_i^2}$, assumed uncorrelated. The noise at the input terminals due to $\overline{v_i^2}$ and $\overline{i_i^2}$ is

$$v_{xA} = v_i \frac{z_i}{z_i + R_S} + i_i \frac{R_S z_i}{R_S + z_i}$$

and thus

$$\overline{v_{xA}^2} = \overline{v_i^2} \frac{|z_i|^2}{|z_i + R_S|^2} + \overline{i_i^2} \frac{|R_S z_i|^2}{|R_S + z_i|^2} \qquad (11.143)$$

The noise power in $R_L$ produced by $\overline{v_i^2}$ and $\overline{i_i^2}$ is

$$N_{oA} = \frac{|G|^2}{R_L} \overline{v_{xA}^2} = \frac{|G|^2}{R_L}\left(\overline{v_i^2} \frac{|z_i|^2}{|z_i + R_S|^2} + \overline{i_i^2} \frac{|R_S z_i|^2}{|R_S + z_i|^2}\right) \qquad (11.144)$$

The noise power in $R_L$ produced by source resistance noise generator $\overline{i_s^2}$ is

$$N_{oB} = \frac{|G|^2}{R_L} \frac{|R_S z_i|^2}{|R_S + z_i|^2} \overline{i_s^2} \qquad (11.145)$$

The noise in the source resistance in a narrow bandwidth $\Delta f$ is

$$\overline{i_s^2} = 4kT \frac{1}{R_S} \Delta f \qquad (11.146)$$

**Figure 11.46** Equivalent input noise representation for the calculation of noise figure.

Substituting (11.146) in (11.145) gives

$$N_{oB} = \frac{|G|^2}{R_L} \frac{|R_S z_i|^2}{|R_S + z_i|^2} 4kT \frac{1}{R_S} \Delta f \tag{11.147}$$

Using the definition of noise figure in (11.142) and substituting from (11.147) and (11.144), we find

$$F = \frac{N_{oA} + N_{oB}}{N_{oB}}$$

$$= 1 + \frac{N_{oA}}{N_{oB}} \tag{11.148}$$

$$= 1 + \frac{\overline{v_i^2}}{4kTR_S \Delta f} + \frac{\overline{i_i^2}}{4kT \dfrac{1}{R_S} \Delta f} \tag{11.149}$$

Equation 11.149 gives the circuit *spot* noise figure assuming negligible correlation between $\overline{v_i^2}$ and $\overline{i_i^2}$. Note that $F$ is *independent* of all circuit parameters $(G, z_i, R_L)$ except the source resistance $R_S$ and the equivalent input noise generators.

It is apparent from (11.149) that $F$ has a minimum as $R_S$ varies. For very low values of $R_S$, the $\overline{v_i^2}$ generator is dominant, whereas for large $R_S$ the $\overline{i_i^2}$ generator is most important. By differentiating (11.149) with respect to $R_S$, we can calculate the value of $R_S$ giving minimum $F$:

$$R_{S(\text{opt})}^2 = \frac{\overline{v_i^2}}{\overline{i_i^2}} \tag{11.150}$$

This result is true in general, even if correlation is significant. A graph of $F$ in decibels versus $R_S$ is shown in Fig. 11.47.

The existence of a minimum in $F$ as $R_S$ is varied is one reason for the widespread use of transformers at the input of low-noise tuned amplifiers. This technique allows the source impedance to be transformed to the value that simultaneously gives the lowest noise figure and causes minimal loss in the circuit.

For example, consider the noise figure of a bipolar transistor at low-to-moderate frequencies, where both flicker noise and high-frequency effects are neglected. From (11.50) and (11.57),

$$\overline{v_i^2} = 4kT \left( r_b + \frac{1}{2g_m} \right) \Delta f$$

$$\overline{i_i^2} = 2qI_B \Delta f = 2q \frac{I_C}{\beta_F} \Delta f$$

Substitution of these values in (11.150) gives

$$R_{S(\text{opt})} = \frac{\sqrt{\beta_F}}{g_m} \sqrt{1 + 2g_m r_b} \tag{11.151}$$

At this value of $R_S$, the noise figure is given by (11.149) as

$$F_{\text{opt}} \simeq 1 + \frac{1}{\sqrt{\beta_F}} \sqrt{1 + 2g_m r_b} \tag{11.152}$$

At a collector current of $I_C = 1$ mA, and with $\beta_F = 100$ and $r_b = 50\ \Omega$, (11.151) gives $R_{S(\text{opt})} = 572\ \Omega$ and $F_{\text{opt}} = 1.22$. In decibels the value is $10 \log_{10} 1.22 = 0.9$ dB. Note that $F_{\text{opt}}$ decreases as $\beta_F$ increases and as $r_b$ and $g_m$ decrease. However, increasing $\beta_F$

**Figure 11.47** Variation in noise figure $F$ with source resistance $R_S$.

and decreasing $g_m$ result in an *increasing* value of $R_{S(opt)}$, and this may prove difficult to realize in practice.

As another example, consider the MOSFET at low frequencies. Neglecting flicker noise, we can calculate the equivalent input generators from Section 11.5.2 as

$$\overline{v_i^2} \simeq 4kT\frac{2}{3}\frac{1}{g_m}\Delta f \tag{11.153}$$

$$\overline{i_i^2} \simeq 0 \tag{11.154}$$

Using these values in (11.149) and (11.150), we find that $R_{S(opt)} \to \infty$ and $F_{opt} \to 0$ dB. Thus the MOS transistor has excellent noise performance from a high source resistance. However, if the source resistance is low (kilohms or less) and transformers cannot be used, the noise figure for the MOS transistor may be worse than for a bipolar transistor. For source resistances of the order of megohms or higher, the MOS transistor usually has significantly *lower* noise figure than a bipolar transistor.

### 11.10.2 Noise Temperature

Noise temperature is an alternative noise representation and is closely related to noise figure. The noise temperature $T_n$ of a circuit is defined as the temperature at which the source resistance $R_S$ must be held so that the noise output from the circuit due to $R_S$ equals the noise output due to the circuit itself. If these conditions are applied to the circuit of Fig. 11.46, the output noise $N_{oA}$ due to the circuit itself is unchanged but the output noise due to the source resistance becomes

$$N'_{oB} = \frac{|G|^2}{R_L}\frac{|R_S z_i|^2}{|R_S + z_i|^2}4kT_n\frac{1}{R_S}\Delta f \tag{11.155}$$

Substituting for $N_{oB}$ from (11.147) in (11.155), we obtain

$$N'_{oB} = N_{oB}\frac{T_n}{T} \tag{11.156}$$

where $T$ is the circuit temperature at which the noise performance is specified (usually taken as 290°K). Substituting (11.156) in (11.148) gives

$$\frac{T_n}{T} = (F - 1) \tag{11.157}$$

where $F$ is specified as a ratio and is *not* in decibels.

Thus noise temperature and noise figure are directly related. The main application of noise temperature provides a convenient expanded measure of noise performance near $F = 1$ for very-low-noise amplifiers. A noise figure of $F = 2$ (3 dB) corresponds to $T_n = 290°K$ and $F = 1.1$ (0.4 dB) corresponds to $T_n = 29°K$.

# PROBLEMS

**11.1** Calculate the noise-voltage spectral density in $V^2/Hz$ at $v_o$ for the circuit in Fig. 11.48, and thus calculate the total noise in a 100-kHz bandwidth. Neglect capacitive effects, flicker noise, and series resistance in the diode.

**11.2** If the diode in Fig. 11.48 shows flicker noise, calculate and plot the output noise voltage spectral density at $v_o$ in $V^2/Hz$ on log scales from $f = 1$ Hz to $f = 10$ MHz. Flicker noise data: in (11.7) use $a = b = 1$, $K_1 = 3 \times 10^{-16}$ A.

+10 V

$20 \text{ k}\Omega$

$v_o$    **Figure 11.48** Diode circuit for Problems 11.1 and 11.2.

**11.3** Repeat Problem 11.2 if a 1000-pF capacitor is connected across the diode. Compare your result with a SPICE simulation.

**11.4** The ac schematic of an amplifier is shown in Fig. 11.49. The circuit is fed from a current source $i_S$ and data are as follows:

$$R_S = 1 \text{ k}\Omega \quad R_L = 10 \text{ k}\Omega \quad I_C = 1 \text{ mA}$$

$$\beta = 50 \quad r_b = 0 \quad r_o = \infty$$

Neglecting capacitive effects and flicker noise, calculate the total noise voltage spectral density at $v_o$ in $V^2/Hz$. Thus calculate the MDS at $i_S$ if the circuit bandwidth is limited to a sharp cutoff at 2 MHz. Compare your result with a SPICE simulation. (This will require setting up a bias circuit.)

**11.5** Calculate the total input- and output-referred noise voltages at 10 Hz, 100 kHz, and 1 GHz for the common-source amplifier shown in Fig. 7.2b. Assume that $W = 100 \text{ }\mu\text{m}$, $L = 1 \text{ }\mu\text{m}$, $I_D = 100 \text{ }\mu\text{A}$, $V_t = 0.6$ V, $k' = 194 \text{ }\mu\text{A/V}^2$, $t_{ox} = 80$ Å, $L_d = 0$, $X_d = 0$, and $K_f = 3 \times 10^{-24}$ F-V$^2$. Ignore gate-current noise in (11.15) and (11.16).

Let $R_S = 100 \text{ k}\Omega$ and $R_L = 10 \text{ k}\Omega$. Verify your result using SPICE. (Add dc sources for SPICE.)

**11.6** Calculate equivalent input noise voltage and current generators for the circuit of Fig. 11.49 (omitting $R_S$). Using these results, calculate the total equivalent input noise current in a 2-MHz bandwidth for the circuit of Fig. 11.49 with $R_S = 1 \text{ k}\Omega$ and compare with the result of Problem 11.4. Neglect correlation between the noise generators.

**Figure 11.49** Amplifier ac schematic for Problems 11.4 and 11.6

**11.7** Four methods of achieving an input impedance greater than 100 kΩ are shown in the ac schematics of Fig. 11.50.

(a) Neglecting flicker noise and capacitive effects, derive expressions for the equivalent input noise voltage and current generators of these circuits. For circuit (i) this will be on the *source* side of the 100 kΩ resistor.

(b) Assuming that following stages limit the bandwidth to dc-20 kHz with a sharp cutoff, calculate the magnitude of the total equivalent input noise voltage in each case. Then compare these circuits for use as low-noise amplifiers from low source impedances.

**11.8** Neglecting capacitive effects, calculate equivalent input noise voltage and current generators for circuit (iv) of Fig. 11.50, assuming that the spectral density of the flicker noise in the MOS transistor drain current equals that of the thermal noise at 100 kHz. Assuming that following stages limit the bandwidth to 0.001 kHz to 20 kHz with a sharp cutoff, calculate the magnitude of the total equivalent input noise voltage. Ignore gate-current noise in (11.15) and (11.16). (Assume $C_{gs} = 0$.)

**11.9** A BiCMOS Darlington is shown in Fig. 11.51. Neglecting frequency effects, calculate

$I_C = 0.5 \text{ mA}, \ \beta = 100, \ r_b = 100 \ \Omega$
(i)

$I_C = 0.5 \text{ mA}, \ \beta = 100, \ r_b = 100 \ \Omega$
(ii)

$I_C = 13 \ \mu\text{A}, \ \beta = 50, \ r_b = 100 \ \Omega$
(iii)

$g_m = 1 \text{ mA/V}$
(iv)

**Figure 11.50** Four ac schematics of circuits realizing an input resistance $R_i > 100 \text{ k}\Omega$.

the equivalent input noise voltage and current generators for this circuit, assuming that the dc value of $V_i$ is adjusted for $I_{C1} = 1$ mA. Device data is $\mu_n C_{ox} = 60 \ \mu\text{A/V}^2$, $V_t = 0.7$ V, $\lambda = 0$, $\gamma = 0$, $W = 100 \ \mu\text{m}$, $L = 1 \ \mu\text{m}$ for the MOSFET and $I_S = 10^{-16}$ A, $V_A = \infty$, $\beta = 100$, $r_b = 100 \ \Omega$ for the bipolar transistor. Use SPICE to check your calculation. Then add $C_{gs} = 150$ fF, $C_{sb} = 50$ fF for the MOSFET and $C_\mu = 50$ fF, $f_T = 10$ GHz for the bipolar transistor and use SPICE to determine the frequency where the spectral density of the equivalent input noise voltage generator $\overline{v_i^2}$ has doubled. Also use SPICE to determine the equiva-

lent input noise current spectral density at that frequency.

**11.10** The ac schematic of a low-input-impedance common-base amplifier is shown in Fig. 11.52.

**(a)** Calculate the equivalent noise voltage and current generators of this circuit at the emitter of $Q_1$ using $I_{C1} = I_{C2} = 1$ mA, $r_{b1} = r_{b2} = 0$, $\beta_1 = \beta_2 = 100$, $f_{T1} = f_{T2} = 400$ MHz. Neglect flicker noise but include capacitive effects in the transistors. Use SPICE to check your result.

**(b)** If $R_S = 5 \text{ k}\Omega$, and later stages limit the bandwidth to a sharp cutoff at 150 MHz, calculate the value of $i_S$ giving an output signal-to-noise ratio of 10 dB.

**11.11** A super-$\beta$ input stage is shown in Fig. 11.53a.

**(a)** Neglecting flicker noise and capacitive effects, calculate the equivalent input noise voltage and current generators $\overline{v^2}$ and $\overline{i^2}$ for this stage. *Data:* $I_{EE} = 1 \ \mu\text{A}$; $\beta_1 = \beta_2 = 5000$; $r_{b1} = r_{b2} = 500 \ \Omega$.

**(b)** If the circuit is fed from source resistances $R_S = 100 \text{ M}\Omega$ as shown in Fig. 11.53b, calculate the total equivalent input noise voltage at $v_s$ in a bandwidth of 1 kHz.

**11.12** Repeat Problem 11.11 if the bipolar transistors are replaced by MOS transistors with $I_G = 0.1$ fA and $g_m = 0.5$ mA/V. Assume $C_{gs} = 0$.

**11.13** If a 100-pF capacitor is connected across the diode in Fig. 11.48, calculate the noise

**Figure 11.51** BiCMOS Darlington circuit for Problem 11.9.

**Figure 11.52** An ac schematic of a common-base amplifier for Problem 11.10.

bandwidth of the circuit and thus calculate the *total* output noise at $v_o$. Neglect flicker noise and series resistance in the diode.

**11.14** A differential input stage is shown in Fig. 11.54.

**(a)** Neglecting flicker noise, calculate expressions for the equivalent input noise voltage and current generators at the base of $Q_1$. Use SPICE to check your result.

**(b)** Assuming the circuit has a dominant pole in its frequency response at 30 MHz and $R_S = 50\,\Omega$, calculate the total equivalent input and output noise voltages. *Data:* $\beta = 100$; $r_b = 200\,\Omega$.

**11.15** Calculate the source resistance giving minimum noise figure and the corresponding noise figure in decibels for a bipolar transistor with parameters

**(a)** $I_C = 2\,\text{mA}$   $\beta_F = 50$   $r_b = 100\,\Omega$

**(b)** $I_C = 10\,\mu\text{A}$   $\beta_F = 100$   $r_b = 300\,\Omega$

**11.16** Repeat Problem 11.15 if the transistor has a flicker noise corner frequency of 1 kHz. Calculate spot noise figure at 500 Hz.

**11.17** Repeat Problem 11.15 if the transistor has a 1-k$\Omega$ emitter resistor.

**11.18** **(a)** Neglecting flicker noise and capacitive effects, calculate the noise figure in decibels of the circuit of Fig. 11.54 with $R_S = 50\,\Omega$.

**(b)** If $R_S$ were made equal to (i) 100 $\Omega$ or (ii) 200 k$\Omega$, would the noise figure increase or decrease? Explain.

**(c)** If $R_S = 200$ k$\Omega$, and each device has a flicker noise corner frequency of 10 kHz, calculate the low frequency where the circuit spot noise figure is 20 dB.

**11.19** **(a)** A shunt-feedback amplifier is shown in Fig. 11.55. Using equivalent input noise generators for the device, calculate the spot noise

(a)

(b)

**Figure 11.53** Super-$\beta$ input stage for Problem 11.11.

**Figure 11.54** Differential-pair input stage for Problem 11.14.

figure of this circuit in decibels for $R_S = 10\ k\Omega$ using the following data.

$$I_C = 0.5\ mA \quad \beta = 50 \quad r_b = 100\ \Omega$$

Neglect flicker noise and capacitive effects.

**(b)** If the device has $f_T = 500$ MHz, calculate the frequency where the noise figure is 3 dB above its low-frequency value.

**11.20** **(a)** Neglecting capacitive effects, calculate the noise figure in decibels of the circuit of Fig. 11.52 with $R_S = 5\ k\Omega$. Use data as in Problem 11.10.

**(b)** If the flicker noise corner frequency for each device is 1 kHz, calculate the low frequency where the spot noise figure is 3 dB above the value in (a).

**11.21** Neglecting flicker noise, calculate the total equivalent input noise voltage for the MC1553 shown in Figure 8.21a. Use $\beta = 100, r_b = 100\ \Omega$ and assume a sharp cutoff in the frequency response at 50 MHz. Then calculate the average noise figure of the circuit with a source resistance of 50 $\Omega$.

**11.22** Calculate the total equivalent input noise current for the shunt-shunt feedback circuit of Fig. 8.48 in a bandwidth from 0.01 Hz to 100 kHz. Use the MOS transistor data in Problem 11.5. Ignore gate-current noise in (11.15) and (11.16).

**11.23** Repeat Problem 11.22 if the MOS transistors in Fig. 8.48 are replaced by bipolar transistors. Assume that $\beta = 200, r_b = 300\ \Omega, I_C = 1$ mA and the flicker noise corner frequency is $f_a = 5$ kHz. Neglect capacitive effects.

**11.24** The BiCMOS amplifier of Fig. 3.78 is to be used as a low-noise transimpedance amplifier. The input is fed from a current source with a shunt source capacitance of $C_S = 1$ pF. Assuming that $C_S$ and $C_{gs1} = 0.5$ pF dominate the frequency response, calculate the equivalent input noise current spectral density of the circuit at low frequencies and at the $-3$-dB frequency of the transfer function. Use data as in Problem 3.17. Use SPICE to check your result, and also to investigate the effect of adding $r_b = 200\ \Omega$ to the bipolar model.

**11.25** A MOS current source of the type shown in Fig. 4.4 is to be designed to achieve minimum output current noise. The two transistors must be identical and the total gate area of the two transistors combined must not exceed 10 $\mu m^2$. Choose the $W$ and $L$ of the devices under two different assumptions:

**(a)** $1/f$ noise dominates.

**(b)** Thermal noise dominates.

**Figure 11.55** An ac schematic of a single-stage shunt-feedback amplifier for Problem 11.19.

Assume that $L_d$ and $X_d$ are zero. The minimum allowed transistor length or width is 0.6 μm. Verify your design using SPICE.

**11.26** Calculate the equivalent input noise voltage at 100 Hz, 1 kHz, and 10 kHz for the CMOS op amp shown in Fig. 6.59. Use the MOS parameters in Table 2.4, and assume that $X_d = 0.1$ μm at the operating point for all transistors operating in the active region. For this problem, assume that the gate of $M_9$ is attached to the positive power supply, and that the $W/L$ of $M_9$ has been optimally chosen to cancel the right-half-plane zero. The flicker-noise coefficient for all transistors is $K_f = 3 \times 10^{-24}$ F-V$^2$. Ignore gate-current noise in (11.15) and (11.16). Verify your result using SPICE.

**11.27** Use SPICE to verify the noise analysis of the 741 op amp given in Section 11.8. Then add

flicker noise generators assuming $a = 1$ in (11.13) and the transistor flicker noise corner frequency is 1 kHz. Which device dominates the noise performance at 1 Hz?

**11.28 (a)** At what frequency are the noise spectral densities, $\overline{i_g^2}/\Delta f$, for the gate-current noise in (11.15) and (11.16) equal? Assume that $W = 50$ μm, $L = 0.5$ μm, $I_G = 0.05$ fA, $I_D = 100$ μA, $V_t = 0.6$ V, $k' = 194$ μA/V$^2$, $t_{ox} = 80$ Å, $L_d = 0$, $X_d = 0$, and $K_f = 3 \times 10^{-24}$ F-V$^2$.

**(b)** For this transistor, considering only the gate-current noise, in what bandwidth (from 0 to $f_{BW}$) are the total input noise currents due to shot noise in (11.15) and coupled thermal noise in (11.16) equal?

# REFERENCES

1. M. Schwartz. *Information Transmission, Modulation, and Noise.* McGraw-Hill, New York, 1959, Chapter 5.

2. W. B. Davenport, Jr., and W. L. Root. *An Introduction to the Theory of Random Signals and Noise.* McGraw-Hill, New York, 1958, Chapter 7.

3. J. L. Lawson and G. E. Uhlenbeck. *Threshold Signals.* McGraw-Hill, New York, 1950, Chapter 4.

4. A. van der Ziel. *Noise.* Prentice-Hall, New York, 1954, Chapter 5.

5. W. B. Davenport, Jr., and W. L. Root, op. cit., Chapter 9.

6. J. L. Plumb and E. R. Chenette. "Flicker Noise Transistors," *IEEE Transactions on Electron Devices,* Vol. ED-10, pp. 304–308, September 1963.

7. R. C. Jaeger and A. J. Broderson. "Low-Frequency Noise Sources in Bipolar Junction Transistors," *IEEE Transactions on Electron Devices,* Vol. ED-17, pp. 128–134, February 1970.

8. M. Nishida. "Effects of Diffusion-Induced Dislocations on the Excess Low-Frequency Noise," *IEEE Transactions on Electron Devices,* Vol. ED-20, pp. 221–226, March 1973.

9. R. G. Meyer, L. Nagel, and S. K. Lui. "Computer Simulation of 1/f Noise Performance of Electronic Circuits," *IEEE Journal of Solid-State Circuits,* Vol. SC-8, pp. 237–240, June 1973.

10. R. H. Haitz. "Controlled Noise Generation with Avalanche Diodes," *IEEE Transactions on* *Electron Devices,* Vol. ED-12, pp. 198–207, April 1965.

11. D. G. Peterson. "Noise Performance of Transistors," *IRE Transactions on Electron Devices,* Vol. Ed-9, pp. 296–303, May 1962.

12. A. van der Ziel. *Noise in Solid State Devices and Circuits.* Wiley, New York, 1986.

13. A. A. Abidi. "High-Frequency Noise Measurements on FETs with Small Dimensions," *IEEE Transactions on Electron Devices,* Vol. 33, no. 11, pp. 1801–1805, November 1986.

14. D. K. Shaeffer and T. H. Lee. "A 1.5-V, 1.5-GHz CMOS Low Noise Amplifier," *IEEE Journal of Solid-State Circuits,* Vol. 32, no. 5, pp. 745–759, May 1997

15. W. R. Bennett. "Methods of Solving Noise Problems," *Proceedings, IRE,* Vol. 44, pp. 609–638, May 1956.

16. E. M. Cherry and D. E. Hooper. *Amplifying Devices and Low-Pass Amplifier Design.* Wiley, New York, 1968, Chapter 8.

17. H. A. Haus, et al. "Representation of Noise in Linear Twoports," *Proceedings, IRE,* Vol. 48, pp. 69–74, January 1960.

18. M. B. Das and J. M. Moore. "Measurements and Interpretation of Low-Frequency Noise in FETS," *IEEE Transactions on Electron Devices,* Vol. ED-21, pp. 247–257, April 1974.

# Fully Differential Operational Amplifiers

## 12.1 Introduction

The analysis of integrated-circuit operational amplifiers (op amps) in Chapter 6 focused on op amps with single-ended outputs. The topic of this chapter is fully differential op amps, which have a differential input and produce a differential output. Fully differential op amps are widely used in modern integrated circuits because they have some advantages over their single-ended counterparts. They provide a larger output voltage swing and are less susceptible to common-mode noise. Also, even-order nonlinearities are not present in the differential output of a balanced circuit. (A *balanced* circuit is symmetric with perfectly matched elements on either side of an axis of symmetry.) A disadvantage of fully differential op amps is that they require two matched feedback networks and a common-mode feedback circuit to control the common-mode output voltage.

In this chapter, the properties of fully differential amplifiers are presented first, followed by some common-mode feedback approaches. A number of fully differential CMOS op amps are covered. Some of the terminology used in this chapter was introduced for a simple fully differential amplifier (a differential pair with resistive loads) in Section 3.5. In most of the chapter, the circuits are assumed to be perfectly balanced. The effects of imbalance are considered in Section 12.7. The circuits in this chapter are CMOS; however, most of the techniques and topologies described can be readily extended to bipolar technologies.

## 12.2 Properties of Fully Differential Amplifiers[1,2]

A fully differential feedback amplifier is shown in Fig. 12.1a. It differs from the single-ended feedback amplifier in Fig. 12.1b in the following two ways. The op amp has two outputs, and two identical resistive networks provide feedback. While many fully differential op-amp topologies exist, the simple fully differential amplifier in Fig. 12.2 will be used for illustration purposes. It consists of a differential pair $M_1$-$M_2$, active loads $M_3$ and $M_4$, and tail current source $M_5$.

Fully differential op amps provide a larger output voltage swing than their single-ended counterparts, which is important when the power-supply voltage is small. The larger output voltage swing provided by a fully differential op amp can be explained using the two feedback circuits in Fig. 12.1. Assume that each op-amp output, $V_{o1}$, $V_{o2}$, or $V_o$, can swing up to $V_{max}$ and down to $V_{min}$. For the single-ended-output circuit in Fig. 12.1b, the peak-to-peak output voltage can be as large as $V_{max} - V_{min}$. In the fully differential circuit in Fig. 12.1a, if $V_{o1}$ swings up to $V_{max}$ and $V_{o2}$ swings down to $V_{min}$, the peak differential output is $V_{max} - V_{min}$. Therefore, the peak-to-peak differential output is $2(V_{max} - V_{min})$. Thus, the output swing of a fully differential op amp is twice as large as that of a similar op amp with a single-ended output.

(a)

(b)

**Figure 12.1.** (a) Fully differential and (b) single-ended inverting amplifiers.

This larger output swing can result in a higher signal-to-noise ratio. Ignoring the noise from the op amp and from the feedback resistor $R_3$, we see that thermal noise associated with the $R_1$ input resistors is the only source of noise. In the single-ended circuit in Fig. 12.1b, the output noise power due to resistor $R_1$ is

$$\overline{v_{oN}^2}(s.e.) = \left(1 + \frac{R_3}{R_1}\right)^2 4kTR_1(BW_N) \qquad (12.1)$$

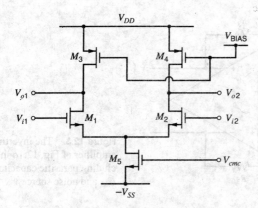

**Figure 12.2.** A simple, one-stage, fully differential op amp.

where $BW_N$ is the equivalent noise bandwidth of the closed-loop amplifier. In the fully differential amplifier in Fig. 12.1, the differential output noise power due to the two $R_1$ resistors is

$$\overline{v_{oN}^2}(diff) = 2\left(1 + \frac{R_3}{R_1}\right)^2 4kTR_1(BW_N) \tag{12.2}$$

because the output noise terms from the two $R_1$ resistors are uncorrelated and hence their contributions add together to give the total output noise power. From (12.1) and (12.2), the output noise power in the fully differential circuit is twice that in the single-ended circuit. Since the peak output signal in the differential circuit is twice that in the single-ended circuit, the maximum output signal power is four times that in the single-ended circuit. The maximum output signal-to-noise ratio (SNR) for a maximum sinusoidal output signal with amplitude $V_{sig(peak)}$ is given by

$$\text{SNR}_{\text{max}} = \frac{\text{maximum output signal power}}{\text{output noise power}} = \frac{\dfrac{V_{sig(peak)}^2}{2}}{\overline{v_{oN}^2}} \tag{12.3}$$

This SNR is twice as large, or 3 dB larger, for the fully differential circuit when compared to the single-ended circuit if the same resistance $R_1$ is used in both circuits and $R_1$ is the dominant noise source.

Fully differential circuits are less susceptible than their single-ended counterparts to common-mode (CM) noise, such as noise on the power supplies that is generated by digital circuits that are integrated on the same substrate as the analog circuits. To explain the reduced sensitivity to CM noise, consider the circuit in Fig. 12.3. This circuit is the same as Fig. 12.1a with two capacitors $C_{ip}$ added. Each capacitor connects from an op-amp input to voltage source $v_n$. Here $C_{ip}$ models parasitic capacitance from the substrate to each op-amp input, and $v_n$ models noise that exists on the power-supply voltage that connects to the substrate. The parasitic capacitors couple equal signals to the op-amp inputs, causing a CM disturbance at the op-amp input. If the op amp is perfectly balanced and has zero CM gain, this CM noise does not affect the CM output voltage. If the op-amp CM gain is nonzero but small, $v_n$ causes a small CM output voltage but does not affect the differential output voltage if the circuit is perfectly balanced. This capacitive coupling to the op-amp inputs can cause a nonzero differential-mode (DM) output voltage if the circuit is not perfectly balanced. For example, mismatch between the $C_{ip}$ capacitors causes the coupled noise at the two op-amp inputs to be unequal and introduces a differential noise signal across the op-amp inputs.

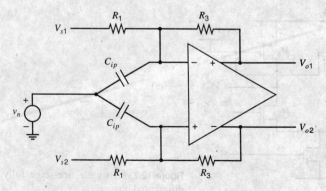

Figure 12.3.  The inverting amplifier of Fig. 12.1a including parasitic capacitors $C_{ip}$ and noise source $v_n$.

Even without the capacitive coupling to the substrate in Fig. 12.3, noise on the positive or negative power supply can couple to the op-amp outputs through the transistors in the op amp (see Section 6.2.6). If the circuit is balanced, such coupling is the same at each op-amp output. Therefore, power-supply noise in a balanced circuit alters the CM output but does not affect the DM output.

Even-order nonlinearities are not present in the differential output of a balanced circuit. The cancellation of even-order nonlinearities can be explained using Fig. 12.1a. Assume that the circuit is perfectly balanced but is not perfectly linear. First, consider the case when the inputs are $V_{s1} = V_a$ and $V_{s2} = V_b$, and let the resulting output voltages be $V_{o1} = V_x$ and $V_{o2} = V_y$. In this case, the differential input and output are

$$V_{sd} = V_a - V_b \quad \text{and} \quad V_{od} = V_x - V_y \qquad (12.4)$$

Next, consider the circuit with the inputs swapped; that is, $V_{s1} = V_b$ and $V_{s2} = V_a$. Then the output voltages will also be swapped ($V_{o1} = V_y$ and $V_{o2} = V_x$) because the circuit is symmetric. In this second case,

$$V_{sd} = V_b - V_a = -(V_a - V_b) \quad \text{and} \quad V_{od} = V_y - V_x = -(V_x - V_y) \quad (12.5)$$

Equations 12.4 and 12.5 show that changing the polarity of the differential input of a balanced circuit causes only a polarity change in the differential output voltage. Therefore, the differential input-output characteristic $f()$ is an odd function; that is, if $V_{od} = f(V_{id})$, then $-V_{od} = f(-V_{id})$. Hence, the differential transfer characteristic of a balanced amplifier exhibits only odd-order nonlinearities, so only odd-order distortion can appear in the differential output when a differential input is applied. Even-order distortion may exist in each individual output $V_{o1}$ and $V_{o2}$, but such distortion in these output voltages is identical and cancels when they are subtracted to form $V_{od}$.

In a balanced, fully differential amplifier, the small-signal differential output voltage is proportional to the small-signal differential input voltage but is independent of the CM input voltage, as was shown in Section 3.5.4. Similarly, the small-signal CM output voltage is proportional to the small-signal CM input voltage but is independent of the differential input voltage.

## 12.3 Small-Signal Models for Balanced Differential Amplifiers

A balanced signal source driving a balanced, fully differential amplifier is shown in Fig. 12.4. A $T$-network small-signal model for the balanced signal source is shown in

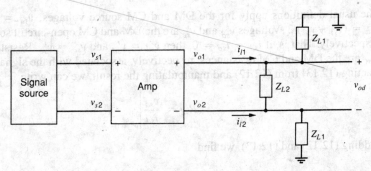

**Figure 12.4.** A block diagram of a fully differential signal source and amplifier driving a complex load.

**Figure 12.5.** A model for a differential signal source.

Fig. 12.5. Equations that describe this model are found as follows. Applying KVL from $v_{s1}$ to ground,

$$v_{s1} = \frac{v'_{sd}}{2} + v'_{sc} + \frac{R_{sd}}{2}i_{s1} + \left(\frac{R_{sc}}{2} - \frac{R_{sd}}{4}\right)(i_{s1} + i_{s2}) \qquad (12.6)$$

Rearranging gives

$$v_{s1} = \frac{v'_{sd}}{2} + v'_{sc} + \frac{R_{sd}}{2}\frac{i_{s1} - i_{s2}}{2} + R_{sc}\frac{i_{s1} + i_{s2}}{2} \qquad (12.7)$$

Define

$$i_{sd} = \frac{i_{s1} - i_{s2}}{2} \qquad (12.8)$$

$$i_{sc} = \frac{i_{s1} + i_{s2}}{2} \qquad (12.9)$$

Then

$$i_{s1} = i_{sd} + i_{sc} \qquad (12.10)$$

$$i_{s2} = -i_{sd} + i_{sc} \qquad (12.11)$$

Substituting (12.8) and (12.9) in (12.7) gives

$$v_{s1} = \frac{v'_{sd}}{2} + v'_{sc} + \frac{R_{sd}}{2}i_{sd} + R_{sc}i_{sc} \qquad (12.12)$$

A similar analysis applied from $v_{s2}$ to ground yields

$$v_{s2} = -\frac{v'_{sd}}{2} + v'_{sc} - \frac{R_{sd}}{2}i_{sd} + R_{sc}i_{sc} \qquad (12.13)$$

The usual definitions apply for the DM and CM source voltages: $v_{sd} = v_{s1} - v_{s2}$ and $v_{sc} = (v_{s1} + v_{s2})/2$. Voltages $v'_{sd}$ and $v'_{sc}$ are the DM and CM open-circuit source voltages, respectively. That is, if $i_{sd} = i_{sc} = 0$, then $v_{sd} = v'_{sd}$ and $v_{sc} = v'_{sc}$. Resistances $R_{sd}$ and $R_{sc}$ are the DM and CM resistances, respectively, associated with the signal source. Subtracting (12.13) from (12.12) and manipulating the result, we can write

$$R_{sd} = \left.\frac{v_{sd}}{i_{sd}}\right|_{v'_{sd}=0} \qquad (12.14)$$

Adding (12.12) and (12.13), we find

$$R_{sc} = \left.\frac{v_{sc}}{i_{sc}}\right|_{v'_{sc}=0} \qquad (12.15)$$

(a)

(b)

**Figure 12.6.** Models for the input impedance of a fully differential amplifier: (a) a T-network model and (b) a $\pi$-network model.

These simple expressions result from the definitions of the CM and DM currents in (12.8) and (12.9), and the standard definitions for the CM and DM voltages.

Two equivalent models for the inputs of the amplifier in Fig. 12.4 are shown in Fig. 12.6. These models are extensions of Fig. 3.61 and (3.197) and (3.198), which were derived to model the inputs for a differential pair with resistive loads. Two equivalent models for the output ports of the amplifier are shown in Fig. 12.7. The equations that describe the model in Fig. 12.7a, which uses voltage-controlled voltage sources, are

$$v_{o1} = a_{dm}\frac{v_{id}}{2} + a_{cm}v_{ic} + \frac{R_{od}}{2}i_{od} + R_{oc}i_{oc} \tag{12.16}$$

$$v_{o2} = -a_{dm}\frac{v_{id}}{2} + a_{cm}v_{ic} - \frac{R_{od}}{2}i_{od} + R_{oc}i_{oc} \tag{12.17}$$

where

$$a_{dm} = \frac{v_{od}}{v_{id}}\bigg|_{i_{od}=0} \qquad a_{cm} = \frac{v_{oc}}{v_{ic}}\bigg|_{i_{oc}=0} \tag{12.18}$$

$$R_{od} = \frac{v_{od}}{i_{od}}\bigg|_{v_{id}=0} \qquad R_{oc} = \frac{v_{oc}}{i_{oc}}\bigg|_{v_{ic}=0} \tag{12.19}$$

and $v_{id} = v_{i1} - v_{i2}$, $v_{ic} = (v_{i1} + v_{i2})/2$, $v_{od} = v_{o1} - v_{o2}$, $v_{oc} = (v_{o1} + v_{o2})/2$, $i_{od} = (i_{o1} - i_{o2})/2$, and $i_{oc} = (i_{o1} + i_{o2})/2$. Figure 12.7b shows an alternative model that uses voltage-controlled current sources, and the corresponding equations are

$$i_{o1} = i_{od} + i_{oc} = G_{md}v_{id} + G_{mc}v_{ic} + \frac{v_{od}}{R_{od}} + \frac{v_{oc}}{R_{oc}} \tag{12.20}$$

$$i_{o2} = -i_{od} + i_{oc} = -G_{md}v_{id} + G_{mc}v_{ic} - \frac{v_{od}}{R_{od}} + \frac{v_{oc}}{R_{oc}} \tag{12.21}$$

where

$$G_{md} = \frac{i_{od}}{v_{id}}\bigg|_{v_{od}=0} \tag{12.22}$$

$$(a)$$

$$(b)$$

**Figure 12.7.** Models for the output ports of a fully differential amplifier: ($a$) a Thévenin-network model and ($b$) a Norton-network model.

$$G_{mc} = \left.\frac{i_{oc}}{v_{ic}}\right|_{v_{oc}=0} \tag{12.23}$$

The parameters for the models in Fig. 12.7 can be computed from the corresponding half-circuits.

The DM and CM output-load impedances can be computed using

$$Z_{Ld} = \frac{v_{od}}{i_{ld}} \tag{12.24}$$

and

$$Z_{Lc} = \frac{v_{oc}}{i_{lc}} \tag{12.25}$$

where $i_{ld} = (i_{l1} - i_{l2})/2$, $i_{lc} = (i_{l1} + i_{l2})/2$, and $i_{l1}$ and $i_{l2}$ are defined in Fig. 12.4. A fully balanced output load can be modeled using a passive network of the form shown in Fig. 12.6a or Fig. 12.6b, with $Z_{id}$ and $Z_{ic}$ replaced by $Z_{Ld}$ and $Z_{Lc}$, respectively.

The DM and CM half-circuits for the amplifier, signal source, and output load in Fig. 12.4 are shown in Figs. 12.8 and 12.9. The DM load $Z_{Ld}$ and the CM load $Z_{Lc}$ can be found using (12.24) and (12.25) for the load network in Fig. 12.4, and the resulting load elements are

$$Z_{Ld} = Z_{L2}\|(2Z_{L1}) \tag{12.26}$$

$$Z_{Lc} = Z_{L1} \tag{12.27}$$

**Figure 12.8.** DM half-circuits for a fully differential signal source and amplifier: (*a*) the input port, (*b*) the output port using a Thévenin equivalent, (*c*) the output port using a Norton equivalent.

**Figure 12.9.** CM half-circuits for a fully differential signal source and amplifier: (*a*) the input port, (*b*) the output port using a Thévenin equivalent, (*c*) the output port using a Norton equivalent.

**Figure 12.10.** A simple small-signal model for a balanced fully differential op amp, assuming infinite input impedance and zero output impedance.

The DM and CM loads are different for the following reason. The axis of symmetry in Fig. 12.4 passes through the middle of $Z_{L2}$. For purely DM signals, points along the axis of symmetry are ac grounds (see Section 3.5.5). Therefore, the load for the DM half-circuit is half of $Z_{L2}$ in parallel with $Z_{L1}$. However, points along the axis of symmetry are open circuits for purely CM signals (see Section 3.5.5). Therefore, $Z_{L2}$ does not affect the load in the CM half-circuit.

These amplifier models can be used to model any balanced, fully differential amplifier, including an op amp. If the model is simplified to just the dependent sources (assuming infinite input impedance and zero output impedance), the equations that describe the model reduce to

$$v_{od} = v_{o1} - v_{o2} = a_{dm}v_{id} \tag{12.28}$$

and

$$v_{oc} = \frac{v_{o1} + v_{o2}}{2} = a_{cm}v_{ic} \tag{12.29}$$

In an ideal, fully differential op amp, $a_{cm} = 0$ and $a_{dm} \to -\infty$. If $a_{cm} = 0$, then $v_{oc} = 0$ if $v_{ic}$ is finite. If $a_{dm} \to -\infty$, then $v_{id} \to 0$ if $v_{od}$ is finite. A simple small-signal model for a balanced, fully differential op amp that is based on (12.28) and (12.29) is shown in Fig. 12.10. Because of its simplicity, this model will be used to illustrate some key points in the following sections.

## 12.4 Common-Mode Feedback

The fully differential feedback amplifier in Fig. 12.1a is redrawn in Fig. 12.11a using the ideal op-amp model from Fig. 12.10. In Fig. 12.11a, the axis of symmetry is shown as a dashed line. The $a_{cm}$ controlled source is shown twice, once on each side of the axis of symmetry. The DM half-circuit is shown in Fig. 12.11b. Here all nodes intersecting the axis of symmetry are connected to ac ground. Using this half-circuit and letting $a_{dm} \to -\infty$, the differential gain is

$$\frac{v_{od}}{v_{sd}} = \frac{v_{od}}{v_{s1} - v_{s2}} = -\frac{R_3}{R_1} \tag{12.30}$$

Thus, the DM output voltage is determined by the DM gain, which is accurately set by the DM feedback loop in Fig. 12.11b. However, the CM output voltage is set by a different feedback loop. The CM half-circuit for Fig. 12.1a is shown in Fig. 12.11c. If $a_{cm} = 0$, the closed-loop CM gain $v_{oc}/v_{sc}$ is zero, and the loop gain (or return ratio) for the CM feedback loop in Fig. 12.11c is zero. Therefore, the CM output voltage $v_{oc}$ is independent of the CM op-amp input voltage $v_{ic}$ and the CM source voltage $v_{sc}$. In practice, $|a_{cm}|$ is nonzero but small in op amps that use an input differential pair with a tail current source because the

**Figure 12.11.** (*a*) The inverting feedback amplifier of Fig. 12.1*a*, using the op-amp model in Fig. 12.10. (*b*) The DM half-circuit. (*c*) The CM half-circuit.

tail current source provides local feedback for CM signals and makes the CM gain of the input stage small. If $|a_{cm}|$ is small, the magnitude of the loop gain (or return ratio) for the CM feedback loop in Fig. 12.11*c* is small, and this feedback loop exerts little control on the CM output voltage. As a result, a different feedback loop with high loop gain is used to control the CM output voltage, as described next.

## 12.4.1 Common-Mode Feedback at Low Frequencies

For the op amp in Fig. 12.2, the ideal operating point biases $M_1$–$M_5$ in the active region and sets the dc CM output voltage $V_{OC}$ to the value that maximizes the swing at the op-amp outputs for which all transistors operate in the active region. However, as described in Section 4.3.5.1, $V_{OC}$ is very sensitive to mismatches and component variations, and the circuit is not practical from a bias stability standpoint. (Section 4.3.5.1 describes the circuit in Fig. 4.24a, which is Fig. 12.2 with the addition of two diode-connected transistors and two ideal current sources that set the dc drain currents.) Accurately setting $V_{OC}$ in Fig. 12.2 to a desired voltage is impossible in practice because $I_{D5}$ is set independently of $|I_{D3}| + |I_{D4}|$.

To set $V_{OC}$ to a desired dc voltage $V_{CM}$ that biases all transistors in the active region and maximizes the output voltage swing, either $V_{BIAS}$ or $V_{GS5}$ must be adjusted so that $I_{D5} = |I_{D3}| + |I_{D4}|$ when $V_{SD3} = V_{SD4} = V_{DD} - V_{CM}$, which makes $V_{OC} = V_{CM}$. We will focus on adjusting $V_{GS5}$. Adjusting $V_{GS5}$ to force $V_{OC} = V_{CM}$ requires the use of feedback in practice. Circuitry is added to form a negative feedback loop that adjusts $V_{GS5}$ to set $V_{OC} = V_{CM}$. Figure 12.12 shows a block diagram of such a feedback loop, which will be referred to as the *common-mode feedback* (CMFB) loop. The added blocks will be called the CM-sense blocks. One CM-sense block, the CM detector, calculates the CM output voltage, $V_{oc} = (V_{o1} + V_{o2})/2$. This voltage is subtracted from the desired CM output voltage, $V_{CM}$. The difference $V_{oc} - V_{CM}$ is scaled by an amplifier with gain $a_{cms}$. Then a dc voltage $V_{CSBIAS}$ is added, and the result is $V_{cms}$, where

$$V_{cms} = a_{cms}(V_{oc} - V_{CM}) + V_{CSBIAS} \qquad (12.31)$$

$V_{cms}$ drives a new op-amp input labeled CMC (for *common-mode control*). The CMC input is chosen so that changing $V_{cmc}$ changes $V_{oc}$ but does not affect $V_{od}$ if the circuit is perfectly balanced. (The voltages $V_{cms}$ and $V_{cmc}$ are equal in Fig. 12.12. The label $V_{cmc}$ will be used when referring to the CMC input of the op amp, while $V_{cms}$ will be used to refer to the output of the CM-sense circuit.) For the op amp in Fig. 12.2, the CMC input is the gate of $M_5$. If the gain in this CMFB loop is high, the negative feedback forces $V_{oc} \approx V_{CM}$ and $V_{cmc}$ to be approximately constant with $V_{cmc} \approx V_{CSBIAS}$. Transistor $M_5$ supplies the tail current for the pair $M_1$ and $M_2$. Bias voltage $V_{CSBIAS}$ is added to provide the nominal dc component of $V_{cmc}$ that sets $|I_{D3}| + |I_{D4}| = I_{D5}$ when $V_{oc} = V_{CM}$.

The magnitude of the small-signal gain from $V_{cmc}$ to $V_{oc}$ is typically much larger than unity. For example, in the op amp in Fig. 12.2, this gain magnitude is high because it is

**Figure 12.12.** A conceptual block diagram of the CMFB loop.

**Figure 12.13.** The simple op-amp model of Fig. 12.10 (a) including the CMC gain $a_{cmc}$ and (b) replacing the $a_{cm}$ and $a_{cmc}$ controlled sources with an equivalent controlled source $a'_{cm}$.

the gain of common-source $M_5$ with a large load resistance at the op-amp output. (This gain is computed in the next example.) Often the magnitude of the gain from $V_{cmc}$ to $V_{oc}$ is large enough to provide all the gain needed in the CMFB loop. Therefore, the CM-sense amplifier $a_{cms}$ can have low gain, and, as a result, a wide bandwidth. Because the CM-sense amplifier is in the CMFB loop, wide bandwidth in this amplifier simplifies the frequency compensation of the CMFB loop. If $V_{oc} = V_{CM}$ in Fig. 12.12, $V_{cmc} = V_{CSBIAS}$. In practice, the bias voltage $V_{CSBIAS}$ is usually generated in the CM-sense-amplifier circuit. Hence, the CM-sense amplifier is designed so that when its differential input voltage is zero, its output voltage equals the nominal bias voltage required at the single-ended CMC input. For the op amp in Fig. 12.2, this bias voltage is $V_{GS5} - V_{SS}$. Practical CM-sense amplifiers that can generate such an output bias voltage will be shown in Section 12.5.

The simple op-amp model in Fig. 12.10 is modified to include the CM control (CMC) input in Fig. 12.13a. Controlled source $a_{cmc}$ models the small-signal voltage gain from this new input to $v_{oc}$. That is,

$$a_{cmc} = \frac{v_{oc}}{v_{cmc}}\bigg|_{v_{ic}=0} \tag{12.32}$$

When this gain is included, the equation for the CM output voltage in (12.29) becomes

$$v_{oc} = a_{cm}v_{ic} + a_{cmc}v_{cmc} \tag{12.33}$$

■ **EXAMPLE**

Compute the three voltage gains in the model in Fig. 12.13a for the op amp in Fig. 12.2. Use the 0.8-$\mu$m CMOS model data in Table 2.3 with $|V_{ov}| = |V_{GS} - V_t| = 0.2$ V and

Figure 12.14. (a) The DM half-circuit for Fig. 12.2, explicitly showing the output load capacitance. (b) The CM half-circuit for Fig. 12.2, explicitly showing the output load capacitance.

$L_{\text{eff}} = 0.8$ μm for all devices. Take $I_{D5} = 200$ μA, $|V_{Ap}| = 20$ V, and $V_{An} = 10$ V. (These $V_A$ values follow from (1.163) and the data in Table 2.3 with $L_{\text{eff}} = 0.8$ μm.) Ignore body effect.

The DM half-circuit is shown in Fig. 12.14a. It is a common-source amplifier with an active load. The low-frequency DM gain is

$$a_{dm} = \frac{v_{od}}{v_{id}} = -g_{m1}(r_{o1}\|r_{o3}) \qquad (12.34)$$

Using (1.181) and $I_{D1} = |I_{D3}|$ in (12.34),

$$a_{dm} = -\frac{2I_{D1}}{V_{ov1}}\left(\frac{V_{A1}}{I_{D1}}\Big\|\frac{|V_{A3}|}{|I_{D3}|}\right) = -\frac{2}{V_{ov1}}\frac{V_{A1}|V_{A3}|}{V_{A1}+|V_{A3}|} = -\frac{2}{0.2}\frac{10 \times 20}{10+20} = -66.7$$

The CM half-circuit is shown in Fig. 12.14b. To form this half-circuit, the original circuit was transformed into a symmetric circuit by splitting $M_5$ into two identical halves in parallel, each called $M_{5h}$ with $(W/L)_{5h} = (W/L)_5/2$ $(W_{5h} = W_5/2, L_{5h} = L_5)$ and $I_{D5h} = I_{D5}/2$. This half-circuit has two inputs, $v_{ic}$ and $v_{cmc}$. First, we find the gain from $v_{cmc}$ to $v_{oc}$ with $v_{ic} = 0$. This circuit consists of common-source $M_{5h}$, common-gate $M_1$, and active load $M_3$. The low-frequency gain is

$$a_{cmc} = \frac{v_{oc}}{v_{cmc}} = -g_{m5h}(R_{o(\text{down})}\|r_{o3}) \qquad (12.35)$$

where $R_{o(\text{down})}$ is the resistance looking into the drain of $M_1$, which is given by

$$R_{o(\text{down})} = r_{o1}(1 + g_{m1}r_{o5h}) \approx r_{o1}(g_{m1}r_{o5h}) \qquad (12.36)$$

Using the approximation in (12.36), (1.181), and $I_{D1} = |I_{D3}| = I_{D5h}$ in (12.35), we find

$$a_{cmc} = -\frac{2I_{D5h}}{V_{ov5h}}\left\{\left[\frac{V_{A1}}{I_{D1}}\left(\frac{2I_{D1}}{V_{ov1}}\frac{V_{A5h}}{I_{D5h}}\right)\right]\middle\|\frac{|V_{A3}|}{|I_{D3}|}\right\} = -\frac{2}{V_{ov5h}}\frac{V_{A1}\left(\dfrac{2V_{A5h}}{V_{ov1}}\right)|V_{A3}|}{V_{A1}\left(\dfrac{2V_{A5h}}{V_{ov1}}\right)+|V_{A3}|}$$

$$= -\frac{2}{0.2}\frac{10\left(\dfrac{2(10)}{0.2}\right)20}{10\left(\dfrac{2(10)}{0.2}\right)+20} = -196$$

Finally, we calculate the gain from $v_{ic}$ to $v_{oc}$ with $v_{cmc} = 0$. In this circuit, $M_1$ is a common-source amplifier with a degeneration resistance that is the output resistance of $M_{5h}$. The gain is

$$a_{cm} = \frac{v_{oc}}{v_{ic}} = -\frac{g_{m1}}{1+g_{m1}r_{o5h}}(R_{o(\text{down})}\|r_{o3}) \approx -\frac{1}{r_{o5h}}(R_{o(\text{down})}\|r_{o3}) \qquad (12.37)$$

The approximation is accurate if $g_{m1}r_{o5h} \gg 1$. Using the approximation in (12.36), (1.181), and $I_{D1} = |I_{D3}| = I_{D5h}$ in (12.37),

$$a_{cm} = -\frac{I_{D5h}}{V_{A5h}}\left\{\left[\frac{V_{A1}}{I_{D1}}\left(\frac{2I_{D1}}{V_{ov1}}\frac{V_{A5h}}{I_{D5h}}\right)\right]\middle\|\frac{|V_{A3}|}{|I_{D3}|}\right\} = -\frac{1}{V_{A5h}}\frac{V_{A1}\left(\dfrac{2V_{A5h}}{V_{ov1}}\right)|V_{A3}|}{V_{A1}\left(\dfrac{2V_{A5h}}{V_{ov1}}\right)+|V_{A3}|}$$

$$= -\frac{1}{10}\frac{10\left(\dfrac{2(10)}{0.2}\right)20}{10\left(\dfrac{2(10)}{0.2}\right)+20} = -1.96 \qquad (12.38)$$

In this example, $|a_{cmc}|$ is much larger than $|a_{cm}|$ because the transconductance in (12.35) is much larger than the degenerated transconductance in (12.37).

The CMFB loop uses negative feedback to make $V_{oc} \approx V_{CM}$. If $V_{CM}$ changes by a small amount from its design value due to parameter variations in the circuit that generates $V_{CM}$, $V_{oc}$ should change by an equal amount so that $V_{oc}$ tracks $V_{CM}$. The ratio $\Delta V_{oc}/\Delta V_{CM}$ is the closed-loop small-signal gain of the CMFB loop, which from Fig. 12.12 is

$$A_{CMFB} = \frac{\Delta V_{oc}}{\Delta V_{CM}} = \frac{v_{oc}}{v_{cm}} = \frac{a_{cms}(-a_{cmc})}{1+a_{cms}(-a_{cmc})} \qquad (12.39)$$

If $a_{cms}(-a_{cmc}) \gg 1$, $A_{CMFB} \approx 1$ and $\Delta V_{oc} \approx \Delta V_{CM}$.

The CM gain from $v_{ic}$ to $v_{oc}$ is affected by the CMFB loop. This gain can be calculated using the CMFB block diagram in Fig. 12.12 and the op-amp model in Fig. 12.13a. The op-amp CM gain when the CMFB is present, which we will call $a'_{cm}$, is found with the DM input signal set to zero. Using (12.31), the small-signal CM-sense voltage is related to the small-signal CM output voltage by

$$v_{cms} = a_{cms}v_{oc} \qquad (12.40)$$

Using this equation, (12.33), and $v_{cms} = v_{cmc}$, we find

$$a'_{cm} = \frac{v_{oc}}{v_{ic}}\bigg|_{\text{with CMFB}} = \frac{a_{cm}}{1+a_{cms}(-a_{cmc})} \qquad (12.41)$$

Therefore, $|a'_{cm}| \ll |a_{cm}|$ if $|a_{cms}(-a_{cmc})| \gg 1$.

The CM gain for a balanced differential amplifier with CMFB can be found using either the model in Fig. 12.13a or 12.13b with $a'_{cm}$ given by (12.41). These models are equivalent because the effect of the controlled source $a_{cmc}$ that is part of the CMFB loop is included in $a'_{cm}$.

▪ **EXAMPLE**

Compute the CM gain from $v_{ic}$ to $v_{oc}$ when the CMFB loop is active, $a'_{cm}$, for the op amp in the last example. Assume that $a_{cms} = 1$.

Substituting values from the last example in (12.41) with $a_{cms} = 1$ gives

$$a'_{cm} = \left.\frac{v_{oc}}{v_{ic}}\right|_{\text{with CMFB}} = \frac{-1.96}{1 + (1)(196)} = -0.01$$

Comparing this result with (12.38), we see that the CMFB has reduced the CM gain by more than two orders of magnitude.

▪

### 12.4.2 Stability and Compensation Considerations in a CMFB Loop

Since the CMFB loop is a negative feedback loop, stability is a key issue. For illustration purposes, consider the op amp in Fig. 12.2 driving a load capacitance and using the CMFB scheme shown in Fig. 12.12. The gain in the CMFB loop is $(-a_{cmc})a_{cms}$. The dominant pole $p_{1c}$ in the CMFB loop is set by the load capacitance and the output resistance in the CM half-circuit in Fig. 12.14b. Ignoring all nondominant poles and using (12.35), we find

$$a_{cmc}(s) = -\frac{g_{m5h}(R_{o(\text{down})}\|r_{o3})}{1 + s(R_{o(\text{down})}\|r_{o3})C_{Lc}} \tag{12.42}$$

At high frequencies $[\omega \gg |p_{1c}| = 1/(R_{o(\text{down})}\|r_{o3})C_{Lc}]$, (12.42) reduces to

$$\left.a_{cmc}(j\omega)\right|_{\omega \gg |p_{1c}|} \approx -\frac{g_{m5h}}{j\omega C_{Lc}} \tag{12.43}$$

This equation follows from the observation that the drain current from $M_{5h}$ flows into the load capacitor at high frequencies. From (12.43), $|a_{cmc}| = 1$ at the frequency

$$\omega_{u,cm} = \frac{g_{m5h}}{C_{Lc}} \tag{12.44}$$

Nondominant poles exist in the CMFB loop, due to capacitance at the source of $M_1$ in Fig. 12.14b and due to poles in the gain $a_{cms}(s)$ of the CM-sense circuit. If the gain roll-off in (12.43) due to the dominant pole does not provide adequate phase margin for the CMFB loop, the unity-gain frequency for the CMFB loop gain can be decreased to increase the phase margin. From (12.44), increasing the CM load capacitance $C_{Lc}$ decreases $\omega_{u,cm}$. However, adding capacitance to the op-amp outputs increases both the CM and DM load capacitances, as can be seen from (12.26) and (12.27). The CMFB loop gain may need a smaller unity-gain frequency than the DM loop gain because the CMFB loop may have more high frequency poles than the DM loop. For example, poles of $a_{cms}(s)$ of the CM-sense amplifier and the pole associated with the capacitance at the source of $M_1$ in Fig. 12.14b are poles in the CMFB loop. However, they are not poles in the DM feedback loop since the source of $M_1$ is an ac ground in the DM half-circuit. As a result, the load capacitance required in (12.43) to provide adequate phase margin for the CMFB

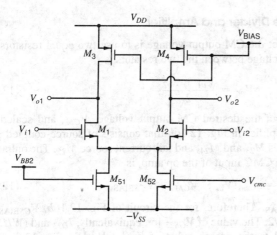

**Figure 12.15.** The op amp of Fig. 12.2 modified by replacing $M_5$ with $M_{51}$ with $V_{g51}$ constant, and $M_{52}$ with $V_{g52} = V_{cmc}$.

loop may result in a larger DM load capacitance than desired, thereby overcompensating the DM feedback loop. While such overcompensation increases the phase margin of the DM feedback loop, it also decreases the unity-gain bandwidth of the DM loop gain and the 3-dB bandwidth of the DM closed-loop gain, which is undesirable when high bandwidth is desired in the DM feedback circuit to amplify a wide-band DM signal.

To overcome this problem, (12.44) shows that decreasing $g_{m5h} = g_{m5}/2$ decreases the unity-gain frequency of the gain $a_{cmc}$ in the CMFB loop and therefore increases the phase margin of the CMFB loop. Assuming that the tail bias current $I_{D5}$ cannot be changed, this decrease could be achieved by decreasing $(W/L)_5$. However, decreasing $(W/L)_5$ increases $V_{ov5}$, which affects the CM input range of the op amp. Alternatively, a reduction in $g_{m5h}$ can be realized by splitting $M_5$ into two parallel transistors, which are labeled $M_{51}$ and $M_{52}$ in Fig. 12.15. Transistor $M_{51}$ has its gate connected to a bias voltage and carries a constant drain current. The gate of $M_{52}$ acts as the CMC input. To keep the bias currents in the op amp the same as in Fig. 12.2, we want

$$I_{D51} + I_{D52} = I_{D5} \tag{12.45}$$

To keep the CM input range of the op amp unchanged, we need

$$V_{ov51} = V_{ov52} = V_{ov5} \tag{12.46}$$

From (1.181), (12.45), and (12.46),

$$g_{m52} = \frac{2I_{D52}}{V_{ov52}} < g_{m5} = \frac{2I_{D5}}{V_{ov5}} \tag{12.47}$$

as desired. For the circuit in Fig. 12.15, $g_{m52h} = g_{m52}/2$ replaces $g_{m5h} = g_{m5}/2$ in (12.42), (12.43), and (12.44). A disadvantage of this approach is that reducing the transconductance in (12.42) reduces the magnitude of the CMC gain, $|a_{cmc}|$, at dc.

## 12.5 CMFB Circuits

In this section, circuits that detect the CM output voltage and generate a signal (a current or a voltage) that is a function of $V_{oc} - V_{CM}$ are described. These circuits are part of the CMFB loop and will be referred to as CM-sense circuits. For simplicity, these circuits are described using the simple, fully differential amplifier shown in Fig. 12.2.

## 12.5.1 CMFB Using Resistive Divider and Amplifier

A straightforward way to detect the CM output voltage is to use two equal resistors, as shown in Fig. 12.16a.[3,4] The voltage between the two resistors is

$$V_{oc} = \frac{V_{o1} + V_{o2}}{2} \qquad (12.48)$$

This voltage is subtracted from the desired CM output voltage, $V_{CM}$, and scaled by the differencing CM-sense amplifier in Fig. 12.16b that consists of source-coupled pair $M_{21}$-$M_{22}$, diode-connected loads $M_{23}$ and $M_{24}$, and tail-current source $M_{25}$. The output of this amplifier, which drives the CMC input of the op amp, is

$$V_{cms} = a_{cms}(V_{oc} - V_{CM}) + V_{CSBIAS} \qquad (12.49)$$

If $V_{oc} = V_{CM}$, $V_{cms} = V_{CSBIAS}$. Therefore, for the circuit of Fig. 12.16b, $V_{CSBIAS} = V_{GS23} - V_{SS}$ when $I_{D23} = I_{D25}/2$. The value of $V_{GS23}$ [or, equivalently, $I_{D23}$ and $(W/L)_{23}$] is chosen so that $I_{D5}$ is equal to the design value of $|I_{D3}| + |I_{D4}|$ in Fig. 12.2 when

(a)

(a)

**Figure 12.16.** (a) CMFB using a resistive divider to detect $V_{oc}$ and a CM-sense amplifier. (b) A schematic for the CM-sense amplifier that can be used with the op amp in Fig. 12.2.

$V_{oc} = V_{CM}$. In (12.49), $a_{cms}$ is the small-signal voltage gain of the CM-sense amplifier

$$a_{cms} = \left. \frac{v_{cms}}{v_{oc}} \right|_{\text{CMFB loop open}} = \frac{1}{2} \frac{g_{m21}}{g_{m23}} \tag{12.50}$$

Here, we have assumed that the CM gain of the CM-sense amplifier is much smaller in magnitude than its DM gain. The factor of 1/2 multiplies $g_{m21}/g_{m23}$ in (12.50) because the output is taken from only one side of the differential amplifier.

■ **EXAMPLE**

Determine the value of $V_{CM}$ that maximizes the output swing for the differential op amp in Fig. 12.2. Use the CMFB scheme in Fig. 12.16a, and design the CM-sense amplifier in Fig. 12.16b. Assume that the CM-sense resistors $R_{cs}$ are very large and can be neglected when computing small-signal voltage gains for the op amp. Use the data and assumptions in the next-to-last example with $V_{DD} = V_{SS} = 2.5$ V. Assume $V_{ic} = 0$. Ignore the body effect.

For the op amp in Fig. 12.2, if the magnitude of its DM gain is large and if the op amp operates in a DM negative feedback loop (for example, as shown in Fig. 12.1a), $V_{id} \approx 0$. Therefore, both op-amp inputs will be close to ground since $V_{ic} = 0$; that is, $V_{i1} = V_{ic} + V_{id}/2 \approx 0$ and $V_{i2} = V_{ic} - V_{id}/2 \approx 0$. The output $V_{o1}$ reaches its lower limit when $M_1$ enters the triode region, which occurs when $V_{gd1} = V_{t1}$; therefore,

$$V_{o1(min)} = -V_{t1} + V_{i1} \approx -V_{t1} = -0.7 \text{ V}$$

(Body effect would increase $V_{t1}$ and decrease $V_{o1(min)}$.) The upper output swing limit occurs when $M_3$ enters the triode region, and

$$V_{o1(max)} = V_{DD} - |V_{ov3}| = 2.5 - 0.2 = 2.3 \text{ V}$$

To maximize the output swing, the dc CM output voltage $V_{OC}$ should be halfway between the swing limits:

$$V_{OC} = \frac{V_{o1(max)} + V_{o1(min)}}{2} = \frac{2.3 + (-0.7)}{2} = 0.8 \text{ V}$$

Therefore, we choose $V_{CM} = 0.8$ V. The resulting peak differential output voltage is

$$V_{od(peak)} = V_{o1(max)} - V_{o2(min)} = V_{o1(max)} - V_{o1(min)} = 2.3 - (-0.7) = 3.0 \text{ V}$$

To design the CM-sense amplifier in Fig. 12.16b, we must choose a value for its low-frequency gain. In the CMFB loop, the loop gain is $(-a_{cmc})a_{cms}$. From the previous example, $a_{cmc} = -196$. If we design for $a_{cms} = 1$, the CMFB loop gain is 196, and (12.39) gives $A_{CMFB} = 0.995$. Therefore, $V_{oc}$ closely tracks changes in $V_{CM}$. With this choice of gain in the CM-sense amplifier in Fig. 12.16b, (12.50) gives

$$a_{cms} = \frac{1}{2} \frac{g_{m21}}{g_{m23}} = \frac{1}{2} \frac{\sqrt{2k_p'(W/L)_{21}|I_{D21}|}}{\sqrt{2k_n'(W/L)_{23}I_{23}}} = \frac{1}{2} \frac{\sqrt{k_p'(W/L)_{21}}}{\sqrt{k_n'(W/L)_{23}}} = 1 \tag{12.51}$$

The dc output voltage of the CM-sense amplifier when $V_{oc} = V_{CM}$ should equal the dc voltage needed at the CMC op-amp input, which is

$$-V_{SS} + V_{GS5} = -V_{SS} + V_{t5} + V_{ov5}$$

This dc voltage is produced by the CM-sense amplifier if $M_5$ and $M_{23}$ have equal overdrive voltages. Assuming that $r_o \rightarrow \infty$, matching $V_{ov5}$ and $V_{ov23}$ requires that $M_5$ and $M_{23}$ have equal drain-current-to-$W/L$ ratios:

$$\frac{I_{D5}}{(W/L)_5} = \frac{I_{D23}}{(W/L)_{23}} \tag{12.52}$$

In (12.51) and (12.52), there are three unknowns: $I_{D23}$, $(W/L)_{23}$, and $(W/L)_{21}$. Therefore, many possible solutions exist. [Note that $(W/L)_5$ can be determined from $V_{ov5} = 0.2$ V (by assumption) and $I_{D5} = 200$ μA.]

One simple solution is $I_{D23} = I_{D5}$ and $(W/L)_{23} = (W/L)_5$. Then $(W/L)_{21}$ can be determined from (12.51). While this solution is simple, it requires as much dc current in the CM-sense amplifier as in the op amp. Equations 12.51 and 12.52 can be solved with $I_{D23} < I_{D5}$, which reduces the power dissipation in the CM-sense amplifier. However, the magnitude of the pole associated with the $M_5$–$M_{23}$ current mirror decreases as $I_{D23}$ decreases. To illustrate this point, we will ignore all capacitors except the gate-source capacitors for $M_5$ and $M_{23}$ and assume $L_{23}$ is fixed. Then the magnitude of the nondominant pole associated with the current mirror is

$$|p_{nd}| = \frac{g_{m23}}{C_{gs5} + C_{gs23}} = \frac{\dfrac{2I_{D23}}{V_{ov23}}}{C_{gs5} + (2/3)C_{ox}W_{23}L_{23}} \tag{12.53}$$

since the small-signal resistance of diode-connected $M_{23}$ is $1/g_{m23}$ (assuming that $r_{o23} \gg 1/g_{m23}$). If $I_{D23}$ is scaled by a factor $x$ ($x < 1$) and if $M_5$ is unchanged, $W_{23}$ must also scale by the factor $x$ to satisfy (12.52). With this scaling, the pole magnitude in (12.53) decreases because the numerator scales by the factor $x$, but the denominator scales by a factor greater than $x$ due to the constant $C_{gs5}$ term in the denominator. This pole appears in the CMFB loop gain. Therefore, the phase margin of the CMFB loop decreases as this pole magnitude decreases due to a decrease in $I_{D23}$.

Finally, we must verify that the CM input range of the CM-sense amplifier includes its CM input voltage, which is $V_{CM} = 0.8$ V. The upper limit of the CM input voltage occurs when $M_{25}$ enters the triode region, when $|V_{DS25}| = |V_{ov25}|$; therefore, we want

$$V_{IC} < V_{DD} - |V_{ov25}| - |V_{GS21}| = V_{DD} - |V_{ov25}| - |V_{tp}| - |V_{ov21}|$$
$$= 2.5 - 0.2 - 0.7 - 0.2 = 1.4 \text{ V}$$

The lower limit of the CM input voltage occurs when $M_{21}$ (or $M_{22}$) enters the triode region (when $V_{GD21} = V_{t21}$); hence,

$$V_{IC} > -V_{SS} + V_{GS23} - |V_{t21}| = -V_{SS} + (V_{tn} + V_{ov23}) - |V_{tp}|$$
$$= -2.5 + (0.7 + 0.2) - 0.7 = -2.3 \text{ V}$$

The applied CM input voltage of 0.8 V falls between these limits; therefore, all transistors operate in the active region as assumed.

In this CMFB approach, the inputs to the CM-sense amplifier are ideally constant, which simplifies its design. One disadvantage of this CM-sense circuit is that the $R_{cs}$ resistors and the input capacitance of the CM-sense amplifier introduce a pole in the transfer function of the CM-sense circuit and therefore in the CMFB loop. A capacitor $C_{cs}$ can be connected in parallel with each sense resistor to introduce a left-half-plane zero in the CM-sense circuit to reduce the effect of the pole at high frequencies. (See Problem 12.18.)

Another disadvantage of this CM-sense circuit is that the sense resistor $R_{cs}$ loads the op-amp output in the DM half-circuit, since the node between the resistors is a DM ac ground. This loading reduces the open-loop differential voltage gain unless $R_{cs}$ is much larger than the output resistance of the DM half-circuit.

**Figure 12.17.** The CMFB scheme of Fig. 12.16 with source followers added as buffers between the op-amp outputs and the $R_{cs}$ resistors.

To avoid this resistive output loading, voltage buffers can be added between the op-amp outputs and the $R_{cs}$ resistors. Source followers are used as buffers in Fig. 12.17. One potential problem is that each source follower introduces a dc offset of $V_{GS}$ between its input and output. To avoid a shift in the CM operating point caused by these offsets, voltage $V_{CM}$ can be buffered by an identical source follower so that the op-amp output voltages and $V_{CM}$ experience equal offsets. However, these offsets limit the op-amp output swing since each source-follower transistor that connects to an op-amp output must remain in the active region over the entire output voltage swing.

The CMFB scheme in Fig. 12.16 can be modified to eliminate the $M_{23}$-$M_5$ current mirror from the CMFB loop, as shown in Fig. 12.18. This modified CM-sense amplifier directly injects currents to control the op-amp CM output.[5] Here, $M_{21}$ in Fig. 12.16b is split into two matched transistors, $M_{21A}$ and $M_{21B}$, and the drain of each transistor connects to an op-amp output. The current injected by $M_{21A}$ and $M_{21B}$ into either output is

$$I_{cms} = \frac{I_{26}}{4} - \frac{g_{m21A}}{2}(V_{oc} - V_{CM})$$

Transistors $M_3$-$M_5$ act as current sources. The CMFB loop will adjust $I_{cms}$ so that

$$|I_{D3}| + |I_{D4}| + 2I_{cms} = I_{D5}$$

If $V_{oc} = V_{CM}$, $M_{21A}$, $M_{21B}$, and $M_{22}$ give $2I_{cms} = I_{26}/2$. Therefore, $I_{26}$ should be chosen so that

$$|I_{D3}| + |I_{D4}| + \frac{I_{26}}{2} = I_{D5}$$

when all devices are active.

An advantage of this approach is that it avoids the pole associated with the $M_5$-$M_{23}$ current mirror in Figs. 12.2 and 12.16. However, $M_{21A}$ and $M_{21B}$ add resistive and capacitive loading at the op-amp outputs. If an op amp uses cascoded devices, $M_{21A}$ and $M_{21B}$ can connect to low-impedance cascode nodes to reduce the impact of this loading.

**Figure 12.18.** A CM-sense amplifier that injects currents into the op amp to control the op-amp CM output voltage. In the CM-sense circuit, $(W/L)_{21A} = (W/L)_{21B} = 0.5(W/L)_{22}$.

### 12.5.2 CMFB Using Two Differential Pairs

A CMFB scheme that uses only transistors is shown in simplified form in Fig. 12.19. Here $M_{21}$-$M_{24}$ are matched. The source-coupled pairs $M_{21}$-$M_{22}$ and $M_{23}$-$M_{24}$ together sense the CM output voltage and generate an output that is proportional to the difference between $V_{oc}$ and $V_{CM}$.[5,6,7] To show this, assume at first that the differential inputs to the two source-coupled pairs, which are $V_{o1} - V_{CM}$ and $V_{o2} - V_{CM}$, are small enough to allow the use of small-signal analysis. Also, assume that the CM gain of these source-coupled pairs is zero. Under these assumptions, the drain currents in $M_{22}$ and $M_{23}$ are

$$I_{d22} = -\frac{I_{20}}{2} - g_{m22}\frac{(V_{o2} - V_{CM})}{2} \tag{12.54}$$

$$I_{d23} = -\frac{I_{20}}{2} - g_{m23}\frac{(V_{o1} - V_{CM})}{2} \tag{12.55}$$

These currents are summed in diode-connected $M_{25}$ to give the CM sensor output current

$$I_{cms} = I_{d25} = -I_{d22} - I_{d23} = I_{20} + g_{m22}\left(\frac{V_{o1} + V_{o2}}{2} - V_{CM}\right)$$

$$= I_{20} + g_{m22}(V_{oc} - V_{CM}) \tag{12.56}$$

since $g_{m22} = g_{m23}$. This last expression shows that the current through $M_{25}$ includes a dc term $I_{20}$ plus a term that is proportional to $V_{oc} - V_{CM}$. The current $I_{d25}$ is mirrored by $M_5$ in Fig. 12.2 to produce the tail current in the op amp, which controls the CM output voltage.

The dc output of the CM-sense circuit should provide the dc voltage needed at the CMC input to give $V_{oc} = V_{CM}$. If $V_{oc} = V_{CM}$, the drain current in $M_{25}$ is

$$I_{D25} = |I_{D22}| + |I_{D23}| = \frac{I_{20}}{2} + \frac{I_{20}}{2} = I_{20} \tag{12.57}$$

**Figure 12.19.** A CMFB approach that uses two differential pairs. This circuit can be used with the op amp in Fig. 12.2.

Choosing $I_{20} = |I_{D3}| + |I_{D4}|$ and $(W/L)_{25} = (W/L)_5$ is one design option. Again, as for the CM-sense amplifier in Fig. 12.16$b$, a smaller value of $I_{20}$ can be used, but such current reduction causes the magnitude of the pole associated with the $M_5$-$M_{25}$ current mirror to decrease. [See the text associated with (12.53).] This scheme does not resistively load the op-amp outputs, but the source-coupled pairs $M_{21}$-$M_{24}$ capacitively load the op-amp outputs.

The above analysis of this CM-sense circuit assumed that $M_{21}$-$M_{24}$ always operate in the active region and that voltages $V_{o1} - V_{CM}$ and $V_{o2} - V_{CM}$ could be treated as small-signal inputs. Even if these voltages become large, the CMFB loop continues to operate as long as $M_{21}$-$M_{24}$ remain on. However, the small-signal analysis is not valid if the transistors leave the active region. If the op-amp outputs become large enough to turn off any of $M_{21}$-$M_{24}$ during a portion of the output swing, the CMFB loop will not operate properly during that part of the output swing. The requirement that $M_{21}$-$M_{24}$ remain on during the entire output swing imposes a limit on the output swing of the op amp. The input voltage range for which both transistors in a differential pair remain on is related to the gate overdrive voltage of those transistors. [See (3.161).] Therefore, to keep $M_{21}$-$M_{24}$ on for a large $V_{o1}$ and $V_{o2}$, $M_{21}$-$M_{24}$ require large overdrives. In contrast, the scheme that uses resistors to detect the CM output voltage does not impose such an output-swing limit since the CM-sense amplifier is driven by $V_{oc}$, which is ideally constant, rather than $V_{o1}$ and $V_{o2}$, which include CM and DM components.

Equation 12.56 implies that this CM-sense circuit is nearly perfect since it produces an output current that includes a constant term plus a term that is proportional to $V_{oc} - V_{CM}$. This result is based on a linear small-signal analysis. However, the inputs to the differential pairs in the CM-sense circuit can include large signals because the op-amp DM output voltage can be large. Next, a large signal analysis of this circuit is carried out.

The drain current in $M_{25}$ is

$$I_{d25} = -I_{d22} - I_{d23} \tag{12.58}$$

The differential input of the $M_{21}$-$M_{22}$ pair is $V_{o2} - V_{CM}$. Using (3.159) and (1.166) gives

$$-I_{d22} = \frac{I_{20}}{2} + \frac{k_p'}{4}\left(\frac{W}{L}\right)_{22}(V_{o2} - V_{CM})\sqrt{4V_{ov22}^2 - (V_{o2} - V_{CM})^2}$$

$$\approx \frac{I_{20}}{2} + \frac{k_p'}{4}\left(\frac{W}{L}\right)_{22}\left(-\frac{V_{od}}{2} + V_{oc} - V_{CM}\right)\sqrt{4V_{ov22}^2 - (V_{od}/2)^2 + (V_{oc} - V_{CM})V_{od}}$$

$$= \frac{I_{20}}{2} + \frac{k_p'}{4}\left(\frac{W}{L}\right)_{22}\left(-\frac{V_{od}}{2} + V_{oc} - V_{CM}\right)\sqrt{4V_{ov22}^2 - (V_{od}/2)^2}\sqrt{1 + \frac{(V_{oc} - V_{CM})V_{od}}{4V_{ov22}^2 - (V_{od}/2)^2}}$$

$$\approx \frac{I_{20}}{2} + \frac{k_p'}{4}\left(\frac{W}{L}\right)_{22}\left(-\frac{V_{od}}{2} + V_{oc} - V_{CM}\right)\sqrt{4V_{ov22}^2 - (V_{od}/2)^2}$$

$$\times \left[1 + \frac{1}{2}\left(\frac{(V_{oc} - V_{CM})V_{od}}{4V_{ov22}^2 - (V_{od}/2)^2}\right) - \frac{1}{8}\left(\frac{(V_{oc} - V_{CM})V_{od}}{4V_{ov22}^2 - (V_{od}/2)^2}\right)^2 + \cdots\right] \quad (12.59)$$

where $|V_{oc} - V_{CM}| \ll |V_{od}|$ was assumed in the first approximation above and $\sqrt{1 + x} \approx 1 + x/2 - x^2/8 + \cdots$, where $x = [(V_{oc} - V_{CM})V_{od}]/[4V_{ov22}^2 - (V_{od}/2)^2]$, was used in the last line.

The differential input of the $M_{23}$-$M_{24}$ pair is $V_{o1} - V_{CM}$. A similar analysis to that above for this differential pair yields

$$-I_{d23} \approx \frac{I_{20}}{2} + \frac{k_p'}{4}\left(\frac{W}{L}\right)_{23}\left(\frac{V_{od}}{2} + V_{oc} - V_{CM}\right)\sqrt{4V_{ov23}^2 - (V_{od}/2)^2}$$

$$\times \left[1 - \frac{1}{2}\left(\frac{(V_{oc} - V_{CM})V_{od}}{4V_{ov23}^2 - (V_{od}/2)^2}\right) - \frac{1}{8}\left(\frac{(V_{oc} - V_{CM})V_{od}}{4V_{ov23}^2 - (V_{od}/2)^2}\right)^2 + \cdots\right] \quad (12.60)$$

Substituting (12.59) and (12.60) in (12.58) with $V_{ov22} = V_{ov23}$ and $(W/L)_{22} = (W/L)_{23}$ gives

$$I_{cms} = I_{d25} \approx I_{20} + \frac{k_p'}{2}\left(\frac{W}{L}\right)_{23}(V_{oc} - V_{CM})\sqrt{4V_{ov23}^2 - (V_{od}/2)^2}$$

$$\times \left[1 - \frac{1}{4}\left(\frac{V_{od}^2}{4V_{ov23}^2 - (V_{od}/2)^2}\right) - \frac{1}{8}\left(\frac{(V_{oc} - V_{CM})V_{od}}{4V_{ov23}^2 - (V_{od}/2)^2}\right)^2 + \cdots\right] \quad (12.61)$$

If $|V_{od}/2| \ll |2V_{ov23}|$, this equation reduces to (12.56). To interpret (12.61), first consider the case when $V_{oc} = V_{CM}$. Then (12.61) shows that the CM-sense output current is constant with $I_{cms} = I_{20}$. Whereas $I_{cms}$ is constant, (12.59) and (12.60) show that $I_{d22}$ and $I_{d23}$ are not constant if $V_{od}$ is nonzero and time-varying, and $I_{d22}$ and $I_{d23}$ are nonlinear functions of $V_{od}$ (see the plot in Fig. 3.51). However, the variation in $I_{d22}$ due to nonzero $V_{od}$ is equal and opposite to the variation in $I_{d23}$ due to $V_{od}$; therefore, these variations cancel when these currents are summed to form $I_{cms}$. Next, consider the case when $V_{oc} \neq V_{CM}$. $V_{oc}$ may not equal $V_{CM}$ due to device mismatch, finite gain in the CMFB loop, or the presence of an ac component in $V_{oc}$. Equation 12.61 shows that $I_{cms}$ has terms that include $V_{od}^2$ that affect $I_{cms}$ when $V_{oc} \neq V_{CM}$. Therefore, even if the transistors are perfectly matched, this CM sensor does not behave like an ideal CM sensor as described by (12.49). The terms that include $V_{od}^2$ stem from the (square-law) nonlinearity associated with the $M_{21}$-$M_{22}$ and $M_{23}$-$M_{24}$ differential pairs that convert $V_{o1} - V_{CM}$ and $V_{o2} - V_{CM}$ into currents. The dependence of $I_{cms}$ on $V_{od}^2$ can cause a shift in the dc CM output voltage. Moreover, if $V_{od}$ is not constant, this dependence can produce an ac component in $V_{oc}$.

## 12.5.3 CMFB Using Transistors in the Triode Region

Another CMFB scheme is shown in Fig. 12.20.[8] The simple op amp of Fig. 12.2 is redrawn here, with $M_5$ replaced by $M_{30}$-$M_{32}$. Transistors $M_{30}$-$M_{35}$ are part of the CMFB

**Figure 12.20.** A CMFB approach that uses transistors $M_{31}$, $M_{32}$, $M_{34}$, and $M_{35}$ biased in the triode region.

loop. Here, $M_{31}$, $M_{32}$, $M_{34}$, and $M_{35}$ operate in the triode region, while $M_{30}$, $M_{33}$, and $M_{36}$ operate in the active region. The desired CM output voltage $V_{CM}$ is connected to the gates of $M_{34}$ and $M_{35}$. To simplify the description of this circuit, assume that $M_{30}$-$M_{35}$ are matched and ignore body effect. Before this CMFB approach is mathematically analyzed, its operation will be explained intuitively. At first, assume that the op-amp outputs in Fig. 12.20 have only a CM component; that is, $V_{o1} = V_{o2} = V_{oc}$. Then the gate voltages of $M_{31}$ and $M_{32}$ equal $V_{oc}$. Since $|I_{D3}| = |I_{D4}| = I_1$, the drain current in $M_{30}$ must equal $2I_1$ to satisfy KCL. Transistors $M_{30}$-$M_{35}$ form a degenerated current mirror and give $I_{D30} = I_{D33} = 2I_1$ when $V_{oc} = V_{CM}$ because $M_{30}$-$M_{35}$ are matched. Therefore, $V_{oc} = V_{CM}$ is a possible operating point for this circuit. Negative feedback forces the circuit to this operating point, as described below. So far, we have assumed that only CM signals are present. Differential signals do not affect the operation of this feedback loop, as shown by the following analysis.

Since $M_{31}$ and $M_{32}$ are matched and operate in the triode region, the sum of their drain currents $I_{cms}$ is [using (1.152)]

$$
\begin{aligned}
I_{cms} = I_{d31} + I_{d32} &= k_n' \left(\frac{W}{L}\right)_{31} \left( (V_{o1} + V_{SS} - V_{t31})V_{ds31} - \frac{V_{ds31}^2}{2} \right) \\
&+ k_n' \left(\frac{W}{L}\right)_{32} \left( (V_{o2} + V_{SS} - V_{t32})V_{ds32} - \frac{V_{ds32}^2}{2} \right) \\
&= 2k_n' \left(\frac{W}{L}\right)_{31} \left( V_{oc} + V_{SS} - V_{tn} - \frac{V_{ds31}}{2} \right) V_{ds31} \quad (12.62)
\end{aligned}
$$

since $V_{ds31} = V_{ds32}$, $V_{t31} = V_{t32} = V_{tn}$, and $(W/L)_{31} = (W/L)_{32}$. This equation shows that $I_{cms}$ is dependent on the CM output voltage and independent of the differential output voltage because changes in the drain currents in $M_{31}$ and $M_{32}$ due to nonzero $V_{od}$ are equal in magnitude and opposite in sign. Therefore, these changes cancel when the drain currents are summed in (12.62).

Applying KVL around the lower transistors $M_{30}$-$M_{35}$ gives

$$V_{ds31} = V_{ds35} + V_{gs33} - V_{gs30} \tag{12.63}$$

Assuming that $I_{d30} \approx I_{d33}$, we have $V_{gs30} \approx V_{gs33}$, and (12.63) reduces to

$$V_{ds31} \approx V_{ds35} \tag{12.64}$$

Since $M_{35}$ operates in the triode region with $I_{D35} = I_1$, rearranging (1.152) gives

$$V_{ds35} = \frac{I_1}{k_n' \left(\dfrac{W}{L}\right)_{35} \left(V_{CM} + V_{SS} - V_{tn} - \dfrac{V_{ds35}}{2}\right)} \tag{12.65}$$

Using (12.64) and (12.65) in (12.62) with $(W/L)_{31} = (W/L)_{35}$ gives

$$
\begin{aligned}
I_{cms} &\approx I_1 \frac{2k_n' \left(\dfrac{W}{L}\right)_{35} \left(V_{oc} + V_{SS} - V_{tn} - \dfrac{V_{ds35}}{2}\right)}{k_n' \left(\dfrac{W}{L}\right)_{35} \left(V_{CM} + V_{SS} - V_{tn} - \dfrac{V_{ds35}}{2}\right)} = 2I_1 \frac{V_{oc} + V_{SS} - V_{tn} - \dfrac{V_{ds35}}{2}}{V_{CM} + V_{SS} - V_{tn} - \dfrac{V_{ds35}}{2}} \\
&= 2I_1 \frac{V_{CM} + V_{SS} - V_{tn} - \dfrac{V_{ds35}}{2}}{V_{CM} + V_{SS} - V_{tn} - \dfrac{V_{ds35}}{2}} + 2I_1 \frac{V_{oc} - V_{CM}}{V_{CM} + V_{SS} - V_{tn} - \dfrac{V_{ds35}}{2}} \\
&= 2I_1 + 2I_1 \frac{V_{oc} - V_{CM}}{V_{CM} + V_{SS} - V_{tn} - \dfrac{V_{ds35}}{2}} \tag{12.66}
\end{aligned}
$$

This last expression shows that the op-amp tail current $I_{cms}$ consists of a constant term $2I_1$ plus a term that depends on $V_{oc} - V_{CM}$. If $|I_{d3}| = |I_{d4}| = I_1$, then KCL requires that $I_{cms} = 2I_1$. Using this value in (12.66) gives $V_{oc} \approx V_{CM}$, as desired. In practice, mismatches can cause $V_{oc}$ to deviate from $V_{CM}$. For example, if the drain currents in $M_3$ and $M_4$ are larger than $I_1$, then (12.66) shows that $V_{oc}$ must be larger than $V_{CM}$ to force $I_{cms}$ to be larger than $2I_1$.

To see that the CMFB loop here is a negative feedback loop, assume that $V_{oc}$ increases. Then the gate-source voltages on $M_{31}$ and $M_{32}$ increase, which in turn increases $I_{cms}$. Increasing $I_{cms}$ causes $V_{sd3} = V_{sd4}$ to increase since $M_3$ and $M_4$ have fixed gate-source voltages. This increase in $V_{sd3} = V_{sd4}$ causes $V_{oc}$ to fall and counteract the assumed increase in $V_{oc}$. In steady state, this CMFB loop forces $V_{oc} \approx V_{CM}$.

One limitation of this scheme is that the CMFB loop will not function properly whenever the output voltage swing is large enough to turn off either $M_{31}$ or $M_{32}$. Therefore, neither op-amp output is allowed to swing within a threshold voltage of $-V_{SS}$. Thus, the op-amp output swing is limited by this CMFB scheme. Another limitation is that the magnitude of the small-signal gain in the CMFB loop is smaller here than in the previous approaches because the transconductance of $M_{31}$ or $M_{32}$ in the triode region is smaller than it is in the active region. (See Problem 12.19.) Reducing the CMFB loop gain reduces the control that the CMFB loop exerts on the CM output voltage. Also, the bandwidth of the CMFB loop is lower here than in other cases due to the low transconductance of $M_{31}$ and $M_{32}$. Bandwidth requirements for the CMFB loop are considered in Section 12.8.

## 12.5.4 Switched-Capacitor CMFB

To overcome the op-amp output swing limitations imposed by the last two CMFB approaches and to avoid resistive output loading of the op amp, capacitors can be used to

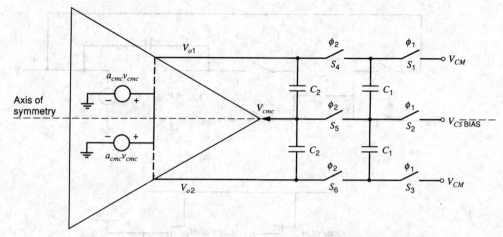

**Figure 12.21.** A CMFB scheme that uses switched capacitors.

detect the CM output voltage. If the CM-sense resistors $R_{cs}$ in Fig. 12.16 are replaced with capacitors, the resistive output loading is eliminated, but these capacitors are open circuits at dc. To avoid a dc bias problem, switched capacitors can be used as the CM detector.[9] A switched-capacitor (SC) CMFB scheme that is often used in switched-capacitor amplifiers and filters (see Section 6.1.7) is shown in Fig. 12.21. Here the network that consists of switches $S_1$-$S_6$ and capacitors $C_1$ and $C_2$ sense the CM output voltage and subtract it from the desired CM output voltage $V_{CM}$. Voltage $V_{CSBIAS}$ is a dc bias voltage. As in Fig. 6.8, assume that each switch is on when its control signal is high and is off when its control signal is low. The switches are controlled by two nonoverlapping clocks, $\phi_1$ and $\phi_2$ (that is, $\phi_1$ and $\phi_2$ are never high at the same time). In this section, we will assume that these switches are ideal. In practice, switches $S_1$-$S_6$ are implemented with MOS transistors. As in the previous section, we use the simple op amp in Fig. 12.2 as the op amp in Fig. 12.21.

The SC CMFB circuit is a linear, balanced, discrete-time circuit. Therefore, all points on the axis of symmetry (shown as a dashed line in Fig. 12.21) operate at ac ground for differential signals. The op-amp CMC input is along the axis of symmetry, so $V_{cmc}$ has a CM component but zero DM component. Therefore, the switched-capacitor circuit is a good CM sensor. To show that voltage $V_{cmc}$ depends on the difference between the actual and desired CM output voltages, consider the CM half-circuit shown in Fig. 12.22a. Capacitor $C_2$ is not switched and connects from $V_{cmc}$ to $V_{oc}$. Since $V_{cmc}$ is the gate voltage of $M_5$ in Fig. 12.2, there is voltage gain from $V_{cmc}$ to $V_{oc}$, which is modeled by controlled source $a_{cmc}$. Comparing this half-circuit to Fig. 6.10a, we see that $C_2$ connected across the gain stage and switched-capacitor $C_1$ form a switched-capacitor integrator. This integrator is in a negative feedback loop since its output $V_{oc}$ is connected back to a switch that connects to $C_1$.

When $\phi_1$ is high, $C_1$ charges to $V_{CM} - V_{CSBIAS}$. When $\phi_2$ is high, $C_1$ connects between $V_{oc}$ and $V_{cmc}$. In steady state, $V_{oc}$ is constant because the applied voltages $V_{CM}$ and $V_{CSBIAS}$ are both dc voltages and because the switched-capacitor integrator operates in a negative feedback loop. After $V_{oc}$ becomes constant, $C_1$ does not transfer charge onto $C_2$ when $\phi_2$ is high. This condition is satisfied if the charge on $C_1$ when $\phi_1$ is high is the same when $\phi_2$ is high, or

$$Q(\phi_1) = C_1(V_{CM} - V_{CSBIAS}) = Q(\phi_2) = C_1(V_{oc} - V_{cmc}) \qquad (12.67)$$

This equation reduces to

$$V_{CM} - V_{oc} = V_{CSBIAS} - V_{cmc} \qquad (12.68)$$

**Figure 12.22.** (*a*) A CM half-circuit for Fig. 12.21. (*b*) Replica bias circuit for generating $V_{CSBIAS}$ for the differential op amp in Fig. 12.2.

If $V_{CSBIAS}$ equals the nominal bias voltage required at the CMC input and if $|a_{cmc}| \gg 1$, $V_{cmc}$ is about constant with $V_{cmc} \approx V_{CSBIAS}$. Then (12.68) reduces to

$$V_{oc} \approx V_{CM} \qquad (12.69)$$

as desired. For the op amp in Fig. 12.2, bias voltage $V_{CSBIAS}$ could be generated by passing a current equal to $|I_{D3}| + |I_{D4}|$ through a diode-connected copy of $M_5$ connected to $-V_{SS}$, as shown in Fig. 12.22*b*. The copies of $M_3$ and $M_4$ have the same source and gate connections as in the op amp and duplicate the currents $|I_{D3}|$ and $|I_{D4}|$ that flow in Fig. 12.2. The voltage $V_{CSBIAS}$ is the gate voltage of the copy of $M_5$. Since this bias circuit uses copies or *replicas* of the transistors in the op amp to generate $V_{CSBIAS}$, this technique is referred to as *replica biasing*.

An advantage of this CMFB approach is that the op-amp output voltage swing is not limited by this CM-sense circuit because it consists only of passive elements (capacitors) and switches. (If a switch is constructed of *n*-channel and *p*-channel transistors in parallel driven by clock $\phi$ and its inverse, respectively, it can pass any signal that falls between the power-supply voltages if $V_{DD} + V_{SS} > V_{tn} + |V_{tp}|$.[10]) In practice, an MOS transistor is not an ideal switch. It must have a $W/L$ that is large enough to give a sufficiently low drain-source resistance when it is on. However, when each transistor turns off, charge from its channel and charge associated with its gate overlap capacitance transfer onto its drain and source nodes. Therefore, the MOS transistors acting as switches will transfer charge onto $C_1$. Let $\Delta Q$ represent the net charge transferred onto $C_1$ each clock period. Including the effect of this charge, (12.67) becomes

$$C_1(V_{CM} - V_{CSBIAS}) = C_1(V_{oc} - V_{cmc}) + \Delta Q \qquad (12.70)$$

or

$$V_{CM} - V_{oc} = V_{CSBIAS} - V_{cmc} + \frac{\Delta Q}{C_1} \qquad (12.71)$$

Comparing (12.71) with (12.68) shows that $\Delta Q/C_1$ introduces an offset in $V_{oc}$, making $V_{oc}$ differ from $V_{CM}$ when $V_{CSBIAS} = V_{cmc}$. If $V_{CM}$ was chosen to maximize the op-amp output swing, a shift in $V_{oc}$ will reduce the op-amp output swing. The magnitude of the charge transferred by ͺach switch transistor increases with its width $W$ [since the gate-channel and overlap capacitances are proportional to $W$ as shown in (1.187) and (2.45)], so a trade-off exists between low switch on-resistance and small charge transfer. From (12.71), increasing $C_1$ reduces the effect of the transferred charge on $V_{oc}$, but increasing $C_1$ increases the capacitive loading at the op-amp outputs when $\phi_2$ is high. ·

## 12.6  Fully Differential Op Amps

Some fully differential op amps are presented in this section. The singled-ended counterpart of each op amp was covered in previous chapters (low-frequency operation in Chapter 6 and compensation in Chapter 9). The two-stage op amp will be covered first, followed by single-stage op amps.

### 12.6.1  A Fully Differential Two-Stage Op Amp

A fully differential two-stage op amp is shown in Fig. 12.23. Compared to its single-ended counterpart in Fig. 6.16, two differences are the addition of $M_9$-$M_{10}$, which is a copy of the common-source stage $M_6$-$M_7$, to generate the second output, and the removal of the gate-to-drain connection on $M_3$ to give a symmetric input stage. The input stage is a complementary version of the differential stage in Fig. 12.2. The common-mode control (CMC) input is the gate of tail current source $M_5$. If the voltage at the gate of $M_5$ changes, the magnitudes of the drain currents in $M_1$-$M_4$ change by equal amounts. Therefore, $V_{ds3}$ and $V_{ds4}$ change by equal amounts. These voltage changes are amplified by the

**Figure 12.23.** A fully differential two-stage CMOS op amp.

**Figure 12.24.** (a) The DM half-circuit and (b) the CM half-circuit for the op amp in Fig. 12.23.

common-source stages $M_6$-$M_7$ and $M_9$-$M_{10}$ to cause equal changes in output voltages $V_{o1}$ and $V_{o2}$, which changes $V_{oc}$. Therefore, the CM output voltage can be controlled by a CMFB loop that connects to the gate of $M_5$.

In Fig. 12.23, two Miller compensation capacitors $C$ are connected across the symmetric second stages. These capacitors compensate both the DM and CM half-circuits, which are shown in Fig. 12.24. Although not shown, any of the approaches described in Chapter 9 for eliminating the right-half-plane zero associated with feedforward through the compensation capacitor could be used here.

The DM half-circuit in Fig. 12.24a is a cascade of two common-source amplifiers with active loads. The low-frequency DM gain is

$$a_{dm0} \equiv \frac{v_{od}}{v_{id}} = -g_{m2}(r_{o2}\|r_{o4})g_{m6}(r_{o6}\|r_{o7}) \tag{12.72}$$

The Miller-compensated second stage can be modeled by the circuit in Fig. 9.21 with $R_1 = r_{o2}\|r_{o4}$, $g_m = g_{m6}$, $R_2 = r_{o6}\|r_{o7}$, $C_1 = C_{1d}$, and $C_2 = C_{2d}$. (The capacitance $C_{1d}$ at the input of the second stage and load capacitance $C_{2d}$ of the second stage are not shown explicitly in Fig. 12.24a.) Therefore, the poles $p_{1d}$ and $p_{2d}$ of the DM half-circuit are given by (9.32) and (9.33). Assume that the op amp is operating in a feedback loop, the feedback factor $f_{dm}$ for the DM feedback loop is frequency-independent, and the right-half-plane zero has been eliminated. Then to achieve 45° phase margin, the magnitude of the DM loop gain should be unity at the frequency $|p_{2d}|$. Since $|gain| \times frequency$ is constant from $p_{1d}$ to $p_{2d}$ due to the one-pole roll-off there, we can write

$$|a_{dm0}f_{dm}p_{1d}| = 1 \cdot |p_{2d}| \tag{12.73}$$

Substituting (12.72), (9.32), and (9.33) in (12.73) gives

$$\frac{g_{m2}}{C} f_{dm} \approx \frac{g_{m6}}{C_{2d}} \tag{12.74}$$

assuming that the DM load capacitance $C_{2d}$ and the compensation capacitor $C$ are much larger than the internal node capacitance $C_{1d}$. If the other values are known, the compensation capacitor is determined by (12.74).

The CM half-circuit is shown in Fig. 12.24b. The first stages of the CM and DM half-circuits are different, but the second stages are identical. To focus on the CMFB loop, we will assume that $v_{ic} = 0$. (Nonzero $v_{ic}$ will be considered later.) In the CM half-circuit, the first stage consists of common-source $M_{5h}$ with common-gate $M_2$ and active load $M_4$. As in Fig. 12.14b, $M_{5h}$ is one half of $M_5$, with $(W/L)_{5h} = (W/L)_5/2$ and $I_{D5h} = I_{D5}/2$. The first stage is followed by the common-source second stage, $M_6$-$M_7$. The low-frequency CMC gain is

$$a_{cmc0} = \frac{v_{oc}}{v_{cmc}} \approx g_{m5h}[(r_{o2}g_{m2}r_{o5h})\|r_{o4}]g_{m6}(r_{o6}\|r_{o7}) \tag{12.75}$$

Capacitance associated with the source of cascode $M_1$ introduces a pole $p_x$ in the CMC gain. If $|p_x|$ is much larger than the magnitude of the nondominant pole $|p_{2c}|$ in (9.33) from the Miller-compensated second stage, pole $p_x$ can be ignored, and the gain $a_{cmc}$ can be approximated as having two poles that are given by (9.32) and (9.33). These poles can be different than the poles in the DM gain for two reasons. First the output load capacitances in the DM and CM half-circuits can be different, and second the output resistances of the first stages in the half-circuits can be different. The zero due to feedforward is the same as for DM gain and can be eliminated as described in Chapter 9. To simplify the following analysis, we will assume that all poles and zeros in the CMFB loop other than the two poles associated with the Miller compensation can be ignored. To achieve 45° phase margin, the magnitude of the CMFB loop gain should fall to unity at $|p_{2c}|$. Therefore,

$$|a_{cmc0}a_{cms0}p_{1c}| = 1 \cdot |p_{2c}| \tag{12.76}$$

where $a_{cms0}$ is the low-frequency gain through the CM-sense circuit

$$a_{cms0} = \left.\frac{v_{cmc}}{v_{oc}}\right|_{\omega=0, \text{ CMFB loop open}} = \left.\frac{v_{cms}}{v_{oc}}\right|_{\omega=0, \text{ CMFB loop open}} \tag{12.77}$$

Substituting (12.75), (9.32), and (9.33) in (12.76) and using $R_1 \approx r_{o2}g_{m2}r_{o5h}$ gives

$$\frac{g_{m5h}}{C}|a_{cms0}| \approx \frac{g_{m6}}{C_{2c}} \tag{12.78}$$

assuming that the CM load capacitance $C_{2c}$ and the compensation capacitor $C$ are much larger than the internal node capacitance $C_{1c}$. The compensation capacitor required for the CMFB loop can be found from (12.78).

Ideally, the compensation capacitor values calculated in (12.74) and (12.78) would be equal, and the CMFB and DM loops would each have a phase margin of 45°. In practice, these values are rarely equal. If the value of $C$ is chosen to be the larger of the values given by (12.74) and (12.78), one feedback loop will have a phase margin of 45°, and the other loop will have a phase margin larger than 45° and will be overcompensated. A drawback of overcompensation is that the unity-gain frequency of the loop gain and the closed-loop bandwidth are smaller than they would be if the loop were optimally compensated. If the larger $C$ is required to compensate the DM feedback loop, using that compensation capacitor will overcompensate the CMFB loop. Since the CMFB ideally operates on only dc signals, reducing its bandwidth may be acceptable. (See Section 12.8 for more on this topic.) If the larger $C$ is required to compensate the CMFB feedback loop, using that compensation capacitor will overcompensate the DM loop. However, reducing the bandwidth of the DM feedback loop by overcompensation is usually undesirable because this loop operates on the DM input signal, which may have a wide bandwidth.

An alternative to using the larger $C$ value that optimally compensates the CMFB loop but overcompensates the DM loop is the following. The value of $C$ that gives a 45° phase margin in the DM loop from (12.74) can be used if $g_{m5h}$ is scaled down to satisfy (12.78). This approach gives a 45° phase margin for both feedback loops without sacrificing bandwidth in the DM loop. Scaling of $g_{m5h} = g_{m5}/2$ could be achieved by reducing $(W/L)_5$, but such scaling would reduce the CM input range of the op amp because decreasing $(W/L)_5$ increases $|V_{ov5}|$. Another solution is to split $M_5$ into two parallel transistors, one that has its gate connected to a bias voltage and the other with its gate connected to CMC, as described in Section 12.4.2 and Fig. 12.15. A drawback of this approach is that reducing $g_{m5h}$ reduces $|a_{cmc0}|$, as can be seen in (12.75).

Ignoring limitations imposed by the CM-sense circuit, we see that each op-amp output in Fig. 12.23 can swing until a transistor in the second stage enters the triode region. The maximum value of $V_{o1}$ is $V_{DD} - |V_{ov7}|$, and its minimum value is $-V_{SS} + V_{ov6}$. Therefore, the peak differential output voltage is

$$V_{od(peak)} = V_{o1(max)} - V_{o2(min)} = V_{o1(max)} - V_{o1(min)} = V_{DD} - |V_{ov7}| - (-V_{SS} + V_{ov6})$$
$$= V_{DD} + V_{SS} - V_{ov6} - |V_{ov7}| \qquad (12.79)$$

The CM input range of the op amp is limited in the positive direction by the tail current source, which transitions from active to triode when $|V_{ds5}| = |V_{ov5}|$; therefore, we want

$$V_{IC} < V_{DD} - |V_{GS1}| - |V_{ov5}| \qquad (12.80)$$

The lower limit of the CM input range occurs when input transistor $M_1$ (or $M_2$) enters the triode region, so

$$V_{IC} > -V_{SS} + V_{GS6} + V_{t1} \qquad (12.81)$$

▪ **EXAMPLE**

Modify the single-ended two-stage op amp from the examples in Section 6.3.5 and Section 9.4.3 into a fully differential op amp. It will be used in the feedback circuit shown in Fig. 12.25, which represents the connections in a switched-capacitor circuit when one clock is high (assuming the switches are ideal). The capacitor values are $C_S = 2\,\text{pF}$, $C_F = 5\,\text{pF}$, and $C_L = 2\,\text{pF}$. Design for 1-V peak output swing and phase margins of 45° or greater in the DM and CMFB loops. Use $V_{DD} = V_{SS} = 1.65$ V, and design for a CM output voltage of 0 V.

**Figure 12.25.** A fully differential op amp with capacitive load and feedback.

**Figure 12.26.** A fully differential two-stage CMOS op amp using the CMFB scheme from Fig. 12.19.

First, we will design the devices to satisfy the bias and low-frequency requirements. Then we will compensate the amplifier. Using the device sizes and bias currents from the example in Section 6.3.5, we have

$$(W/L)_1 = (W/L)_2 = 77 \quad (W/L)_3 = (W/L)_4 = 4 \quad (W/L)_5 = 25$$

$$(W/L)_6 = (W/L)_9 = 16 \quad (W/L)_7 = (W/L)_{10} = 50$$

with $L_{drwn} = 1\ \mu$m, $|I_{D1}| = |I_{D2}| = 100\ \mu$A, and $I_{D6} = 400\ \mu$A. In that example, these values gave a calculated dc gain of $a_{dm0} = -7500$ and a simulated gain of $a_{dm0} = -6200$.

For CMFB, we will use two differential pairs as shown in Fig. 12.26. Since the input stage in Fig. 12.23 is the complement of the op amp in Fig. 12.2, the CMFB circuit in Fig. 12.26 is the complement of the circuit in Fig. 12.19 to allow control of the op-amp tail current $I_{D5}$ through a current mirror formed by $M_5$ and $M_{25}$. Also, the CM-sense output $V_{cms}$ is taken from the drains of $M_{21}$ and $M_{24}$, which makes the gain $a_{cms}$ negative. This inversion is needed here to give negative feedback in the CMFB loop because the CMC gain $a_{cmc}$ is positive at low frequencies in this two-stage op amp. We choose $M_{25}$ to be matched to $M_5$, so they form a unity-gain current mirror. Since the desired tail current is $|I_{D5}| = 200\ \mu$A, we want

$$|I_{D25}| = I_{D26} = I_{D27} = 200\ \mu\text{A}$$

Therefore, each transistor $M_{21}$-$M_{24}$ nominally carries $100\ \mu$A of drain current. These transistors must remain active over the entire range of the op-amp output swing. For a differential output voltage of 1 V peak, each op-amp output ($V_{o1}$ or $V_{o2}$) must swing $\pm 0.5$ V. From (3.161), the transistors in a differential pair remain active as long as the magnitude of the differential input voltage is less than $\sqrt{2}V_{ov}$. Therefore, we want

$$\sqrt{2}V_{ov} = 0.5\ \text{V}$$

or $V_{ov} = 0.35$ V for $M_{21}$-$M_{24}$. From (1.157), we get

$$\left(\frac{W}{L}\right)_{21} = \left(\frac{W}{L}\right)_{22} = \left(\frac{W}{L}\right)_{23} = \left(\frac{W}{L}\right)_{24} = \frac{2I_{D21}}{k_n'(V_{ov21})^2} = \frac{2(100)}{(194)(0.35)^2} = 8.4$$

The only remaining device sizes to be determined are for matched transistors $M_{26}$ and $M_{27}$. Each device acts as a current source carrying 200 µA. For those transistors to act as current sources, they should always be active. Focusing on $M_{26}$, we want $V_{ov26} < V_{ds26(\min)}$. To determine $V_{ds26(\min)}$, consider an extreme case when $M_{21}$ just turns off as $V_{o1}$ swings down to its lowest value. In this case, $M_{22}$ carries 200 µA, and

$$V_{gs22(\max)} = V_{t22} + \sqrt{\frac{2I_{D22(\max)}}{k_n'(W/L)_{22}}} = V_{t22} + \sqrt{\frac{2(200)}{194(8.4)}} = V_{t22} + 0.5 \text{ V}$$

The gate voltage of $M_{22}$ is $V_{CM} = 0$. Therefore, the minimum source-body voltage for $M_{22}$, which is the minimum drain-source voltage of $M_{26}$, is

$$V_{sb22(\min)} = V_{ds26(\min)} = V_{s22(\min)} - (-V_{SS}) = V_{CM} - V_{gs22(\max)} + V_{SS}$$

$$= 0 - (0.5 + V_{t22}) + 1.65 = 1.15 - V_{t22} \qquad (12.82)$$

Since $V_{sb22}$ is not zero, the threshold voltage of $M_{22}$ is given by (1.140) as

$$V_{t22} = V_{tn0} + \gamma \left[ \sqrt{V_{sb22} + 2\phi_f} - \sqrt{2\phi_f} \right] \qquad (12.83)$$

Using the data in Table 2.4, (1.141), and (2.28), we calculate $|\phi_f| = 0.33$ V and $\gamma = 0.28 \text{ V}^{1/2}$ [assuming $V_{sb22}$ is small and using $N_A + N_{si}$ as the effective substrate doping in (1.141)]. Solving (12.82) and (12.83) gives $V_{t22} = 0.67$ V, $V_{s22(\min)} = -1.17$ V, and

$$V_{sb22(\min)} = V_{ds26(\min)} = 1.15 - V_{t22} = 1.15 - 0.67 = 0.48 \text{ V}$$

If we chose $V_{ov26} = 0.38$ V (to allow for a $-0.1$ V shift in $V_{CM}$), then

$$\left(\frac{W}{L}\right)_{26} = \frac{2I_{D26}}{k_n'(V_{ov26})^2} = \frac{2(200)}{(194)(0.38)^2} \approx 14$$

Also, $(W/L)_{27} = 14$ since $M_{26}$ and $M_{27}$ are matched.

In the example in Section 9.4.3, a compensation capacitor of 3.2 pF provided a 45° phase margin for a feedback factor of unity and a 5-pF load. The DM half-circuits for this example with the independent voltage sources $V_{s1}$ and $V_{s2}$ set to zero are shown in Fig. 12.27a. Here, we have assumed that $C_L$ is much larger than the input capacitance of the CM-sense devices $M_{21}$-$M_{24}$. The two feedback networks connect between the two half-circuits in this negative feedback circuit. The feedback factor is less than one because it is set by the capacitive divider formed by $C_F$ and $C_S$. Also, the feedback networks affect the capacitive loading at the outputs. The upper DM half-circuit in Fig. 12.27a is redrawn in Fig. 12.27b with the feedback loop broken. Here, capacitor $C_{idh}$ is the capacitance looking into the gate of $M_1$ in the DM half-circuit, which is the same as the capacitance looking into the gate of $M_2$. Looking into the gate of $M_2$, we see $C_{gs2}$ and overlap capacitance $C_{gd2}$ increased by the Miller effect as in (7.5); therefore,

$$C_{idh} = C_{gs2} + C_{gd2}(1 - a_{dm1}) \approx \frac{2}{3} C_{ox} W_2 L_2 + C_{ol} W_2 (1 - a_{dm1})$$

$$= \frac{2}{3}\left(4.43 \frac{\text{fF}}{\mu\text{m}^2}\right)(77 \ \mu\text{m})(0.82 \ \mu\text{m}) + \left(0.35 \frac{\text{fF}}{\mu\text{m}}\right)(77 \ \mu\text{m})(1 + 137) = 3.9 \text{ pF}$$

**Figure 12.27.** (a) The DM half-circuits for Figs. 12.25 and 12.26. (b) The upper DM half-circuit in (a) with the feedback loop broken.

Here, we used $L_2 = 1\ \mu m - 2L_d = 0.82\ \mu m$ and $a_{dm1} = -g_{m2}(r_{o2}\|r_{o4}) = -137$ for the low-frequency gain of the first stage. These values follow from the example in Section 6.3.5. The total capacitive load from the output to ground in the DM half-circuit is

$$C_{2d} = C_L + \frac{C_F(C_S + C_{idh})}{C_F + C_S + C_{idh}} = 2 + \frac{5(2 + 3.9)}{5 + 2 + 3.9} = 4.7\ \text{pF} \qquad (12.84)$$

Here, we have assumed that $C_L$ is much larger than the junction capacitance and other parasitic capacitances at the op-amp output. The DM feedback factor is

$$f_{dm} = \left.\frac{v_{fb}/2}{v_{od}/2}\right|_{\text{loop broken}} = \frac{C_F}{C_F + C_S + C_{idh}} = \frac{5}{5 + 2 + 3.9} = 0.459 \qquad (12.85)$$

Substituting (12.84), (12.85), and values for $g_{m2} = g_{m1}$ and $g_{m6}$ from the example in Section 9.4.3 into (12.74), we have

$$C \approx \frac{g_{m2}}{g_{m6}} C_{2d} f_{dm} = \frac{1.0}{1.55}(4.7 \text{ pF})(0.459) = 1.39 \text{ pF} \qquad (12.86)$$

This compensation capacitor gives a 45° phase margin in the DM half-circuit (ignoring the right-half-plane zero).

**Figure 12.28.** (*a*) The CM half-circuits for Figs. 12.25 and 12.26. (*b*) The upper CM half-circuit in (*a*) simplified.

**Figure 12.28.** (*c*) The CM half-circuit in (*b*), focusing on the CMFB loop (loop #1).

The CM half-circuits are shown in Fig. 12.28*a* with the source voltages $V_{s1}$ and $V_{s2}$ set to zero. Only the upper CM half-circuit is shown in detail. The capacitive feedback networks connect between the two CM half-circuits. A simplified drawing of the upper CM half-circuit is shown in Fig. 12.28*b*. The key simplification here is that capacitor $C_F$, which was connected to the input of the lower CM half-circuit (which is the gate of $M_1$) in Fig. 12.28*a*, now connects to the gate of $M_2$. This change does not affect the CM analysis because the elements and signals in the two CM half-circuits are identical.

In the CM half-circuit in Fig. 12.28*b*, there are two feedback loops. One loop is the CMFB loop that includes the CM-sense block. We will refer to this loop as loop #1. This loop is a negative feedback loop, since there are three inverting stages in the loop: actively loaded common-source stages $M_{5h}$ and $M_6$, and the inverting CM-sense circuit. The magnitude of the low-frequency gain in this loop is large because each common-source stage provides significant voltage gain. The other feedback loop goes through the op amp from $v_{ic}$ to $v_{oc}$ and then back from $v_{oc}$ to the input $v_{ic}$ through the capacitive divider formed by $C_F$ and $C_S$, and it will be called loop #2. Here, loop #2 is a *positive* feedback loop because it contains two inverting gain stages. This feedback loop is stable, however, because the loop gain in loop #2, which is the product of the forward gain $a'_{cm}$ and the feedback factor through the capacitive divider, has a magnitude that is less than one at all frequencies. The forward gain $a'_{cm}$ in this loop, which is $a'_{cm} = v_{oc}/v_{ic}$ with the CMFB (loop #1) active, has a magnitude that is less than unity due to the presence of the CMFB loop (loop #1), which works to force $v_{oc} \approx 0$. (See Problem 12.27.) To explain this low gain, first consider the CM half-circuit with loop #1 disabled. In this case, if $v_{ic}$ is nonzero, $I_{d2}$ changes, which changes $V_{gs6}$ and produces a nonzero $v_{oc}$. When the CMFB loop #1 is enabled, this loop senses any nonzero $v_{oc}$ and adjusts $V_{cmc}$ to produce a change in $I_{d5}$ that counteracts the change in $I_{d2}$ to give $v_{oc} \approx 0$.

The magnitude responses of the loop gains for these two loops are plotted in Fig. 12.29, ignoring any zeros and poles other than the dominant and nondominant poles, $p_{1c}$ and $p_{2c}$, associated with the Miller-compensated gain stage in Fig. 12.28*b*. Here, loop #1 is assumed to be compensated so that its unity-gain frequency is equal to $|p_{2c}|$, which gives a 45° phase margin. Since loop #2 is stable, we need only focus on the stability and compensation of the high-gain CMFB loop (loop #1).

This CMFB loop is shown in Fig. 12.28*c*. Here, the lumped load capacitance $C_{2c}$ includes the output loading due to $C_L$ and the capacitive feedback network, including the capacitance $C_{ich}$ looking into the gate of $M_2$ in Fig. 12.28*b*. This capacitance is smaller than $C_{idh}$ because $M_2$ has a large source degeneration resistance ($r_{o5h}$) that provides local CM feedback. This feedback increases the impedance (decreases the capacitance) looking into the gate of $M_2$. Also, this feedback reduces the magnitude of the voltage gain from the

**Figure 12.29.** Plots of the loop gains for the two feedback loops in the CM half-circuit in Fig. 12.28$b$.

gate to the drain of $M_2$, which decreases the Miller input capacitance due to $C_{gd2}$. Therefore, assuming $C_{ich} \ll C_S$, we find

$$C_{2c} = C_L + \frac{C_F(C_S + C_{ich})}{C_F + C_S + C_{ich}} \approx C_L + \frac{C_F C_S}{C_F + C_S} = 2 + \frac{5(2)}{5 + 2} = 3.43 \text{ pF}$$

Here, we also assumed that $C_L$ is much larger than the input capacitance of the CM-sense half-circuit. To use (12.78) to calculate the compensation capacitor that gives a 45° phase margin in the CMFB loop, we must find the dc small-signal gain through the CM-sense circuit. In Fig. 12.26, $I_{cms}$ flows through diode-connected $M_{25}$; therefore,

$$v_{cmc} = -\frac{i_{cms}}{g_{m25}} \tag{12.87}$$

if $r_{o25} \gg 1/g_{m25}$. A small-signal version of (12.56) is $i_{cms} = g_{m22}v_{oc} = g_{m21}v_{oc}$. Using this expression and (12.87), the gain $a_{cms}$ at low frequency is

$$|a_{cms0}| = \frac{|v_{cmc}|}{|v_{oc}|}\bigg|_{\text{CMFB loop open}} = \frac{|v_{cmc}|}{|i_{cms}|}\frac{|i_{cms}|}{|v_{oc}|}\bigg|_{\text{CMFB loop open}}$$

$$= \frac{g_{m21}}{g_{m25}} = \frac{\dfrac{2I_{D21}}{V_{ov21}}}{\dfrac{2|I_{D25}|}{|V_{ov25}|}} = \frac{\dfrac{2(100)}{0.35}}{\dfrac{2(200)}{0.5}} = 0.71 \tag{12.88}$$

Solving (12.78) for a 45° phase margin in the CMFB loop, using (12.88) and the value of $g_{m6}$ from the example in Section 9.4.3, gives

$$C = \frac{g_{m5h}}{g_{m6}}|a_{cms0}|C_{2c} = \frac{(g_{m5}/2)}{g_{m6}}|a_{cms0}|C_{2c}$$

$$= \frac{\dfrac{2(200 \text{ μA})}{0.5 \text{ V}}\dfrac{1}{2}}{1.55 \text{ mA/V}}(0.71)(3.43 \text{ pF}) = 0.63 \text{ pF} \tag{12.89}$$

From (12.86) and (12.89), a larger compensation capacitor is required to compensate the DM loop than the CMFB loop. Therefore, using $C = 1.39$ pF will give phase margins of 45° for the DM feedback loop and greater than 45° for the CMFB loop, which is acceptable.

To verify this design, SPICE simulations of this op amp were carried out with $C = 1.39$ pF in series with $R_Z = 758\ \Omega$, which was found to eliminate the right-half-plane zero in the example in Section 9.4.3. The SPICE models are based on the data in Table 2.4. The phase margins of the DM and CMFB loops were simulated using techniques developed for fully differential circuits.[11] The DM feedback loop has a simulated phase margin of 43° and unity-gain frequency of 53 MHz. The CMFB loop has a simulated phase margin of 62° and unity-gain frequency of 24 MHz. Thus, the CMFB loop is overcompensated. Changing the compensation capacitor to 0.63 pF, which is the value calculated from (12.89) to give a 45° phase margin in the CMFB loop, we find the simulated phase margin of the CMFB loop changes to 41°, but the DM phase margin drops to an unacceptably low 29°. These simulation results verify that the formulas in this section give a reasonable estimate for the compensation capacitor.

In the previous example, the op-amp output swing is limited by the linear input range of the CMFB circuit. The output swing could be increased by using either a switched-capacitor or resistive-divider CM detector.

An alternative CMFB approach for the op amp in Fig. 12.23 is to connect the gate of $M_5$ to a dc bias voltage and to use the gates of $M_3$-$M_4$ as the CMC input. In this case, the first gain stage of the CM half-circuit in Fig. 12.28c consists of common-source $M_4$ with a cascoded active load. Also, the pole associated with the capacitance at the source of $M_2$ is not in the signal path of the CMFB loop.

### 12.6.2 Fully Differential Telescopic Cascode Op Amp

A fully differential cascode op amp is shown in Fig. 12.30. Compared to its single-ended complementary counterpart, which is the first stage in Fig. 6.25, the main difference is that diode connections are removed from transistors $M_3$ and $M_{3A}$. Also, the gates of cascode transistors $M_{1A}$-$M_{4A}$ are connected to bias voltages here. The op-amp outputs are taken

**Figure 12.30.** A fully differential CMOS telescopic-cascode op amp.

from the drains of $M_{1A}$ and $M_{2A}$. The resulting circuit is symmetric with each output loaded by a cascoded current source. An advantage of the topology in Fig. 12.30 is that the DM signal path consists only of $n$-channel transistors. That is, only the $n$-channel transistors conduct time-varying currents. The $p$-channel transistors conduct constant currents. Such a configuration maximizes the op-amp speed because $n$-channel transistors have higher mobility and $f_T$ than their $p$-channel counterparts (if the channel lengths and overdrive voltages are the same). One CMFB approach is to set the currents through $M_3$-$M_4$ by connecting their gates to a dc bias voltage (set by a diode-connected transistor that is the input of a current mirror) and use the gate of $M_5$ as the CMC input. In this case, the magnitude of the low-frequency CMC gain $|a_{cmc0}|$ can be large since $M_1$-$M_2$ and $M_{1A}$-$M_{2A}$ provide two levels of NMOS cascoding, and $M_{3A}$-$M_{4A}$ provide one level of PMOS cascoding. This cascoding increases the output resistance, but the two levels of NMOS cascoding introduce high-frequency poles in $a_{cmc}(s)$.

An alternative CMFB approach is to set the current through $M_5$ by connecting its gate to a dc bias voltage and use the gates of $M_3$ and $M_4$ as the CMC input. This approach has one level of cascoding in the CMC gain path, which introduces one high-frequency pole in $a_{cmc}(s)$. Here, however, the amplifying devices in the CMFB loop are $p$-channel $M_3$ and $M_4$, which have lower mobility and $f_T$ than $n$-channel $M_5$ if they have the same channel lengths and overdrive voltages.

The DM and CMFB feedback loops are compensated by the load capacitances at the op-amp outputs. The phase margin of the CMFB loop can be changed without changing the load capacitance, by splitting the transistor(s) that connect to the CMC input into parallel transistors, as described in Section 12.4.2 and shown in Fig. 12.15.

### 12.6.3  Fully Differential Folded-Cascode Op Amp

A fully differential folded-cascode op amp is shown in Fig. 12.31. Compared to its single-ended counterpart shown in Fig. 6.28, the main difference is that the diode connections on $M_3$ and $M_{3A}$ have been eliminated. The resulting circuit is symmetric, and the outputs are taken from the drains of $M_{1A}$ and $M_{2A}$.

**Figure 12.31.**  A fully differential CMOS folded-cascode op amp.

To satisfy KCL, the sum of the currents flowing through $M_3$, $M_4$, and $M_5$ must equal the sum of the drain currents flowing through $M_{11}$ and $M_{12}$. To satisfy KCL with all transistors active and to accurately set $V_{oc}$, CMFB is used. The CMC input could be taken as the gate of $M_5$, the gates of $M_3$-$M_4$, or the gates of $M_{11}$-$M_{12}$, which is shown in Fig. 12.31. With this last option, the CMFB loop contains less nodes than the other two cases, and the gain $a_{cmc}$ is provided by common-source $n$-channel transistor $M_{11}$ (or $M_{12}$), which has a larger $g_m$ than $p$-channel $M_3$ (or $M_4$) if $(W/L)_{11} \approx (W/L)_3$ because $k'_n > k'_p$ and $I_{D11} > |I_{D3}|$.

The DM and CMFB feedback loops are compensated by the capacitances at the op-amp outputs.

The folded-cascode op amp with active cascodes that is shown in Fig. 6.30 can also be converted to a fully differential op amp.[12] As for the folded-cascode op amp, there are three choices for the CMC input.

### 12.6.4 A Differential Op Amp with Two Differential Input Stages

The fully differential op amps presented above have two input terminals that accept one differential input. Those op amps can be used in the amplifier, integrator, and differentiator shown in Fig. 12.32. To implement a fully differential non-inverting gain stage with a very

**Figure 12.32.** Fully differential (a) inverting gain stage, (b) integrator, and (c) differentiator.

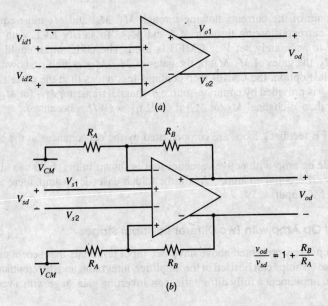

(a)

$$\frac{v_{od}}{v_{sd}} = 1 + \frac{R_B}{R_A}$$

(b)

**Figure 12.33.** (a) An op amp with two pairs of inputs. (b) A noninverting fully differential feedback amplifier.

large input impedance, an op amp with four input terminals is needed. Two inputs connect to the feedback networks and the other two inputs connect to the differential signal source, as shown in Fig. 12.33. Assuming the magnitudes of the op amp gains from $v_{id1}$ and $v_{id2}$ to $v_{od}$ are large, negative feedback forces $v_{id1} \approx 0$ and $v_{id2} \approx 0$. The two pairs of inputs are produced by two source-coupled pairs, as shown for a two-stage op amp in Fig. 12.34. The two source-coupled pairs, $M_1$-$M_2$ and $M_{1X}$-$M_{2X}$, share a pair of current-source loads. Assuming the input pairs are matched, the differential small-signal voltage gain is the same from either input; therefore,

$$v_{od} = a_{dm}(v_{id1} + v_{id2}) \tag{12.90}$$

The CM input range for the op amp must be large enough to include the full range of the input signals, $V_{s1}$ and $V_{s2}$, because they connect directly to op-amp inputs. In this

**Figure 12.34.** A simplified schematic of a two-stage op amp with two pairs of inputs.

op amp, the CMFB loop could adjust either $I_1$ or $I_2$ by controlling the gate voltages of the transistors that generate those currents.

## 12.6.5 Neutralization

In a fully differential op amp, a technique referred to as *capacitive neutralization* can be used to reduce the component of the op-amp input capacitance due to the Miller effect (see Chapter 7). Reducing the input capacitance increases the input impedance, which is desirable. Neutralization is illustrated in Fig. 12.35a. The gate-to-drain overlap capacitances are shown explicitly for $M_1$ and $M_2$. First, ignore the neutralization capacitors $C_n$. Then the DM capacitance looking into either op-amp input (with respect to ground) is

$$C_{idh} = C_{gs1} + C_{gd1}(1 - a_{dm1}) \qquad (12.91)$$

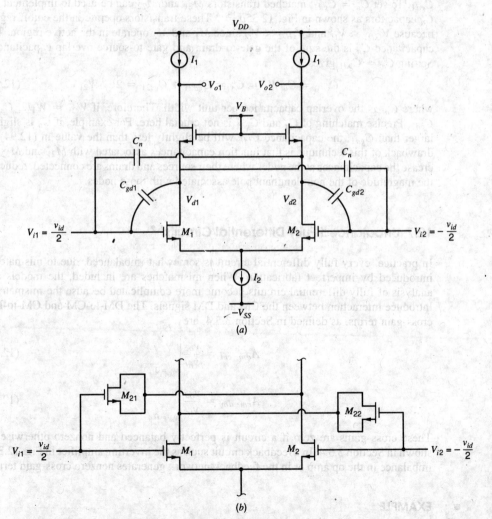

**Figure 12.35.** (a) An example of capacitive neutralization. (b) Using transistors $M_{21}$ and $M_{22}$ in cutoff to implement the neutralization capacitors.

where $a_{dm1}$ is the low-frequency DM gain from the gate to drain of $M_1$:

$$a_{dm1} = \left. \frac{v_{d1}}{(v_{id}/2)} \right|_{\omega=0} \tag{12.92}$$

Because the op amp is balanced, the low-frequency voltage gain across each capacitor $C_n$ is $-a_{dm1}$. Therefore, when $C_n$ is included, the capacitance in (12.91) becomes

$$C_{idh} = C_{gs1} + C_{gd1}(1 - a_{dm1}) + C_n(1 + a_{dm1}) \tag{12.93}$$

If $C_n = C_{gd1}$, (12.93) reduces to

$$C_{idh} = C_{gs1} + 2C_{gd1} \tag{12.94}$$

which is less than the value in (12.91) if $|a_{dm1}| > 1$. The Miller effect on $C_{gd1}$ is canceled here when $C_n = C_{gd1}$ because the gain across $C_n$ is exactly the opposite of the gain across $C_{gd1}$. To set $C_n = C_{gd1}$, matched transistors $M_{21}$ and $M_{22}$ can be used to implement the $C_n$ capacitors as shown in Fig. 12.35b.[13,14] These transistors operate in the cutoff region because $V_{GD2} < V_{t1}$ and $V_{GD2} < V_{t2}$ since $M_1$ and $M_2$ operate in the active region. The capacitance $C_n$ is the sum of the gate-to-drain and gate-to-source overlap capacitances. Setting $C_n = C_{gd1}$ gives

$$C_{gd1} = C_{ol}W_1 = C_n = C_{gd21} + C_{gs21} = 2C_{ol}W_{21} \tag{12.95}$$

where $C_{ol}$ is the overlap capacitance per unit width. Therefore, if $W_{21} = W_1/2$, $C_n = C_{gd1}$. Precise matching of $C_n$ and $C_{gd1}$ is not crucial here. For example, if $C_n$ is slightly larger than $C_{gd1}$, the capacitance $C_{idh}$ will be slightly less than the value in (12.94). A drawback of this technique is that junction capacitances associated with $M_{21}$ and $M_{22}$ increase the capacitances at the nodes where their sources and drains are connected, reducing the magnitude of the non-dominant pole associated with those nodes.

## 12.7 Unbalanced Fully Differential Circuits[1,2]

In practice, every fully differential circuit is somewhat imbalanced, due to mismatches introduced by imperfect fabrication. When mismatches are included, the models and analysis of fully differential circuits become more complicated because the mismatches introduce interaction between the CM and DM signals. The DM-to-CM and CM-to-DM cross-gain terms, as defined in Section 3.5.4, are

$$A_{dm-cm} = \left. \frac{v_{oc}}{v_{id}} \right|_{v_{ic}=0} \tag{12.96}$$

$$A_{cm-dm} = \left. \frac{v_{od}}{v_{ic}} \right|_{v_{id}=0} \tag{12.97}$$

These cross gains are zero if a circuit is perfectly balanced and nonzero otherwise, as shown in Section 3.5.4. In a feedback circuit such as the inverting amplifier in Fig. 12.32a, imbalance in the op amp or in the feedback network generates nonzero cross-gain terms.

■  **EXAMPLE**

Compute the small-signal gains for the inverting amplifier shown in Fig. 12.32a. For simplicity, assume the op amp is balanced, has infinite input impedance, zero output impedance, $a_{dm} \rightarrow -\infty$ and $a'_{cm} = -0.1$. (This $a'_{cm}$ is the CM gain, including the effect of the CMFB loop.) The resistors across the op amp are matched with $R_3 = R_4 = 5\,k\Omega$, but the resistors that connect to the signal source are mismatched with $R_1 = 1.01\,k\Omega$ and $R_2 = 0.99\,k\Omega$. Therefore, the only imbalance in this circuit stems from the mismatch between $R_1$ and $R_2$.

We will analyze this circuit using coupled half-circuits, which were introduced in Section 3.5.6.9. The two coupled half-circuits are shown in Fig. 12.36. The circuits are coupled by the nonzero resistor mismatch

$$\Delta R = R_1 - R_2 = 0.02\,k\Omega$$

The resistance $R$ in the figure is the average value of the mismatched resistors

$$R = \frac{R_1 + R_2}{2} = 1\,k\Omega$$

Letting $a_{dm} \rightarrow -\infty$ in the DM half-circuit gives

$$\frac{v_{od}}{2} = -\frac{R_3}{R}\left(\frac{v_{sd}}{2} - i_{Rc}\frac{\Delta R}{2}\right) \qquad (12.98)$$

Analysis of the CM half-circuit gives

$$v_{oc} = -\frac{R_3}{R}\left(v_{sc} - \frac{i_{Rd}}{2}\frac{\Delta R}{2}\right)\frac{1}{1 + \left[\dfrac{R + R_3}{(-a'_{cm})R}\right]} \qquad (12.99)$$

From these equations and the coupled half-circuits, exact input-output relationships could be found. However, for small mismatches, the approximate method described in Section 3.5.6.9 simplifies the analysis and provides sufficient accuracy for hand calculations. The key simplification in the approximate analysis is that the currents $i_{Rd}$ and $i_{Rc}$ are estimated from their respective half-circuits, ignoring mismatch effects. If the mismatch is ignored

(a)

(b)

**Figure 12.36.** Coupled (a) DM and (b) CM half-circuits for the gain stage in Fig. 12.32a with a balanced op amp and mismatch in the feedback network.

in Fig. 12.36a (i.e., if $\Delta R = 0$), then

$$\frac{i_{Rd}}{2} \approx \frac{\hat{i}_{Rd}}{2} \doteq \frac{v_{sd}}{2R} \tag{12.100}$$

since $v_{id}/2 = 0$ (because $a_{dm} \rightarrow -\infty$). Ignoring resistor mismatch in Fig. 12.36b, we find

$$i_{Rc} \approx \hat{i}_{Rc} = \frac{v_{sc}}{R + R_3}\left(1 + \frac{R_3}{R} \cdot \frac{1}{1 + \left[\dfrac{R + R_3}{(-a'_{cm})R}\right]}\right) \tag{12.101}$$

Using (12.101) in (12.98) gives

$$\frac{v_{od}}{2} := -\frac{R_3}{R}\left\{\frac{v_{sd}}{2} - v_{sc}\frac{\Delta R}{2(R + R_3)}\left(1 + \frac{R_3}{R} \cdot \frac{1}{1 + \left[\dfrac{R + R_3}{(-a'_{cm})R}\right]}\right)\right\} \tag{12.102}$$

Substituting (12.100) into (12.99) gives

$$v_{oc} = -\frac{R_3}{R}\left(v_{sc} - v_{sd}\frac{\Delta R}{4R}\right)\frac{1}{1 + \left[\dfrac{R + R_3}{(-a_{cm})R}\right]} \tag{12.103}$$

From (12.102),

$$A_{dm} = \left.\frac{v_{od}}{v_{sd}}\right|_{v_{sc}=0} = -\frac{R_3}{R} = -\frac{5}{1} = -5$$

$$A_{cm-dm} = \left.\frac{v_{od}}{v_{sc}}\right|_{v_{sd}=0} = \frac{R_3}{R}\frac{\Delta R}{(R + R_3)}\left(1 + \frac{R_3}{R} \cdot \frac{1}{1 + \left[\dfrac{R + R_3}{(-a_{cm})R}\right]}\right)$$

$$= \frac{5}{1} \cdot \frac{0.02}{(1 + 5)}\left(1 + \frac{5}{1} \cdot \frac{1}{1 + \left[\dfrac{1 + 5}{0.1(1)}\right]}\right) = 0.018$$

From (12.103),

$$A_{cm} = \left.\frac{v_{oc}}{v_{sc}}\right|_{v_{sd}=0} = -\frac{R_3}{R}\frac{1}{1 + \left[\dfrac{R + R_3}{(-a_{cm})R}\right]} = -\frac{5}{1} \cdot \frac{1}{1 + \left[\dfrac{1 + 5}{0.1(1)}\right]} = -0.082$$

$$A_{dm-cm} = \left.\frac{v_{oc}}{v_{sd}}\right|_{v_{sc}=0} = \frac{R_3}{R}\frac{\Delta R}{4R}\frac{1}{1 + \left[\dfrac{R + R_3}{(-a_{cm})R}\right]} = \frac{5}{1}\frac{0.02}{4(1)}\frac{1}{1 + \left[\dfrac{1 + 5}{0.1(1)}\right]} = 0.00041$$

The resistor mismatch causes nonzero cross-gain terms in the closed-loop amplifier. Exact
■   analysis of this circuit gives essentially the same gain values as above.

A model for an op amp with mismatch (but assuming infinite input impedance and
zero output impedance, for simplicity) is shown in Fig. 12.37. The equations corresponding

**Figure 12.37.** A simple small-signal model of a fully differential amplifier including cross-gain terms, assuming infinite input impedance and zero output impedance.

to this model are

$$v_{od} = a_{dm}v_{id} + a_{cm-dm}v_{ic} + a_{cmc-dm}v_{cmc} \qquad (12.104)$$

$$v_{oc} = a_{cm}v_{ic} + a_{dm-cm}v_{id} + a_{cmc}v_{cmc} \qquad (12.105)$$

The cross-gain terms $a_{cm-dm}$, $a_{dm-cm}$, and $a_{cmc-dm}$ are zero when the op amp is perfectly balanced. If the CM-sense circuit is not perfectly balanced, its output $v_{cms}$, which ideally is proportional to the CM output, contains a component that depends on the DM output:

$$v_{cms} = a_{cms}v_{oc} + a_{dm-cms}v_{od} \qquad (12.106)$$

Also, $v_{cmc} = v_{cms}$ when the CMFB loop is closed.

To illustrate the effect of feedback on the open-loop op-amp gains, consider the inverting amplifier in Fig. 12.32a with a balanced feedback network ($R_1 = R_2$ and $R_3 = R_4$) but with imbalances in the op amp. The circuit could be analyzed exactly to find the closed-loop gains, but the analysis is difficult. Therefore, we will use the approximate, coupled half-circuit analysis that was used in the last example. The coupled DM and CM half-circuits are shown in Fig. 12.38. The imbalances in the op amp are modeled by the $a_{cm-dm}$, $a_{dm-cm}$, and $a_{cmc-dm}$ controlled sources in Fig. 12.38, based on (12.104) and (12.105). To simplify the analysis, we will assume that the CM-sense circuit is balanced (i.e., $a_{dm-cms} = 0$). Under this assumption, (12.106) reduces to

$$v_{cmc} = v_{cms} = a_{cms}v_{oc} \qquad (12.107)$$

Substituting (12.107) in (12.104) and (12.105) gives

$$v_{od} = a_{dm}v_{id} + a_{cm-dm}v_{ic} + a_{cmc-dm}a_{cms}v_{oc} \qquad (12.108)$$

$$v_{oc} = a_{cm}v_{ic} + a_{dm-cm}v_{id} + a_{cmc}a_{cms}v_{oc} \qquad (12.109)$$

**Figure 12.38.** Coupled (a) DM and (b) CM half-circuits for the gain stage in Fig. 12.32a with an unbalanced op amp and a balanced feedback network.

To carry out the approximate analysis, each half-circuit is first analyzed with the coupling between the half-circuits eliminated. Then the results of these analyses are used to find the closed-loop cross gains. The coupling in the DM half-circuit is eliminated by setting $a_{cm-dm} = 0$ and $a_{cmc-dm} = 0$. With these changes, analysis of Fig. 12.38a gives

$$\hat{v}_{id} = -\frac{R_3}{R_1} \cdot \frac{1}{1 + \dfrac{R_1 + R_3}{(-a_{dm})R_1}} \frac{v_{sd}}{a_{dm}} \tag{12.110}$$

Similarly, the coupling in the CM half-circuit is eliminated by setting $a_{dm-cm} = 0$. With this coupling eliminated, analysis of Fig. 12.38b gives

$$\hat{v}_{ic} = \frac{\hat{v}_{oc}}{a'_{cm}} = -\frac{R_3}{R_1} \cdot \frac{1}{1 + \dfrac{R_1 + R_3}{(-a'_{cm})R_1}} \frac{v_{sc}}{a'_{cm}} \tag{12.111}$$

where

$$a'_{cm} = \frac{a_{cm}}{1 + (-a_{cmc}a_{cms})} \tag{12.112}$$

Assuming $\hat{v}_{id} \approx v_{id}$, $\hat{v}_{ic} \approx v_{ic}$, and $\hat{v}_{oc} \approx v_{oc}$, (12.110) and (12.111) can be used in (12.108) to give

$$v_{od} = -\frac{R_3}{R_1} \cdot \frac{1}{1 + \dfrac{R_1 + R_3}{(-a_{dm})R_1}} v_{sd} + \frac{a'_{cm-dm}}{1 + \dfrac{(-a_{dm})R_1}{R_1 + R_3}} \frac{\dfrac{R_3}{R_3 + R_1}}{1 + \dfrac{(-a'_{cm})R_1}{R_1 + R_3}} v_{sc} \quad (12.113)$$

where

$$a'_{cm-dm} = a_{cm-dm} + a'_{cm}a_{cms}a_{cmc-dm} \quad (12.114)$$

This gain has two components. The first term is $a_{cm-dm}$, which is the CM-to-DM gain of the op amp. The second term is the product of three gains: 1) $a'_{cm}$, which is the gain from $v_{ic}$ to $v_{oc}$ including the effect of the CMFB loop, 2) $a_{cms}$, which is the CM-sense gain from $v_{oc}$ to $v_{cms} = v_{cmc}$, and 3) $a_{cmc-dm}$, which is the gain from $v_{cmc}$ to $v_{od}$ (due to mismatch in the op amp). Therefore, the second term in (12.114) is the gain through an indirect path from $v_{ic}$ to $v_{od}$.

Again assuming $\hat{v}_{id} \approx v_{id}$, $\hat{v}_{ic} \approx v_{ic}$, and $\hat{v}_{oc} \approx v_{oc}$, (12.110) and (12.111) can be used in (12.109) to give

$$v_{oc} = \frac{\dfrac{a'_{cm}R_3}{R_1 + R_3}}{1 + \dfrac{(-a'_{cm})R_1}{R_1 + R_3}} v_{sc} + \frac{a'_{dm-cm}}{1 + \dfrac{(-a'_{cm})R_1}{R_1 + R_3}} \frac{\dfrac{R_3}{R_1 + R_3}}{1 + \dfrac{(-a_{dm})R_1}{R_1 + R_3}} v_{sd} \quad (12.115)$$

where

$$a'_{dm-cm} = \frac{a_{dm-cm}}{1 + (-a_{cmc}a_{cms})} \quad (12.116)$$

Equations 12.113 and 12.115 relate the DM and CM source and output voltages for the feedback amplifier. The open-loop-gain and cross-gain terms in (12.108) and (12.109) have been modified by the feedback. To allow simplification of these gain terms, define

$$T_{dm} = \frac{(-a_{dm})R_1}{R_1 + R_3} \quad (12.117)$$

$$T_{cm} = \frac{(-a'_{cm})R_1}{R_1 + R_3} \quad (12.118)$$

$$T_{cmfb} = -a_{cmc}a_{cms} \quad (12.119)$$

which are the loop gains around the DM, CM, and CMFB loops, respectively. Using (12.117)–(12.119), the closed-loop gain terms in (12.113) can be written as

$$A_{dm} = \left.\frac{v_{od}}{v_{sd}}\right|_{v_{sc}=0} = -\frac{R_3}{R_1} \cdot \frac{1}{1 + \dfrac{1}{T_{dm}}} \approx -\frac{R_3}{R_1} \quad (12.120)$$

where $|T_{dm}| \gg 1$ has been used, and

$$A_{cm-dm} = \left.\frac{v_{od}}{v_{sc}}\right|_{v_{sd}=0} = \frac{a'_{cm-dm}\left(\dfrac{R_3}{R_3 + R_1}\right)}{(1 + T_{dm})(1 + T_{cm})} \quad (12.121)$$

As $|T_{dm}|$ increases, $|A_{cm-dm}|$ decreases. Therefore, $|T_{dm}| \gg 1$ is desired to reduce the magnitude of the closed-loop CM-to-DM cross gain. The $(1 + T_{cm})$ term has little effect here since (12.112) usually gives $|a'_{cm}| \ll 1$; therefore, $(1 + T_{cm}) \approx 1$.

Using (12.116)–(12.119), the closed-loop gain terms in (12.115) can be written as

$$A_{cm} = \left. \frac{v_{oc}}{v_{sc}} \right|_{v_{sd}=0} = \frac{\dfrac{a'_{cm} R_3}{R_1 + R_3}}{1 + T_{cm}} \approx \frac{a'_{cm} R_3}{R_1 + R_3} \qquad (12.122)$$

where $(1 + T_{cm}) \approx 1$ has been used, and

$$A_{dm-cm} = \left. \frac{v_{oc}}{v_{sd}} \right|_{v_{sc}=0} = \frac{a'_{dm-cm}}{1 + T_{cm}} \frac{\dfrac{R_3}{R_1 + R_3}}{1 + T'_{dm}}$$

$$= \frac{a_{dm-cm} \dfrac{R_3}{R_1 + R_3}}{(1 + T_{cmfb})(1 + T_{dm})(1 + T_{cm})} \qquad (12.123)$$

As $|T_{dm}|$ or $|T_{cmfb}|$ increases, $|A_{dm-cm}|$ decreases. Therefore, the DM and CMFB loops work to reduce the closed-loop DM-to-CM cross gain. Again, the $(1 + T_{cm})$ term has little effect here since $|1 + T_{cm}| \approx 1$.

The analysis in this section shows how the closed-loop cross-gain terms for the feedback amplifier in Fig. 12.32a are affected by imbalances in the op amp and feedback network. In practice, the imbalances are usually caused by random mismatches between components, and the effect of such mismatches on circuit performance is often evaluated through SPICE simulations.

## 12.8 Bandwidth of the CMFB Loop

Ideally, a fully differential circuit processes a DM input signal and produces a purely DM output signal. The closed-loop bandwidth required for the DM gain is set by the bandwidth of the DM signal. For example, consider the differential gain stage in Fig. 12.32a. To avoid filtering the signal, the closed-loop bandwidth of the DM gain must be larger than the highest frequency in the applied DM input signal. Since the closed-loop bandwidth is approximately equal to the unity-gain frequency of the DM loop gain (or return ratio), this unity-gain frequency should be about equal to the required closed-loop bandwidth. However, the unity-gain frequency required for the CMFB loop is not so easily determined. Consider a fully differential feedback circuit that is linear and perfectly balanced. If no ac CM signals are present in the circuit, the ac CM output voltage will be zero and the CM output voltage is constant. In such a case, the bandwidth of the CMFB loop is unimportant since it only operates on dc signals.

In practice, there are many sources of ac CM signals. For example, an ac CM signal can be present in the signal source, or CM noise can be introduced by coupling from a noisy power supply. Furthermore, even when the signal source is purely differential, an ac CM signal can be created by circuit imbalance that causes DM-to-CM conversion. Regardless of the source of an ac CM signal, the CMFB works to suppress the ac CM output signal and to give a CM output voltage that is about constant. Suppression of the ac CM output component is important for two reasons. First, if the CM output varies, the DM output swing must be reduced to allow for the CM output swing. Second, if two feedback amplifiers are cascaded, any ac CM output voltage from the first amplifier is a CM input voltage for the second amplifier, and any imbalance in the second amplifier will convert some of its CM input voltage into a DM output voltage.

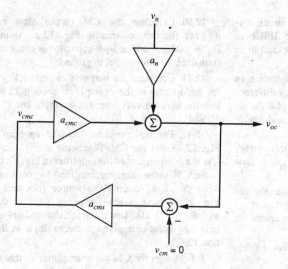

**Figure 12.39.** A model for the CMFB loop with injected noise $v_n$.

To see how the CMFB suppresses the ac CM output signal, consider the small-signal block diagram in Fig. 12.39. Here, $v_n$ is a CM disturbance (for example, an ac signal on the power supply). The signal $v_{cm}$, which is the small-signal component of the applied dc voltage $V_{CM}$, is zero. Also, $a_n$ is the voltage gain from the CM disturbance to the CM output voltage when the CMFB loop is disabled. That is,

$$a_n = \frac{v_{oc}}{v_n}\bigg|_{\text{no CMFB}} = \frac{v_{oc}}{v_n}\bigg|_{v_{cmc}=0} \tag{12.124}$$

When the CMFB is active, the small-signal gain from $v_n$ to $v_{oc}$ becomes

$$A_n = \frac{v_{oc}}{v_n}\bigg|_{\text{with CMFB}} = \frac{a_n}{1 + a_{cms}(-a_{cmc})} \tag{12.125}$$

The CMFB gives $|A_n| \ll |a_n|$ at frequencies where $|a_{cms}(-a_{cmc})| \gg 1$. Therefore, $|a_{cms}(-a_{cmc})| \gg 1$ is desired at frequencies where a significant ac CM output voltage would be generated without CMFB. One possible objective is to satisfy this condition over the bandwidth of DM input signal, or equivalently to make the unity-gain frequencies of the DM and CMFB loops about equal.[15] While desirable, this goal can be difficult to achieve in practice because the CMFB loop often includes more transistors and has more nondominant poles than the DM loop. In any case, suppression of spurious CM signals is an important consideration in determining the required bandwidth of the CMFB loop in practical fully differential amplifiers.

# PROBLEMS

**12.1** What are the swing limits for each output of the differential amplifier in Fig. 12.2? Use $|V_{ov}| = 0.2$ V for all transistors and $V_{tn} = -V_{tp} = 0.6$ V. Assume $V_{DD} = V_{SS} = 2.5$ V, $V_{ic} = 0$ and $\gamma = 0$. Also, assume that the common-mode feedback circuit does not limit the output swing. What value of $V_{OC}$ gives the largest symmetric differen-

tial output swing? What is the peak value of $V_{od}$ in this case?

**12.2** Repeat 12.1 for the two-stage op amp in Fig. 12.23. Assume that switched-capacitor CMFB is used, which does not limit the output swing. Use the data in Problem 12.1.

**12.3** A balanced fully differential circuit displays only odd-order nonlinearity. Use SPICE to verify this fact for the op amp in the example in Section 12.6.1.

**(a)** Either use SPICE to find the distortion in the output waveform for a low-frequency differential sinusoidal input, or use SPICE to plot the dc transfer characteristic $V_{od}$ versus $V_{id}$ and verify that the characteristic is odd.

**(b)** Repeat (a) with a 1% mismatch between $W_1$ and $W_2$. Observe that even-order nonlinearity now exists.

**12.4** For the op amp in Fig. 12.2, use the device data and operating point from the first example in Section 12.4.1. Assume all transistors operate in the active region.

**(a)** Find the element values in the two models for the output ports in Fig. 12.7.

**(b)** Find the element values in the two models for the input ports in Fig. 12.6. (The elements are capacitors.) Use $C_{gs} = 180\,\text{fF}$ and $C_{gd} = 20\,\text{fF}$.

**12.5** For the op amp in Fig. 12.2, use the data from Problem 12.4 except use $I_{D5} = 100\,\mu\text{A}$ and $|V_{ov}| = 0.1\,\text{V}$ for all transistors. Assume all transistors operate in the active region with $C_{gs} = 180\,\text{fF}$ and $C_{gd} = 20\,\text{fF}$.

**(a)** Find the element values in the two models for the output ports in Fig. 12.7.

**(b)** Find the element values in the two models for the input ports in Fig. 12.6. (The elements are capacitors.)

**(c)** Calculate the common-mode control gain $a_{cmc}$.

**12.6** **(a)** For the op amp in Problem 12.5, calculate $a'_{cm}$. Assume that the CMFB scheme in Fig. 12.17 is used and that $a_{cms} = 1$. Recall that $a'_{cm} = v_{oc}/v_{ic}$ when the CMFB loop is active.

**(b)** Use SPICE to plot $|a'_{cm}|$ from 100 Hz to 100 MHz.

**12.7** Repeat Problem 12.5c when the gates of $M_3$ and $M_4$ are the CMC input, and the gate of $M_5$ connects to a bias voltage.

**12.8** The op amp in Problem 12.5 is connected in feedback as shown in Fig. 12.32a. The CMFB is as described in Problem 12.6. Compute the low-frequency closed-loop gains $A_{dm} = v_{od}/v_{sd}$ and $A_{cm} = v_{oc}/v_{sc}$ if $R_1 = R_2 = R_3 = R_4 = 100\,\text{M}\Omega$.

**12.9** Calculate the DM output slew rate $dV_{od}/dt$ for the op amp in Fig. 12.2. Assume $I_{D5} = 200\,\mu\text{A}$ and a 5-pF capacitor is connected from each op-amp output to ground.

**12.10** Calculate the CM output slew rate $dV_{oc}/dt$ for the op amp in Fig. 12.2. Assume $I_{D5} = 200\,\mu\text{A}$ and a 5-pF capacitor is connected from each op-amp output to ground.

**12.11** Compute the output slew rate $dV_{od}/dt$ for the op amp in the example in Section 12.6.1. Use the bias currents from the example and $C = 1.39\,\text{pF}$.

**12.12** For this problem, use the op amp in Fig. 12.23 and the CMFB scheme in Fig. 12.17. Use the complement of the amplifier in Fig. 12.16b as the CM-sense amplifier, modified to give a negative dc gain. Assume the source followers in Fig. 12.17 have a low-frequency gain of 0.95 and $R_{cs} = 15\,\text{k}\Omega$. Use the transistor and op-amp operating-point data given in the example in Section 12.6.1.

**(a)** Design the CM-sense amplifier so that the total low-frequency gain $a_{cms0} = v_{oc}/v_{cms} = -0.71$, which is the same value as in the example in Section 12.6.1.

**(b)** With this CMFB circuit, what are the swing limits for each op-amp output voltage ($V_{o1}$ and $V_{o2}$)? Assume that the biasing current source in each source follower in Fig. 12.17 is implemented with a NMOS transistor, and the current-source and source-follower transistors operate with $V_{GS} = 0.8\,\text{V}$ and $V_{ov} = 0.2\,\text{V}$. For simplicity, assume $V_{GS}$ is constant and take $\gamma = 0$.

**(c)** What value of $V_{CM}$ gives the largest symmetric output swing?

**(d)** Verify that this CMFB circuit works correctly by running a SPICE simulation. Use the value of $V_{CM}$ from part (c).

**12.13** Compute the op-amp CM and DM load capacitances for the output loading in Fig. 12.40a and 12.40b. Assume the inverting voltage buffers in Fig. 12.40b are ideal.

**12.14** **(a)** For the amplifier in Fig. 12.16b, estimate the pole associated with the $RC$ time constant at the $V_{cms}$ output node. Assume $|I_{D25}| = 0.4\,\text{mA}$, $V_{ov23} = 0.2\,\text{V}$, and $V_{OC} = V_{CM}$. Ignore all capacitances except $C_{gs23}$ in parallel with a fixed capacitance of 90 fF. Take $L_{eff} = 0.8\,\mu\text{m}$. Use the data in Table 2.3.

**(b)** Repeat (a) except use $|I_{D25}| = 0.1\,\text{mA}$.

**(c)** Compare the results in (a) and (b). Explain the difference.

**12.15** A differential amplifier with local CMFB is shown in Fig. 12.41. Use $|V_{ov}| = 0.2\,\text{V}$ for all transistors, $V_{tn} = -V_{tp} = 0.6\,\text{V}$, $I_{D5} = 200\,\mu\text{A}$, $V_{An} = 10\,\text{V}$, $|V_{Ap}| = 20\,\text{V}$, and $\gamma = 0$. Assume $V_{DD} = V_{SS} = 2.5\,\text{V}$ and $V_{ic} = 0$.

(a)

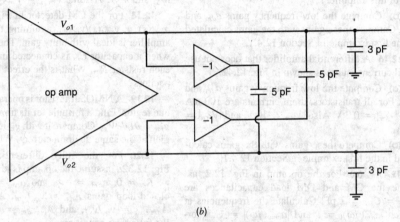

(b)

**Figure 12.40.** Output load networks for Problem 12.13.

**Figure 12.41.** A differential amplifier with local common-mode feedback.

**Figure 12.42.** A differential amplifier without a tail current source.

**(a)** What is the dc common-mode output voltage of this amplifier?

**(b)** Compute the low-frequency gains $a_{dm}$ and $a_{cm}$. Compare these gains with the gains calculated in the first example in Section 12.4.1.

**12.16** A differential amplifier that does not use a tail current source is shown in Fig. 12.42.

**(a)** Compute the low-frequency gains $a_{dm}$ and $a_{cm}$. For all transistors, drain currents are 100 μA and $|V_{ov}| = 0.2$ V. Also, $V_{An} = 10$ V, and $|V_{Ap}| = 20$ V.

**(b)** Compare these gains with the gains calculated in the first example in Section 12.4.1.

**12.17** **(a)** For the op amp in Fig. 12.2, assume the CM and DM load capacitances are $C_{Lc} = C_{Ld} = 2$ pF. Calculate the frequencies at which $|a_{dm}(j\omega)| = 1$ and $|a_{cmc}(j\omega)| = 1$, ignoring other capacitors. Use $|V_{ov}| = 0.25$ V for all transistors, $V_{tn} = -V_{tp} = 0.6$ V, $I_{D5} = 200$ μA, $V_{An} = 20$ V, $|V_{Ap}| = 25$ V, and $\gamma = 0$.

**(b)** Calculate the unity-gain frequencies in part (a) if $C_{Lc} = 2$ pF and $C_{Ld} = 4$ pF.

**(c)** The unity-gain frequency for the CMC gain can be made equal to the DM unity-gain frequency in part (b) by splitting $M_5$ as shown in Fig. 12.15.

How should the 200 μA current be split between $M_{51}$ and $M_{52}$? Assume $V_{ov51} = V_{ov52} = 0.25$ V.

**12.18** For the CM-detector in Fig. 12.43, find $a_{cms}(s) = v_{cms}(s)/v_{oc}(s)$, assuming the CM-sense amplifier is ideal with unity gain. Then find $a_{cms}(s)$ when a capacitor $C_{cs}$ is connected in parallel with each resistor $R_{cs}$. What is the effect of the $C_{cs}$ capacitors?

**12.19** A NMOS transistor is operating in the triode region. Find a formula for its transconductance $g_m = \partial I_d/\partial V_{gs}$. Compare it with $g_m$ in the active region at the same dc drain current. Which is larger?

**12.20** For the fully differential circuit in Fig. 12.32a, assume the op amp is ideal with $R_i = \infty$, $R_o = 0$, $a_{dm} = -\infty$, and $a_{cm} = 0$. Find the closed-loop gains $A_{dm} = v_{od}/v_{sd}$, $A_{cm} = v_{oc}/v_{sc}$, $A_{dm-cm} = v_{oc}/v_{sd}$, and $A_{cm-dm} = v_{od}/v_{sc}$, under the following conditions.

**(a)** $R_1 = R_2 = 1$ kΩ and $R_3 = R_4 = 5$ kΩ.

**(b)** $R_1 = 1.01$ kΩ, $R_2 = 0.99$ kΩ, $R_3 = R_4 = 5$ kΩ.

**12.21** For the circuit in Problem 12.20a, the applied source voltage is a single-ended signal with $V_{s1} = 0.2 V \sin(100t)$ and $V_{s2} = 0$. Assume a CMFB loop forces $V_{OC} = 0$. What are $V_{o1}(t)$,

**Figure 12.43.** Circuit for Problem 12.18.

$V_{DD} = +1.65\text{V}$

**Figure 12.44.** Circuit for Problem 12.23.

$V_{o2}(t)$, $V_{od}(t)$, and $V_{oc}(t)$? What are $V_{i1}(t)$, $V_{i2}(t)$, $V_{id}(t)$, and $V_{ic}(t)$?

**12.22** The op amp in Problem 12.4 is used with the CMFB scheme shown in Fig. 12.17. The circuit is perfectly balanced except that the CM-sense resistors are mismatched with the upper resistor $R_{cs1} = 10.1\ \text{k}\Omega$ and the lower resistor $R_{cs2} = 9.9\ \text{k}\Omega$. Assume the source followers and the CM-sense amplifier are ideal with gains of unity.

(a) Compute the gains $a_{cms}$ and $a_{dm-cms}$ in (12.106).

(b) Compute the low-frequency op-amp gains $v_{od}/v_{id}$, $v_{oc}/v_{ic}$, $v_{od}/v_{ic}$, and $v_{oc}/v_{id}$ with the CMFB active.

(c) Use SPICE to simulate these gains.

**12.23** A fully differential op amp with CMFB is shown in Fig. 12.44. For $M_1$, $M_{1C}$, $M_2$, and $M_{2C}$, use $W/L = (64\ \mu\text{m})/(0.8\ \mu\text{m})$. For $M_3$-$M_4$, $M_{26}$-$M_{27}$ and $M_{11}$, $W/L = (96\ \mu\text{m})/(1.4\ \mu\text{m})$. For $M_{21}$-$M_{24}$, $W/L = (6\ \mu\text{m})/(0.8\ \mu\text{m})$. For $M_{14}$, $M_{25}$, and $M_{52}$, $W/L = (16\ \mu\text{m})/(0.8\ \mu\text{m})$. For $M_{13}$, $W/L = (1.4\ \mu\text{m})/(0.8\ \mu\text{m})$. Take $V_{CM} = -0.65$ V.

(a) Choose $W$ values for $M_{12}$ and $M_{51}$ so that $|I_{D13}| = 20\ \mu\text{A}$. Use $L = 0.8\ \mu\text{m}$ for $M_{51}$ and $L = 1.4\ \mu\text{m}$ for $M_{12}$.

(b) Use SPICE to find the low-frequency op-amp gains $v_{od}/v_{id}$, $v_{oc}/v_{ic}$, $v_{od}/v_{ic}$, and $v_{oc}/v_{id}$ with the CMFB active.

(c) Calculate the output slew rate $dV_{od}/dt$ if a 4-pF capacitor is connected from each op-amp output to ground.

(d) What is the differential output voltage swing of this op amp? Assume $V_{ic} = V_{CM}$, and ignore body effect for this calculation.

(e) Repeat (b) when the input transistors are mismatched with $W_1 = 63\ \mu\text{m}$ and $W_2 = 65\ \mu\text{m}$. (Note: With mismatch, the op-amp offset voltage is not zero.)

(f) Repeat (b) when the load transistors are mismatched with $W_3 = 95\ \mu\text{m}$ and $W_4 = 97\ \mu\text{m}$.

**12.24** The feedback circuit in Fig. 12.45 is a switched-capacitor circuit during one clock phase. Assume the op amp is the folded-cascode op amp in Fig. 12.31.

(a) Calculate the DM and CM output load capacitances, considering only the capacitances in the Fig. 12.45.

(b) If the op-amp bias currents are $|I_{D3}| = |I_{D4}| = 100\ \mu\text{A}$ and $|I_{D5}| = I_{D11} = I_{D12} = 200\ \mu\text{A}$, calculate the DM output slew rate $dV_{od}/dt$.

(c) If all transistors have $|V_{ov}| = 0.15$ V and $V_{DD} = V_{SS} = 2$ V, what is the maximum peak

**Figure 12.45.** Circuit for Problem 12.24.

**Figure 12.46.** A fully differential current-mirror op amp.

differential output swing? Assume $V_{BB3}$ and $V_{BB4}$ are chosen to give maximum swing.

**12.25** In the switched-capacitor CMFB scheme in Fig. 12.21, $C_1 = 0.1$ pF and $C_2 = 0.5$ pF.

**(a)** With $V_{CSBIAS} = -1$ V, $V_{OC} = V_{CM} = 0.5$ V. If $V_{CSBIAS}$ changes to $-1.1$ V, what is the new value of $V_{OC}$? Assume $|a_{cmc}| \gg 1$.

**(b)** Ignoring all capacitors except $C_1$ and $C_2$, what are the CM and DM output load capacitors when the $\phi_1$ switches are on and the $\phi_2$ switches are off?

**(c)** Repeat (b) when the $\phi_2$ switches are on and the $\phi_1$ switches are off.

**12.26** A current-mirror op amp is shown in Fig. 12.46. Assume all NMOS transistors are matched and all PMOS transistors are matched. Use $|V_{ov}| = 0.2$ V for all transistors, $V_{tn} = -V_{tp} = 0.6$ V, $I_{D5} = 200$ μA, $V_{An} = 10$ V, $|V_{Ap}| = 20$ V, and $\gamma = 0$. Assume $V_{DD} = V_{SS} = 1.65$ V and $V_{ic} = 0$.

**(a)** Calculate the model parameters in Fig. 12.7a. Assume the gates of $M_5$, $M_7$, and $M_9$ connect to bias voltages.

**(b)** If the CMC input is the gate of $M_5$ and the gates of $M_7$ and $M_9$ connect to a bias voltage, compute $a_{cmc}$.

**(c)** If the CMC input connects to the gates of $M_7$ and $M_9$ and the gate of $M_5$ connects to a bias voltage, compute $a_{cmc}$.

**(d)** What are the output swing limits for each output? What value of $V_{OC}$ gives the maximum symmetric output swing?

**12.27** Find the low-frequency value of $a'_{cm}$ for the two-stage op amp in the example in Section 12.6.1. Use the data in that example. Recall that $a'_{cm} = v_{oc}/v_{ic}$ when the CMFB loop is active.

**12.28** Assume that the CMFB circuit in the example in Section 12.6.1 is changed so that the CM-sense amplifier has a low-frequency gain $|a_{cms0}| = 2.5$. Determine the compensation capacitor $C$ needed in the op amp to assure that the CMC and DM feedback loops in the example have a phase margin of 45° or larger.

**12.29** Neutralization capacitors $C_n$ are to be added to cancel the Miller effect on $C_{gd1}$ and $C_{gd2}$.

in the two-stage op amp in the example in Section 12.6.1.

(a) Show how the $C_n$ capacitors should be connected in the op amp. What value of $C_n$ should be used?

(b) If these capacitors are constructed from MOS transistors operating in the cutoff region, what type of transistor and what device dimensions should be used?

**12.30** Modify the CMFB schematic in Fig. 12.26 to inject currents at the drains of $M_1$ and $M_2$, in a manner similar to that shown in Fig. 12.18. Give a set of bias current values on the schematic. Assume $I_{D3} = I_{D4} = 150$ μA and $I_{D6} = I_{D9} = 400$ μA.

**12.31** A fully differential op amp with mismatch is connected in the feedback circuit in Fig. 12.32a with $R_1 = R_2 = 10$ kΩ and $R_3 = R_4 = 40$ kΩ. The op amp model is shown in Fig. 12.37 where $a_{dm} = -181$, $a_{cm} = -2.89$, $a_{cmc} = -226$, $a_{dm-cm} = 8.95$, $a_{cm-dm} = 0.15$, and $a_{cmc-dm} = 11.6$. If the gain of the CMFB circuit is $a_{cms} = 0.76$, find the closed-loop gains $A_{dm} = v_{od}/v_{sd}$, $A_{cm} = v_{oc}/v_{sc}$, $A_{dm-cm} = v_{oc}/v_{sd}$, and $A_{cm-dm} = v_{od}/v_{sc}$.

# REFERENCES

1. R. D. Middlebrook. *Differential Amplifiers*. Wiley, New York, 1963.

2. L. J. Giacoletto. *Differential Amplifiers*. Wiley, New York, 1970.

3. W. G. Garrett and T. G. Maxfield. "A Monolithic Differential-Output Operational Amplifier," *Digest of Technical Papers, International Solid-State Circuits Conf.*, pp. 174–175, Philadelphia, PA, February 1972.

4. M. Banu, J. M. Khoury, and Y. Tsividis. "Fully Differential Operational Amplifiers with Accurate Output Balancing," *IEEE Journal of Solid-State Circuits*, Vol. 23, no. 6, pp. 1410–1414, December 1988.

5. P. W. Li, M. J. Chin, P. R. Gray, and R. Castello. "A Ratio Independent Algorithmic Analog-to-Digital Conversion Technique," *IEEE Journal of Solid-State Circuits*, Vol. 19, no. 6, pp. 828–836, December 1984.

6. R. A. Whatley. "Fully Differential Operational Amplifier with DC Common-Mode Feedback," U.S. Patent 4,573,020, February 1986.

7. C.-C. Shih and P. R. Gray. "Reference Refreshing Cyclic Analog-to-Digital and Digital-to-Analog Converters," *IEEE Journal of Solid-State Circuits*, Vol. 21, no. 4, pp. 544–554, August 1986.

8. T. C. Choi, R. T. Kaneshiro, R. W. Broderson, P. R. Gray, W. B. Jett, and M. Wilcox. "High-Frequency CMOS Switched-Capacitor Filters for Communications Application," *IEEE Journal of Solid-State Circuits*, Vol. 18, no. 6, pp. 652–664, December 1983.

9. D. Senderowicz, S. F. Dreyer, J. H. Huggins, C. F. Rahim, and C. A. Laber. "A Family of Differential NMOS Analog Circuits for a PCM Codec Filter Chip," *IEEE Journal of Solid-State Circuits*, Vol. 17, no. 6, pp. 1014–1023, December 1982.

10. D. J. Allstot and W. C. Black, Jr. "Technological Design Considerations for Monolithic MOS Switched-Capacitor Filtering Systems," *Proceedings of the IEEE*, Vol. 71, no. 8, pp. 967–986, August 1983.

11. P. J. Hurst and S. H. Lewis. "Determination of Stability Using Return Ratios in Balanced Fully Differential Feedback Circuits," *IEEE Trans. on Circuits and Systems II*, pp. 805–817, December 1995.

12. K. Bult and G. J. G. M. Geelen. "A Fast-Setting CMOS Op Amp for SC Circuits with 90-dB DC Gain," *IEEE Journal of Solid-State Circuits*, Vol. 25, no. 6, pp. 1379–1384, December 1990.

13. B.-S. Song, M. F. Thompsett, and K. R. Lakshmikumar. "A 12-bit 1-Msample/s Capacitor Error-Averaging Pipelined A/D Converter," *IEEE Journal of Solid-State Circuits*, Vol. 23, no. 6, pp. 1324–1333, December 1988.

14. J. A. Mataya, G. W. Haines, and S. B. Marshall. "IF Amplifier Using $C_c$ Compensated Transistors," *IEEE Journal of Solid-State Circuits*, Vol. 3, pp. 401–407, December 1968.

15. J. F. Duque-Carrillo. "Control of the Common-Mode Component in CMOS Continuous-Time Fully Differential Signal Processing," *Analog Integrated Circuits and Signal Processing, An International Journal*, pp. 131–140, Kluwer Academic Publishers, September 1993.

# Index

865